HAESE MATHEMATICS

Specialists in mathematics publishing

Mathematics
for the international student
Mathematics SL
third edition

Robert Haese

Sandra Haese

Michael Haese

Marjut Mäenpää

Mark Humphries

**for use with
IB Diploma
Programme**

MATHEMATICS FOR THE INTERNATIONAL STUDENT
Mathematics SL third edition

Robert Haese	B.Sc.
Sandra Haese	B.Sc.
Michael Haese	B.Sc.(Hons.), Ph.D.
Marjut Mäenpää	B.Sc., Dip.Ed.
Mark Humphries	B.Sc.(Hons.)

Haese Mathematics
3 Frank Collopy Court, Adelaide Airport, SA 5950, AUSTRALIA
Telephone: +61 8 8355 9444, Fax: +61 8 8355 9471
Email: info@haesemathematics.com.au
Web: www.haesemathematics.com.au

National Library of Australia Card Number & ISBN 978-1-921972-08-9

© Haese Mathematics 2012

Published by Haese Mathematics.
3 Frank Collopy Court, Adelaide Airport, SA 5950, AUSTRALIA

First Edition	2004
Reprinted	2005 three times *(with minor corrections)*, 2006, 2007, 2008 twice
Second Edition	2009
Reprinted	2010 twice *(with minor corrections)*, 2011
Third Edition	2012

Typeset in Times Roman $10\frac{1}{2}$.

The textbook and its accompanying CD have been developed independently of the International Baccalaureate Organization (IBO). The textbook and CD are in no way connected with, or endorsed by, the IBO.

FOREWORD

Mathematics for the International Student: Mathematics SL has been written to embrace the syllabus for the two-year Mathematics SL Course, to be first examined in 2014. It is not our intention to define the course. Teachers are encouraged to use other resources. We have developed this book independently of the International Baccalaureate Organization (IBO) in consultation with many experienced teachers of IB Mathematics. The text is not endorsed by the IBO.

In the third edition, chapters are arranged to follow the same order as the chapters in our *Mathematics HL (Core) third edition*, making it easier for teachers who have combined classes of SL and HL students.

Syllabus references are given at the beginning of each chapter. The new edition reflects the new Mathematics SL syllabus. More lower level questions have been added at the start of the exercises, to make them more suitable for a range of ability levels. Discussion topics for the Theory of Knowledge have been included in this edition. See page 12 for a summary.

In response to the introduction of a calculator-free examination paper, a large number of questions have been added and categorised as 'calculator' or 'non calculator'. In particular, the final chapter contains over 160 examination-style questions.

Comprehensive graphics calculator instructions for Casio fx-9860G Plus, Casio fx-CG20, TI-84 Plus and TI-*n*spire are accessible as printable pages on the CD (see page 16) and, occasionally, where additional help may be needed, more detailed instructions are available from icons located throughout the book. The extensive use of graphics calculators and computer packages throughout the book enables students to realise the importance, application, and appropriate use of technology. No single aspect of technology has been favoured. It is as important that students work with a pen and paper as it is that they use their graphics calculator, or use a spreadsheet or graphing package on computer.

This package is language rich and technology rich. The combination of textbook and interactive Student CD will foster the mathematical development of students in a stimulating way. Frequent use of the interactive features on the CD is certain to nurture a much deeper understanding and appreciation of mathematical concepts. The CD also offers ◀) **Self Tutor** for every worked example. ◀) **Self Tutor** is accessed via the CD – click anywhere on any worked example to hear a teacher's voice explain each step in that worked example. This is ideal for catch-up and revision, or for motivated students who want to do some independent study outside school hours.

For students who may not have a good understanding of the necessary background knowledge for this course, we have provided printable pages of information, examples, exercises, and answers on the Student CD – see 'Background knowledge' (page 16).

The interactive features of the CD allow immediate access to our own specially designed geometry software, graphing software and more. Teachers are provided with a quick and easy way to demonstrate concepts, and students can discover for themselves and re-visit when necessary.

continued next page

It is not our intention that each chapter be worked through in full. Time constraints may not allow for this. Teachers must select exercises carefully, according to the abilities and prior knowledge of their students, to make the most efficient use of time and give as thorough coverage of work as possible. Investigations throughout the book will add to the discovery aspect of the course and enhance student understanding and learning.

In this changing world of mathematics education, we believe that the contextual approach shown in this book, with the associated use of technology, will enhance the students' understanding, knowledge and appreciation of mathematics, and its universal application.

We welcome your feedback.

Email: *info@haesemathematics.com.au*
Web: *www.haesemathematics.com.au*

RCH SHH PMH
EMM MAH

ACKNOWLEDGEMENTS

Cartoon artwork by John Martin. Artwork by Piotr Poturaj and Benjamin Fitzgerald.

Cover design by Piotr Poturaj.

Computer software by Thomas Jansson, Troy Cruickshank, Ashvin Narayanan, Adrian Blackburn, Edward Ross and Tim Lee.

Typeset in Australia by Charlotte Frost.

Editorial review by Catherine Quinn and David Martin.

The authors and publishers would like to thank all those teachers who offered advice and encouragement on this book. Many of them read the page proofs and offered constructive comments and suggestions. These teachers include: Dr. Andrzej Cichy, Paul Thompson, Chris Carter, Glen Whiffen, Leslie Miller, Annette MacDougall, Fatima Remtulla, Sandra Tweedy, Vivienne Verschuren, Dhruv Prajapati, Matt Kaun and Pamela Vollmar. To anyone we may have missed, we offer our apologies.

The publishers wish to make it clear that acknowledging these individuals does not imply any endorsement of this book by any of them, and all responsibility for the content rests with the authors and publishers.

USING THE INTERACTIVE STUDENT CD

The interactive CD is ideal for independent study.

Students can revisit concepts taught in class and undertake their own revision and practice. The CD also has the text of the book, allowing students to leave the textbook at school and keep the CD at home.

By clicking on the relevant icon, a range of interactive features can be accessed:

INTERACTIVE LINK

- **Self Tutor**
- Graphics calculator instructions
- Background knowledge (as printable pages)
- Interactive links to spreadsheets, graphing and geometry software, computer demonstrations and simulations

Graphics calculator instructions: Detailed instructions are available on the CD, as printable pages (see page 16). Click on the icon for Casio fx-9860G Plus, Casio fx-CG20, TI-84 Plus, or TI-$n$spire instructions.

GRAPHICS CALCULATOR INSTRUCTIONS

SELF TUTOR is an exciting feature of this book.

The **Self Tutor** icon on each worked example denotes an active link on the CD.

> Simply 'click' on the **Self Tutor** (or anywhere in the example box) to access the worked example, with a teacher's voice explaining each step necessary to reach the answer.
>
> Play any line as often as you like. See how the basic processes come alive using movement and colour on the screen.
>
> Ideal for students who have missed lessons or need extra help.

Example 2   ◀) **Self Tutor**

A line passes through the point $A(1, 5)$ and has direction vector $\begin{pmatrix} 3 \\ 2 \end{pmatrix}$. Describe the line using:

a a vector equation   **b** parametric equations   **c** a Cartesian equation.

a The vector equation is $\mathbf{r} = \mathbf{a} + t\mathbf{b}$ where

$$\mathbf{a} = \overrightarrow{OA} = \begin{pmatrix} 1 \\ 5 \end{pmatrix} \quad \text{and} \quad \mathbf{b} = \begin{pmatrix} 3 \\ 2 \end{pmatrix}$$

$$\therefore \quad \begin{pmatrix} x \\ y \end{pmatrix} = \begin{pmatrix} 1 \\ 5 \end{pmatrix} + t \begin{pmatrix} 3 \\ 2 \end{pmatrix}, \quad t \in \mathbb{R}$$

b $x = 1 + 3t$ and $y = 5 + 2t$, $t \in \mathbb{R}$

c Now $t = \dfrac{x-1}{3} = \dfrac{y-5}{2}$

$$\therefore \quad 2x - 2 = 3y - 15$$

$$\therefore \quad 2x - 3y = -13$$

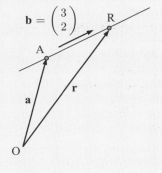

See **Chapter 13, Vector applications**, p. 323

TABLE OF CONTENTS

SYMBOLS AND NOTATION USED IN THIS BOOK

$\mathbb{N}$ the set of positive integers and zero, $\{0, 1, 2, 3, ...\}$

$\mathbb{Z}$ the set of integers, $\{0, \pm 1, \pm 2, \pm 3, ...\}$

$\mathbb{Z}^+$ the set of positive integers, $\{1, 2, 3, ...\}$

$\mathbb{Q}$ the set of rational numbers

$\mathbb{Q}^+$ the set of positive rational numbers, $\{x \mid x > 0, \ x \in \mathbb{Q}\}$

$\mathbb{R}$ the set of real numbers

$\mathbb{R}^+$ the set of positive real numbers, $\{x \mid x > 0, \ x \in \mathbb{R}\}$

$\{x_1, x_2, ...\}$ the set with elements $x_1, x_2, ...$

$n(A)$ the number of elements in set A

$\{x \mid ....\}$ the set of all x such that

$\in$ is an element of

$\notin$ is not an element of

$\varnothing$ the empty (null) set

U the universal set

$\cup$ union

$\cap$ intersection

$\subset$ is a proper subset of

$\subseteq$ is a subset of

A' the complement of the set A

$a^{\frac{1}{n}}, \ \sqrt[n]{a}$ a to the power of $\frac{1}{n}$, nth root of a (if $a \geqslant 0$ then $\sqrt[n]{a} \geqslant 0$)

$a^{\frac{1}{2}}, \ \sqrt{a}$ a to the power $\frac{1}{2}$, square root of a (if $a \geqslant 0$ then $\sqrt{a} \geqslant 0$)

$|x|$ the modulus or absolute value of x

$$|x| = \begin{cases} x \ \text{for} \ x \geqslant 0 & x \in \mathbb{R} \\ -x \ \text{for} \ x < 0 & x \in \mathbb{R} \end{cases}$$

$\equiv$ identity or is equivalent to

$\approx$ is approximately equal to

$>$ is greater than

$\geq$ or $\geqslant$ is greater than or equal to

$<$ is less than

$\leq$ or $\leqslant$ is less than or equal to

   is not greater than

$\not<$ is not less than

$a \mid b$ a divides b

u_n the nth term of a sequence or series

d the common difference of an arithmetic sequence

r the common ratio of a geometric sequence

S_n the sum of the first n terms of a sequence, $u_1 + u_2 + ... + u_n$

S_∞ or S the sum to infinity of a sequence, $u_1 + u_2 + ...$

$\displaystyle\sum_{i=1}^{n} u_i$ $u_1 + u_2 + ... + u_n$

$\dbinom{n}{r}$ the rth binomial coefficient, $r = 0, 1, 2, ...$ in the expansion of $(a+b)^n$

$f : A \rightarrow B$ f is a function under which each element of set A has an image in set B

$f : x \mapsto y$ f is a function which maps x onto y

$f(x)$ the image of x under the function f

f^{-1} the inverse function of the function f

$f \circ g$ the composite function of f and g

$\displaystyle\lim_{x \to a} f(x)$ the limit of $f(x)$ as x tends to a

$\dfrac{dy}{dx}$ the derivative of y with respect to x

$f'(x)$ the derivative of $f(x)$ with respect to x

$\dfrac{d^2y}{dx^2}$ the second derivative of y with respect to x

$f''(x)$ the second derivative of $f(x)$ with respect to x

$\dfrac{d^n y}{dx^n}$ the nth derivative of y with respect to x

$f^{(n)}(x)$ the nth derivative of $f(x)$ with respect to x

$\int y \, dx$ the indefinite integral of y with respect to x

$\displaystyle\int_a^b y \, dx$ the definite integral of y with respect to x between the limits $x = a$ and $x = b$

e^x exponential function of x

$\log_a x$ logarithm to the base a of x

$\ln x$ the natural logarithm of x, $\log_e x$

sin, cos, tan   the circular functions

$A(x, y)$	the point A in the plane with Cartesian coordinates x and y	$x_1, x_2, ...$	observations of a variable
[AB]	the line segment with end points A and B	$f_1, f_2, ...$	frequencies with which the observations $x_1, x_2, x_3, ...$ occur
AB	the length of [AB]	$P(X = x)$	the probability distribution function of the discrete random variable X
(AB)	the line containing points A and B		
$\widehat{A}$	the angle at A	$E(X)$	the expected value of the random variable X
$C\widehat{A}B$	the angle between [CA] and [AB]	μ	population mean
$\triangle ABC$	the triangle whose vertices are A, B, and C	σ	population standard deviation
$\parallel$	is parallel to	σ^2	population variance
$\perp$	is perpendicular to	$\overline{x}$	sample mean
$\mathbf{v}$	the vector $\mathbf{v}$	$s_n^{\,2}$	sample variance
$\overrightarrow{AB}$	the vector represented in magnitude and direction by the directed line segment from A to B	s_n	standard deviation of the sample
		$s_{n-1}^{\,2}$	unbiased estimate of the population variance
$\mathbf{a}$	the position vector $\overrightarrow{OA}$		
$\mathbf{i, j, k}$	unit vectors in the directions of the Cartesian coordinate axes	$B(n, p)$	binomial distribution with parameters n and p
$|\mathbf{a}|$	the magnitude of vector $\mathbf{a}$	$N(\mu, \sigma^2)$	normal distribution with mean μ and variance σ^2
$|\overrightarrow{AB}|$	the magnitude of $\overrightarrow{AB}$	$X \sim B(n, p)$	the random variable X has a binomial distribution with parameters n and p
$\mathbf{v} \bullet \mathbf{w}$	the scalar product of $\mathbf{v}$ and $\mathbf{w}$		
$P(A)$	probability of event A	$X \sim N(\mu, \sigma^2)$	the random variable X has a normal distribution with mean μ and variance σ^2
$P(A')$	probability of the event 'not A'		
$P(A \mid B)$	probability of the event A given B	z	standardised normal random variable, $z = \dfrac{x - \mu}{\sigma}$
		r	Pearson's product-moment correlation coefficient

THEORY OF KNOWLEDGE

Theory of Knowledge is a Core requirement in the International Baccalaureate Diploma Programme.

Students are encouraged to think critically and challenge the assumptions of knowledge. Students should be able to analyse different ways of knowing and areas of knowledge, while considering different cultural and emotional perceptions, fostering an international understanding.

The activities and discussion topics in the below table aim to help students discover and express their views on knowledge issues.

Chapter 3: Exponentials p. 89	**MATHEMATICAL PROOF**
Chapter 4: Logarithms p. 115	**IS MATHEMATICS AN INVENTION OR A DISCOVERY?**
Chapter 6: Sequences and series p. 174	**THE NATURE OF INFINITY**
Chapter 8: The unit circle and radian measure p. 192	**MEASURES OF ANGLE - MATHEMATICS IN NATURE**
Chapter 10: Trigonometric functions p. 236	**MATHEMATICAL LANGUAGE AND SYMBOLS**
Chapter 11: Trigonometric equations and identities p. 272	**MATHEMATICS IN SOCIETY**
Chapter 13: Vector applications p. 337	**ARE ALGEBRA AND GEOMETRY SEPARATE AREAS OF LEARNING? INDEPENDENT DEVELOPMENT OF MATHEMATICS**
Chapter 14: Introduction to differential calculus p. 347	**ZENO'S PARADOX**
Chapter 17: Applications of differential calculus p. 436	**THE SCIENTIFIC METHOD**
Chapter 20: Descriptive statistics p. 538	**MISLEADING STATISTICS**
Chapter 21: Linear modelling p. 561	**MODELLING THE REAL WORLD**
Chapter 22: Probability p. 603	**APPLICATIONS OF PROBABILITY**

THEORY OF KNOWLEDGE

In the previous exercise we saw examples of data which was non-linear, but for which we could *transform* the variables so a linear model could be used.

In other situations we can use quadratic or trigonometric functions to model data.

1 Can all data be modelled by a known mathematical function?

2 How reliable is mathematics in predicting real-world phenomena?

Friedrich Wilhelm Bessel (1784 - 1846) was a German mathematician and astronomer who described the Bessel functions named after him. The Bessel functions are the solutions to a particular class of **differential equation**, which is an equation involving derivative functions. They are used in both classical and quantum physics to describe the dynamics of gravitational systems.

Friedrich Wilhelm Bessel

3 Are the Bessel functions defined by nature or by man?

See **Chapter 21, Linear Modelling**, p. 561

WRITING A MATHEMATICAL EXPLORATION

In addition to sitting examination papers, Mathematics SL students are also required to complete a **mathematical exploration**. This is a short report written by the student, based on a topic of his or her choice, and should focus on the mathematics of that topic. The mathematical exploration comprises 20% of the final mark.

The exploration should be approximately 6-12 pages long, and should be written at a level which is accessible to an audience of your peers. The exploration should also include a bibliography.

Group work should not be used for explorations. Each student's exploration is an individual piece of work.

When deciding on how to structure your exploration, you may wish to include the following sections:

Introduction: This section can be used to explain why the topic has been chosen, and to include any relevant background information.

Aim: A clear statement of intent should be given to provide perspective and direction to your exploration. This should be a short paragraph which outlines the problem or scenario under investigation.

Method and Results: This section can be used to describe the process which was followed to investigate the problem, as well as recording the unprocessed results of your investigations, in the form of a table, for example.

Analysis of Results: In this section, you should use graphs, diagrams, and calculations to analyse your results. Any graphs and diagrams should be included in the appropriate place in the report, and not attached as appendices at the end. You should also form some conjectures based on your analysis.

Conclusion: You should summarise your investigation, giving a clear response to your aim. You should also reflect on your exploration. Limitations and sources of error could be discussed, as well as potential for further exploration.

The exploration will be assessed against five assessment criteria. Refer to the Mathematics SL Subject Guide for more details.

The following two pages contain a short extract of a student's report, used with the permission of Wan Lin Oh. Please note that there is no single structure which must be followed to write a mathematical exploration. The extract displayed is only intended to illustrate some of the key features which should be included.

The electronic version of this extract contains further information, and can be accessed by clicking the icon alongside.

ELECTRONIC EXTRACT

This is an **extract** of a mathematics report used to demonstrate the components of a written report.

1. **Title (and author)**	**Population Trends in China**	2. **Introduction (optional)**
A clear and concise description of the report	Written by Wan Lin Oh	Include background information and definitions of key terms or variables used.

Aim

To determine the model that best fits the population of China from 1950 to 2008 by investigating different functions that best model the population of China from 1950 to 1995 (refer to *Table 1*) initially, and then re-evaluating and modifying this model to include additional data from 1983 to 2008.

Rationale

3. **Aim and Rationale**
Outline the purpose of the task in a clear and succinct manner.
Justify the exploration choice.

The history class had been discussi[...], cultural and social implications of China's "One Child Policy", introduce[...]. This aroused the author's curiosity about the measurable impact that the policy may have had on China's population.

Table 1: Population of China from 1950 to 1995

Year (t)	1950	1955	1960	1965	1970	1975	1980	1985	1990	1995
Population in millions (P)	554.8	609.0	657.5	729.2	830.7	927.8	998.9	1070.0	1155.3	1220.5

Choosing a model

Values from *Table 1* were used to create *Graph 1*:

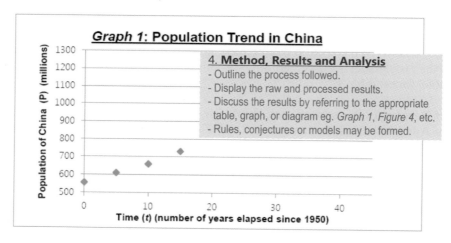

4. **Method, Results and Analysis**
- Outline the process followed.
- Display the raw and processed results.
- Discuss the results by referring to the appropriate table, graph, or diagram eg. *Graph 1*, *Figure 4*, etc.
- Rules, conjectures or models may be formed.

Graph 1 illustrates a positive correlation between the population of China and the number of years since 1950. This means that as time increases, the population of China also increases. *Graph 1* clearly shows that the model is not a linear function, because the graph has turning points and there is no fixed increase in corresponding to a fixed increase in P. Simple observation reveals that it is not a straight line. In addition, *Graph 1* illustrates that the function is not a power function ($P = at^b$) because it does not meet the requirements of a power function; for all positive b values, a power model must go through the origin, however *Graph 1* shows that the model's function does not pass through the origin of $(0, 0)$.

There is a high possibility that the model could be a polynomial function because *Graph 1* indicates that there are turning point(s). A cubic and a quadratic function were then determined and compared.

Analytical Determination of Polynomial Model

As there is a high possibility that the model could be a cubic function (3rd degree polynomial function), an algebraic method can be used in order to determine the equation of the function. In order to determine this cubic equation, four points from the model will be used as there are four...

Conclusion

The aim of this investigation was to investigate a model that best fits the given data from 1950 to 2008. It was initially found that a 3rd degree polynomial function and an exponential function have a good possibility of fitting the given data from *Table 1* which is from year 1950 to 1995 by observing the data plots on the graph.

A cubic function (3rd degree polynomial function) was chosen eventually and consequently an algebraic method using simultaneous equations was developed to produce the equation of the function. Through this method, the equation of the cubic was deduced to be $P(t) = -0.007081t^3 + 0.5304t^2 + 5.263t + 554.8$. In addition, the use of technology was also included in this investigation to further enhance the development of the task by graphing the cubic function to determine how well the cubic function fitted the original data. The cubic graph was then compared with a quadratic function graph of $P(t) = 0.13t^2 + 8.95t + 554.8$. Ultimately, the cubic function was seen as the better fit compared to the quadratic model.

A researcher suggests that the population, P at time t can be modelled by $P(t) = \frac{K}{1+Le^{-Mt}}$. With the use of GeoGebra the parameters, K, L and M were found by trial and error to be 1590, 1.97 and 0.04 respectively. This consequently led to the equation of the logistic function of $P(t) = \frac{1590}{1+1.97e^{-0.04t}}$.

From the comparison of both the cubic and the logistic model, the cubic function was established to be a more accurate model for the given 1950 – 1995 data because the data points matched the model better, however the logistic model produced more likely values under extrapolation.

Additional data on population trends in China fr[...] [...]d by the International Monetary Fund (IMF) was given in Tab[...] graphed with the additional data points and compared. It [...] er model compared to the cubic model because it was able [...] ulation of China much more precisely.

Subsequently a piecewise function was used becau[...] have two distinctly different parts, each with a correspondin[...] domain $0 < t \le 30$. The researcher's model was modified to fit the data for $30 < t \le 58$.

The piecewise function was then defined as

$$P(t) \begin{cases} -0.007081t^3 + 0.5304t^2 + 5.263t + 554.8 & 0 < t \le 30 \\ \dfrac{1590}{1+1.97e^{-0.04t}} & 30 < t \le 58 \end{cases}$$

This modified model matched the data points of the population of China from 1950 to 2008 closely; the model also passed through both the minimum and the maximum of the given data. In addition, the modified model exhibited good long-term behaviour and was able to predict a sensible result beyond the known values.

Limitations

In this investigation, there were several limitations that should be taken into account. Firstly, the best fit model which is the piecewise function model does not take into account the possibility of natural disasters or diseases that may occur in China in the future which will lead to a mass decrease in population. Furthermore, the model also does not consider the population pressures in China such as the one child policy. The one child policy introduced in 1978 but applied in 1979 would cause a decrease in the population in the long term. It is shown in *Graph 14* that after 1979 (P_7), the rate at which the Chinese population is increasing is slower compared to the previous years. This is because this policy leads to an increase in the abortion rate due to many families' preference for males, as males are able to take over the family name. This will consequently lead to a gender imbalance, causing a decrease in population because of the increasing difficulty for Chinese males to find partners. In addition, the model of best fit does not consider the [...] countries, allowing more Chinese people to live longer, which wil[...] term.

[1] http://geography.about.com/od/populationgeography/a/onechild.htm

BACKGROUND KNOWLEDGE

Before starting this course you can make sure that you have a good understanding of the necessary background knowledge. Click on the icon alongside to obtain a printable set of exercises and answers on this background knowledge.

BACKGROUND KNOWLEDGE

Click on the icon to access printable facts about number sets.

NUMBER SETS

Click on the icon to access a printable summary of circle properties.

CIRCLE PROPERTIES

Click on the icon to access a printable summary of measurement facts.

MEASUREMENT FACTS

GRAPHICS CALCULATOR INSTRUCTIONS

Printable graphics calculator instruction booklets are available for the **Casio fx-9860G Plus**, **Casio fx-CG20**, **TI-84 Plus**, and the **TI-*n*spire**. Click on the relevant icon below.

CASIO fx-9860G Plus   **CASIO fx-CG20**   **TI-84 Plus**   **TI-*n*spire**

When additional calculator help may be needed, specific instructions can be printed from icons within the text.

GRAPHICS CALCULATOR INSTRUCTIONS

Chapter 1

Quadratics

Syllabus reference: 2.2, 2.4, 2.7, 2.8

OPENING PROBLEM

Abiola and Badrani are standing 40 metres apart, throwing a ball between them. When Abiola throws the ball, it travels in a smooth arc. At the time when the ball has travelled x metres horizontally towards Badrani, its height is y metres.

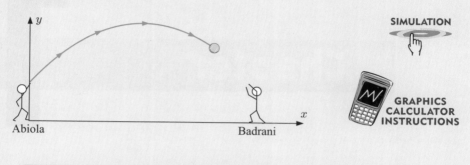

x (m)	0	5	10	15	20	25	30
y (m)	1.25	10	16.25	20	21.25	20	16.25

Things to think about:

a   Use technology to plot these points.

b   What *shape* is the graph of y against x?

c   What is the maximum height reached by the ball?

d   What *formula* gives the height of the ball when it has travelled x metres horizontally towards Badrani?

e   Will the ball reach Badrani before it bounces?

QUADRATICS

A **quadratic equation** is an equation of the form $ax^2 + bx + c = 0$ where a, b, and c are constants, $a \neq 0$.

A **quadratic function** is a function of the form $y = ax^2 + bx + c$, $a \neq 0$.

Quadratic functions are members of the family of **polynomials**.   The first few members of this family are shown in the table.

Polynomial function	Type
$y = ax + b$, $a \neq 0$	linear
$y = ax^2 + bx + c$, $a \neq 0$	quadratic
$y = ax^3 + bx^2 + cx + d$, $a \neq 0$	cubic
$y = ax^4 + bx^3 + cx^2 + dx + e$, $a \neq 0$	quartic

HISTORICAL NOTE

Galileo Galilei (1564 - 1642) was born in Pisa, Tuscany. He was a philosopher who played a significant role in the scientific revolution of that time.

Within his research he conducted a series of experiments on the paths of projectiles, attempting to find a mathematical description of falling bodies.

Two of Galileo's experiments consisted of rolling a ball down a grooved ramp that was placed at a fixed height above the floor and inclined at a fixed angle to the horizontal. In one experiment the ball left the end of the ramp and descended to the floor. In the second, a horizontal shelf was placed at the end of the ramp, and the ball travelled along this shelf before descending to the floor.

In each experiment Galileo altered the release height h of the ball and measured the distance d the ball travelled before landing. The units of measurement were called 'punti' (points).

Galileo

In both experiments Galileo found that once the ball left the ramp or shelf, its path was parabolic and could therefore be modelled by a quadratic function.

A ## QUADRATIC EQUATIONS

Acme Leather Jacket Co. makes and sells x leather jackets each week and their profit function is given by
$P = -12.5x^2 + 550x - 2125$ dollars.

How many jackets must be made and sold each week in order to obtain a weekly profit of $3000?

Clearly we need to solve the equation:

$$-12.5x^2 + 550x - 2125 = 3000$$

We can rearrange the equation to give

$$12.5x^2 - 550x + 5125 = 0,$$

which is of the form $ax^2 + bx + c = 0$ and is thus a quadratic equation.

SOLVING QUADRATIC EQUATIONS

To solve quadratic equations we have the following methods to choose from:

- **factorise** the quadratic and use the **Null Factor law**:

    If $ab = 0$ then $a = 0$ or $b = 0$.

- **complete the square**
- use the **quadratic formula**
- use **technology**.

The **roots** or **solutions** of $ax^2 + bx + c = 0$ are the values of x which satisfy the equation, or make it true.

For example,   consider $x^2 - 3x + 2 = 0$.

$$\begin{aligned} \text{When } x = 2, \quad x^2 - 3x + 2 &= (2)^2 - 3(2) + 2 \\ &= 4 - 6 + 2 \\ &= 0 \ \checkmark \end{aligned}$$

So, $x = 2$ is a root of the equation $x^2 - 3x + 2 = 0$.

SOLVING BY FACTORISATION

Step 1:   If necessary, rearrange the equation so one side is zero.

Step 2:   Fully factorise the other side.

Step 3:   Use the Null Factor law: If $ab = 0$ then $a = 0$ or $b = 0$.

Step 4:   Solve the resulting linear equations.

Caution: Do not be tempted to divide both sides by an expression involving x.
If you do this then you may lose one of the solutions.

For example, consider $x^2 = 5x$.

Correct solution

$$x^2 = 5x$$
$$\therefore \ x^2 - 5x = 0$$
$$\therefore \ x(x - 5) = 0$$
$$\therefore \ x = 0 \text{ or } 5$$

Incorrect solution

$$x^2 = 5x$$
$$\therefore \ \frac{x^2}{x} = \frac{5x}{x}$$
$$\therefore \ x = 5$$

By dividing both sides by x, we lose the solution $x = 0$.

Example 1   ◀) **Self Tutor**

Solve for x: **a** $3x^2 + 5x = 0$ **b** $x^2 = 5x + 6$

a
$$3x^2 + 5x = 0$$
$$\therefore \ x(3x + 5) = 0$$
$$\therefore \ x = 0 \text{ or } 3x + 5 = 0$$
$$\therefore \ x = 0 \text{ or } x = -\tfrac{5}{3}$$

b
$$x^2 = 5x + 6$$
$$\therefore \ x^2 - 5x - 6 = 0$$
$$\therefore \ (x - 6)(x + 1) = 0$$
$$\therefore \ x = 6 \text{ or } -1$$

Example 2   ◀) **Self Tutor**

Solve for x: **a** $4x^2 + 1 = 4x$ **b** $6x^2 = 11x + 10$

a
$$4x^2 + 1 = 4x$$
$$\therefore \ 4x^2 - 4x + 1 = 0$$
$$\therefore \ (2x - 1)^2 = 0$$
$$\therefore \ x = \tfrac{1}{2}$$

b
$$6x^2 = 11x + 10$$
$$\therefore \ 6x^2 - 11x - 10 = 0$$
$$\therefore \ (2x - 5)(3x + 2) = 0$$
$$\therefore \ x = \tfrac{5}{2} \text{ or } -\tfrac{2}{3}$$

Example 3 ◀)) **Self Tutor**

Solve for x: $3x + \dfrac{2}{x} = -7$

RHS is short for
Right Hand Side.

$$3x + \frac{2}{x} = -7$$

$\therefore \; x\left(3x + \dfrac{2}{x}\right) = -7x$ {multiplying both sides by x}

$\therefore \;\; 3x^2 + 2 = -7x$ {expanding the brackets}

$\therefore \;\; 3x^2 + 7x + 2 = 0$ {making the RHS 0}

$\therefore \;\; (x+2)(3x+1) = 0$ {factorising}

$\therefore \;\; x = -2 \text{ or } -\frac{1}{3}$

EXERCISE 1A.1

1   Solve the following by factorisation:

a $4x^2 + 7x = 0$ **b** $6x^2 + 2x = 0$ **c** $3x^2 - 7x = 0$

d $2x^2 - 11x = 0$ **e** $3x^2 = 8x$ **f** $9x = 6x^2$

g $x^2 - 5x + 6 = 0$ **h** $x^2 = 2x + 8$ **i** $x^2 + 21 = 10x$

j $9 + x^2 = 6x$ **k** $x^2 + x = 12$ **l** $x^2 + 8x = 33$

2   Solve the following by factorisation:

a $9x^2 - 12x + 4 = 0$ **b** $2x^2 - 13x - 7 = 0$ **c** $3x^2 = 16x + 12$

d $3x^2 + 5x = 2$ **e** $2x^2 + 3 = 5x$ **f** $3x^2 + 8x + 4 = 0$

g $3x^2 = 10x + 8$ **h** $4x^2 + 4x = 3$ **i** $4x^2 = 11x + 3$

j $12x^2 = 11x + 15$ **k** $7x^2 + 6x = 1$ **l** $15x^2 + 2x = 56$

3   Solve for x:

a $(x+1)^2 = 2x^2 - 5x + 11$ **b** $(x+2)(1-x) = -4$

c $5 - 4x^2 = 3(2x+1) + 2$ **d** $x + \dfrac{2}{x} = 3$

e $2x - \dfrac{1}{x} = -1$ **f** $\dfrac{x+3}{1-x} = -\dfrac{9}{x}$

SOLVING BY 'COMPLETING THE SQUARE'

As you would be aware by now, not all quadratics factorise easily. For example, $x^2 + 4x + 1$ cannot be factorised by simple factorisation. In other words, we cannot write $x^2 + 4x + 1$ in the form $(x-a)(x-b)$ where a, b are rational.

An alternative way to solve equations like $x^2 + 4x + 1 = 0$ is by 'completing the square'.

Equations of the form $ax^2 + bx + c = 0$ can be converted to the form $(x+p)^2 = q$ from which the solutions are easy to obtain.

Example 4

Solve exactly for x: **a** $(x+2)^2 = 7$ **b** $(x-1)^2 = -5$

a $(x+2)^2 = 7$

$\therefore \ x + 2 = \pm\sqrt{7}$

$\therefore \ x = -2 \pm \sqrt{7}$

b $(x-1)^2 = -5$

has no real solutions since the square $(x-1)^2$ cannot be negative.

If $X^2 = a$, then $X = \pm\sqrt{a}$.

Example 5

Solve for exact values of x: $x^2 + 4x + 1 = 0$

$x^2 + 4x + 1 = 0$

$\therefore \ x^2 + 4x = -1$ {put the constant on the RHS}

$\therefore \ x^2 + 4x + 2^2 = -1 + 2^2$ {completing the square}

$\therefore \ (x+2)^2 = 3$ {factorising LHS}

$\therefore \ x + 2 = \pm\sqrt{3}$

$\therefore \ x = -2 \pm \sqrt{3}$

The squared number we add to both sides is $\left(\dfrac{\text{coefficient of } x}{2}\right)^2$

If the coefficient of x^2 is not 1, we first divide throughout to make it 1.

Example 6

Solve exactly for x: $-3x^2 + 12x + 5 = 0$

$-3x^2 + 12x + 5 = 0$

$\therefore \ x^2 - 4x - \frac{5}{3} = 0$ {dividing both sides by -3}

$\therefore \ x^2 - 4x = \frac{5}{3}$ {putting the constant on the RHS}

$\therefore \ x^2 - 4x + 2^2 = \frac{5}{3} + 2^2$ {completing the square}

$\therefore \ (x-2)^2 = \frac{17}{3}$ {factorising LHS}

$\therefore \ x - 2 = \pm\sqrt{\frac{17}{3}}$

$\therefore \ x = 2 \pm \sqrt{\frac{17}{3}}$

EXERCISE 1A.2

1   Solve exactly for x:

   a $(x+5)^2 = 2$ **b** $(x+6)^2 = -11$ **c** $(x-4)^2 = 8$

   d $(x-8)^2 = 7$ **e** $2(x+3)^2 = 10$ **f** $3(x-2)^2 = 18$

   g $(x+1)^2 + 1 = 11$ **h** $(2x+1)^2 = 3$ **i** $(1-3x)^2 - 7 = 0$

2   Solve exactly by completing the square:

a $x^2 - 4x + 1 = 0$

b $x^2 + 6x + 2 = 0$

c $x^2 - 14x + 46 = 0$

d $x^2 = 4x + 3$

e $x^2 + 6x + 7 = 0$

f $x^2 = 2x + 6$

g $x^2 + 6x = 2$

h $x^2 + 10 = 8x$

i $x^2 + 6x = -11$

3   Solve exactly by completing the square:

a $2x^2 + 4x + 1 = 0$

b $2x^2 - 10x + 3 = 0$

c $3x^2 + 12x + 5 = 0$

d $3x^2 = 6x + 4$

e $5x^2 - 15x + 2 = 0$

f $4x^2 + 4x = 5$

THE QUADRATIC FORMULA

In many cases, factorising a quadratic equation or completing the square can be long or difficult. We can instead use the **quadratic formula**:

$$\text{If } \quad ax^2 + bx + c = 0, \quad \text{then} \quad x = \frac{-b \pm \sqrt{b^2 - 4ac}}{2a}.$$

Proof:

If $\quad ax^2 + bx + c = 0, \quad a \neq 0$

then $\quad x^2 + \dfrac{b}{a}x + \dfrac{c}{a} = 0$ {dividing each term by a, as $a \neq 0$}

$\therefore \quad x^2 + \dfrac{b}{a}x \quad = -\dfrac{c}{a}$

$\therefore \quad x^2 + \dfrac{b}{a}x + \left(\dfrac{b}{2a}\right)^2 = -\dfrac{c}{a} + \left(\dfrac{b}{2a}\right)^2$ {completing the square on LHS}

$\therefore \quad \left(x + \dfrac{b}{2a}\right)^2 = \dfrac{b^2 - 4ac}{4a^2}$ {factorising}

$\therefore \quad x + \dfrac{b}{2a} = \pm\sqrt{\dfrac{b^2 - 4ac}{4a^2}}$

$\therefore \quad x = \dfrac{-b \pm \sqrt{b^2 - 4ac}}{2a}$

For example, consider the Acme Leather Jacket Co. equation from page **19**.

We need to solve: $12.5x^2 - 550x + 5125 = 0$
so in this case $a = 12.5, \quad b = -550, \quad c = 5125$

$\therefore \quad x = \dfrac{550 \pm \sqrt{(-550)^2 - 4(12.5)(5125)}}{2(12.5)}$

$= \dfrac{550 \pm \sqrt{46\,250}}{25}$

$\approx 30.60 \text{ or } 13.40$

Trying to factorise this equation or using 'completing the square' would not be easy.

However, for this application the number of jackets x needs to be a whole number, so $x = 13$ or 31 would produce a profit of around $3000 each week.

Example 7   ◀) **Self Tutor**

Solve for x: **a** $x^2 - 2x - 6 = 0$ **b** $2x^2 + 3x - 6 = 0$

a $x^2 - 2x - 6 = 0$ has
$a = 1$, $b = -2$, $c = -6$

$\therefore\ x = \dfrac{-(-2) \pm \sqrt{(-2)^2 - 4(1)(-6)}}{2(1)}$

$\therefore\ x = \dfrac{2 \pm \sqrt{4 + 24}}{2}$

$\therefore\ x = \dfrac{2 \pm \sqrt{28}}{2}$

$\therefore\ x = \dfrac{2 \pm 2\sqrt{7}}{2}$

$\therefore\ x = 1 \pm \sqrt{7}$

b $2x^2 + 3x - 6 = 0$ has
$a = 2$, $b = 3$, $c = -6$

$\therefore\ x = \dfrac{-3 \pm \sqrt{3^2 - 4(2)(-6)}}{2(2)}$

$\therefore\ x = \dfrac{-3 \pm \sqrt{9 + 48}}{4}$

$\therefore\ x = \dfrac{-3 \pm \sqrt{57}}{4}$

EXERCISE 1A.3

1 Use the quadratic formula to solve exactly for x:

   a $x^2 - 4x - 3 = 0$ **b** $x^2 + 6x + 7 = 0$ **c** $x^2 + 1 = 4x$

   d $x^2 + 4x = 1$ **e** $x^2 - 4x + 2 = 0$ **f** $2x^2 - 2x - 3 = 0$

   g $(3x + 1)^2 = -2x$ **h** $(x + 3)(2x + 1) = 9$

2 Rearrange the following equations so they are written in the form $ax^2 + bx + c = 0$, then use the quadratic formula to solve exactly for x.

   a $(x + 2)(x - 1) = 2 - 3x$ **b** $(2x + 1)^2 = 3 - x$ **c** $(x - 2)^2 = 1 + x$

   d $\dfrac{x - 1}{2 - x} = 2x + 1$ **e** $x - \dfrac{1}{x} = 1$ **f** $2x - \dfrac{1}{x} = 3$

SOLVING USING TECHNOLOGY

You can use your graphics calculator to solve quadratic equations.

If the right hand side is zero, you can graph the expression on the left hand side. The x-intercepts of the graph will be the solutions to the quadratic.

GRAPHICS CALCULATOR INSTRUCTIONS

If the right hand side is non-zero, you can either:

- rearrange the equation so the right hand side is zero, then graph the expression and find the x-intercepts, or
- graph the expressions on the left and right hand sides on the same set of axes, then find the x-coordinates of the point where they meet.

Use technology to check your answers to **Exercise 1A.3**.

B THE DISCRIMINANT OF A QUADRATIC

In the quadratic formula, the quantity $b^2 - 4ac$ under the square root sign is called the **discriminant**.

The symbol **delta** Δ is used to represent the discriminant, so $\Delta = b^2 - 4ac$.

The quadratic formula becomes $x = \dfrac{-b \pm \sqrt{\Delta}}{2a}$ where Δ replaces $b^2 - 4ac$.

- If $\Delta = 0$, $x = \dfrac{-b}{2a}$ is the **only solution** (a **repeated** or **double root**)
- If $\Delta > 0$, $\sqrt{\Delta}$ is a positive real number, so there are **two distinct real roots**

$$x = \frac{-b + \sqrt{\Delta}}{2a} \quad \text{and} \quad x = \frac{-b - \sqrt{\Delta}}{2a}$$

- If $\Delta < 0$, $\sqrt{\Delta}$ is not a real number and so there are **no real roots**.
- If a, b, and c are rational and Δ is a **square** then the equation has two rational roots which can be found by factorisation.

Example 8 ◀)) Self Tutor

Use the discriminant to determine the nature of the roots of:

a $2x^2 - 2x + 3 = 0$ **b** $3x^2 - 4x - 2 = 0$

a $\Delta = b^2 - 4ac$
$= (-2)^2 - 4(2)(3)$
$= -20$
Since $\Delta < 0$, there are no real roots.

b $\Delta = b^2 - 4ac$
$= (-4)^2 - 4(3)(-2)$
$= 40$
Since $\Delta > 0$, but 40 is not a square, there are 2 distinct irrational roots.

Example 9 ◀)) Self Tutor

Consider $x^2 - 2x + m = 0$. Find the discriminant Δ, and hence find the values of m for which the equation has:

a a repeated root **b** 2 distinct real roots **c** no real roots.

$x^2 - 2x + m = 0$ has $a = 1$, $b = -2$, and $c = m$
$\therefore \Delta = b^2 - 4ac$
$= (-2)^2 - 4(1)(m)$
$= 4 - 4m$

a For a repeated root
$\Delta = 0$
$\therefore 4 - 4m = 0$
$\therefore 4 = 4m$
$\therefore m = 1$

b For 2 distinct real roots
$\Delta > 0$
$\therefore 4 - 4m > 0$
$\therefore -4m > -4$
$\therefore m < 1$

c For no real roots
$\Delta < 0$
$\therefore 4 - 4m < 0$
$\therefore -4m < -4$
$\therefore m > 1$

Summary:

Factorisation of quadratic	Roots of quadratic	Discriminant value
two distinct linear factors	two real distinct roots	$\Delta > 0$
two identical linear factors	two identical real roots (repeated)	$\Delta = 0$
unable to factorise	no real roots	$\Delta < 0$

Example 10   ◀》 **Self Tutor**

Consider the equation $kx^2 + (k+3)x = 1$.   Find the discriminant Δ and draw its sign diagram.
Hence, find the value of k for which the equation has:

  a   two distinct real roots   **b**   two real roots

  c   a repeated root   **d**   no real roots.

$kx^2 + (k+3)x - 1 = 0$ has $a = k$, $b = (k+3)$, and $c = -1$

$\therefore \ \Delta = b^2 - 4ac$

$\qquad = (k+3)^2 - 4(k)(-1)$ and has sign diagram:

$\qquad = k^2 + 6k + 9 + 4k$

$\qquad = k^2 + 10k + 9$

$\qquad = (k+9)(k+1)$

  a   For two distinct real roots, $\Delta > 0$ $\therefore$ $k < -9$ or $k > -1$.

  b   For two real roots, $\Delta \geqslant 0$ $\therefore$ $k \leqslant -9$ or $k \geqslant -1$.

  c   For a repeated root, $\Delta = 0$ $\therefore$ $k = -9$ or $k = -1$.

  d   For no real roots, $\Delta < 0$ $\therefore$ $-9 < k < -1$.

EXERCISE 1B

1   By using the discriminant only, state the nature of the solutions of:

  a $x^2 + 7x - 3 = 0$ **b** $x^2 - 3x + 2 = 0$ **c** $3x^2 + 2x - 1 = 0$

  d $5x^2 + 4x - 3 = 0$ **e** $x^2 + x + 5 = 0$ **f** $16x^2 - 8x + 1 = 0$

2   By using the discriminant only, determine which of the following quadratic equations have rational roots which can be found by factorisation.

  a $6x^2 - 5x - 6 = 0$ **b** $2x^2 - 7x - 5 = 0$ **c** $3x^2 + 4x + 1 = 0$

  d $6x^2 - 47x - 8 = 0$ **e** $4x^2 - 3x + 2 = 0$ **f** $8x^2 + 2x - 3 = 0$

3   For each of the following quadratic equations, determine the discriminant Δ in simplest form and draw its sign diagram. Hence find the value(s) of m for which the equation has:

     i   a repeated root   **ii**   two distinct real roots   **iii**   no real roots.

  a $x^2 + 4x + m = 0$ **b** $mx^2 + 3x + 2 = 0$ **c** $mx^2 - 3x + 1 = 0$

4   For each of the following quadratic equations, find the discriminant Δ and hence draw its sign diagram. Find all values of k for which the equation has:

     i   two distinct real roots   **ii**   two real roots   **iii**   a repeated root   **iv**   no real roots.

  a $2x^2 + kx - k = 0$ **b** $kx^2 - 2x + k = 0$

  c $x^2 + (k+2)x + 4 = 0$ **d** $2x^2 + (k-2)x + 2 = 0$

  e $x^2 + (3k-1)x + (2k+10) = 0$ **f** $(k+1)x^2 + kx + k = 0$

HISTORICAL NOTE   THE QUADRATIC FORMULA

Thousands of years ago, people knew how to calculate the area of a shape given its side lengths. When they wanted to find the side lengths necessary to give a certain area, however, they ended up with a quadratic equation which they needed to solve.

The first known solution of a quadratic equation is written on the Berlin Papyrus from the Middle Kingdom (2160 - 1700 BC) in Egypt. By 400 BC, the Babylonians were using the method of 'completing the square'.

Pythagoras and Euclid both used geometric methods to explore the problem. Pythagoras noted that the square root wasn't always an integer, but he refused to accept that irrational solutions existed. Euclid also discovered that the square root wasn't always rational, but concluded that irrational numbers *did* exist.

A major jump forward was made in India around 700 AD, when Hindu mathematician Brahmagupta devised a general (but incomplete) solution for the quadratic equation $ax^2 + bx = c$ which was equivalent to $x = \dfrac{\sqrt{4ac + b^2} - b}{2a}$. Taking into account the sign of c, this is one of the two solutions we know today.

> Brahmagupta also added *zero* to our number system!

The final, complete solution as we know it today first came around 1100 AD, by another Hindu mathematician called Baskhara. He was the first to recognise that any positive number has two square roots, which could be negative or irrational. In fact, the quadratic formula is known in some countries today as 'Baskhara's Formula'.

While the Indians had knowledge of the quadratic formula even at this early stage, it took somewhat longer for the quadratic formula to arrive in Europe.

Around 820 AD, the Islamic mathematician Muhammad bin Musa Al-Khwarizmi, who was familiar with the work of Brahmagupta, recognised that for a quadratic equation to have real solutions, the value $b^2 - 4ac$ could not be negative. Al-Khwarizmi's work was brought to Europe by the Jewish mathematician and astronomer Abraham bar Hiyya (also known as Savasorda) who lived in Barcelona around 1100.

Muhammad Al-Khwarizmi

By 1545, Girolamo Cardano had blended the algebra of Al-Khwarizmi with the Euclidean geometry. His work allowed for the existence of complex or imaginary roots, as well as negative and irrational roots.

> From the name Al-Khwarizmi we get the word 'algorithm'.

At the end of the 16th Century the mathematical notation and symbolism was introduced by François Viète in France.

In 1637, when René Descartes published *La Géométrie*, the quadratic formula adopted the form we know today: $x = \dfrac{-b \pm \sqrt{b^2 - 4ac}}{2a}$.

C   QUADRATIC FUNCTIONS

A **quadratic function** has the form $y = ax^2 + bx + c$ where $a \neq 0$.

The simplest quadratic function is $y = x^2$. Its graph can be drawn from a table of values.

x	-3	-2	-1	0	1	2	3
y	9	4	1	0	1	4	9

The graph of a quadratic function is called a **parabola**.

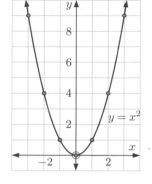

The parabola is one of the **conic sections**, the others being circles, hyperbolae, and ellipses. They are called conic sections because they can be obtained by cutting a cone with a plane. A parabola is produced by cutting the cone with a plane parallel to its slant side.

There are many examples of parabolas in everyday life, including water fountains, suspension bridges, and radio telescopes.

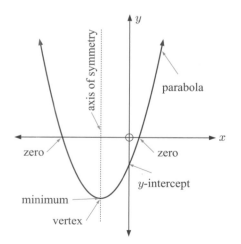

TERMINOLOGY

The graph of a quadratic function $y = ax^2 + bx + c$, $a \neq 0$ is called a **parabola**.

The point where the graph 'turns' is called the **vertex**.

If the graph opens upwards, the y-coordinate of the vertex is the **minimum** or **minimum turning point** and the graph is **concave upwards**.

If the graph opens downwards, the y-coordinate of the vertex is the **maximum** or **maximum turning point** and the graph is **concave downwards**.

The vertical line that passes through the vertex is called the **axis of symmetry**. Every parabola is symmetrical about its axis of symmetry.

The point where the graph crosses the y-axis is the **y-intercept**.

The points (if they exist) where the graph crosses the x-axis are called the **x-intercepts**. They correspond to the **roots** of the equation $y = 0$.

INVESTIGATION 1   GRAPHING $y = a(x - p)(x - q)$

This investigation is best done using a **graphing package** or **graphics calculator**.

What to do:

GRAPHING
PACKAGE

1 **a** Use technology to help you to sketch:

$y = (x - 1)(x - 3),$ $y = 2(x - 1)(x - 3),$ $y = -(x - 1)(x - 3),$

$y = -3(x - 1)(x - 3)$ and $y = -\frac{1}{2}(x - 1)(x - 3)$

 b Find the x-intercepts for each function in **a**.

 c What is the geometrical significance of a in $y = a(x - 1)(x - 3)$?

2 **a** Use technology to help you to sketch:

$y = 2(x - 1)(x - 4),$ $y = 2(x - 3)(x - 5),$ $y = 2(x + 1)(x - 2),$

$y = 2x(x + 5)$ and $y = 2(x + 2)(x + 4)$

 b Find the x-intercepts for each function in **a**.

 c What is the geometrical significance of p and q in $y = 2(x - p)(x - q)$?

3 **a** Use technology to help you to sketch:

$y = 2(x - 1)^2,$ $y = 2(x - 3)^2,$ $y = 2(x + 2)^2,$ $y = 2x^2$

 b Find the x-intercepts for each function in **a**.

 c What is the geometrical significance of p in $y = 2(x - p)^2$?

4 Copy and complete:

  • If a quadratic has the form $y = a(x - p)(x - q)$ then it ...... the x-axis at ......

  • If a quadratic has the form $y = a(x - p)^2$ then it ...... the x-axis at ......

INVESTIGATION 2   GRAPHING $y = a(x - h)^2 + k$

This investigation is also best done using technology.

What to do:

GRAPHING
PACKAGE

1 **a** Use technology to help you to sketch:

$y = (x - 3)^2 + 2,$ $y = 2(x - 3)^2 + 2,$ $y = -2(x - 3)^2 + 2,$

$y = -(x - 3)^2 + 2$ and $y = -\frac{1}{3}(x - 3)^2 + 2$

 b Find the coordinates of the vertex for each function in **a**.

 c What is the geometrical significance of a in $y = a(x - 3)^2 + 2$?

2 **a** Use technology to help you to sketch:

$y = 2(x - 1)^2 + 3,$ $y = 2(x - 2)^2 + 4,$ $y = 2(x - 3)^2 + 1,$

$y = 2(x + 1)^2 + 4,$ $y = 2(x + 2)^2 - 5$ and $y = 2(x + 3)^2 - 2$

 b Find the coordinates of the vertex for each function in **a**.

 c What is the geometrical significance of h and k in $y = 2(x - h)^2 + k$?

3 Copy and complete:

 If a quadratic has the form $y = a(x - h)^2 + k$ then its vertex has coordinates ......

 The graph of $y = a(x - h)^2 + k$ is a ...... of the graph of $y = ax^2$ with vector ......

From **Investigations 1** and **2** you should have discovered that a, the coefficient of x^2, controls the width of the graph and whether it opens upwards or downwards.

> For a quadratic function $y = ax^2 + bx + c$, $a \neq 0$:
>
> - $a > 0$ produces the shape $\smile$ called concave up.
>
> $a < 0$ produces the shape $\frown$ called concave down.
>
> - If $-1 < a < 1$, $a \neq 0$ the graph is wider than $y = x^2$.
>   If $a < -1$ or $a > 1$ the graph is narrower than $y = x^2$.

Summary:

Quadratic form, $a \neq 0$	Graph	Facts
• $y = a(x - p)(x - q)$ p, q are real		x-intercepts are p and q axis of symmetry is $x = \frac{p+q}{2}$ vertex is $\left(\frac{p+q}{2}, f\left(\frac{p+q}{2}\right) \right)$
• $y = a(x - h)^2$ h is real		touches x-axis at h axis of symmetry is $x = h$ vertex is $(h, 0)$
• $y = a(x - h)^2 + k$		axis of symmetry is $x = h$ vertex is (h, k)
• $y = ax^2 + bx + c$		y-intercept c axis of symmetry is $x = \frac{-b}{2a}$ vertex is $\left(-\frac{b}{2a}, c - \frac{b^2}{4a} \right)$ x-intercepts for $\Delta \geqslant 0$ are $\frac{-b \pm \sqrt{\Delta}}{2a}$ where $\Delta = b^2 - 4ac$

$-\dfrac{b}{2a}$ is the **average** of $\dfrac{-b - \sqrt{\Delta}}{2a}$ and $\dfrac{-b + \sqrt{\Delta}}{2a}$

Example 11 ◀◎ **Self Tutor**

Using axes intercepts only, sketch the graphs of:

a $y = 2(x+3)(x-1)$ **b** $y = -2(x-1)(x-2)$ **c** $y = \frac{1}{2}(x+2)^2$

a $y = 2(x+3)(x-1)$
has x-intercepts $-3, 1$
When $x = 0$,
$\quad y = 2(3)(-1)$
$\quad\quad = -6$
$\therefore$ y-intercept is -6

b $y = -2(x-1)(x-2)$
has x-intercepts $1, 2$
When $x = 0$,
$\quad y = -2(-1)(-2)$
$\quad\quad = -4$
$\therefore$ y-intercept is -4

c $y = \frac{1}{2}(x+2)^2$
touches x-axis at -2
When $x = 0$,
$\quad y = \frac{1}{2}(2)^2$
$\quad\quad = 2$
$\therefore$ y-intercept is 2

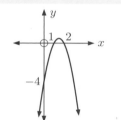

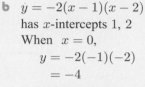

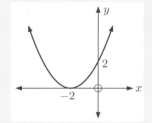

EXERCISE 1C.1

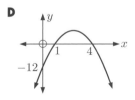

The axis of symmetry is midway between the x-intercepts.

1 Using axes intercepts only, sketch the graphs of:

a $y = (x-4)(x+2)$ **b** $y = -(x-4)(x+2)$

c $y = 2(x+3)(x+5)$ **d** $y = -3x(x+4)$

e $y = 2(x+3)^2$ **f** $y = -\frac{1}{4}(x+2)^2$

2 State the equation of the axis of symmetry for each graph in question **1**.

3 Match each quadratic function with its corresponding graph.

a $y = 2(x-1)(x-4)$ **b** $y = -(x+1)(x-4)$

c $y = (x-1)(x-4)$ **d** $y = (x+1)(x-4)$

e $y = 2(x+4)(x-1)$ **f** $y = -3(x+4)(x-1)$

g $y = -(x-1)(x-4)$ **h** $y = -3(x-1)(x-4)$

A
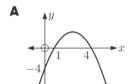

B
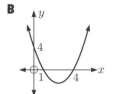

C
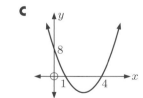

D

E
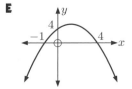

F
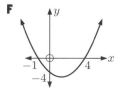

G
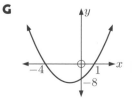

H
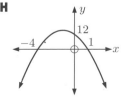

| **Example 12** | ◀) **Self Tutor** |

Use the vertex, axis of symmetry, and y-intercept to graph $y = -2(x+1)^2 + 4$.

The vertex is $(-1, 4)$.

The axis of symmetry is $x = -1$.

When $x = 0$, $y = -2(1)^2 + 4$
$$= 2$$

$a < 0$ so the shape is $\cap$

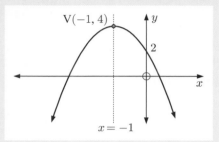

4   Use the vertex, axis of symmetry, and y-intercept to graph:

    a $y = (x-1)^2 + 3$
    b $y = 2(x+2)^2 + 1$
    c $y = -2(x-1)^2 - 3$

    d $y = \frac{1}{2}(x-3)^2 + 2$
    e $y = -\frac{1}{3}(x-1)^2 + 4$
    f $y = -\frac{1}{10}(x+2)^2 - 3$

5   Match each quadratic function with its corresponding graph:

    a $y = -(x+1)^2 + 3$
    b $y = -2(x-3)^2 + 2$
    c $y = x^2 + 2$

    d $y = -(x-1)^2 + 1$
    e $y = (x-2)^2 - 2$
    f $y = \frac{1}{3}(x+3)^2 - 3$

    g $y = -x^2$
    h $y = -\frac{1}{2}(x-1)^2 + 1$
    i $y = 2(x+2)^2 - 1$

A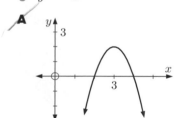

B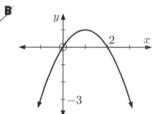

C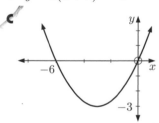

D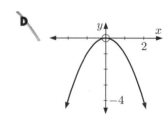

E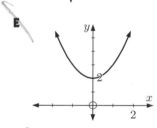

F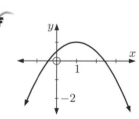

G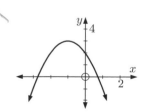

H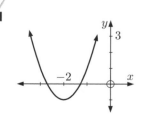

I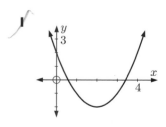

Example 13 ◀) **Self Tutor**

Determine the coordinates of the vertex of $y = 2x^2 - 8x + 1$.

> The vertex is the **maximum** or the **minimum** depending on whether the graph is concave down or concave up.

$y = 2x^2 - 8x + 1$ has $a = 2$, $b = -8$, and $c = 1$

$$\therefore \quad \frac{-b}{2a} = \frac{-(-8)}{2 \times 2} = 2$$

$\therefore$ the axis of symmetry is $x = 2$

When $x = 2$, $y = 2(2)^2 - 8(2) + 1$
$$= -7$$

$\therefore$ the vertex has coordinates $(2, -7)$.

6 Locate the turning point or vertex for each of the following quadratic functions:

    a $y = x^2 - 4x + 2$ **b** $y = x^2 + 2x - 3$ **c** $y = 2x^2 + 4$

    d $y = -3x^2 + 1$ **e** $y = 2x^2 + 8x - 7$ **f** $y = -x^2 - 4x - 9$

    g $y = 2x^2 + 6x - 1$ **h** $y = 2x^2 - 10x + 3$ **i** $y = -\frac{1}{2}x^2 + x - 5$

7 Find the x-intercepts for:

    a $y = x^2 - 9$ **b** $y = 2x^2 - 6$ **c** $y = x^2 + 7x + 10$

    d $y = x^2 + x - 12$ **e** $y = 4x - x^2$ **f** $y = -x^2 - 6x - 8$

    g $y = -2x^2 - 4x - 2$ **h** $y = 4x^2 - 24x + 36$ **i** $y = x^2 - 4x + 1$

    j $y = x^2 + 4x - 3$ **k** $y = x^2 - 6x - 2$ **l** $y = x^2 + 8x + 11$

Example 14 ◀) **Self Tutor**

Consider the quadratic $y = 2x^2 + 6x - 3$.

    a State the axis of symmetry.   **b** Find the coordinates of the vertex.

    c Find the axes intercepts.   **d** Hence, sketch the quadratic.

$y = 2x^2 + 6x - 3$ has $a = 2$, $b = 6$, and $c = -3$.

$a > 0$ so the shape is $\bigvee$

    a $\frac{-b}{2a} = \frac{-6}{4} = -\frac{3}{2}$

        The axis of symmetry is $x = -\frac{3}{2}$.

    b When $x = -\frac{3}{2}$,
        $$y = 2(-\tfrac{3}{2})^2 + 6(-\tfrac{3}{2}) - 3 = -7\tfrac{1}{2}$$
        The vertex is $(-\frac{3}{2}, -7\frac{1}{2})$.

    c When $x = 0$, $y = -3$
        $\therefore$ y-intercept is -3.
        When $y = 0$, $2x^2 + 6x - 3 = 0$
        Using technology,
        $x \approx -3.44$ or 0.436

    d

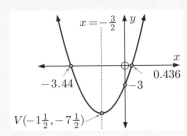

8 For each of the following quadratics:

    i state the axis of symmetry   **ii** find the coordinates of the vertex

    iii find the axes intercepts, if they exist   **iv** sketch the quadratic.

a $y = x^2 - 2x + 5$ **b** $y = x^2 + 4x - 1$ **c** $y = 2x^2 - 5x + 2$

d $y = -x^2 + 3x - 2$ **e** $y = -3x^2 + 4x - 1$ **f** $y = -2x^2 + x + 1$

g $y = 6x - x^2$ **h** $y = -x^2 - 6x - 8$ **i** $y = -\frac{1}{4}x^2 + 2x + 1$

ACTIVITY

Click on the icon to run a card game for quadratic functions.

CARD GAME

SKETCHING GRAPHS BY 'COMPLETING THE SQUARE'

If we wish to find the vertex of a quadratic given in general form $y = ax^2 + bx + c$ then one approach is to convert it to the form $y = a(x - h)^2 + k$ where we can read off the coordinates of the vertex (h, k). One way to do this is to 'complete the square'.

Consider the simple case $y = x^2 - 4x + 1$, for which $a = 1$.

$$y = x^2 - 4x + 1$$
$$\therefore \quad y = \underbrace{x^2 - 4x + 2^2}_{} \underbrace{+ 1 - 2^2}_{}$$
$$\therefore \quad y = \quad (x - 2)^2 \quad - 3$$

To obtain the graph of $y = x^2 - 4x + 1$ from the graph of $y = x^2$, we shift it 2 units to the right and 3 units down.

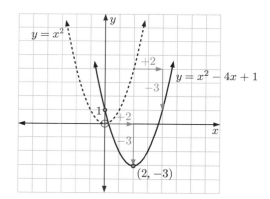

Example 15

    🔊 **Self Tutor**

Write $y = x^2 + 4x + 3$ in the form $y = (x - h)^2 + k$ by 'completing the square'. Hence sketch $y = x^2 + 4x + 3$, stating the coordinates of the vertex.

$$y = x^2 + 4x + 3$$
$$\therefore \quad y = x^2 + 4x + 2^2 + 3 - 2^2$$
$$\therefore \quad y = (x + 2)^2 - 1$$

    shift 2   shift 1

  units left   unit down

The vertex is $(-2, -1)$ and the y-intercept is 3.

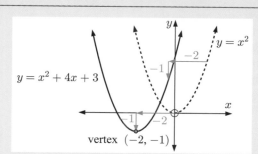

EXERCISE 1C.2

1 Write the following quadratics in the form $y = (x - h)^2 + k$ by 'completing the square'. Hence sketch each function, stating the coordinates of the vertex.

a $y = x^2 - 2x + 3$

b $y = x^2 + 4x - 2$

c $y = x^2 - 4x$

d $y = x^2 + 3x$

e $y = x^2 + 5x - 2$

f $y = x^2 - 3x + 2$

g $y = x^2 - 6x + 5$

h $y = x^2 + 8x - 2$

i $y = x^2 - 5x + 1$

Example 16 ◀)) **Self Tutor**

a Convert $y = 3x^2 - 4x + 1$ to the form $y = a(x - h)^2 + k$ without technology.

b Hence, write down the coordinates of its vertex and sketch the quadratic. Use technology to check your answer.

a $y = 3x^2 - 4x + 1$

$= 3[x^2 - \frac{4}{3}x + \frac{1}{3}]$ {taking out a factor of 3}

$= 3[x^2 - 2(\frac{2}{3})x + (\frac{2}{3})^2 - (\frac{2}{3})^2 + \frac{1}{3}]$ {completing the square}

$= 3[(x - \frac{2}{3})^2 - \frac{4}{9} + \frac{3}{9}]$ {writing as a perfect square}

$= 3[(x - \frac{2}{3})^2 - \frac{1}{9}]$

$= 3(x - \frac{2}{3})^2 - \frac{1}{3}$

b The vertex is $(\frac{2}{3}, -\frac{1}{3})$ and the y-intercept is 1.

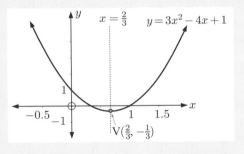

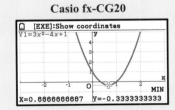

Casio fx-CG20

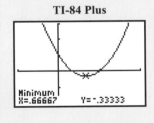

TI-84 Plus

TI-*n*spire

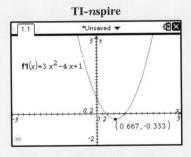

---

2 For each of the following quadratics:

i Write the quadratic in the form $y = a(x - h)^2 + k$ without using technology.

ii State the coordinates of the vertex.

iii Find the y-intercept.

iv Sketch the graph of the quadratic.

v Use technology to check your answers.

a $y = 2x^2 + 4x + 5$

b $y = 2x^2 - 8x + 3$

c $y = 2x^2 - 6x + 1$

d $y = 3x^2 - 6x + 5$

e $y = -x^2 + 4x + 2$

f $y = -2x^2 - 5x + 3$

a is always the factor to be 'taken out'.

3 Use the **graphing package** or your **graphics calculator** to determine the vertex of each of the following functions. *Hence* write each function in the form $y = a(x - h)^2 + k$.

GRAPHING PACKAGE

a $y = x^2 - 4x + 7$

b $y = x^2 + 6x + 3$

c $y = -x^2 + 4x + 5$

d $y = 2x^2 + 6x - 4$

e $y = -2x^2 - 10x + 1$

f $y = 3x^2 - 9x - 5$

THE DISCRIMINANT AND THE QUADRATIC GRAPH

The discriminant of the quadratic equation $ax^2 + bx + c = 0$ is $\Delta = b^2 - 4ac$.

We used Δ to determine the number of real roots of the equation. If they exist, these roots correspond to zeros of the quadratic $y = ax^2 + bx + c$. Δ therefore tells us about the relationship between a quadratic function and the x-axis.

The graphs of $y = x^2 - 2x + 3$, $y = x^2 - 2x + 1$, and $y = x^2 - 2x - 3$ all have the same axis of symmetry, $x = 1$.

Consider the following table:

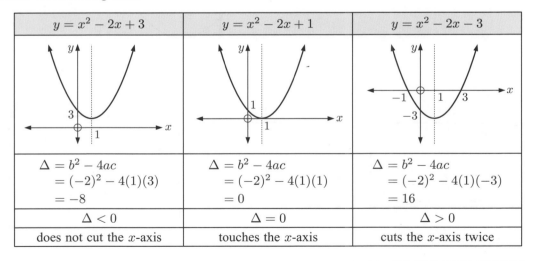

$y = x^2 - 2x + 3$	$y = x^2 - 2x + 1$	$y = x^2 - 2x - 3$
$\begin{aligned}\Delta &= b^2 - 4ac \\ &= (-2)^2 - 4(1)(3) \\ &= -8\end{aligned}$	$\begin{aligned}\Delta &= b^2 - 4ac \\ &= (-2)^2 - 4(1)(1) \\ &= 0\end{aligned}$	$\begin{aligned}\Delta &= b^2 - 4ac \\ &= (-2)^2 - 4(1)(-3) \\ &= 16\end{aligned}$
$\Delta < 0$	$\Delta = 0$	$\Delta > 0$
does not cut the x-axis	touches the x-axis	cuts the x-axis twice

For a quadratic function $y = ax^2 + bx + c$, we consider the discriminant $\Delta = b^2 - 4ac$.

If $\Delta < 0$, the graph does not cut the x-axis.

If $\Delta = 0$, the graph *touches* the x-axis.

If $\Delta > 0$, the graph cuts the x-axis twice.

POSITIVE DEFINITE AND NEGATIVE DEFINITE QUADRATICS

Positive definite quadratics are quadratics which are positive for all values of x. So, $ax^2 + bx + c > 0$ for all $x \in \mathbb{R}$.

Test: A quadratic is **positive definite** if and only if $a > 0$ and $\Delta < 0$.

Negative definite quadratics are quadratics which are negative for all values of x. So, $ax^2 + bx + c < 0$ for all $x \in \mathbb{R}$.

Test: A quadratic is **negative definite** if and only if $a < 0$ and $\Delta < 0$.

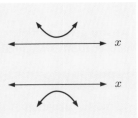

Example 17 ◀)) **Self Tutor**

Use the discriminant to determine the relationship between the graph of each function and the x-axis:

a $y = x^2 + 3x + 4$

b $y = -2x^2 + 5x + 1$

a $a = 1$, $b = 3$, $c = 4$
$\therefore \ \Delta = b^2 - 4ac$
$\quad = 9 - 4(1)(4)$
$\quad = -7$

Since $\Delta < 0$, the graph does not cut the x-axis.
Since $a > 0$, the graph is concave up.

The graph is positive definite, and lies entirely above the x-axis.

b $a = -2$, $b = 5$, $c = 1$
$\therefore \ \Delta = b^2 - 4ac$
$\quad = 25 - 4(-2)(1)$
$\quad = 33$

Since $\Delta > 0$, the graph cuts the x-axis twice.
Since $a < 0$, the graph is concave down.

EXERCISE 1C.3

1 Use the discriminant to determine the relationship between the graph and x-axis for:

a $y = x^2 + x - 2$
b $y = x^2 - 4x + 1$
c $y = -x^2 - 3$
d $y = x^2 + 7x - 2$
e $y = x^2 + 8x + 16$
f $y = -2x^2 + 3x + 1$
g $y = 6x^2 + 5x - 4$
h $y = -x^2 + x + 6$
i $y = 9x^2 + 6x + 1$

2 Show that:

a $x^2 - 3x + 6 > 0$ for all x
b $4x - x^2 - 6 < 0$ for all x
c $2x^2 - 4x + 7$ is positive definite
d $-2x^2 + 3x - 4$ is negative definite.

3 Explain why $3x^2 + kx - 1$ is never positive definite for any value of k.

4 Under what conditions is $2x^2 + kx + 2$ positive definite?

D   FINDING A QUADRATIC FROM ITS GRAPH

If we are given sufficient information on or about a graph we can determine the quadratic function in whatever form is required.

Example 18   ◀) Self Tutor

Find the equation of the quadratic function with graph:

a

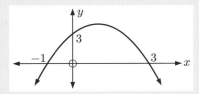

b

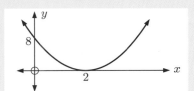

a Since the x-intercepts are -1 and 3,
$y = a(x+1)(x-3)$.
The graph is concave down, so $a < 0$.
When $x = 0$, $y = 3$
$\therefore \quad 3 = a(1)(-3)$
$\therefore \quad a = -1$
The quadratic function is
$y = -(x+1)(x-3)$.

b The graph touches the x-axis at $x = 2$,
so $y = a(x-2)^2$.
The graph is concave up, so $a > 0$.
When $x = 0$, $y = 8$
$\therefore \quad 8 = a(-2)^2$
$\therefore \quad a = 2$
The quadratic function is
$y = 2(x-2)^2$.

Example 19   ◀) Self Tutor

Find the equation of the quadratic function with graph:

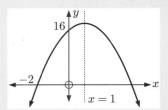

The axis of symmetry $x = 1$ lies midway between the x-intercepts.

$\therefore$ the other x-intercept is 4.

$\therefore$ the quadratic has the form
$$y = a(x+2)(x-4) \quad \text{where} \quad a < 0$$
But when $x = 0$, $y = 16$
$\therefore \quad 16 = a(2)(-4)$
$\therefore \quad a = -2$

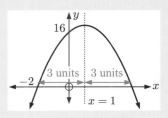

The quadratic is $y = -2(x+2)(x-4)$.

EXERCISE 1D

1 Find the equation of the quadratic with graph:

a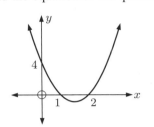

b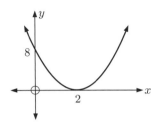

c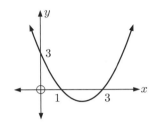

d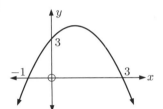

e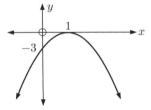

f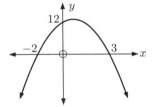

2 Find the quadratic with graph:

a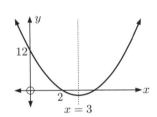

b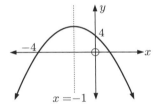

c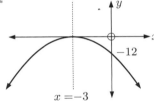

Example 20 🔊 **Self Tutor**

Find the equation of the quadratic whose graph cuts the x-axis at 4 and -3, and which passes through the point $(2, -20)$. Give your answer in the form $y = ax^2 + bx + c$.

Since the x-intercepts are 4 and -3, the quadratic has the form $y = a(x - 4)(x + 3)$ where $a \neq 0$.

When $x = 2$, $y = -20$

$\therefore \quad -20 = a(2 - 4)(2 + 3)$

$\therefore \quad -20 = a(-2)(5)$

$\therefore \quad a = 2$

The quadratic is $y = 2(x - 4)(x + 3)$

$ = 2(x^2 - x - 12)$

$ = 2x^2 - 2x - 24$

3 Find, in the form $y = ax^2 + bx + c$,   the equation of the quadratic whose graph:

    a cuts the x-axis at 5 and 1, and passes through $(2, -9)$

    b cuts the x-axis at 2 and $-\frac{1}{2}$, and passes through $(3, -14)$

    c touches the x-axis at 3 and passes through $(-2, -25)$

    d touches the x-axis at -2 and passes through $(-1, 4)$

    e cuts the x-axis at 3, passes through $(5, 12)$ and has axis of symmetry $x = 2$

    f cuts the x-axis at 5, passes through $(2, 5)$ and has axis of symmetry $x = 1$.

Example 21   ◀)) **Self Tutor**

Find the equation of each quadratic function given its graph:

a
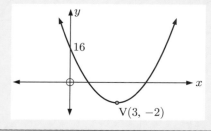

b
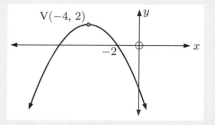

a Since the vertex is $(3, -2)$, the quadratic has the form
$y = a(x - 3)^2 - 2$ where $a > 0$.
When $x = 0$, $y = 16$
$$\therefore \quad 16 = a(-3)^2 - 2$$
$$\therefore \quad 16 = 9a - 2$$
$$\therefore \quad 18 = 9a$$
$$\therefore \quad a = 2$$
The quadratic is $y = 2(x - 3)^2 - 2$.

b Since the vertex is $(-4, 2)$, the quadratic has the form
$y = a(x + 4)^2 + 2$ where $a < 0$.
When $x = -2$, $y = 0$
$$\therefore \quad 0 = a(2)^2 + 2$$
$$\therefore \quad 4a = -2$$
$$\therefore \quad a = -\tfrac{1}{2}$$
The quadratic is
$$y = -\tfrac{1}{2}(x + 4)^2 + 2.$$

---

4 If V is the vertex, find the equation of the quadratic function with graph:

a
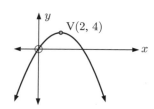

b
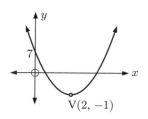

c
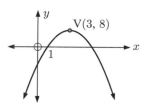

d
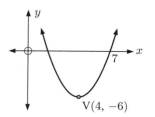

e
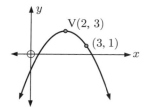

f
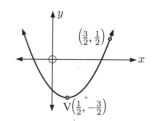

INVESTIGATION 3   FINDING QUADRATIC FUNCTIONS

For the quadratic function $y = 2x^2 + 3x + 7$ we can find a table of values for $x = 1, 2, 3, 4, 5$.

x	0	1	2	3	4	5
y	7	12	21	34	51	72

We turn this table into a **difference table** by adding two further rows:

- the row Δ_1 gives the differences between successive y-values

- the row Δ_2 gives the differences between successive Δ_1-values.

x	0	1	2	3	4	5
y	7	12	21	34	51	72
Δ_1		5	9	13	17	21
Δ_2			4	4	4	4

$9 - 5$ $34 - 21$ $72 - 51$

What to do:

1. Construct difference tables for $x = 0, 1, 2, 3, 4, 5$ for each of the following quadratic functions:

   a $y = x^2 + 4x + 3$ **b** $y = 3x^2 - 4x$

   c $y = 5x - x^2$ **d** $y = 4x^2 - 5x + 2$

2. What do you notice about the Δ_2 row for each of the quadratic functions in **1**?

3. Consider the general quadratic $y = ax^2 + bx + c$, $a \neq 0$.

   a Copy and complete the following difference table:

x	0	1	2	3	4	5
y	ⓒ	$a + b + c$	$4a + 2b + c$	......	......	......
Δ_1	◯	......	......	......	......	
Δ_2		◯	......	......	......	

   b Comment on the Δ_2 row.

   c What can the encircled numbers be used for?

4. Use your observations in **3** to determine, if possible, the quadratic functions with the following tables of values:

   a

x	0	1	2	3	4
y	6	5	8	15	26

   b

x	0	1	2	3	4
y	8	10	18	32	52

   c

x	0	1	2	3	4
y	1	2	-1	-8	-19

   d

x	0	1	2	3	4
y	5	3	-1	-7	-15

5. We wish to determine the **maximum** number of pieces into which a pizza can be cut using n cuts across it.

   For example, for $n = 1$ we have   which has 2 pieces

   for $n = 3$ we have   which has 7 pieces.

a Copy and complete:

Number of cuts, n	0	1	2	3	4	5
Maximum number of pieces, P_n						

b Complete the Δ_1 and Δ_2 rows. Hence determine a quadratic formula for P_n.

c For a huge pizza with 12 cuts across it, find the maximum number of pieces which can result.

E   WHERE FUNCTIONS MEET

Consider the graphs of a quadratic function and a linear function on the same set of axes.

Notice that we could have:

cutting	**touching**	**missing**
(2 points of intersection)	(1 point of intersection)	(no points of intersection)

If the graphs meet, the coordinates of the points of intersection of the graphs can be found by *solving the two equations simultaneously*.

Example 22   ◀)） **Self Tutor**

Find the coordinates of the points of intersection of the graphs with equations $y = x^2 - x - 18$ and $y = x - 3$ without technology.

$y = x^2 - x - 18$ meets $y = x - 3$ where

$$x^2 - x - 18 = x - 3$$
$$\therefore \ x^2 - 2x - 15 = 0 \qquad \{\text{RHS} = 0\}$$
$$\therefore \ (x - 5)(x + 3) = 0 \qquad \{\text{factorising}\}$$
$$\therefore \ x = 5 \text{ or } -3$$

Substituting into $y = x - 3$,   when $x = 5$, $y = 2$ and when $x = -3$, $y = -6$.

$\therefore$ the graphs meet at $(5, 2)$ and $(-3, -6)$.

EXERCISE 1E

1 Without using technology, find the coordinates of the point(s) of intersection of:

    a $y = x^2 - 2x + 8$ and $y = x + 6$ **b** $y = -x^2 + 3x + 9$ and $y = 2x - 3$

    c $y = x^2 - 4x + 3$ and $y = 2x - 6$ **d** $y = -x^2 + 4x - 7$ and $y = 5x - 4$

Example 23   ◀ᴺ Self Tutor

Consider the curves $y = x^2 + 5x + 6$ and $y = 2x^2 + 2x - 4$.

  a Solve for x: $x^2 + 5x + 6 = 2x^2 + 2x - 4$.
  b Solve for x: $x^2 + 5x + 6 > 2x^2 + 2x - 4$.

  a We solve $x^2 + 5x + 6 = 2x^2 + 2x - 4$ using technology.

Casio fx-CG20

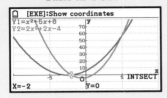

TI-84 Plus

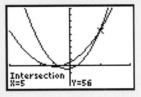

TI-*n*spire

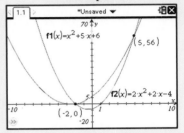

The solutions are: $x = -2$ or 5.

  b

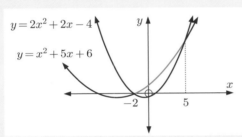

From the graphs we see that
$x^2 + 5x + 6 > 2x^2 + 2x - 4$
when $-2 < x < 5$.

Example 24   ◀ᴺ Self Tutor

$y = 2x + k$ is a tangent to $y = 2x^2 - 3x + 4$.   Find k.

$y = 2x + k$ meets $y = 2x^2 - 3x + 4$ where
$$2x^2 - 3x + 4 = 2x + k$$
$$\therefore \ 2x^2 - 5x + (4 - k) = 0$$

Since the graphs touch, this quadratic has $\Delta = 0$
$$\therefore \ (-5)^2 - 4(2)(4 - k) = 0$$
$$\therefore \ 25 - 8(4 - k) = 0$$
$$\therefore \ 25 - 32 + 8k = 0$$
$$\therefore \ 8k = 7$$
$$\therefore \ k = \tfrac{7}{8}$$

A tangent
touches a curve.

2   Use a **graphing package** or a **graphics calculator** to find the coordinates of the points of intersection (to 2 decimal places) of the graphs with equations:

    a $y = x^2 - 3x + 7$ and $y = x + 5$

    b $y = x^2 - 5x + 2$ and $y = x - 7$

    c $y = -x^2 - 2x + 4$ and $y = x + 8$

    d $y = -x^2 + 4x - 2$ and $y = 5x - 6$

GRAPHING
PACKAGE

3   **a**   **i**   Find where $y = x^2$ meets $y = x + 2$.

        ii   Solve for x: $x^2 > x + 2$.

    b   **i**   Find where $y = x^2 + 2x - 3$ meets $y = x - 1$.

        ii   Solve for x: $x^2 + 2x - 3 > x - 1$.

    c   **i**   Find where $y = 2x^2 - x + 3$ meets $y = 2 + x + x^2$.

        ii   Solve for x: $2x^2 - x + 3 > 2 + x + x^2$.

    d   **i**   Find where $y = \dfrac{4}{x}$ meets $y = x + 3$.

        ii   Solve for x: $\dfrac{4}{x} > x + 3$.

4   For which value of c is the line $y = 3x + c$ a tangent to the parabola with equation $y = x^2 - 5x + 7$?

5   Find the values of m for which the lines $y = mx - 2$ are tangents to the curve with equation $y = x^2 - 4x + 2$.

6   Find the gradients of the lines with y-intercept $(0, 1)$ that are tangents to the curve $y = 3x^2 + 5x + 4$.

7   **a**   For what values of c do the lines $y = x + c$ never meet the parabola with equation $y = 2x^2 - 3x - 7$?

    b   Choose one of the values of c found in part **a** above. Sketch the graphs using technology to illustrate that these curves never meet.

F   PROBLEM SOLVING WITH QUADRATICS

Some real world problems can be solved using a quadratic equation. We are generally only interested in any **real solutions** which result.

Any answer we obtain must be checked to see if it is reasonable. For example:

- if we are finding a length then it must be positive and we reject any negative solutions
- if we are finding 'how many people are present' then clearly the answer must be an integer.

We employ the following general problem solving method:

Step 1:   If the information is given in words, translate it into algebra using a variable such as x for the unknown. Write down the resulting equation. Be sure to define what the variable x represents, and include units if appropriate.

Step 2:   Solve the equation by a suitable method.

Step 3:   Examine the solutions carefully to see if they are acceptable.

Step 4:   Give your answer in a sentence.

Example 25 ◀》 Self Tutor

A rectangle has length 3 cm longer than its width. Its area is 42 cm². Find its width.

If the width is x cm then the length is $(x + 3)$ cm.

$\therefore \quad x(x + 3) = 42$ {equating areas}

$\therefore \quad x^2 + 3x - 42 = 0$

$\therefore \quad x \approx -8.15$ or 5.15 {using technology}

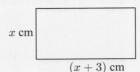

x cm

$(x + 3)$ cm

We reject the negative solution as lengths are positive.

The width is about 5.15 cm.

Example 26 ◀》 Self Tutor

Is it possible to bend a 12 cm length of wire to form the perpendicular sides of a right angled triangle with area 20 cm²?

Suppose the wire is bent x cm from one end.

The area $A = \frac{1}{2}x(12 - x)$

$\therefore \quad \frac{1}{2}x(12 - x) = 20$

$\therefore \quad x(12 - x) = 40$

$\therefore \quad 12x - x^2 - 40 = 0$

$\therefore \quad x^2 - 12x + 40 = 0$

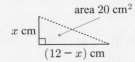

x cm $\quad (12 - x)$ cm

12 cm

becomes

area 20 cm²

x cm

$(12 - x)$ cm

Now $\Delta = (-12)^2 - 4(1)(40)$

$\quad = -16$ which is < 0

There are no real solutions, indicating this situation is **impossible**.

EXERCISE 1F

1 Two integers differ by 12 and the sum of their squares is 74. Find the integers.

2 The sum of a number and its reciprocal is $5\frac{1}{5}$. Find the number.

3 The sum of a natural number and its square is 210. Find the number.

4 The product of two consecutive even numbers is 360. Find the numbers.

5 The product of two consecutive odd numbers is 255. Find the numbers.

6 The number of diagonals of an n-sided polygon is given by the formula $D = \frac{n}{2}(n - 3)$.

A polygon has 90 diagonals. How many sides does it have?

7 The length of a rectangle is 4 cm longer than its width. The rectangle has area 26 cm². Find its width.

8 A rectangular box has a square base with sides of length x cm. Its height is 1 cm longer than its base side length. The total surface area of the box is 240 cm^2.

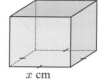

    a Show that the total surface area is given by $A = 6x^2 + 4x$ cm^2.

    b Find the dimensions of the box.

9

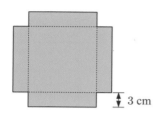

An open box can hold 80 cm^3. It is made from a square piece of tinplate with 3 cm squares cut from each of its 4 corners. Find the dimensions of the original piece of tinplate.

10 Is it possible to bend a 20 cm length of wire into the shape of a rectangle which has an area of 30 cm^2?

11 The rectangle ABCD is divided into a square and a smaller rectangle by [XY] which is parallel to its shorter sides.

The smaller rectangle BCXY is *similar* to the original rectangle, so rectangle ABCD is a **golden rectangle**.

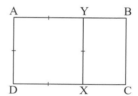

The ratio $\dfrac{AB}{AD}$ is called the **golden ratio**.

Show that the golden ratio is $\dfrac{1 + \sqrt{5}}{2}$.

Hint: Let   AB $= x$ units and AD $= 1$ unit.

12 Two trains travel a 160 km track each day. The express travels 10 km h^{-1} faster and takes 30 minutes less time than the normal train. Find the speed of the express.

13

A group of elderly citizens chartered a bus for \$160. However, at the last minute 8 of them fell ill and had to miss the trip.

As a consequence, the other citizens had to pay an extra \$1 each. How many elderly citizens went on the trip?

14 Answer the **Opening Problem** on page **18**.

15 A truck carrying a wide load needs to pass through the parabolic tunnel shown. The units are metres.

The truck is 5 m high and 4 m wide.

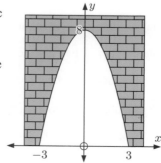

    a Find the quadratic function which describes the shape of the tunnel.

    b Determine whether the truck will fit.

G QUADRATIC OPTIMISATION

The process of finding the maximum or minimum value of a function is called **optimisation**.

For the quadratic function $y = ax^2 + bx + c$, we have already seen that the vertex has x-coordinate $-\dfrac{b}{2a}$.

- If $a > 0$, the **minimum** value of y occurs at $x = -\dfrac{b}{2a}$.

- If $a < 0$, the **maximum** value of y occurs at $x = -\dfrac{b}{2a}$.

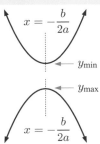

Example 27 ◀ᵛ) **Self Tutor**

Find the maximum or minimum value of the following quadratic functions, and the corresponding value of x:

a $y = x^2 + x - 3$

b $y = 3 + 3x - 2x^2$

a $y = x^2 + x - 3$ has
$a = 1$, $b = 1$, and $c = -3$.
Since $a > 0$, the shape is ∨

The minimum value occurs
when $x = \dfrac{-b}{2a} = -\dfrac{1}{2}$

and $y = (-\tfrac{1}{2})^2 + (-\tfrac{1}{2}) - 3$

$= -3\tfrac{1}{4}$

So, the minimum value of y is $-3\tfrac{1}{4}$,
occurring when $x = -\tfrac{1}{2}$.

b $y = -2x^2 + 3x + 3$ has
$a = -2$, $b = 3$, and $c = 3$.
Since $a < 0$, the shape is ∩

The maximum value occurs
when $x = \dfrac{-b}{2a} = \dfrac{-3}{-4} = \dfrac{3}{4}$

and $y = -2(\tfrac{3}{4})^2 + 3(\tfrac{3}{4}) + 3$

$= 4\tfrac{1}{8}$

So, the maximum value of y is $4\tfrac{1}{8}$,
occurring when $x = \tfrac{3}{4}$.

EXERCISE 1G

1 Find the maximum or minimum values of the following quadratic functions, and the corresponding values of x:

a $y = x^2 - 2x$

b $y = 7 - 2x - x^2$

c $y = 8 + 2x - 3x^2$

d $y = 2x^2 + x - 1$

e $y = 4x^2 - x + 5$

f $y = 7x - 2x^2$

2 The profit in manufacturing x refrigerators per day, is given by the profit relation $P = -3x^2 + 240x - 800$ dollars.

a How many refrigerators should be made each day to maximise the total profit?

b What is the maximum profit?

Example 28   ◀) **Self Tutor**

A gardener has 40 m of fencing to enclose a rectangular
garden plot, where one side is an existing brick wall.
Suppose the two new equal sides are x m long.

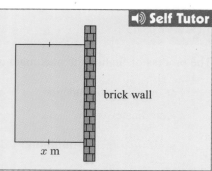

brick wall

a Show that the area enclosed is given by
$A = x(40 - 2x)$ m^2.

b Find the dimensions of the garden of maximum area.

x m

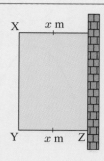

a Side [XY] has length $(40 - 2x)$ m.
Now, area = length × width
∴ $A = x(40 - 2x)$ m^2

b $A = 0$ when $x = 0$ or 20.
The vertex of the function lies midway
between these values, so $x = 10$.
Since $a < 0$, the shape is

∴ the area is maximised when YZ = 10 m and XY = 20 m.

---

3 A rectangular plot is enclosed by 200 m of fencing and has an
area of A square metres. Show that:

a $A = 100x - x^2$ where x m is the length of one of its sides

b the area is maximised if the rectangle is a square.

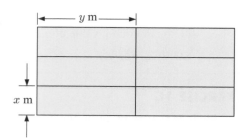

x m

4 Three sides of a rectangular paddock are to be fenced, the fourth side being an existing straight
water drain. If 1000 m of fencing is available, what dimensions should be used for the paddock so
that it encloses the maximum possible area?

5 1800 m of fencing is available to fence six identical
pens as shown in the diagram.

a Explain why $9x + 8y = 1800$.

b Show that the area of each pen is given by
$A = -\frac{9}{8}x^2 + 225x$ m^2.

c If the area enclosed is to be maximised, what are
the dimensions of each pen?

y m

x m

6 500 m of fencing is available
to make 4 rectangular pens
of identical shape. Find the
dimensions that maximise the area
of each pen if the plan is:

a

b

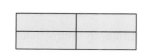

7

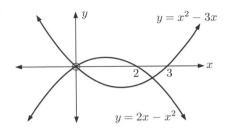

The graphs of $y = x^2 - 3x$ and $y = 2x - x^2$ are illustrated.

a Without using technology, show that the graphs meet where $x = 0$ and $x = 2\frac{1}{2}$.

b Find the maximum vertical separation between the curves for $0 \leqslant x \leqslant 2\frac{1}{2}$.

8 Infinitely many rectangles may be inscribed within the right angled triangle shown alongside. One of them is illustrated.

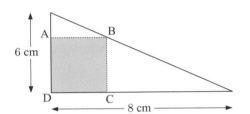

a Let $AB = x$ cm and $BC = y$ cm. Use similar triangles to find y in terms of x.

b Find the dimensions of rectangle ABCD of maximum area.

INVESTIGATION 4 — SUM AND PRODUCT OF ROOTS

What to do:

1 Suppose $ax^2 + bx + c = 0$ has roots p and q.

Prove that $p + q = \dfrac{-b}{a}$ and $pq = \dfrac{c}{a}$.

2 Suppose $2x^2 - 5x + 1 = 0$ has roots p and q. Without finding the values of p and q, find:

a $p + q$ **b** pq **c** $p^2 + q^2$ **d** $\dfrac{1}{p} + \dfrac{1}{q}$

3 Find *all* quadratic equations with roots which are:

a one more than the roots of $2x^2 - 5x + 1 = 0$

b the squares of the roots of $2x^2 - 5x + 1 = 0$

c the reciprocals of the roots of $2x^2 - 5x + 1 = 0$.

REVIEW SET 1A — NON-CALCULATOR

1 Consider the quadratic function $y = -2(x + 2)(x - 1)$.

a State the x-intercepts.   **b** State the equation of the axis of symmetry.

c Find the y-intercept.   **d** Find the coordinates of the vertex.

e Sketch the function.

2 Solve the following equations, giving exact answers:

a $3x^2 - 12x = 0$ **b** $3x^2 - x - 10 = 0$ **c** $x^2 - 11x = 60$

3 Solve using the quadratic formula:

a $x^2 + 5x + 3 = 0$ **b** $3x^2 + 11x - 2 = 0$

4   Solve by 'completing the square': $x^2 + 7x - 4 = 0$

5   Use the vertex, axis of symmetry, and y-intercept to graph:

   a $y = (x - 2)^2 - 4$ **b** $y = -\frac{1}{2}(x + 4)^2 + 6$

6   Find, in the form $y = ax^2 + bx + c$,   the equation of the quadratic whose graph:

   a touches the x-axis at 4 and passes through $(2, 12)$

   b has vertex $(-4, 1)$ and passes through $(1, 11)$.

7   Find the maximum or minimum value of the relation $y = -2x^2 + 4x + 3$ and the value of x at which this occurs.

8   Find the points of intersection of $y = x^2 - 3x$ and $y = 3x^2 - 5x - 24$.

9   For what values of k does the graph of $y = -2x^2 + 5x + k$ not cut the x-axis?

10   Find the values of m for which $2x^2 - 3x + m = 0$ has:

   a a repeated root   **b** two distinct real roots   **c** no real roots.

11   The sum of a number and its reciprocal is $2\frac{1}{30}$. Find the number.

12   Show that no line with a y-intercept of $(0, 10)$ will ever be tangential to the curve with equation $y = 3x^2 + 7x - 2$.

13   The diagram shows a quadratic $y = x^2 + mx + n$.

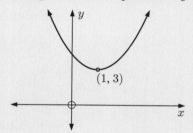

(1, 3)

   a Determine the values of m and n.

   b Find k given that the graph passes through the point $(3, k)$.

REVIEW SET 1B   CALCULATOR

1   Consider the quadratic function $y = 2x^2 + 6x - 3$.

   a Convert it to the form $y = a(x - h)^2 + k$.

   b State the coordinates of the vertex.

   c Find the y-intercept.

   d Sketch the graph of the function.

2   Solve:

   a $(x - 2)(x + 1) = 3x - 4$ **b** $2x - \dfrac{1}{x} = 5$

3   Draw the graph of $y = -x^2 + 2x$.

4   Consider the quadratic function $y = -3x^2 + 8x + 7$. Find the equation of the axis of symmetry, and the coordinates of the vertex.

5   Using the discriminant only, determine the nature of the solutions of:

    a $2x^2 - 5x - 7 = 0$ **b** $3x^2 - 24x + 48 = 0$

6   **a** For what values of c do the lines with equations $y = 3x + c$ intersect the parabola $y = x^2 + x - 5$ in two distinct points?

    b Choose one such value of c from part **a** and find the points of intersection in this case.

7   Consider the quadratic function $y = 2x^2 + 4x - 1$.

    a State the axis of symmetry.   **b** Find the coordinates of the vertex.

    c Find the axes intercepts.   **d** Hence sketch the function.

8   An open square-based container is made by cutting 4 cm square pieces out of a piece of tinplate. If the volume of the container is 120 cm^3, find the size of the original piece of tinplate.

9   Consider $y = -x^2 - 5x + 3$ and $y = x^2 + 3x + 11$.

    a Solve for x: $-x^2 - 5x + 3 = x^2 + 3x + 11$.

    b Hence, or otherwise, determine the values of x for which $x^2 + 3x + 11 > -x^2 - 5x + 3$.

10   Find the maximum or minimum value of the following quadratics, and the corresponding value of x:

    a $y = 3x^2 + 4x + 7$ **b** $y = -2x^2 - 5x + 2$

11   600 m of fencing is used to construct 6 rectangular animal pens as shown.

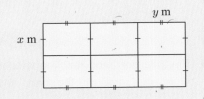

    a Show that the area A of each pen is

        $A = x \left(\dfrac{600 - 8x}{9} \right)$ m^2.

    b Find the dimensions of each pen so that it has the maximum possible area.

    c What is the area of each pen in this case?

12   Two different quadratic functions of the form $y = 9x^2 - kx + 4$ each touch the x-axis.

    a Find the two values of k.

    b Find the point of intersection of the two quadratic functions.

REVIEW SET 1C

1   Consider the quadratic function $y = \frac{1}{2}(x - 2)^2 - 4$.

    a State the equation of the axis of symmetry.

    b Find the coordinates of the vertex.   **c** Find the y-intercept.

    d Sketch the function.

2   Solve the following equations:

    a $x^2 - 5x - 3 = 0$ **b** $2x^2 - 7x - 3 = 0$

3   Solve the following using the quadratic formula:

    a $x^2 - 7x + 3 = 0$ **b** $2x^2 - 5x + 4 = 0$

4   Find the equation of the quadratic function with graph:

a

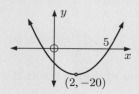

(2, −20)

b

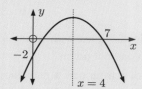

−2   7

$x = 4$

c

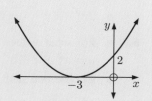

2

−3

5   Use the discriminant only to find the relationship between the graph and the x-axis for:

    a $y = 2x^2 + 3x - 7$ **b** $y = -3x^2 - 7x + 4$

6   Determine whether the following quadratic functions are positive definite, negative definite, or neither:

    a $y = -2x^2 + 3x + 2$ **b** $y = 3x^2 + x + 11$

7   Find the equation of the quadratic function shown:

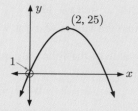

(2, 25)

1

8   Find the y-intercept of the line with gradient -3 that is tangential to the parabola $y = 2x^2 - 5x + 1$.

9   For what values of k would the graph of $y = x^2 - 2x + k$ cut the x-axis twice?

10   Find the quadratic function which cuts the x-axis at 3 and -2 and which has y-intercept 24. Give your answer in the form $y = ax^2 + bx + c$.

11   For what values of m are the lines $y = mx - 10$ tangents to the parabola $y = 3x^2 + 7x + 2$?

12   The diagram shows the parabola $y = a(x + m)(x + n)$ where $m > n$.

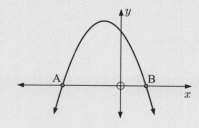

A   B

    a   Find, in terms of m and n, the:

        i   coordinates of the x-intercepts A and B

        ii   equation of the axis of symmetry.

    b   State the sign of:

        i   the discriminant Δ

        ii a.

13   **a**   Determine the equation of:

        i   the quadratic function

        ii   the straight line.

    b   For what values of x is the straight line above the curve?

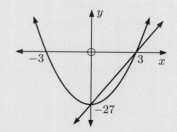

−3   3

−27

Chapter 2

Functions

Syllabus reference: 2.1, 2.2, 2.5

A RELATIONS AND FUNCTIONS

The charges for parking a car in a short-term car park at an airport are shown in the table below. The total charge is *dependent* on the length of time t the car is parked.

Car park charges	
Time t (hours)	*Charge*
0 - 1 hours	$5.00
1 - 2 hours	$9.00
2 - 3 hours	$11.00
3 - 6 hours	$13.00
6 - 9 hours	$18.00
9 - 12 hours	$22.00
12 - 24 hours	$28.00

Looking at this table we might ask: How much would be charged for *exactly* one hour? Would it be $5 or $9?

To avoid confusion, we could adjust the table or draw a graph. We indicate that   2 - 3 hours   really means a time over 2 hours up to and including 3 hours, by writing $2 < t \leqslant 3$ hours.

Car park charges	
Time t (hours)	*Charge*
$0 < t \leqslant 1$ hours	$5.00
$1 < t \leqslant 2$ hours	$9.00
$2 < t \leqslant 3$ hours	$11.00
$3 < t \leqslant 6$ hours	$13.00
$6 < t \leqslant 9$ hours	$18.00
$9 < t \leqslant 12$ hours	$22.00
$12 < t \leqslant 24$ hours	$28.00

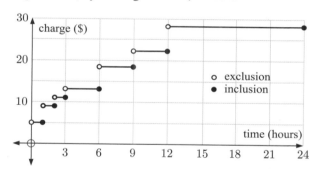

In mathematical terms, we have a relationship between two variables *time* and *charge*, so the schedule of charges is an example of a **relation**.

A relation may consist of a finite number of ordered pairs, such as $\{(1, 5), (-2, 3), (4, 3), (1, 6)\}$, or an infinite number of ordered pairs.

The parking charges example is clearly the latter as every real value of time in the interval $0 < t \leqslant 24$ hours is represented.

The set of possible values of the variable on the horizontal axis is called the **domain** of the relation.

For example:
- the domain for the car park relation is $\{t \mid 0 < t \leqslant 24\}$
- the domain of $\{(1, 5), (-2, 3), (4, 3), (1, 6)\}$ is $\{-2, 1, 4\}$.

The set of possible values on the vertical axis is called the **range** of the relation.

For example:
- the range of the car park relation is $\{5, 9, 11, 13, 18, 22, 28\}$
- the range of $\{(1, 5), (-2, 3), (4, 3), (1, 6)\}$ is $\{3, 5, 6\}$.

We will now look at relations and functions more formally.

RELATIONS

> A **relation** is any set of points which connect two variables.

A relation is often expressed in the form of an **equation** connecting the **variables** x and y. In this case the relation is a set of points (x, y) in the **Cartesian plane**.

This plane is separated into four quadrants according to the signs of x and y.

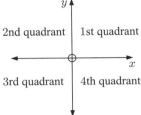

For example, $y = x + 3$ and $x = y^2$ are the equations of two relations. Each equation generates a set of ordered pairs, which we can graph:

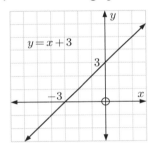 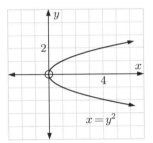

However, a relation may not be able to be defined by an equation. Below are two examples which show this:

(1)

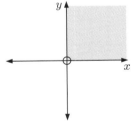

The set of all points in the first quadrant is the relation $x > 0, \ y > 0$

(2)

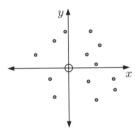

These 13 points form a relation.

FUNCTIONS

> A **function**, sometimes called a **mapping**, is a relation in which no two different ordered pairs have the same x-coordinate or first component.

We can see from the above definition that a function is a special type of relation.

Every function is a relation, but not every relation is a function.

TESTING FOR FUNCTIONS

Algebraic Test:

> If a relation is given as an equation, and the substitution of any value for x results in one and only one value of y, then the relation is a function.

For example:

$y = 3x - 1$ is a function, as for any value of x there is only one corresponding value of y

$x = y^2$ is not a function since if $x = 4$ then $y = \pm 2$.

Geometric Test   or   Vertical Line Test:

> If we draw all possible vertical lines on the graph of a relation, the relation:
> - is a function if each line cuts the graph no more than once
> - is not a function if at least one line cuts the graph more than once.

Example 1   ◀) **Self Tutor**

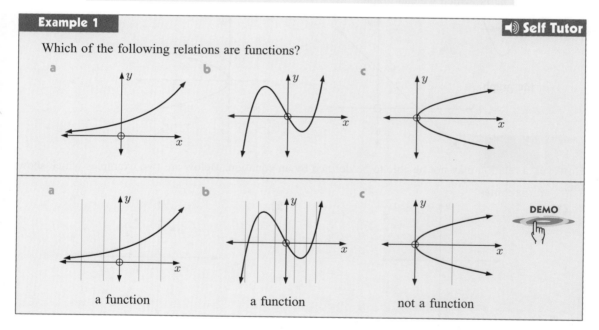

GRAPHICAL NOTE

- If a graph contains a small **open circle** such as ——o—— , this point is **not included**.
- If a graph contains a small **filled-in circle** such as ——•, this point **is included**.
- If a graph contains an **arrow head** at an end such as ——▸ , then the graph continues indefinitely in that general direction, or the shape may repeat as it has done previously.

EXERCISE 2A

1   Which of the following sets of ordered pairs are functions? Give reasons for your answers.

    a $\{(1, 3), (2, 4), (3, 5), (4, 6)\}$ **b** $\{(1, 3), (3, 2), (1, 7), (-1, 4)\}$

    c $\{(2, -1), (2, 0), (2, 3), (2, 11)\}$ **d** $\{(7, 6), (5, 6), (3, 6), (-4, 6)\}$

    e $\{(0, 0), (1, 0), (3, 0), (5, 0)\}$ **f** $\{(0, 0), (0, -2), (0, 2), (0, 4)\}$

2 Use the vertical line test to determine which of the following relations are functions:

a
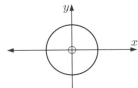

b
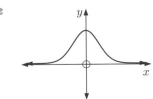

c
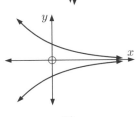

d
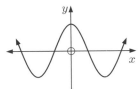

e
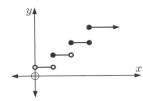

f
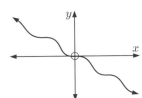

g

h

i

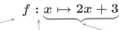

3 Will the graph of a straight line always be a function? Give evidence to support your answer.

4 Give algebraic evidence to show that the relation $x^2 + y^2 = 9$ is not a function.

B | FUNCTION NOTATION

Function machines are sometimes used to illustrate how functions behave.

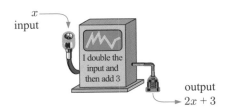

If 4 is the input fed into the machine, the output is $2(4) + 3 = 11$.

The above 'machine' has been programmed to perform a particular function.

If f is used to represent that particular function we can write:

f is the function that will convert x into $2x + 3$.

So, f would convert 2 into $2(2) + 3 = 7$ and
-4 into $2(-4) + 3 = -5$.

This function can be written as:

$$f : x \mapsto 2x + 3$$

function f such that x is converted into $2x + 3$

$f(x)$ is read as "f of x".

Two other equivalent forms we use are $f(x) = 2x + 3$ and $y = 2x + 3$.

$f(x)$ is the value of y for a given value of x, so $y = f(x)$.

f is the function which converts x into $f(x)$, so we write
$f : x \mapsto f(x)$.

$y = f(x)$ is sometimes called the **function value** or **image** of x.

For $f(x) = 2x + 3$:

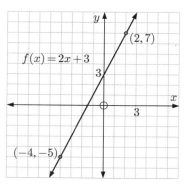

- $f(2) = 2(2) + 3 = 7$ indicates that the point $(2, 7)$ lies on the graph of the function.

- $f(-4) = 2(-4) + 3 = -5$ indicates that the point $(-4, -5)$ also lies on the graph.

A **linear function** is a function of the form $f(x) = ax + b$ where a, b are real constants. The graph of a linear function is a straight line.

Example 2   ◀ッ **Self Tutor**

If $f : x \mapsto 2x^2 - 3x$,   find the value of: **a** $f(5)$ **b** $f(-4)$

$f(x) = 2x^2 - 3x$

a $f(5) = 2(5)^2 - 3(5)$ {replacing x with (5)}
$\quad\quad = 2 \times 25 - 15$
$\quad\quad = 35$

b $f(-4) = 2(-4)^2 - 3(-4)$ {replacing x with (-4)}
$\quad\quad = 2(16) + 12$
$\quad\quad = 44$

Example 3   ◀ッ **Self Tutor**

If $f(x) = 5 - x - x^2$,   find in simplest form: **a** $f(-x)$ **b** $f(x + 2)$

a $f(-x) = 5 - (-x) - (-x)^2$ {replacing x with $(-x)$}
$\quad\quad = 5 + x - x^2$

b $f(x + 2) = 5 - (x + 2) - (x + 2)^2$ {replacing x with $(x + 2)$}
$\quad\quad = 5 - x - 2 - [x^2 + 4x + 4]$
$\quad\quad = 3 - x - x^2 - 4x - 4$
$\quad\quad = -x^2 - 5x - 1$

EXERCISE 2B

1 If $f : x \mapsto 3x + 2$,   find the value of:

  a $f(0)$ **b** $f(2)$ **c** $f(-1)$ **d** $f(-5)$ **e** $f(-\frac{1}{3})$

2 If $f : x \mapsto 3x - x^2 + 2$,   find the value of:

  a $f(0)$ **b** $f(3)$ **c** $f(-3)$ **d** $f(-7)$ **e** $f(\frac{3}{2})$

3 If $g : x \mapsto x - \dfrac{4}{x}$, find the value of:

    a $g(1)$ **b** $g(4)$ **c** $g(-1)$ **d** $g(-4)$ **e** $g(-\tfrac{1}{2})$

4 If $f(x) = 7 - 3x$, find in simplest form:

    a $f(a)$ **b** $f(-a)$ **c** $f(a+3)$ **d** $f(b-1)$ **e** $f(x+2)$ **f** $f(x+h)$

5 If $F(x) = 2x^2 + 3x - 1$, find in simplest form:

    a $F(x+4)$ **b** $F(2-x)$ **c** $F(-x)$ **d** $F(x^2)$ **e** $F(x^2-1)$ **f** $F(x+h)$

6 Suppose $G(x) = \dfrac{2x+3}{x-4}$.

    a Evaluate: **i** $G(2)$ **ii** $G(0)$ **iii** $G(-\tfrac{1}{2})$

    b Find a value of x such that $G(x)$ does not exist.

    c Find $G(x+2)$ in simplest form.

    d Find x if $G(x) = -3$.

7 f represents a function. What is the difference in meaning between f and $f(x)$?

8 The value of a photocopier t years after purchase is given by $V(t) = 9650 - 860t$ euros.

    a Find $V(4)$ and state what $V(4)$ means.

    b Find t when $V(t) = 5780$ and explain what this represents.

    c Find the original purchase price of the photocopier.

9 On the same set of axes draw the graphs of three different functions $f(x)$ such that $f(2) = 1$ and $f(5) = 3$.

10 Find a linear function $f(x) = ax + b$ for which $f(2) = 1$ and $f(-3) = 11$.

11 Given $f(x) = ax + \dfrac{b}{x}$, $f(1) = 1$, and $f(2) = 5$, find constants a and b.

12 Given $T(x) = ax^2 + bx + c$, $T(0) = -4$, $T(1) = -2$, and $T(2) = 6$, find a, b, and c.

C   DOMAIN AND RANGE

> The **domain** of a relation is the set of values of x in the relation.
>
> The **range** of a relation is the set of values of y in the relation.

The domain and range of a relation are often described using **set notation**.

For example:

(1)

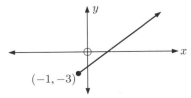

All values of $x \geqslant -1$ are included, so the domain is $\{x \mid x \geqslant -1\}$.

All values of $y \geqslant -3$ are included, so the range is $\{y \mid y \geqslant -3\}$.

(2)

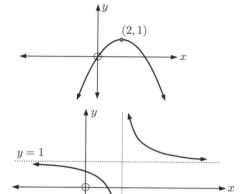

x can take any value,
so the domain is $\{x \mid x \in \mathbb{R}\}$.
y cannot be > 1,
so the range is $\{y \mid y \leqslant 1\}$.

(3)

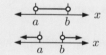

x can take all values except 2,
so the domain is $\{x \mid x \neq 2\}$.
y can take all values except 1,
so the range is $\{y \mid y \neq 1\}$.

NUMBER LINE GRAPHS

We can illustrate sets of values on a number line graph. For example:

$\{x \mid x \geqslant 3\}$ is read 'the set of all x such that x is greater than or equal to 3' and has number line graph

$\{x \mid x < 2\}$ has number line graph

$\{x \mid -2 < x \leqslant 1\}$ has number line graph

$\{x \mid x \leqslant 0 \ \text{or} \ x > 4\}$ has number line graph

For numbers *between* a and b we write $a < x < b$.

For numbers '*outside*' a and b we write $x < a$ or $x > b$.

DOMAIN AND RANGE OF FUNCTIONS

To fully describe a function, we need both a rule *and* a domain.

For example, we can specify $f(x) = x^2$ where $x \geqslant 0$.

If a domain is not specified, we use the **natural domain**, which is the largest part of $\mathbb{R}$ for which $f(x)$ is defined.

For example, consider the domains in the table opposite:

Click on the icon to obtain software for finding the domain and range of different functions.

DOMAIN AND RANGE

$f(x)$	Natural domain
x^2	$x \in \mathbb{R}$
$\sqrt{x}$	$x \geqslant 0$
$\dfrac{1}{x}$	$x \neq 0$
$\dfrac{1}{\sqrt{x}}$	$x > 0$

Example 4   ◀ঃ) **Self Tutor**

For each of the following graphs state the domain and range:

a

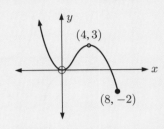

b

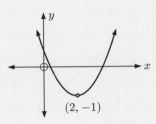

a	Domain is $\{x \mid x \leqslant 8\}$	b	Domain is $\{x \mid x \in \mathbb{R}\}$
	Range is $\{y \mid y \geqslant -2\}$		Range is $\{y \mid y \geqslant -1\}$

Example 5   ◀ঃ) **Self Tutor**

State the domain and range of each of the following functions:

     a $f(x) = \sqrt{x - 5}$ **b** $f(x) = \dfrac{1}{x - 5}$ **c** $f(x) = \dfrac{1}{\sqrt{x - 5}}$

a $\sqrt{x - 5}$ is defined when $x - 5 \geqslant 0$
                           $\therefore \ x \geqslant 5$
   $\therefore$ the domain is $\{x \mid x \geqslant 5\}$.
A square root cannot be negative.
   $\therefore$ the range is $\{y \mid y \geqslant 0\}$.

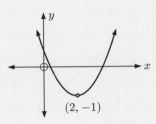

b $\dfrac{1}{x - 5}$ is defined when $x - 5 \neq 0$
                         $\therefore \ x \neq 5$
   $\therefore$ the domain is $\{x \mid x \neq 5\}$.
No matter how large or small x is, $y = f(x)$
is never zero.
   $\therefore$ the range is $\{y \mid y \neq 0\}$.

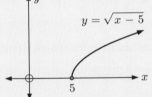

c $\dfrac{1}{\sqrt{x - 5}}$ is defined when $x - 5 > 0$
                         $\therefore \ x > 5$
   $\therefore$ the domain is $\{x \mid x > 5\}$.
$y = f(x)$ is always positive and never zero.
   $\therefore$ the range is $\{y \mid y > 0\}$.

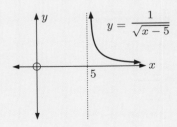

EXERCISE 2C

1 For each of the following graphs, find the domain and range:

a

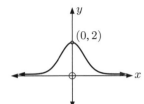

b

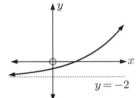

c

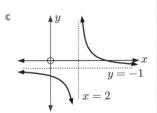

d

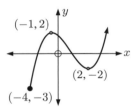

e

f

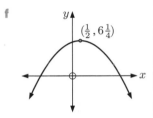

g

h

i

2 State the values of x for which $f(x)$ is defined, and hence state the domain of the function.

a $f(x) = \sqrt{x + 6}$

b $f : x \mapsto \dfrac{1}{x^2}$

c $f(x) = \dfrac{-7}{\sqrt{3 - 2x}}$

3 Find the domain and range of each of the following functions:

a $f : x \mapsto 2x - 1$

b $f(x) = 3$

c $f : x \mapsto \sqrt{x}$

d $f(x) = \dfrac{1}{x + 1}$

e $f(x) = -\dfrac{1}{\sqrt{x}}$

f $f : x \mapsto \dfrac{1}{3 - x}$

4 Use technology to help sketch graphs of the following functions. Find the domain and range of each.

a $f(x) = \sqrt{x - 2}$

b $f : x \mapsto \dfrac{1}{x^2}$

c $f : x \mapsto \sqrt{4 - x}$

d $y = x^2 - 7x + 10$

e $f(x) = \sqrt{x^2 + 4}$

f $f(x) = \sqrt{x^2 - 4}$

g $f : x \mapsto 5x - 3x^2$

h $f : x \mapsto x + \dfrac{1}{x}$

i $y = \dfrac{x + 4}{x - 2}$

j $y = x^3 - 3x^2 - 9x + 10$

k $f : x \mapsto \dfrac{3x - 9}{x^2 - x - 2}$

l $y = x^2 + x^{-2}$

m $y = x^3 + \dfrac{1}{x^3}$

n $f : x \mapsto x^4 + 4x^3 - 16x + 3$

DOMAIN
AND RANGE

INVESTIGATION 1   FLUID FILLING FUNCTIONS

When water is added at a **constant rate** to a cylindrical container, the depth of water in the container is a linear function of time. This is because the volume of water added is directly proportional to the time taken to add it. If the water was *not* added at a constant rate, depth of water over time would *not* be a linear function.

The linear depth-time graph for a cylindrical container is shown alongside.

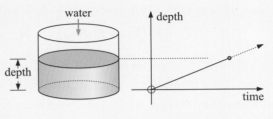

In this investigation we explore the changes in the graph for different shaped containers such as the conical vase.

DEMO

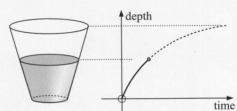

What to do:

1   By examining the shape of each container, predict the depth-time graph when water is added at a constant rate.

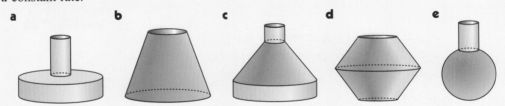

2   Use the water filling demonstration to check your answers to question **1**.

3   Write a brief report on the connection between the shape of a vessel and the corresponding shape of its depth-time graph. First examine cylindrical containers, then conical, then other shapes. Gradients of curves must be included in your report.

4   Suggest containers which would have the following depth-time graphs:

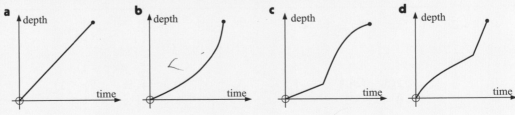

D   COMPOSITE FUNCTIONS

Given $f : x \mapsto f(x)$ and $g : x \mapsto g(x)$, the **composite function** of f and g will convert x into $f(g(x))$.

$f \circ g$ is used to represent the composite function of f and g. It means "f following g".

$$(\boldsymbol{f \circ g})(\boldsymbol{x}) = \boldsymbol{f(g(x))} \quad \text{or} \quad \boldsymbol{f \circ g : x \mapsto f(g(x))}.$$

Consider $f : x \mapsto x^4$ and $g : x \mapsto 2x + 3$.

$f \circ g$ means that g converts x to $2x + 3$ and then f converts $(2x + 3)$ to $(2x + 3)^4$.

This is illustrated by the two function machines below.

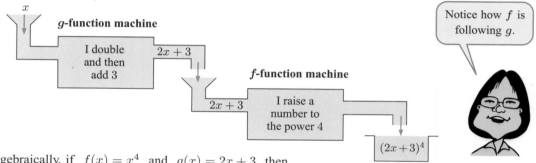

Notice how f is following g.

Algebraically, if $f(x) = x^4$ and $g(x) = 2x + 3$ then

$$\begin{aligned}(f \circ g)(x) &= f(g(x)) \\ &= f(2x + 3) \quad \text{\{g operates on x first\}} \\ &= (2x + 3)^4 \quad \text{\{f operates on $g(x)$ next\}}\end{aligned}$$

and $\quad \begin{aligned}(g \circ f)(x) &= g(f(x)) \\ &= g(x^4) \quad \text{\{f operates on x first\}} \\ &= 2(x^4) + 3 \quad \text{\{g operates on $f(x)$ next\}} \\ &= 2x^4 + 3\end{aligned}$

So, $f(g(x)) \neq g(f(x))$.

In general, $(f \circ g)(x) \neq (g \circ f)(x)$.

Example 6   ◀) Self Tutor

Given $f : x \mapsto 2x + 1$ and $g : x \mapsto 3 - 4x$, find in simplest form:

a $(f \circ g)(x)$ **b** $(g \circ f)(x)$

$f(x) = 2x + 1$ and $g(x) = 3 - 4x$

a $\begin{aligned}(f \circ g)(x) &= f(g(x)) \\ &= f(3 - 4x) \\ &= 2(3 - 4x) + 1 \\ &= 6 - 8x + 1 \\ &= 7 - 8x\end{aligned}$

b $\begin{aligned}(g \circ f)(x) &= g(f(x)) \\ &= g(2x + 1) \\ &= 3 - 4(2x + 1) \\ &= 3 - 8x - 4 \\ &= -8x - 1\end{aligned}$

In the previous example you should have observed how we can substitute an expression into a function.

If $f(x) = 2x + 1$ then $\qquad f(\Delta) = 2(\Delta) + 1$

and so $\quad f(3 - 4x) = 2(3 - 4x) + 1$.

Example 7

◀ Self Tutor

Given $\quad f(x) = 6x - 5$ and $g(x) = x^2 + x$, determine:

a $\quad (g \circ f)(-1)$

b $\quad (f \circ f)(0)$

a $\qquad (g \circ f)(-1) = g(f(-1))$

$\qquad$ Now $\quad f(-1) = 6(-1) - 5$

$\qquad\qquad\qquad = -11$

$\qquad \therefore\ (g \circ f)(-1) = g(-11)$

$\qquad\qquad\qquad = (-11)^2 + (-11)$

$\qquad\qquad\qquad = 110$

b $\qquad (f \circ f)(0) = f(f(0))$

$\qquad$ Now $\quad f(0) = 6(0) - 5$

$\qquad\qquad\qquad = -5$

$\qquad \therefore\ (f \circ f)(0) = f(-5)$

$\qquad\qquad\qquad = 6(-5) - 5$

$\qquad\qquad\qquad = -35$

The domain of the composite of two functions depends on the domain of the original functions.

For example, consider $f(x) = x^2$ with domain $x \in \mathbb{R}$ and $g(x) = \sqrt{x}$ with domain $x \geqslant 0$.

$\qquad (f \circ g)(x) = f(g(x))$

$\qquad\qquad\qquad = (\sqrt{x})^2$ The domain of $(f \circ g)(x)$ is $x \geqslant 0$, not $\mathbb{R}$, since $(f \circ g)(x)$

$\qquad\qquad\qquad = x$ is defined using function $g(x)$.

EXERCISE 2D

1 Given $\quad f : x \mapsto 2x + 3$ and $g : x \mapsto 1 - x$, find in simplest form:

a $\quad (f \circ g)(x)$

b $\quad (g \circ f)(x)$

c $\quad (f \circ g)(-3)$

2 Given $\quad f(x) = 2 + x$ and $g(x) = 3 - x$, find:

a $\quad (f \circ f)(x)$

b $\quad (f \circ g)(x)$

c $\quad (g \circ f)(x)$

3 Given $\quad f(x) = \sqrt{6 - x}$ and $g(x) = 5x - 7$, find:

a $\quad (g \circ g)(x)$

b $\quad (f \circ g)(1)$

c $\quad (g \circ f)(6)$

4 Given $\quad f : x \mapsto x^2$ and $g : x \mapsto 2 - x$, find $(f \circ g)(x)$ and $(g \circ f)(x)$.

Find also the domain and range of $f \circ g$ and $g \circ f$.

5 Suppose $\quad f : x \mapsto x^2 + 1$ and $g : x \mapsto 3 - x$.

a Find in simplest form: $\qquad$ i $\quad (f \circ g)(x)$ $\qquad$ ii $\quad (g \circ f)(x)$

b Find the value(s) of x such that $(g \circ f)(x) = f(x)$.

6 a If $ax + b = cx + d$ for all values of x, show that $a = c$ and $b = d$.

Hint: If it is true for all x, it is true for $x = 0$ and $x = 1$.

b Given $\quad f(x) = 2x + 3$ and $g(x) = ax + b$ and that $(f \circ g)(x) = x$ for all values of x, deduce that $a = \frac{1}{2}$ and $b = -\frac{3}{2}$.

c Is the result in b true if $(g \circ f)(x) = x$ for all x?

7 Given $f(x) = \sqrt{1 - x}$ and $g(x) = x^2$, find:

   a $(f \circ g)(x)$

   b the domain and range of $(f \circ g)(x)$

E   SIGN DIAGRAMS

Sometimes we do not wish to draw a time-consuming graph of a function but wish to know when the function is positive, negative, zero or undefined. A **sign diagram** enables us to do this and is relatively easy to construct.

For the function $f(x)$, the sign diagram consists of:

- a **horizontal line** which is really the x-axis
- **positive** (+) and **negative** (−) signs indicating that the graph is **above** and **below** the x-axis respectively
- the **zeros** of the function, which are the x-intercepts of the graph of $y = f(x)$, and the **roots** of the equation $f(x) = 0$
- values of x where the graph is undefined.

DEMO

Consider the three functions given below.

Function	$y = (x + 2)(x - 1)$	$y = -2(x - 1)^2$	$y = \dfrac{4}{x}$
Graph			
Sign diagram	$\begin{array}{ccc} + & - & + \\ \hline & -2 \quad\; 1 & x \end{array}$	$\begin{array}{cc} - & - \\ \hline & 1 \quad x \end{array}$	$\begin{array}{cc} - & + \\ \hline & 0 \quad x \end{array}$

From these signs you should notice that:

- A sign change occurs about a zero of the function for single linear factors such as $(x + 2)$ and $(x - 1)$. This indicates **cutting** of the x-axis.
- No sign change occurs about a zero of the function for squared linear factors such as $(x - 1)^2$. This indicates **touching** of the x-axis.
- $\begin{array}{c} \vdots \\ 0 \end{array}$ indicates that a function is **undefined** at $x = 0$.

> In general:
> - when a linear factor has an **odd power** there is a change of sign about that zero
> - when a linear factor has an **even power** there is no sign change about that zero.

Example 8

◀)) **Self Tutor**

Draw sign diagrams for:

a

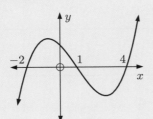

b

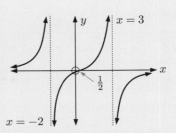

a

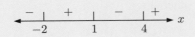

b

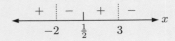

EXERCISE 2E

1 Draw sign diagrams for these graphs:

a

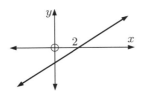

b

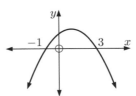

c

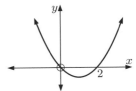

d

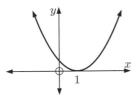

e

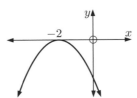

f

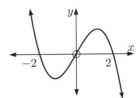

g

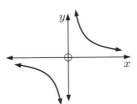

h

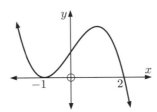

i

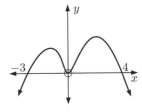

j

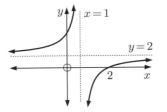

k

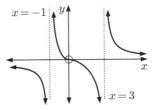

l

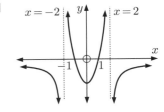

Example 9   ◀) **Self Tutor**

Draw a sign diagram for:

a $(x+3)(x-1)$

b $2(2x+5)(3-x)$

a $(x+3)(x-1)$ has zeros -3 and 1.

> We substitute any number > 1.
> When $x = 2$ we have $(5)(1) > 0$,
> so we put a $+$ sign here.

As the factors are single, the signs alternate.

b $2(2x+5)(3-x)$ has zeros $-\frac{5}{2}$ and 3.

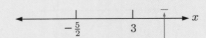

> We substitute any number > 3.
> When $x = 5$ we have $2(15)(-2) < 0$,
> so we put a $-$ sign here.

As the factors are single, the signs alternate.

Example 10   ◀) **Self Tutor**

Draw a sign diagram for:

a $12 - 3x^2$

b $-4(x-3)^2$

a $12 - 3x^2 = -3(x^2 - 4)$
$= -3(x+2)(x-2)$

which has zeros -2 and 2.

> We substitute any number > 2.
> When $x = 3$ we have $-3(5)(1) < 0$,
> so we put a $-$ sign here.

As the factors are single, the signs alternate.

b $-4(x-3)^2$ has zero 3.

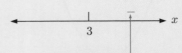

> We substitute any number > 3.
> When $x = 4$ we have $-4(1)^2 < 0$,
> so we put a $-$ sign here.

As the factor is squared, the signs do not change.

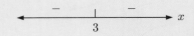

---

2 Draw sign diagrams for:

a $(x+4)(x-2)$

b $x(x-3)$

c $x(x+2)$

d $-(x+1)(x-3)$

e $(2x-1)(3-x)$

f $(5-x)(1-2x)$

g $x^2 - 9$

h $4 - x^2$

i $5x - x^2$

j $x^2 - 3x + 2$

k $2 - 8x^2$

l $6x^2 + x - 2$

m $6 - 16x - 6x^2$

n $-2x^2 + 9x + 5$

o $-15x^2 - x + 2$

3 Draw sign diagrams for:

    a $(x+2)^2$ **b** $(x-3)^2$ **c** $-(x+2)^2$

    d $-(x-4)^2$ **e** x^2-2x+1 **f** $-x^2+4x-4$

    g $4x^2-4x+1$ **h** $-x^2-6x-9$ **i** $-4x^2+12x-9$

Example 11   ◀) **Self Tutor**

Draw a sign diagram for $\dfrac{x-1}{2x+1}$.

$\dfrac{x-1}{2x+1}$ is zero when $x=1$ and undefined when $x=-\frac{1}{2}$.

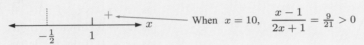

When $x=10$, $\dfrac{x-1}{2x+1}=\frac{9}{21}>0$

Since $(x-1)$ and $(2x+1)$ are single factors, the signs alternate.

---

4 Draw sign diagrams for:

    a $\dfrac{x+2}{x-1}$ **b** $\dfrac{x}{x+3}$ **c** $\dfrac{2x+3}{4-x}$ **d** $\dfrac{4x-1}{2-x}$

    e $\dfrac{3x}{x-2}$ **f** $\dfrac{-8x}{3-x}$ **g** $\dfrac{(x-1)^2}{x}$ **h** $\dfrac{4x}{(x+1)^2}$

    i $\dfrac{(x+2)(x-1)}{3-x}$ **j** $\dfrac{x(x-1)}{2-x}$ **k** $\dfrac{x^2-4}{-x}$ **l** $\dfrac{3-x}{2x^2-x-6}$

F   RATIONAL FUNCTIONS

We have seen that a linear function has the form $y=ax+b$.

When we divide a linear function by another linear function, the result is a **rational function**.

Rational functions are characterised by **asymptotes**, which are lines the function gets closer and closer to but never reaches.

The rational functions we consider in this course can be written in the form $y=\dfrac{ax+b}{cx+d}$.   These functions have asymptotes which are horizontal and vertical.

RECIPROCAL FUNCTIONS

A **reciprocal function** is a function of the form $x\mapsto\dfrac{k}{x}$ or $f(x)=\dfrac{k}{x}$,   where $k\neq0$.

The simplest example of a reciprocal function is $f(x)=\dfrac{1}{x}$.

The graph of $f(x) = \dfrac{1}{x}$ is called a **rectangular hyperbola**.

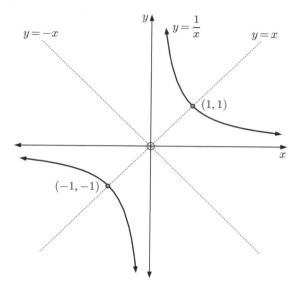

Notice that:

- $f(x) = \dfrac{1}{x}$ is undefined when $x = 0$

- The graph of $f(x) = \dfrac{1}{x}$ exists in the first and third quadrants only.

- $f(x) = \dfrac{1}{x}$ is symmetric about $y = x$ and $y = -x$.

- as $x \to \infty$, $f(x) \to 0$ (from above)
  as $x \to -\infty$, $f(x) \to 0$ (from below)
  as $x \to 0$ (from the right), $f(x) \to \infty$
  as $x \to 0$ (from the left), $f(x) \to -\infty$

- The **asymptotes** of $f(x) = \dfrac{1}{x}$ are the x-axis and the y-axis.

GRAPHING PACKAGE

$\to$ reads *"approaches"* or *"tends to"*

INVESTIGATION 2   RECIPROCAL FUNCTIONS

In this investigation we explore reciprocal functions of the form $y = \dfrac{k}{x}$, $k \neq 0$.

DEMO

What to do:

1   Use the slider to vary the value of k for $k > 0$.

   a Sketch the graphs of $y = \dfrac{1}{x}$, $y = \dfrac{2}{x}$, and $y = \dfrac{4}{x}$ on the same set of axes.

   b Describe the effect of varying k on the graph of $y = \dfrac{k}{x}$.

2   Use the slider to vary the value of k for $k < 0$.

   a Sketch the graphs of $y = -\dfrac{1}{x}$, $y = -\dfrac{2}{x}$, and $y = -\dfrac{4}{x}$ on the same set of axes.

   b Describe the effect of varying k on the graph of $y = \dfrac{k}{x}$.

RATIONAL FUNCTIONS OF THE FORM $y = \dfrac{ax+b}{cx+d}, \ c \neq 0$

The graph of $f(x) = \dfrac{2x+1}{x-1}$ is shown below.

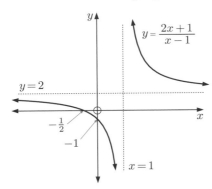

Notice that when $x = 1$, $f(x)$ is undefined.

The graph approaches the vertical line $x = 1$, so $x = 1$ is a vertical asymptote.

Notice that $f(0.999) = -2998$ and $f(1.001) = 3002$.

We can write: as $x \to 1$ (from the left), $f(x) \to -\infty$

as $x \to 1$ (from the right), $f(x) \to \infty$

or   as $x \to 1^-$, $f(x) \to -\infty$

as $x \to 1^+$, $f(x) \to \infty$.

To determine the equation of a vertical asymptote, consider the values of x which make the function undefined.

The sign diagram of $y = \dfrac{2x+1}{x-1}$ is $\xleftarrow{\ +\ |\ \ -\ \ |\ \ +\ } x$ and can be used to discuss the function
$ -\frac{1}{2} \qquad 1$

near its vertical asymptote without having to graph the function.

The graph also approaches the horizontal line $y = 2$, so $y = 2$ is a horizontal asymptote.

Notice that $f(1000) = \dfrac{2001}{999} \approx 2.003$ and $f(-1000) = \dfrac{-1999}{-1001} \approx 1.997$

We can write:

as $x \to \infty$, $y \to 2$ (from above)   *or*   as $x \to \infty$, $y \to 2^+$

as $x \to -\infty$, $y \to 2$ (from below)   *or*   as $x \to -\infty$, $y \to 2^-$.

We can also write: as $|x| \to \infty$, $f(x) \to 2$.

This indicates that as x becomes very large (either positive or negative) the function approaches the value 2.

> To determine the equation of a horizontal asymptote, we consider the behaviour of the function as $|x| \to \infty$.

INVESTIGATION 3   FINDING ASYMPTOTES

What to do:

GRAPHING PACKAGE

1 Use the **graphing package** supplied or a **graphics calculator** to examine the following functions for asymptotes:

a $y = -1 + \dfrac{3}{x-2}$ 　　　　**b** $y = \dfrac{3x+1}{x+2}$ 　　　　**c** $y = \dfrac{2x-9}{3-x}$

2 State the domain of each of the functions in **1**.

3 How can we tell directly from the function, what its vertical asymptote is?

DISCUSSION

Can a function cross a vertical asymptote?

Example 12   ◄) **Self Tutor**

Consider the function $y = \dfrac{6}{x-2} + 4$.

  a Find the asymptotes of the function.   **b** Find the axes intercepts.
  c Use technology to help sketch the function, including the features from **a** and **b**.

---

  a The vertical asymptote is $x = 2$.
       The horizontal asymptote is $y = 4$.

  b When $y = 0$, $\dfrac{6}{x-2} = -4$

$$\therefore \quad -4(x-2) = 6$$
$$\therefore \quad -4x + 8 = 6$$
$$\therefore \quad -4x = -2$$
$$\therefore \quad x = \tfrac{1}{2}$$

When $x = 0$, $y = \dfrac{6}{-2} + 4 = 1$

So, the x-intercept is $\tfrac{1}{2}$ and the
y-intercept is 1.

c
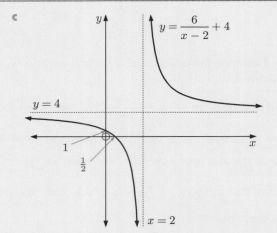

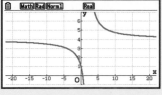

Further examples of asymptotic behaviour are seen in exponential, logarithmic, and some trigonometric functions.

EXERCISE 2F

1 For the following functions:
  i   determine the equations of the asymptotes
  ii   state the domain and range
  iii find the axes intercepts
  iv   discuss the behaviour of the function as it approaches its asymptotes
  v   sketch the graph of the function.

  a $f : x \mapsto \dfrac{3}{x-2}$ **b** $y = 2 - \dfrac{3}{x+1}$ **c** $f : x \mapsto \dfrac{x+3}{x-2}$ **d** $f(x) = \dfrac{3x-1}{x+2}$

2 Consider the function $y = \dfrac{ax + b}{cx + d}$, where a, b, c, d are constants and $c \neq 0$.

    a State the domain of the function.

    b State the equation of the vertical asymptote.

    c Show that for $c \neq 0$, $\dfrac{ax + b}{cx + d} = \dfrac{a}{c} + \dfrac{b - \frac{ad}{c}}{cx + d}$.

    Hence determine the equation of the horizontal asymptote.

ACTIVITY

Click on the icon to run a card game for rational functions.

GAME

G   INVERSE FUNCTIONS

The operations of $+$ and $-$, $\times$ and $\div$, squaring and finding the square root, are **inverse operations** as one undoes what the other does.

For example, $x + 3 - 3 = x$, $x \times 3 \div 3 = x$ and $\sqrt{8^2} = 8$.

The function $y = 2x + 3$ can be "undone" by its *inverse* function $y = \dfrac{x - 3}{2}$.

We can think of this as two machines. If the machines are inverses then the second machine *undoes* what the first machine does.

No matter what value of x enters the first machine, it is returned as the output from the second machine.

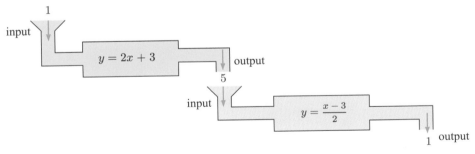

A function $y = f(x)$ *may or may not* have an inverse function.

If $y = f(x)$ has an **inverse function**, this new function:

- is denoted $f^{-1}(x)$
- must indeed be a function, and so must satisfy the vertical line test
- is the reflection of $y = f(x)$ in the line $y = x$
- satisfies $(f \circ f^{-1})(x) = x$ and $(f^{-1} \circ f)(x) = x$.

The function $y = x$, defined as $f : x \mapsto x$, is the **identity function**.

f^{-1} is **not** the reciprocal of f.

$f^{-1}(x) \neq \dfrac{1}{f(x)}$

If (x, y) lies on f, then (y, x) lies on f^{-1}. Reflecting the function in the line $y = x$ has the algebraic effect of interchanging x and y.

For example, $f : y = 5x + 2$ becomes $f^{-1} : x = 5y + 2$.

> The domain of f^{-1} is equal to the range of f.
>
> The range of f^{-1} is equal to the domain of f.

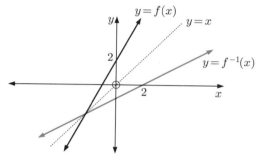

$y = f^{-1}(x)$ is the inverse of $y = f(x)$ as:

• it is also a function
• it is the reflection of $y = f(x)$ in the line $y = x$.

The parabola shown in red is the reflection of $y = f(x)$ in $y = x$, but it is *not* the inverse function of $y = f(x)$ as it fails the vertical line test.

In this case the function $y = f(x)$ does not have an inverse.

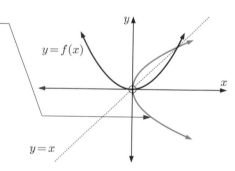

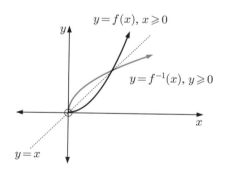

Now consider the same function $y = f(x)$ but with the restricted domain $x \geqslant 0$.

The function does now have an inverse function, as shown alongside. However, domain restrictions like this are beyond this course.

Example 13   ◀ Self Tutor

Consider $f : x \mapsto 2x + 3$.

a On the same axes, graph f and its inverse function f^{-1}.

b Find $f^{-1}(x)$ using:

   i coordinate geometry and the gradient of $y = f^{-1}(x)$ from **a**
   ii variable interchange.

c Check that $(f \circ f^{-1})(x) = (f^{-1} \circ f)(x) = x$

a $f(x) = 2x + 3$ passes through $(0, 3)$ and $(2, 7)$.
$\therefore$ $f^{-1}(x)$ passes through $(3, 0)$ and $(7, 2)$.

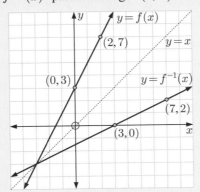

If f includes point (a, b) then f^{-1} includes point (b, a).

b **i** $y = f^{-1}(x)$ has gradient $\dfrac{2 - 0}{7 - 3} = \dfrac{1}{2}$

Its equation is $\dfrac{y - 0}{x - 3} = \dfrac{1}{2}$

$\therefore$ $y = \dfrac{x - 3}{2}$

$\therefore$ $f^{-1}(x) = \dfrac{x - 3}{2}$

ii f is $y = 2x + 3$,
$\therefore$ f^{-1} is $x = 2y + 3$
$\therefore$ $x - 3 = 2y$
$\therefore$ $\dfrac{x - 3}{2} = y$
$\therefore$ $f^{-1}(x) = \dfrac{x - 3}{2}$

c $(f \circ f^{-1})(x)$ and
$= f(f^{-1}(x))$
$= f\left(\dfrac{x - 3}{2}\right)$
$= 2\left(\dfrac{x - 3}{2}\right) + 3$
$= x$

$(f^{-1} \circ f)(x)$
$= f^{-1}(f(x))$
$= f^{-1}(2x + 3)$
$= \dfrac{(2x + 3) - 3}{2}$
$= \dfrac{2x}{2}$
$= x$

The reciprocal function $f(x) = \dfrac{1}{x}$, $x \neq 0$, is said to be a **self-inverse function** as $f = f^{-1}$.

This is because the graph of $y = \dfrac{1}{x}$ is symmetrical about the line $y = x$.

Any function which has an inverse, and whose graph is symmetrical about the line $y = x$, is a **self-inverse function**.

Graphics calculator tip:

When graphing f, f^{-1}, and $y = x$ on the same set of axes, it is best to set the scale so that $y = x$ makes a $45°$ angle with both axes.

EXERCISE 2G

1 For each of the following functions f:
    i On the same set of axes, graph $y = x$, $y = f(x)$, and $y = f^{-1}(x)$.
    ii Find $f^{-1}(x)$ using coordinate geometry and the gradient of $y = f^{-1}(x)$ from **i**.
    iii Find $f^{-1}(x)$ using variable interchange.

a $f : x \mapsto 3x + 1$

b $f : x \mapsto \dfrac{x + 2}{4}$

2 For each of the following functions f:

    i find $f^{-1}(x)$

    ii sketch $y = f(x)$, $y = f^{-1}(x)$, and $y = x$ on the same set of axes

    iii show that $(f^{-1} \circ f)(x) = (f \circ f^{-1})(x) = x$, the identity function.

    a $f : x \mapsto 2x + 5$ **b** $f : x \mapsto \dfrac{3 - 2x}{4}$ **c** $f : x \mapsto x + 3$

3 Copy the graphs of the following functions and draw the graphs of $y = x$ and $y = f^{-1}(x)$ on the same set of axes.

a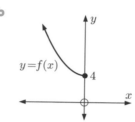

b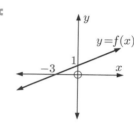

c

PRINTABLE GRAPHS

d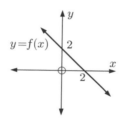

e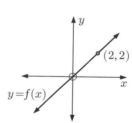

f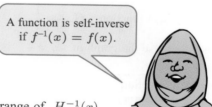

4 For the graph of $y = f(x)$ given in **3 a**, state:

    a the domain of $f(x)$ **b** the range of $f(x)$

    c the domain of $f^{-1}(x)$ **d** the range of $f^{-1}(x)$.

5   **a** Comment on the results from **3 e** and **f**.

    b Draw a linear function that is a self-inverse function.

> A function is self-inverse if $f^{-1}(x) = f(x)$.

    c Draw a rational function other than $y = \dfrac{1}{x}$, that is a self-inverse function.

6 If the domain of $H(x)$ is $\{x \mid -2 \leqslant x < 3\}$, state the range of $H^{-1}(x)$.

7 Given $f(x) = 2x - 5$, find $(f^{-1})^{-1}(x)$. What do you notice?

8 Sketch the graph of $f : x \mapsto x^3$ and its inverse function $f^{-1}(x)$.

9 Given $f : x \mapsto \dfrac{1}{x}$, $x \neq 0$, find f^{-1} algebraically and show that f is a self-inverse function.

10 Show that $f : x \mapsto \dfrac{3x - 8}{x - 3}$, $x \neq 3$ is a self-inverse function by:

    a reference to its graph   **b** using algebra.

11 Consider the function $f(x) = \frac{1}{2}x - 1$.

    a Find $f^{-1}(x)$.   **b** Find: **i** $(f \circ f^{-1})(x)$ **ii** $(f^{-1} \circ f)(x)$.

12 Consider the functions $f : x \mapsto 2x + 5$ and $g : x \mapsto \dfrac{8 - x}{2}$.

    a Find $g^{-1}(-1)$.   **b** Show that $f^{-1}(-3) - g^{-1}(6) = 0$.

    c Find x such that $(f \circ g^{-1})(x) = 9$.

13 Consider the functions $f : x \mapsto 5^x$ and $g : x \mapsto \sqrt{x}$.

    a Find: **i** $f(2)$ **ii** $g^{-1}(4)$. **b** Solve the equation $(g^{-1} \circ f)(x) = 25$.

14 Given $f : x \mapsto 2x$ and $g : x \mapsto 4x - 3$, show that $(f^{-1} \circ g^{-1})(x) = (g \circ f)^{-1}(x)$.

15 Which of these functions is a self-inverse function?

    a $f(x) = 2x$ **b** $f(x) = x$ **c** $f(x) = -x$

    d $f(x) = \dfrac{2}{x}$ **e** $f(x) = -\dfrac{6}{x}$

16 The **horizontal line test** says:

For a function to have an inverse function, no horizontal line can cut its graph more than once.

    a Explain why this is a valid test for the existence of an inverse function.

    b Which of the following functions have an inverse function?

  i 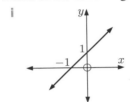 **ii** 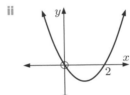 **iii**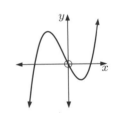

REVIEW SET 2A   NON-CALCULATOR

1 For each graph, state:

    i the domain   **ii** the range   **iii** whether the graph shows a function.

  a 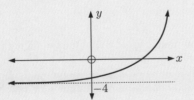 **b**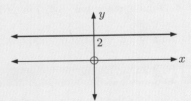

  c 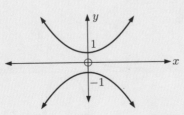 **d**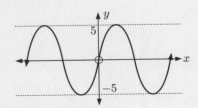

2 If $f(x) = 2x - x^2$, find: **a** $f(2)$ **b** $f(-3)$ **c** $f(-\tfrac{1}{2})$.

3 Suppose $f(x) = ax + b$ where a and b are constants. If $f(1) = 7$ and $f(3) = -5$, find a and b.

4 If $g(x) = x^2 - 3x$, find in simplest form: **a** $g(x+1)$ **b** $g(x^2 - 2)$

5 For each of the following graphs determine:

      i the domain and range   **ii** the x and y-intercepts

      iii whether it is a function.

a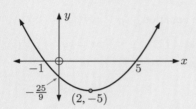

b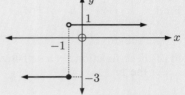

6 Draw a sign diagram for:

    a $(3x+2)(4-x)$ **b** $\dfrac{x-3}{x^2 + 4x + 4}$

7 If $f(x) = ax + b$, $f(2) = 1$, and $f^{-1}(3) = 4$, find a and b.

8 Copy the following graphs and draw the inverse function on the same set of axes:

a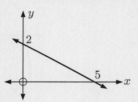

b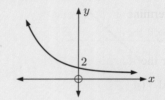

9 Find $f^{-1}(x)$ given that $f(x)$ is: **a** $4x + 2$ **b** $\dfrac{3 - 5x}{4}$

10 Consider $f(x) = x^2$ and $g(x) = 1 - 6x$.

    a Show that $f(-3) = g(-\frac{4}{3})$.   **b** Find $(f \circ g)(-2)$.

    c Find x such that $g(x) = f(5)$.

11 Given $f : x \mapsto 3x + 6$ and $h : x \mapsto \dfrac{x}{3}$, show that $(f^{-1} \circ h^{-1})(x) = (h \circ f)^{-1}(x)$.

REVIEW SET 2B   CALCULATOR

1 For each of the following graphs, find the domain and range:

a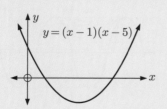

b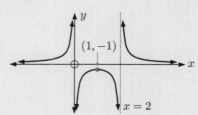

2 If $f(x) = 2x - 3$ and $g(x) = x^2 + 2$, find in simplest form:

    a $(f \circ g)(x)$ **b** $(g \circ f)(x)$

3 Draw a sign diagram for:

a $\dfrac{x^2 - 6x - 16}{x - 3}$

b $\dfrac{x + 9}{x + 5} + x$

4 Consider $f(x) = \dfrac{1}{x^2}$.

a For what value of x is $f(x)$ undefined, or not a real number?

b Sketch the graph of this function using technology.

c State the domain and range of the function.

5 Consider the function $f(x) = \dfrac{ax + 3}{x - b}$.

a Find a and b given that $y = f(x)$ has asymptotes with equations $x = -1$ and $y = 2$.

b Write down the domain and range of $f^{-1}(x)$.

6 Consider the function $f : x \mapsto \dfrac{4x + 1}{2 - x}$.

a Determine the equations of the asymptotes.

b State the domain and range of the function.

c Discuss the behaviour of the function as it approaches its asymptotes.

d Determine the axes intercepts.

e Sketch the function.

7 Consider the functions $f(x) = 3x + 1$ and $g(x) = \dfrac{2}{x}$.

a Find $(g \circ f)(x)$.

b Given $(g \circ f)(x) = -4$, solve for x.

c Let $h(x) = (g \circ f)(x)$, $x \neq -\frac{1}{3}$.

   i Write down the equations of the asymptotes of $h(x)$.

   ii Sketch the graph of $h(x)$ for $-3 \leqslant x \leqslant 2$.

   iii State the range of $h(x)$ for the domain $-3 \leqslant x \leqslant 2$.

8 Consider $f : x \mapsto 2x - 7$.

a On the same set of axes graph $y = x$, $y = f(x)$, and $y = f^{-1}(x)$.

b Find $f^{-1}(x)$ using variable interchange.

c Show that $(f \circ f^{-1})(x) = (f^{-1} \circ f)(x) = x$, the identity function.

9 The graph of the function $f(x) = -3x^2$, $0 \leqslant x \leqslant 2$ is shown alongside.

a Sketch the graph of $y = f^{-1}(x)$.

b State the range of f^{-1}.

c Solve:

   i $f(x) = -10$

   ii $f^{-1}(x) = 1$

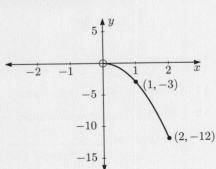

REVIEW SET 2C

1 For each of the following graphs, find the domain and range:

    a

    b

2 Given $f(x) = x^2 + 3$, find:

    a $f(-3)$
        b x such that $f(x) = 4$.

3 State the value(s) of x for which $f(x)$ is undefined:

    a $f(x) = 10 + \dfrac{3}{2x - 1}$
        b $f(x) = \sqrt{x + 7}$

4 Draw a sign diagram for:

    a $f(x) = x(x + 4)(3x + 1)$
        b $f(x) = \dfrac{-11}{(x + 1)(x + 8)}$

5 Given $h(x) = 7 - 3x$, find:

    a $h(2x - 1)$ in simplest form
        b x such that $h(2x - 1) = -2$.

6 If $f(x) = 1 - 2x$ and $g(x) = \sqrt{x}$, find in simplest form:

    a $(f \circ g)(x)$
        b $(g \circ f)(x)$

7 Suppose $f(x) = ax^2 + bx + c$. Find a, b, and c if $f(0) = 5$, $f(-2) = 21$, and $f(3) = -4$.

8 Copy the following graphs and draw the graph of each inverse function on the same set of axes:

    a

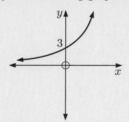

    b

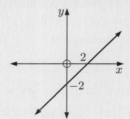

9 Find the inverse function $f^{-1}(x)$ for:

    a $f(x) = 7 - 4x$
        b $f(x) = \dfrac{3 + 2x}{5}$

10 Given $f : x \mapsto 5x - 2$ and $h : x \mapsto \dfrac{3x}{4}$, show that $(f^{-1} \circ h^{-1})(x) = (h \circ f)^{-1}(x)$.

11 Given $f(x) = 2x + 11$ and $g(x) = x^2$, find $(g \circ f^{-1})(3)$.

12 Sketch a function with domain $\{x \mid x \neq 4\}$, range $\{y \mid y \neq -1\}$, and

    sign diagram

Chapter 3

Exponentials

Syllabus reference: 1.2, 2.2, 2.6, 2.7, 2.8

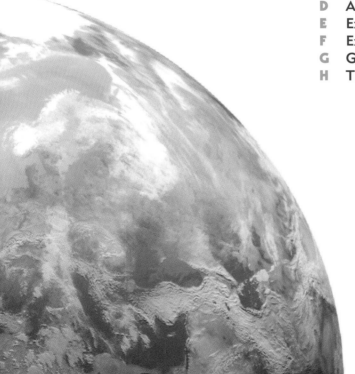

OPENING PROBLEM

The interior of a freezer has temperature $-10°C$. When a packet of peas is placed in the freezer, its temperature after t minutes is given by $T(t) = -10 + 32 \times 2^{-0.2t}$ $°C$.

Things to think about:

a   What was the temperature of the packet of peas:
   i   when it was first placed in the freezer   ii   after 5 minutes
   iii   after 10 minutes   iv   after 15 minutes?

b   What does the graph of temperature over time look like?

c   According to this model, will the temperature of the packet of peas ever reach $-10°C$? Explain your answer.

We often deal with numbers that are repeatedly multiplied together. Mathematicians use **exponents**, also called **powers**, or **indices**, to construct such expressions.

Exponents have many applications in the areas of finance, engineering, physics, electronics, biology, and computer science. Problems encountered in these areas may involve situations where quantities increase or decrease over time. Such problems are often examples of **exponential growth** or **decay**.

A   EXPONENTS

Rather than writing $3 \times 3 \times 3 \times 3 \times 3$, we can write this product as 3^5.

If n is a positive integer, then a^n is the product of n factors of a.

$$a^n = \underbrace{a \times a \times a \times a \times \ldots\ldots \times a}_{n \text{ factors}}$$

We say that a is the **base**, and n is the **exponent** or **index**.

base   power, index or exponent

NEGATIVE BASES

$(-1)^1 = -1$ $(-2)^1 = -2$
$(-1)^2 = -1 \times -1 = 1$ $(-2)^2 = -2 \times -2 = 4$
$(-1)^3 = -1 \times -1 \times -1 = -1$ $(-2)^3 = -2 \times -2 \times -2 = -8$
$(-1)^4 = -1 \times -1 \times -1 \times -1 = 1$ $(-2)^4 = -2 \times -2 \times -2 \times -2 = 16$

From the patterns above we can see that:

A **negative** base raised to an **odd** exponent is **negative**.
A **negative** base raised to an **even** exponent is **positive**.

CALCULATOR USE

Although different calculators vary in the appearance of keys, they all perform operations of raising to powers in a similar manner. Click on the icon for instructions for calculating exponents.

GRAPHICS CALCULATOR INSTRUCTIONS

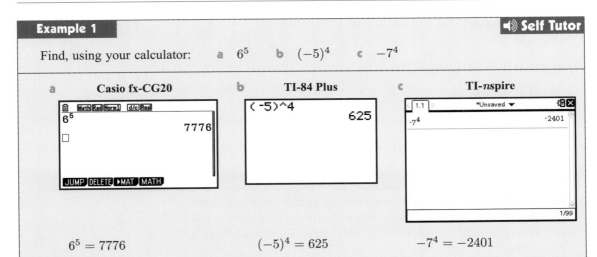

Example 1 ◀)) **Self Tutor**

Find, using your calculator: **a** 6^5 **b** $(-5)^4$ **c** -7^4

a Casio fx-CG20

b TI-84 Plus

c TI-*n*spire

$$6^5 = 7776 \qquad (-5)^4 = 625 \qquad -7^4 = -2401$$

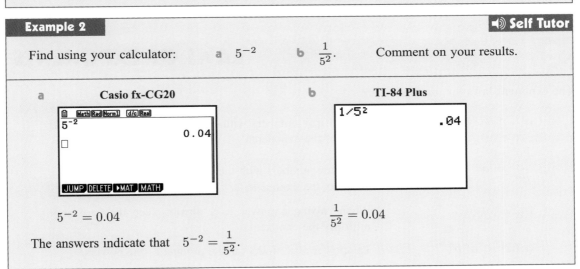

Example 2 ◀)) **Self Tutor**

Find using your calculator: **a** 5^{-2} **b** $\dfrac{1}{5^2}$. Comment on your results.

a Casio fx-CG20

b TI-84 Plus

$$5^{-2} = 0.04 \qquad \frac{1}{5^2} = 0.04$$

The answers indicate that $5^{-2} = \dfrac{1}{5^2}$.

EXERCISE 3A

1 List the first six powers of:

  a 2   **b** 3   **c** 4

2 Copy and complete the values of these common powers:

  a $5^1 = ...$, $5^2 = ...$, $5^3 = ...$, $5^4 = ...$

  b $6^1 = ...$, $6^2 = ...$, $6^3 = ...$, $6^4 = ...$

  c $7^1 = ...$, $7^2 = ...$, $7^3 = ...$, $7^4 = ...$

3 Simplify, then use a calculator to check your answer:

  a $(-1)^5$ **b** $(-1)^6$ **c** $(-1)^{14}$ **d** $(-1)^{19}$ **e** $(-1)^8$ **f** -1^8

  g $-(-1)^8$ **h** $(-2)^5$ **i** -2^5 **j** $-(-2)^6$ **k** $(-5)^4$ **l** $-(-5)^4$

4 Use your calculator to find the value of the following, recording the entire display:

  a 4^7 **b** 7^4 **c** -5^5 **d** $(-5)^5$ **e** 8^6 **f** $(-8)^6$

  g -8^6 **h** 2.13^9 **i** -2.13^9 **j** $(-2.13)^9$

5 Use your calculator to find the values of the following:

    a 9^{-1} **b** $\dfrac{1}{9^1}$ **c** 6^{-2} **d** $\dfrac{1}{6^2}$ **e** 3^{-4} **f** $\dfrac{1}{3^4}$

    g 17^0 **h** $(0.366)^0$

    What do you notice?

6 Consider 3^1, 3^2, 3^3, 3^4, 3^5 ....   Look for a pattern and hence find the last digit of 3^{101}.

7 What is the last digit of 7^{217}?

HISTORICAL NOTE

Nicomachus discovered an interesting number pattern involving cubes and sums of odd numbers. Nicomachus was born in Roman Syria (now Jerash, Jordan) around 100 AD. He wrote in Greek and was a Pythagorean.

$$1 = 1^3$$
$$3 + 5 = 8 = 2^3$$
$$7 + 9 + 11 = 27 = 3^3$$
$$\vdots$$

B   LAWS OF EXPONENTS

The **exponent laws** for m, $n \in \mathbb{Z}$ are:

$a^m \times a^n = a^{m+n}$	To **multiply** numbers with the **same base**, keep the base and **add** the exponents.
$\dfrac{a^m}{a^n} = a^{m-n}, \quad a \neq 0$	To **divide** numbers with the same base, keep the base and **subtract** the exponents.
$(a^m)^n = a^{m \times n}$	When **raising** a **power** to a **power**, keep the base and **multiply** the exponents.
$(ab)^n = a^n b^n$	The power of a product is the product of the powers.
$\left(\dfrac{a}{b}\right)^n = \dfrac{a^n}{b^n}, \quad b \neq 0$	The power of a quotient is the quotient of the powers.
$a^0 = 1, \quad a \neq 0$	Any non-zero number raised to the power of zero is 1.
$a^{-n} = \dfrac{1}{a^n}$ and $\dfrac{1}{a^{-n}} = a^n$ and in particular $a^{-1} = \dfrac{1}{a}, \quad a \neq 0.$	

Example 3   ◀) Self Tutor

Simplify using the exponent laws: **a** $3^5 \times 3^4$ **b** $\dfrac{5^3}{5^5}$ **c** $\left(m^4\right)^3$

a $3^5 \times 3^4$
    $= 3^{5+4}$
    $= 3^9$

b $\dfrac{5^3}{5^5}$
    $= 5^{3-5}$
    $= 5^{-2}$
    $= \frac{1}{25}$

c $\left(m^4\right)^3$
    $= m^{4 \times 3}$
    $= m^{12}$

Example 4   ◀)) **Self Tutor**

Write as powers of 2:

   a 16   **b** $\frac{1}{16}$ **c** 1   **d** 4×2^n **e** $\frac{2^m}{8}$

a 16	**b** $\quad\frac{1}{16}$	**c** $\quad 1$	**d** $\quad 4 \times 2^n$	**e** $\quad\frac{2^m}{8}$
$= 2 \times 2 \times 2 \times 2$	$= \frac{1}{2^4}$	$= 2^0$	$= 2^2 \times 2^n$	
$= 2^4$	$= 2^{-4}$		$= 2^{2+n}$	$= \frac{2^m}{2^3}$
				$= 2^{m-3}$

EXERCISE 3B

1 Simplify using the laws of exponents:

  a $5^4 \times 5^7$ **b** $d^2 \times d^6$ **c** $\frac{k^8}{k^3}$ **d** $\frac{7^5}{7^6}$ **e** $\left(x^2\right)^5$ **f** $\left(3^4\right)^4$

  g $\frac{p^3}{p^7}$ **h** $n^3 \times n^9$ **i** $\left(5^t\right)^3$ **j** $7^x \times 7^2$ **k** $\frac{10^3}{10^q}$ **l** $\left(c^4\right)^m$

2 Write as powers of 2:

  a 4   **b** $\frac{1}{4}$ **c** 8   **d** $\frac{1}{8}$ **e** 32   **f** $\frac{1}{32}$

  g 2   **h** $\frac{1}{2}$ **i** 64   **j** $\frac{1}{64}$ **k** 128   **l** $\frac{1}{128}$

3 Write as powers of 3:

  a 9   **b** $\frac{1}{9}$ **c** 27   **d** $\frac{1}{27}$ **e** 3   **f** $\frac{1}{3}$

  g 81   **h** $\frac{1}{81}$ **i** 1   **j** 243   **k** $\frac{1}{243}$

4 Write as a single power of 2:

  a 2×2^a **b** 4×2^b **c** 8×2^t **d** $(2^{x+1})^2$ **e** $(2^{1-n})^{-1}$

  f $\frac{2^c}{4}$ **g** $\frac{2^m}{2^{-m}}$ **h** $\frac{4}{2^{1-n}}$ **i** $\frac{2^{x+1}}{2^x}$ **j** $\frac{4^x}{2^{1-x}}$

5 Write as a single power of 3:

  a 9×3^p **b** 27^a **c** 3×9^n **d** 27×3^d **e** 9×27^t

  f $\frac{3^y}{3}$ **g** $\frac{3}{3^y}$ **h** $\frac{9}{27^t}$ **i** $\frac{9^a}{3^{1-a}}$ **j** $\frac{9^{n+1}}{3^{2n-1}}$

Example 5   ◀)) **Self Tutor**

Write in simplest form, without brackets:

  a $\left(-3a^2\right)^4$ **b** $\left(-\dfrac{2a^2}{b}\right)^3$

a $\quad \left(-3a^2\right)^4$	**b** $\quad \left(-\dfrac{2a^2}{b}\right)^3$
$= (-3)^4 \times (a^2)^4$	$= \dfrac{(-2)^3 \times (a^2)^3}{b^3}$
$= 81 \times a^{2 \times 4}$	$= \dfrac{-8a^6}{b^3}$
$= 81a^8$	

6 Write without brackets:

a $(2a)^2$

b $(3b)^3$

c $(ab)^4$

d $(pq)^3$

e $\left(\dfrac{m}{n}\right)^2$

f $\left(\dfrac{a}{3}\right)^3$

g $\left(\dfrac{b}{c}\right)^4$

h $\left(\dfrac{2a}{b}\right)^0$

i $\left(\dfrac{m}{3n}\right)^4$

j $\left(\dfrac{xy}{2}\right)^3$

7 Write the following in simplest form, without brackets:

a $(-2a)^2$

b $(-6b^2)^2$

c $(-2a)^3$

d $(-3m^2n^2)^3$

e $(-2ab^4)^4$

f $\left(\dfrac{-2a^2}{b^2}\right)^3$

g $\left(\dfrac{-4a^3}{b}\right)^2$

h $\left(\dfrac{-3p^2}{q^3}\right)^2$

Example 6	◀)) Self Tutor
Write without negative exponents: $\dfrac{a^{-3}b^2}{c^{-1}}$	$a^{-3} = \dfrac{1}{a^3}$ and $\dfrac{1}{c^{-1}} = c^1$ $\therefore \quad \dfrac{a^{-3}b^2}{c^{-1}} = \dfrac{b^2c}{a^3}$

8 Write without negative exponents:

a ab^{-2}

b $(ab)^{-2}$

c $(2ab^{-1})^2$

d $(3a^{-2}b)^2$

e $\dfrac{a^2b^{-1}}{c^2}$

f $\dfrac{a^2b^{-1}}{c^{-2}}$

g $\dfrac{1}{a^{-3}}$

h $\dfrac{a^{-2}}{b^{-3}}$

i $\dfrac{2a^{-1}}{d^2}$

j $\dfrac{12a}{m^{-3}}$

Example 7	◀)) Self Tutor
Write $\dfrac{1}{2^{1-n}}$ in non-fractional form.	$\dfrac{1}{2^{1-n}} = 2^{-(1-n)}$ $= 2^{-1+n}$ $= 2^{n-1}$

9 Write in non-fractional form:

a $\dfrac{1}{a^n}$

b $\dfrac{1}{b^{-n}}$

c $\dfrac{1}{3^{2-n}}$

d $\dfrac{a^n}{b^{-m}}$

e $\dfrac{a^{-n}}{a^{2+n}}$

10 Simplify, giving your answers in simplest rational form:

a $\left(\dfrac{5}{3}\right)^0$

b $\left(\dfrac{7}{4}\right)^{-1}$

c $\left(\dfrac{1}{6}\right)^{-1}$

d $\dfrac{3^3}{3^0}$

e $\left(\dfrac{4}{3}\right)^{-2}$

f $2^1 + 2^{-1}$

g $\left(1\tfrac{2}{3}\right)^{-3}$

h $5^2 + 5^1 + 5^{-1}$

11 Write as powers of 2, 3 and/or 5:

a $\dfrac{1}{9}$

b $\dfrac{1}{16}$

c $\dfrac{1}{125}$

d $\dfrac{3}{5}$

e $\dfrac{4}{27}$

f $\dfrac{2^c}{8 \times 9}$

g $\dfrac{9^k}{10}$

h $\dfrac{6^p}{75}$

12 Read about Nicomachus' pattern on page **84** and find the series of odd numbers for:

a 5^3

b 7^3

c 12^3

C   RATIONAL EXPONENTS

The exponent laws used previously can also be applied to **rational exponents**, or exponents which are written as a fraction.

For $a > 0$, notice that $\quad a^{\frac{1}{2}} \times a^{\frac{1}{2}} = a^{\frac{1}{2}+\frac{1}{2}} = a^1 = a$ {exponent laws}
and $\quad \sqrt{a} \times \sqrt{a} = a$ also.

So, $\quad a^{\frac{1}{2}} = \sqrt{a}$ {by direct comparison}

Likewise $a^{\frac{1}{3}} \times a^{\frac{1}{3}} \times a^{\frac{1}{3}} = a^1 = a$
and $\sqrt[3]{a} \times \sqrt[3]{a} \times \sqrt[3]{a} = a$

suggests $\quad a^{\frac{1}{3}} = \sqrt[3]{a}$

In general, $\quad a^{\frac{1}{n}} = \sqrt[n]{a}$ where $\sqrt[n]{a}$ reads 'the nth root of a', for $n \in \mathbb{Z}^+$.

We can now determine that $\quad \sqrt[n]{a^m}$

$$= (a^m)^{\frac{1}{n}}$$
$$= a^{\frac{m}{n}} \qquad \therefore \quad a^{\frac{m}{n}} = \sqrt[n]{a^m} \quad \text{for } a > 0, \ n \in \mathbb{Z}^+, \ m \in \mathbb{Z}$$

Example 8   ◀)) Self Tutor

Write as a single power of 2:   **a** $\sqrt[3]{2}$ **b** $\dfrac{1}{\sqrt{2}}$ **c** $\sqrt[5]{4}$

a $\quad \sqrt[3]{2}$

$\quad = 2^{\frac{1}{3}}$

b $\quad \dfrac{1}{\sqrt{2}}$

$\quad = \dfrac{1}{2^{\frac{1}{2}}}$

$\quad = 2^{-\frac{1}{2}}$

c $\quad \sqrt[5]{4}$

$\quad = (2^2)^{\frac{1}{5}}$

$\quad = 2^{2 \times \frac{1}{5}}$

$\quad = 2^{\frac{2}{5}}$

EXERCISE 3C

1 Write as a single power of 2:

  a $\sqrt[5]{2}$ **b** $\dfrac{1}{\sqrt[5]{2}}$ **c** $2\sqrt{2}$ **d** $4\sqrt{2}$ **e** $\dfrac{1}{\sqrt[3]{2}}$

  f $2 \times \sqrt[3]{2}$ **g** $\dfrac{4}{\sqrt{2}}$ **h** $(\sqrt{2})^3$ **i** $\dfrac{1}{\sqrt[3]{16}}$ **j** $\dfrac{1}{\sqrt{8}}$

2 Write as a single power of 3:

  a $\sqrt[3]{3}$ **b** $\dfrac{1}{\sqrt[3]{3}}$ **c** $\sqrt[4]{3}$ **d** $3\sqrt{3}$ **e** $\dfrac{1}{9\sqrt{3}}$

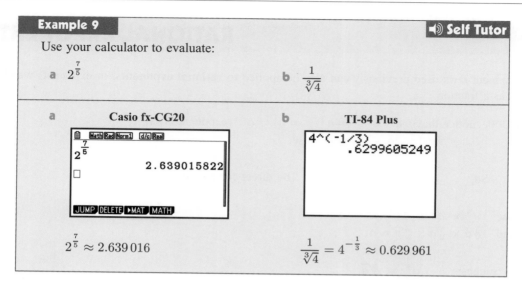

Example 9   ◀ﹱ **Self Tutor**

Use your calculator to evaluate:

a $2^{\frac{7}{5}}$

b $\dfrac{1}{\sqrt[3]{4}}$

a   Casio fx-CG20   **b**   TI-84 Plus

$2^{\frac{7}{5}} \approx 2.639\,016$ $\dfrac{1}{\sqrt[3]{4}} = 4^{-\frac{1}{3}} \approx 0.629\,961$

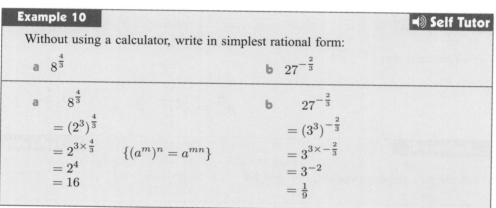

Example 10   ◀ﹱ **Self Tutor**

Without using a calculator, write in simplest rational form:

a $8^{\frac{4}{3}}$

b $27^{-\frac{2}{3}}$

a $8^{\frac{4}{3}}$

$= (2^3)^{\frac{4}{3}}$

$= 2^{3 \times \frac{4}{3}}$ $\{(a^m)^n = a^{mn}\}$

$= 2^4$

$= 16$

b $27^{-\frac{2}{3}}$

$= (3^3)^{-\frac{2}{3}}$

$= 3^{3 \times -\frac{2}{3}}$

$= 3^{-2}$

$= \frac{1}{9}$

3 Write the following in the form a^x where a is a prime number and x is rational:

a $\sqrt[3]{7}$ **b** $\sqrt[4]{27}$ **c** $\sqrt[5]{16}$ **d** $\sqrt[3]{32}$ **e** $\sqrt[7]{49}$

f $\dfrac{1}{\sqrt[3]{7}}$ **g** $\dfrac{1}{\sqrt[4]{27}}$ **h** $\dfrac{1}{\sqrt[5]{16}}$ **i** $\dfrac{1}{\sqrt[3]{32}}$ **j** $\dfrac{1}{\sqrt[7]{49}}$

4 Use your calculator to find:

a $3^{\frac{3}{4}}$ **b** $2^{\frac{7}{8}}$ **c** $2^{-\frac{1}{3}}$ **d** $4^{-\frac{3}{5}}$ **e** $\sqrt[4]{8}$

f $\sqrt[5]{27}$ **g** $\dfrac{1}{\sqrt[3]{7}}$

5 Without using a calculator, write in simplest rational form:

a $4^{\frac{3}{2}}$ **b** $8^{\frac{5}{3}}$ **c** $16^{\frac{3}{4}}$ **d** $25^{\frac{3}{2}}$ **e** $32^{\frac{2}{5}}$

f $4^{-\frac{1}{2}}$ **g** $9^{-\frac{3}{2}}$ **h** $8^{-\frac{4}{3}}$ **i** $27^{-\frac{4}{3}}$ **j** $125^{-\frac{2}{3}}$

THEORY OF KNOWLEDGE

A **rational number** is a number which can be written in the form $\dfrac{p}{q}$ where p and q are integers, $q \neq 0$. It has been proven that a rational number has a decimal expansion which either terminates or recurs.

If we begin to write the decimal expansion of $\sqrt{2}$, there is no indication that it will terminate or recur, and we might therefore suspect that $\sqrt{2}$ is irrational.

$$1.414\,213\,562\,373\,095\,048\,801\,688\,724\,209\,698\,078\,569\,671\,875\,376\,948\,073....$$

However, we cannot *prove* that $\sqrt{2}$ is irrational by writing out its decimal expansion, as we would have to write an infinite number of decimal places. We might therefore *believe* that $\sqrt{2}$ is irrational, but it may also seem impossible to *prove* it.

1   If something has not yet been proven, does that make it untrue?

2   Is the state of an idea being true or false dependent on our ability to prove it?

In fact, we can quite easily prove that $\sqrt{2}$ is irrational by using a method called **proof by contradiction**. In this method we suppose that the opposite is true of what we want to show is true, and follow a series of logical steps until we arrive at a contradiction. The contradiction confirms that our original supposition must be false.

Proof: Suppose $\sqrt{2}$ is rational, so $\sqrt{2} = \dfrac{p}{q}$ for some (positive) integers p and q, $q \neq 0$.

We assume this fraction has been written in lowest terms, so p and q have no common factors.

Squaring both sides, $2 = \dfrac{p^2}{q^2}$

$$\therefore \quad p^2 = 2q^2 \quad \text{.... (1)}$$

$\therefore$ p^2 is even, and so p must be even.

Thus $p = 2k$ for some $k \in \mathbb{Z}^+$.

Substituting into (1), $4k^2 = 2q^2$

$$\therefore \quad q^2 = 2k^2$$

$\therefore$ q^2 is even, and so q must be even.

Here we have a contradiction, as p and q have no common factors.

Thus our original supposition is false, and $\sqrt{2}$ is irrational.

3   Is proof by contradiction unique to mathematics, or do we use it elsewhere?

D   ALGEBRAIC EXPANSION AND FACTORISATION

EXPANSION

We can use the usual expansion laws to simplify expressions containing exponents:

$$a(b + c) = ab + ac$$
$$(a + b)(c + d) = ac + ad + bc + bd$$
$$(a + b)(a - b) = a^2 - b^2$$
$$(a + b)^2 = a^2 + 2ab + b^2$$
$$(a - b)^2 = a^2 - 2ab + b^2$$

Example 11   ◀) **Self Tutor**

Expand and simplify: $x^{-\frac{1}{2}}(x^{\frac{3}{2}} + 2x^{\frac{1}{2}} - 3x^{-\frac{1}{2}})$

$x^{-\frac{1}{2}}(x^{\frac{3}{2}} + 2x^{\frac{1}{2}} - 3x^{-\frac{1}{2}})$

$= x^{-\frac{1}{2}} \times x^{\frac{3}{2}} + x^{-\frac{1}{2}} \times 2x^{\frac{1}{2}} - x^{-\frac{1}{2}} \times 3x^{-\frac{1}{2}}$ {each term is $\times$ by $x^{-\frac{1}{2}}$}

$= x^1 + 2x^0 - 3x^{-1}$ {adding exponents}

$= x + 2 - \dfrac{3}{x}$

Example 12   ◀) **Self Tutor**

Expand and simplify: **a** $(2^x + 3)(2^x + 1)$ **b** $(7^x + 7^{-x})^2$

a $(2^x + 3)(2^x + 1)$

$= 2^x \times 2^x + 2^x + 3 \times 2^x + 3$

$= 2^{2x} + 4 \times 2^x + 3$

$= 4^x + 2^{2+x} + 3$

b $(7^x + 7^{-x})^2$

$= (7^x)^2 + 2 \times 7^x \times 7^{-x} + (7^{-x})^2$

$= 7^{2x} + 2 \times 7^0 + 7^{-2x}$

$= 7^{2x} + 2 + 7^{-2x}$

EXERCISE 3D.1

1 Expand and simplify:

a $x^2(x^3 + 2x^2 + 1)$

b $2^x(2^x + 1)$

c $x^{\frac{1}{2}}(x^{\frac{1}{2}} + x^{-\frac{1}{2}})$

d $7^x(7^x + 2)$

e $3^x(2 - 3^{-x})$

f $x^{\frac{1}{2}}(x^{\frac{3}{2}} + 2x^{\frac{1}{2}} + 3x^{-\frac{1}{2}})$

g $2^{-x}(2^x + 5)$

h $5^{-x}(5^{2x} + 5^x)$

i $x^{-\frac{1}{2}}(x^2 + x + x^{\frac{1}{2}})$

2 Expand and simplify:

a $(2^x - 1)(2^x + 3)$

b $(3^x + 2)(3^x + 5)$

c $(5^x - 2)(5^x - 4)$

d $(2^x + 3)^2$

e $(3^x - 1)^2$

f $(4^x + 7)^2$

g $(x^{\frac{1}{2}} + 2)(x^{\frac{1}{2}} - 2)$

h $(2^x + 3)(2^x - 3)$

i $(x^{\frac{1}{2}} + x^{-\frac{1}{2}})(x^{\frac{1}{2}} - x^{-\frac{1}{2}})$

j $(x + \frac{2}{x})^2$

k $(7^x - 7^{-x})^2$

l $(5 - 2^{-x})^2$

FACTORISATION AND SIMPLIFICATION

Example 13	◀ Self Tutor

Factorise: **a** $2^{n+3} + 2^n$ **b** $2^{n+3} + 8$ **c** $2^{3n} + 2^{2n}$

$$
\begin{aligned}
\textbf{a} \quad & 2^{n+3} + 2^n \\
= \ & 2^n 2^3 + 2^n \\
= \ & 2^n(2^3 + 1) \\
= \ & 2^n \times 9
\end{aligned}
\qquad
\begin{aligned}
\textbf{b} \quad & 2^{n+3} + 8 \\
= \ & 2^n 2^3 + 8 \\
= \ & 8(2^n) + 8 \\
= \ & 8(2^n + 1)
\end{aligned}
\qquad
\begin{aligned}
\textbf{c} \quad & 2^{3n} + 2^{2n} \\
= \ & 2^{2n} 2^n + 2^{2n} \\
= \ & 2^{2n}(2^n + 1)
\end{aligned}
$$

Example 14	◀ Self Tutor

Factorise: **a** $4^x - 9$ **b** $9^x + 4(3^x) + 4$

$$
\begin{aligned}
\textbf{a} \quad & 4^x - 9 \\
= \ & (2^x)^2 - 3^2 && \{\text{compare} \quad a^2 - b^2 = (a+b)(a-b)\} \\
= \ & (2^x + 3)(2^x - 3)
\end{aligned}
$$

$$
\begin{aligned}
\textbf{b} \quad & 9^x + 4(3^x) + 4 \\
= \ & (3^x)^2 + 4(3^x) + 4 && \{\text{compare} \quad a^2 + 4a + 4\} \\
= \ & (3^x + 2)^2 && \{\text{as} \quad a^2 + 4a + 4 = (a+2)^2\}
\end{aligned}
$$

EXERCISE 3D.2

1 Factorise:

a $5^{2x} + 5^x$ **b** $3^{n+2} + 3^n$ **c** $7^n + 7^{3n}$

d $5^{n+1} - 5$ **e** $6^{n+2} - 6$ **f** $4^{n+2} - 16$

2 Factorise:

a $9^x - 4$ **b** $4^x - 25$ **c** $16 - 9^x$

d $25 - 4^x$ **e** $9^x - 4^x$ **f** $4^x + 6(2^x) + 9$

g $9^x + 10(3^x) + 25$ **h** $4^x - 14(2^x) + 49$ **i** $25^x - 4(5^x) + 4$

3 Factorise:

a $4^x + 9(2^x) + 18$ **b** $4^x - 2^x - 20$ **c** $9^x + 9(3^x) + 14$

d $9^x + 4(3^x) - 5$ **e** $25^x + 5^x - 2$ **f** $49^x - 7^{x+1} + 12$

Example 15	◀ Self Tutor

Simplify: **a** $\dfrac{6^n}{3^n}$ **b** $\dfrac{4^n}{6^n}$

$$
\begin{aligned}
\textbf{a} \quad & \frac{6^n}{3^n} \quad \textbf{or} \quad \frac{6^n}{3^n} \\
& = \frac{2^n 3^n}{3^n{}_1} \qquad = \left(\frac{6}{3}\right)^n \\
& = 2^n \qquad\qquad = 2^n
\end{aligned}
\qquad
\begin{aligned}
\textbf{b} \quad & \frac{4^n}{6^n} \quad \textbf{or} \quad \frac{4^n}{6^n} \\
& = \frac{2^n 2^n}{2^n 3^n} \qquad = \left(\frac{4}{6}\right)^n \\
& = \frac{2^n}{3^n} \qquad\quad = \left(\frac{2}{3}\right)^n
\end{aligned}
$$

Example 16 🔊 **Self Tutor**

Simplify: **a** $\dfrac{3^n + 6^n}{3^n}$ **b** $\dfrac{2^{m+2} - 2^m}{2^m}$ **c** $\dfrac{2^{m+3} + 2^m}{9}$

a $\dfrac{3^n + 6^n}{3^n}$

$= \dfrac{3^n + 2^n 3^n}{3^n}$

$= \dfrac{3^n(1 + 2^n)}{3^n{}_1}$

$= 1 + 2^n$

b $\dfrac{2^{m+2} - 2^m}{2^m}$

$= \dfrac{2^m 2^2 - 2^m}{2^m}$

$= \dfrac{2^m(4 - 1)}{2^m{}_1}$

$= 3$

c $\dfrac{2^{m+3} + 2^m}{9}$

$= \dfrac{2^m 2^3 + 2^m}{9}$

$= \dfrac{2^m(8 + 1)}{9{}_1}$

$= 2^m$

4 Simplify:

a $\dfrac{12^n}{6^n}$ **b** $\dfrac{20^a}{2^a}$ **c** $\dfrac{6^b}{2^b}$ **d** $\dfrac{4^n}{20^n}$

e $\dfrac{35^x}{7^x}$ **f** $\dfrac{6^a}{8^a}$ **g** $\dfrac{5^{n+1}}{5^n}$ **h** $\dfrac{5^{n+1}}{5}$

5 Simplify:

a $\dfrac{6^m + 2^m}{2^m}$ **b** $\dfrac{2^n + 12^n}{2^n}$ **c** $\dfrac{8^n + 4^n}{2^n}$

d $\dfrac{12^x - 3^x}{3^x}$ **e** $\dfrac{6^n + 12^n}{1 + 2^n}$ **f** $\dfrac{5^{n+1} - 5^n}{4}$

g $\dfrac{5^{n+1} - 5^n}{5^n}$ **h** $\dfrac{4^n - 2^n}{2^n}$ **i** $\dfrac{2^n - 2^{n-1}}{2^n}$

6 Simplify:

a $2^n(n+1) + 2^n(n-1)$ **b** $3^n\left(\dfrac{n-1}{6}\right) - 3^n\left(\dfrac{n+1}{6}\right)$

E   EXPONENTIAL EQUATIONS

An **exponential equation** is an equation in which the unknown occurs as part of the index or exponent.

For example: $2^x = 8$ and $30 \times 3^x = 7$ are both exponential equations.

There are a number of methods we can use to solve exponential equations. These include graphing, using technology, and by using **logarithms**, which we will study in **Chapter 4**. However, in some cases we can solve algebraically by the following observation:

If $2^x = 8$ then $2^x = 2^3$.   Thus $x = 3$,   and this is the only solution.

> If the base numbers are the same, we can **equate exponents**.
> If $a^x = a^k$ then $x = k$.

Example 17   🔊 **Self Tutor**

Solve for x:

a $2^x = 16$

b $3^{x+2} = \frac{1}{27}$

a $\qquad 2^x = 16$	b $\qquad 3^{x+2} = \frac{1}{27}$
$\therefore \quad 2^x = 2^4$	$\therefore \quad 3^{x+2} = 3^{-3}$
$\therefore \quad x = 4$	$\therefore \quad x + 2 = -3$
	$\therefore \quad x = -5$

Once we have the same base we then equate the exponents.

Example 18   🔊 **Self Tutor**

Solve for x:

a $4^x = 8$

b $9^{x-2} = \frac{1}{3}$

a $\qquad 4^x = 8$	b $\qquad 9^{x-2} = \frac{1}{3}$
$\therefore \quad (2^2)^x = 2^3$	$\therefore \quad (3^2)^{x-2} = 3^{-1}$
$\therefore \quad 2^{2x} = 2^3$	$\therefore \quad 3^{2(x-2)} = 3^{-1}$
$\therefore \quad 2x = 3$	$\therefore \quad 2(x-2) = -1$
$\therefore \quad x = \frac{3}{2}$	$\therefore \quad 2x - 4 = -1$
	$\therefore \quad 2x = 3$
	$\therefore \quad x = \frac{3}{2}$

EXERCISE 3E

1 Solve for x:

a $2^x = 8$ b $5^x = 25$ c $3^x = 81$ d $7^x = 1$

e $3^x = \frac{1}{3}$ f $2^x = \sqrt{2}$ g $5^x = \frac{1}{125}$ h $4^{x+1} = 64$

i $2^{x-2} = \frac{1}{32}$ j $3^{x+1} = \frac{1}{27}$ k $7^{x+1} = 343$ l $5^{1-2x} = \frac{1}{5}$

2 Solve for x:

a $8^x = 32$ b $4^x = \frac{1}{8}$ c $9^x = \frac{1}{27}$ d $25^x = \frac{1}{5}$

e $27^x = \frac{1}{9}$ f $16^x = \frac{1}{32}$ g $4^{x+2} = 128$ h $25^{1-x} = \frac{1}{125}$

i $4^{4x-1} = \frac{1}{2}$ j $9^{x-3} = 27$ k $(\frac{1}{2})^{x+1} = 8$ l $(\frac{1}{3})^{x+2} = 9$

m $81^x = 27^{-x}$ n $(\frac{1}{4})^{1-x} = 32$ o $(\frac{1}{7})^x = 49$ p $(\frac{1}{3})^{x+1} = 243$

3 Solve for x, if possible:

a $4^{2x+1} = 8^{1-x}$ b $9^{2-x} = (\frac{1}{3})^{2x+1}$ c $2^x \times 8^{1-x} = \frac{1}{4}$

4 Solve for x:

a $3 \times 2^x = 24$ b $7 \times 2^x = 56$ c $3 \times 2^{x+1} = 24$

d $12 \times 3^{-x} = \frac{4}{3}$ e $4 \times (\frac{1}{3})^x = 36$ f $5 \times (\frac{1}{2})^x = 20$

Example 19

◀)) **Self Tutor**

Solve for x: $4^x + 2^x - 20 = 0$

$4^x + 2^x - 20 = 0$

$\therefore \quad (2^x)^2 + 2^x - 20 = 0$ {compare $a^2 + a - 20 = 0$}

$\therefore \quad (2^x - 4)(2^x + 5) = 0$ {$a^2 + a - 20 = (a-4)(a+5)$}

$\therefore \quad 2^x = 4$ or $2^x = -5$

$\therefore \quad 2^x = 2^2$ {2^x cannot be negative}

$\therefore \quad x = 2$

5 Solve for x:

   a $4^x - 6(2^x) + 8 = 0$ **b** $4^x - 2^x - 2 = 0$ **c** $9^x - 12(3^x) + 27 = 0$

   d $9^x = 3^x + 6$ **e** $25^x - 23(5^x) - 50 = 0$ **f** $49^x + 1 = 2(7^x)$

Check your answers using technology. You can get instructions for doing this by clicking on the icon.

GRAPHICS CALCULATOR INSTRUCTIONS

F   # EXPONENTIAL FUNCTIONS

We have already seen how to evaluate b^n when $n \in \mathbb{Q}$, or in other words when n is a rational number.

But what about b^n when $n \in \mathbb{R}$, so n is real but not necessarily rational?

To answer this question, we can look at graphs of exponential functions.

> The most simple general **exponential function** has the form $y = b^x$ where $b > 0$, $b \neq 1$.

For example, $y = 2^x$ is an exponential function.

We construct a table of values from which we graph the function:

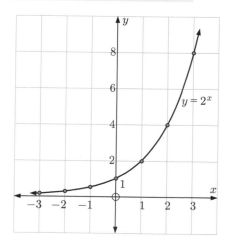

x	-3	-2	-1	0	1	2	3
y	$\frac{1}{8}$	$\frac{1}{4}$	$\frac{1}{2}$	1	2	4	8

When $x = -10$, $y = 2^{-10} \approx 0.001$.
When $x = -50$, $y = 2^{-50} \approx 8.88 \times 10^{-16}$.

As x becomes large and negative, the graph of $y = 2^x$ approaches the x-axis from above but never touches it, since 2^x becomes very small but never zero.

So, as $x \to -\infty$, $y \to 0^+$.

We say that $y = 2^x$ is '**asymptotic** to the x-axis' or '$y = 0$ is a **horizontal asymptote**'.

We now have a well-defined meaning for b^n where b, $n \in \mathbb{R}$ because simple exponential functions have smooth increasing or decreasing graphs.

INVESTIGATION 1   GRAPHS OF EXPONENTIAL FUNCTIONS

In this investigation we examine the graphs of various families of exponential functions.

Click on the icon to run the **dynamic graphing package**, or else you could use your **graphics calculator**.

DYNAMIC GRAPHING PACKAGE

What to do:

1 Explore the family of curves of the form $y = b^x$ where $b > 0$.
For example, consider $y = 2^x$, $y = 3^x$, $y = 10^x$, and $y = (1.3)^x$.

  a What effect does changing b have on the shape of the graph?

  b What is the y-intercept of each graph?

  c What is the horizontal asymptote of each graph?

2 Explore the family of curves of the form $y = 2^x + d$ where d is a constant.
For example, consider $y = 2^x$, $y = 2^x + 1$, and $y = 2^x - 2$.

  a What effect does changing d have on the position of the graph?

  b What effect does changing d have on the shape of the graph?

  c What is the horizontal asymptote of each graph?

  d What is the horizontal asymptote of $y = 2^x + d$?

  e To graph $y = 2^x + d$ from $y = 2^x$ what transformation is used?

3 Explore the family of curves of the form $y = 2^{x-c}$.
For example, consider $y = 2^x$, $y = 2^{x-1}$, $y = 2^{x+2}$, and $y = 2^{x-3}$.

  a What effect does changing c have on the position of the graph?

  b What effect does changing c have on the shape of the graph?

  c What is the horizontal asymptote of each graph?

  d To graph $y = 2^{x-c}$ from $y = 2^x$ what transformation is used?

4 Explore the relationship between $y = b^x$ and $y = b^{-x}$ where $b > 0$.
For example, consider $y = 2^x$ and $y = 2^{-x}$.

  a What is the y-intercept of each graph?

  b What is the horizontal asymptote of each graph?

  c What transformation moves $y = 2^x$ to $y = 2^{-x}$?

5 Explore the family of curves of the form $y = a \times 2^x$ where a is a constant.

  a Consider functions where $a > 0$, such as $y = 2^x$, $y = 3 \times 2^x$, and $y = \frac{1}{2} \times 2^x$.
  Comment on the effect on the graph.

  b Consider functions where $a < 0$, such as $y = -2^x$, $y = -3 \times 2^x$, and $y = -\frac{1}{2} \times 2^x$.
  Comment on the effect on the graph.

  c What is the horizontal asymptote of each graph? Explain your answer.

From your investigation you should have discovered that:

> For the general exponential function $y = a \times b^{x-c} + d$ where $b > 0$, $b \neq 1$, $a \neq 0$:
>
> - b controls how steeply the graph increases or decreases
> - c controls horizontal translation
> - d controls vertical translation
> - the equation of the horizontal asymptote is $y = d$
>
> - if $a > 0$, $b > 1$
>   the function is
>   increasing.
>
> - if $a > 0$, $0 < b < 1$
>   the function is
>   decreasing.
>
> - if $a < 0$, $b > 1$
>   the function is
>   decreasing.
>
> - if $a < 0$, $0 < b < 1$
>   the function is
>   increasing.

We can sketch reasonably accurate graphs of exponential functions using:

- the horizontal asymptote
- the y-intercept
- two other points, for example, when $x = 2$, $x = -2$

> All exponential graphs are similar in shape and have a horizontal asymptote.

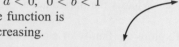

Example 20 ◀) **Self Tutor**

Sketch the graph of $y = 2^{-x} - 3$.

Hence state the domain and range of $f(x) = 2^{-x} - 3$.

For $y = 2^{-x} - 3$,
the horizontal asymptote is $y = -3$.

When $x = 0$, $y = 2^0 - 3$
$$= 1 - 3$$
$$= -2$$
∴   the y-intercept is -2.

When $x = 2$, $y = 2^{-2} - 3$
$$= \tfrac{1}{4} - 3$$
$$= -2\tfrac{3}{4}$$

When $x = -2$, $y = 2^2 - 3 = 1$

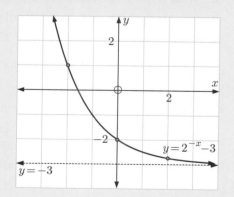

The domain is $\{x \mid x \in \mathbb{R}\}$.   The range is $\{y \mid y > -3\}$.

Consider the graph of $y = 2^x$ alongside. We can use the graph to estimate:

- the value of 2^x for a given value of x, for example $2^{1.8} \approx 3.5$ {point A}
- the solutions of the exponential equation $2^x = b$, for example if $2^x = 5$ then $x \approx 2.3$ {point B}.

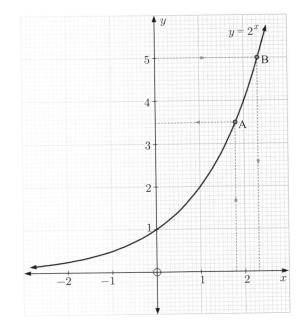

EXERCISE 3F

1 Use the graph above to estimate the value of:

     a $2^{\frac{1}{2}}$ or $\sqrt{2}$ **b** $2^{0.8}$ **c** $2^{1.5}$ **d** $2^{-\sqrt{2}}$

2 Use the graph above to estimate the solution to:

     a $2^x = 3$ **b** $2^x = 0.6$

3 Use the graph of $y = 2^x$ to explain why $2^x = 0$ has no solutions.

4 Draw freehand sketches of the following pairs of graphs using your observations from the previous investigation:

     a $y = 2^x$ and $y = 2^x - 2$ **b** $y = 2^x$ and $y = 2^{-x}$

     c $y = 2^x$ and $y = 2^{x-2}$ **d** $y = 2^x$ and $y = 2(2^x)$

GRAPHING PACKAGE

5 Draw freehand sketches of the following pairs of graphs:

     a $y = 3^x$ and $y = 3^{-x}$ **b** $y = 3^x$ and $y = 3^x + 1$

     c $y = 3^x$ and $y = -3^x$ **d** $y = 3^x$ and $y = 3^{x-1}$

6 For each of the functions below:

     i sketch the graph of the function

     ii state the domain and range

     iii use your calculator to find the value of y when $x = \sqrt{2}$

     iv discuss the behaviour of y as $x \to \pm\infty$

     v determine the horizontal asymptotes.

     a $y = 2^x + 1$ **b** $y = 2 - 2^x$ **c** $y = 2^{-x} + 3$ **d** $y = 3 - 2^{-x}$

G   GROWTH AND DECAY

In this section we will examine situations where quantities are either increasing or decreasing exponentially. These situations are known as **growth** and **decay** modelling, and occur frequently in the world around us.

Populations of animals, people, and bacteria usually *grow* in an exponential way.

Radioactive substances, and items that depreciate in value, usually *decay* exponentially.

GROWTH

Consider a population of 100 mice which under favourable conditions is increasing by 20% each week.

To increase a quantity by 20%, we multiply it by 1.2.

If P_n is the population after n weeks, then:

$P_0 = 100$ {the *original* population}

$P_1 = P_0 \times 1.2 = 100 \times 1.2$

$P_2 = P_1 \times 1.2 = 100 \times (1.2)^2$

$P_3 = P_2 \times 1.2 = 100 \times (1.2)^3$,   and so on.

From this pattern we see that $P_n = 100 \times (1.2)^n$.

So, the graph of the population is a smooth curve given by the exponential function $P_n = 100 \times (1.2)^n$.

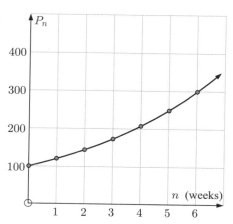

Example 21   ◀) Self Tutor

An entomologist monitoring a grasshopper plague notices that the area affected by the grasshoppers is given by $A_n = 1000 \times 2^{0.2n}$ hectares, where n is the number of weeks after the initial observation.

a   Find the original affected area.

b   Find the affected area after: i   5 weeks   ii   10 weeks   iii   12 weeks.

c   Draw the graph of A_n against n.

a $A_0 = 1000 \times 2^0$

$\quad = 1000 \times 1$

$\quad = 1000$ $\therefore$ the original affected area was 1000 ha.

b   i $A_5 = 1000 \times 2^1$

$\qquad = 2000$

The affected area is 2000 ha.

ii $A_{10} = 1000 \times 2^2$

$\qquad = 4000$

The affected area is 4000 ha.

iii $A_{12} = 1000 \times 2^{0.2 \times 12}$

$\qquad = 1000 \times 2^{2.4}$

$\qquad \approx 5280$

The area affected is about 5280 ha.

c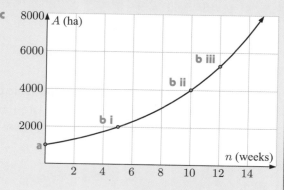

EXERCISE 3G.1

1   The weight W_t of bacteria in a culture t hours after establishment is given by $W_t = 100 \times 2^{0.1t}$ grams.

   a   Find the initial weight.

   b   Find the weight after: i   4 hours   ii   10 hours   iii   24 hours.

   c   Sketch the graph of W_t against t using the results of a and b only.

   d   Use technology to graph $Y_1 = 100 \times 2^{0.1X}$ and check your answers to a, b, and c.

2   A breeding program to ensure the survival of pygmy possums is established with an initial population of 50 (25 pairs). From a previous program, the expected population P_n in n years' time is given by $P_n = P_0 \times 2^{0.3n}$.

   a   What is the value of P_0?

   b   What is the expected population after: i   2 years   ii   5 years   iii   10 years?

   c   Sketch the graph of P_n against n using a and b only.

   d   Use technology to graph $Y_1 = 50 \times 2^{0.3X}$ and check your answers to b.

3   A species of bear is introduced to a large island off Alaska where previously there were no bears. 6 pairs of bears were introduced in 1998. It is expected that the population will increase according to $B_t = B_0 \times 2^{0.18t}$ where t is the time since the introduction.

   a   Find B_0.   b   Find the expected bear population in 2018.

   c   Find the expected percentage increase from 2008 to 2018.

4   The speed V_t of a chemical reaction is given by $V_t = V_0 \times 2^{0.05t}$ where t is the temperature in °C.

   a   Find the reaction speed at: i   0°C   ii   20°C.

   b   Find the percentage increase in reaction speed at 20°C compared with 0°C.

   c   Find $\left(\dfrac{V_{50} - V_{20}}{V_{20}} \right) \times 100\%$ and explain what this calculation means.

DECAY

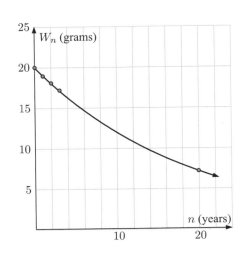

Consider a radioactive substance with original weight 20 grams. It *decays* or reduces by 5% each year. The multiplier for this is 95% or 0.95.

If W_n is the weight after n years, then:

$$W_0 = 20 \text{ grams}$$
$$W_1 = W_0 \times 0.95 = 20 \times 0.95 \text{ grams}$$
$$W_2 = W_1 \times 0.95 = 20 \times (0.95)^2 \text{ grams}$$
$$W_3 = W_2 \times 0.95 = 20 \times (0.95)^3 \text{ grams}$$

$$\vdots$$

$$W_{20} = 20 \times (0.95)^{20} \approx 7.2 \text{ grams}$$

$$\vdots$$

$$W_{100} = 20 \times (0.95)^{100} \approx 0.1 \text{ grams}$$

and from this pattern we see that $W_n = 20 \times (0.95)^n$.

Example 22   ◀)) **Self Tutor**

When a diesel-electric generator is switched off, the current dies away according to the formula
$I(t) = 24 \times (0.25)^t$ amps, where t is the time in seconds after the power is cut.

a Find $I(t)$ when $t = 0, 1, 2$ and 3.

b What current flowed in the generator at the instant when it was switched off?

c Plot the graph of $I(t)$ for $t \geqslant 0$ using the information above.

d Use your graph or technology to find how long it takes for the current to reach 4 amps.

a $I(t) = 24 \times (0.25)^t$ amps

$I(0)$	$I(1)$	$I(2)$	$I(3)$
$= 24 \times (0.25)^0$	$= 24 \times (0.25)^1$	$= 24 \times (0.25)^2$	$= 24 \times (0.25)^3$
$= 24$ amps	$= 6$ amps	$= 1.5$ amps	$= 0.375$ amps

b When $t = 0$, $I(0) = 24$

When the generator was switched off, 24 amps of current flowed in the circuit.

c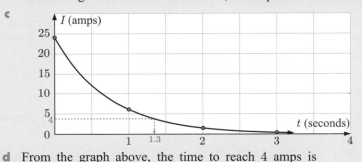

d From the graph above, the time to reach 4 amps is
about 1.3 seconds.   *or*

By finding the **point of intersection** of
$Y_1 = 24 \times (0.25)^{\wedge}X$ and $Y_2 = 4$ on a graphics
calculator, the solution is ≈ 1.29 seconds.

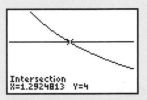

Example 23   ◀)) **Self Tutor**

The weight of radioactive material remaining after t years is given by
$W_t = W_0 \times 2^{-0.001t}$ grams.

a Find the original weight.

b Find the percentage remaining after 200 years.

a When $t = 0$, the weight remaining is $W_0 \times 2^0 = W_0$

∴ W_0 is the original weight.

b When $t = 200$, $W_{200} = W_0 \times 2^{-0.001 \times 200}$

$= W_0 \times 2^{-0.2}$

$\approx W_0 \times 0.8706$

$\approx 87.06\%$ of W_0

After 200 years, 87.1% of the material remains.

EXERCISE 3G.2

1   The weight of a radioactive substance t years after being set aside is given by
    $W(t) = 250 \times (0.998)^t$ grams.

   a   How much radioactive substance was initially set aside?

   b   Determine the weight of the substance after:

       i   400 years   ii   800 years   iii   1200 years.

   c   Sketch the graph of $W(t)$ for $t \geqslant 0$ using a and b only.

   d   Use your graph or graphics calculator to find how long it takes for the substance to decay to
       125 grams.

2   The temperature T of a liquid which has been placed in a refrigerator is given by
    $T(t) = 100 \times 2^{-0.02t}$ °C   where t is the time in minutes.

   a   Find the initial temperature of the liquid.

   b   Find the temperature after:

       i   15 minutes   ii   20 minutes   iii   78 minutes.

   c   Sketch the graph of $T(t)$ for $t \geqslant 0$ using a and b only.

3   Answer the **Opening Problem** on page **82**.

4   The weight W_t grams of radioactive substance remaining after t years is given by
    $W_t = 1000 \times 2^{-0.03t}$ grams.

   a   Find the initial weight of the radioactive substance.

   b   Find the weight remaining after:

       i   10 years   ii   100 years   iii   1000 years.

   c   Graph W_t against t using a and b only.

   d   Use your graph or graphics calculator to find the time when 10 grams of the substance remains.

   e   Write an expression for the amount of substance that has decayed after t years.

5   The weight W_t of a radioactive uranium-235 sample remaining after t years is given by the formula
    $W_t = W_0 \times 2^{-0.0002t}$ grams, $t \geqslant 0$.   Find:

   a   the original weight   b   the percentage weight loss after 1000 years

   c   the time required until $\frac{1}{512}$ of the sample remains.

H   THE NATURAL EXPONENTIAL e^x

We have seen that the simplest exponential functions are
of the form $f(x) = b^x$ where $b > 0$, $b \neq 1$.

Graphs of some of these functions are shown alongside.

We can see that for all positive values of the base b, the
graph is always positive.

Hence $b^x > 0$ for all $b > 0$.

There are an infinite number of possible choices for the
base number.

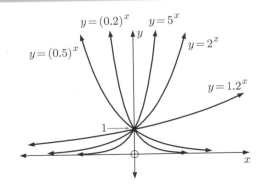

However, where exponential data is examined in science, engineering, and finance, the base $e \approx 2.7183$ is commonly used.

e is a special number in mathematics. It is irrational like π, and just as π is the ratio of a circle's circumference to its diameter, e also has a physical meaning. We explore this meaning in the following investigation.

INVESTIGATION 2   CONTINUOUS COMPOUND INTEREST

A formula for calculating the amount to which an investment grows is $u_n = u_0(1 + i)^n$ where:

u_n is the final amount, u_0 is the initial amount,

   i is the interest rate per compounding period,

   n is the number of periods or number of times the interest is compounded.

We will investigate the final value of an investment for various values of n, and allow n to get extremely large.

What to do:

1 Suppose $1000 is invested for one year at a fixed rate of 6% per annum. Use your calculator to find the final amount or *maturing value* if the interest is paid:

   a annually $(n = 1,\ i = 6\% = 0.06)$ **b** quarterly $(n = 4,\ i = \frac{6\%}{4} = 0.015)$

   c monthly   **d** daily

   e by the second   **f** by the millisecond.

2 Comment on your answers from **1**.

3 If r is the percentage rate per year, t is the number of years, and N is the number of interest payments per year, then $i = \dfrac{r}{N}$ and $n = Nt$.

   The growth formula becomes $u_n = u_0 \left(1 + \dfrac{r}{N}\right)^{Nt}$.

   If we let $a = \dfrac{N}{r}$, show that $u_n = u_0 \left[\left(1 + \dfrac{1}{a}\right)^a\right]^{rt}$.

4 For continuous compound growth, the number of interest payments per year N gets very large.

   a Explain why a gets very large as N gets very large.

   b Copy and complete the table, giving your answers as accurately as technology permits.

a	$\left(1 + \dfrac{1}{a}\right)^a$
10	
100	
1000	
10 000	
100 000	
1 000 000	
10 000 000	

5 You should have found that for very large values of a,

$$\left(1 + \frac{1}{a}\right)^a \approx 2.718\,281\,828\,459....$$

Use the $\boxed{e^x}$ key of your calculator to find the value of e^1. What do you notice?

6 For continuous growth, $u_n = u_0 e^{rt}$ where u_0 is the initial amount

   r is the annual percentage rate

   t is the number of years

   Use this formula to find the final value if $1000 is invested for 4 years at a fixed rate of 6% per annum, where the interest is calculated continuously.

From **Investigation 2** we observe that:

If interest is paid *continuously* or *instantaneously* then the formula for calculating a compounding amount $u_n = u_0(1 + i)^n$ can be replaced by $u_n = u_0 e^{rt}$, where r is the percentage rate per annum and t is the number of years.

HISTORICAL NOTE

The natural exponential e was first described in 1683 by Swiss mathematician Jacob Bernoulli. He discovered the number while studying compound interest, just as we did in **Investigation 2**.

The natural exponential was first called e by Swiss mathematician and physicist Leonhard Euler in a letter to the German mathematician Christian Goldbach in 1731. The number was then published with this notation in 1736.

In 1748 Euler evaluated e correct to 18 decimal places.

One may think that e was chosen because it was the first letter of Euler's name or for the word exponential, but it is likely that it was just the next vowel available since he had already used a in his work.

Leonhard Euler

EXERCISE 3H

3, 7, 9, 13

GRAPHING PACKAGE

1 Sketch, on the same set of axes, the graphs of $y = 2^x$, $y = e^x$, and $y = 3^x$. Comment on any observations.

2 Sketch, on the same set of axes, the graphs of $y = e^x$ and $y = e^{-x}$. What is the geometric connection between these two graphs?

3 For the general exponential function $y = ae^{kx}$, what is the y-intercept?

4 Consider $y = 2e^x$.
   a Explain why y can never be < 0.   **b** Find y if: **i** $x = -20$ **ii** $x = 20$.

5 Find, to 3 significant figures, the value of:
   a e^2 **b** e^3 **c** $e^{0.7}$ **d** $\sqrt{e}$ **e** e^{-1}

6 Write the following as powers of e:
   a $\sqrt{e}$ **b** $\dfrac{1}{\sqrt{e}}$ **c** $\dfrac{1}{e^2}$ **d** $e\sqrt{e}$

7 Simplify:
   a $\left(e^{0.36}\right)^{\frac{t}{2}}$ **b** $\left(e^{0.064}\right)^{\frac{t}{16}}$ **c** $\left(e^{-0.04}\right)^{\frac{t}{8}}$ **d** $\left(e^{-0.836}\right)^{\frac{t}{5}}$

8 Find, to five significant figures, the values of:
   a $e^{2.31}$ **b** $e^{-2.31}$ **c** $e^{4.829}$
   d $e^{-4.829}$ **e** $50e^{-0.1764}$ **f** $80e^{-0.6342}$
   g $1000e^{1.2642}$ **h** $0.25e^{-3.6742}$

9 On the same set of axes, sketch and clearly label the graphs of:

$$f : x \mapsto e^x, \qquad g : x \mapsto e^{x-2}, \qquad h : x \mapsto e^x + 3$$

State the domain and range of each function.

10 On the same set of axes, sketch and clearly label the graphs of:

$$f : x \mapsto e^x, \qquad g : x \mapsto -e^x, \qquad h : x \mapsto 10 - e^x$$

State the domain and range of each function.

11 Expand and simplify:

   a $(e^x + 1)^2$
          b $(1 + e^x)(1 - e^x)$
          c $e^x(e^{-x} - 3)$

12 The weight of bacteria in a culture is given by $W(t) = 2e^{\frac{t}{2}}$ grams where t is the time in hours after the culture was set to grow.

   a Find the weight of the culture when:

      i $t = 0$
         ii $t = 30$ min
         iii $t = 1\frac{1}{2}$ hours
         iv $t = 6$ hours.

   b Use **a** to sketch the graph of $W(t) = 2e^{\frac{t}{2}}$.

13 Solve for x:

   a $e^x = \sqrt{e}$
          b $e^{\frac{1}{2}x} = \dfrac{1}{e^2}$

14 The current flowing in an electrical circuit t seconds after it is switched off is given by $I(t) = 75e^{-0.15t}$ amps.

   a What current is still flowing in the circuit after:

      i 1 second
         ii 10 seconds?

   b Use your graphics calculator to sketch $I(t) = 75e^{-0.15t}$ and $I = 1$.

   c Hence find how long it will take for the current to fall to 1 amp.

15 Consider the function $f(x) = e^x$.

   a On the same set of axes, sketch $y = f(x)$, $y = x$, and $y = f^{-1}(x)$.

   b State the domain and range of f^{-1}.

ACTIVITY

Click on the icon to run a card game for exponential functions.

CARD GAME

RESEARCH
RESEARCHING e

What to do:

1 The 'bell curve' which models statistical distributions is shown alongside. Research the equation of this curve.

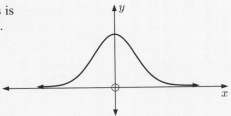

2 The function $f(x) = 1 + x + \frac{1}{2}x^2 + \frac{1}{2 \times 3}x^3 + \frac{1}{2 \times 3 \times 4}x^4 + \ldots$ has infinitely many terms. It can be shown that $f(x) = e^x$.

Check this statement by finding an approximation for $f(1)$ using its first 20 terms.

REVIEW SET 3A
NON-CALCULATOR

1 Simplify:

  a $-(-1)^{10}$ **b** $-(-3)^3$ **c** $3^0 - 3^{-1}$

2 Simplify using the laws of exponents:

  a $a^4 b^5 \times a^2 b^2$ **b** $6xy^5 \div 9x^2 y^5$ **c** $\dfrac{5(x^2 y)^2}{(5x^2)^2}$

3 Let $f(x) = 3^x$.

  a Write down the value of: **i** $f(4)$ **ii** $f(-1)$

  b Find the value of k such that $f(x+2) = k\, f(x), \quad k \in \mathbb{Z}$.

4 Write without brackets or negative exponents:

  a $x^{-2} \times x^{-3}$ **b** $2(ab)^{-2}$ **c** $2ab^{-2}$

5 Write as a single power of 3:

  a $\dfrac{27}{9^a}$ **b** $(\sqrt{3})^{1-x} \times 9^{1-2x}$

6 Evaluate:

  a $8^{\frac{2}{3}}$ **b** $27^{-\frac{2}{3}}$

7 Write without negative exponents:

  a mn^{-2} **b** $(mn)^{-3}$ **c** $\dfrac{m^2 n^{-1}}{p^{-2}}$ **d** $(4m^{-1}n)^2$

8 Expand and simplify:

  a $(3 - e^x)^2$ **b** $(\sqrt{x} + 2)(\sqrt{x} - 2)$ **c** $2^{-x}(2^{2x} + 2^x)$

9 Find the value of x:

  a $2^{x-3} = \frac{1}{32}$ **b** $9^x = 27^{2-2x}$ **c** $e^{2x} = \dfrac{1}{\sqrt{e}}$

10 Match each equation to its corresponding graph:

a $y = -e^x$ b $y = 3 \times 2^x$ c $y = e^x + 1$ d $y = 3^{-x}$ e $y = -e^{-x}$

A
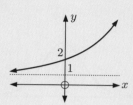

B
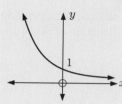

C
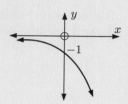

D
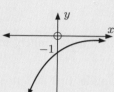

E
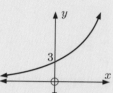

11 Suppose $y = a^x$.   Express in terms of y:

a a^{2x} b a^{-x} c $\dfrac{1}{\sqrt{a^x}}$

REVIEW SET 3B   CALCULATOR

1 a Write 4×2^n as a power of 2.

   b Evaluate $7^{-1} - 7^0$.

   c Write $\left(\frac{2}{3}\right)^{-3}$ in simplest fractional form.

   d Write $\left(\dfrac{2a^{-1}}{b^2}\right)^2$ without negative exponents or brackets.

2 Evaluate, correct to 3 significant figures:

   a $3^{\frac{3}{4}}$ b $27^{-\frac{1}{5}}$ c $\sqrt[4]{100}$

3 If $f(x) = 3 \times 2^x$,   find the value of:

   a $f(0)$ b $f(3)$ c $f(-2)$

4 Suppose $f(x) = 2^{-x} + 1$.

   a Find $f(\frac{1}{2})$.   b Find a such that $f(a) = 3$.

5 On the same set of axes draw the graphs of $y = 2^x$ and $y = 2^x - 4$. Include on your graph the y-intercept and the equation of the horizontal asymptote of each function.

6 The temperature of a dish t minutes after it is removed from the microwave, is given by $T = 80 \times (0.913)^t$ °C.

   a Find the initial temperature of the dish.

   b Find the temperature after: i $t = 12$ ii $t = 24$ iii $t = 36$ minutes.

   c Draw the graph of T against t for $t \geqslant 0$, using the above or technology.

   d Hence, find the time taken for the temperature of the dish to fall to 25°C.

7 Consider $y = 3^x - 5$.

    a Find y when $x = 0, \pm 1, \pm 2$.
    b Discuss y as $x \to \pm\infty$.

    c Sketch the graph of $y = 3^x - 5$.
    d State the equation of any asymptote.

8 **a** On the same set of axes, sketch and clearly label the graphs of:

        $f : x \mapsto e^x, \quad g : x \mapsto e^{x-1}, \quad h : x \mapsto 3 - e^x$

    b State the domain and range of each function in **a**.

9 Consider $y = 3 - 2^{-x}$.

    a Find y when $x = 0, \pm 1, \pm 2$.
    b Discuss y as $x \to \pm\infty$.

    c Sketch the graph of $y = 3 - 2^{-x}$.
    d State the equation of any asymptote.

10 The weight of a radioactive substance after t years is given by $W = 1500 \times (0.993)^t$ grams.

    a Find the original amount of radioactive material.

    b Find the amount of radioactive material remaining after:

       i 400 years
       ii 800 years.

    c Sketch the graph of W against t, $t \geqslant 0$, using the above or technology.

    d Hence, find the time taken for the weight to reduce to 100 grams.

REVIEW SET 3C

1 Given the graph of $y = 3^x$ shown, estimate solutions to the exponential equations:

    a $3^x = 5$

    b $3^x = \frac{1}{2}$

    c $6 \times 3^x = 20$

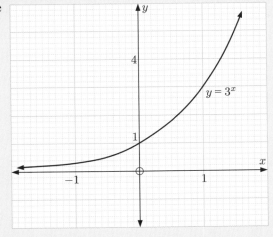

2 Simplify using the laws of exponents:

    a $(a^7)^3$
    b $pq^2 \times p^3q^4$
    c $\dfrac{8ab^5}{2a^4b^4}$

3 Write the following as a power of 2:

    a 2×2^{-4}
    b $16 \div 2^{-3}$
    c 8^4

4 Write without brackets or negative exponents:

    a b^{-3}
    b $(ab)^{-1}$
    c ab^{-1}

5 Simplify $\dfrac{2^{x+1}}{2^{1-x}}$.

6 Write as powers of 5 in simplest form:

  a 1   **b** $5\sqrt{5}$ **c** $\dfrac{1}{\sqrt[4]{5}}$ **d** 25^{a+3}

7 Expand and simplify:

  a $e^x(e^{-x} + e^x)$ **b** $(2^x + 5)^2$ **c** $(x^{\frac{1}{2}} - 7)(x^{\frac{1}{2}} + 7)$

8 Solve for x:
  a $6 \times 2^x = 192$ **b** $4 \times (\frac{1}{3})^x = 324$

9 The point $(1, \sqrt{8})$ lies on the graph of $y = 2^{kx}$.   Find the value of k.

10 Solve for x without using a calculator:

  a $2^{x+1} = 32$ **b** $4^{x+1} = \left(\frac{1}{8}\right)^x$

11 Consider $y = 2e^{-x} + 1$.
  a Find y when $x = 0, \pm 1, \pm 2$.
  b Discuss y as $x \to \pm\infty$.
  c Sketch the graph of $y = 2e^{-x} + 1$.
  d State the equation of any asymptote.

Chapter 4

Logarithms

OPENING PROBLEM

In a plentiful springtime, a population of 1000 mice will double every week.

The population after t weeks is given by the exponential function $P(t) = 1000 \times 2^t$ mice.

Things to think about:

a What does the graph of the population over time look like?

b How long will it take for the population to reach 20 000 mice?

c Can we write a function for t in terms of P, which determines the time at which the population P is reached?

d What does the graph of this function look like?

A   LOGARITHMS IN BASE 10

Consider the exponential function $f : x \mapsto 10^x$ or $f(x) = 10^x$.

The graph of $y = f(x)$ is shown alongside, along with its inverse function f^{-1}.

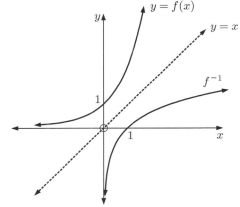

Since f is defined by $y = 10^x$,

$\quad f^{-1}$ is defined by $x = 10^y$.

$\qquad$ {interchanging x and y}

y is the exponent to which the base 10 is raised in order to get x.

We write this as $y = \log_{10} x$ and say that y is the **logarithm in base 10, of x**.

Logarithms are thus defined to be the inverse of exponential functions:

$$\text{If} \quad f(x) = 10^x \quad \text{then} \quad f^{-1}(x) = \log_{10} x.$$

WORKING WITH LOGARITHMS

Many positive numbers can be easily written in the form 10^x.

For example:
$$10\,000 = 10^4$$
$$1000 = 10^3$$
$$100 = 10^2$$
$$10 = 10^1$$
$$1 = 10^0$$
$$0.1 = 10^{-1}$$
$$0.01 = 10^{-2}$$
$$0.001 = 10^{-3}$$

Numbers like $\sqrt{10}$, $10\sqrt{10}$ and $\dfrac{1}{\sqrt[5]{10}}$ can also be written in the form 10^x as follows:

$$\sqrt{10} = 10^{\frac{1}{2}} \qquad\qquad 10\sqrt{10} = 10^1 \times 10^{0.5} \qquad\qquad \dfrac{1}{\sqrt[5]{10}} = 10^{-\frac{1}{5}}$$
$$= 10^{0.5} \qquad\qquad\qquad\qquad = 10^{1.5} \qquad\qquad\qquad\qquad = 10^{-0.2}$$

In fact, all positive numbers can be written in the form 10^x by using logarithms in base 10.

> The **logarithm in base 10** of a positive number is the exponent when the number is written as a power of 10.

For example:

- Since $1000 = 10^3$, we write $\log_{10} 1000 = 3$ or $\log 1000 = 3$.
- Since $0.01 = 10^{-2}$, we write $\log_{10}(0.01) = -2$ or $\log(0.01) = -2$.

$$a = 10^{\log a} \quad \text{for any } a > 0.$$

Notice that a must be positive since $10^x > 0$ for all $x \in \mathbb{R}$.

Notice also that $\quad \log 1000 = \log 10^3 = 3$
and $\qquad\qquad\qquad \log 0.01 = \log 10^{-2} = -2$.

We hence conclude that $\quad \boldsymbol{\log 10^x = x} \quad$ for any $x \in \mathbb{R}$.

> If no base is indicated we assume it means base 10. $\log a$ means $\log_{10} a$.

Example 1 ◀)) **Self Tutor**

a Without using a calculator, find: **i** $\log 100$ **ii** $\log(\sqrt[4]{10})$.

b Check your answers using technology.

a **i** $\log 100 = \log 10^2 = 2$ **ii** $\log(\sqrt[4]{10}) = \log(10^{\frac{1}{4}}) = \frac{1}{4}$

b **i** Casio fx-CG20 **ii** TI-84 Plus

```
Math Rad Norm1 d/c Real
log 100
                    2
□


JUMP DELETE ▶MAT MATH
```

```
log(4 ×√10)
                .25
```

GRAPHICS CALCULATOR INSTRUCTIONS

$\log 100 = 2$ $\qquad\qquad \log(\sqrt[4]{10}) = 0.25$

EXERCISE 4A

1 Without using a calculator, find:

a $\log 10\,000$ **b** $\log 0.001$ **c** $\log 10$ **d** $\log 1$

e $\log \sqrt{10}$ **f** $\log(\sqrt[3]{10})$ **g** $\log\left(\dfrac{1}{\sqrt[4]{10}}\right)$ **h** $\log\left(10\sqrt{10}\right)$

i $\log \sqrt[3]{100}$ **j** $\log\left(\dfrac{100}{\sqrt{10}}\right)$ **k** $\log\left(10 \times \sqrt[3]{10}\right)$ **l** $\log\left(1000\sqrt{10}\right)$

Check your answers using your calculator.

2 Simplify:

  a $\log 10^n$ **b** $\log (10^a \times 100)$ **c** $\log \left(\dfrac{10}{10^m} \right)$ **d** $\log \left(\dfrac{10^a}{10^b} \right)$

Example 2   ◀ッ **Self Tutor**

Use your calculator to write the following in the form 10^x where x is correct to 4 decimal places:

  a 8   **b** 800   **c** 0.08

a 8	**b** 800	**c** 0.08
$= 10^{\log 8}$	$= 10^{\log 800}$	$= 10^{\log 0.08}$
$\approx 10^{0.9031}$	$\approx 10^{2.9031}$	$\approx 10^{-1.0969}$

---

3 Use your calculator to write the following in the form 10^x where x is correct to 4 decimal places:

  a 6   **b** 60   **c** 6000   **d** 0.6   **e** 0.006
  f 15   **g** 1500   **h** 1.5   **i** 0.15   **j** 0.000 15

Example 3   ◀ッ **Self Tutor**

  a Use your calculator to find: **i** $\log 2$ **ii** $\log 20$
  b Explain why $\log 20 = \log 2 + 1$.

  a   **i** $\log 2 \approx 0.3010$ **b** $\log 20 = \log(2 \times 10)$
       ii $\log 20 \approx 1.3010$ {calculator} $\approx \log(10^{0.3010} \times 10^1)$
                                                                      $\approx \log 10^{1.3010}$ {adding exponents}
                                                                      ≈ 1.3010
                                                                      $\approx \log 2 + 1$

---

4 **a** Use your calculator to find: **i** $\log 3$ **ii** $\log 300$
    b Explain why $\log 300 = \log 3 + 2$.

5 **a** Use your calculator to find: **i** $\log 5$ **ii** $\log 0.05$
    b Explain why $\log 0.05 = \log 5 - 2$.

Example 4   ◀ッ **Self Tutor**

  Find x if:

    a $\log x = 3$ **b** $\log x \approx -0.271$

  a $x = 10^{\log x}$ **b** $x = 10^{\log x}$
     $\therefore$ $x = 10^3$ $\therefore$ $x \approx 10^{-0.271}$
     $\therefore$ $x = 1000$ $\therefore$ $x \approx 0.536$

6 Find x if:

a $\log x = 2$

b $\log x = 1$

c $\log x = 0$

d $\log x = -1$

e $\log x = \frac{1}{2}$

f $\log x = -\frac{1}{2}$

g $\log x = 4$

h $\log x = -5$

i $\log x \approx 0.8351$

j $\log x \approx 2.1457$

k $\log x \approx -1.378$

l $\log x \approx -3.1997$

B — LOGARITHMS IN BASE a

In the previous section we defined logarithms in base 10 as the inverse of the exponential function $f(x) = 10^x$.

If $f(x) = 10^x$ then $f^{-1}(x) = \log_{10} x$.

We can use the same principle to define logarithms in other bases:

If $f(x) = a^x$ then $f^{-1}(x) = \log_a x$.

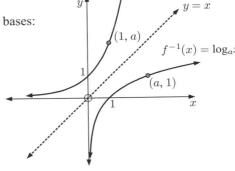

If $b = a^x$, $a \neq 1$, $a > 0$, we say that x is the **logarithm in base a, of b**, and that $b = a^x \Leftrightarrow x = \log_a b$, $b > 0$.

$b = a^x \Leftrightarrow x = \log_a b$ is read as "$b = a^x$ if and only if $x = \log_a b$". It is a short way of writing:
"if $b = a^x$ then $x = \log_a b$, and if $x = \log_a b$ then $b = a^x$".

$b = a^x$ and $x = \log_a b$ are *equivalent* or *interchangeable* statements.

For example:
- $8 = 2^3$ means that $3 = \log_2 8$ and vice versa.
- $\log_5 25 = 2$ means that $25 = 5^2$ and vice versa.

If $y = a^x$ then $x = \log_a y$, and so $\quad x = \log_a a^x$.

If $x = a^y$ then $y = \log_a x$, and so $\quad x = a^{\log_a x}$ provided $x > 0$.

Example 5 ◀) Self Tutor

a Write an equivalent exponential equation for $\log_{10} 1000 = 3$.

b Write an equivalent logarithmic equation for $3^4 = 81$.

---

a From $\log_{10} 1000 = 3$ we deduce that $10^3 = 1000$.

b From $3^4 = 81$ we deduce that $\log_3 81 = 4$.

EXERCISE 4B

1 Write an equivalent exponential equation for:

   a $\log_{10} 100 = 2$ **b** $\log_{10} 10\,000 = 4$ **c** $\log_{10}(0.1) = -1$

   d $\log_{10} \sqrt{10} = \frac{1}{2}$ **e** $\log_2 8 = 3$ **f** $\log_3 9 = 2$

   g $\log_2(\frac{1}{4}) = -2$ **h** $\log_3 \sqrt{27} = 1.5$ **i** $\log_5(\frac{1}{\sqrt{5}}) = -\frac{1}{2}$

2 Write an equivalent logarithmic equation for:

   a $2^2 = 4$ **b** $4^3 = 64$ **c** $5^2 = 25$

   d $7^2 = 49$ **e** $2^6 = 64$ **f** $2^{-3} = \frac{1}{8}$

   g $10^{-2} = 0.01$ **h** $2^{-1} = \frac{1}{2}$ **i** $3^{-3} = \frac{1}{27}$

Example 6
◀) **Self Tutor**

Find:

   a $\log_2 16$ **b** $\log_5 0.2$ **c** $\log_{10} \sqrt[5]{100}$ **d** $\log_2\left(\frac{1}{\sqrt{2}}\right)$

a $\quad\log_2 16$	**b** $\quad\log_5 0.2$	**c** $\quad\log_{10}\sqrt[5]{100}$	**d** $\quad\log_2\left(\frac{1}{\sqrt{2}}\right)$
$= \log_2 2^4$	$= \log_5(\frac{1}{5})$	$= \log_{10}\left(10^2\right)^{\frac{1}{5}}$	$= \log_2 2^{-\frac{1}{2}}$
$= 4$	$= \log_5 5^{-1}$	$= \log_{10} 10^{\frac{2}{5}}$	$= -\frac{1}{2}$
	$= -1$	$= \frac{2}{5}$	

---

3 Find:

   a $\log_{10} 100\,000$ **b** $\log_{10}(0.01)$ **c** $\log_3 \sqrt{3}$ **d** $\log_2 8$

   e $\log_2 64$ **f** $\log_2 128$ **g** $\log_5 25$ **h** $\log_5 125$

   i $\log_2(0.125)$ **j** $\log_9 3$ **k** $\log_4 16$ **l** $\log_{36} 6$

   m $\log_3 243$ **n** $\log_2 \sqrt[3]{2}$ **o** $\log_a a^n$ **p** $\log_8 2$

   q $\log_t\left(\frac{1}{t}\right)$ **r** $\log_6 6\sqrt{6}$ **s** $\log_4 1$ **t** $\log_9 9$

4 Use your calculator to find:

   a $\log_{10} 152$ **b** $\log_{10} 25$ **c** $\log_{10} 74$ **d** $\log_{10} 0.8$

5 Solve for x:

   a $\log_2 x = 3$ **b** $\log_4 x = \frac{1}{2}$ **c** $\log_x 81 = 4$ **d** $\log_2(x-6) = 3$

6 Simplify:

   a $\log_4 16$ **b** $\log_2 4$ **c** $\log_3\left(\frac{1}{3}\right)$ **d** $\log_{10} \sqrt[4]{1000}$

   e $\log_7\left(\frac{1}{\sqrt{7}}\right)$ **f** $\log_5(25\sqrt{5})$ **g** $\log_3\left(\frac{1}{\sqrt{27}}\right)$ **h** $\log_4\left(\frac{1}{2\sqrt{2}}\right)$

   i $\log_x x^2$ **j** $\log_x \sqrt{x}$ **k** $\log_m m^3$ **l** $\log_x(x\sqrt{x})$

   m $\log_n\left(\frac{1}{n}\right)$ **n** $\log_a\left(\frac{1}{a^2}\right)$ **o** $\log_a\left(\frac{1}{\sqrt{a}}\right)$ **p** $\log_m \sqrt{m^5}$

THEORY OF KNOWLEDGE

Acharya Virasena was an 8th century Indian mathematician. Among other areas, he worked with the concept of *ardhaccheda*, which is how many times a number of the form 2^n can be divided by 2. The result is the integer n, and is the logarithm of the number 2^n in base 2.

In 1544, the German Michael Stifel published *Arithmetica Integra* which contains a table expressing many other integers as powers of 2. To do this, he had created an early version of a logarithmic table.

In the late 16th century, astronomers spent a large part of their working lives doing the complex and tedious calculations of spherical trigonometry needed to understand the movement of celestial bodies. In 1614, the Scottish mathematician John Napier formally proposed the idea of a logarithm, and algebraic methods for dealing with them. It was said that Napier effectively doubled the life of an astronomer by reducing the time required to do calculations.

John Napier

Just six years later, Joost Bürgi from Switzerland published a geometric approach for logarithms developed completely independently from John Napier.

1 Can anyone claim to have *invented* logarithms?

2 Can we consider the process of mathematical discovery an *evolution* of ideas?

Many areas of mathematics have been developed over centuries as several mathematicians have worked in a particular area, or taken the knowledge from one area and applied it to another field. Sometimes the process is held up because a method for solving a particular class of problem has not yet been found. In other cases, pure mathematicians have published research papers on seemingly useless mathematical ideas, which have then become vital in applications much later.

In *Everybody Counts*: *A report to the nation on the future of Mathematical Education* by the National Academy of Sciences (National Academy Press, 1989), there is an excellent section on the Nature of Mathematics. It includes:

"Even the most esoteric and abstract parts of mathematics - number theory and logic, for example - are now used routinely in applications (for example, in computer science and cryptography). Fifty years ago, the leading British mathematician G.H. Hardy could boast that number theory was the most pure and least useful part of mathematics. Today, Hardy's mathematics is studied as an essential prerequisite to many applications, including control of automated systems, data transmission from remote satellites, protection of financial records, and efficient algorithms for computation."

3 Should we only study the mathematics we need to enter our chosen profession?

4 Why should we explore mathematics for its own sake, rather than to address the needs of science?

C   LAWS OF LOGARITHMS

INVESTIGATION   DISCOVERING THE LAWS OF LOGARITHMS

What to do:

1   Use your calculator to find:

   a $\log 2 + \log 3$ **b** $\log 3 + \log 7$ **c** $\log 4 + \log 20$

   d $\log 6$ **e** $\log 21$ **f** $\log 80$

   From your answers, suggest a possible simplification for $\log a + \log b$.

2   Use your calculator to find:

   a $\log 6 - \log 2$ **b** $\log 12 - \log 3$ **c** $\log 3 - \log 5$

   d $\log 3$ **e** $\log 4$ **f** $\log(0.6)$

   From your answers, suggest a possible simplification for $\log a - \log b$.

3   Use your calculator to find:

   a $3 \log 2$ **b** $2 \log 5$ **c** $-4 \log 3$

   d $\log(2^3)$ **e** $\log(5^2)$ **f** $\log(3^{-4})$

   From your answers, suggest a possible simplification for $n \log a$.

From the **Investigation**, you should have discovered the three important **laws of logarithms**:

If A and B are both
positive then:

- $\log A + \log B = \log(AB)$

- $\log A - \log B = \log\left(\dfrac{A}{B}\right)$

- $n \log A = \log\left(A^n\right)$

More generally, in any base c where $c \neq 1$, $c > 0$, we have these **laws of logarithms**:

If A and B are both
positive then:

- $\log_c A + \log_c B = \log_c(AB)$

- $\log_c A - \log_c B = \log_c\left(\dfrac{A}{B}\right)$

- $n \log_c A = \log_c\left(A^n\right)$

Proof:

- $c^{\log_c A + \log_c B}$
  $= c^{\log_c A} \times c^{\log_c B}$
  $= A \times B$
  $= c^{\log_c(AB)}$
  $\therefore \ \log_c A + \log_c B = \log_c(AB)$

- $c^{\log_c A - \log_c B}$
  $= \dfrac{c^{\log_c A}}{c^{\log_c B}}$
  $= \dfrac{A}{B}$
  $= c^{\log_c\left(\frac{A}{B}\right)}$
  $\therefore \ \log_c A - \log_c B = \log_c\left(\dfrac{A}{B}\right)$

- $c^{n \log_c A}$
  $$= (c^{\log_c A})^n$$
  $$= A^n$$
  $$= c^{\log_c (A^n)}$$
  $$\therefore \quad n \log_c A = \log_c(A^n)$$

Example 7

Use the laws of logarithms to write the following as a single logarithm or as an integer:

a $\log 5 + \log 3$ **b** $\log_3 24 - \log_3 8$ **c** $\log_2 5 - 1$

a	**b**	**c**
$\log 5 + \log 3$	$\log_3 24 - \log_3 8$	$\log_2 5 - 1$
$= \log(5 \times 3)$	$= \log_3\left(\frac{24}{8}\right)$	$= \log_2 5 - \log_2 2^1$
$= \log 15$	$= \log_3 3$	$= \log_2\left(\frac{5}{2}\right)$
	$= 1$	

Example 8

Simplify by writing as a single logarithm or as a rational number:

a $2\log 7 - 3\log 2$ **b** $2\log 3 + 3$ **c** $\dfrac{\log 8}{\log 4}$

a	**b**	**c**
$2\log 7 - 3\log 2$	$2\log 3 + 3$	$\dfrac{\log 8}{\log 4} = \dfrac{\log 2^3}{\log 2^2}$
$= \log(7^2) - \log(2^3)$	$= \log(3^2) + \log(10^3)$	$= \dfrac{3\log 2}{2\log 2}$
$= \log 49 - \log 8$	$= \log 9 + \log 1000$	$= \dfrac{3}{2}$
$= \log\left(\frac{49}{8}\right)$	$= \log(9000)$	

EXERCISE 4C.1

1 Write as a single logarithm or as an integer:

  a $\log 8 + \log 2$ **b** $\log 4 + \log 5$ **c** $\log 40 - \log 5$

  d $\log p - \log m$ **e** $\log_4 8 - \log_4 2$ **f** $\log 5 + \log(0.4)$

  g $\log 2 + \log 3 + \log 4$ **h** $1 + \log_2 3$ **i** $\log 4 - 1$

  j $\log 5 + \log 4 - \log 2$ **k** $2 + \log 2$ **l** $t + \log w$

  m $\log_m 40 - 2$ **n** $\log_3 6 - \log_3 2 - \log_3 3$ **o** $\log 50 - 4$

  p $3 - \log_5 50$ **q** $\log_5 100 - \log_5 4$ **r** $\log\left(\frac{4}{3}\right) + \log 3 + \log 7$

2 Write as a single logarithm or integer:

  a $5\log 2 + \log 3$ **b** $2\log 3 + 3\log 2$ **c** $3\log 4 - \log 8$

  d $2\log_3 5 - 3\log_3 2$ **e** $\frac{1}{2}\log_6 4 + \log_6 3$ **f** $\frac{1}{3}\log\left(\frac{1}{8}\right)$

  g $3 - \log 2 - 2\log 5$ **h** $1 - 3\log 2 + \log 20$ **i** $2 - \frac{1}{2}\log_n 4 - \log_n 5$

3 Simplify without using a calculator:

a $\dfrac{\log 4}{\log 2}$

b $\dfrac{\log_5 27}{\log_5 9}$

c $\dfrac{\log 8}{\log 2}$

d $\dfrac{\log 3}{\log 9}$

e $\dfrac{\log_3 25}{\log_3 (0.2)}$

f $\dfrac{\log_4 8}{\log_4 (0.25)}$

Check your answers using a calculator.

Example 9   ◀) **Self Tutor**

Show that:

a $\log \left(\frac{1}{9}\right) = -2 \log 3$

b $\log 500 = 3 - \log 2$

a $\log \left(\frac{1}{9}\right)$
$= \log(3^{-2})$
$= -2 \log 3$

b $\log 500$
$= \log \left(\frac{1000}{2}\right)$
$= \log 1000 - \log 2$
$= \log 10^3 - \log 2$
$= 3 - \log 2$

---

4 Show that:

a $\log 9 = 2 \log 3$

b $\log \sqrt{2} = \frac{1}{2} \log 2$

c $\log \left(\frac{1}{8}\right) = -3 \log 2$

d $\log \left(\frac{1}{5}\right) = -\log 5$

e $\log 5 = 1 - \log 2$

f $\log 5000 = 4 - \log 2$

5 If $p = \log_b 2$, $q = \log_b 3$,   and $r = \log_b 5$ write in terms of p, q, and r:

a $\log_b 6$

b $\log_b 45$

c $\log_b 108$

d $\log_b \left(\frac{5\sqrt{3}}{2}\right)$

e $\log_b \left(\frac{5}{32}\right)$

f $\log_b (0.\overline{2})$

> $0.\overline{2}$ means $0.222\,222 \ldots.$

6 If $\log_2 P = x$, $\log_2 Q = y$,   and $\log_2 R = z$ write in terms of x, y, and z:

a $\log_2 (PR)$

b $\log_2 (RQ^2)$

c $\log_2 \left(\dfrac{PR}{Q}\right)$

d $\log_2 (P^2 \sqrt{Q})$

e $\log_2 \left(\dfrac{Q^3}{\sqrt{R}}\right)$

f $\log_2 \left(\dfrac{R^2 \sqrt{Q}}{P^3}\right)$

7 If $\log_t M = 1.29$ and $\log_t N^2 = 1.72$ find:

a $\log_t N$

b $\log_t (MN)$

c $\log_t \left(\dfrac{N^2}{\sqrt{M}}\right)$

LOGARITHMIC EQUATIONS

We can use the laws of logarithms to write equations in a different form. This can be particularly useful if an unknown appears as an exponent.

For the logarithmic function, for every value of y, there is only one corresponding value of x. We can therefore take the logarithm of both sides of an equation without changing the solution. However, we can only do this if both sides are positive.

Example 10   ◀)) **Self Tutor**

Write these as logarithmic equations (in base 10):

a $y = a^2 b$ b $y = \dfrac{a}{b^3}$ c $P = \dfrac{20}{\sqrt{n}}$

a $\qquad y = a^2 b$ b $\qquad y = \dfrac{a}{b^3}$

$\therefore \quad \log y = \log(a^2 b)$

$\therefore \quad \log y = \log a^2 + \log b$ $\therefore \quad \log y = \log\left(\dfrac{a}{b^3}\right)$

$\therefore \quad \log y = 2\log a + \log b$ $\therefore \quad \log y = \log a - \log b^3$

$\qquad\qquad\qquad\qquad\qquad\qquad\qquad \therefore \quad \log y = \log a - 3\log b$

c $\qquad P = \left(\dfrac{20}{\sqrt{n}}\right)$

$\therefore \quad \log P = \log\left(\dfrac{20}{n^{\frac{1}{2}}}\right)$

$\therefore \quad \log P = \log 20 - \log n^{\frac{1}{2}}$

$\therefore \quad \log P = \log 20 - \tfrac{1}{2}\log n$

Example 11   ◀)) **Self Tutor**

Write the following equations without logarithms:

a $\log A = \log b + 2\log c$ b $\log_2 M = 3\log_2 a - 2$

a $\qquad \log A = \log b + 2\log c$ b $\qquad \log_2 M = 3\log_2 a - 2$

$\therefore \quad \log A = \log b + \log c^2$ $\therefore \quad \log_2 M = \log_2 a^3 - \log_2 2^2$

$\therefore \quad \log A = \log(bc^2)$ $\therefore \quad \log_2 M = \log_2\left(\dfrac{a^3}{4}\right)$

$\therefore \qquad A = bc^2$ $\therefore \qquad M = \dfrac{a^3}{4}$

EXERCISE 4C.2

1 Write the following as logarithmic equations (in base 10), assuming all terms are positive:

a $y = 2^x$ b $y = 20b^3$ c $M = ad^4$ d $T = 5\sqrt{d}$

e $R = b\sqrt{l}$ f $Q = \dfrac{a}{b^n}$ g $y = ab^x$ h $F = \dfrac{20}{\sqrt{n}}$

i $L = \dfrac{ab}{c}$ j $N = \sqrt{\dfrac{a}{b}}$ k $S = 200 \times 2^t$ l $y = \dfrac{a^m}{b^n}$

2 Write the following equations without logarithms:

a $\log D = \log e + \log 2$ b $\log_a F = \log_a 5 - \log_a t$

c $\log P = \tfrac{1}{2}\log x$ d $\log_n M = 2\log_n b + \log_n c$

e $\log B = 3\log m - 2\log n$ f $\log N = -\tfrac{1}{3}\log p$

g $\log P = 3\log x + 1$ h $\log_a Q = 2 - \log_a x$

3 **a** Write $y = 3 \times 2^x$ as a logarithmic equation in base 2.

  b Hence write x in terms of y.

  c Find x when:

  i $y = 3$ **ii** $y = 12$ **iii** $y = 30$

4 Solve for x:

  a $\log_3 27 + \log_3(\frac{1}{3}) = \log_3 x$

  b $\log_5 x = \log_5 8 - \log_5(6 - x)$

  c $\log_5 125 - \log_5 \sqrt{5} = \log_5 x$

  d $\log_{20} x = 1 + \log_{20} 10$

  e $\log x + \log(x + 1) = \log 30$

  f $\log(x + 2) - \log(x - 2) = \log 5$

D | NATURAL LOGARITHMS

In **Chapter 3** we came across the **natural exponential** $e \approx 2.718\,28$.

Given the exponential function $f(x) = e^x$,   the inverse function $f^{-1} = \log_e x$ is the logarithm in base e.

We use $\ln x$ to represent $\log_e x$, and call $\ln x$ the **natural logarithm** of x.

$y = \ln x$ is the reflection of $y = e^x$ in the mirror line $y = x$.

Notice that:

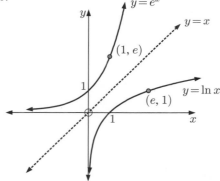

- $\ln 1 = \ln e^0 = 0$
- $\ln e = \ln e^1 = 1$
- $\ln e^2 = 2$
- $\ln \sqrt{e} = \ln e^{\frac{1}{2}} = \frac{1}{2}$
- $\ln\left(\frac{1}{e}\right) = \ln e^{-1} = -1$

$$\boxed{\ln e^x = x \quad \text{and} \quad e^{\ln x} = x.}$$

Since $a^x = \left(e^{\ln a}\right)^x = e^{x \ln a}$, $\boxed{a^x = e^{x \ln a}, \quad a > 0.}$

Example 12   ◀ｳ **Self Tutor**

Use your calculator to write the following in the form e^k where k is correct to 4 decimal places:

  a 50   **b** 0.005

  a   50

    $= e^{\ln 50}$ {using $x = e^{\ln x}$}

    $\approx e^{3.9120}$

  b   0.005

    $= e^{\ln 0.005}$

    $\approx e^{-5.2983}$

EXERCISE 4D.1

1   Without using a calculator find:

    a $\ln e^2$ **b** $\ln e^3$ **c** $\ln \sqrt{e}$ **d** $\ln 1$

    e $\ln\left(\dfrac{1}{e}\right)$ **f** $\ln \sqrt[3]{e}$ **g** $\ln\left(\dfrac{1}{e^2}\right)$ **h** $\ln\left(\dfrac{1}{\sqrt{e}}\right)$

    Check your answers using a calculator.

2   Simplify:

    a $e^{\ln 3}$ **b** $e^{2\ln 3}$ **c** $e^{-\ln 5}$ **d** $e^{-2\ln 2}$

3   Explain why $\ln(-2)$ and $\ln 0$ cannot be found.

4   Simplify:

    a $\ln e^a$ **b** $\ln(e \times e^a)$ **c** $\ln\left(e^a \times e^b\right)$ **d** $\ln(e^a)^b$ **e** $\ln\left(\dfrac{e^a}{e^b}\right)$

Example 13   ◄⑴ **Self Tutor**

Find x if:

    a $\ln x = 2.17$ **b** $\ln x = -0.384$

    a $\ln x = 2.17$ **b** $\ln x = -0.384$

    $\therefore \ x = e^{2.17}$ $\therefore \ x = e^{-0.384}$

    $\therefore \ x \approx 8.76$ $\therefore \ x \approx 0.681$

If $\ln x = a$
then $x = e^a$.

---

5   Use your calculator to write the following in the form e^k where k is correct to 4 decimal places:

    a 6   **b** 60   **c** 6000   **d** 0.6   **e** 0.006

    f 15   **g** 1500   **h** 1.5   **i** 0.15   **j** 0.000 15

6   Find x if:

    a $\ln x = 3$ **b** $\ln x = 1$ **c** $\ln x = 0$ **d** $\ln x = -1$

    e $\ln x = -5$ **f** $\ln x \approx 0.835$ **g** $\ln x \approx 2.145$ **h** $\ln x \approx -3.2971$

LAWS OF NATURAL LOGARITHMS

The laws for natural logarithms are the laws for logarithms written in base e:

For positive A and B:

    • $\ln A + \ln B = \ln(AB)$ • $\ln A - \ln B = \ln\left(\dfrac{A}{B}\right)$ • $n \ln A = \ln(A^n)$

Example 14   ◀) **Self Tutor**

Use the laws of logarithms to write the following as a single logarithm:

| a $\ln 5 + \ln 3$ | b $\ln 24 - \ln 8$ | c $\ln 5 - 1$ |

a	$\ln 5 + \ln 3$	b	$\ln 24 - \ln 8$	c	$\ln 5 - 1$
	$= \ln(5 \times 3)$		$= \ln\left(\frac{24}{8}\right)$		$= \ln 5 - \ln e^1$
	$= \ln 15$		$= \ln 3$		$= \ln\left(\frac{5}{e}\right)$

Example 15   ◀) **Self Tutor**

Use the laws of logarithms to simplify:

| a $2\ln 7 - 3\ln 2$ | b $2\ln 3 + 3$ |

a	$2\ln 7 - 3\ln 2$	b	$2\ln 3 + 3$
	$= \ln(7^2) - \ln(2^3)$		$= \ln(3^2) + \ln e^3$
	$= \ln 49 - \ln 8$		$= \ln 9 + \ln e^3$
	$= \ln\left(\frac{49}{8}\right)$		$= \ln(9e^3)$

Example 16   ◀) **Self Tutor**

Show that:

| a $\ln\left(\frac{1}{9}\right) = -2\ln 3$ | b $\ln 500 \approx 6.9078 - \ln 2$ |

a	$\ln\left(\frac{1}{9}\right)$	b	$\ln 500 = \ln\left(\frac{1000}{2}\right)$
	$= \ln(3^{-2})$		$= \ln 1000 - \ln 2$
	$= -2\ln 3$		$\approx 6.9078 - \ln 2$

EXERCISE 4D.2

1 Write as a single logarithm or integer:

a $\ln 15 + \ln 3$	b $\ln 15 - \ln 3$	c $\ln 20 - \ln 5$
d $\ln 4 + \ln 6$	e $\ln 5 + \ln(0.2)$	f $\ln 2 + \ln 3 + \ln 5$
g $1 + \ln 4$	h $\ln 6 - 1$	i $\ln 5 + \ln 8 - \ln 2$
j $2 + \ln 4$	k $\ln 20 - 2$	l $\ln 12 - \ln 4 - \ln 3$

2 Write in the form $\ln a, \ a \in \mathbb{Q}$:

a $5\ln 3 + \ln 4$	b $3\ln 2 + 2\ln 5$	c $3\ln 2 - \ln 8$
d $3\ln 4 - 2\ln 2$	e $\frac{1}{3}\ln 8 + \ln 3$	f $\frac{1}{3}\ln(\frac{1}{27})$
g $-\ln 2$	h $-\ln(\frac{1}{2})$	i $-2\ln(\frac{1}{4})$

3 Show that:

a $\ln 27 = 3\ln 3$	b $\ln\sqrt{3} = \frac{1}{2}\ln 3$	c $\ln(\frac{1}{16}) = -4\ln 2$
d $\ln(\frac{1}{6}) = -\ln 6$	e $\ln\left(\frac{1}{\sqrt{2}}\right) = -\frac{1}{2}\ln 2$	f $\ln\left(\frac{e}{5}\right) = 1 - \ln 5$

4 Show that:

    a $\ln \sqrt[3]{5} = \frac{1}{3}\ln 5$
          b $\ln(\frac{1}{32}) = -5\ln 2$

    c $\ln\left(\dfrac{1}{\sqrt[5]{2}}\right) = -\frac{1}{5}\ln 2$
          d $\ln\left(\dfrac{e^2}{8}\right) = 2 - 3\ln 2$

Example 17   ◀) **Self Tutor**

Write the following equations without logarithms:

    a $\ln A = 2\ln c + 3$
          b $\ln M = 3\ln a - 2$

a $\ln A = 2\ln c + 3$

$\therefore \quad \ln A - 2\ln c = 3$

$\therefore \quad \ln A - \ln c^2 = 3$

$\therefore \quad \ln\left(\dfrac{A}{c^2}\right) = 3$

$\therefore \quad \dfrac{A}{c^2} = e^3$

$\therefore \quad A = c^2 e^3$

b $\ln M = 3\ln a - 2$

$\therefore \quad \ln M - 3\ln a = -2$

$\therefore \quad \ln M - \ln a^3 = -2$

$\therefore \quad \ln\left(\dfrac{M}{a^3}\right) = -2$

$\therefore \quad \dfrac{M}{a^3} = e^{-2}$

$\therefore \quad M = \dfrac{a^3}{e^2}$

---

5 Write the following equations without logarithms, assuming all terms are positive:

    a $\ln D = \ln x + 1$
    b $\ln F = -\ln p + 2$
    c $\ln P = \frac{1}{2}\ln x$

    d $\ln M = 2\ln y + 3$
    e $\ln B = 3\ln t - 1$
    f $\ln N = -\frac{1}{3}\ln g$

    g $\ln Q \approx 3\ln x + 2.159$
    h $\ln D \approx 0.4\ln n - 0.6582$

E   EXPONENTIAL EQUATIONS USING LOGARITHMS

In **Chapter 3** we found solutions to simple exponential equations where we could make equal bases and then equate exponents. However, it is not always easy to make the bases the same. In these situations we use **logarithms** to find the exact solution.

Example 18   ◀) **Self Tutor**

Consider the equation $2^x = 30$.

    a Solve for x, giving an exact answer, by using: **a** base 2   **b** base 10.

    b Comment on your answers.

a   **i** $2^x = 30$

        $\therefore \quad x = \log_2 30$

   ii $2^x = 30$

        $\therefore \quad \log 2^x = \log 30$ {find the logarithm of each side}

        $\therefore \quad x\log 2 = \log 30$ $\{\log(A^n) = n\log A\}$

        $\therefore \quad x = \dfrac{\log 30}{\log 2}$

b From **a**, $\log_2 30 = \dfrac{\log 30}{\log 2}$.

If $a^x = b$ then $x = \log_a b$.

Example 19

◄) **Self Tutor**

Find x exactly:

    a $e^x = 30$ **b** $3e^{\frac{x}{2}} = 21$

    a $e^x = 30$ **b** $3e^{\frac{x}{2}} = 21$

         $\therefore \quad x = \ln 30$ $\therefore \quad e^{\frac{x}{2}} = 7$

                                          $\therefore \quad \dfrac{x}{2} = \ln 7$

                                          $\therefore \quad x = 2\ln 7$

EXERCISE 4E

1 Solve for x, giving an exact answer in base 10:

    a $2^x = 10$ **b** $3^x = 20$ **c** $4^x = 100$

    d $\left(\frac{1}{2}\right)^x = 0.0625$ **e** $\left(\frac{3}{4}\right)^x = 0.1$ **f** $10^x = 0.000\,01$

2 Solve for x, giving an exact answer:

    a $e^x = 10$ **b** $e^x = 1000$ **c** $2e^x = 0.3$

    d $e^{\frac{x}{2}} = 5$ **e** $e^{2x} = 18$ **f** $e^{-\frac{x}{2}} = 1$

Example 20

◄) **Self Tutor**

Consider the equation $P = 200 \times 2^{0.04t}$.

    a Rearrange the equation to give t in terms of P.

    b Hence find the value of t when $P = 6$.

    a $P = 200 \times 2^{0.04t}$

         $\therefore \quad 2^{0.04t} = \dfrac{P}{200}$ {dividing both sides by 200}

         $\therefore \quad \log 2^{0.04t} = \log\left(\dfrac{P}{200}\right)$ {finding the logarithm of each side}

         $\therefore \quad 0.04t \times \log 2 = \log\left(\dfrac{P}{200}\right)$ $\{ \log(A)^n = n\log A \}$

            $\therefore \quad t = \dfrac{\log\left(\frac{P}{200}\right)}{0.04 \times \log 2}$

    b When $P = 6$, $t = \dfrac{\log\left(\frac{6}{200}\right)}{0.04 \times \log 2} \approx -126$

3 Consider the equation $R = 200 \times 2^{0.25t}$.

    a Rearrange the equation to give t in terms of R.

    b Hence find t when: **i** $R = 600$ **ii** $R = 1425$

4 Consider the equation $M = 20 \times 5^{-0.02x}$.

    a Rearrange the equation to give x in terms of M.

    b Hence find x when: **i** $M = 100$ **ii** $M = 232$

Example 21

Find algebraically the exact points of intersection of $y = e^x - 3$ and $y = 1 - 3e^{-x}$.
Check your solution using technology.

The functions meet where

$$e^x - 3 = 1 - 3e^{-x}$$
$$\therefore \quad e^x - 4 + 3e^{-x} = 0$$
$$\therefore \quad e^{2x} - 4e^x + 3 = 0 \quad \{\text{multiplying each term by } e^x\}$$
$$\therefore \quad (e^x - 1)(e^x - 3) = 0$$
$$\therefore \quad e^x = 1 \text{ or } 3$$
$$\therefore \quad x = \ln 1 \text{ or } \ln 3$$
$$\therefore \quad x = 0 \text{ or } \ln 3$$

When $x = 0$, $y = e^0 - 3 = -2$
When $x = \ln 3$, $y = e^{\ln 3} - 3 = 0$

$\therefore$ the functions meet at $(0, -2)$ and at $(\ln 3, 0)$.

GRAPHING
PACKAGE

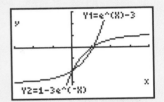

5   Solve for x, giving an exact answer:

a $4 \times 2^{-x} = 0.12$

b $300 \times 5^{0.1x} = 1000$

c $32 \times 3^{-0.25x} = 4$

d $20 \times e^{2x} = 840$

e $50 \times e^{-0.03x} = 0.05$

f $41e^{0.3x} - 27 = 0$

6   Solve for x:

a $e^{2x} = 2e^x$

b $e^x = e^{-x}$

c $e^{2x} - 5e^x + 6 = 0$

d $e^x + 2 = 3e^{-x}$

e $1 + 12e^{-x} = e^x$

f $e^x + e^{-x} = 3$

7   Find algebraically the point(s) of intersection of:

a $y = e^x$ and $y = e^{2x} - 6$

b $y = 2e^x + 1$ and $y = 7 - e^x$

c $y = 3 - e^x$ and $y = 5e^{-x} - 3$

Check your answers using technology.

F   THE CHANGE OF BASE RULE

$$\log_b a = \frac{\log_c a}{\log_c b} \quad \text{for } a, b, c > 0 \text{ and } b, c \neq 1.$$

Proof: If $\log_b a = x$, then $b^x = a$

$$\therefore \quad \log_c b^x = \log_c a \qquad \{\text{taking logarithms in base } c\}$$
$$\therefore \quad x \log_c b = \log_c a \qquad \{\text{power law of logarithms}\}$$
$$\therefore \quad x = \frac{\log_c a}{\log_c b}$$
$$\therefore \quad \log_b a = \frac{\log_c a}{\log_c b}$$

Example 22   ◀)) **Self Tutor**

Find $\log_2 9$ by:

  a letting $\log_2 9 = x$ **b** changing to base 10   **c** changing to base e.

a Let $\log_2 9 = x$
$$\therefore \quad 9 = 2^x$$
$$\therefore \quad \log 2^x = \log 9$$
$$\therefore \quad x \log 2 = \log 9$$
$$\therefore \quad x = \frac{\log 9}{\log 2} \approx 3.17$$

b $\log_2 9 = \dfrac{\log_{10} 9}{\log_{10} 2}$
$$\approx 3.17$$

c $\log_2 9 = \dfrac{\ln 9}{\ln 2}$
$$\approx 3.17$$

Example 23   ◀)) **Self Tutor**

Solve for x exactly:

$8^x - 5(4^x) = 0$

$$8^x - 5(4^x) = 0$$
$$\therefore \quad 2^{3x} - 5(2^{2x}) = 0$$
$$\therefore \quad 2^{2x}(2^x - 5) = 0$$
$$\therefore \quad 2^x = 5 \quad \{\text{as } 2^{2x} > 0 \text{ for all } x\}$$
$$\therefore \quad x = \log_2 5 = \frac{\log 5}{\log 2}$$

EXERCISE 4F

1 Use the rule $\log_b a = \dfrac{\log_{10} a}{\log_{10} b}$ to find, correct to 3 significant figures:

  a $\log_3 12$ **b** $\log_{\frac{1}{2}} 1250$ **c** $\log_3(0.067)$ **d** $\log_{0.4}(0.006\,984)$

2 Use the rule $\log_b a = \dfrac{\ln a}{\ln b}$ to solve, correct to 3 significant figures:

  a $2^x = 0.051$ **b** $4^x = 213.8$ **c** $3^{2x+1} = 4.069$

3 Solve for x exactly:

  a $25^x - 3(5^x) = 0$ **b** $8(9^x) - 3^x = 0$ **c** $2^x - 2(4^x) = 0$

4 Solve for x exactly: $\log_4 x^3 + \log_2 \sqrt{x} = 8$

G   GRAPHS OF LOGARITHMIC FUNCTIONS

Consider the general exponential function $f(x) = a^x$, $a > 0$, $a \neq 1$.

The graph of $y = a^x$ is:

For $0 < a < 1$:

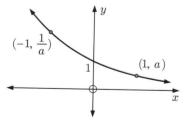

For $a > 1$:

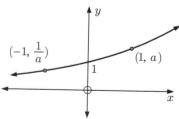

The **horizontal asymptote** for all of these functions is the x-axis $y = 0$.

The inverse function f^{-1} is given by $x = a^y$,   so $y = \log_a x$.

> If $f(x) = a^x$ where $a > 0$, $a \neq 1$,   then $f^{-1}(x) = \log_a x$.

Since $f^{-1}(x) = \log_a x$ is an inverse function, it is a reflection of $f(x) = a^x$ in the line $y = x$.
We may therefore deduce the following properties:

Function	$f(x) = a^x$	$f^{-1}(x) = \log_a x$
Domain	$\{x \mid x \in \mathbb{R}\}$	$\{x \mid x > 0\}$
Range	$\{y \mid y > 0\}$	$\{y \mid y \in \mathbb{R}\}$
Asymptote	horizontal $y = 0$	vertical $x = 0$

The graph of $y = \log_a x$ for $0 < a < 1$:

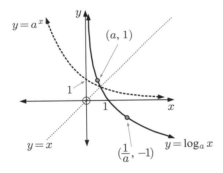

The graph of $y = \log_a x$ for $a > 1$:

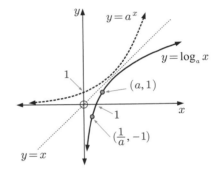

The **vertical asymptote** of $y = \log_a x$ is the y-axis $x = 0$.

Since we can only find logarithms of positive numbers, the domain of $f^{-1}(x) = \log_a x$ is $\{x \mid x > 0\}$.

> In general, $y = \log_a(g(x))$ is defined when $g(x) > 0$.

When graphing f, f^{-1}, and $y = x$ on your graphics calculator, it is best to set the scale so that $y = x$ makes a $45°$ angle with both axes.

Example 24
◀》 **Self Tutor**

Consider the function $f(x) = \log_2(x - 1) + 1$.
a Find the domain and range of f.
b Find any asymptotes and axes intercepts.
c Sketch the graph of f showing all important features.
d Find f^{-1} and explain how to verify your answer.

a $x - 1 > 0$ when $x > 1$
So, the domain is $\{x \mid x > 1\}$ and the range is $y \in \mathbb{R}$.

b As $x \to 1$ from the right, $y \to -\infty$, so the vertical asymptote is $x = 1$.

As $x \to \infty$, $y \to \infty$.

When $x = 0$, y is undefined, so there is no y-intercept.

When $y = 0$, $\log_2(x - 1) = -1$

$$\therefore \quad x - 1 = 2^{-1}$$
$$\therefore \quad x = 1\tfrac{1}{2}$$

So, the x-intercept is $1\tfrac{1}{2}$.

c To graph the function using your calculator, it may be necessary to change the base to base 10 or base e.

So, we graph $y = \dfrac{\log(x - 1)}{\log 2} + 1$

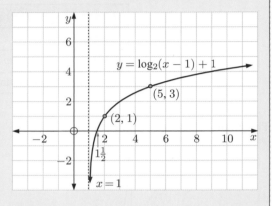

d f is defined by $y = \log_2(x - 1) + 1$

$\therefore$ f^{-1} is defined by $x = \log_2(y - 1) + 1$

$$\therefore \quad x - 1 = \log_2(y - 1)$$
$$\therefore \quad y - 1 = 2^{x-1}$$
$$\therefore \quad y = 2^{x-1} + 1$$
$$\therefore \quad f^{-1}(x) = 2^{x-1} + 1$$

which has the horizontal asymptote $y = 1$ ✓

Its domain is $\{x \mid x \in \mathbb{R}\}$, and its range is $\{y \mid y > 1\}$.

Example 25 ◄) **Self Tutor**

Consider the function $f : x \mapsto e^{x-3}$.

a Find the equation defining f^{-1}.

b Sketch the graphs of f and f^{-1} on the same set of axes.

c State the domain and range of f and f^{-1}.

d Find any asymptotes and intercepts of f and f^{-1}.

a $f(x) = e^{x-3}$

$\therefore$ f^{-1} is $x = e^{y-3}$

$$\therefore \quad y - 3 = \ln x$$
$$\therefore \quad y = 3 + \ln x$$

So, $f^{-1}(x) = 3 + \ln x$

b
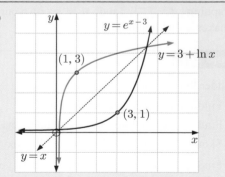

c

Function	f	f^{-1}
Domain	$x \in \mathbb{R}$	$x > 0$
Range	$y > 0$	$y \in \mathbb{R}$

d For f: Horizontal asymptote is $y = 0$, y-intercept is $(0, e^{-3})$.

For f^{-1}: Vertical asymptote is $x = 0$, x-intercept is $(e^{-3}, 0)$.

EXERCISE 4G

1 For the following functions f:

    i Find the domain and range.

    ii Find any asymptotes and axes intercepts.

    iii Sketch the graph of $y = f(x)$ showing all important features.

    iv Solve $f(x) = -1$ algebraically and check the solution on your graph.

    v Find f^{-1} and explain how to verify your answer.

  a $f : x \mapsto \log_3(x + 1), \quad x > -1$ **b** $f : x \mapsto 1 - \log_3(x + 1), \quad x > -1$

  c $f : x \mapsto \log_5(x - 2) - 2, \quad x > 0$ **d** $f : x \mapsto 1 - \log_5(x - 2), \quad x > 2$

  e $f : x \mapsto 1 - 2\log_2 x, \quad x > 0$

2 For the following functions f:

    i Find the equation of f^{-1}.

    ii Sketch the graphs of f and f^{-1} on the same set of axes.

    iii State the domain and range of f and f^{-1}.

    iv Find any asymptotes and intercepts of f and f^{-1}.

  a $f(x) = e^x + 5$ **b** $f(x) = e^{x+1} - 3$

  c $f(x) = \ln x - 4, \quad x > 0$ **d** $f(x) = \ln(x - 1) + 2, \quad x > 1$

3 Given $f : x \mapsto e^{2x}$ and $g : x \mapsto 2x - 1$, find:

  a $(f^{-1} \circ g)(x)$ **b** $(g \circ f)^{-1}(x)$

4 Consider the graphs A and B. One of them is the graph of $y = \ln x$ and the other is the graph of $y = \ln(x - 2)$.

  a Identify which is which. Give evidence for your answer.

  b Copy the graphs onto a new set of axes and add to them the graph of $y = \ln(x + 2)$.

  c Find the equation of the vertical asymptote for each graph.

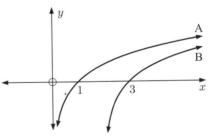

5 Kelly said that in order to graph $y = \ln(x^2), \; x > 0$, you could first graph $y = \ln x$ and then double the distance of each point on the graph from the x-axis. Is Kelly correct? Explain your answer.

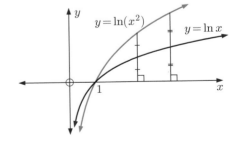

6 Consider the function $f : x \mapsto e^{x+3} + 2$.

   a Find the defining equation for f^{-1}.

   b Find the values of x for which:

   i $f(x) < 2.1$ **ii** $f(x) < 2.01$ **iii** $f(x) < 2.001$ **iv** $f(x) < 2.0001$

   Hence conjecture the horizontal asymptote for the graph of f.

   c Determine the equation of the horizontal asymptote of $f(x)$ by discussing the behaviour of $f(x)$ as $x \to \pm\infty$.

   d Hence, determine the vertical asymptote and the domain of f^{-1}.

ACTIVITY

Click on the icon to obtain a card game for logarithmic functions.

CARD GAME

H   GROWTH AND DECAY

In **Chapter 3** we showed how exponential functions can be used to model a variety of growth and decay situations. These included the growth of populations and the decay of radioactive substances. In this section we consider more growth and decay problems, focussing particularly on how logarithms can be used in their solution.

POPULATION GROWTH

Example 26   ◀ Self Tutor

A farmer monitoring an insect plague notices that the area affected by the insects is given by $A_n = 1000 \times 2^{0.7n}$ hectares, where n is the number of weeks after the initial observation.

   a Draw an accurate graph of A_n against n and use your graph to estimate the time taken for the affected area to reach 5000 ha.

   b Check your answer to **a** using logarithms and using suitable technology.

a
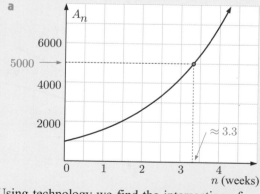

b   When $A_n = 5000$,

$$1000 \times 2^{0.7n} = 5000$$

$$\therefore \quad 2^{0.7n} = 5$$

$$\therefore \quad \log 2^{0.7n} = \log 5$$

$$\therefore \quad 0.7n \log 2 = \log 5$$

$$\therefore \quad n = \frac{\log 5}{0.7 \times \log 2}$$

$$\therefore \quad n \approx 3.32$$

∴   it takes about 3 weeks and 2 days.

Using technology we find the intersection of $y = 1000 \times 2^{0.7x}$ and $y = 5000$. This confirms $n \approx 3.32$.

FINANCIAL GROWTH

Suppose an amount u_1 is invested at a fixed rate for each compounding period. In this case the value of the investment after n periods is given by $u_{n+1} = u_1 \times r^n$ where r is the multiplier corresponding to the given rate of interest. In order to find n algebraically, we need to use **logarithms**.

Example 27 ◀) **Self Tutor**

Iryna has €5000 to invest in an account that pays 5.2% p.a. interest compounded annually. Find, using logarithms, how long it will take for her investment to reach €20 000.

$u_{n+1} = 20\,000$ after n years	Now $u_{n+1} = u_1 \times r^n$
$u_1 = 5000$	$\therefore\quad 20\,000 = 5000 \times (1.052)^n$
$r = 105.2\% = 1.052$	$\therefore\quad (1.052)^n = 4$
	$\therefore\quad \log(1.052)^n = \log 4$
	$\therefore\quad n \times \log 1.052 = \log 4$
	$\therefore\quad n = \dfrac{\log 4}{\log 1.052} \approx 27.3$ years

Rounding up here, it will take about 28 years to reach €20 000.

EXERCISE 4H

1   The weight W_t of bacteria in a culture t hours after establishment is given by
   $W_t = 20 \times 2^{0.15t}$ grams. Find, using logarithms, the time for the weight of the culture to reach:

   a   30 grams   b   100 grams.

2   The mass M_t of bacteria in a culture t hours after establishment is given by
   $M_t = 25 \times e^{0.1t}$ grams. Show that the time required for the mass of the culture to reach 50 grams
   is $10 \ln 2$ hours.

3   A biologist is modelling an infestation of fire ants. He determines that the area affected by the
   ants is given by $A_n = 2000 \times e^{0.57n}$ hectares, where n is the number of weeks after the initial
   observation.

   a   Draw an accurate graph of A_n against n.

   b   Use your graph to estimate the time taken for the infested area to reach 10 000 ha.

   c   Check your answer to b using: i   logarithms   ii   suitable technology.

4   A house is expected to increase in value at an average rate of 7.5% p.a. If the house is worth
   £160 000 now, when would you expect it to be worth £250 000?

5   Thabo has $10 000 to invest in an account that pays 4.8% p.a. compounded annually. How long
   will it take for his investment to grow to $15 000?

6   Dien invests $15 000 at 8.4% p.a. compounded *monthly*. He will withdraw his money when it
   reaches $25 000, at which time he plans to travel. The formula $u_{n+1} = u_1 \times r^n$ can be used to
   model the investment, where n is the time in months.

   a   Explain why $r = 1.007$.   b   After how many months will Dien withdraw the money?

7   The mass M_t of radioactive substance remaining after t years is given by
   $M_t = 1000 \times e^{-0.04t}$ grams. Find the time taken for the mass to:

   a   halve   b   reach 25 grams   c   reach 1% of its original value.

8 A man jumps from an aeroplane. His speed of descent is given by $V = 50(1 - e^{-0.2t})$ m s^{-1}, where t is the time in seconds. Show that it will take $5 \ln 5$ seconds for the man's speed to reach 40 m s^{-1}.

9 Answer the **Opening Problem** on page **110**.

10 The temperature of a liquid t minutes after it is placed in a refrigerator, is given by $T = 4 + 96 \times e^{-0.03t}$ °C.   Find the time required for the temperature to reach:

    a 25°C   **b** 5°C.

11 The weight of radioactive substance remaining after t years is given by $W = 1000 \times 2^{-0.04t}$ grams.

    a Sketch the graph of W against t.

    b Write a function for t in terms of W.

    c Hence find the time required for the weight to reach:

       i 20 grams   **ii** 0.001 grams.

12 The weight of radioactive uranium remaining after t years is given by the formula $W(t) = W_0 \times 2^{-0.0002t}$ grams, $t \geqslant 0$. Find the time required for the weight to fall to:

    a 25% of its original value   **b** 0.1% of its original value.

13 The current I flowing in a transistor radio t seconds after it is switched off is given by $I = I_0 \times 2^{-0.02t}$ amps.   Show that it takes $\dfrac{50}{\log 2}$ seconds for the current to drop to 10% of its original value.

14 A parachutist jumps from the basket of a stationary hot air balloon. His speed of descent is given by $V = 60(1 - 2^{-0.2t})$ m s^{-1} where t is the time in seconds. Find the time taken for his speed to reach 50 m s^{-1}.

REVIEW SET 4A   NON-CALCULATOR

1 Find the following, showing all working.

    a $\log_4 64$ **b** $\log_2 256$ **c** $\log_2(0.25)$ **d** $\log_{25} 5$

    e $\log_8 1$ **f** $\log_{81} 3$ **g** $\log_9(0.\overline{1})$ **h** $\log_k \sqrt{k}$

2 Find:

    a $\log \sqrt{10}$ **b** $\log \dfrac{1}{\sqrt[3]{10}}$ **c** $\log(10^a \times 10^{b+1})$

3 Simplify:

    a $4 \ln 2 + 2 \ln 3$ **b** $\frac{1}{2} \ln 9 - \ln 2$ **c** $2 \ln 5 - 1$ **d** $\frac{1}{4} \ln 81$

4 Find:

    a $\ln(e\sqrt{e})$ **b** $\ln\left(\dfrac{1}{e^3}\right)$ **c** $\ln(e^{2x})$ **d** $\ln\left(\dfrac{e}{e^x}\right)$

5 Write as a single logarithm:

    a $\log 16 + 2 \log 3$ **b** $\log_2 16 - 2 \log_2 3$ **c** $2 + \log_4 5$

6 Write as logarithmic equations:

    a $P = 3 \times b^x$ **b** $m = \dfrac{n^3}{p^2}$

7 Show that $\log_3 7 \times 2\log_7 x = 2\log_3 x$.

8 Write the following equations without logarithms:

   a $\log T = 2\log x - \log y$ **b** $\log_2 K = \log_2 n + \frac{1}{2}\log_2 t$

9 Write in the form $a \ln k$ where a and k are positive whole numbers and k is prime:

   a $\ln 32$ **b** $\ln 125$ **c** $\ln 729$

10 Copy and complete:

Function	$y = \log_2 x$	$y = \ln(x + 5)$
Domain		
Range		

11 If $A = \log_5 2$ and $B = \log_5 3$, write in terms of A and B:

   a $\log_5 36$ **b** $\log_5 54$ **c** $\log_5(8\sqrt{3})$ **d** $\log_5(20.25)$ **e** $\log_5(0.\overline{8})$

12 Solve for x:

   a $3e^x - 5 = -2e^{-x}$ **b** $2\ln x - 3\ln\left(\frac{1}{x}\right) = 10$

REVIEW SET 4B   CALCULATOR

1 Write in the form 10^x giving x correct to 4 decimal places:

   a 32 **b** 0.0013 **c** 8.963×10^{-5}

2 Find x if:

   a $\log_2 x = -3$ **b** $\log_5 x \approx 2.743$ **c** $\log_3 x \approx -3.145$

3 Write the following equations without logarithms:

   a $\log_2 k \approx 1.699 + x$ **b** $\log_a Q = 3\log_a P + \log_a R$

   c $\log A \approx 5\log B - 2.602$

4 Solve for x, giving exact answers:

   a $5^x = 7$ **b** $20 \times 2^{2x+1} = 640$

5 The weight of a radioactive isotope after t years is given by $W_t = 2500 \times 3^{-\frac{t}{3000}}$ grams.

   a Find the initial weight of the isotope.

   b Find the time taken for the isotope to reduce to 30% of its original weight.

   c Find the percentage weight loss after 1500 years.

   d Sketch the graph of W_t against t.

6 Show that the solution to $16^x - 5 \times 8^x = 0$ is $x = \log_2 5$.

7 Solve for x, giving exact answers:

   a $\ln x = 5$ **b** $3\ln x + 2 = 0$ **c** $e^x = 400$

   d $e^{2x+1} = 11$ **e** $25e^{\frac{x}{2}} = 750$

8 A population of seals is given by $P_t = P_0 2^{\frac{t}{3}}$ where t is the time in years, $t \geqslant 0$.

   a Find the time required for the population to double in size.

   b Find the percentage increase in population during the first 4 years.

9 Consider $g : x \mapsto 2e^x - 5$.

  a Find the defining equation of g^{-1}.

  b Sketch the graphs of g and g^{-1} on the same set of axes.

  c State the domain and range of g and g^{-1}.

  d State the asymptotes and intercepts of g and g^{-1}.

10 Consider $f(x) = e^x$ and $g(x) = \ln(x + 4)$, $x > -4$. Find:

  a $(f \circ g)(5)$ **b** $(g \circ f)(0)$

REVIEW SET 4C

1 Without using a calculator, find the base 10 logarithms of:

  a $\sqrt{1000}$ **b** $\dfrac{10}{\sqrt[3]{10}}$ **c** $\dfrac{10^a}{10^{-b}}$

2 Simplify:

  a $e^{4\ln x}$ **b** $\ln(e^5)$ **c** $\ln(\sqrt{e})$

  d $10^{\log x + \log 3}$ **e** $\ln\left(\dfrac{1}{e^x}\right)$ **f** $\dfrac{\log x^2}{\log_3 9}$

3 Write in the form e^x, where x is correct to 4 decimal places:

  a 20   **b** 3000   **c** 0.075

4 Solve for x:

  a $\log x = 3$ **b** $\log_3(x + 2) = 1.732$ **c** $\log_2\left(\dfrac{x}{10}\right) = -0.671$

5 Write as a single logarithm:

  a $\ln 60 - \ln 20$ **b** $\ln 4 + \ln 1$ **c** $\ln 200 - \ln 8 + \ln 5$

6 Write as logarithmic equations:

  a $M = ab^n$ **b** $T = \dfrac{5}{\sqrt{l}}$ **c** $G = \dfrac{a^2 b}{c}$

7 Solve for x:

  a $3^x = 300$ **b** $30 \times 5^{1-x} = 0.15$ **c** $3^{x+2} = 2^{1-x}$

8 Solve exactly for x:

  a $e^{2x} = 3e^x$ **b** $e^{2x} - 7e^x + 12 = 0$

9 Write the following equations without logarithms:

  a $\ln P = 1.5 \ln Q + \ln T$ **b** $\ln M = 1.2 - 0.5 \ln N$

10 For the function $g : x \mapsto \log_3(x + 2) - 2$:

  a Find the domain and range.

  b Find any asymptotes and axes intercepts for the graph of the function.

  c Find the defining equation for g^{-1}. Explain how to verify your answer.

  d Sketch the graphs of g, g^{-1}, and $y = x$ on the same axes.

11 The weight of a radioactive isotope remaining after t weeks is given by

$W_t = 8000 \times e^{-\frac{t}{20}}$ grams. Find the time for the weight to:

  a halve   **b** reach 1000 g   **c** reach 0.1% of its original value.

Transforming functions

Syllabus reference: 2.2, 2.3

OPENING PROBLEM

Blood glucose levels are measured in millimoles per litre (mmol/L) of blood. In most people, blood glucose levels range from about 4 to 6 mmol/L, depending on food intake. For patients with Type 1 diabetes, blood glucose levels are frequently outside the normal range. Regular monitoring of glucose levels is important to assist with management of the condition.

The blood glucose levels of a patient are modelled by $G(t) = 19te^{-t} + 4$ mmol/L, where t is the time in hours since the evening meal, for $0 \leqslant t \leqslant 12$.

Things to think about:

a Sketch the graph of $G(t)$ on the domain $0 \leqslant t \leqslant 12$.

b What is the highest blood glucose level reached during this time period? When does it occur?

c Guidelines state that blood glucose levels should be less than 8 mmol/L before sleep. For how many hours should the patient wait following their meal before they sleep?

A GRAPHING FUNCTIONS

There are several families of functions that we are already familiar with:

Name	General form	Function notation
Linear	$f(x) = ax + b, \quad a \neq 0$	$f : x \mapsto ax + b, \quad a \neq 0$
Quadratic	$f(x) = ax^2 + bx + c, \quad a \neq 0$	$f : x \mapsto ax^2 + bx + c, \quad a \neq 0$
Cubic	$f(x) = ax^3 + bx^2 + cx + d, \ a \neq 0$	$f : x \mapsto ax^3 + bx^2 + cx + d, \ a \neq 0$
Exponential	$f(x) = a^x, \quad a > 0, \quad a \neq 1$	$f : x \mapsto a^x, \quad a > 0, \quad a \neq 1$
Logarithmic	$f(x) = \log_e x \quad$ or $\quad f(x) = \ln x$	$f : x \mapsto \log_e x \quad$ or $\quad f : x \mapsto \ln x$
Reciprocal	$f(x) = \dfrac{k}{x}, \quad x \neq 0, \quad k \neq 0$	$f : x \mapsto \dfrac{k}{x}, \quad x \neq 0, \quad k \neq 0$

These families of functions have different and distinctive graphs. We can compare them by considering important graphical features such as:

- the **axes intercepts** where the graph cuts the x and y-axes
- **turning points** which could be a **local minimum** or **local maximum**
- values of x for which the function does not exist
- the presence of **asymptotes**, which are lines or curves that the graph approaches.

Many real world situations are modelled by mathematical functions which are difficult to analyse using algebra. However, we can use technology to help us graph and investigate the key features of an unfamiliar function.

If there is no domain or range specified, start with a large viewing window. This ensures we do not miss any features of the function.

Example 1

Consider the function $y = \dfrac{2^x}{x} - 2$.   Use technology to help answer the following:

a   Find the axes intercepts.

b   Find any turning points of the function.

c   Find any asymptotes of the function.

d   State the domain and range of the function.

e   Sketch the function, showing its key features.

a   When $x = 0$, y is undefined. There is no y-intercept.

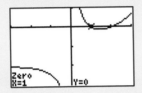 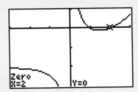

The x-intercepts are 1 and 2.

b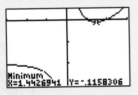

There is a local minimum at $(1.44, -0.116)$.

c   As $x \to -\infty$, $y \to -2$ from below.
So, the horizontal asymptote is $y = -2$.
As $x \to 0$ from the left, $y \to -\infty$.
As $x \to 0$ from the right, $y \to \infty$.
So, the vertical asymptote is $x = 0$.

d   The domain is $\{x \mid x \neq 0\}$.
The range is
$\{y \mid y < -2$ or $y \geqslant -0.116\}$.

e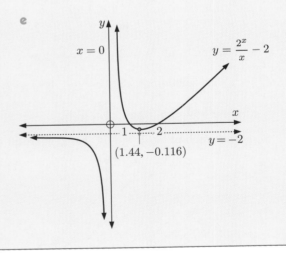

If we are asked to **sketch** a function, it will show the graph's general shape and its key features.

If we are asked to **draw** a function, it should be done more carefully to scale.

WHERE GRAPHS MEET

Suppose we graph two functions $f(x)$ and $g(x)$ on the same set of axes. The x-coordinates of points where the graphs meet are the solutions to the equation $f(x) = g(x)$.

We can use this property to solve equations graphically, but we must make sure the graphs are drawn accurately.

Example 2   ◀) **Self Tutor**

a Draw the functions $y = \dfrac{1}{x}$ and $y = 2 - x$ on the same set of axes, with the domain $-4 \leqslant x \leqslant 4$.

b Hence find any solutions to the equation $2 - x = \dfrac{1}{x}$ on the domain $-4 \leqslant x \leqslant 4$.

c On the domain $x \in \mathbb{R}$, for what values of k does $x + \dfrac{1}{x} = k$ have:

   i one solution   **ii** no solutions   **iii** two solutions?

a

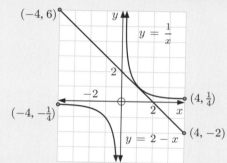

The Table menu on your calculator can be used to find endpoints.

b The graphs of $y = 2 - x$ and $y = \dfrac{1}{x}$ meet when $x = 1$.

$\therefore$ the solution of $2 - x = \dfrac{1}{x}$ is $x = 1$.

c If $x + \dfrac{1}{x} = k$ then $k - x = \dfrac{1}{x}$.

The graph of $y = k - x$ has y-intercept k and gradient -1.

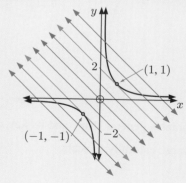

i Using **b** as a guide, we see there is one solution if $k = 2$ or -2. {green lines}

ii There are no solutions if $-2 < k < 2$. {blue lines}

iii There are two solutions if $k < -2$ or $k > 2$. {red lines}

EXERCISE 5A

1 For each of the functions given, use technology to answer the following:

   i Find the axes intercepts.

   ii Find any turning points of the function.

   iii Find any asymptotes of the function.

   iv State the domain and range of the function.

   v Sketch the function, showing its key features.

   a $y = \frac{1}{2}x(x-4)(x+3)$ **b** $y = \frac{4}{5}x^4 + 5x^3 + 5x^2 + 2$ on $-5 \leqslant x \leqslant 1$

   c $y = x \, 2^{-x}$ **d** $y = \dfrac{1 - x^2}{(x+2)^2}$ on $-5 \leqslant x \leqslant 5$

   e $y = \dfrac{1}{1 + 2^{-x}}$ **f** $y = \dfrac{x^2}{2^x} - 1$

2 **a** Sketch the graphs of $f(x) = x^2 - \dfrac{4}{x}$ and $g(x) = -x^2 + 11$ for $-6 \leqslant x \leqslant 6$.

   b One of the solutions to $f(x) = g(x)$ is $x \approx 2.51$. Use technology to determine the two negative solutions.

3 Find the maximum value of:

   a $y = -x^4 + 2x^3 + 5x^2 + x + 2$ on the interval $0 \leqslant x \leqslant 4$

   b $y = -2x^4 + 5x^2 + x + 2$ on the interval:

   i $-2 \leqslant x \leqslant 2$ **ii** $-2 \leqslant x \leqslant 0$ **iii** $0 \leqslant x \leqslant 2$.

4 Sketch the graphs of $f(x) = e^{-x^2}$ and $g(x) = x^2$ on the same set of axes.

   Hence solve $x^2 = e^{-x^2}$.

5 Part of the graph of $y = f(x)$ is shown alongside.

   a Copy the graph, and on the same set of axes draw the graph of $g(x) = -1$, $-5 \leqslant x \leqslant 4$.

   b Hence state the number of solutions of $f(x) = g(x)$ on the domain $-5 \leqslant x \leqslant 4$.

   c Consider the function $h(x) = k$ on the domain $-5 \leqslant x \leqslant 4$. For what values of k does $f(x) = h(x)$ have:

   i three solutions   **ii** two solutions

   iii one solution   **iv** no solutions?

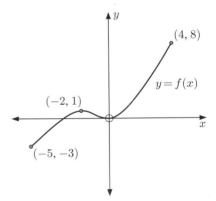

6 Answer the **Opening Problem** on page **136**.

B   TRANSFORMATION OF GRAPHS

Having studied the key features of graphs, we now consider how the graphs of different members of a family of functions are related.

INVESTIGATION 1   FUNCTION FAMILIES

In this investigation you are encouraged to use the graphing package supplied. Click on the icon to access this package.

What to do:

GRAPHING
PACKAGE

1 From the menu, graph on the same set of axes:
$y = 2x + 1$, $y = 2x + 3$, $y = 2x - 1$
Comment on all lines of the form $y = 2x + b$.

2 From the menu, graph on the same set of axes:
$y = x + 2$, $y = 2x + 2$, $y = 4x + 2$, $y = -x + 2$, $y = -\frac{1}{2}x + 2$
Comment on all lines of the form $y = ax + 2$.

3 On the same set of axes graph:
$y = x^2$, $y = 2x^2$, $y = \frac{1}{2}x^2$, $y = -x^2$, $y = -3x^2$, $y = -\frac{1}{5}x^2$
Comment on all functions of the form $y = ax^2$, $a \neq 0$.

4 On the same set of axes graph:
$y = x^2$, $y = (x - 1)^2 + 2$, $y = (x + 1)^2 - 3$, $y = (x - 2)^2 - 1$
and other functions of the form $y = (x - h)^2 + k$ of your choice.
Comment on the functions of this form.

5 On the same set of axes, graph these functions:

a $y = \dfrac{1}{x}$, $y = \dfrac{3}{x}$, $y = \dfrac{10}{x}$

b $y = \dfrac{-1}{x}$, $y = \dfrac{-2}{x}$, $y = \dfrac{-5}{x}$

c $y = \dfrac{1}{x}$, $y = \dfrac{1}{x - 2}$, $y = \dfrac{1}{x + 3}$

d $y = \dfrac{1}{x}$, $y = \dfrac{1}{x} + 2$, $y = \dfrac{1}{x} - 2$

e $y = \dfrac{2}{x}$, $y = \dfrac{2}{x - 1} + 2$, $y = \dfrac{2}{x + 2} - 1$

Write a brief report on your discoveries.

From the **Investigation** you should have observed how different parts of a function's equation can affect its graph.

In particular, we can perform **transformations** of graphs to give the graph of a related function. These transformations include **translations**, **stretches**, and **reflections**.

In this chapter we will consider transformations of the function $y = f(x)$ into:

- $y = f(x) + b$, b is a constant
- $y = f(x - a)$, a is a constant
- $y = pf(x)$, p is a positive constant
- $y = f(qx)$, q is a positive constant
- $y = -f(x)$
- $y = f(-x)$

Example 3

◀) **Self Tutor**

If $f(x) = x^2$, find in simplest form:

   a $f(2x)$ **b** $f\left(\dfrac{x}{3}\right)$ **c** $2f(x) + 1$ **d** $f(x + 3) - 4$

a $f(2x)$	**b** $f\left(\dfrac{x}{3}\right)$	**c** $2f(x) + 1$	**d** $f(x + 3) - 4$
$= (2x)^2$	$= \left(\dfrac{x}{3}\right)^2$	$= 2x^2 + 1$	$= (x + 3)^2 - 4$
$= 4x^2$	$= \dfrac{x^2}{9}$		$= x^2 + 6x + 9 - 4$
			$= x^2 + 6x + 5$

EXERCISE 5B

1 If $f(x) = x$, find in simplest form:

   a $f(2x)$ **b** $f(x) + 2$ **c** $\frac{1}{2}f(x)$ **d** $2f(x) + 3$

2 If $f(x) = x^2$, find in simplest form:

   a $f(3x)$ **b** $f\left(\dfrac{x}{2}\right)$ **c** $3f(x)$ **d** $2f(x - 1) + 5$

3 If $f(x) = x^3$, find in simplest form:

   a $f(4x)$ **b** $\frac{1}{2}f(2x)$ **c** $f(x + 1)$ **d** $2f(x + 1) - 3$

   Hint: $(x + 1)^3 = x^3 + 3x^2 + 3x + 1$.   See the binomial theorem in **Chapter 7**.

4 If $f(x) = 2^x$, find in simplest form:

   a $f(2x)$ **b** $f(-x) + 1$ **c** $f(x - 2) + 3$ **d** $2f(x) + 3$

5 If $f(x) = \dfrac{1}{x}$, find in simplest form:

   a $f(-x)$ **b** $f(\frac{1}{2}x)$ **c** $2f(x) + 3$ **d** $3f(x - 1) + 2$

C   TRANSLATIONS $y = f(x) + b$ AND $y = f(x - a)$

INVESTIGATION 2   **TRANSLATIONS**

What to do:

GRAPHING
PACKAGE

1 **a** For $f(x) = x^3$, find in simplest form:

     i $f(x) + 2$ **ii** $f(x) - 3$ **iii** $f(x) + 6$

   b Graph all four functions on the same set of axes.

   c What effect does the constant b have when $y = f(x)$ is transformed to $y = f(x) + b$?

2 **a** For $f(x) = x^2$, find in simplest form:

     i $f(x - 2)$ **ii** $f(x + 1)$ **iii** $f(x - 5)$

   b Graph all four functions on the same set of axes.

   c What effect does the constant a have when $y = f(x)$ is transformed to $y = f(x - a)$?

- For $y = f(x) + b$, the effect of b is to **translate** the graph **vertically** through b units.
  - ▸ If $b > 0$ it moves **upwards**.   ▸ If $b < 0$ it moves **downwards**.
- For $y = f(x - a)$, the effect of a is to **translate** the graph **horizontally** through a units.
  - ▸ If $a > 0$ it moves to the **right**.   ▸ If $a < 0$ it moves to the **left**.
- For $y = f(x - a) + b$, the graph is translated horizontally a units and vertically b units.
  We say it is **translated by the vector** $\binom{a}{b}$.

EXERCISE 5C

1 **a** Sketch the graph of $f(x) = x^2$.

    b On the same set of axes sketch the graphs of:

       i $y = f(x) + 2$ or $y = x^2 + 2$ **ii** $y = f(x) - 3$ or $y = x^2 - 3$.

    c What is the connection between the graphs of $y = f(x)$ and $y = f(x) + b$ if:

       i $b > 0$ **ii** $b < 0$?

GRAPHING
PACKAGE

2 For each of the following functions f, sketch on the same set of axes the graphs of $y = f(x)$, $y = f(x) + 1$, and $y = f(x) - 2$.

    a $f(x) = 2^x$ **b** $f(x) = x^3$ **c** $f(x) = \dfrac{1}{x}$ **d** $f(x) = (x - 1)^2$

3 **a** On the same set of axes, graph $f(x) = x^2$, $y = f(x - 3)$, and $y = f(x + 2)$.

    b What is the connection between the graphs of $y = f(x)$ and $y = f(x - a)$ if:

       i $a > 0$ **ii** $a < 0$?

4 For each of the following functions f, sketch on the same set of axes the graphs of $y = f(x)$, $y = f(x - 1)$, and $y = f(x + 2)$.

    a $f(x) = x^3$ **b** $f(x) = \ln x$ **c** $f(x) = \dfrac{1}{x}$ **d** $f(x) = (x + 1)^2 + 2$

5 For each of the following functions f, sketch on the same set of axes the graphs of $y = f(x)$, $y = f(x - 2) + 3$, and $y = f(x + 1) - 4$.

    a $f(x) = x^2$ **b** $f(x) = e^x$ **c** $f(x) = \dfrac{1}{x}$

6 Copy these functions and then draw the graph of $y = f(x - 2) - 3$.

    a

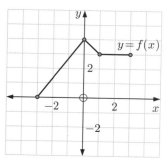

    b

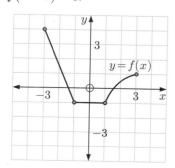

7 The graph of $f(x) = x^2 - 2x + 2$ is translated 3 units right to $g(x)$. Find $g(x)$ in the form $g(x) = ax^2 + bx + c$.

8 Suppose $f(x) = x^2$ is transformed to $g(x) = (x - 3)^2 + 2$.

    a Find the images of the following points on $f(x)$:

        i $(0, 0)$ **ii** $(-3, 9)$ **iii** where $x = 2$

    b Find the points on $f(x)$ which correspond to the following points on $g(x)$:

        i $(1, 6)$ **ii** $(-2, 27)$ **iii** $(1\frac{1}{2}, 4\frac{1}{4})$

D   STRETCHES $y = p\,f(x)$, $p > 0$ AND $y = f(qx)$, $q > 0$

INVESTIGATION 3   STRETCHES

What to do:

GRAPHING PACKAGE

1   **a** For $f(x) = x + 2$, find in simplest form:

        i $3f(x)$ **ii** $\frac{1}{2}f(x)$ **iii** $5f(x)$

  b Graph all four functions on the same set of axes.

  c What effect does the constant p have when $y = f(x)$ is transformed to $y = pf(x)$, $p > 0$?

2   **a** For $f(x) = x^2$, find in simplest form:

        i $f(2x)$ **ii** $f(3x)$ **iii** $f(\frac{x}{4})$

  b Graph all four functions on the same set of axes.

  c What effect does the constant q have when $y = f(x)$ is transformed to $y = f(qx)$, $q > 0$?

- For $y = pf(x)$, $p > 0$, the effect of p is to **vertically stretch** the graph by the **scale factor** p.
  - ▸ If $p > 1$ it moves points of $y = f(x)$ **further away** from the x-axis.
  - ▸ If $0 < p < 1$ it moves points of $y = f(x)$ **closer** to the x-axis.

- For $y = f(qx)$, $q > 0$, the effect of q is to **horizontally stretch** the graph by the **scale factor** $\dfrac{1}{q}$.
  - ▸ If $q > 1$ it moves points of $y = f(x)$ **closer** to the y-axis.
  - ▸ If $0 < q < 1$ it moves points of $y = f(x)$ **further away** from the y-axis.

EXERCISE 5D

1 Sketch, on the same set of axes, the graphs of $y = f(x)$, $y = 2f(x)$, and $y = 3f(x)$ for each of:

    a $f(x) = x^2$ **b** $f(x) = x^3$ **c** $f(x) = e^x$

    d $f(x) = \ln x$ **e** $f(x) = \dfrac{1}{x}$

2 Sketch, on the same set of axes, the graphs of $y = f(x)$, $y = \frac{1}{2}f(x)$, and $y = \frac{1}{4}f(x)$ for each of:

    a $f(x) = x^2$ **b** $f(x) = x^3$ **c** $f(x) = e^x$

3 Sketch, on the same set of axes, the graphs of $y = f(x)$ and $y = f(2x)$ for each of:

   a $y = x^2$ **b** $y = (x - 1)^2$ **c** $y = (x + 3)^2$

4 Sketch, on the same set of axes, the graphs of $y = f(x)$ and $y = f(\frac{x}{2})$ for each of:

   a $y = x^2$ **b** $y = 2x$ **c** $y = (x + 2)^2$

5 Sketch, on the same set of axes, the graphs of $y = f(x)$ and $y = f(3x)$ for each of:

   a $y = x$ **b** $y = x^2$ **c** $y = e^x$

6 Consider the function $f : x \mapsto x^2$.
On the same set of axes sketch the graphs of:

   a $y = f(x)$, $y = 3f(x - 2) + 1$, and $y = 2f(x + 1) - 3$

   b $y = f(x)$, $y = f(x - 3)$, $y = f(\frac{x}{2} - 3)$, $y = 2f(\frac{x}{2} - 3)$, and $y = 2f(\frac{x}{2} - 3) + 4$

   c $y = f(x)$ and $y = \frac{1}{4}f(2x + 5) + 1$.

7   **a** Given that the following points lie on $y = f(x)$, find the coordinates of the point each moves to under the transformation $y = 3f(2x)$:

     i $(3, -5)$ **ii** $(1, 2)$ **iii** $(-2, 1)$

  b Find the points on $y = f(x)$ which are moved to the following points under the transformation $y = 3f(2x)$:

     i $(2, 1)$ **ii** $(-3, 2)$ **iii** $(-7, 3)$

E   REFLECTIONS $y = -f(x)$ AND $y = f(-x)$

INVESTIGATION 4   REFLECTIONS

What to do:

GRAPHING PACKAGE

1 Consider $f(x) = x^3 - 2$.

   a Find in simplest form:

     i $-f(x)$ **ii** $f(-x)$

   b Graph $y = f(x)$, $y = -f(x)$, and $y = f(-x)$ on the same set of axes.

2 Consider $f(x) = e^x$.

   a Find in simplest form:

     i $-f(x)$ **ii** $f(-x)$

   b Graph $y = f(x)$, $y = -f(x)$, and $y = f(-x)$ on the same set of axes.

3 What transformation moves:

   a $y = f(x)$ to $y = -f(x)$ **b** $y = f(x)$ to $y = f(-x)$?

- For $y = -f(x)$, we **reflect** $y = f(x)$ in the x-axis.
- For $y = f(-x)$, we **reflect** $y = f(x)$ in the y-axis.

EXERCISE 5E

1   On the same set of axes, sketch the graphs of $y = f(x)$ and $y = -f(x)$ for:

    a $f(x) = 3x$
    b $f(x) = e^x$
    c $f(x) = x^2$

    d $f(x) = \ln x$
    e $f(x) = x^3 - 2$
    f $f(x) = 2(x + 1)^2$

2   **a** Find $f(-x)$ for:

      i $f(x) = 2x + 1$
      ii $f(x) = x^2 + 2x + 1$
      iii $f(x) = x^3$

    b Graph $y = f(x)$ and $y = f(-x)$ for:

      i $f(x) = 2x + 1$
      ii $f(x) = x^2 + 2x + 1$
      iii $f(x) = x^3$

3   The function $f(x) = x^3 - \ln x$ is reflected in the x-axis to $g(x)$. Find $g(x)$.

4   The function $f(x) = x^4 - 2x^3 - 3x^2 + 5x - 7$ is reflected in the y-axis to $g(x)$. Find $g(x)$.

5   The function $y = f(x)$ is transformed to $g(x) = -f(x)$.

    a Find the points on $g(x)$ corresponding to the following points on $f(x)$:

      i $(3, 0)$
      ii $(2, -1)$
      iii $(-3, 2)$

    b Find the points on $f(x)$ that have been transformed to the following points on $g(x)$:

      i $(7, -1)$
      ii $(-5, 0)$
      iii $(-3, -2)$

6   The function $y = f(x)$ is transformed to $h(x) = f(-x)$.

    a Find the image points on $h(x)$ for the following points on $f(x)$:

      i $(2, -1)$
      ii $(0, 3)$
      iii $(-1, 2)$

    b Find the points on $f(x)$ corresponding to the following points on $h(x)$:

      i $(5, -4)$
      ii $(0, 3)$
      iii $(2, 3)$

7   Copy the graph of $y = f(x)$ alongside, then draw the graph of:

    a $y = -f(x)$
    b $y = f(-x)$

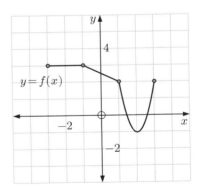

8   A function $f(x)$ is transformed to the function $g(x) = -f(-x)$.

    a Describe the nature of the transformation.

    b If $(3, -7)$ lies on $y = f(x)$, find the transformed point on $y = g(x)$.

    c Find the point on $f(x)$ that transforms to the point $(-5, -1)$.

F   MISCELLANEOUS TRANSFORMATIONS

A summary of all the transformations is given in the printable concept map.

CONCEPT
MAP

Example 4   ◀) **Self Tutor**

Consider $f(x) = \frac{1}{2}x + 1$.   On separate sets of axes graph:

a $y = f(x)$ and $y = f(x + 2)$ **b** $y = f(x)$ and $y = f(x) + 2$

c $y = f(x)$ and $y = 2f(x)$ **d** $y = f(x)$ and $y = -f(x)$

a 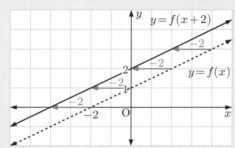   **b**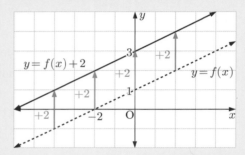

c 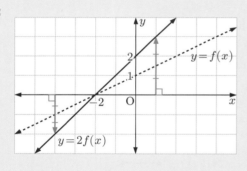   **d**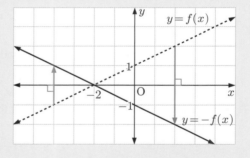

EXERCISE 5F

1   Consider $f(x) = x^2 - 1$.

Invariant points do not move
under a transformation.

a   Graph $y = f(x)$ and state its axes intercepts.

b   Graph the functions:

    i $y = f(x) + 3$ **ii** $y = f(x - 1)$

    iii $y = 2f(x)$ **iv** $y = -f(x)$

c   What transformation on $y = f(x)$ has occurred in each case in **b**?

d   On the same set of axes graph $y = f(x)$ and $y = -2f(x)$.
Describe the transformation.

e   What points on $y = f(x)$ are invariant when $y = f(x)$ is
transformed to $y = -2f(x)$?

2 On each of the following $f(x)$ is mapped onto $g(x)$ using a single transformation.

    i Describe the transformation fully.   **ii** Write $g(x)$ in terms of $f(x)$.

a
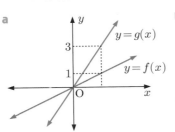

b
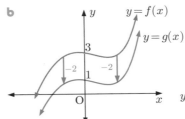

c
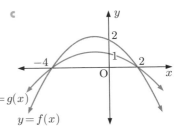

3 Copy the following graphs for $y = f(x)$ and sketch the graphs of $y = -f(x)$ on the same axes.

a
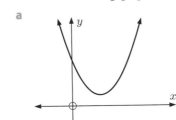

b
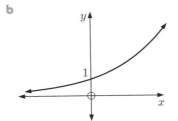

c
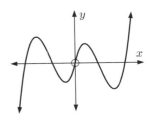

4 Given the following graphs of $y = f(x)$, sketch graphs of $y = f(-x)$:

a

b
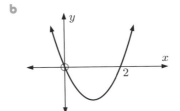

c
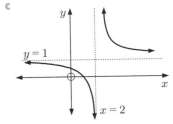

5 The scales on the graphs below are the same. Match each equation to its graph.

  A $y = x^4$ **B** $y = 2x^4$ **C** $y = \frac{1}{2}x^4$ **D** $y = 6x^4$

a
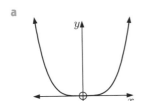

b
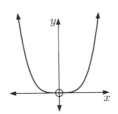

c
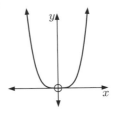

d
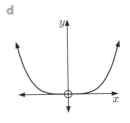

6 For the graph of $y = f(x)$ given, sketch the graph of:

  a $y = 2f(x)$ **b** $y = \frac{1}{2}f(x)$

  c $y = f(x+2)$ **d** $y = f(2x)$

  e $y = f(\frac{1}{2}x)$

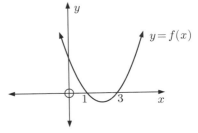

7

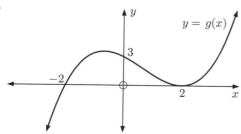

For the graph of $y = g(x)$ given, sketch the graph of:

a $y = g(x) + 2$ **b** $y = -g(x)$

c $y = g(-x)$ **d** $y = g(x + 1)$

8 For the graph of $y = h(x)$ given, sketch the graph of:

a $y = h(x) + 1$ **b** $y = \frac{1}{2}h(x)$

c $y = h(-x)$ **d** $y = h\left(\frac{x}{2}\right)$

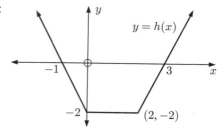

REVIEW SET 5A   NON-CALCULATOR

1 If $f(x) = x^2 - 2x$, find in simplest form:

   a $f(3)$ **b** $f(2x)$ **c** $f(-x)$ **d** $3f(x) - 2$

2 If $f(x) = 5 - x - x^2$, find in simplest form:

   a $f(-1)$ **b** $f(x - 1)$ **c** $f\left(\frac{x}{2}\right)$ **d** $2f(x) - f(-x)$

3 The graph of $f(x) = 3x^3 - 2x^2 + x + 2$ is translated to its image $g(x)$ by the vector $\binom{1}{-2}$. Write the equation of $g(x)$ in the form $g(x) = ax^3 + bx^2 + cx + d$.

4 The graph of $y = f(x)$ is shown alongside.
The x-axis is a tangent to $f(x)$ at $x = a$ and $f(x)$ cuts the x-axis at $x = b$.
On the same diagram, sketch the graph of $y = f(x - c)$ where $0 < c < b - a$.
Indicate the x-intercepts of $y = f(x - c)$.

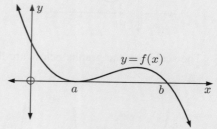

5 For the graph of $y = f(x)$, sketch graphs of:

   a $y = f(-x)$ **b** $y = -f(x)$

   c $y = f(x + 2)$ **d** $y = f(x) + 2$

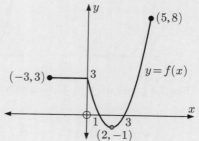

6 Consider the function $f : x \mapsto x^2$.
On the same set of axes graph:

   a $y = f(x)$ **b** $y = f(x - 1)$ **c** $y = 3f(x - 1)$ **d** $y = 3f(x - 1) + 2$

7 The graph of $y = f(x)$ is shown alongside.

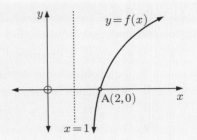

   a Sketch the graph of $y = g(x)$ where
$g(x) = f(x + 3) - 1$.

   b State the equation of the vertical asymptote of
$y = g(x)$.

   c Identify the point A′ on the graph of
$y = g(x)$ which corresponds to point A.

REVIEW SET 5B   CALCULATOR

1 Use your calculator to help graph $f(x) = (x + 1)^2 - 4$. Include all axes intercepts, and the coordinates of the turning point of the function.

2 Consider the function $f : x \mapsto x^2$. On the same set of axes graph:

   a $y = f(x)$ **b** $y = f(x + 2)$ **c** $y = 2f(x + 2)$ **d** $y = 2f(x + 2) - 3$

3 Consider $f : x \mapsto \dfrac{2^x}{x}$.

   a Does the function have any axes intercepts?

   b Find the equations of the asymptotes of the function.

   c Find any turning points of the function.

   d Sketch the function for $-4 \leqslant x \leqslant 4$.

4 Consider $f : x \mapsto 2^{-x}$.

   a Use your calculator to help graph the function.

   b True or false?

      i As $x \to \infty$, $2^{-x} \to 0$.   **ii** As $x \to -\infty$, $2^{-x} \to 0$.

      iii The y-intercept is $\frac{1}{2}$.   **iv** $2^{-x} > 0$ for all x.

5 The graph of the function $f(x) = (x + 1)^2 + 4$ is translated 2 units to the right and 4 units up.

   a Find the function $g(x)$ corresponding to the translated graph.

   b State the range of $f(x)$.

   c State the range of $g(x)$.

6 For each of the following functions:

      i Find $y = f(x)$, the result when the function is translated by $\begin{pmatrix} 1 \\ -2 \end{pmatrix}$.

      ii Sketch the original function and its translated function on the same set of axes. Clearly state any asymptotes of each function.

      iii State the domain and range of each function.

   a $y = \dfrac{1}{x}$ **b** $y = 2^x$ **c** $y = \log_4 x$

7 Sketch the graph of $f(x) = x^2 + 1$, and on the same set of axes sketch the graphs of:

   a $-f(x)$ **b** $f(2x)$ **c** $f(x) + 3$

REVIEW SET 5C

1 Consider the graph of $y = f(x)$ shown.

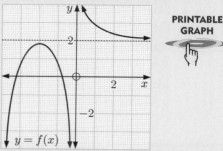

PRINTABLE GRAPH

 a Use the graph to determine:
   i the coordinates of the turning point
   ii the equation of the vertical asymptote
   iii the equation of the horizontal asymptote
   iv the x-intercepts.

 b Graph the function $g : x \mapsto x + 1$ on the same set of axes.

 c Hence estimate the coordinates of the points of intersection of $y = f(x)$ and $y = g(x)$.

2 Sketch the graph of $f(x) = -x^2$, and on the same set of axes sketch the graph of:

 a $y = f(-x)$ 　　 **b** $y = -f(x)$ 　　 **c** $y = f(2x)$ 　　 **d** $y = f(x - 2)$

3 The graph of a cubic function $y = f(x)$ is shown alongside.

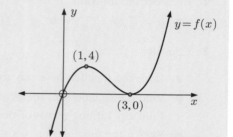

 a Sketch the graph of $g(x) = -f(x - 1)$.

 b State the coordinates of the turning points of $y = g(x)$.

4 The graph of $f(x) = x^2$ is transformed to the graph of $g(x)$ by a reflection and a translation as illustrated. Find the formula for $g(x)$ in the form $g(x) = ax^2 + bx + c$.

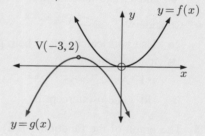

5 Given the graph of $y = f(x)$, sketch graphs of:

 a $f(-x)$ 　　　　 **b** $f(x + 1)$

 c $f(x) - 3$.

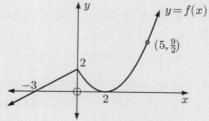

6 The graph of $f(x) = x^3 + 3x^2 - x + 4$ is translated to its image $y = g(x)$ by the vector $\binom{-1}{3}$. Write the equation of $g(x)$ in the form $g(x) = ax^3 + bx^2 + cx + d$.

7 **a** Find the equation of the line that results when the line $f(x) = 3x + 2$ is translated:
   i 2 units to the left 　　　　 **ii** 6 units upwards.

 b Show that when the linear function $f(x) = ax + b$, $a > 0$ is translated k units to the left, the resulting line is the same as when $f(x)$ is translated ka units upwards.

Chapter

6

Sequences and series

Syllabus reference: 1.1

Contents:

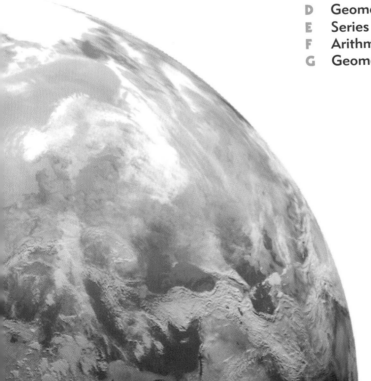

OPENING PROBLEM   THE LEGEND OF SISSA IBN DAHIR

Around 1260 AD, the Kurdish historian Ibn Khallikan recorded the following story about Sissa ibn Dahir and a chess game against the Indian King Shihram. (The story is also told in the Legend of the Ambalappuzha Paal Payasam, where the Lord Krishna takes the place of Sissa ibn Dahir, and they play a game of chess with the prize of rice grains rather than wheat.)

King Shihram was a tyrant king, and his subject Sissa ibn Dahir wanted to teach him how important all of his people were. He invented the game of chess for the king, and the king was greatly impressed. He insisted on Sissa ibn Dahir naming his reward, and the wise man asked for one grain of wheat for the first square, two grains of wheat for the second square, four grains of wheat for the third square, and so on, doubling the wheat on each successive square on the board.

The king laughed at first and agreed, for there was so little grain on the first few squares. By halfway he was surprised at the amount of grain being paid, and soon he realised his great error: that he owed more grain than there was in the world.

Things to think about:

a How can we describe the number of grains of wheat for each square?

b What expression gives the number of grains of wheat for the nth square?

c Find the total number of grains of wheat that the king owed.

To help understand problems like the **Opening Problem**, we need to study **sequences** and their sums which are called **series**.

A   NUMBER SEQUENCES

In mathematics it is important that we can:
- **recognise** a pattern in a set of numbers,
- **describe** the pattern in words, and
- **continue** the pattern.

A **number sequence** is an ordered list of numbers defined by a rule.

The numbers in the sequence are said to be its **members** or its **terms**.

A sequence which continues forever is called an **infinite sequence**.

A sequence which terminates is called a **finite sequence**.

For example,   3, 7, 11, 15, ...   form an infinite number sequence.

The first term is 3, the second term is 7, the third term is 11, and so on.

We can describe this pattern in words:

 "The sequence starts at 3 and each term is 4 more than the previous term."

Thus, the fifth term is 19 and the sixth term is 23.

The sequence   3, 7, 11, 15, 19, 23   which terminates with the sixth term, is a finite number sequence.

Example 1	◀ Self Tutor

Describe the sequence: 14, 17, 20, 23, ...   and write down the next two terms.

The sequence starts at 14, and each term is 3 more than the previous term.

The next two terms are 26 and 29.

EXERCISE 6A

1 Write down the first four terms of the sequence if you start with:
   a 4 and add 9 each time
   b 45 and subtract 6 each time
   c 2 and multiply by 3 each time
   d 96 and divide by 2 each time.

2 For each of the following write a description of the sequence and find the next 2 terms:
   a 8, 16, 24, 32, ...
   b 2, 5, 8, 11, ...
   c 36, 31, 26, 21, ...
   d 96, 89, 82, 75, ...
   e 1, 4, 16, 64, ...
   f 2, 6, 18, 54, ...
   g 480, 240, 120, 60, ...
   h 243, 81, 27, 9, ...
   i 50 000, 10 000, 2000, 400, ...

3 Describe the following number patterns and write down the next 3 terms:
   a 1, 4, 9, 16, ...
   b 1, 8, 27, 64, ...
   c 2, 6, 12, 20, ...

4 Find the next two terms of:
   a 95, 91, 87, 83, ...
   b 5, 20, 80, 320, ...
   c 1, 16, 81, 256, ...
   d 2, 3, 5, 7, 11, ...
   e 2, 4, 7, 11, ...
   f 9, 8, 10, 7, 11, ...

B   THE GENERAL TERM OF A NUMBER SEQUENCE

Sequences may be defined in one of the following ways:

- listing all terms (of a finite sequence)
- listing the first few terms and assuming that the pattern represented continues indefinitely
- giving a description in words
- using a formula which represents the **general term** or **nth term**.

Consider the illustrated tower of bricks. The first row has three bricks, the second row has four bricks, and the third row has five bricks.

If u_n represents the number of bricks in row n (from the top) then $u_1 = 3$, $u_2 = 4$, $u_3 = 5$, $u_4 = 6$, ...

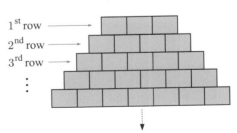

1st row
2nd row
3rd row

This sequence can be specified by:

- **listing terms**   3, 4, 5, 6, ...

- **using words**   "The top row has three bricks and each successive row under it has one more brick than the previous row."

- **using an explicit formula** $u_n = n + 2$ is the **general term** or **nth term** formula for $n = 1, 2, 3, 4, ...$

     Check: $u_1 = 1 + 2 = 3$ ✓ $u_2 = 2 + 2 = 4$ ✓
          $u_3 = 3 + 2 = 5$ ✓

- **a pictorial or graphical representation**

   Early members of a sequence can be graphed with each represented by a dot.

   The dots *must not* be joined because n must be an integer.

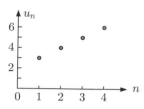

THE GENERAL TERM

The **general term** or ***n*th term** of a sequence is represented by a symbol with a subscript, for example u_n, T_n, t_n, or A_n. The general term is defined for $n = 1, 2, 3, 4, ...$

$\{u_n\}$ represents the sequence that can be generated by using u_n as the nth term.

The general term u_n is a function where $n \mapsto u_n$. The domain is $n \in \mathbb{Z}^+$ for an infinite sequence, or a subset of $\mathbb{Z}^+$ for a finite sequence.

For example, $\{2n + 1\}$ generates the sequence $3, 5, 7, 9, 11, ...$

EXERCISE 6B

1   A sequence is defined by $u_n = 3n - 2$. Find:

   a u_1 **b** u_5 **c** u_{27}

2   Consider the sequence defined by $u_n = 2n + 5$.

   a Find the first four terms of the sequence.   **b** Display these members on a graph.

3   Evaluate the first *five* terms of the sequence:

   a $\{2n\}$ **b** $\{2n + 2\}$ **c** $\{2n - 1\}$ **d** $\{2n - 3\}$

   e $\{2n + 3\}$ **f** $\{2n + 11\}$ **g** $\{3n + 1\}$ **h** $\{4n - 3\}$

4   Evaluate the first *five* terms of the sequence:

   a $\{2^n\}$ **b** $\{3 \times 2^n\}$ **c** $\{6 \times (\frac{1}{2})^n\}$ **d** $\{(-2)^n\}$

5   Evaluate the first *five* terms of the sequence $\{15 - (-2)^n\}$.

You can use technology to help generate sequences from a formula.

Click on the appropriate icon for instructions.

GRAPHICS CALCULATOR INSTRUCTIONS

RESEARCH   **THE FIBONACCI SEQUENCE**

Leonardo Pisano Bigollo, known commonly as Fibonacci, was born in Pisa around 1170 AD. He is best known for the **Fibonacci sequence** $0, 1, 1, 2, 3, 5, 8, 13, 21, ...$ which starts with 0 and 1, and then each subsequent member of the sequence is the sum of the preceding two members.

1   Where do we see the Fibonacci sequence in nature?

2   Can we write a formula for the general term u_n of the Fibonacci sequence? How else can the Fibonacci sequence be described using symbols?

C   ARITHMETIC SEQUENCES

> An **arithmetic sequence** is a sequence in which each term differs from the previous one by the same fixed number.
>
> It can also be referred to as an **arithmetic progression**.

For example:

- the tower of bricks in the previous section forms an arithmetic sequence where the difference between terms is 1
- 2, 5, 8, 11, 14, ... is arithmetic as $5 - 2 = 8 - 5 = 11 - 8 = 14 - 11 = $ ....
- 31, 27, 23, 19, ... is arithmetic as $27 - 31 = 23 - 27 = 19 - 23 = $ ....

ALGEBRAIC DEFINITION

> $\{u_n\}$ is **arithmetic** $\Leftrightarrow u_{n+1} - u_n = d$ for all positive integers n where d is a constant called the **common difference**.

The symbol $\Leftrightarrow$ means 'if and only if'. It implies both:

- if $\{u_n\}$ is arithmetic then $u_{n+1} - u_n$ is a constant
- if $u_{n+1} - u_n$ is a constant then $\{u_n\}$ is arithmetic.

THE NAME 'ARITHMETIC'

If a, b and c are any consecutive terms of an arithmetic sequence then

$$b - a = c - b \quad \{\text{equating common differences}\}$$
$$\therefore \ 2b = a + c$$
$$\therefore \ b = \frac{a + c}{2}$$

So, the middle term is the **arithmetic mean** of the terms on either side of it.

THE GENERAL TERM FORMULA

Suppose the first term of an arithmetic sequence is u_1 and the common difference is d.

Then $u_2 = u_1 + d$, $u_3 = u_1 + 2d$, $u_4 = u_1 + 3d$,   and so on.

Hence $u_n = u_1 + \underbrace{(n - 1)}\, d$

term number

the coefficient of d is
one less than the term number

> For an **arithmetic sequence** with **first term u_1** and **common difference d** the **general term** or **nth term** is $u_n = u_1 + (n - 1)d.$

Example 2   🔊 **Self Tutor**

Consider the sequence   2, 9, 16, 23, 30, ...

  a Show that the sequence is arithmetic.

  b Find a formula for the general term u_n.

  c Find the 100th term of the sequence.

  d Is   i 828   ii 2341   a term of the sequence?

a $9 - 2 = 7$	The difference between successive terms is constant.
$16 - 9 = 7$	So, the sequence is arithmetic, with $u_1 = 2$ and $d = 7$.
$23 - 16 = 7$	
$30 - 23 = 7$	

b $u_n = u_1 + (n - 1)d$ **c** If $n = 100$,

$\therefore \ u_n = 2 + 7(n - 1)$ $u_{100} = 7(100) - 5$

$\therefore \ u_n = 7n - 5$ $= 695$

d   **i**   Let $u_n = 828$ **ii**   Let $u_n = 2341$

$\therefore \ 7n - 5 = 828$ $\therefore \ 7n - 5 = 2341$

$\therefore \ \ 7n = 833$ $\therefore \ \ 7n = 2346$

$\therefore \ \ n = 119$ $\therefore \ \ n = 335\tfrac{1}{7}$

$\therefore$ 828 is a term of the sequence,   But n must be an integer, so 2341

and in fact is the 119th term.   is not a member of the sequence.

EXERCISE 6C.1

1 Find the 10th term of each of the following arithmetic sequences:

  a 19, 25, 31, 37, ...   b 101, 97, 93, 89, ...   c 8, $9\tfrac{1}{2}$, 11, $12\tfrac{1}{2}$, ...

2 Find the 15th term of each of the following arithmetic sequences:

  a 31, 36, 41, 46, ...   b 5, −3, −11, −19, ...   c $a, a + d, a + 2d, a + 3d$, ...

3 Consider the sequence   6, 17, 28, 39, 50, ...

  a Show that the sequence is arithmetic.   b Find the formula for its general term.

  c Find its 50th term.   d Is 325 a member?

  e Is 761 a member?

4 Consider the sequence   87, 83, 79, 75, 71, ...

  a Show that the sequence is arithmetic.   b Find the formula for its general term.

  c Find the 40th term.   d Which term of the sequence is −297?

5 A sequence is defined by $u_n = 3n - 2$.

  a Prove that the sequence is arithmetic.   **Hint:** Find $u_{n+1} - u_n$.

  b Find u_1 and d.   c Find the 57th term.

  d What is the largest term of the sequence that is smaller than 450? Which term is this?

6 A sequence is defined by $u_n = \dfrac{71 - 7n}{2}$.

  a Prove that the sequence is arithmetic.   b Find u_1 and d.   c Find u_{75}.

  d For what values of n are the terms of the sequence less than −200?

Example 3 ◀)) *Self Tutor*

Find k given that $3k + 1$, k, and -3 are consecutive terms of an arithmetic sequence.

Since the terms are consecutive, $\quad k - (3k + 1) = -3 - k \quad$ {equating differences}
$$\therefore \quad k - 3k - 1 = -3 - k$$
$$\therefore \quad -2k - 1 = -3 - k$$
$$\therefore \quad -1 + 3 = -k + 2k$$
$$\therefore \quad k = 2$$

or   Since the middle term is the arithmetic mean of the terms on either side of it,

$$k = \frac{(3k + 1) + (-3)}{2}$$
$$\therefore \quad 2k = 3k - 2$$
$$\therefore \quad k = 2$$

7 Find k given the consecutive arithmetic terms:

   a $32, k, 3$
   b $k, 7, 10$
   c $k + 1, 2k + 1, 13$

   d $k - 1, 2k + 3, 7 - k$
   e $k, k^2, k^2 + 6$
   f $5, k, k^2 - 8$

Example 4 ◀)) *Self Tutor*

Find the general term u_n for an arithmetic sequence with $u_3 = 8$ and $u_8 = -17$.

$u_3 = 8 \qquad \therefore \quad u_1 + 2d = 8 \qquad$ .... (1) $\qquad$ {using $u_n = u_1 + (n - 1)d$}
$u_8 = -17 \quad \therefore \quad u_1 + 7d = -17 \qquad$ .... (2)

We now solve (1) and (2) simultaneously:

$$-u_1 - 2d = -8 \qquad \text{\{multiplying both sides of (1) by } -1\}$$
$$u_1 + 7d = -17$$
$$\therefore \quad 5d = -25 \qquad \text{\{adding the equations\}}$$
$$\therefore \quad d = -5$$

So, in (1): $\qquad u_1 + 2(-5) = 8 \qquad\qquad$ *Check:*
$$\therefore \quad u_1 - 10 = 8 \qquad\qquad u_3 = 23 - 5(3)$$
$$\therefore \quad u_1 = 18 \qquad\qquad\qquad = 23 - 15$$
$$\text{Now} \quad u_n = u_1 + (n - 1)d \qquad\qquad = 8 \;\checkmark$$
$$\therefore \quad u_n = 18 - 5(n - 1) \qquad u_8 = 23 - 5(8)$$
$$\therefore \quad u_n = 18 - 5n + 5 \qquad\qquad = 23 - 40$$
$$\therefore \quad u_n = 23 - 5n \qquad\qquad\quad = -17 \;\checkmark$$

8 Find the general term u_n for an arithmetic sequence with:

   a $u_7 = 41$ and $u_{13} = 77$
        b $u_5 = -2$ and $u_{12} = -12\frac{1}{2}$

   c seventh term 1 and fifteenth term -39

   d eleventh and eighth terms being -16 and $-11\frac{1}{2}$ respectively.

Example 5   ◄)) **Self Tutor**

Insert four numbers between 3 and 12 so that all six numbers are in arithmetic sequence.

Suppose the common difference is d.

$\therefore$ the numbers are   3, $3+d$, $3+2d$, $3+3d$, $3+4d$, and 12

$$\therefore \quad 3 + 5d = 12$$
$$\therefore \quad 5d = 9$$
$$\therefore \quad d = \tfrac{9}{5} = 1.8$$

So, the sequence is   3, 4.8, 6.6, 8.4, 10.2, 12.

9 **a** Insert three numbers between 5 and 10 so that all five numbers are in arithmetic sequence.

  b Insert six numbers between -1 and 32 so that all eight numbers are in arithmetic sequence.

10 Consider the arithmetic sequence   36, $35\tfrac{1}{3}$, $34\tfrac{2}{3}$, ...

  a Find u_1 and d.   **b** Which term of the sequence is -30?

11 An arithmetic sequence starts 23, 36, 49, 62, ...   What is the first term of the sequence to exceed 100 000?

ARITHMETIC SEQUENCE PROBLEMS

Example 6   ◄)) **Self Tutor**

Ryan is a cartoonist. His comic strip has just been bought by a newspaper, so he sends them the 28 comic strips he has drawn so far. Each week after the first he mails 3 more comic strips to the newspaper.

  a Find the total number of comic strips sent after 1, 2, 3, and 4 weeks.
  b Show that the total number of comic strips sent after n weeks forms an arithmetic sequence.
  c Find the number of comic strips sent after 15 weeks.
  d When does Ryan send his 120th comic strip?

  a *Week 1:*   28 comic strips   *Week 3:* $31+3=34$ comic strips
     Week 2: $28+3=31$ comic strips   *Week 4:* $34+3=37$ comic strips

  b Every week, Ryan sends 3 comic strips, so the difference between successive weeks is always 3. We have an arithmetic sequence with $u_1 = 28$ and common difference $d = 3$.

  c $u_n = u_1 + (n-1)d$
     $ = 28 + (n-1) \times 3$ $\therefore \quad u_{15} = 25 + 3 \times 15$
     $ = 25 + 3n$ $\phantom{\therefore \quad u_{15}} = 70$

   After 15 weeks Ryan has sent 70 comic strips.

  d We want to find n such that $u_n = 120$
        $\therefore \quad 25 + 3n = 120$
        $\therefore \quad 3n = 95$
        $\therefore \quad n = 31\tfrac{2}{3}$

   Ryan sends the 120th comic strip in the 32nd week.

EXERCISE 6C.2

1   A luxury car manufacturer sets up a factory for a new model. In the first month only 5 cars are produced. After this, 13 cars are assembled every month.

   a   List the total number of cars that have been made in the factory by the end of each of the first six months.

   b   Explain why the total number of cars made after n months forms an arithmetic sequence.

   c   How many cars are made in the first year?

   d   How long is it until the 250th car is manufactured?

2   Valéria joins a social networking website. After 1 week she has 34 online friends. At the end of 2 weeks she has 41 friends, after 3 weeks she has 48 friends, and after 4 weeks she has 55 friends.

   a   Show that Valéria's number of friends forms an arithmetic sequence.

   b   Assuming the pattern continues, find the number of online friends Valéria will have after 12 weeks.

   c   After how many weeks will Valéria have 150 online friends?

3   A farmer feeds his cattle herd with hay every day in July. The amount of hay in his barn at the end of day n is given by the arithmetic sequence $u_n = 100 - 2.7n$ tonnes.

   a   Write down the amount of hay in the barn on the first three days of July.

   b   Find and interpret the common difference.

   c   Find and interpret u_{25}.

   d   How much hay is in the barn at the beginning of August?

D   GEOMETRIC SEQUENCES

A sequence is **geometric** if each term can be obtained from the previous one by multiplying by the same non-zero constant.

A geometric sequence is also referred to as a **geometric progression**.

For example: 2, 10, 50, 250, ...   is a geometric sequence as each term can be obtained by multiplying the previous term by 5.

Notice that $\frac{10}{2} = \frac{50}{10} = \frac{250}{50} = 5$,   so each term divided by the previous one gives the same constant.

ALGEBRAIC DEFINITION

$\{u_n\}$ is **geometric** $\Leftrightarrow$ $\dfrac{u_{n+1}}{u_n} = r$ for all positive integers n where r is a constant called the **common ratio**.

For example:
   • 2, 10, 50, 250, ...   is geometric with $r = 5$.
   • 2, −10, 50, −250, ...   is geometric with $r = -5$.

THE NAME 'GEOMETRIC'

If a, b, and c are any consecutive terms of a geometric sequence then $\dfrac{b}{a} = \dfrac{c}{b}$.

$\therefore$ $b^2 = ac$ and so $b = \pm\sqrt{ac}$ where $\sqrt{ac}$ is the **geometric mean** of a and c.

THE GENERAL TERM FORMULA

Suppose the first term of a geometric sequence is u_1 and the common ratio is r.

Then $u_2 = u_1 r$, $u_3 = u_1 r^2$, $u_4 = u_1 r^3$,   and so on.

Hence $u_n = u_1 r^{n-1}$

term number   The power of r is one less than the term number.

> For a **geometric sequence** with **first term u_1** and **common ratio r**,
> the **general term** or **nth term** is $u_n = u_1 r^{n-1}$.

Example 7
◀) Self Tutor

Consider the sequence 8, 4, 2, 1, $\frac{1}{2}$, ...

a Show that the sequence is geometric.   **b** Find the general term u_n.

c Hence, find the 12th term as a fraction.

a $\dfrac{4}{8} = \dfrac{1}{2}$ $\dfrac{2}{4} = \dfrac{1}{2}$ $\dfrac{1}{2} = \dfrac{1}{2}$ $\dfrac{\frac{1}{2}}{1} = \dfrac{1}{2}$

Consecutive terms have a common ratio of $\frac{1}{2}$.

$\therefore$ the sequence is geometric with $u_1 = 8$ and $r = \frac{1}{2}$.

b $u_n = u_1 r^{n-1}$

$\therefore$ $u_n = 8 \left(\frac{1}{2}\right)^{n-1}$ or $u_n = 2^3 \times (2^{-1})^{n-1}$

$\qquad\qquad\qquad\qquad\qquad = 2^3 \times 2^{-n+1}$

$\qquad\qquad\qquad\qquad\qquad = 2^{3+(-n+1)}$

$\qquad\qquad\qquad\qquad\qquad = 2^{4-n}$

c $u_{12} = 8 \times \left(\frac{1}{2}\right)^{11}$

$\qquad = \frac{1}{256}$

EXERCISE 6D.1

1 For the geometric sequence with first two terms given, find b and c:

  a 2, 6, b, c, ...   **b** 10, 5, b, c, ...   **c** 12, -6, b, c, ...

2 Find the 6th term in each of the following geometric sequences:

  a 3, 6, 12, 24, ...   **b** 2, 10, 50, ...   **c** 512, 256, 128, ...

3 Find the 9th term in each of the following geometric sequences:

  a 1, 3, 9, 27, ...   **b** 12, 18, 27, ...   **c** $\frac{1}{16}$, $-\frac{1}{8}$, $\frac{1}{4}$, $-\frac{1}{2}$, ...   **d** a, ar, ar^2, ...

4 **a** Show that the sequence 5, 10, 20, 40, ...   is geometric.

  b Find u_n and hence find the 15th term.

5 **a** Show that the sequence $12, -6, 3, -\frac{3}{2}, \ldots$ is geometric.

    b Find u_n and hence write the 13th term as a rational number.

6 Show that the sequence $8, -6, 4.5, -3.375, \ldots$ is geometric. Hence find the 10th term as a decimal.

7 Show that the sequence $8, 4\sqrt{2}, 4, 2\sqrt{2}, \ldots$ is geometric. Hence show that the general term of the sequence is $u_n = 2^{\frac{7}{2} - \frac{1}{2}n}$.

Example 8 ◀ **Self Tutor**

$k - 1$, $2k$, and $21 - k$ are consecutive terms of a geometric sequence. Find k.

Since the terms are geometric, $\quad \dfrac{2k}{k - 1} = \dfrac{21 - k}{2k} \quad$ {equating the common ratio r}

$$\therefore \quad 4k^2 = (21 - k)(k - 1)$$
$$\therefore \quad 4k^2 = 21k - 21 - k^2 + k$$
$$\therefore \quad 5k^2 - 22k + 21 = 0$$
$$\therefore \quad (5k - 7)(k - 3) = 0$$
$$\therefore \quad k = \tfrac{7}{5} \text{ or } 3$$

Check: If $k = \frac{7}{5}$ the terms are: $\frac{2}{5}, \frac{14}{5}, \frac{98}{5}$. ✓ $\{r = 7\}$

       If $k = 3$ the terms are: $2, 6, 18$. ✓ $\{r = 3\}$

---

8 Find k given that the following are consecutive terms of a geometric sequence:

    a $7, k, 28$ **b** $k, 3k, 20 - k$ **c** $k, k + 8, 9k$

Example 9 ◀ **Self Tutor**

A geometric sequence has $u_2 = -6$ and $u_5 = 162$. Find its general term.

$$u_2 = u_1 r = -6 \quad \ldots \text{ (1)}$$
$$\text{and} \quad u_5 = u_1 r^4 = 162 \quad \ldots \text{ (2)}$$
$$\text{Now} \quad \frac{u_1 r^4}{u_1 r} = \frac{162}{-6} \quad \{(2) \div (1)\}$$
$$\therefore \quad r^3 = -27$$
$$\therefore \quad r = \sqrt[3]{-27}$$
$$\therefore \quad r = -3$$
$$\text{Using (1),} \quad u_1(-3) = -6$$
$$\therefore \quad u_1 = 2$$
$$\text{Thus} \quad u_n = 2 \times (-3)^{n-1}.$$

---

9 Find the general term u_n of the geometric sequence which has:

    a $u_4 = 24$ and $u_7 = 192$ **b** $u_3 = 8$ and $u_6 = -1$

    c $u_7 = 24$ and $u_{15} = 384$ **d** $u_3 = 5$ and $u_7 = \frac{5}{4}$

Example 10   Self Tutor

Find the first term of the sequence $6, 6\sqrt{2}, 12, 12\sqrt{2}, ...$ which exceeds 1400.

The sequence is geometric with $u_1 = 6$ and $r = \sqrt{2}$

$$\therefore \ u_n = 6 \times (\sqrt{2})^{n-1}.$$

We need to find n such that $u_n > 1400$.

Using a graphics calculator with $Y_1 = 6 \times (\sqrt{2})^{\wedge}(X - 1),$ we view a *table of values*:

Casio fx-CG20	TI-84 Plus	TI-*n*spire
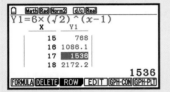	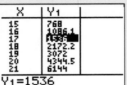	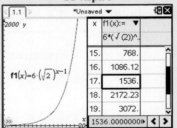

The first term to exceed 1400 is $u_{17} = 1536$.

---

10 **a** Find the first term of the sequence $2, 6, 18, 54, ...$ which exceeds $10\,000$.

  b Find the first term of the sequence $4, 4\sqrt{3}, 12, 12\sqrt{3}, ...$ which exceeds 4800.

  c Find the first term of the sequence $12, 6, 3, 1.5, ...$ which is less than 0.0001.

GEOMETRIC SEQUENCE PROBLEMS

Problems of **growth** and **decay** involve repeated multiplications by a constant number. We can therefore use geometric sequences to model these situations.

Example 11   Self Tutor

The initial population of rabbits on a farm was 50.
The population increased by 7% each week.

  a How many rabbits were present after:

   i 15 weeks   **ii** 30 weeks?

  b How long would it take for the population to reach 500?

There is a fixed percentage increase each week, so the population forms a geometric sequence.

$u_1 = 50$ and $r = 1.07$

$u_2 = 50 \times 1.07^1 =$ the population after 1 week

$u_3 = 50 \times 1.07^2 =$ the population after 2 weeks

$\vdots$

$u_{n+1} = 50 \times 1.07^n =$ the population after n weeks.

a **i** $u_{16} = 50 \times (1.07)^{15}$
≈ 137.95
There were 138 rabbits.

ii $u_{31} = 50 \times (1.07)^{30}$
≈ 380.61
There were 381 rabbits.

b We need to solve $50 \times (1.07)^n = 500$
$\therefore \quad (1.07)^n = 10$
$\therefore \quad n = \dfrac{\ln 10}{\ln(1.07)} \approx 34.03$

or **trial and error** on your calculator gives $n \approx 34$ weeks.

or finding the **point of intersection** of $Y_1 = 50 \times 1.07^{\wedge}X$ and $Y_2 = 500$, the solution is ≈ 34.0 weeks.

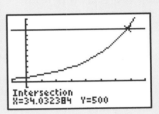

The population will reach 500 early in the 35th week.

EXERCISE 6D.2

1 A nest of ants initially contains 500 individuals. The population is increasing by 12% each week.

  a How many ants will there be after:

    i 10 weeks   **ii** 20 weeks?

  b Use technology to find how many weeks it will take for the ant population to reach 2000.

2 The animal *Eraticus* is endangered. Since 1995 there has only been one colony remaining, and in 1995 the population of the colony was 555. The population has been steadily decreasing by 4.5% per year.

  a Find the population in the year 2010.

  b In which year would we expect the population to have declined to 50?

3

A herd of 32 deer is to be left unchecked on a large island off the coast of Alaska. It is estimated that the size of the herd will increase each year by 18%.

  a Estimate the size of the herd after:

    i 5 years   **ii** 10 years.

  b How long will it take for the herd size to reach 5000?

4 An endangered species of marsupials has a population of 178. However, with a successful breeding program it is expected to increase by 32% each year.

  a Find the expected population size after: **i** 10 years   **ii** 25 years.

  b How long will it take for the population to reach 10 000?

COMPOUND INTEREST

Suppose you invest $1000 in the bank. You leave the money in the bank for 3 years, and are paid an interest rate of 10% per annum (p.a.). The interest is added to your investment each year, so the total value *increases*.

per annum means each year

The percentage increase each year is 10%, so at the end of the year you will have $100\% + 10\% = 110\%$ of the value at its start. This corresponds to a *multiplier* of 1.1 .

After one year your investment is worth $\$1000 \times 1.1 = \$1100$.

After two years it is worth
$$\$1100 \times 1.1$$
$$= \$1000 \times 1.1 \times 1.1$$
$$= \$1000 \times (1.1)^2 = \$1210$$

After three years it is worth
$$\$1210 \times 1.1$$
$$= \$1000 \times (1.1)^2 \times 1.1$$
$$= \$1000 \times (1.1)^3 = \$1331$$

This suggests that if the money is left in your account for n years it would amount to $\$1000 \times (1.1)^n$.

Observe that:

$u_1 = \$1000$	$=$ initial investment
$u_2 = u_1 \times 1.1$	$=$ amount after 1 year
$u_3 = u_1 \times (1.1)^2$	$=$ amount after 2 years
$u_4 = u_1 \times (1.1)^3$	$=$ amount after 3 years
$\vdots$	
$u_{n+1} = u_1 \times (1.1)^n$	$=$ amount after n years

THE COMPOUND INTEREST FORMULA

We can calculate the value of a compounding investment using the formula
$$u_{n+1} = u_1 \times r^n$$

where
$u_1 =$ initial investment
$r =$ growth multiplier for each period
$n =$ number of compounding periods
$u_{n+1} =$ amount after n compounding periods.

Example 12   ◀) **Self Tutor**

$5000 is invested for 4 years at 7% p.a. compound interest, compounded annually. What will it amount to at the end of this period? Give your answer to the nearest cent.

$u_5 = u_1 \times r^4$ is the amount after 4 years

$= 5000 \times (1.07)^4$ {for a 7% increase 100% becomes 107%}

≈ 6553.98

The investment will amount to $6553.98.

EXERCISE 6D.3

1 **a** What will an investment of $3000 at 10% p.a. compound interest amount to after 3 years?

   b How much of this is interest?

2 How much compound interest is earned by investing €20 000 at 12% p.a. if the investment is over a 4 year period?

3 **a** What will an investment of ¥30 000 at 10% p.a. compound interest amount to after 4 years?

   b How much of this is interest?

4 How much compound interest is earned by investing $80 000 at 9% p.a. if the investment is over a 3 year period?

5 What will an investment of ¥100 000 amount to after 5 years if it earns 8% p.a. compounded twice annually?

6 What will an investment of £45 000 amount to after 21 months if it earns 7.5% p.a. compounded quarterly?

Example 13
🔊 **Self Tutor**

How much should I invest now if I need a maturing value of €10 000 in 4 years' time, and I am able to invest at 8% p.a. compounded twice annually? Give your answer to the nearest cent.

The initial investment u_1 is unknown.

The investment is compounded twice annually, so the multiplier $r = 1 + \dfrac{0.08}{2} = 1.04$.

There are $4 \times 2 = 8$ compounding periods, so $n = 8$

$$\therefore \quad u_{n+1} = u_9$$

Now $\quad u_9 = u_1 \times r^8 \qquad \{\text{using} \quad u_{n+1} = u_1 \times r^n\}$

$\therefore \quad 10\,000 = u_1 \times (1.04)^8$

$\therefore \quad u_1 = \dfrac{10\,000}{(1.04)^8}$

$\therefore \quad u_1 \approx 7306.90$

I should invest €7306.90 now.

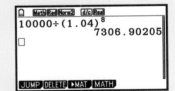

---

7 How much money must be invested now if you require $20 000 for a holiday in 4 years' time and the money can be invested at a fixed rate of 7.5% p.a. compounded annually?

8 What initial investment is required to produce a maturing amount of £15 000 in 60 months' time given a guaranteed fixed interest rate of 5.5% p.a. compounded annually?

9 How much should I invest now to yield €25 000 in 3 years' time, if the money can be invested at a fixed rate of 8% p.a. compounded quarterly?

10 What initial investment will yield ¥40 000 in 8 years' time if your money can be invested at 9% p.a. compounded monthly?

E

SERIES

A **series** is the sum of the terms of a sequence.

For the **finite** sequence $\{u_n\}$ with n terms, the corresponding series is $u_1 + u_2 + u_3 + ... + u_n$.

The sum of this series is $S_n = u_1 + u_2 + u_3 + ... + u_n$ and this will always be a finite real number.

For the **infinite** sequence $\{u_n\}$, the corresponding series is $u_1 + u_2 + u_3 + ... + u_n + ...$

In many cases, the sum of an infinite series cannot be calculated. In some cases, however, it does converge to a finite number.

SIGMA NOTATION

$u_1 + u_2 + u_3 + u_4 + ... + u_n$ can be written more compactly using **sigma notation**.

The symbol $\sum$ is called **sigma**. It is the equivalent of capital S in the Greek alphabet.

We write $u_1 + u_2 + u_3 + u_4 + ... + u_n$ as $\displaystyle\sum_{k=1}^{n} u_k$.

$\displaystyle\sum_{k=1}^{n} u_k$ reads "the sum of all numbers of the form u_k where $k = 1, 2, 3, ...,$ up to n".

Example 14
◀) **Self Tutor**

Consider the sequence $1, 4, 9, 16, 25, ...$

a Write down an expression for S_n.

b Find S_n for $n = 1, 2, 3, 4$, and 5.

a $S_n = 1^2 + 2^2 + 3^2 + 4^2 + ... + n^2$

    {all terms are squares}

$= \displaystyle\sum_{k=1}^{n} k^2$

b $S_1 = 1$

$S_2 = 1 + 4 = 5$

$S_3 = 1 + 4 + 9 = 14$

$S_4 = 1 + 4 + 9 + 16 = 30$

$S_5 = 1 + 4 + 9 + 16 + 25 = 55$

Example 15
◀) **Self Tutor**

Expand and evaluate: **a** $\displaystyle\sum_{k=1}^{7} (k+1)$ **b** $\displaystyle\sum_{k=1}^{5} \frac{1}{2^k}$

a $\displaystyle\sum_{k=1}^{7} (k+1)$

$= 2 + 3 + 4 + 5 + 6 + 7 + 8$

$= 35$

b $\displaystyle\sum_{k=1}^{5} \frac{1}{2^k}$

$= \dfrac{1}{2} + \dfrac{1}{4} + \dfrac{1}{8} + \dfrac{1}{16} + \dfrac{1}{32}$

$= \dfrac{31}{32}$

You can also use technology to evaluate the sum of a series in sigma notation. Click on the icon for instructions.

GRAPHICS
CALCULATOR
INSTRUCTIONS

PROPERTIES OF SIGMA NOTATION

$$\sum_{k=1}^{n} (a_k + b_k) = \sum_{k=1}^{n} a_k + \sum_{k=1}^{n} b_k$$

If c is a constant, $\displaystyle\sum_{k=1}^{n} ca_k = c \sum_{k=1}^{n} a_k$ and $\displaystyle\sum_{k=1}^{n} c = cn.$

EXERCISE 6E

1   For the following sequences:

   i   write down an expression for S_n **ii**   find S_5.

   a   3, 11, 19, 27, ...   **b**   42, 37, 32, 27, ...   **c**   12, 6, 3, $1\frac{1}{2}$, ...

   d   2, 3, $4\frac{1}{2}$, $6\frac{3}{4}$, ...   **e**   1, $\frac{1}{2}$, $\frac{1}{4}$, $\frac{1}{8}$, ...   **f**   1, 8, 27, 64, ...

2   Expand and evaluate:

   a $\displaystyle\sum_{k=1}^{3} 4k$ **b** $\displaystyle\sum_{k=1}^{6} (k+1)$ **c** $\displaystyle\sum_{k=1}^{4} (3k-5)$

   d $\displaystyle\sum_{k=1}^{5} (11-2k)$ **e** $\displaystyle\sum_{k=1}^{7} k(k+1)$ **f** $\displaystyle\sum_{k=1}^{5} 10 \times 2^{k-1}$

3   For $u_n = 3n - 1$,   write $u_1 + u_2 + u_3 + ... + u_{20}$ using sigma notation and evaluate the sum.

4   Show that:

   a $\displaystyle\sum_{k=1}^{n} c = cn$ **b** $\displaystyle\sum_{k=1}^{n} ca_k = c \sum_{k=1}^{n} a_k$ **c** $\displaystyle\sum_{k=1}^{n} (a_k + b_k) = \sum_{k=1}^{n} a_k + \sum_{k=1}^{n} b_k$

5   **a**   Expand $\displaystyle\sum_{k=1}^{n} k.$

   b   Now write the sum with terms in the reverse order, placing each term under a term in the original expansion. Add each term with the one under it.

   c   Hence write an expression for the sum S_n of the first n integers.

   d   Hence find a and b if $\displaystyle\sum_{k=1}^{n} (ak + b) = 8n^2 + 11n$ for all positive integers n.

F   ARITHMETIC SERIES

An **arithmetic series** is the sum of the terms of an arithmetic sequence.

For example: 21, 23, 25, 27, ..., 49   is a finite arithmetic sequence.

21 + 23 + 25 + 27 + ... + 49   is the corresponding arithmetic series.

SUM OF A FINITE ARITHMETIC SERIES

If the first term is u_1 and the common difference is d, the terms are u_1, $u_1 + d$, $u_1 + 2d$, $u_1 + 3d$, and so on.

Suppose that u_n is the final term of an arithmetic series.

So, $S_n = u_1 + (u_1 + d) + (u_1 + 2d) + ... + (u_n - 2d) + (u_n - d) + u_n$

But $S_n = u_n + (u_n - d) + (u_n - 2d) + ... + (u_1 + 2d) + (u_1 + d) + u_1$ {reversing them}

Adding these two equations vertically we get

$$2S_n = \underbrace{(u_1 + u_n) + (u_1 + u_n) + (u_1 + u_n) + ... + (u_1 + u_n) + (u_1 + u_n) + (u_1 + u_n)}_{n \text{ of these}}$$

$\therefore$ $2S_n = n(u_1 + u_n)$

$\therefore$ $S_n = \dfrac{n}{2}(u_1 + u_n)$ where $u_n = u_1 + (n-1)d$

The sum of a finite arithmetic series with first term u_1, common difference d, and last term u_n, is

$$S_n = \frac{n}{2}(u_1 + u_n) \quad \text{or} \quad S_n = \frac{n}{2}(2u_1 + (n-1)d).$$

For example, from **Exercise 6E** question **5**, we observe that the sum of the first n integers is

$$1 + 2 + 3 + ... + n = \frac{n(n+1)}{2} \quad \text{for} \quad n \in \mathbb{Z}^+.$$

Example 16   ◀) **Self Tutor**

Find the sum of $4 + 7 + 10 + 13 + ...$ to 50 terms.

The series is arithmetic with $u_1 = 4$, $d = 3$ and $n = 50$.

Now $S_n = \dfrac{n}{2}(2u_1 + (n-1)d)$

$\therefore$ $S_{50} = \dfrac{50}{2}(2 \times 4 + 49 \times 3)$

$= 3875$

Example 17   ◀) **Self Tutor**

Find the sum of $-6 + 1 + 8 + 15 + ... + 141$.

The series is arithmetic with $u_1 = -6$, $d = 7$ and $u_n = 141$.

First we need to find n.

Now $u_n = 141$

$\therefore$ $u_1 + (n-1)d = 141$

$\therefore$ $-6 + 7(n-1) = 141$

$\therefore$ $7(n-1) = 147$

$\therefore$ $n - 1 = 21$

$\therefore$ $n = 22$

Using $S_n = \dfrac{n}{2}(u_1 + u_n)$,

$S_{22} = \dfrac{22}{2}(-6 + 141)$

$= 11 \times 135$

$= 1485$

You can also use technology to evaluate series, although for some calculator models this is tedious.

GRAPHICS CALCULATOR INSTRUCTIONS

EXERCISE 6F

1   Find the sum of:

    a $3 + 7 + 11 + 15 + ...$ to 20 terms
    b $\frac{1}{2} + 3 + 5\frac{1}{2} + 8 + ...$ to 50 terms

    c $100 + 93 + 86 + 79 + ...$ to 40 terms
    d $50 + 48\frac{1}{2} + 47 + 45\frac{1}{2} + ...$ to 80 terms.

2   Find the sum of:

    a $5 + 8 + 11 + 14 + ... + 101$
    b $50 + 49\frac{1}{2} + 49 + 48\frac{1}{2} + ... + (-20)$

    c $8 + 10\frac{1}{2} + 13 + 15\frac{1}{2} + ... + 83$

3   Evaluate these arithmetic series:

    a $\displaystyle\sum_{k=1}^{10} (2k + 5)$
    b $\displaystyle\sum_{k=1}^{15} (k - 50)$
    c $\displaystyle\sum_{k=1}^{20} \left(\frac{k + 3}{2}\right)$

    Hint: List the first 3 terms and the last term. Check your answers using technology.

4   An arithmetic series has seven terms. The first term is 5 and the last term is 53. Find the sum of the series.

5   An arithmetic series has eleven terms. The first term is 6 and the last term is -27. Find the sum of the series.

6   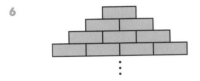 A bricklayer builds a triangular wall with layers of bricks as shown. If the bricklayer uses 171 bricks, how many layers did he build?

7   A soccer stadium has 25 sections of seating. Each section has 44 rows of seats, with 22 seats in the first row, 23 in the second row, 24 in the third row, and so on. How many seats are there in:

    a row 44 of one section
    b each section
    c the whole stadium?

8   Find the sum of:

    a the first 50 multiples of 11
    b the multiples of 7 between 0 and 1000

    c the integers between 1 and 100 which are not divisible by 3.

9   Consider the series of odd numbers $1 + 3 + 5 + 7 + ...$

    a What is the nth odd number u_n?
    b Prove that the sum of the first n odd integers is n^2.
    c Check your answer to **b** by finding S_1, S_2, S_3, and S_4.

10   Find the first two terms of an arithmetic sequence if the sixth term is 21 and the sum of the first seventeen terms is 0.

11   Three consecutive terms of an arithmetic sequence have a sum of 12 and a product of -80. Find the terms.   **Hint:**   Let the terms be $x - d$, x, and $x + d$.

12   Five consecutive terms of an arithmetic sequence have a sum of 40. The product of the first, middle and last terms is 224. Find the terms of the sequence.

INVESTIGATION 1 — STADIUM SEATING

A circular stadium consists of sections as illustrated, with aisles in between. The diagram shows the 13 tiers of concrete steps for the final section, Section K. Seats are placed along every concrete step, with each seat 0.45 m wide. The arc AB at the front of the first row, is 14.4 m long, while the arc CD at the back of the back row, is 20.25 m long.

1 How wide is each concrete step?

2 What is the length of the arc of the back of Row 1, Row 2, Row 3, and so on?

3 How many seats are there in Row 1, Row 2, Row 3, ..., Row 13?

4 How many sections are there in the stadium?

5 What is the total seating capacity of the stadium?

6 What is the radius r of the 'playing surface'?

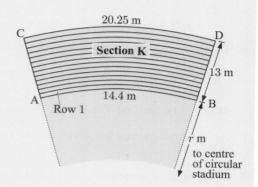

G — GEOMETRIC SERIES

A **geometric series** is the sum of the terms of a geometric sequence.

For example: $1, 2, 4, 8, 16, ..., 1024$ is a finite geometric sequence.

$1 + 2 + 4 + 8 + 16 + ... + 1024$ is the corresponding finite geometric series.

If we are adding the first n terms of an infinite geometric sequence, we are then calculating a finite geometric series called the nth partial sum of the corresponding infinite series.

If we are adding all of the terms in a geometric sequence which goes on and on forever, we have an infinite geometric series.

SUM OF A FINITE GEOMETRIC SERIES

If the first term is u_1 and the common ratio is r, then the terms are: $u_1, u_1 r, u_1 r^2, u_1 r^3, ...$

So, $S_n = u_1 + \underset{u_2}{u_1 r} + \underset{u_3}{u_1 r^2} + \underset{u_4}{u_1 r^3} + ... + \underset{u_{n-1}}{u_1 r^{n-2}} + \underset{u_n}{u_1 r^{n-1}}$

For a finite geometric series with $r \neq 1$,

$$S_n = \frac{u_1(r^n - 1)}{r - 1} \quad \text{or} \quad S_n = \frac{u_1(1 - r^n)}{1 - r}.$$

Proof:

$$\text{If } S_n = u_1 + u_1 r + u_1 r^2 + u_1 r^3 + \dots + u_1 r^{n-2} + u_1 r^{n-1} \qquad (*)$$

$$\text{then } rS_n = (u_1 r + u_1 r^2 + u_1 r^3 + u_1 r^4 + \dots + u_1 r^{n-1}) + u_1 r^n$$

$$\therefore \; rS_n = (S_n - u_1) + u_1 r^n \qquad \{\text{from } (*)\}$$

$$\therefore \; rS_n - S_n = u_1 r^n - u_1$$

$$\therefore \; S_n(r-1) = u_1(r^n - 1)$$

$$\therefore \; S_n = \frac{u_1(r^n - 1)}{r - 1} \quad \text{or} \quad \frac{u_1(1 - r^n)}{1 - r} \quad \text{provided } r \neq 1.$$

In the case $r = 1$ we have a sequence in which all terms are the same, and $S_n = u_1 n$.

Example 18   ◀») Self Tutor

Find the sum of $2 + 6 + 18 + 54 + \dots$ to 12 terms.

The series is geometric with $u_1 = 2$, $r = 3$, and $n = 12$.

$$S_n = \frac{u_1(r^n - 1)}{r - 1}$$

$$\therefore \; S_{12} = \frac{2(3^{12} - 1)}{3 - 1}$$

$$= 531\,440$$

Example 19   ◀») Self Tutor

Find a formula for S_n, the sum of the first n terms of the series $9 - 3 + 1 - \frac{1}{3} + \dots$

The series is geometric with $u_1 = 9$ and $r = -\frac{1}{3}$

$$S_n = \frac{u_1(1 - r^n)}{1 - r} = \frac{9(1 - (-\frac{1}{3})^n)}{\frac{4}{3}}$$

$$\therefore \; S_n = \tfrac{27}{4}(1 - (-\tfrac{1}{3})^n)$$

This answer cannot be simplified as we do not know if n is odd or even.

EXERCISE 6G.1

1 Find the sum of the following series:

   a $12 + 6 + 3 + 1.5 + \dots$ to 10 terms

   b $\sqrt{7} + 7 + 7\sqrt{7} + 49 + \dots$ to 12 terms

   c $6 - 3 + 1\frac{1}{2} - \frac{3}{4} + \dots$ to 15 terms

   d $1 - \frac{1}{\sqrt{2}} + \frac{1}{2} - \frac{1}{2\sqrt{2}} + \dots$ to 20 terms

2 Find a formula for S_n, the sum of the first n terms of the series:

   a $\sqrt{3} + 3 + 3\sqrt{3} + 9 + \dots$

   b $12 + 6 + 3 + 1\frac{1}{2} + \dots$

   c $0.9 + 0.09 + 0.009 + 0.0009 + \dots$

   d $20 - 10 + 5 - 2\frac{1}{2} + \dots$

3 A geometric sequence has partial sums $S_1 = 3$ and $S_2 = 4$.

   a State the first term u_1.

   b Calculate the common ratio r.

   c Calculate the fifth term u_5 of the series.

4   Evaluate these geometric series:

a $\displaystyle\sum_{k=1}^{10} 3 \times 2^{k-1}$

b $\displaystyle\sum_{k=1}^{12} (\tfrac{1}{2})^{k-2}$

c $\displaystyle\sum_{k=1}^{25} 6 \times (-2)^k$

5   Each year a salesperson is paid a bonus of \$2000 which is banked into the same account. It earns a fixed rate of interest of 6% p.a. with interest being paid annually. The total amount in the account at the end of each year is calculated as follows:

$$A_0 = 2000$$
$$A_1 = A_0 \times 1.06 + 2000$$
$$A_2 = A_1 \times 1.06 + 2000 \quad \text{and so on.}$$

a   Show that $A_2 = 2000 + 2000 \times 1.06 + 2000 \times (1.06)^2$.

b   Show that $A_3 = 2000[1 + 1.06 + (1.06)^2 + (1.06)^3]$.

c   Find the total bank balance after 10 years, assuming there are no fees or withdrawals.

6   Consider $S_n = \tfrac{1}{2} + \tfrac{1}{4} + \tfrac{1}{8} + \tfrac{1}{16} + \,....\, + \dfrac{1}{2^n}$.

a   Find $S_1, S_2, S_3, S_4,$ and S_5 in fractional form.

b   From **a** guess the formula for S_n.

c   Find S_n using $S_n = \dfrac{u_1(1 - r^n)}{1 - r}$.

d   Comment on S_n as n gets very large.

e   What is the relationship between the given diagram and **d**?

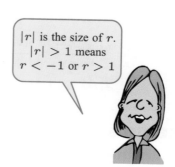

SUM OF AN INFINITE GEOMETRIC SERIES

To examine the sum of all the terms of an infinite geometric sequence, we need to consider $S_n = \dfrac{u_1(1 - r^n)}{1 - r}$ when n gets very large.

$|r|$ is the size of r.
$|r| > 1$ means
$r < -1$ or $r > 1$

If $|r| > 1$, the series is said to be **divergent** and the sum becomes infinitely large.

For example, when $r = 2$, $1 + 2 + 4 + 8 + 16 + ...$ is infinitely large.

If $|r| < 1$, or in other words $-1 < r < 1$, then as n becomes very large, r^n approaches 0.

For example, when $r = \tfrac{1}{2}$, $1 + \tfrac{1}{2} + \tfrac{1}{4} + \tfrac{1}{8} + \tfrac{1}{16} + ... = 2$.

This means that S_n will get closer and closer to $\dfrac{u_1}{1 - r}$.

> If $|r| < 1$, an infinite geometric series of the form $u_1 + u_1 r + u_1 r^2 + ... = \displaystyle\sum_{k=1}^{\infty} u_1 r^{k-1}$
> will **converge** to the sum $\boldsymbol{S = \dfrac{u_1}{1 - r}}$.

We call this the **limiting sum** of the series.

This result can be used to find the value of recurring decimals.

Example 20   ◀)) **Self Tutor**

Write $0.\overline{7}$ as a rational number.

$0.\overline{7} = \frac{7}{10} + \frac{7}{100} + \frac{7}{1000} + \frac{7}{10\,000} + ...$

which is a geometric series with infinitely many terms.

In this case, $u_1 = \frac{7}{10}$ and $r = \frac{1}{10}$

$\therefore \quad S = \frac{u_1}{1-r} = \frac{\frac{7}{10}}{1 - \frac{1}{10}} = \frac{7}{9}$

$\therefore \quad 0.\overline{7} = \frac{7}{9}$

EXERCISE 6G.2

1 Consider $0.\overline{3} = \frac{3}{10} + \frac{3}{100} + \frac{3}{1000} + ...$ which is an infinite geometric series.

   a Find: **i** u_1 **ii** r

   b Using **a**, show that $0.\overline{3} = \frac{1}{3}$.

2 Write as a rational number: **a** $0.\overline{4}$ **b** $0.\overline{16}$ **c** $0.\overline{312}$

3 Use $S = \frac{u_1}{1-r}$ to check your answer to **Exercise 6G.1** question **6d**.

4 Find the sum of each of the following infinite geometric series:

   a $18 + 12 + 8 + \frac{16}{3} + ...$ **b** $18.9 - 6.3 + 2.1 - 0.7 + ...$

5 Find each of the following:

   a $\displaystyle\sum_{k=1}^{\infty} \frac{3}{4^k}$ **b** $\displaystyle\sum_{k=0}^{\infty} 6\left(-\frac{2}{5}\right)^k$

6 The sum of the first three terms of a convergent infinite geometric series is 19. The sum of the series is 27. Find the first term and the common ratio.

7 The second term of a convergent infinite geometric series is $\frac{8}{5}$. The sum of the series is 10. Show that there are two possible series, and find the first term and the common ratio in each case.

8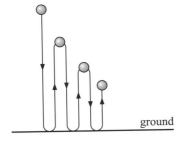

   When dropped, a ball takes 1 second to hit the ground. It then takes 90% of this time to rebound to its new height, and this continues until the ball comes to rest.

   a Show that the total time of motion is given by
   $1 + 2(0.9) + 2(0.9)^2 + 2(0.9)^3 + ...$

   b Find S_n for the series in **a**.

   c How long does it take for the ball to come to rest?

Note: This diagram is inaccurate as the motion is really up and down on the same spot. It has been separated out to help us visualise what is happening.

ACTIVITY

Click on the icon to run a card game for sequences and series.

SEQUENCES AND SERIES

THEORY OF KNOWLEDGE

The German mathematician Leopold Kronecker (1823 - 1891) made important contributions in number theory and algebra. Several things are named after him, including formulae, symbols, and a theorem.

Kronecker made several well-known quotes, including:

"God made integers; all else is the work of man."

"A mathematical object does not exist unless it can be constructed from natural numbers in a finite number of steps."

Leopold Kronecker

1 What do you understand by the term *infinity*?

2 If the entire world were made of grains of sand, could you count them? Would the number of grains of sand be infinite?

Consider an infinite geometric series with first term u_1 and common ratio r.

If $|r| < 1$, the series will converge to the sum $S = \dfrac{u_1}{1-r}$.

Proof: If the first term is u_1 and the common ratio is r, the terms are u_1, $u_1 r$, $u_1 r^2$, $u_1 r^3$, and so on.

Suppose the sum of the corresponding infinite series is

$$S = u_1 + u_1 r + u_1 r^2 + u_1 r^3 + u_1 r^4 + \ldots \quad (*)$$

We multiply (*) by r to obtain $rS = u_1 r + u_1 r^2 + u_1 r^3 + u_1 r^4 + \ldots$

$$\therefore \quad rS = S - u_1 \quad \text{\{comparing with (*)\}}$$

$$\therefore \quad S(r-1) = -u_1$$

$$\therefore \quad S = \frac{u_1}{1-r} \quad \text{\{provided } r \neq 1\}$$

3 Can we explain through intuition how a sum of non-zero terms, which goes on and on for ever and ever, could actually be a finite number?

In the case $r = -1$, the terms are u_1, $-u_1$, u_1, $-u_1$, ...

If we take partial sums of the series, the answer is always u_1 or 0.

4 What is the sum of the infinite series when $r = -1$? Is it infinite? Is it defined?

Substituting $r = -1$ into the formula above gives $S = \dfrac{u_1}{2}$. Could this possibly be the answer?

INVESTIGATION 2   VON KOCH'S SNOWFLAKE CURVE

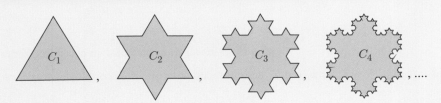

In this investigation we consider a **limit curve** named after the Swedish mathematician Niels Fabian Helge von Koch (1870 - 1924).

To draw **Von Koch's Snowflake curve** we:

DEMO

- start with an equilateral triangle, C_1
- then divide each side into 3 equal parts
- then on each middle part draw an equilateral triangle
- then delete the side of the smaller triangle which lies on C_1.

The resulting curve is C_2. By repeating this process on every edge of C_2, we generate curve C_3.

We hence obtain a sequence of special curves C_1, C_2, C_3, C_4, ...   and Von Koch's curve is the limiting case when n is infinitely large.

Your task is to investigate the perimeter and area of Von Koch's curve.

What to do:

1 Suppose C_1 has a perimeter of 3 units. Find the perimeter of C_2, C_3, C_4, and C_5.

    Hint: becomes   so 3 parts become 4 parts.

    Remembering that Von Koch's curve is C_n, where n is infinitely large, find the perimeter of Von Koch's curve.

2 Suppose the area of C_1 is 1 unit^2. Explain why the areas of C_2, C_3, C_4, and C_5 are:

    $A_2 = 1 + \frac{1}{3}$ units^2 $A_3 = 1 + \frac{1}{3}[1 + \frac{4}{9}]$ units^2

    $A_4 = 1 + \frac{1}{3}[1 + \frac{4}{9} + (\frac{4}{9})^2]$ units^2 $A_5 = 1 + \frac{1}{3}[1 + \frac{4}{9} + (\frac{4}{9})^2 + (\frac{4}{9})^3]$ units^2.

Use your calculator to find A_n where $n = 1, 2, 3, 4, 5, 6,$ and 7, giving answers which are as accurate as your calculator permits.
What do you think will be the area within Von Koch's snowflake curve?

3 Is there anything remarkable about your answers to **1** and **2**?

4 Similarly, investigate the sequence of curves obtained by adding squares on successive curves from the middle third of each side. These are the curves C_1, C_2, C_3, ... shown below.

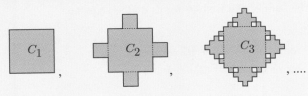

REVIEW SET 6A   NON-CALCULATOR

1 Identify the following sequences as arithmetic, geometric, or neither:

    a $7, -1, -9, -17, ...$ **b** $9, 9, 9, 9, ...$ **c** $4, -2, 1, -\frac{1}{2}, ...$

    d $1, 1, 2, 3, 5, 8, ...$ **e** the set of all multiples of 4 in ascending order.

2 Find k if $3k$, $k-2$, and $k+7$ are consecutive terms of an arithmetic sequence.

3 Show that $28, 23, 18, 13, ...$ is an arithmetic sequence. Hence find u_n and the sum S_n of the first n terms in simplest form.

4 Find k given that 4, k, and $k^2 - 1$ are consecutive terms of a geometric sequence.

5 Determine the general term of a geometric sequence given that its sixth term is $\frac{16}{3}$ and its tenth term is $\frac{256}{3}$.

6 Insert six numbers between 23 and 9 so that all eight numbers are in arithmetic sequence.

7 Find, in simplest form, a formula for the general term u_n of:

    a $86, 83, 80, 77, ...$ **b** $\frac{3}{4}, 1, \frac{7}{6}, \frac{9}{7}, ...$ **c** $100, 90, 81, 72.9, ...$

    Hint: One of these sequences is neither arithmetic nor geometric.

8 Expand and hence evaluate: **a** $\displaystyle\sum_{k=1}^{7} k^2$ **b** $\displaystyle\sum_{k=1}^{8} \frac{k+3}{k+2}$

9 Find the sum of each of the following infinite geometric series:

    a $18 - 12 + 8 - ....$ **b** $8 + 4\sqrt{2} + 4 + ...$

10 A ball bounces from a height of 3 metres and returns to 80% of its previous height on each bounce. Find the total distance travelled by the ball until it stops bouncing.

11 The sum of the first n terms of an infinite sequence is $\dfrac{3n^2 + 5n}{2}$ for all $n \in \mathbb{Z}^+$.

    a Find the nth term.   **b** Prove that the sequence is arithmetic.

REVIEW SET 6B   CALCULATOR

1 A sequence is defined by $u_n = 6(\frac{1}{2})^{n-1}$.

    a Prove that the sequence is geometric.   **b** Find u_1 and r.

    c Find the 16th term of the sequence to 3 significant figures.

2 Consider the sequence $24, 23\frac{1}{4}, 22\frac{1}{2}, ...$

    a Which term of the sequence is -36?   **b** Find the value of u_{35}.

    c Find S_{40}, the sum of the first 40 terms of the sequence.

3 Find the sum of:

    a the first 23 terms of $3 + 9 + 15 + 21 + ...$

    b the first 12 terms of $24 + 12 + 6 + 3 + ...$

4 Find the first term of the sequence $5, 10, 20, 40, ...$ which exceeds $10\,000$.

5 What will an investment of €6000 at 7% p.a. compound interest amount to after 5 years if the interest is compounded:

    a annually   **b** quarterly   **c** monthly?

6 The nth term of a sequence is given by the formula $u_n = 5n - 8$.

    a Find the value of u_{10}.

    b Write down an expression for $u_{n+1} - u_n$ and simplify it.

    c Hence explain why the sequence is arithmetic.

    d Evaluate $u_{15} + u_{16} + u_{17} + ... + u_{30}$.

7 A geometric sequence has $u_6 = 24$ and $u_{11} = 768$. Determine the general term of the sequence and hence find:

    a u_{17} **b** the sum of the first 15 terms.

8 Find the first term of the sequence $24, 8, \frac{8}{3}, \frac{8}{9}, ...$ which is less than 0.001.

9   **a** Determine the number of terms in the sequence $128, 64, 32, 16, ..., \frac{1}{512}$.

    b Find the sum of these terms.

10 Find the sum of each of the following infinite geometric series:

    a $1.21 - 1.1 + 1 - ....$ **b** $\frac{14}{3} + \frac{4}{3} + \frac{8}{21} + ...$

11 How much should be invested at a fixed rate of 9% p.a. compound interest if you need it to amount to $20 000 after 4 years with interest paid monthly?

12 In 2004 there were 3000 iguanas on a Galapagos island. Since then, the population of iguanas on the island has increased by 5% each year.

    a How many iguanas were on the island in 2007?

    b In what year will the population first exceed 10 000?

REVIEW SET 6C

1 A sequence is defined by $u_n = 68 - 5n$.

    a Prove that the sequence is arithmetic.   **b** Find u_1 and d.

    c Find the 37th term of the sequence.

    d State the first term of the sequence which is less than -200.

2   **a** Show that the sequence $3, 12, 48, 192, ...$ is geometric.

    b Find u_n and hence find u_9.

3 Find the general term of the arithmetic sequence with $u_7 = 31$ and $u_{15} = -17$. Hence, find the value of u_{34}.

4 Write using sigma notation:

    a $4 + 11 + 18 + 25 + ...$ for n terms   **b** $\frac{1}{4} + \frac{1}{8} + \frac{1}{16} + \frac{1}{32} + ...$ for n terms.

5 Evaluate:

    a $\displaystyle\sum_{k=1}^{8} \left(\frac{31 - 3k}{2} \right)$ **b** $\displaystyle\sum_{k=1}^{15} 50(0.8)^{k-1}$ **c** $\displaystyle\sum_{k=7}^{\infty} 5\left(\frac{2}{5} \right)^{k-1}$

6 How many terms of the series $11 + 16 + 21 + 26 + ...$ are needed to exceed a sum of 450?

7 £12 500 is invested in an account which pays 8.25% p.a. compounded. Find the value of the investment after 5 years if the interest is compounded:

    a half-yearly   **b** monthly.

8 The sum of the first two terms of an infinite geometric series is 90. The third term is 24.

    a Show that there are two possible series. Find the first term and the common ratio in each case.

    b Show that both series converge and find their respective sums.

9 Seve is training for a long distance walk. He walks for 10 km in the first week, then each week thereafter he walks an additional 500 m. If he continues this pattern for a year, how far does Seve walk:

    a in the last week   **b** in total?

10 **a** Under what conditions will the series $\displaystyle\sum_{k=1}^{\infty} 50(2x-1)^{k-1}$ converge?

       Explain your answer.

    b Find $\displaystyle\sum_{k=1}^{\infty} 50(2x-1)^{k-1}$ if $x = 0.3$.

Chapter **7**

The binomial expansion

Syllabus reference: 1.3

Contents:

OPENING PROBLEM

Consider the cube alongside, which has sides of length $(a + b)$ cm.

The cube has been subdivided into 8 blocks by making 3 cuts parallel to the cube's surfaces as shown.

We know that the total volume of the cube is $(a+b)^3$ cm³. However, we can also find an expression for the cube's volume by adding the volumes of the 8 individual blocks.

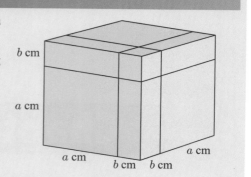

b cm

a cm

a cm   *a* cm

b cm   *b* cm

Things to think about:

a How many of the blocks that make up the cube have dimensions:

   i a by a by a **ii** a by a by b

   iii a by b by b **iv** b by b by b?

b By adding the volumes of the blocks, can you find an expression which is equivalent to $(a + b)^3$?

ANIMATION

A   BINOMIAL EXPANSIONS

> The sum $a + b$ is called a **binomial** as it contains two terms.
>
> Any expression of the form $(a + b)^n$ is called a **power of a binomial**.

All binomials raised to a power can be expanded using the same general principles. In this chapter, therefore, we consider the expansion of the general expression $(a + b)^n$ where $n \in \mathbb{N}$.

Consider the following algebraic expansions:

$(a + b)^1 = a + b$

$(a + b)^2 = a^2 + 2ab + b^2$

$$\begin{aligned}(a + b)^3 &= (a + b)(a + b)^2 \\ &= (a + b)(a^2 + 2ab + b^2) \\ &= a^3 + 2a^2b + ab^2 + a^2b + 2ab^2 + b^3 \\ &= a^3 + 3a^2b + 3ab^2 + b^3\end{aligned}$$

> The **binomial expansion** of $(a + b)^2$ is $a^2 + 2ab + b^2$.
>
> The **binomial expansion** of $(a + b)^3$ is $a^3 + 3a^2b + 3ab^2 + b^3$.

INVESTIGATION 1   THE BINOMIAL EXPANSION

What to do:

1 Expand $(a + b)^4$ in the same way as for $(a + b)^3$ above.
   Hence expand $(a + b)^5$ and $(a + b)^6$.

2 The cubic expansion $(a + b)^3 = a^3 + 3a^2b + 3ab^2 + b^3$ contains 4 terms. Observe that their coefficients are: 1 3 3 1

   a What happens to the powers of a and b in each term of the expansion of $(a + b)^3$?

b Does the pattern in **a** continue for the expansions of $(a+b)^4$, $(a+b)^5$, and $(a+b)^6$?

c Write down the triangle of coefficients to row 6:

$n=0$				1		
$n=1$			1		1	
$n=2$		1		2		1
$n=3$	1		3		3		1 $\longleftarrow$ row 3

$\vdots$

3 The triangle of coefficients in **c** above is called **Pascal's triangle**. Investigate:

  a the predictability of each row from the previous one

  b a formula for finding the sum of the numbers in the nth row of Pascal's triangle.

4   **a** Use your results from **3** to predict the elements of the 7th row of Pascal's triangle.

  b Hence write down the binomial expansion of $(a+b)^7$.

  c Check your result algebraically by using $(a+b)^7 = (a+b)(a+b)^6$ and your results from **1**.

From the **Investigation** we obtained
$$(a+b)^4 = a^4 + 4a^3b + 6a^2b^2 + 4ab^3 + b^4$$
$$= a^4 + 4a^3b^1 + 6a^2b^2 + 4a^1b^3 + b^4$$

Notice that:

- As we look from left to right across the expansion, the powers of a decrease by 1, while the powers of b increase by 1.
- The sum of the powers of a and b in each term of the expansion is 4.
- The number of terms in the expansion is $4+1 = 5$.
- The coefficients of the terms are row 4 of Pascal's triangle.

For the expansion of $(a+b)^n$ where $n \in \mathbb{N}$:

- As we look from left to right across the expansion, the powers of a *decrease* by 1, while the powers of b *increase* by 1.
- The sum of the powers of a and b in each term of the expansion is n.
- The number of terms in the expansion is $n+1$.
- The coefficients of the terms are row n of Pascal's triangle.

In the following examples we see how the general binomial expansion $(a+b)^n$ may be put to use.

Example 1 ◀)) **Self Tutor**

Using $(a+b)^3 = a^3 + 3a^2b + 3ab^2 + b^3$, find the binomial expansion of:

a $(2x+3)^3$ **b** $(x-5)^3$

a In the expansion of $(a+b)^3$ we substitute $a=(2x)$ and $b=(3)$.

$\therefore (2x+3)^3 = (2x)^3 + 3(2x)^2(3) + 3(2x)^1(3)^2 + (3)^3$
$\qquad\qquad = 8x^3 + 36x^2 + 54x + 27$

Brackets are essential!

b We substitute $a=(x)$ and $b=(-5)$

$\therefore (x-5)^3 = (x)^3 + 3(x)^2(-5) + 3(x)(-5)^2 + (-5)^3$
$\qquad\qquad = x^3 - 15x^2 + 75x - 125$

Example 2   ◆) **Self Tutor**

Find the:

a 5th row of Pascal's triangle

b binomial expansion of $\left(x - \dfrac{2}{x}\right)^5$.

a
$$1 \longleftarrow \text{the 0th row, for } (a+b)^0$$
$$1 \quad 1 \longleftarrow \text{the 1st row, for } (a+b)^1$$
$$1 \quad 2 \quad 1$$
$$1 \quad 3 \quad 3 \quad 1$$
$$1 \quad 4 \quad 6 \quad 4 \quad 1$$
$$1 \quad 5 \quad 10 \quad 10 \quad 5 \quad 1 \longleftarrow \text{the 5th row, for } (a+b)^5$$

b Using the coefficients obtained in **a**, $(a+b)^5 = a^5 + 5a^4b + 10a^3b^2 + 10a^2b^3 + 5ab^4 + b^5$

Letting $a = (x)$ and $b = \left(\dfrac{-2}{x}\right)$, we find

$$\left(x - \frac{2}{x}\right)^5 = (x)^5 + 5(x)^4\left(\frac{-2}{x}\right) + 10(x)^3\left(\frac{-2}{x}\right)^2 + 10(x)^2\left(\frac{-2}{x}\right)^3 + 5(x)\left(\frac{-2}{x}\right)^4 + \left(\frac{-2}{x}\right)^5$$

$$= x^5 - 10x^3 + 40x - \frac{80}{x} + \frac{80}{x^3} - \frac{32}{x^5}$$

EXERCISE 7A

1 Use the binomial expansion of $(a+b)^3$ to expand and simplify:

a $(p+q)^3$

b $(x+1)^3$

c $(x-3)^3$

d $(2+x)^3$

e $(3x-1)^3$

f $(2x+5)^3$

g $(2a-b)^3$

h $\left(3x - \dfrac{1}{3}\right)^3$

i $\left(2x + \dfrac{1}{x}\right)^3$

2 Use $(a+b)^4 = a^4 + 4a^3b + 6a^2b^2 + 4ab^3 + b^4$ to expand and simplify:

a $(1+x)^4$

b $(p-q)^4$

c $(x-2)^4$

d $(3-x)^4$

e $(1+2x)^4$

f $(2x-3)^4$

g $(2x+b)^4$

h $\left(x + \dfrac{1}{x}\right)^4$

i $\left(2x - \dfrac{1}{x}\right)^4$

3 Expand and simplify:

a $(x+2)^5$

b $(x-2y)^5$

c $(1+2x)^5$

d $\left(x - \dfrac{1}{x}\right)^5$

4 **a** Write down the 6th row of Pascal's triangle.

   b Find the binomial expansion of:

   i $(x+2)^6$

   ii $(2x-1)^6$

   iii $\left(x + \dfrac{1}{x}\right)^6$

5 The first two terms in a binomial expansion are shown below:
$$(a+b)^3 = 8 + 12e^x + \dots.$$

   a Find a and b.

   b Hence determine the remaining two terms of the expansion.

6   Expand and simplify:

    a $(1 + \sqrt{2})^3$
        b $(\sqrt{5} + 2)^4$
        c $(2 - \sqrt{2})^5$

7   **a**   Expand $(2 + x)^6$.

    b   Use the expansion of **a** to find the value of $(2.01)^6$.

8   Expand and simplify $(2x + 3)(x + 1)^4$.

9   Find the coefficient of:

    a $a^3 b^2$ in the expansion of $(3a + b)^5$
        b $a^3 b^3$ in the expansion of $(2a + 3b)^6$.

.B   THE BINOMIAL COEFFICIENT $\binom{n}{r}$

INVESTIGATION 2   THE BINOMIAL COEFFICIENT

The numbers in Pascal's triangle are called **binomial coefficients** because of their importance in the binomial expansion.

You can use your calculator to find binomial coefficients.

GRAPHICS CALCULATOR INSTRUCTIONS

What to do:

1   Write down the first 6 rows of Pascal's triangle.

2   Use a graphics calculator to find the **binomial coefficient** $\binom{n}{r}$ for $n = 3$ and $r = 0, 1, 2,$ and 3.
    What do you notice about these numbers?

3   Use your calculator to find $\binom{4}{0}$, $\binom{4}{1}$, $\binom{4}{2}$, $\binom{4}{3}$, and $\binom{4}{4}$.
    What do you notice about these numbers?

4   Use your calculator to help you write down the expansion for $(a + b)^5$.

5   Copy and complete:
    In the expansion of $(a + b)^5$, the binomial coefficient $\binom{5}{r}$ is the coefficient of $a^{\cdots} b^{\cdots}$.

6   Copy and complete:
    In the expansion of $(a + b)^n$, the binomial coefficient $\binom{n}{r}$ is the coefficient of $a^{\cdots} b^{\cdots}$.

From the **Investigation** above you should have found that $\binom{n}{0} = \binom{n}{n} = 1$ for all n.

To calculate the other binomial coefficients we can use a formula. It involves the product of consecutive positive integers, so to keep it simple we introduce **factorial notation**.

FACTORIAL NOTATION

For $n \geqslant 1$, $n!$ is the product of the first n positive integers.

$$n! = n(n - 1)(n - 2)(n - 3)\ldots \times 3 \times 2 \times 1$$

$n!$ is read "n factorial".

For example, the product $6 \times 5 \times 4 \times 3 \times 2 \times 1$ can be written as 6!.

Notice that $8 \times 7 \times 6$ can be written using factorial numbers only as

$$8 \times 7 \times 6 = \frac{8 \times 7 \times 6 \times 5 \times 4 \times 3 \times 2 \times 1}{5 \times 4 \times 3 \times 2 \times 1} = \frac{8!}{5!}$$

The **factorial rule** is $\boxed{n! = n \times (n-1)! \quad \text{for} \ n \geqslant 1}$

which can be extended to $n! = n(n-1)(n-2)!$ and so on.

Using the factorial rule with $n = 1$,   we have $1! = 1 \times 0!$

We hence define $\boxed{0! = 1}$

Example 3
◀) **Self Tutor**

What integer is equal to: **a** $4!$ **b** $\dfrac{5!}{3!}$ **c** $\dfrac{7!}{4! \times 3!}$?

a $4! = 4 \times 3 \times 2 \times 1 = 24$

b $\dfrac{5!}{3!} = \dfrac{5 \times 4 \times 3 \times 2 \times 1}{3 \times 2 \times 1} = 5 \times 4 = 20$

c $\dfrac{7!}{4! \times 3!} = \dfrac{7 \times 6 \times 5 \times 4 \times 3 \times 2 \times 1}{4 \times 3 \times 2 \times 1 \times 3 \times 2 \times 1} = 35$

THE BINOMIAL COEFFICIENT

The **binomial coefficient** is defined by

$$\binom{n}{r} = \underbrace{\frac{n(n-1)(n-2)\ldots.(n-r+2)(n-r+1)}{r(r-1)(r-2)\ldots.2 \times 1}}_{\text{factor form}} = \underbrace{\frac{n!}{r!(n-r)!}}_{\text{factorial form}}$$

The binomial coefficient is sometimes written ^nC_r or C_r^n.

Example 4
◀) **Self Tutor**

Use the formula $\binom{n}{r} = \dfrac{n!}{r!(n-r)!}$ to evaluate:

a $\binom{5}{2}$ **b** $\binom{11}{7}$

a $\binom{5}{2} = \dfrac{5!}{2!(5-2)!}$

$= \dfrac{5!}{2! \times 3!}$

$= \dfrac{5 \times 4 \times 3 \times 2 \times 1}{2 \times 1 \times 3 \times 2 \times 1}$

$= 10$

b $\binom{11}{7} = \dfrac{11!}{7!(11-7)!}$

$= \dfrac{11!}{7! \times 4!}$

$= \dfrac{11 \times 10 \times 9 \times 8 \times 7 \times 6 \times 5 \times 4 \times 3 \times 2 \times 1}{7 \times 6 \times 5 \times 4 \times 3 \times 2 \times 1 \times 4 \times 3 \times 2 \times 1}$

$= \dfrac{7920}{24}$

$= 330$

EXERCISE 7B

1 Find $n!$ for $n = 0, 1, 2, 3, ..., 10$.

2 Simplify without using a calculator:

   a $\dfrac{6!}{4!}$ **b** $\dfrac{100!}{99!}$ **c** $\dfrac{7!}{5! \times 2!}$

3 Simplify: **a** $\dfrac{n!}{(n-1)!}$ **b** $\dfrac{(n+2)!}{n!}$

4 Use the formula $\dbinom{n}{r} = \dfrac{n!}{r!(n-r)!}$ to evaluate:

   a $\dbinom{3}{1}$ **b** $\dbinom{4}{2}$ **c** $\dbinom{7}{3}$ **d** $\dbinom{10}{4}$

5 **a** Use the formula $\dbinom{n}{r} = \dfrac{n!}{r!(n-r)!}$ to evaluate:

     i $\dbinom{8}{2}$ **ii** $\dbinom{8}{6}$

   b Can you explain these results using Pascal's triangle?

C   THE BINOMIAL THEOREM

The binomial theorem states that

$$(a+b)^n = a^n + \binom{n}{1} a^{n-1}b + ... + \binom{n}{r} a^{n-r}b^r + ... + b^n$$

where $\binom{n}{r}$ is the **binomial coefficient** of $a^{n-r}b^r$ and $r = 0, 1, 2, 3, ..., n$.

The **general term** or $(r+1)$th term in the binomial expansion is $T_{r+1} = \binom{n}{r} a^{n-r}b^r$.

Using the same sigma notation as in **Chapter 6**, we write $(a+b)^n = \displaystyle\sum_{r=0}^{n} \binom{n}{r} a^{n-r}b^r$.

Example 5   ◀) **Self Tutor**

Write down the first three and last two terms of the expansion of $\left(2x + \dfrac{1}{x}\right)^{12}$.
Do not simplify your answer.

$$\left(2x + \frac{1}{x}\right)^{12} = (2x)^{12} + \binom{12}{1}(2x)^{11}\left(\frac{1}{x}\right)^1 + \binom{12}{2}(2x)^{10}\left(\frac{1}{x}\right)^2 + ...$$

$$.... + \binom{12}{11}(2x)^1\left(\frac{1}{x}\right)^{11} + \left(\frac{1}{x}\right)^{12}$$

EXERCISE 7C

1 Write down the first three and last two terms of the following binomial expansions. Do not simplify your answers.

   a $(1+2x)^{11}$ **b** $\left(3x + \dfrac{2}{x}\right)^{15}$ **c** $\left(2x - \dfrac{3}{x}\right)^{20}$

Example 6   ◀) Self Tutor

Find the 7th term of $\left(3x - \dfrac{4}{x^2}\right)^{14}$. Do not simplify your answer.

$a = (3x)$, $b = \left(\dfrac{-4}{x^2}\right)$,   and $n = 14$

Given the general term $T_{r+1} = \binom{n}{r} a^{n-r} b^r$,   we let $r = 6$

$$\therefore \ T_7 = \binom{14}{6} (3x)^8 \left(\dfrac{-4}{x^2}\right)^6$$

2 Without simplifying, write down:

   a the 6th term of $(2x + 5)^{15}$

   b the 4th term of $(x^2 + y)^9$

   c the 10th term of $\left(x - \dfrac{2}{x}\right)^{17}$

   d the 9th term of $\left(2x^2 - \dfrac{1}{x}\right)^{21}$.

Example 7   ◀) Self Tutor

In the expansion of $\left(x^2 + \dfrac{4}{x}\right)^{12}$, find:

   a the coefficient of x^6

   b the constant term

$a = (x^2)$, $b = \left(\dfrac{4}{x}\right)$,   and $n = 12$

$\therefore$ the general term $T_{r+1} = \binom{12}{r} (x^2)^{12-r} \left(\dfrac{4}{x}\right)^r$

$$= \binom{12}{r} x^{24-2r} \times \dfrac{4^r}{x^r}$$

$$= \binom{12}{r} 4^r x^{24-3r}$$

a If $24 - 3r = 6$
    then $3r = 18$
    $\therefore \ r = 6$
    $\therefore \ T_7 = \binom{12}{6} 4^6 x^6$
    $\therefore$ the coefficient of x^6 is
    $\binom{12}{6} 4^6$ or $3\,784\,704$.

b If $24 - 3r = 0$
    then $3r = 24$
    $\therefore \ r = 8$
    $\therefore \ T_9 = \binom{12}{8} 4^8 x^0$
    $\therefore$ the constant term is
    $\binom{12}{8} 4^8$ or $32\,440\,320$.

3 Consider the expansion of $(x + b)^7$.

   a Write down the general term of the expansion.

   b Find b given that the coefficient of x^4 is -280.

4 Find the coefficient of:

   a x^{10} in the expansion of $(3 + 2x^2)^{10}$

   b x^3 in the expansion of $\left(2x^2 - \dfrac{3}{x}\right)^6$

   c $x^6 y^3$ in the expansion of $(2x^2 - 3y)^6$

   d x^{12} in the expansion of $\left(2x^2 - \dfrac{1}{x}\right)^{12}$.

5 Find the constant term in the expansion of:

    a $\left(x + \dfrac{2}{x^2}\right)^{15}$
                  b $\left(x - \dfrac{3}{x^2}\right)^{9}$.

6 **a** Write down the first 6 rows of Pascal's triangle.

    b Find the sum of the numbers in:

        i row 1   **ii** row 2   **iii** row 3   **iv** row 4   **v** row 5.

    c Copy and complete:

        The sum of the numbers in row n of Pascal's triangle is ......

    d Show that $(1 + x)^n = \binom{n}{0} + \binom{n}{1} x + \binom{n}{2} x^2 + \; .... \; + \binom{n}{n-1} x^{n-1} + \binom{n}{n} x^n$.

        Hence deduce that $\binom{n}{0} + \binom{n}{1} + \binom{n}{2} + \; .... \; + \binom{n}{n-1} + \binom{n}{n} = 2^n$.

Example 8   ◀》 **Self Tutor**

Find the coefficient of x^5 in the expansion of $(x + 3)(2x - 1)^6$.

$(x + 3)(2x - 1)^6$

$= (x + 3)[(2x)^6 + \binom{6}{1}(2x)^5(-1) + \binom{6}{2}(2x)^4(-1)^2 + \; ....]$

$= (x + 3)(2^6 x^6 - \binom{6}{1} 2^5 x^5 + \binom{6}{2} 2^4 x^4 - \; ....)$

                — (1) —
          —————— (2) ——————

So, the terms containing x^5 are $\binom{6}{2} 2^4 x^5$ from (1)

                and $-3 \binom{6}{1} 2^5 x^5$ from (2)

$\therefore$ the coefficient of x^5 is $\binom{6}{2} 2^4 - 3 \binom{6}{1} 2^5 = -336$

---

7 **a** Find the coefficient of x^5 in the expansion of $(x + 2)(x^2 + 1)^8$.

    b Find the term containing x^6 in the expansion of $(2 - x)(3x + 1)^9$. Simplify your answer.

8 Consider the expression $\left(x^2 y - 2y^2\right)^6$. Find the term in which x and y are raised to the same power.

9 **a** The third term of $(1 + x)^n$ is $36x^2$. Find the fourth term.

    b If $(1 + kx)^n = 1 - 12x + 60x^2 - \; .... \;$, find the values of k and n.

10 Find a if the coefficient of x^{11} in the expansion of $\left(x^2 + \dfrac{1}{ax}\right)^{10}$ is 15.

REVIEW SET 7A

1 Use the formula $\binom{n}{r} = \dfrac{n!}{r!(n - r)!}$ to evaluate $\binom{6}{4}$.

2 Use the binomial expansion to find: **a** $(x - 2y)^3$ **b** $(3x + 2)^4$

3 Find the constant term in the expansion of $\left(2x^2 - \dfrac{1}{x}\right)^6$.

4 Use Pascal's triangle to expand $(a + b)^6$.

Hence, find the binomial expansion of: **a** $(x - 3)^6$ **b** $\left(1 + \dfrac{1}{x}\right)^6$

5 Expand and simplify $(\sqrt{3} + 2)^5$. Give your answer in the form $a + b\sqrt{3}$ where $a, b \in \mathbb{Z}$.

6 Consider the expansion of $\left(3x^2 + \dfrac{1}{x}\right)^6$.

    a How many terms does the expansion include?

    b Find the constant term.

    c Show that the expansion has no terms involving x^5.

7 The first two terms in a binomial expansion are shown below:
$$(a + b)^4 = e^{4x} - 4e^{2x} + \ldots.$$

    a Find a and b.   **b** Copy and complete the expansion.

REVIEW SET 7B

1 Find the coefficient of x^3 in the expansion of $(x + 5)^6$.

2 Use the expansion of $(4 + x)^3$ to find the exact value of $(4.02)^3$.

3 Find the coefficient of x^{-6} in the expansion of $\left(2x - \dfrac{3}{x^2}\right)^{12}$.

4 Find the term containing x^5 in the expansion of $(2x + 3)(x - 2)^6$.

5 Find k in the expansion $(m - 2n)^{10} = m^{10} - 20m^9 n + km^8 n^2 - \ldots + 1024n^{10}$.

6 Find c given that the expansion $(1 + cx)(1 + x)^4$ includes the term $22x^3$.

7   **a** Write down the first four and last two terms of the binomial expansion $(2 + x)^n$.

    b Hence evaluate the series $2^n + \binom{n}{1} 2^{n-1} + \binom{n}{2} 2^{n-2} + \binom{n}{3} 2^{n-3} + \ldots + 2n + 1$.

The unit circle and radian measure

Syllabus reference: 3.1, 3.2, 3.3

Contents:

OPENING PROBLEM

Consider an equilateral triangle with sides 2 cm long. Altitude [AN] bisects side [BC] and the vertical angle BAC.

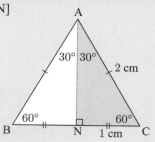

Things to think about:

a Can you use this figure to explain why $\sin 30° = \frac{1}{2}$?

b Use your calculator to find the values of $\sin 30°$, $\sin 150°$, $\sin 390°$, $\sin 1110°$, and $\sin(-330°)$.
Can you explain your results even though the angles are not between $0°$ and $90°$?

A   RADIAN MEASURE

DEGREE MEASUREMENT OF ANGLES

We have seen previously that one full revolution makes an angle of $360°$, and the angle on a straight line is $180°$. Hence, one **degree**, $1°$, can be defined as $\frac{1}{360}$th of one full revolution. This measure of angle is commonly used by surveyors and architects.

For greater accuracy we define one **minute**, $1'$, as $\frac{1}{60}$th of one degree and one **second**, $1''$, as $\frac{1}{60}$th of one minute. Obviously a minute and a second are very small angles.

Most graphics calculators can convert fractions of angles measured in degrees into minutes and seconds. This is also useful for converting fractions of hours into minutes and seconds for time measurement, as one minute is $\frac{1}{60}$th of one hour, and one second is $\frac{1}{60}$th of one minute.

 GRAPHICS CALCULATOR INSTRUCTIONS

RADIAN MEASUREMENT OF ANGLES

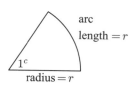

An angle is said to have a measure of 1 **radian** (1^c) if it is subtended at the centre of a circle by an arc equal in length to the radius.

The symbol 'c' is used for radian measure but is usually omitted. By contrast, the degree symbol is *always* used when the measure of an angle is given in degrees.

From the diagram to the right, it can be seen that 1^c is slightly smaller than $60°$. In fact, $1^c \approx 57.3°$.

The word 'radian' is an abbreviation of 'radial angle'.

DEGREE-RADIAN CONVERSIONS

If the radius of a circle is r, then an arc of length πr, or half the circumference, will subtend an angle of π radians.

Therefore, π radians $\equiv 180°$.

So, $1^c = \left(\frac{180}{\pi}\right)^\circ \approx 57.3^\circ$ and $1^\circ = \left(\frac{\pi}{180}\right)^c \approx 0.0175^c$.

To convert from degrees to radians, we multiply by $\frac{\pi}{180}$.

To convert from radians to degrees, we multiply by $\frac{180}{\pi}$.

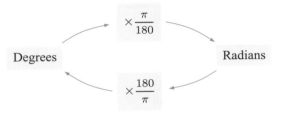

We indicate degrees with a small $^\circ$.
To indicate radians we use a small ^{c} or else use no symbol at all.

Example 1   🔊 **Self Tutor**

Convert 45° to radians in terms of π.

$45^\circ = (45 \times \frac{\pi}{180})$ radians   *or* $180^\circ = \pi$ radians

$= \frac{\pi}{4}$ radians $\therefore \left(\frac{180}{4}\right)^\circ = \frac{\pi}{4}$ radians

$\therefore\ 45^\circ = \frac{\pi}{4}$ radians

Angles in radians may be expressed either in terms of π or as decimals.

Example 2   🔊 **Self Tutor**

Convert 126.5° to radians.

126.5°
$= (126.5 \times \frac{\pi}{180})$ radians
≈ 2.21 radians

EXERCISE 8A

1 Convert to radians, in terms of π:

a 90°	b 60°	c 30°	d 18°	e 9°
f 135°	g 225°	h 270°	i 360°	j 720°
k 315°	l 540°	m 36°	n 80°	o 230°

2 Convert to radians, correct to 3 significant figures:

a 36.7°	b 137.2°	c 317.9°	d 219.6°	e 396.7°

Example 3   🔊 **Self Tutor**

Convert $\frac{5\pi}{6}$ to degrees.

$\frac{5\pi}{6}$
$= \left(\frac{5\pi}{6} \times \frac{180}{\pi}\right)^\circ$
$= 150^\circ$

3 Convert the following radian measures to degrees:

a $\frac{\pi}{5}$ b $\frac{3\pi}{5}$ c $\frac{3\pi}{4}$ d $\frac{\pi}{18}$ e $\frac{\pi}{9}$

f $\frac{7\pi}{9}$ g $\frac{\pi}{10}$ h $\frac{3\pi}{20}$ i $\frac{7\pi}{6}$ j $\frac{\pi}{8}$

Example 4   ◀)) **Self Tutor**

Convert 0.638 radians to degrees.

$$0.638 \text{ radians}$$
$$= (0.638 \times \tfrac{180}{\pi})°$$
$$\approx 36.6°$$

---

4 Convert the following radians to degrees. Give your answers correct to 2 decimal places.

a 2   b 1.53   c 0.867   d 3.179   e 5.267

5 Copy and complete, giving answers in terms of π:

a

Degrees	0	45	90	135	180	225	270	315	360
Radians									

b

Degrees	0	30	60	90	120	150	180	210	240	270	300	330	360
Radians													

THEORY OF KNOWLEDGE

There are several theories for why one complete turn was divided into 360 degrees:

- 360 is approximately the number of days in a year.
- The Babylonians used a counting system in base 60. If they drew 6 equilateral triangles within a circle as shown, and divided each angle into 60 subdivisions, then there were 360 subdivisions in one turn. The division of an hour into 60 minutes, and a minute into 60 seconds, is from this base 60 counting system.

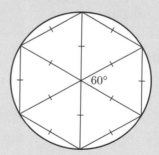

- 360 has 24 divisors, including every integer from 1 to 10 except 7.

The idea of measuring an angle by the length of an arc dates to around 1400 and the Persian mathematician Al-Kashi. The concept of a radian is generally credited to Roger Cotes, however, who described it as we know it today.

1 What other measures of angle are there?

2 Which is the most *natural* unit of angle measure?

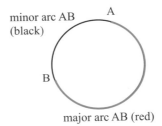

B ARC LENGTH AND SECTOR AREA

You should be familiar with these terms relating to the parts of a circle:

An arc, sector, or segment is described as:

- **minor** if it involves less than half the circle.
- **major** if it involves more than half the circle.

For example:

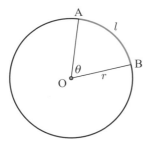

minor segment

major segment

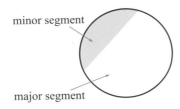

minor arc AB (black)

major arc AB (red)

ARC LENGTH

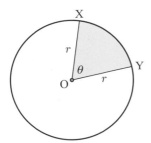

In the diagram, the **arc length** AB is l. Angle θ is measured in **radians**. We use a ratio to obtain:

$$\frac{\text{arc length}}{\text{circumference}} = \frac{\theta}{2\pi}$$

$$\therefore \frac{l}{2\pi r} = \frac{\theta}{2\pi}$$

$$\therefore l = \theta r$$

> For θ in radians,   arc length $l = \theta r$.
>
> For θ in degrees,   arc length $l = \frac{\theta}{360} \times 2\pi r$.

AREA OF SECTOR

In the diagram, the area of minor sector XOY is shaded. θ is measured in **radians**. We use a ratio to obtain:

$$\frac{\text{area of sector}}{\text{area of circle}} = \frac{\theta}{2\pi}$$

$$\therefore \frac{A}{\pi r^2} = \frac{\theta}{2\pi}$$

$$\therefore A = \tfrac{1}{2}\theta r^2$$

> For θ in radians,   area of sector $A = \frac{1}{2}\theta r^2$.
>
> For θ in degrees,   area of sector $A = \frac{\theta}{360} \times \pi r^2$.

Example 5   🔊 Self Tutor

A sector has radius 12 cm and angle 3 radians. Find its:

   a arc length   **b** area

   a arc length $= \theta r$
                  $= 3 \times 12$
                  $= 36$ cm

   b area $= \frac{1}{2}\theta r^2$
             $= \frac{1}{2} \times 3 \times 12^2$
             $= 216$ cm^2

EXERCISE 8B

1 Use radians to find the arc length and area of a sector of a circle of:

   a radius 9 cm and angle $\frac{7\pi}{4}$ **b** radius 4.93 cm and angle 4.67 radians.

2 A sector has an angle of 107.9° and an arc length of 5.92 m. Find its:

   a radius   **b** area.

3 A sector has an angle of 1.19 radians and an area of 20.8 cm^2. Find its:

   a radius   **b** perimeter.

Example 6   🔊 Self Tutor

Find the area of a sector with radius 8.2 cm and arc length 13.3 cm.

$$l = \theta r \quad \{\theta \text{ in radians}\}$$
$$\therefore \ \theta = \frac{l}{r} = \frac{13.3}{8.2}$$
$$\therefore \ \text{area} = \frac{1}{2}\theta r^2$$
$$= \frac{1}{2} \times \frac{13.3}{8.2} \times 8.2^2$$
$$\approx 54.5 \text{ cm}^2$$

4 Find, in radians, the angle of a sector of:

   a radius 4.3 m and arc length 2.95 m   **b** radius 10 cm and area 30 cm^2.

5 Find θ (in radians) for each of the following, and hence find the area of each figure:

   a   **b**   **c**

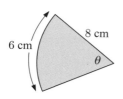
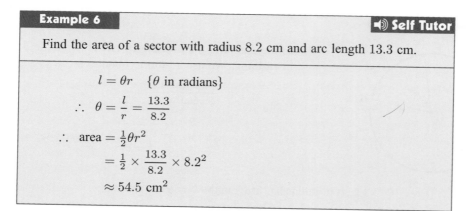
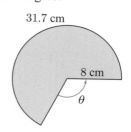

6 Find the arc length and area of a sector of radius 5 cm and angle 2 radians.

7 If a sector has radius $2x$ cm and arc length x cm, show that its area is x^2 cm^2.

8   The cone 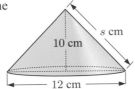 is made from this sector:

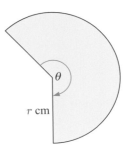

Find correct to 3 significant figures:

   a   the slant length s cm

   c   the arc length of the sector

   b   the value of r

   d   the sector angle θ in radians.

9

The end wall of a building has the shape illustrated, where the centre of arc AB is at C. Find:

   a α to 4 significant figures

   b θ to 4 significant figures

   c   the area of the wall.

10

[AT] is a tangent to the given circle.   OA $= 13$ cm   and the circle has radius 5 cm. Find the perimeter of the shaded region.

11   A **nautical mile** (nmi) is the distance on the Earth's surface that subtends an angle of 1 minute (or $\frac{1}{60}$ of a degree) of the Great Circle arc measured from the centre of the Earth.
A **knot** is a speed of 1 nautical mile per hour.

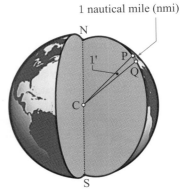

1 nautical mile (nmi)

   a   Given that the radius of the Earth is 6370 km, show that 1 nmi is approximately equal to 1.853 km.

   b   Calculate how long it would take a plane to fly from Perth to Adelaide (a distance of 2130 km) if the plane can fly at 480 knots.

12

fence

6 m

post   sheep

A sheep is tethered to a post which is 6 m from a long fence. The length of rope is 9 m. Find the area which the sheep can feed on.

C   THE UNIT CIRCLE AND THE TRIGONOMETRIC RATIOS

The **unit circle** is the circle with centre $(0, 0)$ and radius 1 unit.

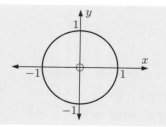

CIRCLES WITH CENTRE $(0, 0)$

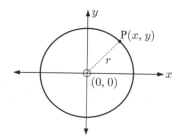

Consider a circle with centre $(0, 0)$ and radius r units. Suppose $P(x, y)$ is any point on this circle.

Since $OP = r$,

$$\sqrt{(x-0)^2 + (y-0)^2} = r \quad \text{\{distance formula\}}$$
$$\therefore \; x^2 + y^2 = r^2$$

$x^2 + y^2 = r^2$ is the equation of a circle with centre $(0, 0)$ and radius r.
The equation of the **unit circle** is $x^2 + y^2 = 1$.

ANGLE MEASUREMENT

Suppose P lies anywhere on the unit circle and A is $(1, 0)$.
Let θ be the angle measured from [OA] on the positive x-axis.

> θ is **positive** for anticlockwise rotations and **negative** for clockwise rotations.

For example, $\theta = 210°$ and $\phi = -150°$.

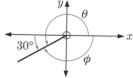

You can explore angle measurement further by clicking on the icon.

DYNAMIC ANGLES

DEFINITION OF SINE AND COSINE

Consider a point $P(a, b)$ which lies on the unit circle in the first quadrant. [OP] makes an angle θ with the x-axis as shown.

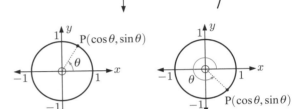

Using right angled triangle trigonometry:

$$\cos \theta = \frac{\text{ADJ}}{\text{HYP}} = \frac{a}{1} = a$$

$$\sin \theta = \frac{\text{OPP}}{\text{HYP}} = \frac{b}{1} = b$$

$$\tan \theta = \frac{\text{OPP}}{\text{ADJ}} = \frac{b}{a} = \frac{\sin \theta}{\cos \theta}$$

In general, for a point P anywhere on the unit circle:

- **$\cos \theta$** is the x-coordinate of P
- **$\sin \theta$** is the y-coordinate of P

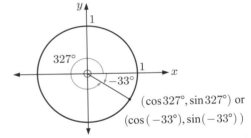

We can hence find the coordinates of any point on the unit circle with given angle θ measured from the positive x-axis.

For example:

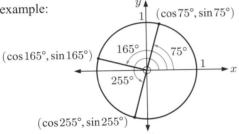

Since the unit circle has equation $x^2 + y^2 = 1$, $(\cos \theta)^2 + (\sin \theta)^2 = 1$ for all θ.

We commonly write this as $\qquad \cos^2 \theta + \sin^2 \theta = 1.$

For all points on the unit circle, $-1 \leqslant x \leqslant 1$ and $-1 \leqslant y \leqslant 1$.

So, $\qquad -1 \leqslant \cos \theta \leqslant 1$ and $-1 \leqslant \sin \theta \leqslant 1$ for all θ.

DEFINITION OF TANGENT

Suppose we extend [OP] to meet the tangent at $A(1, 0)$. The intersection between these lines occurs at Q, and as P moves so does Q.

The position of Q relative to A is defined as the **tangent function**.

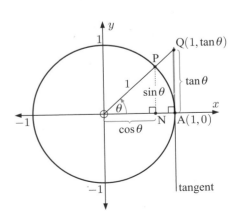

Notice that $\triangle$s ONP and OAQ are equiangular and therefore similar.

Consequently $\dfrac{\text{AQ}}{\text{OA}} = \dfrac{\text{NP}}{\text{ON}}$ and hence $\dfrac{\text{AQ}}{1} = \dfrac{\sin \theta}{\cos \theta}.$

Under the definition that $\text{AQ} = \tan \theta$, $\qquad \tan \theta = \dfrac{\sin \theta}{\cos \theta}.$

INVESTIGATION 1   THE TRIGONOMETRIC RATIOS

In this investigation we explore the signs of the trigonometric ratios in each quadrant of the unit circle.

THE UNIT CIRCLE

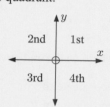

What to do:

1   Click on the icon to run the Unit Circle software.
    Drag the point P slowly around the circle.
    Note the *sign* of each trigonometric ratio in each quadrant.

Quadrant	$\cos\theta$	$\sin\theta$	$\tan\theta$
1	positive		
2			
3			
4			

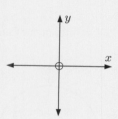

2   Hence note down the trigonometric ratios which are *positive* in each quadrant.

From the **Investigation** you should have discovered that:

- $\sin\theta$, $\cos\theta$, and $\tan\theta$ are positive in quadrant 1
- only $\sin\theta$ is positive in quadrant 2
- only $\tan\theta$ is positive in quadrant 3
- only $\cos\theta$ is positive in quadrant 4.

We can use a letter to show which trigonometric ratios are positive in each quadrant. The A stands for *all* of the ratios.

You might like to remember them using

    All Silly Turtles Crawl.

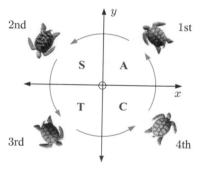

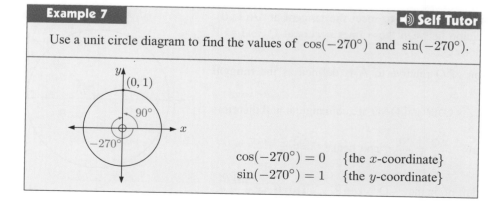

| Example 7 | ◀ Self Tutor |

Use a unit circle diagram to find the values of $\cos(-270°)$ and $\sin(-270°)$.

$\cos(-270°) = 0$ {the x-coordinate}
$\sin(-270°) = 1$ {the y-coordinate}

PERIODICITY OF TRIGONOMETRIC RATIOS

Since there are 2π radians in a full revolution, if we add any integer multiple of 2π to θ (in radians) then the position of P on the unit circle is unchanged.

For θ in radians and $k \in \mathbb{Z}$,
$$\cos(\theta + 2k\pi) = \cos\theta \quad \text{and} \quad \sin(\theta + 2k\pi) = \sin\theta.$$

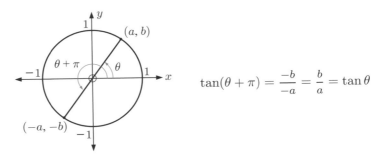

$$\tan(\theta + \pi) = \frac{-b}{-a} = \frac{b}{a} = \tan\theta$$

For θ in radians and $k \in \mathbb{Z}$, $\quad \tan(\theta + k\pi) = \tan\theta$.

This **periodic** feature is an important property of the trigonometric functions.

EXERCISE 8C

1 For each unit circle illustrated:
   i   state the exact coordinates of points A, B, and C in terms of sine and cosine
   ii use your calculator to give the coordinates of A, B, and C correct to 3 significant figures.

a
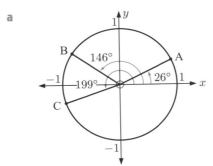

b
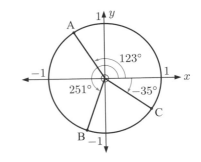

2 With the aid of a unit circle, complete the following table:

θ (degrees)	0°	90°	180°	270°	360°	450°
θ (radians)						
sine						
cosine						
tangent						

3 **a** Use your calculator to evaluate: **i** $\frac{1}{\sqrt{2}}$ **ii** $\frac{\sqrt{3}}{2}$

   b Copy and complete the following table. Use your calculator to evaluate the trigonometric ratios, then **a** to write them exactly.

θ (degrees)	30°	45°	60°	135°	150°	240°	315°
θ (radians)							
sine							
cosine							
tangent							

4 **a** Use your calculator to evaluate:

   i $\sin 100°$ **ii** $\sin 80°$ **iii** $\sin 120°$ **iv** $\sin 60°$
   v $\sin 150°$ **vi** $\sin 30°$ **vii** $\sin 45°$ **viii** $\sin 135°$

   b Use the results from **a** to copy and complete:
   $$\sin(180° - \theta) = \ldots\ldots$$

   c Justify your answer using the diagram alongside:

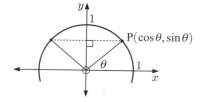

   d Find the obtuse angle with the same sine as:
   i 45°   **ii** 51°   **iii** $\frac{\pi}{3}$ **iv** $\frac{\pi}{6}$

5 **a** Use your calculator to evaluate:

   i $\cos 70°$ **ii** $\cos 110°$ **iii** $\cos 60°$ **iv** $\cos 120°$
   v $\cos 25°$ **vi** $\cos 155°$ **vii** $\cos 80°$ **viii** $\cos 100°$

   b Use the results from **a** to copy and complete:
   $$\cos(180° - \theta) = \ldots\ldots$$

   c Justify your answer using the diagram alongside:

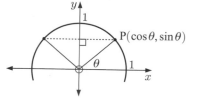

   d Find the obtuse angle which has the negative cosine of:
   i 40°   **ii** 19°   **iii** $\frac{\pi}{5}$ **iv** $\frac{2\pi}{5}$

6 Without using your calculator, find:

   a $\sin 137°$ if $\sin 43° \approx 0.6820$ **b** $\sin 59°$ if $\sin 121° \approx 0.8572$
   c $\cos 143°$ if $\cos 37° \approx 0.7986$ **d** $\cos 24°$ if $\cos 156° \approx -0.9135$
   e $\sin 115°$ if $\sin 65° \approx 0.9063$ **f** $\cos 132°$ if $\cos 48° \approx 0.6691$

7 **a** Copy and complete:

Quadrant	Degree measure	Radian measure	$\cos\theta$	$\sin\theta$	$\tan\theta$
1	$0° < \theta < 90°$	$0 < \theta < \frac{\pi}{2}$	positive	positive	
2					
3					
4					

b In which quadrants are the following true?

    i $\cos\theta$ is positive.   **ii** $\cos\theta$ is negative.

    iii $\cos\theta$ and $\sin\theta$ are both negative.   **iv** $\cos\theta$ is negative and $\sin\theta$ is positive.

8 **a** If $A\widehat{O}P = \theta$ and $B\widehat{O}Q = \theta$ also, what is the measure of $A\widehat{O}Q$?

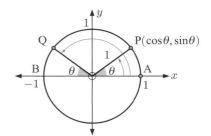

  b Copy and complete:

    [OQ] is a reflection of [OP] in the ......
and so Q has coordinates ......

  c What trigonometric formulae can be deduced from **a** and **b**?

9 **a** Copy and complete:

θ^c	$\sin\theta$	$\sin(-\theta)$	$\cos\theta$	$\cos(-\theta)$
0.75				
1.772				
3.414				
6.25				
-1.17				

  b What do you suspect is true from **a** for a general angle θ?

  c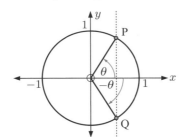

    The coordinates of P in the figure are $(\cos\theta,\ \sin\theta)$.

    i By finding the coordinates of Q in terms of θ in *two different* ways, prove that your suspicion in **b** is correct.

    ii Hence explain why $\cos(2\pi - \theta) = \cos\theta$.

D   APPLICATIONS OF THE UNIT CIRCLE

The identity $\cos^2\theta + \sin^2\theta = 1$ is essential for finding trigonometric ratios.

Example 8	◀ΰ **Self Tutor**

Find exactly the possible values of $\cos\theta$ for $\sin\theta = \frac{2}{3}$. Illustrate your answers.

$$\cos^2\theta + \sin^2\theta = 1$$
$$\therefore\ \cos^2\theta + \left(\tfrac{2}{3}\right)^2 = 1$$
$$\therefore\ \cos^2\theta = \tfrac{5}{9}$$
$$\therefore\ \cos\theta = \pm\tfrac{\sqrt{5}}{3}$$

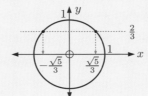

EXERCISE 8D.1

1 Find the possible exact values of $\cos \theta$ for:

    a $\sin \theta = \frac{1}{2}$ **b** $\sin \theta = -\frac{1}{3}$ **c** $\sin \theta = 0$ **d** $\sin \theta = -1$

2 Find the possible exact values of $\sin \theta$ for:

    a $\cos \theta = \frac{4}{5}$ **b** $\cos \theta = -\frac{3}{4}$ **c** $\cos \theta = 1$ **d** $\cos \theta = 0$

Example 9   ◀) **Self Tutor**

If $\sin \theta = -\frac{3}{4}$ and $\pi < \theta < \frac{3\pi}{2}$, find $\cos \theta$ and $\tan \theta$. Give exact values.

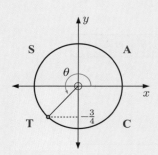

Now $\cos^2 \theta + \sin^2 \theta = 1$

$\therefore \;\; \cos^2 \theta + \frac{9}{16} = 1$

$\therefore \;\; \cos^2 \theta = \frac{7}{16}$

$\therefore \;\; \cos \theta = \pm \frac{\sqrt{7}}{4}$

But $\pi < \theta < \frac{3\pi}{2}$, so θ is a quadrant 3 angle

$\therefore \;\; \cos \theta$ is negative.

$\therefore \;\; \cos \theta = -\frac{\sqrt{7}}{4}$

and $\tan \theta = \dfrac{\sin \theta}{\cos \theta} = \dfrac{-\frac{3}{4}}{-\frac{\sqrt{7}}{4}} = \dfrac{3}{\sqrt{7}}$

---

3 Without using a calculator, find:

    a $\sin \theta$ if $\cos \theta = \frac{2}{3}$ and $0 < \theta < \frac{\pi}{2}$ **b** $\cos \theta$ if $\sin \theta = \frac{2}{5}$ and $\frac{\pi}{2} < \theta < \pi$

    c $\cos \theta$ if $\sin \theta = -\frac{3}{5}$ and $\frac{3\pi}{2} < \theta < 2\pi$ **d** $\sin \theta$ if $\cos \theta = -\frac{5}{13}$ and $\pi < \theta < \frac{3\pi}{2}$.

Example 10   ◀) **Self Tutor**

If $\tan \theta = -2$ and $\frac{3\pi}{2} < \theta < 2\pi$, find $\sin \theta$ and $\cos \theta$. Give exact answers.

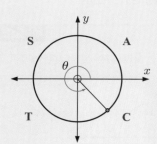

$\tan \theta = \dfrac{\sin \theta}{\cos \theta} = -2$

$\therefore \;\; \sin \theta = -2 \cos \theta$

Now $\sin^2 \theta + \cos^2 \theta = 1$

$\therefore \;\; (-2 \cos \theta)^2 + \cos^2 \theta = 1$

$\therefore \;\; 4 \cos^2 \theta + \cos^2 \theta = 1$

$\therefore \;\; 5 \cos^2 \theta = 1$

$\therefore \;\; \cos \theta = \pm \frac{1}{\sqrt{5}}$

But $\frac{3\pi}{2} < \theta < 2\pi$, so θ is a quadrant 4 angle.

$\therefore \;\; \cos \theta$ is positive and $\sin \theta$ is negative.

$\therefore \;\; \cos \theta = \frac{1}{\sqrt{5}}$ and $\sin \theta = -\frac{2}{\sqrt{5}}$.

4   **a** If $\sin x = \frac{1}{3}$ and $\frac{\pi}{2} < x < \pi$,   find $\tan x$ exactly.

   b If $\cos x = \frac{1}{5}$ and $\frac{3\pi}{2} < x < 2\pi$,   find $\tan x$ exactly.

   c If $\sin x = -\frac{1}{\sqrt{3}}$ and $\pi < x < \frac{3\pi}{2}$,   find $\tan x$ exactly.

   d If $\cos x = -\frac{3}{4}$ and $\frac{\pi}{2} < x < \pi$,   find $\tan x$ exactly.

5   Find exact values for $\sin x$ and $\cos x$ given that:

   a $\tan x = \frac{2}{3}$ and $0 < x < \frac{\pi}{2}$
              b $\tan x = -\frac{4}{3}$ and $\frac{\pi}{2} < x < \pi$

   c $\tan x = \frac{\sqrt{5}}{3}$ and $\pi < x < \frac{3\pi}{2}$
         d $\tan x = -\frac{12}{5}$ and $\frac{3\pi}{2} < x < 2\pi$

6   Suppose $\tan x = k$ where k is a constant and $\pi < x < \frac{3\pi}{2}$.   Write expressions for $\sin x$ and $\cos x$ in terms of k.

FINDING ANGLES WITH PARTICULAR TRIGONOMETRIC RATIOS

From **Exercise 8C** you should have discovered that:

> For θ in radians:
> - $\sin(\pi - \theta) = \sin \theta$
> - $\cos(\pi - \theta) = -\cos \theta$
> - $\cos(2\pi - \theta) = \cos \theta$

We need results such as these, and also the periodicity of the trigonometric ratios, to find angles which have a particular sine, cosine, or tangent.

Example 11   ◀) **Self Tutor**

Find the two angles θ on the unit circle, with $0 \leqslant \theta \leqslant 2\pi$,   such that:

  a $\cos \theta = \frac{1}{3}$
          b $\sin \theta = \frac{3}{4}$
          c $\tan \theta = 2$

---

  a Using technology,
$$\cos \theta = \frac{1}{3}$$
$$\cos^{-1}\left(\tfrac{1}{3}\right) \approx 1.23$$

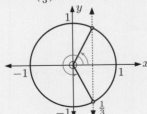

  b Using technology,
$$\sin \theta = \frac{3}{4}$$
$$\sin^{-1}\left(\tfrac{3}{4}\right) \approx 0.848$$

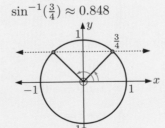

  c Using technology,
$$\tan \theta = 2$$
$$\tan^{-1}(2) \approx 1.11$$

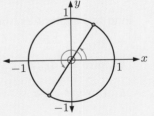

  $\therefore \ \theta \approx 1.23$ or $2\pi - 1.23$
$\therefore \ \theta \approx 1.23$ or 5.05

  $\therefore \ \theta \approx 0.848$ or $\pi - 0.848$
$\therefore \ \theta \approx 0.848$ or 2.29

  $\therefore \ \theta \approx 1.11$ or $\pi + 1.11$
$\therefore \ \theta \approx 1.11$ or 4.25

Example 12
🔊 Self Tutor

Find two angles θ on the unit circle, with $0 \leqslant \theta \leqslant 2\pi$, such that:

a $\sin \theta = -0.4$ **b** $\cos \theta = -\frac{2}{3}$ **c** $\tan \theta = -\frac{1}{3}$

a $\sin \theta = -0.4$

Using technology,

$\sin^{-1}(-0.4) \approx -0.412$

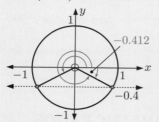

But $0 \leqslant \theta \leqslant 2\pi$

∴ $\theta \approx \pi + 0.412$ or

     $2\pi - 0.412$

∴ $\theta \approx 3.55$ or   5.87

b $\cos \theta = -\frac{2}{3}$

Using technology,

$\cos^{-1}(-\frac{2}{3}) \approx 2.30$

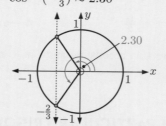

But $0 \leqslant \theta \leqslant 2\pi$

∴ $\theta \approx 2.30$ or

     $2\pi - 2.30$

∴ $\theta \approx 2.30$ or   3.98

c $\tan \theta = -\frac{1}{3}$

Using technology,

$\tan^{-1}(-\frac{1}{3}) \approx -0.322$

But $0 \leqslant \theta \leqslant 2\pi$

∴ $\theta \approx \pi - 0.322$ or

     $2\pi - 0.322$

∴ $\theta \approx 2.82$ or   5.96

The green arrow shows the angle that the calculator gives.

EXERCISE 8D.2

1   Find two angles θ on the unit circle, with $0 \leqslant \theta \leqslant 2\pi$, such that:

     a $\tan \theta = 4$ **b** $\cos \theta = 0.83$ **c** $\sin \theta = \frac{3}{5}$

     d $\cos \theta = 0$ **e** $\tan \theta = 1.2$ **f** $\cos \theta = 0.7816$

     g $\sin \theta = \frac{1}{11}$ **h** $\tan \theta = 20.2$ **i** $\sin \theta = \frac{39}{40}$

2   Find two angles θ on the unit circle, with $0 \leqslant \theta \leqslant 2\pi$, such that:

     a $\cos \theta = -\frac{1}{4}$ **b** $\sin \theta = 0$ **c** $\tan \theta = -3.1$

     d $\sin \theta = -0.421$ **e** $\tan \theta = -6.67$ **f** $\cos \theta = -\frac{2}{17}$

     g $\tan \theta = -\sqrt{5}$ **h** $\cos \theta = \frac{-1}{\sqrt{3}}$ **i** $\sin \theta = -\frac{\sqrt{2}}{\sqrt{5}}$

INVESTIGATION 2   PARAMETRIC EQUATIONS

Usually we write functions in the form $y = f(x)$.

For example: $y = 3x + 7$, $y = x^2 - 6x + 8$, $y = \sin x$

However, sometimes it is useful to express **both** x and y in terms of another variable t, called the **parameter**. In this case we say we have **parametric equations**.

GRAPHICS
CALCULATOR
INSTRUCTIONS

What to do:

1 **a** Use your graphics calculator to plot $\{(x, y) \mid x = \cos t, \; y = \sin t, \; 0° \leqslant t \leqslant 360°\}$.
      Use the same scale on both axes.
      Note: Your calculator will need to be set to degrees.

   b Describe the resulting graph. Is it the graph of a function?

   c Evaluate $x^2 + y^2$.   Hence determine the equation of this graph in terms of x and y only.

2 Use your graphics calculator to plot:

   a $\{(x, y) \mid x = 2\cos t, \; y = \sin(2t), \; 0° \leqslant t \leqslant 360°\}$

   b $\{(x, y) \mid x = 2\cos t, \; y = 2\sin(3t), \; 0° \leqslant t \leqslant 360°\}$

   c $\{(x, y) \mid x = 2\cos t, \; y = \cos t - \sin t, \; 0° \leqslant t \leqslant 360°\}$

   d $\{(x, y) \mid x = \cos^2 t + \sin 2t, \; y = \cos t, \; 0° \leqslant t \leqslant 360°\}$

   e $\{(x, y) \mid x = \cos^3 t, \; y = \sin t, \; 0° \leqslant t \leqslant 360°\}$

E   MULTIPLES OF $\frac{\pi}{6}$ AND $\frac{\pi}{4}$

Angles which are multiples of $\frac{\pi}{6}$ and $\frac{\pi}{4}$ occur frequently, so it is important for us to write their trigonometric ratios exactly.

MULTIPLES OF $\frac{\pi}{4}$ OR $45°$

Triangle OBP is isosceles as angle OPB also measures $45°$.

Letting   OB = BP = a,

$$a^2 + a^2 = 1^2 \qquad \{\text{Pythagoras}\}$$
$$\therefore \;\; 2a^2 = 1$$
$$\therefore \;\; a^2 = \tfrac{1}{2}$$
$$\therefore \;\; a = \tfrac{1}{\sqrt{2}} \quad \text{as} \;\; a > 0$$

So, P is $(\tfrac{1}{\sqrt{2}}, \tfrac{1}{\sqrt{2}})$ where $\tfrac{1}{\sqrt{2}} \approx 0.707$.

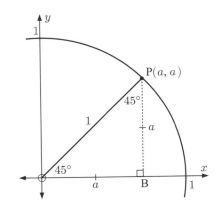

$$\cos \tfrac{\pi}{4} = \tfrac{1}{\sqrt{2}} \quad \text{and} \quad \sin \tfrac{\pi}{4} = \tfrac{1}{\sqrt{2}}$$

You should remember these values. If you forget, draw a right angled isosceles triangle with side length 1.

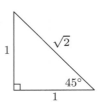

For **multiples of** $\frac{\pi}{4}$, the number $\frac{1}{\sqrt{2}}$ is the important thing to remember. The signs of the coordinates are determined by which quadrant the angle is in.

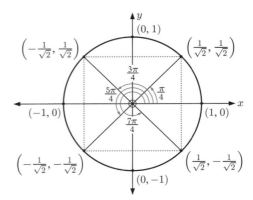

MULTIPLES OF $\frac{\pi}{6}$ OR $30°$

Since OA $=$ OP, triangle OAP is isosceles.

The remaining angles are therefore also $60°$, and so triangle AOP is equilateral.

The altitude [PN] bisects base [OA],

$$\text{so} \quad \text{ON} = \tfrac{1}{2}$$

If P is $(\tfrac{1}{2}, k)$, then $(\tfrac{1}{2})^2 + k^2 = 1 \quad$ {Pythagoras}

$$\therefore \quad k^2 = \tfrac{3}{4}$$

$$\therefore \quad k = \tfrac{\sqrt{3}}{2} \quad \{\text{as } k > 0\}$$

So, P is $(\tfrac{1}{2}, \tfrac{\sqrt{3}}{2})$ where $\tfrac{\sqrt{3}}{2} \approx 0.866$.

$$\cos \tfrac{\pi}{3} = \tfrac{1}{2} \quad \text{and} \quad \sin \tfrac{\pi}{3} = \tfrac{\sqrt{3}}{2}$$

Now $\text{N}\widehat{\text{P}}\text{O} = \tfrac{\pi}{6} = 30°$.

Hence $\quad \cos \tfrac{\pi}{6} = \tfrac{\sqrt{3}}{2} \quad \text{and} \quad \sin \tfrac{\pi}{6} = \tfrac{1}{2}$

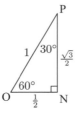

You should remember these values. If you forget, divide in two an equilateral triangle with side length 2.

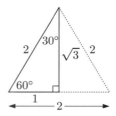

For **multiples of** $\frac{\pi}{6}$, the numbers $\frac{1}{2}$ and $\frac{\sqrt{3}}{2}$ are important. The exact coordinates of each point are found by symmetry.

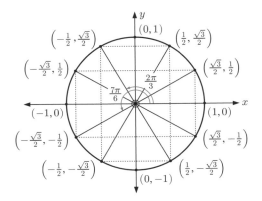

SUMMARY

- For **multiples of** $\frac{\pi}{2}$, the coordinates of the points on the unit circle involve 0 and ± 1.

- For *other* **multiples of** $\frac{\pi}{4}$, the coordinates involve $\pm\frac{1}{\sqrt{2}}$.

- For *other* **multiples of** $\frac{\pi}{6}$, the coordinates involve $\pm\frac{1}{2}$ and $\pm\frac{\sqrt{3}}{2}$.

You should be able to use this summary to find the trigonometric ratios for angles which are multiples of $\frac{\pi}{6}$ and $\frac{\pi}{4}$.

For example, consider the angles:

- $225° = \frac{5\pi}{4}$

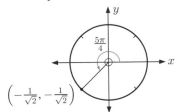

$\frac{5\pi}{4}$ is in quadrant 3, so the signs are both negative and both have $\frac{1}{\sqrt{2}}$ size.

- $300° = \frac{5\pi}{3}$ which is a multiple of $\frac{\pi}{6}$.

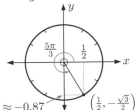

$\frac{5\pi}{3}$ is in quadrant 4, so the signs are $(+, -)$ and from the diagram the x-value is $\frac{1}{2}$.

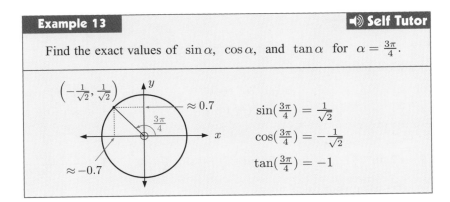

Example 13   ◀) **Self Tutor**

Find the exact values of $\sin\alpha$, $\cos\alpha$, and $\tan\alpha$ for $\alpha = \frac{3\pi}{4}$.

$\sin\left(\frac{3\pi}{4}\right) = \frac{1}{\sqrt{2}}$

$\cos\left(\frac{3\pi}{4}\right) = -\frac{1}{\sqrt{2}}$

$\tan\left(\frac{3\pi}{4}\right) = -1$

Example 14   ◀) **Self Tutor**

Find the exact values of $\sin\frac{4\pi}{3}$, $\cos\frac{4\pi}{3}$, and $\tan\frac{4\pi}{3}$.

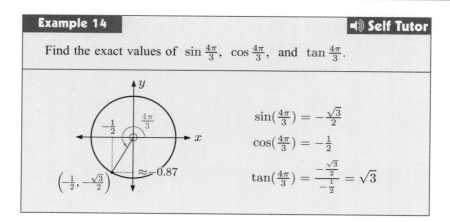

$$\sin(\tfrac{4\pi}{3}) = -\tfrac{\sqrt{3}}{2}$$

$$\cos(\tfrac{4\pi}{3}) = -\tfrac{1}{2}$$

$$\tan(\tfrac{4\pi}{3}) = \frac{-\frac{\sqrt{3}}{2}}{-\frac{1}{2}} = \sqrt{3}$$

EXERCISE 8E

1 Use a unit circle diagram to find exact values for $\sin\theta$, $\cos\theta$, and $\tan\theta$ for θ equal to:

  a $\frac{\pi}{4}$ **b** $\frac{3\pi}{4}$ **c** $\frac{7\pi}{4}$ **d** π **e** $\frac{-3\pi}{4}$

2 Use a unit circle diagram to find exact values for $\sin\beta$, $\cos\beta$, and $\tan\beta$ for β equal to:

  a $\frac{\pi}{6}$ **b** $\frac{2\pi}{3}$ **c** $\frac{7\pi}{6}$ **d** $\frac{5\pi}{3}$ **e** $\frac{11\pi}{6}$

3 Find the exact values of:

  a $\cos 120°$, $\sin 120°$, and $\tan 120°$ **b** $\cos(-45°)$, $\sin(-45°)$, and $\tan(-45°)$

4 **a** Find the exact values of $\cos 90°$ and $\sin 90°$.

    b What can you say about $\tan 90°$?

Example 15   ◀) **Self Tutor**

Without using a calculator, show that $8\sin(\frac{\pi}{3})\cos(\frac{5\pi}{6}) = -6$.

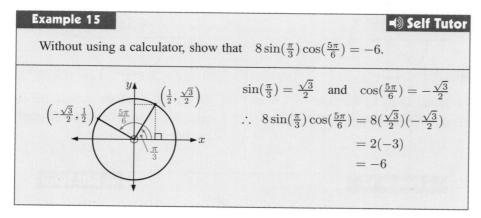

$$\sin(\tfrac{\pi}{3}) = \tfrac{\sqrt{3}}{2} \quad \text{and} \quad \cos(\tfrac{5\pi}{6}) = -\tfrac{\sqrt{3}}{2}$$

$$\therefore \quad 8\sin(\tfrac{\pi}{3})\cos(\tfrac{5\pi}{6}) = 8(\tfrac{\sqrt{3}}{2})(-\tfrac{\sqrt{3}}{2})$$

$$= 2(-3)$$

$$= -6$$

5 Without using a calculator, evaluate:

  a $\sin^2 60°$ **b** $\sin 30° \cos 60°$ **c** $4\sin 60° \cos 30°$

  d $1 - \cos^2(\frac{\pi}{6})$ **e** $\sin^2(\frac{2\pi}{3}) - 1$ **f** $\cos^2(\frac{\pi}{4}) - \sin(\frac{7\pi}{6})$

  g $\sin(\frac{3\pi}{4}) - \cos(\frac{5\pi}{4})$ **h** $1 - 2\sin^2(\frac{7\pi}{6})$ **i** $\cos^2(\frac{5\pi}{6}) - \sin^2(\frac{5\pi}{6})$

  j $\tan^2(\frac{\pi}{3}) - 2\sin^2(\frac{\pi}{4})$ **k** $2\tan(-\frac{5\pi}{4}) - \sin(\frac{3\pi}{2})$ **l** $\dfrac{2\tan 150°}{1 - \tan^2 150°}$

Check all answers using your calculator.

Example 16   ◀)) **Self Tutor**

Find all angles $0 \leqslant \theta \leqslant 2\pi$ with a cosine of $\frac{1}{2}$.

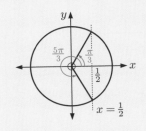

Since the cosine is $\frac{1}{2}$, we draw the vertical line $x = \frac{1}{2}$.

Because $\frac{1}{2}$ is involved, we know the required angles are multiples of $\frac{\pi}{6}$.

They are $\frac{\pi}{3}$ and $\frac{5\pi}{3}$.

6 Find all angles between $0°$ and $360°$ with:

   a a sine of $\frac{1}{2}$ **b** a sine of $\frac{\sqrt{3}}{2}$ **c** a cosine of $\frac{1}{\sqrt{2}}$

   d a cosine of $-\frac{1}{2}$ **e** a cosine of $-\frac{1}{\sqrt{2}}$ **f** a sine of $-\frac{\sqrt{3}}{2}$

7 Find all angles between 0 and 2π (inclusive) which have:

   a a tangent of 1 **b** a tangent of -1 **c** a tangent of $\sqrt{3}$

   d a tangent of 0 **e** a tangent of $\frac{1}{\sqrt{3}}$ **f** a tangent of $-\sqrt{3}$

8 Find all angles between 0 and 4π with:

   a a cosine of $\frac{\sqrt{3}}{2}$ **b** a sine of $-\frac{1}{2}$ **c** a sine of -1

9 Find θ if $0 \leqslant \theta \leqslant 2\pi$ and:

   a $\cos\theta = \frac{1}{2}$ **b** $\sin\theta = \frac{\sqrt{3}}{2}$ **c** $\cos\theta = -1$ **d** $\sin\theta = 1$

   e $\cos\theta = -\frac{1}{\sqrt{2}}$ **f** $\sin^2\theta = 1$ **g** $\cos^2\theta = 1$ **h** $\cos^2\theta = \frac{1}{2}$

   i $\tan\theta = -\frac{1}{\sqrt{3}}$ **j** $\tan^2\theta = 3$

10 Find *all* values of θ for which $\tan\theta$ is: **a** zero   **b** undefined.

F   **THE EQUATION OF A STRAIGHT LINE**

If a straight line makes an angle of θ with the positive x-axis then its gradient is $m = \tan\theta$.

Proof:

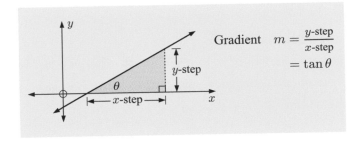

Gradient $m = \dfrac{y\text{-step}}{x\text{-step}}$

$= \tan\theta$

Example 17
◄ᵉ Self Tutor

Find the equation of
the given line:

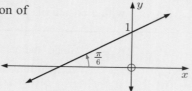

The line has gradient $m = \tan\frac{\pi}{6} = \frac{1}{\sqrt{3}}$ and y-intercept 1.

∴   the line has equation $y = \frac{1}{\sqrt{3}}x + 1$.

EXERCISE 8F

1 Find the equation of each line:

a
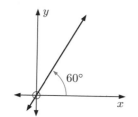

b
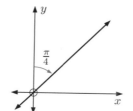

c
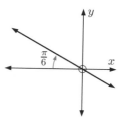

2 Find the equation of each line:

a
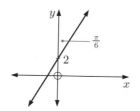

b
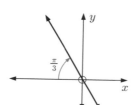

c
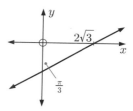

REVIEW SET 8A   NON-CALCULATOR

1 Convert these to radians in terms of π:

    a 120°   **b** 225°   **c** 150°   **d** 540°

2 Find the acute angles that would have the same:

    a sine as $\frac{2\pi}{3}$ **b** sine as 165°   **c** cosine as 276°.

3 Find:

    a $\sin 159°$ if $\sin 21° \approx 0.358$ **b** $\cos 92°$ if $\cos 88° \approx 0.035$

    c $\cos 75°$ if $\cos 105° \approx -0.259$ **d** $\sin(-133°)$ if $\sin 47° \approx 0.731$.

4 Use a unit circle diagram to find:

    a $\cos 360°$ and $\sin 360°$ **b** $\cos(-\pi)$ and $\sin(-\pi)$.

5 Explain how to use the unit circle to find θ when $\cos\theta = -\sin\theta$, $0 \leqslant \theta \leqslant 2\pi$.

6 Find exact values for $\sin\theta$, $\cos\theta$, and $\tan\theta$ for θ equal to:

    a $\frac{2\pi}{3}$ **b** $\frac{8\pi}{3}$

7 If $\sin x = -\frac{1}{4}$ and $\pi < x < \frac{3\pi}{2}$, find $\tan x$ exactly.

8 If $\cos \theta = \frac{3}{4}$ find the possible values of $\sin \theta$.

9 Evaluate:

     a $2\sin(\frac{\pi}{3})\cos(\frac{\pi}{3})$ **b** $\tan^2(\frac{\pi}{4}) - 1$ **c** $\cos^2(\frac{\pi}{6}) - \sin^2(\frac{\pi}{6})$

10 Given $\tan x = -\frac{3}{2}$ and $\frac{3\pi}{2} < x < 2\pi$, find: **a** $\sin x$ **b** $\cos x$.

11

Find the perimeter and area of the sector.

12 Suppose $\cos \theta = \frac{\sqrt{11}}{\sqrt{17}}$ and θ is acute. Find the exact value of $\tan \theta$.

REVIEW SET 8B   CALCULATOR

1 Determine the coordinates of the point on the unit circle corresponding to an angle of:

     a $320°$ **b** $163°$

2 Convert to radians to 4 significant figures:

     a $71°$ **b** $124.6°$ **c** $-142°$

3 Convert these radian measurements to degrees, to 2 decimal places:

     a 3 **b** 1.46 **c** 0.435 **d** -5.271

4 Determine the area of a sector of angle $\frac{5\pi}{12}$ and radius 13 cm.

5 Find the coordinates of the points M, N, and P on the unit circle.

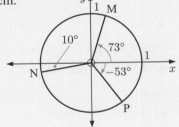

6 Find the angle [OA] makes with the positive x-axis if the x-coordinate of the point A on the unit circle is -0.222.

7 Find all angles between $0°$ and $360°$ which have:

     a a cosine of $-\frac{\sqrt{3}}{2}$ **b** a sine of $\frac{1}{\sqrt{2}}$ **c** a tangent of $-\sqrt{3}$

8 Find θ for $0 \leqslant \theta \leqslant 2\pi$ if:

     a $\cos \theta = -1$ **b** $\sin^2 \theta = \frac{3}{4}$

9 Find the obtuse angles which have the same:

     a sine as $47°$ **b** sine as $\frac{\pi}{15}$ **c** cosine as $186°$

10 Find the perimeter and area of a sector of radius 11 cm and angle $63°$.

11 Find the radius and area of a sector of perimeter 36 cm with an angle of $\frac{2\pi}{3}$.

12 Find two angles on the unit circle with $0 \leqslant \theta \leqslant 2\pi$, such that:

   a $\cos\theta = \frac{2}{3}$ **b** $\sin\theta = -\frac{1}{4}$ **c** $\tan\theta = 3$

REVIEW SET 8C

1 Convert these radian measurements to degrees:

   a $\frac{2\pi}{5}$ **b** $\frac{5\pi}{4}$ **c** $\frac{7\pi}{9}$ **d** $\frac{11\pi}{6}$

2 Illustrate the regions where $\sin\theta$ and $\cos\theta$ have the same sign.

3 Use a unit circle diagram to find:

   a $\cos(\frac{3\pi}{2})$ and $\sin(\frac{3\pi}{2})$ **b** $\cos(-\frac{\pi}{2})$ and $\sin(-\frac{\pi}{2})$

4 Suppose $m = \sin p$, where p is acute. Write an expression in terms of m for:

   a $\sin(\pi - p)$ **b** $\sin(p + 2\pi)$ **c** $\cos p$ **d** $\tan p$

5

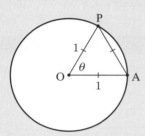

   a State the value of θ in:

      i degrees   **ii** radians.

   b State the arc length AP.

   c State the area of the minor *sector* OAP.

6 Without a calculator, evaluate $\tan^2(\frac{2\pi}{3})$.

7 Show that $\cos(\frac{3\pi}{4}) - \sin(\frac{3\pi}{4}) = -\sqrt{2}$.

8 If $\cos\theta = -\frac{3}{4}$, $\frac{\pi}{2} < \theta < \pi$ find the exact value of:

   a $\sin\theta$ **b** $\tan\theta$ **c** $\sin(\theta + \pi)$

9 Without using a calculator, evaluate:

   a $\tan^2 60° - \sin^2 45°$ **b** $\cos^2(\frac{\pi}{4}) + \sin(\frac{\pi}{2})$ **c** $\cos(\frac{5\pi}{3}) - \tan(\frac{5\pi}{4})$

10 Simplify:

   a $\sin(\pi - \theta) - \sin\theta$ **b** $\cos\theta\tan\theta$

11

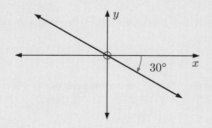

   a Find the equation of the line drawn.

   b Find the exact value of k given the point $(k, 2)$ lies on the line.

12 Three circles with radius r are drawn as shown, each with its centre on the circumference of the other two circles. A, B and C are the centres of the three circles.

Prove that an expression for the area of the shaded region is $A = \dfrac{r^2}{2}(\pi - \sqrt{3})$.

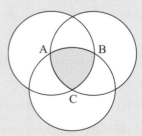

Chapter

9

Non-right angled triangle trigonometry

Syllabus reference: 3.6

Contents:
A Areas of triangles
B The cosine rule
C The sine rule
D Using the sine and cosine rules

OPENING PROBLEM

A triangular sail is to be cut from a section of cloth. Two of the sides must have lengths 4 m and 6 m as illustrated. The total area for the sail must be 11.6 m², the maximum allowed for the boat to race in its class.

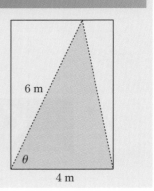

Things to think about:

a Can you find the size of the angle θ between the two sides of given length?

b Can you find the length of the third side of the sail?

A   AREAS OF TRIANGLES

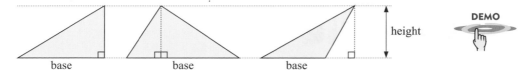

If we know the base and height measurements of a triangle we can calculate the area using **area $= \frac{1}{2}$ base $\times$ height**.

However, cases arise where we do not know the height but we can use trigonometry to calculate the area.

These cases are:

- knowing two sides and the **included angle** between them

- knowing all three sides

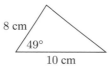

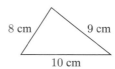

USING THE INCLUDED ANGLE

Triangle ABC has angles of size A, B, and C. The sides opposite these angles are labelled a, b, and c respectively.

Using trigonometry, we can develop an alternative area formula that does not depend on a perpendicular height.

Any triangle that is not right angled must be either acute or obtuse. We will consider both cases: ·

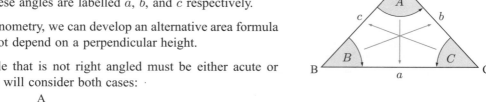

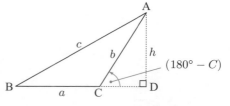

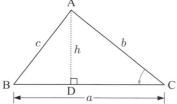

In both triangles the altitude h is constructed from A to D on [BC] (extended if necessary).

$$\sin C = \frac{h}{b} \qquad\qquad \sin(180° - C) = \frac{h}{b}$$

$$\therefore \quad h = b\sin C \qquad\qquad \therefore \quad h = b\sin(180° - C)$$

$$\text{But} \quad \sin(180° - C) = \sin C$$

$$\therefore \quad h = b\sin C$$

So, since area $= \frac{1}{2}ah$, we now have   **Area $= \frac{1}{2}ab\sin C$.**

Using different altitudes we can show that the area is also $\frac{1}{2}bc\sin A$ or $\frac{1}{2}ac\sin B$.

Given the lengths of two sides of a triangle, and the size of the included angle between them, the area of the triangle is

half of the product of two sides and the sine of the included angle.

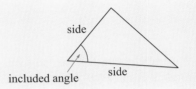

side

included angle   side

Example 1   ◀) **Self Tutor**

Find the area of triangle ABC.

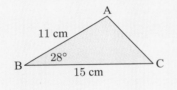

A

11 cm

28°

B

15 cm

C

$\text{Area} = \frac{1}{2}ac\sin B$

$\quad = \frac{1}{2} \times 15 \times 11 \times \sin 28°$

$\quad \approx 38.7 \text{ cm}^2$

If we rearrange the area formula to find the included angle between two sides, we need to use the **inverse** sine function denoted $\sin^{-1}$. For help with this and the other inverse trigonometric functions you should consult the Background Knowledge chapter on the CD.

LINK

Example 2   ◀) **Self Tutor**

A triangle has sides of length 10 cm and 11 cm and an area of 50 cm². Determine the two possible measures of the included angle. Give your answers accurate to 1 decimal place.

If the included angle is θ, then $\quad \frac{1}{2} \times 10 \times 11 \times \sin\theta = 50$

$$\therefore \quad \sin\theta = \frac{50}{55}$$

Now $\quad \sin^{-1}\left(\frac{50}{55}\right) \approx 65.4°$

$\therefore \quad \theta \approx 65.4°$ or $180° - 65.4°$

$\therefore \quad \theta \approx 65.4°$ or $114.6°$

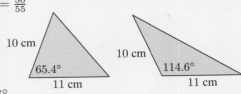

10 cm

65.4°

11 cm

10 cm

114.6°

11 cm

The two different possible angles are 65.4° and 114.6°.

EXERCISE 9A

1 Find the area of:

a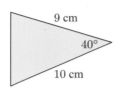

9 cm
40°
10 cm

b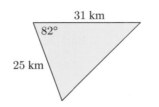

31 km
82°
25 km

c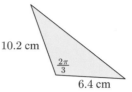

10.2 cm
$\frac{2\pi}{3}$
6.4 cm

2 If triangle ABC has area 150 cm², find the value of x:

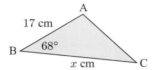

17 cm
A
B   68°
x cm   C

3 A parallelogram has two adjacent sides with lengths 4 cm and 6 cm respectively. If the included angle measures 52°, find the area of the parallelogram.

4 A rhombus has sides of length 12 cm and an angle of 72°. Find its area.

5 Find the area of a regular hexagon with sides of length 12 cm.

6 A rhombus has an area of 50 cm² and an internal angle of size 63°. Find the length of its sides.

7 A regular pentagonal garden plot has centre of symmetry O and an area of 338 m². Find the distance OA.

8 Find the possible values of the included angle of a triangle with:

a sides of length 5 cm and 8 cm, and area 15 cm²

b sides of length 45 km and 53 km, and area 800 km².

9 The Australian 50 cent coin has the shape of a regular dodecagon, which is a polygon with 12 sides.

Eight of these 50 cent coins will fit exactly on an Australian $10 note as shown. What fraction of the $10 note is *not* covered?

10 Find the shaded area in:

a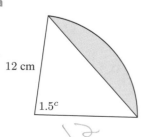

12 cm
1.5ᶜ

b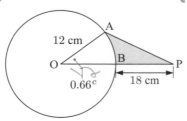

12 cm
A
O   B
0.66ᶜ   18 cm   P

c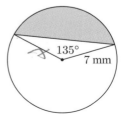

135°
7 mm

11   ADB is an arc of the circle with centre C and radius
7.3 cm. AEB is an arc of the circle with centre F and
radius 8.7 cm.
Find the shaded area.

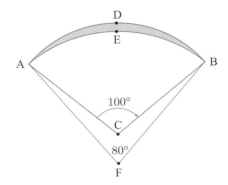

| **B** | **THE COSINE RULE** |

The **cosine rule** involves the sides and angles of a triangle.

In any $\triangle ABC$:

$$a^2 = b^2 + c^2 - 2bc \cos A$$
$$or \quad b^2 = a^2 + c^2 - 2ac \cos B$$
$$or \quad c^2 = a^2 + b^2 - 2ab \cos C$$

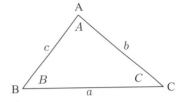

We will develop the first formula for both an acute and an obtuse triangle.

Proof:

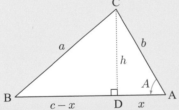 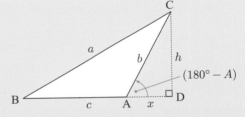

In both triangles draw the altitude from C down to [AB] (extended if necessary), meeting
it at D.

Let $AD = x$ and let $CD = h$.

Apply the theorem of Pythagoras in $\triangle BCD$:

$$a^2 = h^2 + (c - x)^2 \qquad\qquad a^2 = h^2 + (c + x)^2$$
$$\therefore \ a^2 = h^2 + c^2 - 2cx + x^2 \qquad \therefore \ a^2 = h^2 + c^2 + 2cx + x^2$$

In both cases, applying Pythagoras to $\triangle ADC$ gives $h^2 + x^2 = b^2$.

$\therefore \ h^2 = b^2 - x^2$,   and we substitute this into the equations above.

$$\therefore \ a^2 = b^2 + c^2 - 2cx \qquad\qquad \therefore \ a^2 = b^2 + c^2 + 2cx$$

In $\triangle ADC$, $\cos A = \dfrac{x}{b}$ \qquad\qquad $\cos(180° - A) = \dfrac{x}{b}$

$$\therefore \ b \cos A = x \qquad\qquad\qquad \therefore \ -\cos A = \dfrac{x}{b}$$
$$\therefore \ a^2 = b^2 + c^2 - 2bc \cos A \qquad\qquad \therefore \ -b \cos A = x$$
$$\therefore \ a^2 = b^2 + c^2 - 2bc \cos A$$

The other variations of the cosine rule could be developed by rearranging the vertices of $\triangle ABC$.

Note that if $A = 90°$ then $\cos A = 0$ and $a^2 = b^2 + c^2 - 2bc \cos A$ reduces to $a^2 = b^2 + c^2$, which is the **Pythagorean Rule**.

The **cosine rule** can be used to solve problems involving triangles given:

- **two sides** and an **included angle**
- **three sides**.

If we are given **two sides** and a **non-included angle**, then when we try to find the third side we obtain a quadratic equation. This is an *ambiguous* case where there may be two plausible solutions. We may not be able to solve for the length uniquely if there are two positive, plausible solutions to the quadratic equation.

Example 3   ◄) **Self Tutor**

Find, correct to 2 decimal places, the length of [BC].

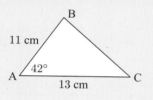

By the cosine rule:

$$BC^2 = 11^2 + 13^2 - 2 \times 11 \times 13 \times \cos 42°$$

$\therefore\ BC \approx \sqrt{(11^2 + 13^2 - 2 \times 11 \times 13 \times \cos 42°)}$

$\therefore\ BC \approx 8.801$

$\therefore$ [BC] is 8.80 cm in length.

Rearrangement of the original cosine rule formulae can be used for finding angles if we know all three sides. The formulae for finding the angles are:

$$\cos A = \frac{b^2 + c^2 - a^2}{2bc} \qquad \cos B = \frac{c^2 + a^2 - b^2}{2ca} \qquad \cos C = \frac{a^2 + b^2 - c^2}{2ab}$$

We then need to use the **inverse** cosine function $\cos^{-1}$ to evaluate the angle.

Example 4   ◄) **Self Tutor**

In triangle ABC, AB = 7 cm, BC = 5 cm, and CA = 8 cm.

  a Find the measure of $B\widehat{C}A$.

  b Find the exact area of triangle ABC.

a

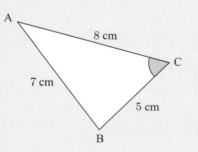

By the cosine rule:

$$\cos C = \frac{(5^2 + 8^2 - 7^2)}{(2 \times 5 \times 8)}$$

$\therefore\ C = \cos^{-1}\left(\dfrac{5^2 + 8^2 - 7^2}{2 \times 5 \times 8}\right)$

$\therefore\ C = \cos^{-1}(\tfrac{1}{2})$

$\therefore\ C = 60°$

So, $B\widehat{C}A$ measures 60°.

b The area of $\triangle ABC = \tfrac{1}{2} \times 8 \times 5 \times \sin 60°$

$= 20 \times \dfrac{\sqrt{3}}{2} \qquad \{\sin 60° = \dfrac{\sqrt{3}}{2}\}$

$= 10\sqrt{3}$ cm²

$a^2 = b^2 + c^2 - 2bc\cos A$

EXERCISE 9B

1 Find the length of the remaining side in the given triangle:

a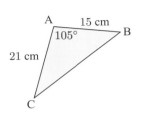

b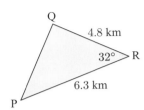

c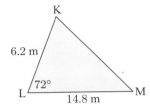

2 Find the measure of all angles of:

3 **a** Find the measure of obtuse $P\widehat{Q}R$.
   b Hence find the area of $\triangle PQR$.

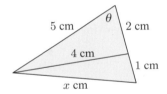

4 **a** Find the smallest angle of a triangle with sides 11 cm, 13 cm, and 17 cm.
   b Find the largest angle of a triangle with sides 4 cm, 7 cm, and 9 cm.

The smallest angle is opposite the shortest side.

5 **a** Find $\cos\theta$ but not θ.
   b Find the value of x.

6 Find the exact value of x in each of the following diagrams:

a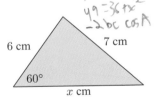

b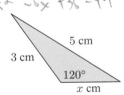

c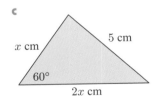

7 Solve the **Opening Problem** on page **214**.

8 Find x in each of the following diagrams:

a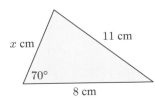

b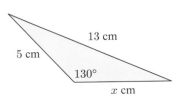

9 Show that there are two plausible values
for x in this triangle:

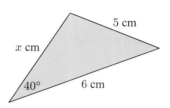

C   THE SINE RULE

The **sine rule** is a set of equations which connects the lengths of the sides of any triangle with the sines of the angles of the triangle. The triangle does not have to be right angled for the sine rule to be used.

In any triangle ABC with sides a, b, and c units in length,
and opposite angles A, B, and C respectively,

$$\frac{\sin A}{a} = \frac{\sin B}{b} = \frac{\sin C}{c} \quad or \quad \frac{a}{\sin A} = \frac{b}{\sin B} = \frac{c}{\sin C}.$$

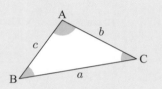

Proof: The area of any triangle ABC is given by $\frac{1}{2} bc \sin A = \frac{1}{2} ac \sin B = \frac{1}{2} ab \sin C.$

Dividing each expression by $\frac{1}{2} abc$ gives $\dfrac{\sin A}{a} = \dfrac{\sin B}{b} = \dfrac{\sin C}{c}.$

The sine rule is used to solve problems involving triangles, given:

- **two angles** and **one side**
- **two sides** and a **non-included angle**.

FINDING SIDE LENGTHS

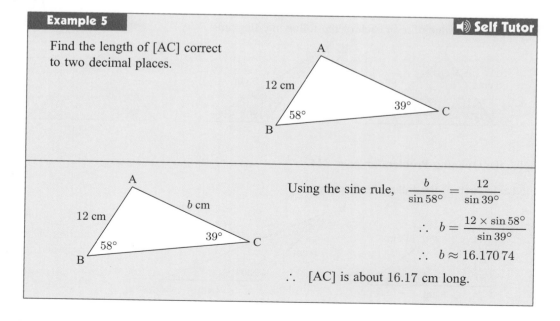

Example 5   ◀》 **Self Tutor**

Find the length of [AC] correct
to two decimal places.

Using the sine rule, $\dfrac{b}{\sin 58°} = \dfrac{12}{\sin 39°}$

$$\therefore \quad b = \frac{12 \times \sin 58°}{\sin 39°}$$

$$\therefore \quad b \approx 16.170\,74$$

$\therefore$ [AC] is about 16.17 cm long.

EXERCISE 9C.1

1 Find the value of x:

a
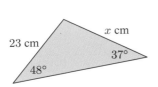

b
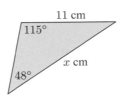

c
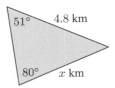

2 Consider triangle ABC.

    a Given $A = 63°$, $B = 49°$, and $b = 18$ cm, find a.

    b Given $A = 82°$, $C = 25°$, and $c = 34$ cm, find b.

    c Given $B = 21°$, $C = 48°$, and $a = 6.4$ cm, find c.

FINDING ANGLES

The problem of finding angles using the sine rule is more complicated because there may be two possible answers. For example, if $\sin\theta = \frac{\sqrt{3}}{2}$ then $\theta = 60°$ or $120°$. We call this situation an **ambiguous case**.

DEMO

You can click on the icon to obtain an interactive demonstration of the ambiguous case, or else you can work through the following investigation.

INVESTIGATION	THE AMBIGUOUS CASE

You will need a blank sheet of paper, a ruler, a protractor, and a compass for the tasks that follow. In each task you will be required to construct triangles from given information. You could also do this using a computer package such as 'The Geometer's Sketchpad'.

What to do:

Task 1: Draw $AB = 10$ cm. At A construct an angle of $30°$. Using B as the centre, draw an arc of a circle of radius 6 cm. Let C denote the point where the arc intersects the ray from A. How many different possible points C are there, and therefore how many different triangles ABC may be constructed?

Task 2: As before, draw $AB = 10$ cm and construct a $30°$ angle at A. This time draw an arc of radius 5 cm centred at B. How many different triangles are possible?

Task 3: Repeat, but this time draw an arc of radius 3 cm centred at B. How many different triangles are possible?

Task 4: Repeat, but this time draw an arc of radius 12 cm centred at B. How many different triangles are possible now?

You should have discovered that when you are given two sides and a non-included angle there are a number of different possibilities. You could get two triangles, one triangle, or it may be impossible to draw any triangles at all for some given dimensions.

Now consider the calculations involved in each of the cases of the investigation.

Task 1:   Given: $c = 10$ cm, $a = 6$ cm, $A = 30°$

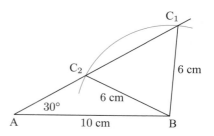

$$\frac{\sin C}{c} = \frac{\sin A}{a}$$

$$\therefore \quad \sin C = \frac{c \sin A}{a}$$

$$\therefore \quad \sin C = \frac{10 \times \sin 30°}{6} \approx 0.8333$$

Because $\sin \theta = \sin(180° - \theta)$ there are two possible angles:
$C \approx 56.44°$ or $180° - 56.44° = 123.56°$

Task 2:   Given: $c = 10$ cm, $a = 5$ cm, $A = 30°$

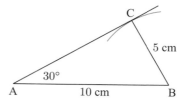

$$\frac{\sin C}{c} = \frac{\sin A}{a}$$

$$\therefore \quad \sin C = \frac{c \sin A}{a}$$

$$\therefore \quad \sin C = \frac{10 \times \sin 30°}{5} = 1$$

There is only one possible solution for C in the range from $0°$ to $180°$, and that is $C = 90°$. Only one triangle is therefore possible. Complete the solution of the triangle yourself.

Task 3:   Given: $c = 10$ cm, $a = 3$ cm, $A = 30°$

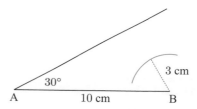

$$\frac{\sin C}{c} = \frac{\sin A}{a}$$

$$\therefore \quad \sin C = \frac{c \sin A}{a}$$

$$\therefore \quad \sin C = \frac{10 \times \sin 30°}{3} \approx 1.6667$$

There is no angle that has a sine value > 1. Therefore there is *no solution* for this given data, and no triangles can be drawn to match the information given.

Task 4:   Given: $c = 10$ cm, $a = 12$ cm, $A = 30°$

$$\frac{\sin C}{c} = \frac{\sin A}{a}$$

$$\therefore \quad \sin C = \frac{c \sin A}{a}$$

$$\therefore \quad \sin C = \frac{10 \times \sin 30°}{12} \approx 0.4167$$

Two angles have a sine
ratio of 0.4167 :

$C \approx 24.62°$ *or*
$\qquad 180° - 24.62° = 155.38°$

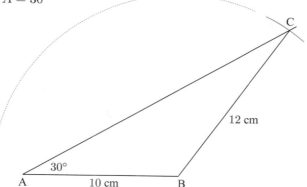

However, in this case only one of these two angles is valid. If $A = 30°$ then C cannot possibly equal $155.38°$ because $30° + 155.38° > 180°$.

Therefore, there is only one possible solution, $C \approx 24.62°$.

Conclusion: Each situation using the sine rule with two sides and a non-included angle must be examined very carefully.

Example 6   ◀)) **Self Tutor**

Find the measure of angle C in triangle ABC if AC $= 7$ cm, AB $= 11$ cm, and angle B measures $25°$.

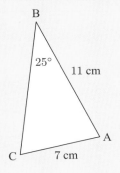

$$\frac{\sin C}{c} = \frac{\sin B}{b} \quad \text{\{sine rule\}}$$

$$\therefore \quad \frac{\sin C}{11} = \frac{\sin 25°}{7}$$

$$\therefore \quad \sin C = \frac{11 \times \sin 25°}{7}$$

$$\therefore \quad C = \sin^{-1}\left(\frac{11 \times \sin 25°}{7}\right) \quad \begin{array}{l}\text{or its supplement}\\ \text{\{as } C \text{ may be obtuse\}}\end{array}$$

$$\therefore \quad C \approx 41.6° \quad \text{or} \quad 180° - 41.6°$$

$$\therefore \quad C \approx 41.6° \quad \text{or} \quad 138.4°$$

$\therefore$ C measures $41.6°$ if angle C is acute, or $138.4°$ if angle C is obtuse.

In this case there is insufficient information to determine the actual shape of the triangle. There are two possible triangles.

Sometimes there is information in the question which enables us to **reject** one of the answers.

Example 7   ◀)) **Self Tutor**

Find the measure of angle L in triangle KLM given that angle K measures $56°$, LM $= 16.8$ m, and KM $= 13.5$ m.

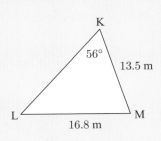

$$\frac{\sin L}{13.5} = \frac{\sin 56°}{16.8} \quad \text{\{by the sine rule\}}$$

$$\therefore \quad \sin L = \frac{13.5 \times \sin 56°}{16.8}$$

$$\therefore \quad L = \sin^{-1}\left(\frac{13.5 \times \sin 56°}{16.8}\right) \quad \text{or its supplement}$$

$$\therefore \quad L \approx 41.8° \quad \text{or} \quad 180° - 41.8°$$

$$\therefore \quad L \approx 41.8° \quad \text{or} \quad 138.2°$$

We reject $L \approx 138.2°$, since $138.2° + 56° > 180°$ which is impossible in a triangle.

$\therefore$ $L \approx 41.8°$, a unique solution in this case.

EXERCISE 9C.2

1 Triangle ABC has angle $B = 40°$, $b = 8$ cm, and $c = 11$ cm. Find the two possible measures of angle C.

2 Consider triangle ABC.

   a Given $a = 14.6$ cm, $b = 17.4$ cm, and $A\widehat{B}C = 65°$, find the measure of $B\widehat{A}C$.

   b Given $b = 43.8$ cm, $c = 31.4$ cm, and $A\widehat{C}B = 43°$, find the measure of $A\widehat{B}C$.

   c Given $a = 6.5$ km, $c = 4.8$ km, and $B\widehat{A}C = 71°$, find the measure of $A\widehat{C}B$.

3 Is it possible to have a triangle with the measurements shown? Explain your answer.

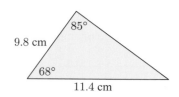

4 Given AD = 20 cm, find the magnitude of $A\widehat{B}C$ and hence the length BD.

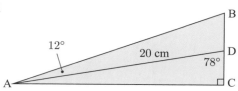

5 Find x and y in the given figure.

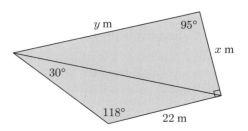

6 Triangle ABC has $\widehat{A} = 58°$, AB = 5.1 cm, AC = 8 cm, and BC = 6.84 cm.

    a Find $\widehat{B}$ correct to the nearest degree using the sine rule.

    b Find $\widehat{B}$ correct to the nearest degree using the cosine rule.

    c Copy and complete: "When faced with using either the sine rule or the cosine rule it is better to use the ...... as it avoids ......"

7 In triangle ABC, $A\widehat{B}C = 30°$, AC = 9 cm, and AB = 7 cm.   Find the area of the triangle.

8 Find the exact value of x, giving your answer in the form $a + b\sqrt{2}$ where $a, b \in \mathbb{Q}$.

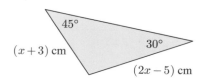

D   USING THE SINE AND COSINE RULES

If we are given a problem involving a triangle, we must first decide which rule is best to use.

If the triangle is right angled then the trigonometric ratios or Pythagoras' Theorem can be used. For some problems we can add an extra line or two to the diagram to create a right angled triangle.

However, if we do not have a right angled triangle then we usually have to choose between the sine and cosine rules. In these cases the following checklist may be helpful:

Use the **cosine rule** when given:

- three sides
- two sides and an included angle.

Use the **sine rule** when given:

- one side and two angles ,
- two sides and a non-included angle, but beware of an *ambiguous case* which can occur when the smaller of the two given sides is opposite the given angle.

Example 8   ◀) **Self Tutor**

The angles of elevation to the top of a mountain are measured from two beacons A and B at sea.

The measurements are shown on the diagram.

If the beacons are 1473 m apart, how high is the mountain?

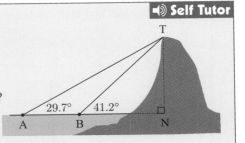

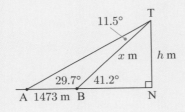

Let BT be x m and NT be h m.

$\widehat{ATB} = 41.2° - 29.7°$ {exterior angle of $\triangle$}
        $= 11.5°$

We find x in $\triangle ABT$ using the sine rule:

$$\frac{x}{\sin 29.7°} = \frac{1473}{\sin 11.5°}$$

$$\therefore \; x = \frac{1473}{\sin 11.5°} \times \sin 29.7°$$

$$\approx 3660.62$$

Now, in $\triangle BNT$, $\sin 41.2° = \frac{h}{x} \approx \frac{h}{3660.62}$

$$\therefore \; h \approx \sin 41.2° \times 3660.62$$

$$\approx 2410$$

The mountain is about 2410 m high.

EXERCISE 9D

1   Rodrigo wishes to determine the height of a flagpole. He takes a sighting to the top of the flagpole from point P. He then moves further away from the flagpole by 20 metres to point Q and takes a second sighting. The information is shown in the diagram alongside. How high is the flagpole?

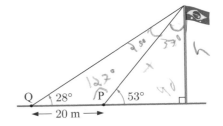

2

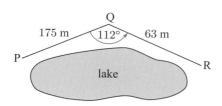

To get from P to R, a park ranger had to walk along a path to Q and then to R as shown.
What is the distance in a straight line from P to R?

3 A golfer played his tee shot a distance of 220 m to point A. He then played a 165 m six iron to the green. If the distance from tee to green is 340 m, determine the angle the golfer was off line with his tee shot.

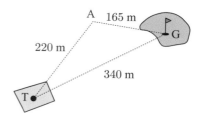

4

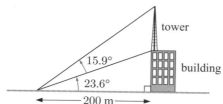

A communications tower is constructed on top of a building as shown. Find the height of the tower.

5 Hikers Ritva and Esko leave point P at the same time. Ritva walks 4 km on a bearing of 040°, then a further 6 km on a bearing of 155°.

Esko hikes directly from P to the camp site.

  a How far does Esko hike?

  b In which direction does Esko hike?

  c Ritva hikes at 10 km h⁻¹ and Esko hikes at 6 km h⁻¹.

    i Who will arrive at the camp site first?

    ii How long will this person need to wait before the other person arrives?

  d On what bearing should the hikers walk from the camp site to return to P?

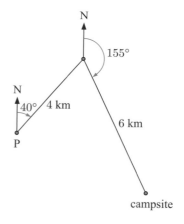

6 A football goal is 5 metres wide. When a player is 26 metres from one goal post and 23 metres from the other, he shoots for goal. What is the angle of view of the goals that the player sees?

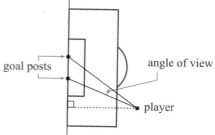

7 A tower 42 metres high stands on top of a hill. From a point some distance from the base of the hill, the angle of elevation to the top of the tower is 13.2° and the angle of elevation to the bottom of the tower is 8.3°. Find the height of the hill.

8   From the foot of a building I have to look 22° upwards to sight the top of a tree. From the top of the building, 150 metres above ground level, I have to look down at an angle of 50° below the horizontal to sight the tree top.

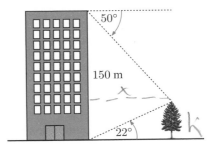

   a   How high is the tree?

   b   How far from the building is this tree?

Example 9   ◀ᴺ) **Self Tutor**

Find the measure of RP̂V.

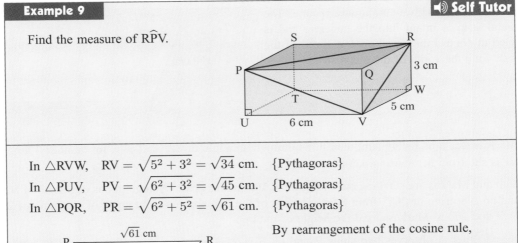

In △RVW, RV $= \sqrt{5^2 + 3^2} = \sqrt{34}$ cm. {Pythagoras}

In △PUV, PV $= \sqrt{6^2 + 3^2} = \sqrt{45}$ cm. {Pythagoras}

In △PQR, PR $= \sqrt{6^2 + 5^2} = \sqrt{61}$ cm. {Pythagoras}

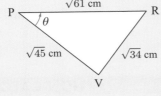

By rearrangement of the cosine rule,

$$\cos\theta = \frac{(\sqrt{61})^2 + (\sqrt{45})^2 - (\sqrt{34})^2}{2\sqrt{61}\sqrt{45}}$$

$$= \frac{61 + 45 - 34}{2\sqrt{61}\sqrt{45}}$$

$$= \frac{72}{2\sqrt{61}\sqrt{45}}$$

$$\therefore \ \theta = \cos^{-1}\left(\frac{36}{\sqrt{61}\sqrt{45}}\right) \approx 46.6°$$

$\therefore$ RP̂V measures about 46.6°.

---

9   Find the measure of PQ̂R in the rectangular box shown.

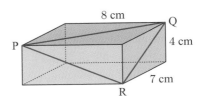

10   Two observation posts A and B are 12 km apart. A third observation post C is located such that CÂB is 42° and CB̂A is 67°. Find the distance of C from A and from B.

11 Stan and Olga are considering buying a sheep farm. A surveyor has supplied them with the given accurate sketch. Find the area of the property, giving your answer in:

   a km²   **b** hectares.

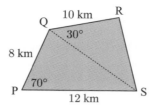

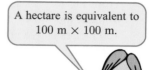

A hectare is equivalent to 100 m × 100 m.

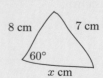

12 Thabo and Palesa start at point A. They each walk in a straight line at an angle of 120° to one another. Thabo walks at 6 km h⁻¹ and Palesa walks at 8 km h⁻¹. How far apart are they after 45 minutes?

13 The cross-section design of the kerbing for a driverless-bus roadway is shown opposite. The metal strip is inlaid into the concrete and is used to control the direction and speed of the bus. Find the width of the metal strip.

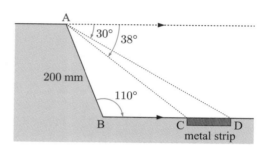

14 An orienteer runs for $4\frac{1}{2}$ km, then turns through an angle of 32° and runs for another 6 km. How far is she from her starting point?

15 Sam and Markus are standing on level ground 100 metres apart. A large tree is due north of Markus and on a bearing of 065° from Sam. The top of the tree appears at an angle of elevation of 25° to Sam and 15° to Markus. Find the height of the tree.

16 A helicopter A observes two ships B and C. B is 23.8 km from the helicopter and C is 31.9 km from it. The angle of view BÂC from the helicopter to B and C, is 83.6°. How far are the ships apart?

REVIEW SET 9A   NON-CALCULATOR

1 Determine the area of the triangle.

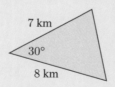

7 km
30°
8 km

2 You are given enough details of a triangle so that you could use either the cosine rule or the sine rule to find an unknown. Which rule should you use? Explain your answer.

3 Kady was asked to draw the illustrated triangle exactly.

   a Use the cosine rule to find x.

   b What should Kady's response be?

8 cm   7 cm
60°
x cm

4 A triangle has sides of length 7 cm and 13 cm, and its area is 42 cm². Find the sine of the included angle.

5

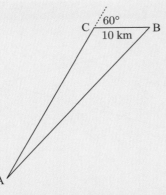

A boat is meant to be sailing directly from A to B. However, it travels in a straight line to C before the captain realises he is off course. The boat is turned through an angle of 60°, then travels another 10 km to B. The trip would have been 4 km shorter if the boat had gone straight from A to B. How far did the boat travel?

6 Show that the yellow shaded area is given by
$A = \frac{49}{2}\left(\frac{13\pi}{18} - \sin\left(\frac{13\pi}{18}\right)\right)$.

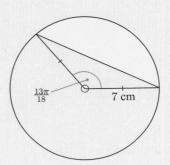

REVIEW SET 9B   CALCULATOR

1 Determine the value of x:

a

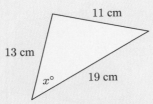

b

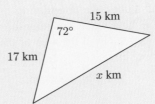

2 Find the unknown side and angles:

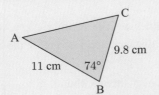

3 Find the area of quadrilateral ABCD:

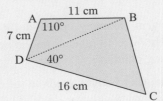

4 A vertical tree is growing on the side of a hill with gradient 10° to the horizontal. From a point 50 m downhill from the tree, the angle of elevation to the top of the tree is 18°. Find the height of the tree.

5 From point A, the angle of elevation to the top of a tall building is 20°. On walking 80 m towards the building, the angle of elevation is now 23°. How tall is the building?

6 Peter, Sue, and Alix are sea-kayaking. Peter is 430 m from Sue on a bearing of 113°. Alix is on a bearing of 210° and is 310 m from Sue. Find the distance and bearing of Peter from Alix.

REVIEW SET 9C

1 Find the value of x:

a

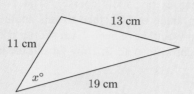

b

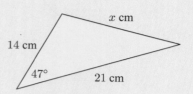

2 Find the value of x if the triangle has area 80 cm^2.

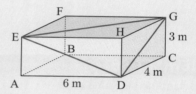

3 Find the measure of $E\hat{D}G$:

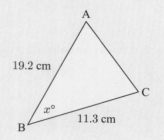

4 Anke and Lucas are considering buying a block of land. The land agent supplies them with the given accurate sketch. Find the area of the property, giving your answer in:

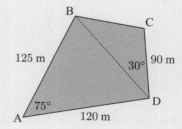

    a m^2 **b** hectares.

5 A family in Germany drives at 140 km h^{-1} for 45 minutes on the bearing 032°, and then 180 km h^{-1} for 40 minutes on the bearing 317°. Find the distance and bearing of the car from its starting point.

6 Soil contractor Frank was given the following dimensions over the telephone:

The triangular garden plot ABC has $C\hat{A}B$ measuring 44°, [AC] is 8 m long, and [BC] is 6 m long. Soil to a depth of 10 cm is required.

    a Explain why Frank needs extra information from his client.

    b What is the maximum volume of soil needed if his client is unable to supply the necessary information?

Chapter 10

Trigonometric functions

Syllabus reference: 3.4

Contents:

OPENING PROBLEM

A Ferris wheel rotates at a constant speed. The wheel's radius is 10 m and the bottom of the wheel is 2 m above ground level. From a point in front of the wheel, Andrew is watching a green light on the perimeter of the wheel. Andrew notices that the green light moves in a circle. He estimates how high the light is above ground level at two second intervals and draws a scatter diagram of his results.

Things to think about:

a What does his scatter diagram look like?

b What function can be used to model the data?

c How could this function be used to find:

  i the light's position at any point in time

  ii the times when the light is at its maximum and minimum heights?

d What part of the function would indicate the time interval over which one complete cycle occurs?

Click on the icon to visit a simulation of the Ferris wheel. You will be able to view the light from:

  DEMO

- in front of the wheel
- a side-on position
- above the wheel.

You can then observe the graph of the green light's position as the wheel rotates at a constant rate.

A   PERIODIC BEHAVIOUR

Periodic phenomena occur all the time in the physical world. For example, in:

- seasonal variations in our climate
- variations in average maximum and minimum monthly temperatures
- the number of daylight hours at a particular location
- tidal variations in the depth of water in a harbour
- the phases of the moon
- animal populations.

These phenomena illustrate variable behaviour which is repeated over time. The repetition may be called **periodic**, **oscillatory**, or **cyclic** in different situations.

In this chapter we will see how trigonometric functions can be used to model periodic phenomena.

OBSERVING PERIODIC BEHAVIOUR

The table below shows the mean monthly maximum temperature for Cape Town, South Africa.

Month	Jan	Feb	Mar	Apr	May	Jun	Jul	Aug	Sep	Oct	Nov	Dec
Temp T (°C)	28	27	$25\frac{1}{2}$	22	$18\frac{1}{2}$	16	15	16	18	$21\frac{1}{2}$	24	26

On the scatter diagram alongside we plot the temperature T on the vertical axis. We assign January as $t = 1$ month, February as $t = 2$ months, and so on for the 12 months of the year.

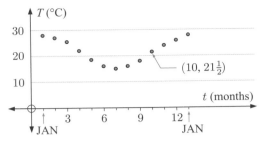

The temperature shows a variation from an average of 28°C in January through a range of values across the months. The cycle will approximately repeat itself for each subsequent 12 month period. By the end of the chapter we will be able to establish a **periodic function** which approximately fits this set of points.

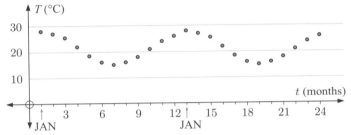

HISTORICAL NOTE

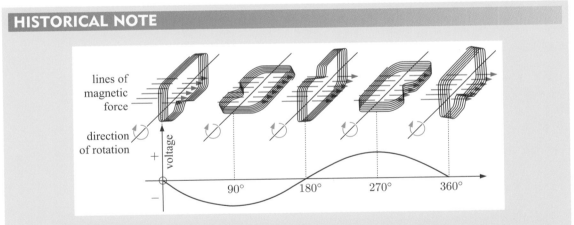

In 1831 **Michael Faraday** discovered that an electric current was generated by rotating a coil of wire in a magnetic field. The electric current produced showed a voltage which varied between positive and negative values as the coil rotated through 360°.

Graphs with this basic shape, where the cycle is repeated over and over, are called **sine waves**.

GATHERING PERIODIC DATA

Data on a number of periodic phenomena can be found online or in other publications. For example:

- Maximum and minimum monthly temperatures can be found at   www.weatherbase.com
- Tidal details can be obtained from daily newspapers or internet sites such as
  http://tidesandcurrents.noaa.gov   or   http://www.bom.gov.au/oceanography

TERMINOLOGY USED TO DESCRIBE PERIODICITY

A **periodic function** is one which repeats itself over and over in a horizontal direction, in intervals of the same length.

The **period** of a periodic function is the length of one repetition or cycle.

$f(x)$ is a periodic function with period $p \Leftrightarrow f(x + p) = f(x)$ for all x, and p is the smallest positive value for this to be true.

A **cycloid** is an example of a periodic function. It is the curve traced out by a point on a circle as the circle rolls across a flat surface in a straight line.

DEMO

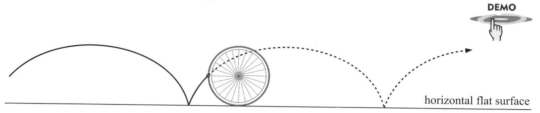

horizontal flat surface

Use a **graphing package** to examine the function $f(x) = x - [x]$
where $[x]$ is "the largest integer less than or equal to x".
Is $f(x)$ periodic?   What is its period?

GRAPHING PACKAGE

WAVES

In this course we are mainly concerned with periodic phenomena which show a wave pattern:

the wave

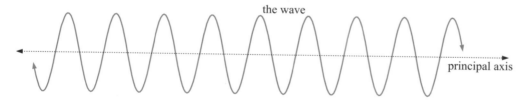

principal axis

The wave oscillates about a horizontal line called the **principal axis** or **mean line** which has equation $y = \dfrac{\text{max} + \text{min}}{2}$.

A **maximum point** occurs at the top of a crest, and a **minimum point** at the bottom of a trough.

The **amplitude** is the distance between a maximum (or minimum) point and the principal axis.

$$\text{amplitude} = \frac{\text{max} - \text{min}}{2}$$

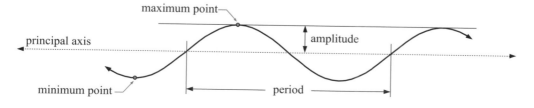

maximum point

principal axis

amplitude

minimum point

period

EXERCISE 10A

1   Which of these graphs show periodic behaviour?

a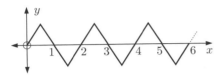

b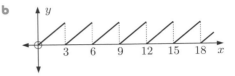

c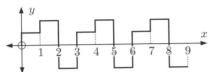

d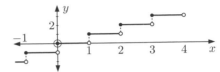

e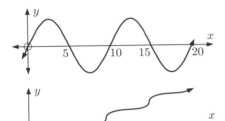

f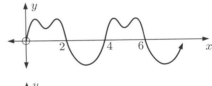

g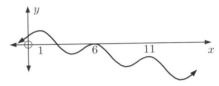

h (graph)

2   The following tabled values show the height above the ground of a point on a bicycle wheel as the bicycle is wheeled along a flat surface.

Distance travelled (cm)	0	20	40	60	80	100	120	140	160	180	200
Height above ground (cm)	0	6	23	42	57	64	59	43	23	7	1

Distance travelled (cm)	220	240	260	280	300	320	340	360	380	400
Height above ground (cm)	5	27	40	55	63	60	44	24	9	3

a   Plot the graph of height against distance.

b   Is it reasonable to fit a curve to this data, or should we leave it as discrete points?

c   Is the data periodic? If so, estimate:

   i   the equation of the principal axis   **ii**   the maximum value

   iii   the period   **iv**   the amplitude.

3   Draw a scatter diagram for each set of data below.   Is there any evidence to suggest the data is periodic?

a

x	0	1	2	3	4	5	6	7	8	9	10	11	12
y	0	1	1.4	1	0	−1	−1.4	−1	0	1	1.4	1	0

b

x	0	2	3	4	5	6	7	8	9	10	12
y	0	4.7	3.4	1.7	2.1	5.2	8.9	10.9	10.2	8.4	10.4

GRAPHICS
CALCULATOR
INSTRUCTIONS

THEORY OF KNOWLEDGE

In mathematics we clearly define terms so there is no misunderstanding of their exact meaning.

We can understand the need for specific definitions by considering integers and rational numbers:

- 2 is an integer, and is also a rational number since $2 = \frac{4}{2}$.

- $\frac{4}{2}$ is a rational number, and is also an integer since $\frac{4}{2} = 2$.

- $\frac{4}{3}$ is a rational number, but is *not* an integer.

Symbols are frequently used in mathematics to take the place of phrases. For example:

- $=$ is read as "is equal to"
- $\in$ is read as "is an element of" or "is in".
- $\sum$ is read as "the sum of all"

1 Is mathematics a language?

2 Why is it important that mathematicians use the same notation?

3 Does a mathematical argument need to read like a good piece of English?

The word *similar* is used in mathematics to describe two figures which are in proportion. This is different to how *similar* is used in everyday speech.

Likewise the words *function*, *domain*, *range*, *period*, and *wave* all have different or more specific mathematical meanings.

4 What is the difference between *equal*, *equivalent*, and *the same*?

5 Are there any words which we use only in mathematics? What does this tell us about the nature of mathematics and the world around us?

B   THE SINE FUNCTION

In previous studies of trigonometry we have only considered static situations where an angle is fixed. However, when an object moves around a circle, the situation is dynamic. The angle θ between the radius [OP] and the positive x-axis continually changes with time.

Consider again the **Opening Problem** in which a Ferris wheel of radius 10 m revolves at constant speed. We let P represent the green light on the wheel.

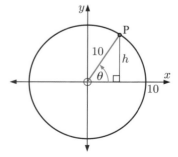

The height of P relative to the x-axis can be determined using right angled triangle trigonometry.

$$\sin \theta = \frac{h}{10}, \quad \text{so} \quad h = 10 \sin \theta.$$

As time goes by, θ changes and so does h.

So, we can write h as a function of θ, or alternatively we can write h as a function of time t.

Suppose the Ferris wheel observed by Andrew takes 100 seconds for a full revolution. The graph below shows the height of the light above or below the principal axis against the time in seconds.

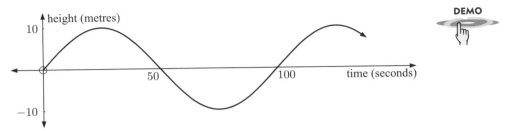

DEMO

We observe that the amplitude is 10 metres and the period is 100 seconds.

THE BASIC SINE CURVE

Suppose point P moves around the unit circle so the angle [OP] makes with the positive horizontal axis is x. In this case P has coordinates $(\cos x, \sin x)$.

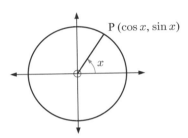

If we project the values of $\sin x$ from the unit circle to a set of axes alongside, we can obtain the graph of $y = \sin x$.

Note carefully that x on the unit circle diagram is an *angle*, and becomes the horizontal coordinate of the sine function.

Unless indicated otherwise, you should assume that x is measured in radians. Degrees are only included on this graph for the sake of completeness.

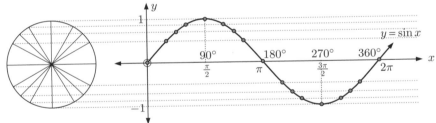

Click on the icon to generate the sine function for yourself.

You should observe that the sine function can be continued beyond $0 \leqslant x \leqslant 2\pi$ in either direction.

SINE FUNCTION

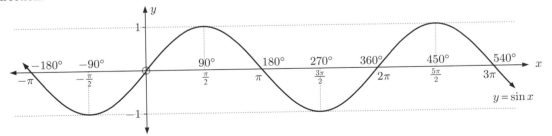

The unit circle repeats itself after one full revolution, so its *period* is 2π.

The *maximum* value is 1 and the *minimum* is -1, as $-1 \leqslant y \leqslant 1$ on the unit circle.

The *amplitude* is 1.

TRANSFORMATIONS OF THE SINE CURVE

In the investigations that follow, we will consider applying transformations to the sine curve $y = \sin x$. Using the transformations we learnt in **Chapter 5**, we can generate the curve for the general sine function $y = a\sin(b(x - c)) + d$.

INVESTIGATION 1   THE FAMILY $y = a\sin x, \; a \neq 0$

Click on the icon to explore the family $y = a\sin x, \; a \neq 0$.

Notice that x is measured in radians.

DYNAMIC SINE FUNCTION

What to do:

1 Use the slider to vary the value of a. Observe the changes to the graph of the function.

2 Use the software to help complete the table:

a	Function	Maximum	Minimum	Period	Amplitude
1	$y = \sin x$	1	-1	2π	1
2	$y = 2\sin x$				
0.5	$y = 0.5\sin x$				
-1	$y = -\sin x$				
a	$y = a\sin x$				

3 How does a affect the function $y = a\sin x$?

4 State the amplitude of:

   a $y = 3\sin x$ **b** $y = \sqrt{7}\sin x$ **c** $y = -2\sin x$

INVESTIGATION 2   THE FAMILY $y = \sin bx, \; b > 0$

Click on the icon to explore the family $y = \sin bx, \; b > 0$.

DYNAMIC SINE FUNCTION

What to do:

1 Use the slider to vary the value of b. Observe the changes to the graph of the function.

2 Use the software to help complete the table:

b	Function	Maximum	Minimum	Period	Amplitude
1	$y = \sin x$	1	-1	2π	1
2	$y = \sin 2x$				
$\frac{1}{2}$	$y = \sin(\frac{1}{2}x)$				
b	$y = \sin bx$				

3 How does b affect the function $y = \sin bx$?

4 State the period of:

   a $y = \sin 3x$ **b** $y = \sin(\frac{1}{3}x)$ **c** $y = \sin(1.2x)$ **d** $y = \sin bx$

From the previous **Investigations** you should have found:

Family $y = a \sin x$, $a \neq 0$

- a affects the amplitude of the graph;   amplitude $= |a|$
- The graph is a vertical stretch of $y = \sin x$ with scale factor $|a|$.
- If $a < 0$, the graph of $y = \sin x$ is also reflected in the x-axis.

Family $y = \sin bx$, $b > 0$

- The graph is a horizontal stretch of $y = \sin x$ with scale factor $\dfrac{1}{b}$.
- period $= \dfrac{2\pi}{b}$

$|a|$ is the modulus of a. It is the *size* of a, and cannot be negative.

Example 1   ◀⑴ **Self Tutor**

Without using technology, sketch the graphs of:

  a $y = 2 \sin x$ **b** $y = -2 \sin x$ for $0 \leqslant x \leqslant 2\pi$.

  a   This is a vertical stretch of $y = \sin x$ with scale factor 2.
      The amplitude is 2 and the period is 2π.

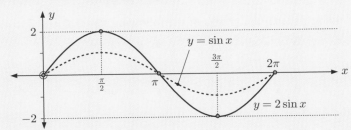

  b   The amplitude is 2 and the period is 2π. It is the reflection of $y = 2 \sin x$ in the x-axis.

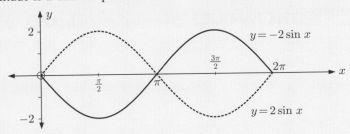

Example 2

◀)) **Self Tutor**

Without using technology, sketch the graph of $y = \sin 2x$ for $0 \leqslant x \leqslant 2\pi$.

This is a horizontal stretch of $y = \sin x$ with scale factor $\frac{1}{2}$.

The period is $\frac{2\pi}{2} = \pi$.

$\therefore$ the maximum values are π units apart.

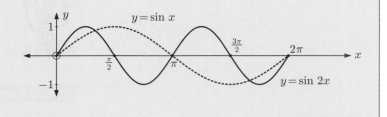

Since $\sin 2x$ has half the period of $\sin x$, the first maximum is at $\frac{\pi}{4}$ not $\frac{\pi}{2}$.

EXERCISE 10B.1

1 Without using technology, sketch the graphs of the following for $0 \leqslant x \leqslant 2\pi$:

    a $y = 3\sin x$ **b** $y = -3\sin x$ **c** $y = \frac{3}{2}\sin x$ **d** $y = -\frac{3}{2}\sin x$

2 Without using technology, sketch the graphs of the following for $0 \leqslant x \leqslant 3\pi$:

    a $y = \sin 3x$ **b** $y = \sin\left(\frac{x}{2}\right)$ **c** $y = \sin(-2x)$

3 State the period of:

    a $y = \sin 4x$ **b** $y = \sin(-4x)$ **c** $y = \sin\left(\frac{x}{3}\right)$ **d** $y = \sin(0.6x)$

4 Find b given that the function $y = \sin bx$, $b > 0$ has period:

    a 5π **b** $\frac{2\pi}{3}$ **c** 12π **d** 4 **e** 100

INVESTIGATION 3   THE FAMILIES $y = \sin(x - c)$ AND $y = \sin x + d$

Click on the icon to explore the families $y = \sin(x - c)$ and $y = \sin x + d$.

DYNAMIC SINE FUNCTION

What to do:

1 Use the slider to vary the value of c. Observe the changes to the graph of the function.

2 Use the software to help complete the table:

c	Function	Maximum	Minimum	Period	Amplitude
0	$y = \sin x$	1	-1	2π	1
-2	$y = \sin(x - 2)$				
2	$y = \sin(x + 2)$				
$-\frac{\pi}{3}$	$y = \sin\left(x - \frac{\pi}{3}\right)$				
c	$y = \sin(x - c)$				

3 What transformation moves $y = \sin x$ to $y = \sin(x - c)$?

4 Return the value of c to zero, and now vary the value of d. Observe the changes to the graph of the function.

5 Use the software to help complete the table:

d	Function	Maximum	Minimum	Period	Amplitude
0	$y = \sin x$	1	-1	2π	1
3	$y = \sin x + 3$				
-2	$y = \sin x - 2$				
d	$y = \sin x + d$				

6 What transformation moves $y = \sin x$ to $y = \sin x + d$?

7 What transformation moves $y = \sin x$ to $y = \sin(x - c) + d$?

From **Investigation 3** we observe that:

- $y = \sin(x - c)$ is a **horizontal translation** of $y = \sin x$ through c units.
- $y = \sin x + d$ is a **vertical translation** of $y = \sin x$ through d units.
- $y = \sin(x - c) + d$ is a **translation** of $y = \sin x$ through vector $\binom{c}{d}$.

Example 3 ◀) **Self Tutor**

On the same set of axes graph for $0 \leqslant x \leqslant 4\pi$:

a $y = \sin x$ and $y = \sin(x - 1)$ **b** $y = \sin x$ and $y = \sin x - 1$

a This is a horizontal translation of $y = \sin x$ to the right by 1 unit.

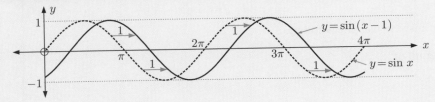

b This is a vertical translation of $y = \sin x$ downwards by 1 unit.

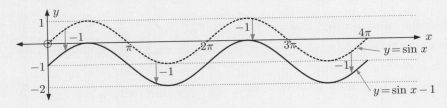

THE GENERAL SINE FUNCTION

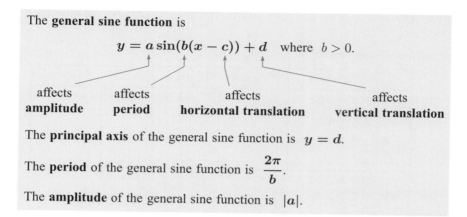

The **general sine function** is

$$y = a\sin(b(x - c)) + d \quad \text{where} \ b > 0.$$

affects   affects   affects   affects
amplitude   **period**   **horizontal translation**   **vertical translation**

The **principal axis** of the general sine function is $y = d$.

The **period** of the general sine function is $\dfrac{2\pi}{b}$.

The **amplitude** of the general sine function is $|a|$.

Consider $y = 2\sin(3(x - \frac{\pi}{4})) + 1$. It is a translation of $y = 2\sin 3x$ with translation vector $\begin{pmatrix} \frac{\pi}{4} \\ 1 \end{pmatrix}$.

So, starting with $y = \sin x$ we would:

- double the amplitude to produce $y = 2\sin x$,   then
- divide the period by 3 to produce $y = 2\sin 3x$,   then

- translate by $\begin{pmatrix} \frac{\pi}{4} \\ 1 \end{pmatrix}$ to produce $y = 2\sin(3(x - \frac{\pi}{4})) + 1$.

EXERCISE 10B.2

1   Sketch the graphs of the following for $0 \leqslant x \leqslant 4\pi$:

    a $y = \sin x - 2$ **b** $y = \sin(x - 2)$

    c $y = \sin(x + 2)$ **d** $y = \sin x + 2$

    e $y = \sin(x + \frac{\pi}{4})$ **f** $y = \sin(x - \frac{\pi}{6}) + 1$

    GRAPHING PACKAGE

    Check your answers using technology.

2   State the period of:

    a $y = \sin 5t$ **b** $y = \sin\left(\frac{t}{4}\right)$ **c** $y = \sin(-2t)$

3   Find b in $y = \sin bx$ if $b > 0$ and the period is:

    a 3π **b** $\frac{\pi}{10}$ **c** 100π **d** 50

4   State the transformation(s) which map:

    a $y = \sin x$ onto $y = \sin x - 1$ **b** $y = \sin x$ onto $y = \sin(x - \frac{\pi}{4})$

    c $y = \sin x$ onto $y = 2\sin x$ **d** $y = \sin x$ onto $y = \sin 4x$

    e $y = \sin x$ onto $y = \frac{1}{2}\sin x$ **f** $y = \sin x$ onto $y = \sin\left(\frac{x}{4}\right)$

    g $y = \sin x$ onto $y = -\sin x$ **h** $y = \sin x$ onto $y = -3 + \sin(x + 2)$

    i $y = \sin x$ onto $y = 2\sin 3x$ **j** $y = \sin x$ onto $y = \sin(x - \frac{\pi}{3}) + 2$

C — MODELLING USING SINE FUNCTIONS

When patterns of variation can be identified and quantified using a formula or equation, predictions may be made about behaviour in the future. Examples of this include tidal movement which can be predicted many months ahead, and the date of a future full moon.

In this section we use sine functions to model periodic biological and physical phenomena.

MEAN MONTHLY TEMPERATURE

Consider again the mean monthly maximum temperature for Cape Town over a 12 month period:

Month	Jan	Feb	Mar	Apr	May	Jun	Jul	Aug	Sep	Oct	Nov	Dec
Temp T (°C)	28	27	$25\frac{1}{2}$	22	$18\frac{1}{2}$	16	15	16	18	$21\frac{1}{2}$	24	26

The graph over a two year period is shown below:

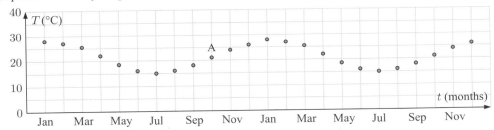

We attempt to model this data using the general sine function $y = a\sin(b(x - c)) + d$,

$$\text{or in this case} \quad T = a\sin(b(t - c)) + d.$$

The period is 12 months, so $\frac{2\pi}{b} = 12$ and $\therefore$ $b = \frac{\pi}{6}$.

The amplitude $= \frac{\text{max} - \text{min}}{2} \approx \frac{28 - 15}{2} \approx 6.5$, so $a \approx 6.5$.

The principal axis is midway between the maximum and minimum, so $d \approx \frac{28 + 15}{2} \approx 21.5$.

So, the model is $T \approx 6.5\sin(\frac{\pi}{6}(t - c)) + 21.5$ for some constant c.

On the original graph, point A lies on the principal axis, and is the first point shown at which we are starting a new period. Since A is at $(10, 21.5)$, $c = 10$.

The model is therefore $T \approx 6.5\sin(\frac{\pi}{6}(t - 10)) + 21.5$, and we can superimpose it on the original data as follows.

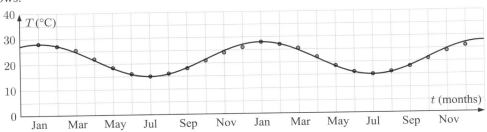

TIDAL MODELS

The tides at Juneau, Alaska were recorded over a two day period. The results are shown in the table opposite:

Day 1	high tide	1:18 pm
	low tide	6:46 am, 7:13 pm
Day 2	high tide	1:31 am, 2:09 pm
	low tide	7:30 am, 7:57 pm

Suppose high tide corresponds to height 1 and low tide to height -1.

Plotting these times with t being the time after midnight before the first low tide, we get:

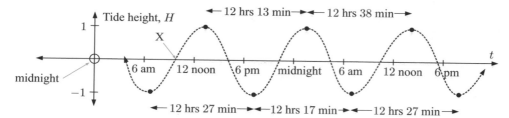

We attempt to model this periodic data using $H = a \sin(b(t - c)) + d$.

The principal axis is $H = 0$, so $d = 0$.

The amplitude is 1, so $a = 1$.

The graph shows that the 'average' period is about 12 hours 24 min ≈ 12.4 hours.

But the period is $\dfrac{2\pi}{b}$, so $\dfrac{2\pi}{b} \approx 12.4$ and $\therefore$ $b \approx \dfrac{2\pi}{12.4} \approx 0.507$.

The model is now $H \approx \sin(0.507(t - c))$ for some constant c.

We find point X which is midway between the *first minimum* 6:46 am and the *following maximum* 1:18 pm. Its x-coordinate is $\dfrac{6.77 + 13.3}{2} \approx 10.0$, so $c \approx 10.0$.

So, the model is $H \approx \sin(0.507(t - 10.0))$.

Below is our original graph of seven plotted points and our model which attempts to fit them.

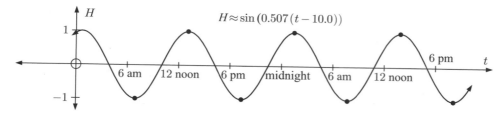

Use your **graphics calculator** to check this result.
The times must be given in hours after midnight, so
the low tide at 6:46 am is $(6.77, -1)$,
the high tide at 1:18 pm is $(13.3, 1)$, and so on.

**GRAPHICS
CALCULATOR
INSTRUCTIONS**

EXERCISE 10C

1   Below is a table which shows the mean monthly maximum temperatures for a city in Greece.

Month	Jan	Feb	Mar	Apr	May	Jun	July	Aug	Sept	Oct	Nov	Dec
Temperature (°C)	15	14	15	18	21	25	27	26	24	20	18	16

   a   Use a sine function of the form $T \approx a\sin(b(t-c))+d$ to model the data. Find good estimates
       of the constants a, b, c and d without using technology. Use Jan $\equiv 1$, Feb $\equiv 2$, and so on.

   b   Use technology to check your answer to a. How well does your model fit?

2   The data in the table shows the mean monthly temperatures for Christchurch, New Zealand.

Month	Jan	Feb	Mar	Apr	May	Jun	July	Aug	Sept	Oct	Nov	Dec
Temperature (°C)	15	16	$14\frac{1}{2}$	12	10	$7\frac{1}{2}$	7	$7\frac{1}{2}$	$8\frac{1}{2}$	$10\frac{1}{2}$	$12\frac{1}{2}$	14

   a   Find a sine model for this data in the form $T \approx a\sin(b(t-c))+d$.   Assume Jan $\equiv 1$,
       Feb $\equiv 2$, and so on. Do not use technology.

   b   Use technology to check your answer to a.

3   At the Mawson base in Antarctica, the mean monthly temperatures for the last 30 years are:

Month	Jan	Feb	Mar	Apr	May	Jun	July	Aug	Sept	Oct	Nov	Dec
Temperature (°C)	0	0	−4	−9	−14	−17	−18	−19	−17	−13	−6	−2

   a   Find a sine model for this data without using technology.
       Use Jan $\equiv 1$, Feb $\equiv 2$, and so on.

   b   How appropriate is the model?

4   Some of the largest tides in the world are observed in Canada's Bay of Fundy. The difference
    between high and low tides is 14 metres, and the average time difference between high tides is
    about 12.4 hours.

   a   Find a sine model for the height of the tide H in terms of the time t.

   b   Sketch the graph of the model over one period.

5   Revisit the **Opening Problem** on page **232**.
    The wheel takes 100 seconds to complete one
    revolution. Find the sine model which gives the height
    of the light above the ground at any point in time.
    Assume that at time $t = 0$, the light is at its lowest
    point.

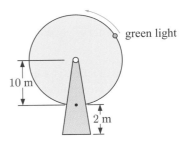

D   THE COSINE FUNCTION

We return to the Ferris wheel and now view the movement of the green light from above.

Now $\cos \theta = \dfrac{d}{10}$ so $d = 10 \cos \theta$

The graph being generated over time is therefore a **cosine function**.

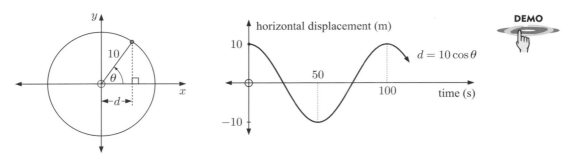

DEMO

The cosine curve $y = \cos x$,   like the sine curve $y = \sin x$,   has a **period** of 2π, an **amplitude** of 1, and its **range** is $-1 \leqslant y \leqslant 1$.

Use your graphics calculator or graphing package to check these features.

GRAPHICS
CALCULATOR
INSTRUCTIONS

GRAPHING
PACKAGE

Now view the relationship between the sine and cosine functions.

You should observe that $y = \cos x$ and $y = \sin x$ are identical in shape, but the cosine function is $\frac{\pi}{2}$ units left of the sine function under a horizontal translation.

This suggests that $\cos x = \sin \left(x + \frac{\pi}{2} \right)$.

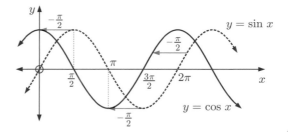

Use your graphing package or graphics calculator to check this by graphing $y = \cos x$ and $y = \sin \left(x + \frac{\pi}{2} \right)$ on the same set of axes.

GRAPHING
PACKAGE

THE GENERAL COSINE FUNCTION

> The **general cosine function** is $y = a\cos(b(x - c)) + d$ where $a \neq 0$, $b > 0$.

Since the cosine function is a horizontal translation of the sine function, the constants a, b, c, and d have the same effects as for the general sine function. Click on the icon to check this.

DYNAMIC
COSINE
FUNCTION

Example 4   ◀) **Self Tutor**

On the same set of axes graph $y = \cos x$ and $y = \cos\left(x - \frac{\pi}{3}\right)$ for $-2\pi \leqslant x \leqslant 2\pi$.

$y = \cos\left(x - \frac{\pi}{3}\right)$ is a horizontal translation of $y = \cos x$ through $\frac{\pi}{3}$ units to the right.

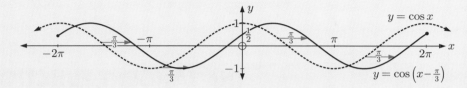

Example 5   ◀) **Self Tutor**

Without using technology, sketch the graph of $y = 3\cos 2x$ for $0 \leqslant x \leqslant 2\pi$.

Notice that $a = 3$, so the amplitude is $|3| = 3$.

$b = 2$, so the period is $\dfrac{2\pi}{b} = \dfrac{2\pi}{2} = \pi$.

To obtain this from $y = \cos x$, we have a vertical stretch with scale factor 3 followed by a horizontal stretch with scale factor $\frac{1}{2}$, as the period has been halved.

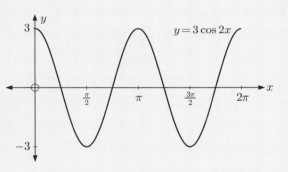

EXERCISE 10D

1 Given the graph of $y = \cos x$, sketch the graphs of:

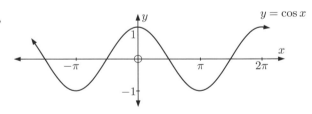

    a $y = \cos x + 2$ **b** $y = \cos x - 1$ **c** $y = \cos\left(x - \frac{\pi}{4}\right)$

    d $y = \cos\left(x + \frac{\pi}{6}\right)$ **e** $y = \frac{2}{3}\cos x$ **f** $y = \frac{3}{2}\cos x$

    g $y = -\cos x$ **h** $y = \cos\left(x - \frac{\pi}{6}\right) + 1$ **i** $y = \cos\left(x + \frac{\pi}{4}\right) - 1$

    j $y = \cos 2x$ **k** $y = \cos\left(\frac{x}{2}\right)$ **l** $y = 3\cos 2x$

2 Without graphing them, state the periods of:

    a $y = \cos 3x$ **b** $y = \cos\left(\frac{x}{3}\right)$ **c** $y = \cos\left(\frac{\pi}{50}x\right)$

3 The general cosine function is $y = a\cos(b(x - c)) + d$.
    State the geometrical significance of a, b, c, and d.

4 Find the cosine function shown in the graph:

a
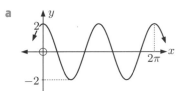

b
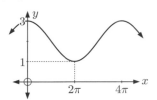

c
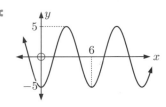

E | THE TANGENT FUNCTION

We have seen that if $P(\cos\theta, \sin\theta)$ is a point which is free to move around the unit circle, and if [OP] is extended to meet the tangent at $A(1, 0)$, the intersection between these lines occurs at $Q(1, \tan\theta)$.

This enables us to define the **tangent function**

$$\tan\theta = \frac{\sin\theta}{\cos\theta}.$$

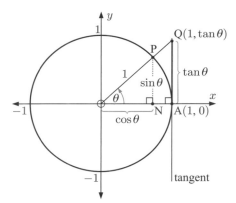

For θ in quadrant 2, $\sin\theta$ is positive and $\cos\theta$ is negative and so $\tan\theta = \dfrac{\sin\theta}{\cos\theta}$ is negative.

As before, [OP] is extended to meet the tangent at A at $Q(1, \tan\theta)$.

For θ in quadrant 3, $\sin\theta$ and $\cos\theta$ are both negative and so $\tan\theta$ is positive. This is clearly demonstrated as Q is back above the x-axis.

For θ in quadrant 4, $\sin\theta$ is negative and $\cos\theta$ is positive. $\tan\theta$ is again negative.

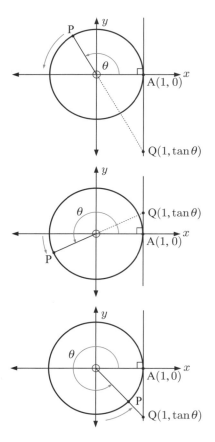

What happens to $\tan\theta$ when P is at $(0, 1)$ and $(0, -1)$?

THE GRAPH OF $y = \tan x$

Since $\tan x = \dfrac{\sin x}{\cos x}$, $\tan x$ will be undefined whenever $\cos x = 0$.

The zeros of the function $y = \cos x$ correspond to vertical asymptotes of the function $y = \tan x$.

The graph of $y = \tan x$ is

DEMO

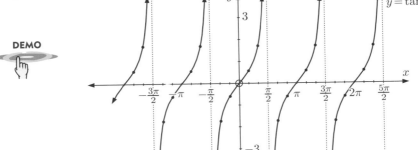

We observe that $y = \tan x$ has:

- **period** of π
- **range** $y \in \mathbb{R}$
- **vertical asymptotes** $x = \frac{\pi}{2} + k\pi$ for all $k \in \mathbb{Z}$.

Click on the icon to explore how the tangent function is produced from the unit circle.

TANGENT FUNCTION

THE GENERAL TANGENT FUNCTION

The **general tangent function** is $y = a\tan(b(x - c)) + d, \quad a \neq 0, \ b > 0$.

- The **principal axis** is $y = d$.
- The **period** of this function is $\dfrac{\pi}{b}$.
- The **amplitude** of this function is undefined.

Click on the icon to explore the properties of this function.

DYNAMIC TANGENT FUNCTION

- Discuss how to find the x-intercepts of $y = \tan x$.
- What must $\tan(x - \pi)$ simplify to?
- How many solutions does the equation $\tan x = 2$ have?

Example 6

◀》 **Self Tutor**

Without using technology, sketch the graph of $y = \tan(x + \frac{\pi}{4})$ for $0 \leqslant x \leqslant 3\pi$.

$y = \tan(x + \frac{\pi}{4})$ is a horizontal translation of $y = \tan x$ through $-\frac{\pi}{4}$

$y = \tan x$ has vertical asymptotes $x = \frac{\pi}{2}$, $x = \frac{3\pi}{2}$, and $x = \frac{5\pi}{2}$

Its x-axis intercepts are 0, π, 2π, and 3π.

$\therefore \quad y = \tan(x + \frac{\pi}{4})$ has vertical asymptotes $x = \frac{\pi}{4}$, $x = \frac{5\pi}{4}$, $x = \frac{9\pi}{4}$, and x-intercepts $\frac{3\pi}{4}$, $\frac{7\pi}{4}$, and $\frac{11\pi}{4}$.

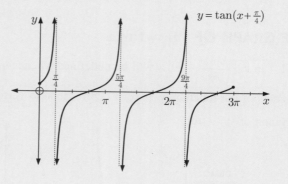

Example 7

◀》 **Self Tutor**

Without using technology, sketch the graph of $y = \tan 2x$ for $-\pi \leqslant x \leqslant \pi$.

$y = \tan 2x$ is a horizontal stretch of $y = \tan x$ with scale factor $\frac{1}{2}$.

Since $b = 2$, the period is $\frac{\pi}{2}$.

The vertical asymptotes are $x = \pm\frac{\pi}{4}$, $x = \pm\frac{3\pi}{4}$, and the x-axis intercepts are at 0, $\pm\frac{\pi}{2}$, $\pm\pi$.

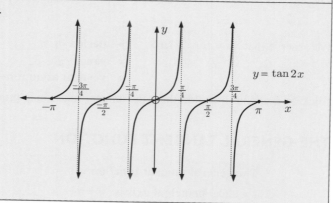

EXERCISE 10E

1 **a** *Sketch* the following functions for $0 \leqslant x \leqslant 3\pi$:

  i $y = \tan(x - \frac{\pi}{2})$ **ii** $y = -\tan x$ **iii** $y = \tan 3x$

b Use technology to check your answers to **a**.
   Look in particular for asymptotes and the x-intercepts.

GRAPHING PACKAGE

2 Describe the transformation(s) which moves the first curve to the second curve:

  a $y = \tan x$ to $y = \tan(x - 1) + 2$ **b** $y = \tan x$ to $y = -\tan x$

  c $y = \tan x$ to $y = 2\tan\left(\frac{x}{2}\right)$

3 State the period of:

  a $y = \tan x$ **b** $y = \tan 3x$ **c** $y = \tan nx$, $n \neq 0$

GRAPHING PACKAGE

F   GENERAL TRIGONOMETRIC FUNCTIONS

In the previous sections we have explored properties of the sine, cosine, and tangent functions, and observed how they can be transformed into more general trigonometric functions.

The following tables summarise our observations:

FEATURES OF CIRCULAR FUNCTIONS					
Function	Sketch for $0 \leqslant x \leqslant 2\pi$	Period	Amplitude	Domain	Range
$y = \sin x$		2π	1	$x \in \mathbb{R}$	$-1 \leqslant y \leqslant 1$
$y = \cos x$		2π	1	$x \in \mathbb{R}$	$-1 \leqslant y \leqslant 1$
$y = \tan x$		π	undefined	$x \neq \pm\frac{\pi}{2}, \pm\frac{3\pi}{2}, \ldots$	$y \in \mathbb{R}$

GENERAL TRIGONOMETRIC FUNCTIONS				
General function	a affects vertical stretch	$b > 0$ affects horizontal stretch	c affects horizontal translation	d affects vertical translation
$y = a\sin(b(x - c)) + d$ $y = a\cos(b(x - c)) + d$	amplitude $= \lvert a \rvert$	period $= \dfrac{2\pi}{b}$	• $c > 0$ moves the graph right • $c < 0$ moves the graph left	• $d > 0$ moves the graph up • $d < 0$ moves the graph down
$y = a\tan(b(x - c)) + d$	amplitude undefined	period $= \dfrac{\pi}{b}$		• principal axis is $y = d$

EXERCISE 10F

1   State the amplitude, where appropriate, of:

   a $y = \sin 4x$
   b $y = 2\tan\left(\frac{x}{2}\right)$
   c $y = -\cos\left(3\left(x - \frac{\pi}{4}\right)\right)$

2   State the period of:

   a $y = -\tan x$
   b $y = \cos\left(\frac{x}{3}\right) - 1$
   c $y = \sin\left(2\left(x - \frac{\pi}{4}\right)\right)$

3 Find b given:

    a $y = \sin bx$ has period 2π **b** $y = \cos bx$ has period $\frac{2\pi}{3}$

    c $y = \tan bx$ has period $\frac{\pi}{2}$ **d** $y = \sin bx$ has period 4

4 Sketch the graphs of these functions for $0 \leqslant x \leqslant 2\pi$:

    a $y = \frac{2}{3}\cos x$ **b** $y = \sin x + 1$ **c** $y = \tan(x + \frac{\pi}{2})$

    d $y = 3\cos 2x$ **e** $y = \sin(x + \frac{\pi}{4}) - 1$ **f** $y = \tan x - 2$

5 State the maximum and minimum values, where appropriate, of:

    a $y = -\sin 5x$ **b** $y = 3\cos x$ **c** $y = 2\tan x$

    d $y = -\cos 2x + 3$ **e** $y = 1 + 2\sin x$ **f** $y = \sin(x - \frac{\pi}{2}) - 3$

6 State the transformation(s) which map(s):

    a $y = \sin x$ onto $y = \frac{1}{2}\sin x$ **b** $y = \cos x$ onto $y = \cos(\frac{x}{4})$

    c $y = \sin x$ onto $y = -\sin x$ **d** $y = \cos x$ onto $y = \cos x - 2$

    e $y = \tan x$ onto $y = \tan(x + \frac{\pi}{4})$ **f** $y = \sin x$ onto $y = \sin(-x)$

7 Find m and n given the following graph is of the function $y = m\sin x + n$.

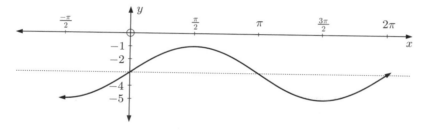

8 Find p and q given the following graph is of the function $y = \tan pt + q$.

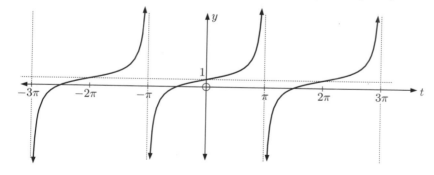

REVIEW SET 10A   NON-CALCULATOR

1 Which of the following graphs display periodic behaviour?

a

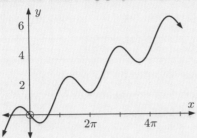

b

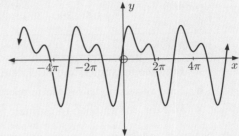

2 Draw the graph of $y = 4 \sin x$ for $0 \leqslant x \leqslant 2\pi$.

3 State the minimum and maximum values of:

    a $1 + \sin x$ **b** $-2 \cos 3x$

4 State the period of:

    a $y = 4 \sin(\frac{x}{5})$ **b** $y = -2 \cos(4x)$ **c** $y = 4 \cos(\frac{x}{2}) + 4$ **d** $y = \frac{1}{2} \tan(3x)$

5 Complete the table:

Function	Period	Amplitude	Domain	Range
$y = -3 \sin(\frac{x}{4}) + 1$				
$y = \tan 2x$				
$y = 3 \cos \pi x$				

6 Find the cosine function represented in each of the following graphs:

a

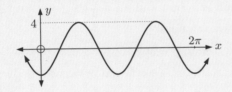

b

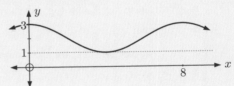

REVIEW SET 10B   CALCULATOR

1 For each set of data below, draw a scatter diagram and state if the data exhibits approximately periodic behaviour.

    a

x	0	1	2	3	4	5	6	7	8	9	10	11	12
y	2.7	0.8	−1.7	−3	−2.1	0.3	2.5	2.9	1.3	−1.3	−2.9	−2.5	−0.3

    b

x	0	1	2	3	4	5	6	7	8	9
y	5	3.5	6	−1.5	4	−2.5	−0.8	0.9	2.6	4.3

2 Draw the graph of $y = \sin 3x$ for $0 \leqslant x \leqslant 2\pi$.

3 State the period of: **a** $y = 4 \sin(\frac{x}{3})$ **b** $y = -2 \tan 4x$

4 Draw the graph of $y = 0.6 \cos(2.3x)$ for $0 \leqslant x \leqslant 5$.

5 A robot on Mars records the temperature every Mars day. A summary series, showing every one hundredth Mars day, is shown in the table below.

Number of Mars days	0	100	200	300	400	500	600	700	800	900	1000	1100	1200	1300
Temp. (°C)	−43	−15	−5	−21	−59	−79	−68	−50	−27	−8	−15	−70	−78	−68

  a Find the maximum and minimum temperatures recorded by the robot.

  b Find a sine model for the temperature T in terms of the number of Mars days n.

  c Use this information to estimate the length of a Mars year.

6 State the minimum and maximum values of:

  a $y = 5\sin x - 3$ **b** $y = \frac{1}{3}\cos x + 1$

REVIEW SET 10C

1 Consider the graph alongside.

  a Explain why this graph shows periodic behaviour.

  b State:

  i the period

  ii the maximum value

  iii the minimum value

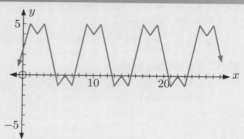

2 Find b given that the function $y = \sin bx$, $b > 0$ has period:

  a 6π **b** $\frac{\pi}{12}$ **c** 9

3 **a** Without using technology, draw the graph of $f(x) = \sin(x - \frac{\pi}{3}) + 2$ for $0 \leqslant x \leqslant 2\pi$.

  b For what values of k will $f(x) = k$ have solutions?

4 On the same set of axes, for the domain $0 \leqslant x \leqslant 2\pi$, sketch:

  a $y = \cos x$ and $y = \cos x - 3$ **b** $y = \cos x$ and $y = \cos(x - \frac{\pi}{4})$

  c $y = \cos x$ and $y = 3\cos 2x$ **d** $y = \cos x$ and $y = 2\cos(x - \frac{\pi}{3}) + 3$

5 The table below gives the mean monthly maximum temperature for Perth Airport in Western Australia.

Month	Jan	Feb	Mar	Apr	May	Jun	Jul	Aug	Sep	Oct	Nov	Dec
Temp (°C)	31.5	31.8	29.5	25.4	21.5	18.8	17.7	18.3	20.1	22.4	25.5	28.8

  a A sine function of the form $T \approx a\sin(b(t - c)) + d$ is used to model the data. Find good estimates of the constants a, b, c, and d without using technology. Use Jan $\equiv 1$, Feb $\equiv 2$, and so on.

  b Check your answer to **a** using technology. How well does your model fit?

6 State the transformation(s) which map(s):

  a $y = \cos x$ onto $y = \cos(x - \frac{\pi}{3}) + 1$ **b** $y = \tan x$ onto $y = -2\tan x$

  c $y = \sin x$ onto $y = \sin(3x)$

Chapter **11**

Trigonometric equations and identities

Syllabus reference: 3.3, 3.5

OPENING PROBLEM

Andrew is watching a Ferris wheel rotate at constant speed. There are many lights around the Ferris wheel, and Andrew watches a green light closely. The height of the green light after t seconds is given by $H(t) = 10\sin(\frac{\pi}{50}(t-25)) + 12$ metres.

Things to think about:

a At what height will the green light be after 50 seconds?

b How long does it take for the wheel to complete a full circle?

c At what times in the first three minutes will the green light be 16 metres above the ground?

A   TRIGONOMETRIC EQUATIONS

Linear equations such as $2x + 3 = 11$ have exactly one solution. Quadratic equations of the form $ax^2 + bx + c = 0$, $a \neq 0$ have at most two real solutions.

Trigonometric equations generally have infinitely many solutions unless a restricted domain such as $0 \leqslant x \leqslant 3\pi$ is given.

For example, in the **Opening Problem**, the green light will be 16 metres above the ground when $10\sin(\frac{\pi}{50}(t-25)) + 12 = 16$ metres.

This is a trigonometric equation, and it has infinitely many solutions provided the wheel keeps rotating. For this reason we need to specify if we are interested in the first three minutes of its rotation, which is when $0 \leqslant t \leqslant 180$.

We will examine solving trigonometric equations using:

- pre-prepared graphs
- technology
- algebra.

GRAPHICAL SOLUTION OF TRIGONOMETRIC EQUATIONS

Sometimes simple trigonometric graphs are available on grid paper. In such cases we can estimate solutions straight from the graph.

Example 1   ◀)) Self Tutor

Solve $\cos x = 0.4$ for $0 \leqslant x \leqslant 10$ radians using the graph of $y = \cos x$.

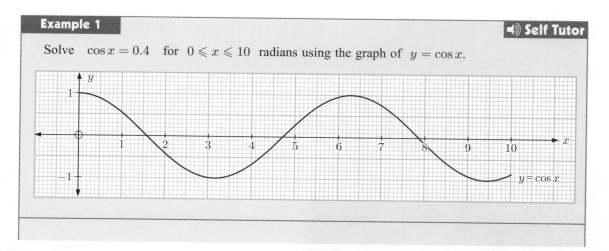

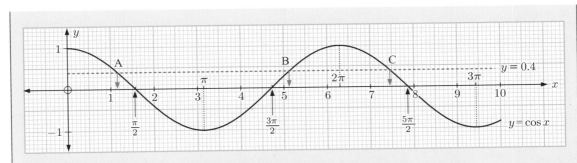

$y = 0.4$ meets $y = \cos x$ at A, B, and C. Hence $x \approx 1.2,\ 5.1,$ or 7.4.

The solutions of $\cos x = 0.4$ for $0 \leqslant x \leqslant 10$ radians are $1.2,\ 5.1,$ and 7.4.

EXERCISE 11A.1

1

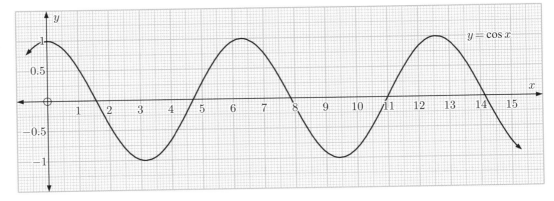

Use the graph of $y = \sin x$ to find, correct to 1 decimal place, the solutions of:

  a $\sin x = 0.3$ for $0 \leqslant x \leqslant 15$ **b** $\sin x = -0.4$ for $5 \leqslant x \leqslant 15$.

2

Use the graph of $y = \cos x$ to find, correct to 1 decimal place, the solutions of:

  a $\cos x = 0.4$ for $0 \leqslant x \leqslant 10$ **b** $\cos x = -0.3$ for $4 \leqslant x \leqslant 12$.

3

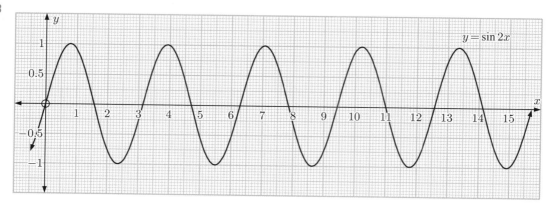

Use the graph of $y = \sin 2x$ to find, correct to 1 decimal place, the solutions of:

a $\sin 2x = 0.7$ for $0 \leqslant x \leqslant 16$ **b** $\sin 2x = -0.3$ for $0 \leqslant x \leqslant 16$.

4

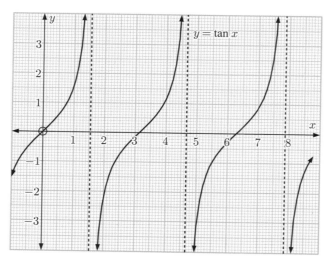

The graph of $y = \tan x$ is illustrated.

a Use the graph to estimate: **i** $\tan 1$ **ii** $\tan 2.3$
     Check your answers with a calculator.

b Find, correct to 1 decimal place, the solutions of:
     i $\tan x = 2$ for $0 \leqslant x \leqslant 8$ **ii** $\tan x = -1.4$ for $2 \leqslant x \leqslant 7$.

SOLVING TRIGONOMETRIC EQUATIONS USING TECHNOLOGY

Trigonometric equations may be solved using either a **graphing package** or a **graphics calculator**.

When using a graphics calculator make sure that the **mode** is set to **radians**.

GRAPHING PACKAGE

Example 2

◄) **Self Tutor**

Solve $2\sin x - \cos x = 4 - x$ for $0 \leqslant x \leqslant 2\pi$.

We graph the functions $Y_1 = 2\sin X - \cos X$ and $Y_2 = 4 - X$ on the same set of axes.

We need to use **window** settings just larger than the domain.

In this case, $X\min = -\frac{\pi}{6}$ $X\max = \frac{13\pi}{6}$ $X\text{scale} = \frac{\pi}{6}$

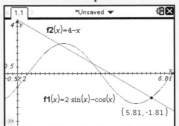

GRAPHICS
CALCULATOR
INSTRUCTIONS

Casio fx-CG20	TI-84 Plus	TI-*n*spire

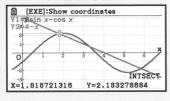 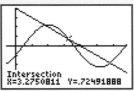

The solutions are $x \approx 1.82$, 3.28, and 5.81.

EXERCISE 11A.2

1   Solve for x on the domain $0 < x < 12$:

   a $\sin x = 0.431$ **b** $\cos x = -0.814$ **c** $3\tan x - 2 = 0$

2   Solve for x on the domain $-5 \leqslant x \leqslant 5$:

   a $5\cos x - 4 = 0$ **b** $2\tan x + 13 = 0$ **c** $8\sin x + 3 = 0$

3   Solve each of the following for $0 \leqslant x \leqslant 2\pi$:

   a $\sin(x + 2) = 0.0652$ **b** $\sin^2 x + \sin x - 1 = 0$

   c $x\tan\left(\dfrac{x^2}{10}\right) = x^2 - 6x + 1$ **d** $2\sin(2x)\cos x = \ln x$

4   Solve for x: $\cos(x - 1) + \sin(x + 1) = 6x + 5x^2 - x^3$ for $-2 \leqslant x \leqslant 6$.

> Make sure you find *all* the solutions on the given domain.

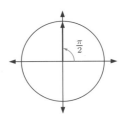

SOLVING TRIGONOMETRIC EQUATIONS USING ALGEBRA

Using a calculator we get approximate decimal or **numerical** solutions to trigonometric equations.

Sometimes exact solutions are needed in terms of π, and these arise when the solutions are multiples of $\frac{\pi}{6}$ or $\frac{\pi}{4}$. Exact solutions obtained using algebra are called **analytical** solutions.

We use the periodicity of the trigonometric functions to give us all solutions in the required domain. Remember that $\sin x$ and $\cos x$ both have period 2π, and $\tan x$ has period π.

For example, consider $\sin x = 1$. We know from the unit circle that a solution is $x = \frac{\pi}{2}$. However, since the period of $\sin x$ is 2π, there are infinitely many solutions spaced 2π apart.

In general, $x = \frac{\pi}{2} + k2\pi$ is a solution for any $k \in \mathbb{Z}$.

In this course we will be solving equations on a fixed domain. This means there will be a finite number of solutions.

Reminder:

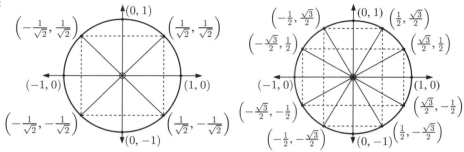

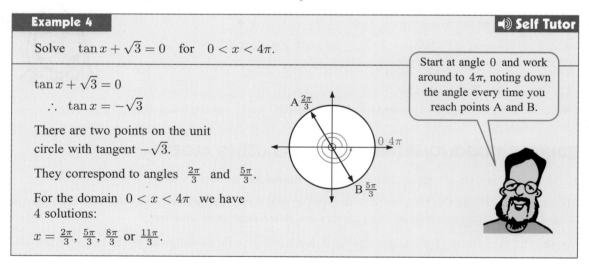

Example 3

Solve for x: $2 \sin x - 1 = 0$, $0 \leqslant x \leqslant \pi$

$2 \sin x - 1 = 0$

$\therefore \ \sin x = \frac{1}{2}$

There are two points on the unit circle with sine $\frac{1}{2}$.

They correspond to angles $\frac{\pi}{6}$ and $\frac{5\pi}{6}$.

These are the only solutions in the domain $0 \leqslant x \leqslant \pi$,

so $x = \frac{\pi}{6}$ or $\frac{5\pi}{6}$.

Since the tangent function is periodic with period π we see that $\tan(x + \pi) = \tan x$ for all values of x. This means that equal $\tan$ values are π units apart.

Example 4

Solve $\tan x + \sqrt{3} = 0$ for $0 < x < 4\pi$.

$\tan x + \sqrt{3} = 0$

$\therefore \ \tan x = -\sqrt{3}$

There are two points on the unit circle with tangent $-\sqrt{3}$.

They correspond to angles $\frac{2\pi}{3}$ and $\frac{5\pi}{3}$.

For the domain $0 < x < 4\pi$ we have 4 solutions:

$x = \frac{2\pi}{3}, \ \frac{5\pi}{3}, \ \frac{8\pi}{3}$ or $\frac{11\pi}{3}$.

> Start at angle 0 and work around to 4π, noting down the angle every time you reach points A and B.

EXERCISE 11A.3

1 Solve for x on the domain $0 \leqslant x \leqslant 4\pi$:

    a $2 \cos x - 1 = 0$ **b** $\sqrt{2} \sin x = 1$ **c** $\tan x = 1$

2 Solve for x on the domain $-2\pi \leqslant x \leqslant 2\pi$:

    a $2 \sin x - \sqrt{3} = 0$ **b** $\sqrt{2} \cos x + 1 = 0$ **c** $\tan x = -1$

Example 5   ◀)) Self Tutor

Solve exactly for $0 \leqslant x \leqslant 3\pi$:

  a $\sin x = -\frac{1}{2}$ **b** $\sin 2x = -\frac{1}{2}$ **c** $\sin(x - \frac{\pi}{6}) = -\frac{1}{2}$

The three equations all have the form $\sin \theta = -\frac{1}{2}$.

There are two points on the unit circle with sine $-\frac{1}{2}$.

They correspond to angles $\frac{7\pi}{6}$ and $\frac{11\pi}{6}$.

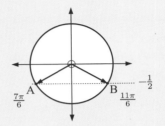

a In this case θ is simply x, so we have the domain $0 \leqslant x \leqslant 3\pi$.
The only solutions for this domain are $x = \frac{7\pi}{6}$ or $\frac{11\pi}{6}$.

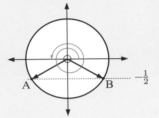

Start at 0 and work around to 3π, noting down the angle every time you reach points A and B.

b In this case θ is $2x$.
If $0 \leqslant x \leqslant 3\pi$ then $0 \leqslant 2x \leqslant 6\pi$.
$\therefore \ 2x = \frac{7\pi}{6}, \frac{11\pi}{6}, \frac{19\pi}{6}, \frac{23\pi}{6}, \frac{31\pi}{6},$ or $\frac{35\pi}{6}$
$\therefore \ x = \frac{7\pi}{12}, \frac{11\pi}{12}, \frac{19\pi}{12}, \frac{23\pi}{12}, \frac{31\pi}{12},$ or $\frac{35\pi}{12}$

c In this case θ is $x - \frac{\pi}{6}$.
If $0 \leqslant x \leqslant 3\pi$ then $-\frac{\pi}{6} \leqslant x - \frac{\pi}{6} \leqslant \frac{17\pi}{6}$.
$\therefore \ x - \frac{\pi}{6} = -\frac{\pi}{6}, \frac{7\pi}{6},$ or $\frac{11\pi}{6}$
$\therefore \ x = 0, \frac{4\pi}{3},$ or 2π

Start at $-\frac{\pi}{6}$ and work around to $\frac{17\pi}{6}$, noting down the angle every time you reach points A and B.

3 If $0 \leqslant x \leqslant 2\pi$, what are the possible values of:

  a $2x$ **b** $\frac{x}{3}$ **c** $x + \frac{\pi}{2}$ **d** $x - \frac{\pi}{6}$ **e** $2\left(x - \frac{\pi}{4}\right)$ **f** $-x$

4 If $-\pi \leqslant x \leqslant \pi$, what are the possible values of:

  a $3x$ **b** $\frac{x}{4}$ **c** $x - \frac{\pi}{2}$ **d** $2x + \frac{\pi}{2}$ **e** $-2x$ **f** $\pi - x$

5 Solve exactly for $0 \leqslant x \leqslant 3\pi$:

  a $\cos x = \frac{1}{2}$ **b** $\cos 2x = \frac{1}{2}$ **c** $\cos(x + \frac{\pi}{3}) = \frac{1}{2}$

Example 6
🔊 **Self Tutor**

Find exact solutions of $\sqrt{2}\cos(x - \frac{3\pi}{4}) + 1 = 0$ for $0 \leqslant x \leqslant 6\pi$.

Rearranging $\sqrt{2}\cos(x - \frac{3\pi}{4}) + 1 = 0$, we find $\cos(x - \frac{3\pi}{4}) = -\frac{1}{\sqrt{2}}$.

We recognise $\frac{1}{\sqrt{2}}$ as a special fraction for multiples of $\frac{\pi}{4}$, and we identify two points on the unit circle with cosine $-\frac{1}{\sqrt{2}}$.

Since $0 \leqslant x \leqslant 6\pi$,

$$-\frac{3\pi}{4} \leqslant x - \frac{3\pi}{4} \leqslant \frac{21\pi}{4}$$

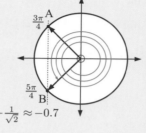

Start at $-\frac{3\pi}{4}$ and work around to $\frac{21\pi}{4}$, noting down the angle every time you reach points A and B.

So, $x - \frac{3\pi}{4} = -\frac{3\pi}{4}, \frac{3\pi}{4}, \frac{5\pi}{4}, \frac{11\pi}{4}, \frac{13\pi}{4}, \frac{19\pi}{4}$, or $\frac{21\pi}{4}$

$\therefore \ x = 0, \frac{3\pi}{2}, 2\pi, \frac{7\pi}{2}, 4\pi, \frac{11\pi}{2}$, or 6π

6 Find the exact solutions of:

a $\cos x = -\frac{1}{2}, \ 0 \leqslant x \leqslant 5\pi$

b $2\sin x - 1 = 0, \ -360° \leqslant x \leqslant 360°$

c $2\cos x + \sqrt{3} = 0, \ 0 \leqslant x \leqslant 3\pi$

d $\cos(x - \frac{2\pi}{3}) = \frac{1}{2}, \ -2\pi \leqslant x \leqslant 2\pi$

e $2\sin(x + \frac{\pi}{3}) = 1, \ -3\pi \leqslant x \leqslant 3\pi$

f $\sqrt{2}\sin(x - \frac{\pi}{4}) + 1 = 0, \ 0 \leqslant x \leqslant 3\pi$

g $3\cos 2x + 3 = 0, \ 0 \leqslant x \leqslant 3\pi$

h $4\cos 3x + 2 = 0, \ -\pi \leqslant x \leqslant \pi$

i $\sin(4(x - \frac{\pi}{4})) = 0, \ 0 \leqslant x \leqslant \pi$

j $2\sin(2(x - \frac{\pi}{3})) = -\sqrt{3}, \ 0 \leqslant x \leqslant 2\pi$

Example 7
🔊 **Self Tutor**

Find exact solutions of $\tan(2x - \frac{\pi}{3}) = 1$ for $-\pi \leqslant x \leqslant \pi$.

There are two points on the unit circle which have tangent 1.

Since $-\pi \leqslant x \leqslant \pi$,

$$-2\pi \leqslant 2x \leqslant 2\pi$$

$$\therefore -\frac{7\pi}{3} \leqslant 2x - \frac{\pi}{3} \leqslant \frac{5\pi}{3}$$

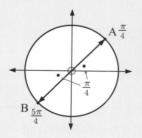

Start at $-\frac{7\pi}{3}$ and work around to $\frac{5\pi}{3}$, noting down the angle every time you reach points A and B.

So, $2x - \frac{\pi}{3} = -\frac{7\pi}{4}, -\frac{3\pi}{4}, \frac{\pi}{4}$, or $\frac{5\pi}{4}$

$\therefore \ 2x = -\frac{17\pi}{12}, -\frac{5\pi}{12}, \frac{7\pi}{12}$, or $\frac{19\pi}{12}$

$\therefore \ x = -\frac{17\pi}{24}, -\frac{5\pi}{24}, \frac{7\pi}{24}$, or $\frac{19\pi}{24}$

7 Find the exact solutions of $\tan x = \sqrt{3}$ for $0 \leqslant x \leqslant 2\pi$. Hence solve the following equations for $0 \leqslant x \leqslant 2\pi$:

a $\tan(x - \frac{\pi}{6}) = \sqrt{3}$

b $\tan 4x = \sqrt{3}$

c $\tan^2 x = 3$

8 Find exactly the zeros of:

a $y = \sin 2x$ for $0° \leqslant x \leqslant 180°$

b $y = \sin(x - \frac{\pi}{4})$ for $0 \leqslant x \leqslant 3\pi$

Example 8   🔊 **Self Tutor**

Find the exact solutions of $\sqrt{3}\sin x = \cos x$ for $0° \leqslant x \leqslant 360°$.

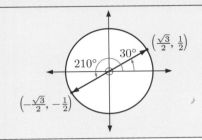

$$\sqrt{3}\sin x = \cos x$$

$$\therefore \quad \frac{\sin x}{\cos x} = \frac{1}{\sqrt{3}} \quad \{\text{dividing both sides by } \sqrt{3}\cos x\}$$

$$\therefore \quad \tan x = \frac{1}{\sqrt{3}}$$

$$\therefore \quad x = 30° \quad \text{or} \quad 210°$$

9 a Use your graphics calculator to sketch the graphs of $y = \sin x$ and $y = \cos x$ on the same set of axes on the domain $0 \leqslant x \leqslant 2\pi$.

 b Find the x-coordinates of the points of intersection of the two graphs.

10 Find the exact solutions to these equations for $0 \leqslant x \leqslant 2\pi$:

 a $\sin x = -\cos x$ **b** $\sin(3x) = \cos(3x)$ **c** $\sin(2x) = \sqrt{3}\cos(2x)$

Check your answers using a graphics calculator by finding the points of intersection of the appropriate graphs.

B	**USING TRIGONOMETRIC MODELS**

Having discussed the solution of trigonometric equations, we can now put into use the trigonometric model from **Chapter 10**.

Example 9   🔊 **Self Tutor**

The height of the tide above mean sea level on January 24th at Cape Town is modelled approximately by $h(t) = 3\sin(\frac{\pi t}{6})$ metres where t is the number of hours after midnight.

 a Graph $y = h(t)$ for $0 \leqslant t \leqslant 24$.

 b When is high tide and what is the maximum height?

 c What is the height of the tide at 2 pm?

 d A ship can cross the harbour provided the tide is at least 2 m above mean sea level. When is crossing possible on January 24th?

a $h(0) = 0$

  $h(t) = 3\sin(\frac{\pi t}{6})$ has period $= \dfrac{2\pi}{\frac{\pi}{6}} = 2\pi \times \frac{6}{\pi} = 12$ hours

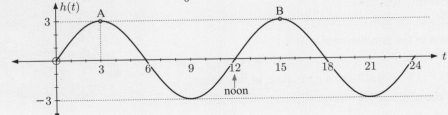

b High tide is at 3 am and 3 pm. The maximum height is 3 m above the mean as seen at points A and B.

c At 2 pm, $t = 14$ and $h(14) = 3\sin(\frac{14\pi}{6}) \approx 2.60$ m.

So, the tide is 2.6 m above the mean.

d

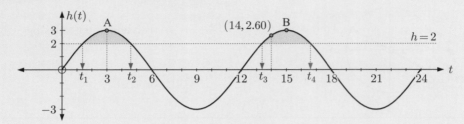

We need to solve $h(t) = 2$, so $3\sin(\frac{\pi t}{6}) = 2$.

Using a graphics calculator with $Y_1 = 3\sin(\frac{\pi X}{6})$ and $Y_2 = 2$

we obtain $t_1 \approx 1.39$, $t_2 \approx 4.61$, $t_3 \approx 13.39$, $t_4 \approx 16.61$

Now 1.39 hours = 1 hour 23 minutes, and so on.

So, the ship can cross between 1:23 am and 4:37 am or 1:23 pm and 4:37 pm.

EXERCISE 11B

1 Answer the **Opening Problem** on page **256**.

2 The population of grasshoppers after t weeks where $0 \leqslant t \leqslant 12$ is estimated by $P(t) = 7500 + 3000\sin(\frac{\pi t}{8})$.

   a Find: **i** the initial estimate   **ii** the estimate after 5 weeks.

   b What is the greatest population size over this interval and when does it occur?

   c When is the population: **i** 9000   **ii** 6000?

   d During what time interval(s) does the population size exceed 10 000?

3 The model for the height of a light on a certain Ferris wheel is $H(t) = 20 - 19\sin(\frac{2\pi t}{3})$,   where H is the height in metres above the ground, and t is in minutes.

   a Where is the light at time $t = 0$?

   b At what time is the light at its lowest in the first revolution of the wheel?

   c How long does the wheel take to complete one revolution?

   d Sketch the graph of the function $H(t)$ over one revolution.

4 The population of water buffalo is given by $P(t) = 400 + 250\sin(\frac{\pi t}{2})$ where t is the number of years since the first estimate was made.

   a What was the initial estimate?

   b What was the population size after:

   i 6 months   **ii** two years?

   c Find $P(1)$. What is the significance of this value?

   d Find the smallest population size and when it first occurred.

   e Find the first time when the herd exceeded 500.

5 A paint spot X lies on the outer rim of the wheel of a paddle-steamer.

The wheel has radius 3 m. It rotates anticlockwise at a constant rate, and X is seen entering the water every 4 seconds.

H is the distance of X above the bottom of the boat. At time $t = 0$, X is at its highest point.

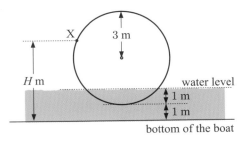

a Find a cosine model for H in the form $H(t) = a\cos(b(t+c)) + d$.

b At what time t does X first enter the water?

6 Over a 28 day period, the cost per litre of petrol was modelled by
$C(t) = 9.2\sin(\frac{\pi}{7}(t-4)) + 107.8$ cents L^{-1}.

a True or false?

   i "The cost per litre oscillates about 107.8 cents with maximum price $1.17 per litre."

   ii "Every 14 days, the cycle repeats itself."

b What was the cost of petrol on day 7, to the nearest tenth of a cent per litre?

c On which days was the petrol priced at $1.10 per litre?

d What was the minimum cost per litre and when did it occur?

C   TRIGONOMETRIC RELATIONSHIPS

There are a vast number of trigonometric relationships. However, we only need to remember a few because we can obtain the rest by rearrangement or substitution.

SIMPLIFYING TRIGONOMETRIC EXPRESSIONS

For any given angle θ, $\sin\theta$ and $\cos\theta$ are real numbers. $\tan\theta$ is also real whenever it is defined. The algebra of trigonometry is therefore identical to the algebra of real numbers.

An expression like $2\sin\theta + 3\sin\theta$ compares with $2x + 3x$ when we wish to do simplification, and so $2\sin\theta + 3\sin\theta = 5\sin\theta$.

To simplify complicated trigonometric expressions, we often use the identities:

$$\sin^2\theta + \cos^2\theta = 1$$

$$\tan\theta = \frac{\sin\theta}{\cos\theta}$$

We can also use rearrangements of these formulae, such as $\sin^2\theta = 1 - \cos^2\theta$ and $\cos^2\theta = 1 - \sin^2\theta$.

Example 10   ◆) **Self Tutor**

Simplify:

a $3\cos\theta + 4\cos\theta$

b $\tan\alpha - 3\tan\alpha$

a $3\cos\theta + 4\cos\theta = 7\cos\theta$
   {compare with $3x + 4x = 7x$}

b $\tan\alpha - 3\tan\alpha = -2\tan\alpha$
   {compare with $x - 3x = -2x$}

Example 11   ◀» **Self Tutor**

Simplify:

a $2 - 2\sin^2\theta$

b $\cos^2\theta\sin\theta + \sin^3\theta$

---

a $2 - 2\sin^2\theta$
$= 2(1 - \sin^2\theta)$
$= 2\cos^2\theta$
    $\{\text{as}\quad \cos^2\theta + \sin^2\theta = 1\}$

b $\cos^2\theta\sin\theta + \sin^3\theta$
$= \sin\theta(\cos^2\theta + \sin^2\theta)$
$= \sin\theta \times 1$
$= \sin\theta$

Example 12   ◀» **Self Tutor**

Expand and simplify: $(\cos\theta - \sin\theta)^2$

$(\cos\theta - \sin\theta)^2$
$= \cos^2\theta - 2\cos\theta\sin\theta + \sin^2\theta$ $\{\text{using}\quad (a - b)^2 = a^2 - 2ab + b^2\}$
$= \cos^2\theta + \sin^2\theta - 2\cos\theta\sin\theta$
$= 1 - 2\cos\theta\sin\theta$

EXERCISE 11C.1

1 Simplify:

a $\sin\theta + \sin\theta$

b $2\cos\theta + \cos\theta$

c $3\sin\theta - \sin\theta$

d $3\sin\theta - 2\sin\theta$

e $\tan\theta - 3\tan\theta$

f $2\cos^2\theta - 5\cos^2\theta$

2 Simplify:

a $3\sin^2\theta + 3\cos^2\theta$

b $-2\sin^2\theta - 2\cos^2\theta$

c $-\cos^2\theta - \sin^2\theta$

d $3 - 3\sin^2\theta$

e $4 - 4\cos^2\theta$

f $\cos^3\theta + \cos\theta\sin^2\theta$

g $\cos^2\theta - 1$

h $\sin^2\theta - 1$

i $2\cos^2\theta - 2$

j $\dfrac{1 - \sin^2\theta}{\cos^2\theta}$

k $\dfrac{1 - \cos^2\theta}{\sin\theta}$

l $\dfrac{\cos^2\theta - 1}{-\sin\theta}$

3 Simplify:

a $3\tan x - \dfrac{\sin x}{\cos x}$

b $\dfrac{\sin^2 x}{\cos^2 x}$

c $\tan x\cos x$

d $\dfrac{\sin x}{\tan x}$

e $3\sin x + 2\cos x\tan x$

f $\dfrac{2\tan x}{\sin x}$

4 Expand and simplify if possible:

a $(1 + \sin\theta)^2$

b $(\sin\alpha - 2)^2$

c $(\tan\alpha - 1)^2$

d $(\sin\alpha + \cos\alpha)^2$

e $(\sin\beta - \cos\beta)^2$

f $-(2 - \cos\alpha)^2$

5 Expand and simplify: $(\sin x + \tan x)(\sin x - \tan x)$

FACTORISING TRIGONOMETRIC EXPRESSIONS

Example 13

◀) **Self Tutor**

Factorise: **a** $\cos^2 \alpha - \sin^2 \alpha$ **b** $\tan^2 \theta - 3 \tan \theta + 2$

a $\cos^2 \alpha - \sin^2 \alpha$
$= (\cos \alpha + \sin \alpha)(\cos \alpha - \sin \alpha)$ $\{a^2 - b^2 = (a+b)(a-b)\}$

b $\tan^2 \theta - 3 \tan \theta + 2$
$= (\tan \theta - 2)(\tan \theta - 1)$ $\{x^2 - 3x + 2 = (x-2)(x-1)\}$

Example 14

◀) **Self Tutor**

Simplify:

a $\dfrac{2 - 2\cos^2 \theta}{1 + \cos \theta}$ **b** $\dfrac{\cos \theta - \sin \theta}{\cos^2 \theta - \sin^2 \theta}$

a $\dfrac{2 - 2\cos^2 \theta}{1 + \cos \theta}$

$= \dfrac{2(1 - \cos^2 \theta)}{1 + \cos \theta}$

$= \dfrac{2(1 + \cos\theta)(1 - \cos \theta)}{(1 + \cos\theta)}$

$= 2(1 - \cos \theta)$

b $\dfrac{\cos \theta - \sin \theta}{\cos^2 \theta - \sin^2 \theta}$

$= \dfrac{(\cos\theta - \sin\theta)}{(\cos \theta + \sin \theta)(\cos\theta - \sin\theta)}$

$= \dfrac{1}{\cos \theta + \sin \theta}$

EXERCISE 11C.2

1 Factorise:

a $1 - \sin^2 \theta$

b $\sin^2 \alpha - \cos^2 \alpha$

c $\tan^2 \alpha - 1$

d $2 \sin^2 \beta - \sin \beta$

e $2 \cos \phi + 3 \cos^2 \phi$

f $3 \sin^2 \theta - 6 \sin \theta$

g $\tan^2 \theta + 5 \tan \theta + 6$

h $2 \cos^2 \theta + 7 \cos \theta + 3$

i $6 \cos^2 \alpha - \cos \alpha - 1$

2 Simplify:

a $\dfrac{1 - \sin^2 \alpha}{1 - \sin \alpha}$

b $\dfrac{\tan^2 \beta - 1}{\tan \beta + 1}$

c $\dfrac{\cos^2 \phi - \sin^2 \phi}{\cos \phi + \sin \phi}$

d $\dfrac{\cos^2 \phi - \sin^2 \phi}{\cos \phi - \sin \phi}$

e $\dfrac{\sin \alpha + \cos \alpha}{\sin^2 \alpha - \cos^2 \alpha}$

f $\dfrac{3 - 3 \sin^2 \theta}{6 \cos \theta}$

3 Show that:

a $(\cos \theta + \sin \theta)^2 + (\cos \theta - \sin \theta)^2$ simplifies to 2

b $(2 \sin \theta + 3 \cos \theta)^2 + (3 \sin \theta - 2 \cos \theta)^2$ simplifies to 13

c $(1 - \cos \theta) \left(1 + \dfrac{1}{\cos \theta}\right)$ simplifies to $\tan \theta \sin \theta$

d $\left(1 + \dfrac{1}{\sin \theta}\right) (\sin \theta - \sin^2 \theta)$ simplifies to $\cos^2 \theta$

e $\dfrac{\sin\theta}{1+\cos\theta} + \dfrac{1+\cos\theta}{\sin\theta}$ simplifies to $\dfrac{2}{\sin\theta}$

f $\dfrac{\sin\theta}{1-\cos\theta} - \dfrac{\sin\theta}{1+\cos\theta}$ simplifies to $\dfrac{2}{\tan\theta}$

g $\dfrac{1}{1-\sin\theta} + \dfrac{1}{1+\sin\theta}$ simplifies to $\dfrac{2}{\cos^2\theta}$.

Use a graphing package to check these simplifications by graphing each function on the same set of axes.

GRAPHING
PACKAGE

D   DOUBLE ANGLE FORMULAE

INVESTIGATION   DOUBLE ANGLE FORMULAE

What to do:

1 Copy and complete, using angles of your choice as well:

θ	$\sin 2\theta$	$2\sin\theta$	$2\sin\theta\cos\theta$	$\cos 2\theta$	$2\cos\theta$	$\cos^2\theta - \sin^2\theta$
0.631						
57.81°						
−3.697						

2 Write down any discoveries from your table of values in **1**.

3 In the diagram alongside, the semi-circle has radius
1 unit, and $\widehat{PAB} = \theta$.

$\widehat{APO} = \theta$ {$\triangle AOP$ is isosceles}
$\widehat{PON} = 2\theta$ {exterior angle of a triangle}

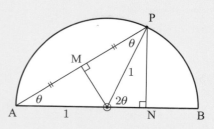

a Find in terms of θ, the lengths of:

  i [OM]   **ii** [AM]
  iii [ON]   **iv** [PN]

b Use $\triangle ANP$ and the lengths in **1** to show that:

  i $\cos\theta = \dfrac{\sin 2\theta}{2\sin\theta}$ **ii** $\cos\theta = \dfrac{1+\cos 2\theta}{2\cos\theta}$

c Hence deduce that:

  i $\sin 2\theta = 2\sin\theta\cos\theta$ **ii** $\cos 2\theta = 2\cos^2\theta - 1$

The **double angle formulae** are:

$$\sin 2\theta = 2\sin\theta\cos\theta$$
$$\cos 2\theta = \cos^2\theta - \sin^2\theta$$
$$= 1 - 2\sin^2\theta$$
$$= 2\cos^2\theta - 1$$

GRAPHING PACKAGE

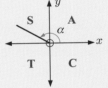

Example 15   ◀») **Self Tutor**

Given that $\sin\alpha = \frac{3}{5}$ and $\cos\alpha = -\frac{4}{5}$ find:

a $\sin 2\alpha$ b $\cos 2\alpha$

a $\quad \sin 2\alpha$
$\quad = 2\sin\alpha\cos\alpha$
$\quad = 2(\frac{3}{5})(-\frac{4}{5})$
$\quad = -\frac{24}{25}$

b $\quad \cos 2\alpha$
$\quad = \cos^2\alpha - \sin^2\alpha$
$\quad = (-\frac{4}{5})^2 - (\frac{3}{5})^2$
$\quad = \frac{7}{25}$

Example 16   ◀») **Self Tutor**

If $\sin\alpha = \frac{5}{13}$ where $\frac{\pi}{2} < \alpha < \pi$, find the exact value of $\sin 2\alpha$.

α is in quadrant 2, so $\cos\alpha$ is negative.

Now $\cos^2\alpha + \sin^2\alpha = 1$

$\therefore \quad \cos^2\alpha + \frac{25}{169} = 1$

$\therefore \quad \cos^2\alpha = \frac{144}{169}$ But $\sin 2\alpha = 2\sin\alpha\cos\alpha$

$\therefore \quad \cos\alpha = \pm\frac{12}{13}$ $\therefore \ \sin 2\alpha = 2(\frac{5}{13})(-\frac{12}{13})$

$\therefore \quad \cos\alpha = -\frac{12}{13}$ $\qquad = -\frac{120}{169}$

EXERCISE 11D

1 If $\sin\theta = \frac{4}{5}$ and $\cos\theta = \frac{3}{5}$ find the exact values of:

a $\sin 2\theta$ b $\cos 2\theta$ c $\tan 2\theta$

2 a If $\cos A = \frac{1}{3}$, find $\cos 2A$.   b If $\sin\phi = -\frac{2}{3}$, find $\cos 2\phi$.

3 If $\sin\alpha = -\frac{2}{3}$ where $\pi < \alpha < \frac{3\pi}{2}$, find the exact value of:

a $\cos\alpha$ b $\sin 2\alpha$

4 If $\cos\beta = \frac{2}{5}$ where $270° < \beta < 360°$, find the exact value of:

a $\sin\beta$ b $\sin 2\beta$

Example 17   ◀) **Self Tutor**

If α is acute and $\cos 2\alpha = \frac{3}{4}$ find the exact values of: a $\cos \alpha$ b $\sin \alpha$.

a $\cos 2\alpha = 2\cos^2 \alpha - 1$

$\therefore \quad \frac{3}{4} = 2\cos^2 \alpha - 1$

$\therefore \quad \cos^2 \alpha = \frac{7}{8}$

$\therefore \quad \cos \alpha = \pm\frac{\sqrt{7}}{2\sqrt{2}}$

$\therefore \quad \cos \alpha = \frac{\sqrt{7}}{2\sqrt{2}}$

$\{$as α is acute, $\cos \alpha > 0\}$

b $\sin \alpha = \sqrt{1 - \cos^2 \alpha}$

$\{$as α is acute, $\sin \alpha > 0\}$

$\therefore \quad \sin \alpha = \sqrt{1 - \frac{7}{8}}$

$\therefore \quad \sin \alpha = \sqrt{\frac{1}{8}}$

$\therefore \quad \sin \alpha = \frac{1}{2\sqrt{2}}$

5   If α is acute and $\cos 2\alpha = -\frac{7}{9}$, find without a calculator: a $\cos \alpha$ b $\sin \alpha$.

Example 18   ◀) **Self Tutor**

Use an appropriate 'double angle formula' to simplify:

a $3\sin \theta \cos \theta$ b $4\cos^2 2B - 2$

a $3\sin \theta \cos \theta$

$= \frac{3}{2}(2\sin \theta \cos \theta)$

$= \frac{3}{2}\sin 2\theta$

b $4\cos^2 2B - 2$

$= 2(2\cos^2 2B - 1)$

$= 2\cos 2(2B)$

$= 2\cos 4B$

6   Find the exact value of $\left[\cos(\frac{\pi}{12}) + \sin(\frac{\pi}{12})\right]^2$.

7   Use an appropriate 'double angle' formula to simplify:

a $2\sin \alpha \cos \alpha$
b $4\cos \alpha \sin \alpha$
c $\sin \alpha \cos \alpha$

d $2\cos^2 \beta - 1$
e $1 - 2\cos^2 \phi$
f $1 - 2\sin^2 N$

g $2\sin^2 M - 1$
h $\cos^2 \alpha - \sin^2 \alpha$
i $\sin^2 \alpha - \cos^2 \alpha$

j $2\sin 2A \cos 2A$
k $2\cos 3\alpha \sin 3\alpha$
l $2\cos^2 4\theta - 1$

m $1 - 2\cos^2 3\beta$
n $1 - 2\sin^2 5\alpha$
o $2\sin^2 3D - 1$

p $\cos^2 2A - \sin^2 2A$
q $\cos^2(\frac{\alpha}{2}) - \sin^2(\frac{\alpha}{2})$
r $2\sin^2 3P - 2\cos^2 3P$

8   Show that:

a $(\sin \theta + \cos \theta)^2 = 1 + \sin 2\theta$ b $\cos^4 \theta - \sin^4 \theta = \cos 2\theta$

GRAPHING
PACKAGE

9   Solve exactly for x where $0 \leqslant x \leqslant 2\pi$:

a $\sin 2x + \sin x = 0$ b $\sin 2x - 2\cos x = 0$

c $\sin 2x + 3\sin x = 0$

10   Use the double angle formula to show that:

a $\sin^2 \theta = \frac{1}{2} - \frac{1}{2}\cos 2\theta$ b $\cos^2 \theta = \frac{1}{2} + \frac{1}{2}\cos 2\theta$

E TRIGONOMETRIC EQUATIONS IN QUADRATIC FORM

Sometimes we may be given trigonometric equations in quadratic form.

For example, $2\sin^2 x + \sin x = 0$ and $2\cos^2 x + \cos x - 1 = 0$ are clearly quadratic equations where the variables are $\sin x$ and $\cos x$ respectively.

These equations can be factorised by quadratic factorisation and then solved for x.

Example 19 ◀ϑ **Self Tutor**

Solve for x on $0 \leqslant x \leqslant 2\pi$, giving your answers as exact values:

a $2\sin^2 x + \sin x = 0$

b $2\cos^2 x + \cos x - 1 = 0$

a $\qquad 2\sin^2 x + \sin x = 0$

$\therefore \quad \sin x(2\sin x + 1) = 0$

$\therefore \quad \sin x = 0$ or $-\tfrac{1}{2}$

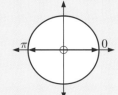

$\sin x = 0$ when
$x = 0,\ \pi,$ or 2π

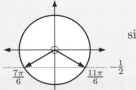

$\sin x = -\tfrac{1}{2}$ when
$x = \tfrac{7\pi}{6}$ or $\tfrac{11\pi}{6}$

b $\qquad 2\cos^2 x + \cos x - 1 = 0$

$\therefore \quad (2\cos x - 1)(\cos x + 1) = 0$

$\therefore \quad \cos x = \tfrac{1}{2}$ or -1

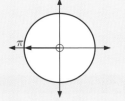

$\cos x = \tfrac{1}{2}$ when
$x = \tfrac{\pi}{3}$ or $\tfrac{5\pi}{3}$

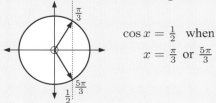

$\cos x = -1$ when
$x = \pi$

The solutions are:
$x = 0,\ \pi,\ \tfrac{7\pi}{6},\ \tfrac{11\pi}{6},$ or 2π.

The solutions are:
$x = \tfrac{\pi}{3},\ \pi,$ or $\tfrac{5\pi}{3}$.

EXERCISE 11E

1 Solve for $0 \leqslant x \leqslant 2\pi$ giving your answers as exact values:

    a $2\sin^2 x + \sin x = 0$
    b $2\cos^2 x = \cos x$
    c $2\cos^2 x + \cos x - 1 = 0$

    d $2\sin^2 x + 3\sin x + 1 = 0$
    e $\sin^2 x = 2 - \cos x$

2 Solve for $0 \leqslant x \leqslant 2\pi$ giving your answers as exact values:

    a $\cos 2x - \cos x = 0$
    b $\cos 2x + 3\cos x = 1$
    c $\cos 2x + \sin x = 0$

    d $\sin 4x = \sin 2x$
    e $\sin x + \cos x = \sqrt{2}$
    f $2\cos^2 x = 3\sin x$

THEORY OF KNOWLEDGE

Trigonometry appears to be one of the most useful disciplines of mathematics, having great importance in building and engineering. Its study has been driven by the need to solve real world problems throughout history.

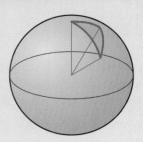

The study of trigonometry began when Greek, Babylonian, and Arabic astronomers needed to calculate the positions of stars and planets. These early mathematicians considered the trigonometry of spherical triangles, which are triangles on the surface of a sphere.

Trigonometric functions were developed by Hipparchus around 140 BC, and then by Ptolemy and Menelaus around 100 AD.

Around 500 AD, Hindu mathematicians published a table called the *Aryabhata*. It was a table of lengths of half chords, which are the lengths $AM = r \sin x$ in the diagram. This is trigonometry of triangles in a plane, as we study in schools today.

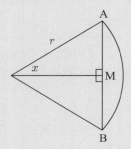

1   How do society and culture affect mathematical knowledge?

2   Should congruence and similarity, or the work of Pythagoras, be considered part of modern trigonometry?

3   Is the angle sum of a triangle always equal to $180°$?

REVIEW SET 11A   NON-CALCULATOR

1

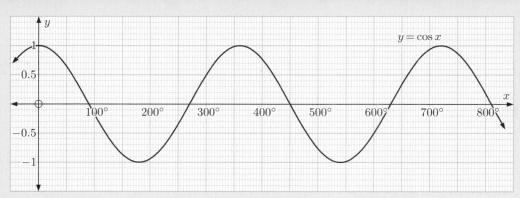

Use the graph of $y = \cos x$ to find the solutions of:

a $\cos x = -0.4$, $0 \leqslant x \leqslant 800°$

b $\cos x = 0.9$, $0 \leqslant x \leqslant 600°$

2 Solve in terms of π:

    a $2\sin x = -1$ for $0 \leqslant x \leqslant 4\pi$
        b $\sqrt{2}\sin x - 1 = 0$ for $-2\pi \leqslant x \leqslant 2\pi$

3 Find the x-intercepts of:

    a $y = 2\sin 3x + \sqrt{3}$ for $0 \leqslant x \leqslant 2\pi$
        b $y = \sqrt{2}\sin(x + \frac{\pi}{4})$ for $0 \leqslant x \leqslant 3\pi$

4 Solve $\sqrt{2}\cos(x + \frac{\pi}{4}) - 1 = 0$ for $0 \leqslant x \leqslant 4\pi$.

5 Simplify:

    a $\dfrac{1 - \cos^2\theta}{1 + \cos\theta}$
        b $\dfrac{\sin\alpha - \cos\alpha}{\sin^2\alpha - \cos^2\alpha}$
        c $\dfrac{4\sin^2\alpha - 4}{8\cos\alpha}$

6 If $\sin\alpha = -\frac{3}{4}$, $\pi \leqslant \alpha \leqslant \frac{3\pi}{2}$, find the value of $\cos\alpha$ and hence the value of $\sin 2\alpha$.

7 Show that $\dfrac{\sin 2\alpha - \sin\alpha}{\cos 2\alpha - \cos\alpha + 1}$ simplifies to $\tan\alpha$.

REVIEW SET 11B   CALCULATOR

1 Solve for $0 \leqslant x \leqslant 8$:

    a $\sin x = 0.382$
        b $\tan(\frac{x}{2}) = -0.458$

2 Solve:

    a $\cos x = 0.4379$ for $0 \leqslant x \leqslant 10$
        b $\cos(x - 2.4) = -0.6014$ for $0 \leqslant x \leqslant 6$

3 If $\sin A = \frac{5}{13}$ and $\cos A = \frac{12}{13}$, find: **a** $\sin 2A$ **b** $\cos 2A$ **c** $\tan 2A$

4 **a** Solve for $0 \leqslant x \leqslant 10$:

        i $\tan x = 4$
        ii $\tan(\frac{x}{4}) = 4$
        iii $\tan(x - 1.5) = 4$

    b Find exact solutions for x given $-\pi \leqslant x \leqslant \pi$:

        i $\tan(x + \frac{\pi}{6}) = -\sqrt{3}$
        ii $\tan 2x = -\sqrt{3}$
        iii $\tan^2 x - 3 = 0$

    c Solve $3\tan(x - 1.2) = -2$ for $0 \leqslant x \leqslant 10$.

5 Solve for $0 \leqslant x \leqslant 2\pi$:

    a $\cos x = 0.3$
        b $2\sin(3x) = \sqrt{2}$
        c $43 + 8\sin x = 50.1$

6 An ecologist studying a species of water beetle estimates the population of a colony over an eight week period. If t is the number of weeks after the initial estimate is made, then the population in thousands can be modelled by $P(t) = 5 + 2\sin(\frac{\pi t}{3})$ where $0 \leqslant t \leqslant 8$.

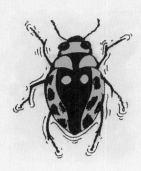

    a What was the initial population?

    b What were the smallest and largest populations?

    c During what time interval(s) did the population exceed 6000?

7 Solve for x: $3\cos x + \sin 2x = 1$ for $0 \leqslant x \leqslant 10$.

REVIEW SET 11C

1 Consider $y = \sin(\frac{x}{3})$ on the domain $-7 \leqslant x \leqslant 7$. Use the graph to solve, correct to 1 decimal place:

   a $\sin(\frac{x}{3}) = -0.9$ **b** $\sin(\frac{x}{3}) = \frac{1}{4}$

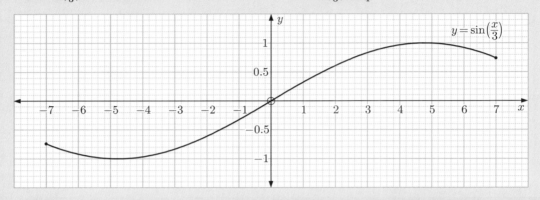

2 Solve algebraically for $0 \leqslant x \leqslant 2\pi$, giving answers in terms of π:

   a $\sin^2 x - \sin x - 2 = 0$ **b** $4\sin^2 x = 1$

3 Find the exact solutions of:

   a $\tan(x - \frac{\pi}{3}) = \frac{1}{\sqrt{3}}, \quad 0 \leqslant x \leqslant 4\pi$ **b** $\cos(x + \frac{2\pi}{3}) = \frac{1}{2}, \quad -2\pi \leqslant x \leqslant 2\pi$

4 Simplify:

   a $\cos^3 \theta + \sin^2 \theta \cos \theta$ **b** $\dfrac{\cos^2 \theta - 1}{\sin \theta}$

   c $5 - 5\sin^2 \theta$ **d** $\dfrac{\sin^2 \theta - 1}{\cos \theta}$

5 Expand and simplify if possible:

   a $(2\sin \alpha - 1)^2$ **b** $(\cos \alpha - \sin \alpha)^2$

6 Show that:

   a $\dfrac{\cos \theta}{1 + \sin \theta} + \dfrac{1 + \sin \theta}{\cos \theta} = \dfrac{2}{\cos \theta}$ **b** $\left(1 + \dfrac{1}{\cos \theta}\right)(\cos \theta - \cos^2 \theta) = \sin^2 \theta$

7 If $\tan \theta = -\frac{2}{3}$, $\frac{\pi}{2} < \theta < \pi$, find $\sin \theta$ and $\cos \theta$ exactly.

Chapter 12

Vectors

Syllabus reference: 4.1, 4.2

OPENING PROBLEM

An aeroplane in calm conditions is flying at 800 km h^{-1} due east. A cold wind suddenly blows from the south-west at 35 km h^{-1}, pushing the aeroplane slightly off course.

Things to think about:

a How can we illustrate the plane's movement and the wind using a scale diagram?

b What operation do we need to perform to find the effect of the wind on the aeroplane?

c Can you use a scale diagram to determine the resulting speed and direction of the aeroplane?

A   VECTORS AND SCALARS

In the **Opening Problem**, the effect of the wind on the aeroplane is determined by both its speed *and* its direction. The effect would be different if the wind was blowing against the aeroplane rather than from behind it.

> Quantities which have only magnitude are called **scalars**.
>
> Quantities which have both magnitude and direction are called **vectors**.

The *speed* of the plane is a scalar. It describes its size or strength.

The *velocity* of the plane is a vector. It includes both its speed and also its direction.

Other examples of vector quantities are:

- acceleration
- force
- displacement
- momentum

For example, farmer Giles needs to remove a fence post. He starts by pushing on the post sideways to loosen the ground. Giles has a choice of how hard to push the post and in which direction. The force he applies is therefore a vector.

DIRECTED LINE SEGMENT REPRESENTATION

We can represent a vector quantity using a **directed line segment** or **arrow**.

The **length of the arrow** represents the size or magnitude of the quantity, and the **arrowhead** shows its direction.

For example, if farmer Giles pushes the post with a force of 50 Newtons (N) to the north-east, we can draw a scale diagram of the force relative to the north line.

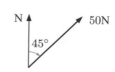

Scale: 1 cm represents 25 N

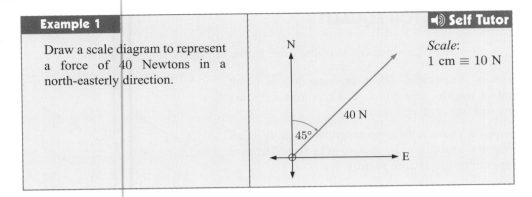

Example 1   🔊 **Self Tutor**

Draw a scale diagram to represent a force of 40 Newtons in a north-easterly direction.

Scale:
1 cm ≡ 10 N

EXERCISE 12A.1

1   Using a scale of 1 cm represents 10 units, sketch a vector to represent:

   a   30 Newtons in a south-easterly direction

   b   25 $m\,s^{-1}$ in a northerly direction

   c   an excavator digging a tunnel at a rate of 30 cm min^{-1} at an angle of $30°$ to the ground

   d   an aeroplane taking off at an angle of $10°$ to the runway with a speed of 50 $m\,s^{-1}$.

2   If ——————➤ represents a velocity of 50 $m\,s^{-1}$ due east, draw a directed line segment representing a velocity of:

   a   100 $m\,s^{-1}$ due west   **b**   75 $m\,s^{-1}$ north-east.

3   Draw a scale diagram to represent the following vectors:

   a   a force of 30 Newtons in the NW direction

   b   a velocity of 36 $m\,s^{-1}$ vertically downwards

   c   a displacement of 4 units at an angle of $15°$ to the positive x-axis

   d   an aeroplane taking off at an angle of $8°$ to the runway at a speed of 150 $km\,h^{-1}$.

VECTOR NOTATION

Consider the vector from the origin O to the point A. We call this the **position vector** of point A.

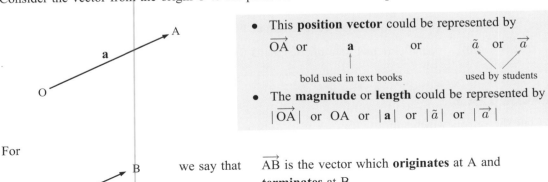

• This **position vector** could be represented by

$\overrightarrow{OA}$ or   **a**   or $\tilde{a}$ or $\overrightarrow{a}$

↑

bold used in text books   used by students

• The **magnitude** or **length** could be represented by

$|\overrightarrow{OA}|$ or OA or $|\mathbf{a}|$ or $|\tilde{a}|$ or $|\overrightarrow{a}|$

For

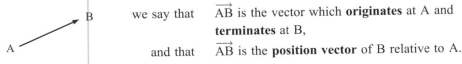

we say that $\overrightarrow{AB}$ is the vector which **originates** at A and **terminates** at B,

and that $\overrightarrow{AB}$ is the **position vector** of B relative to A.

GEOMETRIC VECTOR EQUALITY

> Two vectors are **equal** if they have the same magnitude and direction.

Equal vectors are **parallel** and in the same direction, and are **equal in length**. The arrows that represent them are translations of one another.

We can draw a vector with given magnitude and direction from *any* point, so we consider vectors to be **free**. They are sometimes referred to as **free vectors**.

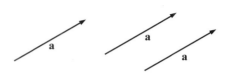

GEOMETRIC NEGATIVE VECTORS

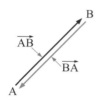

$\overrightarrow{AB}$ and $\overrightarrow{BA}$ have the same length, but they have opposite directions.

We say that $\overrightarrow{BA}$ is the negative of $\overrightarrow{AB}$ and write $\overrightarrow{BA} = -\overrightarrow{AB}$.

a and $-$**a** are parallel and equal in length, but opposite in direction.

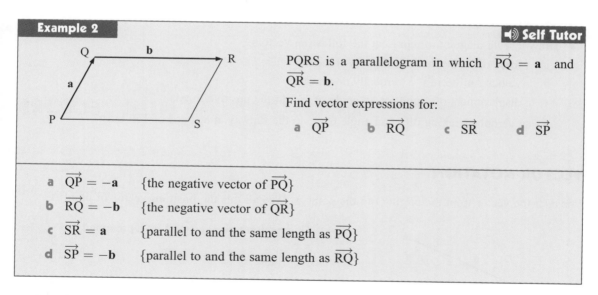

Example 2   ◀) **Self Tutor**

PQRS is a parallelogram in which $\overrightarrow{PQ} = $ **a** and $\overrightarrow{QR} = $ **b**.

Find vector expressions for:

a $\overrightarrow{QP}$ b $\overrightarrow{RQ}$ c $\overrightarrow{SR}$ d $\overrightarrow{SP}$

a $\overrightarrow{QP} = -$**a**   {the negative vector of $\overrightarrow{PQ}$}

b $\overrightarrow{RQ} = -$**b**   {the negative vector of $\overrightarrow{QR}$}

c $\overrightarrow{SR} = $ **a**   {parallel to and the same length as $\overrightarrow{PQ}$}

d $\overrightarrow{SP} = -$**b**   {parallel to and the same length as $\overrightarrow{RQ}$}

EXERCISE 12A.2

1 State the vectors which are:

    a equal in magnitude   b parallel

    c in the same direction   d equal

    e negatives of one another.

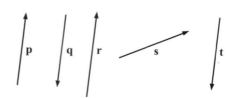

2 The figure alongside consists of two equilateral triangles. A, B, and C lie on a straight line.

$\overrightarrow{AB} = \mathbf{p}$, $\overrightarrow{AE} = \mathbf{q}$,   and $\overrightarrow{DC} = \mathbf{r}$.

Which of the following statements are true?

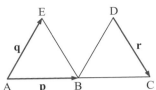

    a $\overrightarrow{EB} = \mathbf{r}$ **b** $|\mathbf{p}| = |\mathbf{q}|$ **c** $\overrightarrow{BC} = \mathbf{r}$

    d $\overrightarrow{DB} = \mathbf{q}$ **e** $\overrightarrow{ED} = \mathbf{p}$ **f** $\mathbf{p} = \mathbf{q}$

3

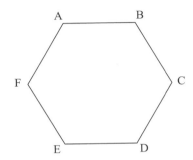

ABCDEF is a regular hexagon.

a Write down the vector which:

    i originates at B and terminates at C

    ii is equal to $\overrightarrow{AB}$.

b Write down *all* vectors which:

    i are the negative of $\overrightarrow{EF}$

    ii have the same length as $\overrightarrow{ED}$.

c Write down a vector which is parallel to $\overrightarrow{AB}$ and twice its length.

DISCUSSION

- Could we have a zero vector?
- What would its length be?
- What would its direction be?

B   GEOMETRIC OPERATIONS WITH VECTORS

In previous years we have often used vectors for problems involving distances and directions. The vectors in this case are **displacements**.

A typical problem could be:

    A runner runs east for 4 km and then south for 2 km.

    How far is she from her starting point and in what direction?

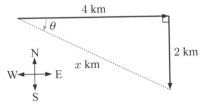

In problems like these we use trigonometry and Pythagoras' theorem to find the unknown lengths and angles.

GEOMETRIC VECTOR ADDITION

Suppose we have three towns P, Q, and R.

A trip from P to Q followed by a trip from Q to R has the same origin and destination as a trip from P to R.

This can be expressed in vector form as the sum $\overrightarrow{PQ} + \overrightarrow{QR} = \overrightarrow{PR}$.

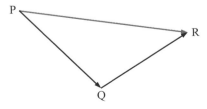

This triangular diagram could take all sorts of shapes, but in each case the sum will be true. For example:

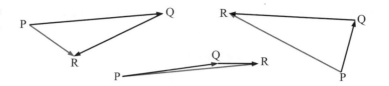

After considering diagrams like those above, we can now define vector addition geometrically:

To construct **a** + **b**:

Step 1: Draw **a**.

Step 2: At the arrowhead end of **a**, draw **b**.

Step 3: Join the beginning of **a** to the arrowhead end of **b**. This is vector **a** + **b**.

Example 3

Given **a** and **b** as shown, construct **a** + **b**.

THE ZERO VECTOR

Having defined vector addition, we are now able to state that:

The **zero vector 0** is a vector of length 0.

For any vector **a**: $\mathbf{a} + \mathbf{0} = \mathbf{0} + \mathbf{a} = \mathbf{a}$

$\mathbf{a} + (-\mathbf{a}) = (-\mathbf{a}) + \mathbf{a} = \mathbf{0}$.

When we write the zero vector by hand, we usually write $\overrightarrow{0}$.

Example 4

Find a single vector which is equal to:

a $\overrightarrow{BC} + \overrightarrow{CA}$

b $\overrightarrow{BA} + \overrightarrow{AE} + \overrightarrow{EC}$

c $\overrightarrow{AB} + \overrightarrow{BC} + \overrightarrow{CA}$

d $\overrightarrow{AB} + \overrightarrow{BC} + \overrightarrow{CD} + \overrightarrow{DE}$

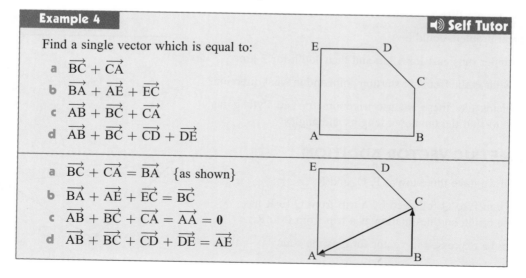

a $\overrightarrow{BC} + \overrightarrow{CA} = \overrightarrow{BA}$ {as shown}

b $\overrightarrow{BA} + \overrightarrow{AE} + \overrightarrow{EC} = \overrightarrow{BC}$

c $\overrightarrow{AB} + \overrightarrow{BC} + \overrightarrow{CA} = \overrightarrow{AA} = \mathbf{0}$

d $\overrightarrow{AB} + \overrightarrow{BC} + \overrightarrow{CD} + \overrightarrow{DE} = \overrightarrow{AE}$

EXERCISE 12B.1

1   Use the given vectors **p** and **q** to construct **p** + **q**:

a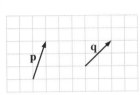

b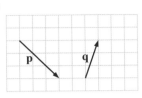

c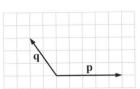

d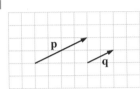

e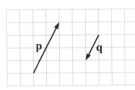

f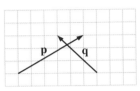

2   Find a single vector which is equal to:

a $\overrightarrow{AB} + \overrightarrow{BC}$

b $\overrightarrow{BC} + \overrightarrow{CD}$

c $\overrightarrow{AB} + \overrightarrow{BA}$

d $\overrightarrow{AB} + \overrightarrow{BC} + \overrightarrow{CD}$

e $\overrightarrow{AC} + \overrightarrow{CB} + \overrightarrow{BD}$

f $\overrightarrow{BC} + \overrightarrow{CA} + \overrightarrow{AB}$

3   a   Given   and   use vector diagrams to find:

   i   **p** + **q**   ii   **q** + **p**.

   b   For any two vectors **p** and **q**,   is   **p** + **q** = **q** + **p**?

4   Consider:

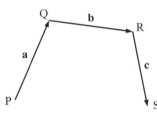

One way of finding $\overrightarrow{PS}$ is:
$$\overrightarrow{PS} = \overrightarrow{PR} + \overrightarrow{RS}$$
$$= (\mathbf{a} + \mathbf{b}) + \mathbf{c}.$$

Use the diagram to show that
$(\mathbf{a} + \mathbf{b}) + \mathbf{c} = \mathbf{a} + (\mathbf{b} + \mathbf{c}).$

5   Answer the **Opening Problem** on page **276**.

GEOMETRIC VECTOR SUBTRACTION

To subtract one vector from another, we simply **add its negative**. $\mathbf{a} - \mathbf{b} = \mathbf{a} + (-\mathbf{b})$

For example,

given   and   then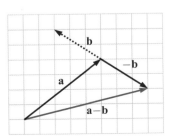

Example 5   ◀) **Self Tutor**

For **r**, **s**, and **t** shown, find geometrically:

  a   **r** − **s**
  b   **s** − **t** − **r**

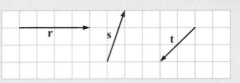

a

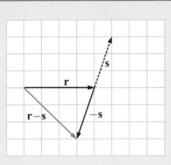

b

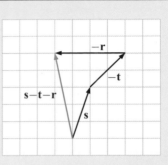

Example 6   ◀) **Self Tutor**

For points A, B, C, and D, simplify the following vector expressions:

  a $\overrightarrow{AB} - \overrightarrow{CB}$ b $\overrightarrow{AC} - \overrightarrow{BC} - \overrightarrow{DB}$

a $\overrightarrow{AB} - \overrightarrow{CB}$
   $= \overrightarrow{AB} + \overrightarrow{BC}$ {as $\overrightarrow{BC} = -\overrightarrow{CB}$}
   $= \overrightarrow{AC}$

b $\overrightarrow{AC} - \overrightarrow{BC} - \overrightarrow{DB}$
   $= \overrightarrow{AC} + \overrightarrow{CB} + \overrightarrow{BD}$
   $= \overrightarrow{AD}$

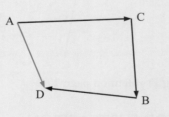

EXERCISE 12B.2

1   For the following vectors **p** and **q**, show how to construct   **p** − **q**:

  a   b   c   d

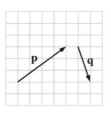   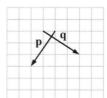   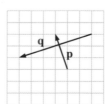   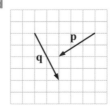

2 For the vectors illustrated, show how to construct:

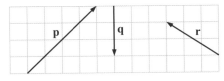

   a $p + q - r$ **b** $p - q - r$ **c** $r - q - p$

3 For points A, B, C, and D, simplify the following vector expressions:

  a $\overrightarrow{AC} + \overrightarrow{CB}$ **b** $\overrightarrow{AD} - \overrightarrow{BD}$ **c** $\overrightarrow{AC} + \overrightarrow{CA}$

  d $\overrightarrow{AB} + \overrightarrow{BC} + \overrightarrow{CD}$ **e** $\overrightarrow{BA} - \overrightarrow{CA} + \overrightarrow{CB}$ **f** $\overrightarrow{AB} - \overrightarrow{CB} - \overrightarrow{DC}$

VECTOR EQUATIONS

Whenever we have vectors which form a closed polygon, we can write a **vector equation** which relates the variables.

The vector equation can usually be written in several ways, but they are all equivalent.

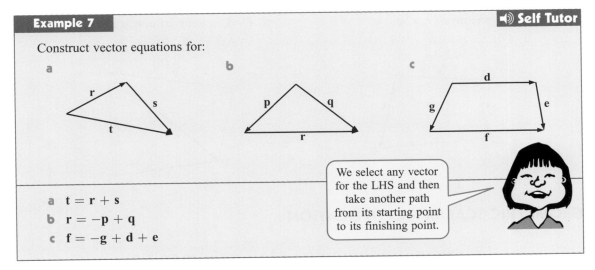

a $t = r + s$
b $r = -p + q$
c $f = -g + d + e$

EXERCISE 12B.3

1 Construct vector equations for:

  a 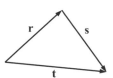   **b** 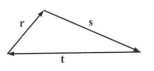   **c**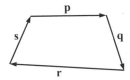

  d 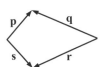   **e**   **f**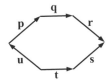

Example 8

◀) **Self Tutor**

Find, in terms of **r**, **s**, and **t**:

  a $\overrightarrow{RS}$ b $\overrightarrow{SR}$ c $\overrightarrow{ST}$

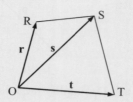

a	$\overrightarrow{RS}$	b	$\overrightarrow{SR}$	c	$\overrightarrow{ST}$
	$= \overrightarrow{RO} + \overrightarrow{OS}$		$= \overrightarrow{SO} + \overrightarrow{OR}$		$= \overrightarrow{SO} + \overrightarrow{OT}$
	$= -\overrightarrow{OR} + \overrightarrow{OS}$		$= -\overrightarrow{OS} + \overrightarrow{OR}$		$= -\overrightarrow{OS} + \overrightarrow{OT}$
	$= -\mathbf{r} + \mathbf{s}$		$= -\mathbf{s} + \mathbf{r}$		$= -\mathbf{s} + \mathbf{t}$
	$= \mathbf{s} - \mathbf{r}$		$= \mathbf{r} - \mathbf{s}$		$= \mathbf{t} - \mathbf{s}$

2   **a**   Find, in terms of **r**, **s**, and **t**:

    i $\overrightarrow{OB}$ **ii** $\overrightarrow{CA}$ **iii** $\overrightarrow{OC}$

    b   Find, in terms of **p**, **q**, and **r**:

    i $\overrightarrow{AD}$ **ii** $\overrightarrow{BC}$ **iii** $\overrightarrow{AC}$

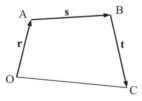
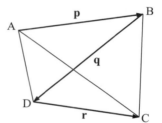

GEOMETRIC SCALAR MULTIPLICATION

A **scalar** is a non-vector quantity. It has a size but no direction.

We can multiply vectors by scalars such as 2 and -3, or in fact any $k \in \mathbb{R}$.

If **a** is a vector, we define $2\mathbf{a} = \mathbf{a} + \mathbf{a}$ and $3\mathbf{a} = \mathbf{a} + \mathbf{a} + \mathbf{a}$

            so $-3\mathbf{a} = 3(-\mathbf{a}) = (-\mathbf{a}) + (-\mathbf{a}) + (-\mathbf{a})$.

If **a** is   **a**   then

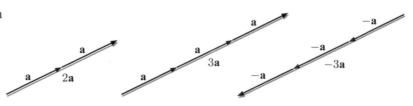

So,   **2a**   is in the same direction as **a** but is twice as long as **a**

     3a   is in the same direction as **a** but is three times longer than **a**

   $-$**3a**   has the opposite direction to **a** and is three times longer than **a**.

If **a** is a vector and k is a scalar, then k**a** is also a vector and we are performing **scalar multiplication**.

VECTOR SCALAR
MULTIPLICATION

If $k > 0$, k**a** and **a** have the same direction.
If $k < 0$, k**a** and **a** have opposite directions.
If $k = 0$, k**a** = **0**, the zero vector.

Example 9 🔊 **Self Tutor**

Given vectors and ,

construct geometrically: a $2\mathbf{r} + \mathbf{s}$ b $\mathbf{r} - 3\mathbf{s}$

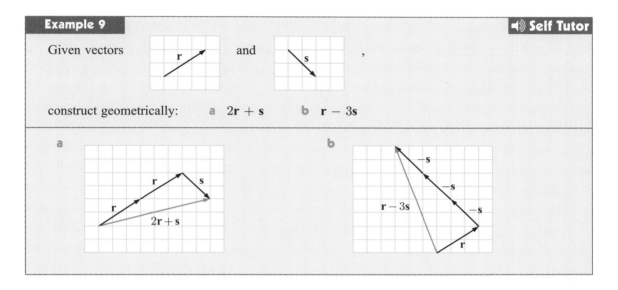

Example 10 🔊 **Self Tutor**

Sketch vectors **p** and **q** if: a $\mathbf{p} = 3\mathbf{q}$ b $\mathbf{p} = -\tfrac{1}{2}\mathbf{q}$

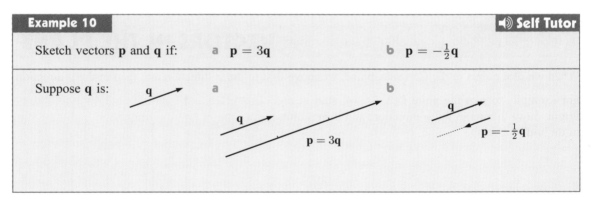

EXERCISE 12B.4

1 Given vectors and , construct geometrically:

a $-\mathbf{r}$ b $2\mathbf{s}$ c $\tfrac{1}{2}\mathbf{r}$ d $-\tfrac{3}{2}\mathbf{s}$

e $2\mathbf{r} - \mathbf{s}$ f $2\mathbf{r} + 3\mathbf{s}$ g $\tfrac{1}{2}\mathbf{r} + 2\mathbf{s}$ h $\tfrac{1}{2}(\mathbf{r} + 3\mathbf{s})$

2 Sketch vectors **p** and **q** if:

a $\mathbf{p} = \mathbf{q}$ b $\mathbf{p} = -\mathbf{q}$ c $\mathbf{p} = 2\mathbf{q}$ d $\mathbf{p} = \tfrac{1}{3}\mathbf{q}$ e $\mathbf{p} = -3\mathbf{q}$

3 **a** Copy this diagram and on it mark the
points:

     i X such that $\overrightarrow{MX} = \overrightarrow{MN} + \overrightarrow{MP}$

     ii Y such that $\overrightarrow{MY} = \overrightarrow{MN} - \overrightarrow{MP}$

     iii Z such that $\overrightarrow{PZ} = 2\overrightarrow{PM}$

  b What type of figure is MNYZ?

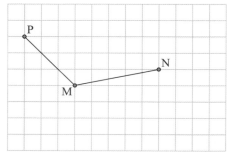

4

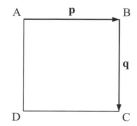

ABCD is a square. Its diagonals [AC] and [BD] intersect at
M. If $\overrightarrow{AB} = \mathbf{p}$ and $\overrightarrow{BC} = \mathbf{q}$, find in terms of **p** and **q**:

  a $\overrightarrow{CD}$ **b** $\overrightarrow{AC}$ **c** $\overrightarrow{AM}$ **d** $\overrightarrow{BM}$

5

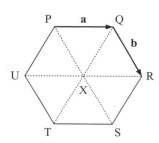

PQRSTU is a regular hexagon.

If $\overrightarrow{PQ} = \mathbf{a}$ and $\overrightarrow{QR} = \mathbf{b}$, find in terms of **a** and **b**:

  a $\overrightarrow{PX}$ **b** $\overrightarrow{PS}$ **c** $\overrightarrow{QX}$ **d** $\overrightarrow{RS}$

C   VECTORS IN THE PLANE

When we plot points in the Cartesian plane, we move first in the x-direction and then in the y-direction.

For example, to plot the point P(2, 5), we start at the
origin, move 2 units in the x-direction, and then 5 units
in the y-direction.

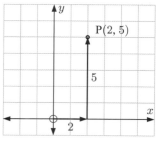

In transformation geometry, translating a point a units in the x-direction and b units in the y-direction

can be achieved using the translation vector $\begin{pmatrix} a \\ b \end{pmatrix}$.

So, the vector from O to P is $\overrightarrow{OP} = \begin{pmatrix} 2 \\ 5 \end{pmatrix}$.

> **i** and **j** are examples of **unit
> vectors** because they have
> length 1.

Suppose that $\mathbf{i} = \begin{pmatrix} 1 \\ 0 \end{pmatrix}$ is a translation 1 unit in the positive x-direction

and that $\mathbf{j} = \begin{pmatrix} 0 \\ 1 \end{pmatrix}$ is a translation 1 unit in the positive y-direction.

We can see that moving from O to P is equivalent to
two lots of **i** plus 5 lots of **j**.

$$\overrightarrow{OP} = 2\mathbf{i} + 5\mathbf{j}$$

$$\therefore \quad \begin{pmatrix} 2 \\ 5 \end{pmatrix} = 2 \begin{pmatrix} 1 \\ 0 \end{pmatrix} + 5 \begin{pmatrix} 0 \\ 1 \end{pmatrix}$$

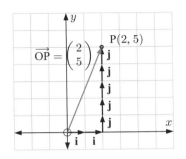

The point $P(x, y)$ has **position vector** $\overrightarrow{OP} = \begin{pmatrix} x \\ y \end{pmatrix} = x\mathbf{i} + y\mathbf{j}$

component form   unit vector form

$\mathbf{i} = \begin{pmatrix} 1 \\ 0 \end{pmatrix}$ is the **base unit vector** in the x-direction.

$\mathbf{j} = \begin{pmatrix} 0 \\ 1 \end{pmatrix}$ is the **base unit vector** in the y-direction.

The set of vectors $\{\mathbf{i}, \mathbf{j}\} = \left\{ \begin{pmatrix} 1 \\ 0 \end{pmatrix}, \begin{pmatrix} 0 \\ 1 \end{pmatrix} \right\}$ is the **standard basis** for the 2-dimensional (x, y)
coordinate system.

All vectors in the plane can be described in terms of the base unit vectors **i** and **j**.

For example: $\mathbf{a} = 3\mathbf{i} - \mathbf{j}$
$\mathbf{b} = -4\mathbf{i} + 3\mathbf{j}$

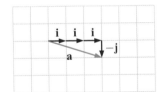
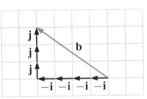

Two vectors are **equal** if their components are equal.

Example 11   ◀) Self Tutor

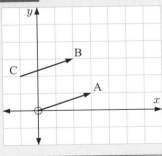

a Write $\overrightarrow{OA}$ and $\overrightarrow{CB}$ in component form and in unit
vector form.

b Comment on your answers in **a**.

a $\overrightarrow{OA} = \begin{pmatrix} 3 \\ 1 \end{pmatrix} = 3\mathbf{i} + \mathbf{j}$ $\overrightarrow{CB} = \begin{pmatrix} 3 \\ 1 \end{pmatrix} = 3\mathbf{i} + \mathbf{j}$

b The vectors $\overrightarrow{OA}$ and $\overrightarrow{CB}$ are equal.

EXERCISE 12C

1 Write the illustrated vectors in component form and in unit vector form:

a
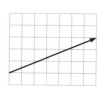

b

c

d

e

f

2 Write each vector in unit vector form, and illustrate it using an arrow diagram:

a $\begin{pmatrix} 3 \\ 4 \end{pmatrix}$ b $\begin{pmatrix} 2 \\ 0 \end{pmatrix}$ c $\begin{pmatrix} 2 \\ -5 \end{pmatrix}$ d $\begin{pmatrix} -1 \\ -3 \end{pmatrix}$

3

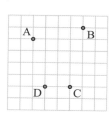

Find in component form and in unit vector form:

a $\overrightarrow{BA}$ b $\overrightarrow{BC}$ c $\overrightarrow{DC}$

d $\overrightarrow{AC}$ e $\overrightarrow{CA}$ f $\overrightarrow{DB}$

4 Write in component form and illustrate using a directed line segment:

a $\mathbf{i} + 2\mathbf{j}$ b $-\mathbf{i} + 3\mathbf{j}$ c $-5\mathbf{j}$ d $4\mathbf{i} - 2\mathbf{j}$

5 Write the zero vector **0** in component form.

D   THE MAGNITUDE OF A VECTOR

Consider vector $\mathbf{v} = \begin{pmatrix} 2 \\ 3 \end{pmatrix} = 2\mathbf{i} + 3\mathbf{j}$.

The **magnitude** or **length** of **v** is represented by $|\mathbf{v}|$.

By Pythagoras, $|\mathbf{v}|^2 = 2^2 + 3^2 = 4 + 9 = 13$
$\therefore$ $|\mathbf{v}| = \sqrt{13}$ units   {since $|\mathbf{v}| > 0$}

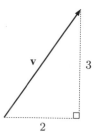

If $\mathbf{v} = \begin{pmatrix} v_1 \\ v_2 \end{pmatrix} = v_1\mathbf{i} + v_2\mathbf{j}$,   the **magnitude** or **length** of v is $|\mathbf{v}| = \sqrt{v_1{}^2 + v_2{}^2}$.

Example 12   ◀) **Self Tutor**

If $\mathbf{p} = \begin{pmatrix} 3 \\ -5 \end{pmatrix}$ and $\mathbf{q} = 2\mathbf{i} - 5\mathbf{j}$ find: **a** $|\mathbf{p}|$ **b** $|\mathbf{q}|$

a $\mathbf{p} = \begin{pmatrix} 3 \\ -5 \end{pmatrix}$

$\therefore |\mathbf{p}| = \sqrt{3^2 + (-5)^2}$

$= \sqrt{34}$ units

b As $2\mathbf{i} - 5\mathbf{j} = \begin{pmatrix} 2 \\ -5 \end{pmatrix}$,

$|\mathbf{q}| = \sqrt{2^2 + (-5)^2}$

$= \sqrt{29}$ units.

UNIT VECTORS

A **unit vector** is any vector which has a length of one unit.

$\mathbf{i} = \begin{pmatrix} 1 \\ 0 \end{pmatrix}$ and $\mathbf{j} = \begin{pmatrix} 0 \\ 1 \end{pmatrix}$ are the base unit vectors in the positive x and y-directions respectively.

Example 13   ◀) **Self Tutor**

Find k given that $\begin{pmatrix} -\frac{1}{3} \\ k \end{pmatrix}$ is a unit vector.

Since $\begin{pmatrix} -\frac{1}{3} \\ k \end{pmatrix}$ is a unit vector, $\sqrt{(-\frac{1}{3})^2 + k^2} = 1$

$\therefore \sqrt{\frac{1}{9} + k^2} = 1$

$\therefore \frac{1}{9} + k^2 = 1$ {squaring both sides}

$\therefore k^2 = \frac{8}{9}$

$\therefore k = \pm\frac{\sqrt{8}}{3}$

EXERCISE 12D

1 Find the magnitude of:

   a $\begin{pmatrix} 3 \\ 4 \end{pmatrix}$ **b** $\begin{pmatrix} -4 \\ 3 \end{pmatrix}$ **c** $\begin{pmatrix} 2 \\ 0 \end{pmatrix}$ **d** $\begin{pmatrix} -2 \\ 2 \end{pmatrix}$ **e** $\begin{pmatrix} 0 \\ -3 \end{pmatrix}$

2 Find the length of:

   a $\mathbf{i} + \mathbf{j}$ **b** $5\mathbf{i} - 12\mathbf{j}$ **c** $-\mathbf{i} + 4\mathbf{j}$ **d** $3\mathbf{i}$ **e** $k\mathbf{j}$

3 Which of the following are unit vectors?

   a $\begin{pmatrix} 0 \\ -1 \end{pmatrix}$ **b** $\begin{pmatrix} -\frac{1}{\sqrt{2}} \\ \frac{1}{\sqrt{2}} \end{pmatrix}$ **c** $\begin{pmatrix} \frac{2}{3} \\ \frac{1}{3} \end{pmatrix}$ **d** $\begin{pmatrix} -\frac{3}{5} \\ -\frac{4}{5} \end{pmatrix}$ **e** $\begin{pmatrix} \frac{2}{7} \\ -\frac{5}{7} \end{pmatrix}$

4 Find k for the unit vectors:

a $\begin{pmatrix} 0 \\ k \end{pmatrix}$ b $\begin{pmatrix} k \\ 0 \end{pmatrix}$ c $\begin{pmatrix} k \\ 1 \end{pmatrix}$ d $\begin{pmatrix} k \\ k \end{pmatrix}$ e $\begin{pmatrix} \frac{1}{2} \\ k \end{pmatrix}$

5 Given $\mathbf{v} = \begin{pmatrix} 8 \\ p \end{pmatrix}$ and $|\mathbf{v}| = \sqrt{73}$ units, find the possible values of p.

E   OPERATIONS WITH PLANE VECTORS

ALGEBRAIC VECTOR ADDITION

Consider adding vectors $\mathbf{a} = \begin{pmatrix} a_1 \\ a_2 \end{pmatrix}$ and $\mathbf{b} = \begin{pmatrix} b_1 \\ b_2 \end{pmatrix}$.

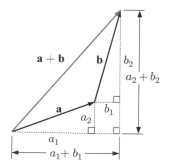

Notice that:

- the horizontal step for $\mathbf{a} + \mathbf{b}$ is $a_1 + b_1$
- the vertical step for $\mathbf{a} + \mathbf{b}$ is $a_2 + b_2$.

If $\mathbf{a} = \begin{pmatrix} a_1 \\ a_2 \end{pmatrix}$ and $\mathbf{b} = \begin{pmatrix} b_1 \\ b_2 \end{pmatrix}$ then $\mathbf{a} + \mathbf{b} = \begin{pmatrix} a_1 + b_1 \\ a_2 + b_2 \end{pmatrix}$.

Example 14   ◀)) **Self Tutor**

If $\mathbf{a} = \begin{pmatrix} 1 \\ -3 \end{pmatrix}$ and $\mathbf{b} = \begin{pmatrix} 4 \\ 7 \end{pmatrix}$, find $\mathbf{a} + \mathbf{b}$. Check your answer graphically.

$\mathbf{a} + \mathbf{b} = \begin{pmatrix} 1 \\ -3 \end{pmatrix} + \begin{pmatrix} 4 \\ 7 \end{pmatrix}$

$= \begin{pmatrix} 1+4 \\ -3+7 \end{pmatrix}$

$= \begin{pmatrix} 5 \\ 4 \end{pmatrix}$

Graphical check:

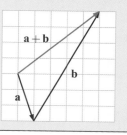

ALGEBRAIC NEGATIVE VECTORS

In the diagram we see the vector $\mathbf{a} = \begin{pmatrix} 2 \\ 3 \end{pmatrix}$

and its negative $-\mathbf{a} = \begin{pmatrix} -2 \\ -3 \end{pmatrix}$.

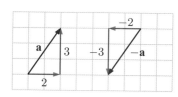

If $\mathbf{a} = \begin{pmatrix} a_1 \\ a_2 \end{pmatrix}$ then $-\mathbf{a} = \begin{pmatrix} -a_1 \\ -a_2 \end{pmatrix}$.

ALGEBRAIC VECTOR SUBTRACTION

To subtract one vector from another, we simply **add its negative**.

So, if $\mathbf{a} = \begin{pmatrix} a_1 \\ a_2 \end{pmatrix}$ and $\mathbf{b} = \begin{pmatrix} b_1 \\ b_2 \end{pmatrix}$

then
$$= \mathbf{a} + (-\mathbf{b})$$
$$= \begin{pmatrix} a_1 \\ a_2 \end{pmatrix} + \begin{pmatrix} -b_1 \\ -b_2 \end{pmatrix}$$
$$= \begin{pmatrix} a_1 - b_1 \\ a_2 - b_2 \end{pmatrix}$$

If $\mathbf{a} = \begin{pmatrix} a_1 \\ a_2 \end{pmatrix}$ and $\mathbf{b} = \begin{pmatrix} b_1 \\ b_2 \end{pmatrix}$, then $\mathbf{a} - \mathbf{b} = \begin{pmatrix} a_1 - b_1 \\ a_2 - b_2 \end{pmatrix}$.

Example 15	◄» Self Tutor

Given $\mathbf{p} = \begin{pmatrix} 3 \\ -2 \end{pmatrix}$, $\mathbf{q} = \begin{pmatrix} 1 \\ 4 \end{pmatrix}$, and $\mathbf{r} = \begin{pmatrix} -2 \\ -5 \end{pmatrix}$, find:

a $\mathbf{q} - \mathbf{p}$ **b** $\mathbf{p} - \mathbf{q} - \mathbf{r}$

a $\mathbf{q} - \mathbf{p}$
$$= \begin{pmatrix} 1 \\ 4 \end{pmatrix} - \begin{pmatrix} 3 \\ -2 \end{pmatrix}$$
$$= \begin{pmatrix} 1 - 3 \\ 4 + 2 \end{pmatrix}$$
$$= \begin{pmatrix} -2 \\ 6 \end{pmatrix}$$

b $\mathbf{p} - \mathbf{q} - \mathbf{r}$
$$= \begin{pmatrix} 3 \\ -2 \end{pmatrix} - \begin{pmatrix} 1 \\ 4 \end{pmatrix} - \begin{pmatrix} -2 \\ -5 \end{pmatrix}$$
$$= \begin{pmatrix} 3 - 1 + 2 \\ -2 - 4 + 5 \end{pmatrix}$$
$$= \begin{pmatrix} 4 \\ -1 \end{pmatrix}$$

ALGEBRAIC SCALAR MULTIPLICATION

We have already seen a geometric approach for integer scalar multiplication:

Consider $\mathbf{a} = \begin{pmatrix} 1 \\ 3 \end{pmatrix}$.

$$2\mathbf{a} = \mathbf{a} + \mathbf{a} = \begin{pmatrix} 1 \\ 3 \end{pmatrix} + \begin{pmatrix} 1 \\ 3 \end{pmatrix} = \begin{pmatrix} 2 \\ 6 \end{pmatrix} = \begin{pmatrix} 2 \times 1 \\ 2 \times 3 \end{pmatrix}$$

$$3\mathbf{a} = \mathbf{a} + \mathbf{a} + \mathbf{a} = \begin{pmatrix} 1 \\ 3 \end{pmatrix} + \begin{pmatrix} 1 \\ 3 \end{pmatrix} + \begin{pmatrix} 1 \\ 3 \end{pmatrix} = \begin{pmatrix} 3 \\ 9 \end{pmatrix} = \begin{pmatrix} 3 \times 1 \\ 3 \times 3 \end{pmatrix}$$

If k is any scalar and $\mathbf{v} = \begin{pmatrix} v_1 \\ v_2 \end{pmatrix}$, then $k\mathbf{v} = \begin{pmatrix} kv_1 \\ kv_2 \end{pmatrix}$.

Notice that:

- $(-1)\mathbf{v} = \begin{pmatrix} (-1)v_1 \\ (-1)v_2 \end{pmatrix} = \begin{pmatrix} -v_1 \\ -v_2 \end{pmatrix} = -\mathbf{v}$ • $(0)\mathbf{v} = \begin{pmatrix} (0)v_1 \\ (0)v_2 \end{pmatrix} = \begin{pmatrix} 0 \\ 0 \end{pmatrix} = \mathbf{0}$

Example 16   🔊 **Self Tutor**

For $\mathbf{p} = \begin{pmatrix} 4 \\ 1 \end{pmatrix}$, $\mathbf{q} = \begin{pmatrix} 2 \\ -3 \end{pmatrix}$ find: **a** $3\mathbf{q}$ **b** $\mathbf{p} + 2\mathbf{q}$ **c** $\frac{1}{2}\mathbf{p} - 3\mathbf{q}$

a $3\mathbf{q}$

$= 3 \begin{pmatrix} 2 \\ -3 \end{pmatrix}$

$= \begin{pmatrix} 6 \\ -9 \end{pmatrix}$

b $\mathbf{p} + 2\mathbf{q}$

$= \begin{pmatrix} 4 \\ 1 \end{pmatrix} + 2 \begin{pmatrix} 2 \\ -3 \end{pmatrix}$

$= \begin{pmatrix} 4 + 2(2) \\ 1 + 2(-3) \end{pmatrix}$

$= \begin{pmatrix} 8 \\ -5 \end{pmatrix}$

c $\frac{1}{2}\mathbf{p} - 3\mathbf{q}$

$= \frac{1}{2} \begin{pmatrix} 4 \\ 1 \end{pmatrix} - 3 \begin{pmatrix} 2 \\ -3 \end{pmatrix}$

$= \begin{pmatrix} \frac{1}{2}(4) - 3(2) \\ \frac{1}{2}(1) - 3(-3) \end{pmatrix}$

$= \begin{pmatrix} -4 \\ 9\frac{1}{2} \end{pmatrix}$

Example 17   🔊 **Self Tutor**

If $\mathbf{p} = 3\mathbf{i} - 5\mathbf{j}$ and $\mathbf{q} = -\mathbf{i} - 2\mathbf{j}$, find $|\mathbf{p} - 2\mathbf{q}|$.

$\mathbf{p} - 2\mathbf{q} = 3\mathbf{i} - 5\mathbf{j} - 2(-\mathbf{i} - 2\mathbf{j})$
$\qquad\quad = 3\mathbf{i} - 5\mathbf{j} + 2\mathbf{i} + 4\mathbf{j}$
$\qquad\quad = 5\mathbf{i} - \mathbf{j}$

$\therefore\ |\mathbf{p} - 2\mathbf{q}| = \sqrt{5^2 + (-1)^2}$
$\qquad\qquad\quad = \sqrt{26}$ units

EXERCISE 12E

1 If $\mathbf{a} = \begin{pmatrix} -3 \\ 2 \end{pmatrix}$, $\mathbf{b} = \begin{pmatrix} 1 \\ 4 \end{pmatrix}$, and $\mathbf{c} = \begin{pmatrix} -2 \\ -5 \end{pmatrix}$ find:

VECTOR RACE GAME

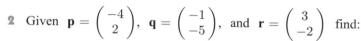

    a $\mathbf{a} + \mathbf{b}$ **b** $\mathbf{b} + \mathbf{a}$ **c** $\mathbf{b} + \mathbf{c}$ **d** $\mathbf{c} + \mathbf{b}$

    e $\mathbf{a} + \mathbf{c}$ **f** $\mathbf{c} + \mathbf{a}$ **g** $\mathbf{a} + \mathbf{a}$ **h** $\mathbf{b} + \mathbf{a} + \mathbf{c}$

2 Given $\mathbf{p} = \begin{pmatrix} -4 \\ 2 \end{pmatrix}$, $\mathbf{q} = \begin{pmatrix} -1 \\ -5 \end{pmatrix}$, and $\mathbf{r} = \begin{pmatrix} 3 \\ -2 \end{pmatrix}$ find:

    a $\mathbf{p} - \mathbf{q}$ **b** $\mathbf{q} - \mathbf{r}$ **c** $\mathbf{p} + \mathbf{q} - \mathbf{r}$

    d $\mathbf{p} - \mathbf{q} - \mathbf{r}$ **e** $\mathbf{q} - \mathbf{r} - \mathbf{p}$ **f** $\mathbf{r} + \mathbf{q} - \mathbf{p}$

3 Consider $\mathbf{a} = \begin{pmatrix} a_1 \\ a_2 \end{pmatrix}$.

    a Use vector addition to show that $\mathbf{a} + \mathbf{0} = \mathbf{a}$.

    b Use vector subtraction to show that $\mathbf{a} - \mathbf{a} = \mathbf{0}$.

4 For $\mathbf{p} = \begin{pmatrix} 1 \\ 5 \end{pmatrix}$, $\mathbf{q} = \begin{pmatrix} -2 \\ 4 \end{pmatrix}$, and $\mathbf{r} = \begin{pmatrix} -3 \\ -1 \end{pmatrix}$ find:

    a $-3\mathbf{p}$ **b** $\frac{1}{2}\mathbf{q}$ **c** $2\mathbf{p} + \mathbf{q}$ **d** $\mathbf{p} - 2\mathbf{q}$

    e $\mathbf{p} - \frac{1}{2}\mathbf{r}$ **f** $2\mathbf{p} + 3\mathbf{r}$ **g** $2\mathbf{q} - 3\mathbf{r}$ **h** $2\mathbf{p} - \mathbf{q} + \frac{1}{3}\mathbf{r}$

5 Consider $\mathbf{p} = \begin{pmatrix} 1 \\ 1 \end{pmatrix}$ and $\mathbf{q} = \begin{pmatrix} 2 \\ -1 \end{pmatrix}$. Find geometrically and then comment on the results:

    a $\mathbf{p} + \mathbf{p} + \mathbf{q} + \mathbf{q} + \mathbf{q}$ **b** $\mathbf{p} + \mathbf{q} + \mathbf{p} + \mathbf{q} + \mathbf{q}$ **c** $\mathbf{q} + \mathbf{p} + \mathbf{q} + \mathbf{p} + \mathbf{q}$

6 For $\mathbf{r} = \begin{pmatrix} 2 \\ 3 \end{pmatrix}$ and $\mathbf{s} = \begin{pmatrix} -1 \\ 4 \end{pmatrix}$ find:

    a $|\mathbf{r}|$ **b** $|\mathbf{s}|$ **c** $|\mathbf{r} + \mathbf{s}|$ **d** $|\mathbf{r} - \mathbf{s}|$ **e** $|\mathbf{s} - 2\mathbf{r}|$

7 If $\mathbf{p} = \begin{pmatrix} 1 \\ 3 \end{pmatrix}$ and $\mathbf{q} = \begin{pmatrix} -2 \\ 4 \end{pmatrix}$ find:

    a $|\mathbf{p}|$ **b** $|2\mathbf{p}|$ **c** $|-2\mathbf{p}|$ **d** $|3\mathbf{p}|$ **e** $|-3\mathbf{p}|$

    f $|\mathbf{q}|$ **g** $|4\mathbf{q}|$ **h** $|-4\mathbf{q}|$ **i** $|\tfrac{1}{2}\mathbf{q}|$ **j** $|-\tfrac{1}{2}\mathbf{q}|$

8 Suppose $\mathbf{x} = \begin{pmatrix} x_1 \\ x_2 \end{pmatrix}$ and $\mathbf{a} = \begin{pmatrix} a_1 \\ a_2 \end{pmatrix}$. Show by equating components, that if $k\mathbf{x} = \mathbf{a}$ then

$\mathbf{x} = \tfrac{1}{k}\mathbf{a}$.

9 From your answers in **7**, you should have noticed that $|k\mathbf{v}| = |k||\mathbf{v}|$.

So, (the length of $k\mathbf{v}$) = (the modulus of k) × (the length of $\mathbf{v}$).

By letting $\mathbf{v} = \begin{pmatrix} v_1 \\ v_2 \end{pmatrix}$, prove that $|k\mathbf{v}| = |k||\mathbf{v}|$.

> The *modulus* of k is its *size*.

THE VECTOR BETWEEN TWO POINTS

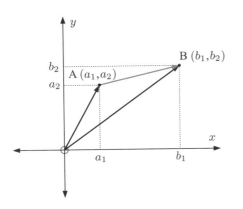

In the diagram, point A has position vector $\overrightarrow{OA} = \begin{pmatrix} a_1 \\ a_2 \end{pmatrix}$,

and point B has position vector $\overrightarrow{OB} = \begin{pmatrix} b_1 \\ b_2 \end{pmatrix}$.

$$\therefore \quad \overrightarrow{AB} = \overrightarrow{AO} + \overrightarrow{OB}$$
$$= -\overrightarrow{OA} + \overrightarrow{OB}$$
$$= \overrightarrow{OB} - \overrightarrow{OA}$$
$$= \begin{pmatrix} b_1 \\ b_2 \end{pmatrix} - \begin{pmatrix} a_1 \\ a_2 \end{pmatrix}$$
$$= \begin{pmatrix} b_1 - a_1 \\ b_2 - a_2 \end{pmatrix}$$

The **position vector of B relative to A** is $\overrightarrow{AB} = \overrightarrow{OB} - \overrightarrow{OA} = \begin{pmatrix} b_1 - a_1 \\ b_2 - a_2 \end{pmatrix}$.

We can also observe this in terms of transformations.

In translating point A to point B in the diagram, the translation vector is $\begin{pmatrix} b_1 - a_1 \\ b_2 - a_2 \end{pmatrix}$.

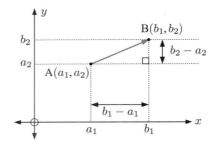

In general, for two points A and B with position vectors **a** and **b** respectively, we observe

$$\overrightarrow{AB} = -\mathbf{a} + \mathbf{b}$$
$$= \mathbf{b} - \mathbf{a}$$
$$= \begin{pmatrix} b_1 - a_1 \\ b_2 - a_2 \end{pmatrix}$$

and

$$\overrightarrow{BA} = -\mathbf{b} + \mathbf{a}$$
$$= \mathbf{a} - \mathbf{b}$$
$$= \begin{pmatrix} a_1 - b_1 \\ a_2 - b_2 \end{pmatrix}$$

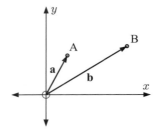

Example 18   ◀)) **Self Tutor**

Given points A$(-1, 2)$, B$(3, 4)$, and C$(4, -5)$, find the position vector of:

    a B from O   **b** B from A   **c** A from C

a The position vector of B relative to O is $\overrightarrow{OB} = \begin{pmatrix} 3 - 0 \\ 4 - 0 \end{pmatrix} = \begin{pmatrix} 3 \\ 4 \end{pmatrix}$.

b The position vector of B relative to A is $\overrightarrow{AB} = \begin{pmatrix} 3 - -1 \\ 4 - 2 \end{pmatrix} = \begin{pmatrix} 4 \\ 2 \end{pmatrix}$.

c The position vector of A relative to C is $\overrightarrow{CA} = \begin{pmatrix} -1 - 4 \\ 2 - -5 \end{pmatrix} = \begin{pmatrix} -5 \\ 7 \end{pmatrix}$.

Example 19   ◀)) **Self Tutor**

[AB] is the diameter of a circle with centre C$(-1, 2)$. If B is $(3, 1)$, find:

    a $\overrightarrow{BC}$ **b** the coordinates of A.

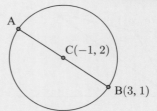

a $\overrightarrow{BC} = \begin{pmatrix} -1 - 3 \\ 2 - 1 \end{pmatrix} = \begin{pmatrix} -4 \\ 1 \end{pmatrix}$

b If A has coordinates (a, b), then $\overrightarrow{CA} = \begin{pmatrix} a - (-1) \\ b - 2 \end{pmatrix} = \begin{pmatrix} a + 1 \\ b - 2 \end{pmatrix}$

But $\overrightarrow{CA} = \overrightarrow{BC}$, so $\begin{pmatrix} a+1 \\ b-2 \end{pmatrix} = \begin{pmatrix} -4 \\ 1 \end{pmatrix}$

$\therefore$ $a+1 = -4$ and $b-2 = 1$

$\therefore$ $a = -5$ and $b = 3$

$\therefore$ A is $(-5, 3)$.

EXERCISE 12F

1 Find $\overrightarrow{AB}$ given:

    a A(2, 3) and B(4, 7)   **b** A(3, −1) and B(1, 4)   **c** A(−2, 7) and B(1, 4)

    d B(3, 0) and A(2, 5)   **e** B(6, −1) and A(0, 4)   **f** B(0, 0) and A(−1, −3)

2 Consider the point A(1, 4). Find the coordinates of:

    a B given $\overrightarrow{AB} = \begin{pmatrix} 3 \\ -2 \end{pmatrix}$ **b** C given $\overrightarrow{CA} = \begin{pmatrix} -1 \\ 2 \end{pmatrix}$.

3 [PQ] is the diameter of a circle with centre C.

    a Find $\overrightarrow{PC}$.

    b Hence find the coordinates of Q.

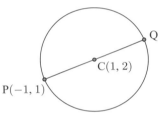

4

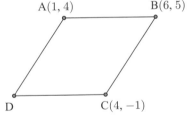

ABCD is a parallelogram.

    a Find $\overrightarrow{AB}$.

    b Find $\overrightarrow{CD}$.

    c Hence find the coordinates of D.

5 A(−1, 3) and B(3, k) are two points which are 5 units apart.

    a Find $\overrightarrow{AB}$ and $|\overrightarrow{AB}|$.

    b Hence, find the two possible values of k.

    c Show, by illustration, why k should have two possible values.

$|\overrightarrow{AB}|$ is the magnitude of $\overrightarrow{AB}$.

6

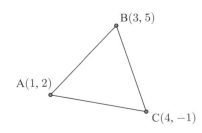

    a Find $\overrightarrow{AB}$ and $\overrightarrow{AC}$.

    b Explain why $\overrightarrow{BC} = -\overrightarrow{AB} + \overrightarrow{AC}$.

    c Hence find $\overrightarrow{BC}$.

    d Check your answer to **c** by direct evaluation.

7   **a**   Given $\overrightarrow{BA} = \begin{pmatrix} 2 \\ -3 \end{pmatrix}$ and $\overrightarrow{BC} = \begin{pmatrix} -3 \\ 1 \end{pmatrix}$, find $\overrightarrow{AC}$.

    b   Given $\overrightarrow{AB} = \begin{pmatrix} -1 \\ 3 \end{pmatrix}$ and $\overrightarrow{CA} = \begin{pmatrix} 2 \\ -1 \end{pmatrix}$, find $\overrightarrow{CB}$.

    c   Given $\overrightarrow{PQ} = \begin{pmatrix} -1 \\ 4 \end{pmatrix}$, $\overrightarrow{RQ} = \begin{pmatrix} 2 \\ 1 \end{pmatrix}$, and $\overrightarrow{RS} = \begin{pmatrix} -3 \\ 2 \end{pmatrix}$, find $\overrightarrow{SP}$.

8

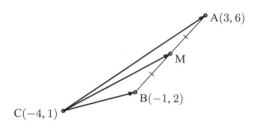

    a   Find the coordinates of M.

    b   Find vectors $\overrightarrow{CA}$, $\overrightarrow{CM}$, and $\overrightarrow{CB}$.

    c   Verify that $\overrightarrow{CM} = \frac{1}{2}\overrightarrow{CA} + \frac{1}{2}\overrightarrow{CB}$.

G   VECTORS IN SPACE

To specify points in **3-dimensional space** we need a point of reference O, called the **origin**.

Through O we draw 3 **mutually perpendicular** lines and call them the X, Y, and Z-axes. We often think of the YZ-plane as the plane of the page, with the X-axis coming directly out of the page. However, we cannot of course draw this.

In the diagram alongside the **coordinate planes** divide space into 8 regions, with each pair of planes intersecting on the axes.

The **positive direction** of each axis is a solid line whereas the **negative direction** is 'dashed'.

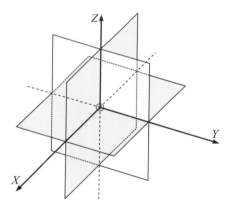

Any point P in space can be specified by an **ordered triple** of numbers (x, y, z) where x, y, and z are the **steps** in the X, Y, and Z directions from the origin O, to P.

The **position vector** of P is

$$\overrightarrow{OP} = \begin{pmatrix} x \\ y \\ z \end{pmatrix} = x\mathbf{i} + y\mathbf{j} + z\mathbf{k}$$

where $\mathbf{i} = \begin{pmatrix} 1 \\ 0 \\ 0 \end{pmatrix}$, $\mathbf{j} = \begin{pmatrix} 0 \\ 1 \\ 0 \end{pmatrix}$, and $\mathbf{k} = \begin{pmatrix} 0 \\ 0 \\ 1 \end{pmatrix}$

are the **base unit vectors** in the X, Y, and Z directions respectively.

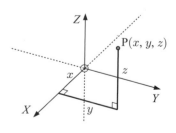

The set of vectors $\{\mathbf{i}, \mathbf{j}, \mathbf{k}\} = \left\{ \begin{pmatrix} 1 \\ 0 \\ 0 \end{pmatrix}, \begin{pmatrix} 0 \\ 1 \\ 0 \end{pmatrix}, \begin{pmatrix} 0 \\ 0 \\ 1 \end{pmatrix} \right\}$

is the **standard basis** for the 3-dimensional (x, y, z) coordinate system.

To help us visualise the 3-D position of a point on our 2-D paper, it is useful to complete a rectangular prism or box with the origin O as one vertex, the axes as sides adjacent to it, and P being the vertex opposite O.

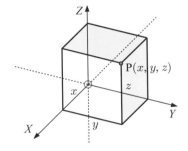

3-D POINT PLOTTER

THE MAGNITUDE OF A VECTOR

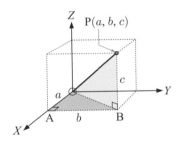

Triangle OAB is right angled at A

$\therefore \quad OB^2 = a^2 + b^2 \quad \dots (1) \quad$ {Pythagoras}

Triangle OBP is right angled at B

$\therefore \quad OP^2 = OB^2 + c^2 \qquad$ {Pythagoras}

$\therefore \quad OP^2 = a^2 + b^2 + c^2 \qquad$ {using (1)}

$\therefore \quad OP = \sqrt{a^2 + b^2 + c^2}$

The magnitude or length of the vector $\mathbf{v} = \begin{pmatrix} v_1 \\ v_2 \\ v_3 \end{pmatrix}$ is $|\mathbf{v}| = \sqrt{v_1^2 + v_2^2 + v_3^2}$.

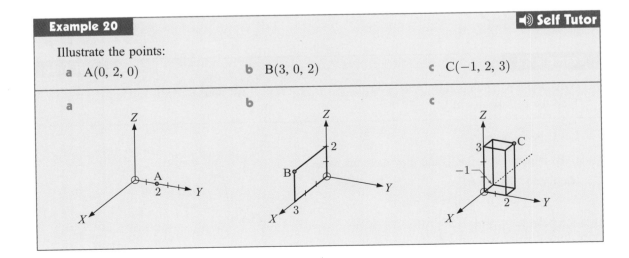

Example 20   ◆) **Self Tutor**

Illustrate the points:

a $A(0, 2, 0)$ **b** $B(3, 0, 2)$ **c** $C(-1, 2, 3)$

THE VECTOR BETWEEN TWO POINTS

If $A(x_1, y_1, z_1)$ and $B(x_2, y_2, z_2)$ are two points in space then:

$$\overrightarrow{AB} = \overrightarrow{OB} - \overrightarrow{OA} = \begin{pmatrix} x_2 - x_1 \\ y_2 - y_1 \\ z_2 - z_1 \end{pmatrix} \begin{matrix} \leftarrow x\text{-step} \\ \leftarrow y\text{-step} \\ \leftarrow z\text{-step} \end{matrix}$$

$\overrightarrow{AB}$ is called the 'vector AB' or the '**position vector of B relative to A**'.

The magnitude of $\overrightarrow{AB}$ is $AB = \sqrt{(x_2 - x_1)^2 + (y_2 - y_1)^2 + (z_2 - z_1)^2}$ which is the distance between the points A and B.

Example 21   ◀》 **Self Tutor**

If P is $(-3, 1, 2)$ and Q is $(1, -1, 3)$, find: **a** $\overrightarrow{OP}$ **b** $\overrightarrow{PQ}$ **c** $|\overrightarrow{PQ}|$

a $\overrightarrow{OP} = \begin{pmatrix} -3 \\ 1 \\ 2 \end{pmatrix}$ **b** $\overrightarrow{PQ} = \begin{pmatrix} 1 - (-3) \\ -1 - 1 \\ 3 - 2 \end{pmatrix} = \begin{pmatrix} 4 \\ -2 \\ 1 \end{pmatrix}$ **c** $|\overrightarrow{PQ}| = \sqrt{4^2 + (-2)^2 + 1^2}$
$= \sqrt{21}$ units

VECTOR EQUALITY

Two vectors are **equal** if they have the same magnitude and direction.

If $\mathbf{a} = \begin{pmatrix} a_1 \\ a_2 \\ a_3 \end{pmatrix}$ and $\mathbf{b} = \begin{pmatrix} b_1 \\ b_2 \\ b_3 \end{pmatrix}$, then $\mathbf{a} = \mathbf{b} \iff a_1 = b_1, \ a_2 = b_2, \ a_3 = b_3$.

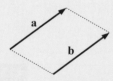

If $\mathbf{a}$ and $\mathbf{b}$ do not coincide, then they are opposite sides of a parallelogram, and lie in the same plane.

Example 22   ◀》 **Self Tutor**

ABCD is a parallelogram. A is $(-1, 2, 1)$, B is $(2, 0, -1)$, and D is $(3, 1, 4)$. Find the coordinates of C.

Let C be (a, b, c).

[AB] is parallel to [DC], and they have the same length, so $\overrightarrow{DC} = \overrightarrow{AB}$

$\therefore \begin{pmatrix} a - 3 \\ b - 1 \\ c - 4 \end{pmatrix} = \begin{pmatrix} 3 \\ -2 \\ -2 \end{pmatrix}$

A$(-1, 2, 1)$ B$(2, 0, -1)$

D$(3, 1, 4)$ C(a, b, c)

$\therefore \quad a - 3 = 3, \quad b - 1 = -2, \quad$ and $\quad c - 4 = -2$

$\therefore \quad a = 6, \qquad b = -1, \qquad$ and $\quad c = 2$

So, C is $(6, -1, 2)$.

Check: Midpoint of [DB] is $\left(\dfrac{3+2}{2}, \dfrac{1+0}{2}, \dfrac{4+-1}{2} \right)$ which is $\left(\frac{5}{2}, \frac{1}{2}, \frac{3}{2} \right)$.

Midpoint of [AC] is $\left(\dfrac{-1+6}{2}, \dfrac{2+-1}{2}, \dfrac{1+2}{2} \right)$ which is $\left(\frac{5}{2}, \frac{1}{2}, \frac{3}{2} \right)$.

The midpoints are the same, so the diagonals of the parallelogram bisect. ✓

EXERCISE 12G

1 Consider the point $T(3, -1, 4)$.

    a Draw a diagram to locate the position of T in space.   **b** Find $\overrightarrow{OT}$.

    c How far is it from O to T?

2 Illustrate P and find its distance from the origin O:

    a $P(0, 0, -3)$ **b** $P(0, -1, 2)$ **c** $P(3, 1, 4)$ **d** $P(-1, -2, 3)$

3 Given $A(-3, 1, 2)$ and $B(1, 0, -1)$ find:

    a $\overrightarrow{AB}$ and $\overrightarrow{BA}$ **b** the lengths $|\overrightarrow{AB}|$ and $|\overrightarrow{BA}|$.

4 Given $A(3, 1, 0)$ and $B(-1, 1, 2)$ find $\overrightarrow{OA}$, $\overrightarrow{OB}$, and $\overrightarrow{AB}$.

5 Given $M(4, -2, -1)$ and $N(-1, 2, 0)$ find:

    a the position vector of M relative to N   **b** the position vector of N relative to M

    c the distance between M and N.

6 Consider $A(-1, 2, 5)$, $B(2, 0, 3)$, and $C(-3, 1, 0)$.

    a Find the position vector $\overrightarrow{OA}$ and its length OA.

    b Find the position vector $\overrightarrow{AB}$ and its length AB.

    c Find the position vector $\overrightarrow{AC}$ and its length AC.

    d Find the position vector $\overrightarrow{CB}$ and its length CB.

    e Hence classify triangle ABC.

7 Find the shortest distance from $Q(3, 1, -2)$ to:

    a the Y-axis   **b** the origin   **c** the YOZ plane.

8 Show that $P(0, 4, 4)$, $Q(2, 6, 5)$, and $R(1, 4, 3)$ are vertices of an isosceles triangle.

9 Use side lengths to classify triangle ABC given the coordinates:

    a $A(0, 0, 3)$, $B(2, 8, 1)$, and $C(-9, 6, 18)$ **b** $A(1, 0, -3)$, $B(2, 2, 0)$, and $C(4, 6, 6)$.

10 The vertices of triangle ABC are $A(5, 6, -2)$, $B(6, 12, 9)$, and $C(2, 4, 2)$.

    a Use distances to show that the triangle is right angled.

    b Hence find the area of the triangle.

11 A sphere has centre $C(-1, 2, 4)$ and diameter $[AB]$ where A is $(-2, 1, 3)$.
Find the coordinates of B and the radius of the sphere.

12 **a** State the coordinates of any general point A on the Y-axis.

b Use **a** and the diagram opposite to find the coordinates of two points on the Y-axis which are $\sqrt{14}$ units from $B(-1, -1, 2)$.

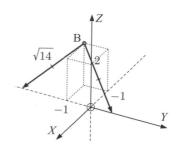

13 Find a, b, and c if:

a $\begin{pmatrix} a - 4 \\ b - 3 \\ c + 2 \end{pmatrix} = \begin{pmatrix} 1 \\ 3 \\ -4 \end{pmatrix}$

b $\begin{pmatrix} a - 5 \\ b - 2 \\ c + 3 \end{pmatrix} = \begin{pmatrix} 3 - a \\ 2 - b \\ 5 - c \end{pmatrix}$

14 Find k given the unit vector:

a $\begin{pmatrix} -\frac{1}{2} \\ k \\ \frac{1}{4} \end{pmatrix}$

b $\begin{pmatrix} k \\ \frac{2}{3} \\ -\frac{1}{3} \end{pmatrix}$

A unit vector has length 1.

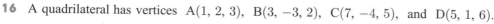

15 $A(-1, 3, 4)$, $B(2, 5, -1)$, $C(-1, 2, -2)$, and $D(r, s, t)$ are four points in space.

Find r, s, and t if: **a** $\overrightarrow{AC} = \overrightarrow{BD}$ **b** $\overrightarrow{AB} = \overrightarrow{DC}$

16 A quadrilateral has vertices $A(1, 2, 3)$, $B(3, -3, 2)$, $C(7, -4, 5)$, and $D(5, 1, 6)$.

a Find $\overrightarrow{AB}$ and $\overrightarrow{DC}$.

b What can be deduced about the quadrilateral ABCD?

17 PQRS is a parallelogram. P is $(-1, 2, 3)$, Q is $(1, -2, 5)$, and R is $(0, 4, -1)$.

a Use vectors to find the coordinates of S.

b Use midpoints of diagonals to check your answer.

H   OPERATIONS WITH VECTORS IN SPACE

The rules for algebra with vectors readily extend from 2-D to 3-D:

$$\text{If } \mathbf{a} = \begin{pmatrix} a_1 \\ a_2 \\ a_3 \end{pmatrix} \text{ and } \mathbf{b} = \begin{pmatrix} b_1 \\ b_2 \\ b_3 \end{pmatrix} \text{ then } \mathbf{a} + \mathbf{b} = \begin{pmatrix} a_1 + b_1 \\ a_2 + b_2 \\ a_3 + b_3 \end{pmatrix}, \quad \mathbf{a} - \mathbf{b} = \begin{pmatrix} a_1 - b_1 \\ a_2 - b_2 \\ a_3 - b_3 \end{pmatrix},$$

$$\text{and } k\mathbf{a} = \begin{pmatrix} ka_1 \\ ka_2 \\ ka_3 \end{pmatrix} \text{ for any scalar } k.$$

INVESTIGATION   PROPERTIES OF VECTORS IN SPACE

There are several properties or rules which are valid for the addition of real numbers. For example, we know that $a + b = b + a$.

Our task is to identify some similar properties of vectors.

What to do:

1   Use general vectors $\mathbf{a} = \begin{pmatrix} a_1 \\ a_2 \\ a_3 \end{pmatrix}$, $\mathbf{b} = \begin{pmatrix} b_1 \\ b_2 \\ b_3 \end{pmatrix}$, and $\mathbf{c} = \begin{pmatrix} c_1 \\ c_2 \\ c_3 \end{pmatrix}$ to find:

      a $\mathbf{a} + \mathbf{b}$ and $\mathbf{b} + \mathbf{a}$ **b** $\mathbf{a} + \mathbf{0}$

      c $\mathbf{a} + (-\mathbf{a})$ and $(-\mathbf{a} + \mathbf{a})$ **d** $(\mathbf{a} + \mathbf{b}) + \mathbf{c}$ and $\mathbf{a} + (\mathbf{b} + \mathbf{c})$

2   Summarise your observations from **1**. Do they match the rules for real numbers?

3   Prove that for scalar k and vectors $\mathbf{a} = \begin{pmatrix} a_1 \\ a_2 \\ a_3 \end{pmatrix}$ and $\mathbf{b} = \begin{pmatrix} b_1 \\ b_2 \\ b_3 \end{pmatrix}$:

      a $|k\mathbf{a}| = |k|\,|\mathbf{a}|$ **b** $k(\mathbf{a} + \mathbf{b}) = k\mathbf{a} + k\mathbf{b}$

From the **Investigation** you should have found that for vectors $\mathbf{a}$, $\mathbf{b}$, $\mathbf{c}$ and $k \in \mathbb{R}$:

-      $\mathbf{a} + \mathbf{b} = \mathbf{b} + \mathbf{a}$ {commutative property}

-    $(\mathbf{a} + \mathbf{b}) + \mathbf{c} = \mathbf{a} + (\mathbf{b} + \mathbf{c})$ {associative property}

-      $\mathbf{a} + \mathbf{0} = \mathbf{0} + \mathbf{a} = \mathbf{a}$ {additive identity}

-    $\mathbf{a} + (-\mathbf{a}) = (-\mathbf{a}) + \mathbf{a} = \mathbf{0}$ {additive inverse}

-      $\underbrace{|k\mathbf{a}|}_{\text{length of } k\mathbf{a}} = \underbrace{|k|}_{} \underbrace{|\mathbf{a}|}_{\text{length of } \mathbf{a}}$ where $k\mathbf{a}$ is parallel to $\mathbf{a}$

            modulus of k

-    $k(\mathbf{a} + \mathbf{b}) = k\mathbf{a} + k\mathbf{b}$ {distributive property}

The rules for solving vector equations are similar to those for solving real number equations. However, there is no such thing as dividing a vector by a scalar. Instead, we multiply by the reciprocal scalar.

For example,   if $2\mathbf{x} = \mathbf{a}$ then $\mathbf{x} = \frac{1}{2}\mathbf{a}$ and *not* $\dfrac{\mathbf{a}}{2}$.

          $\dfrac{\mathbf{a}}{2}$ has no meaning in vector algebra.

Two useful rules are:

-    if $\mathbf{x} + \mathbf{a} = \mathbf{b}$ then $\mathbf{x} = \mathbf{b} - \mathbf{a}$
-    if $k\mathbf{x} = \mathbf{a}$ then $\mathbf{x} = \frac{1}{k}\mathbf{a}$ $(k \neq 0)$

To establish these   if $\mathbf{x} + \mathbf{a} = \mathbf{b}$ and if $k\mathbf{x} = \mathbf{a}$

notice that: then $\mathbf{x} + \mathbf{a} + (-\mathbf{a}) = \mathbf{b} + (-\mathbf{a})$ then $\frac{1}{k}(k\mathbf{x}) = \frac{1}{k}\mathbf{a}$

               $\therefore \quad \mathbf{x} + \mathbf{0} = \mathbf{b} - \mathbf{a}$ $\therefore \quad 1\mathbf{x} = \frac{1}{k}\mathbf{a}$

                  $\therefore \quad \mathbf{x} = \mathbf{b} - \mathbf{a}$ $\therefore \quad \mathbf{x} = \frac{1}{k}\mathbf{a}$

Example 23   ◀》 **Self Tutor**

Solve for **x**:   **a** $3\mathbf{x} - \mathbf{r} = \mathbf{s}$ **b** $\mathbf{c} - 2\mathbf{x} = \mathbf{d}$

a $3\mathbf{x} - \mathbf{r} = \mathbf{s}$	**b** $\mathbf{c} - 2\mathbf{x} = \mathbf{d}$
$\therefore \quad 3\mathbf{x} = \mathbf{s} + \mathbf{r}$	$\therefore \quad \mathbf{c} - \mathbf{d} = 2\mathbf{x}$
$\therefore \quad \mathbf{x} = \tfrac{1}{3}(\mathbf{s} + \mathbf{r})$	$\therefore \quad \tfrac{1}{2}(\mathbf{c} - \mathbf{d}) = \mathbf{x}$

Example 24   ◀》 **Self Tutor**

If $\mathbf{a} = \begin{pmatrix} -1 \\ 3 \\ 2 \end{pmatrix}$, find $|2\mathbf{a}|$.

$$|2\mathbf{a}| = 2\,|\mathbf{a}|$$
$$= 2\sqrt{(-1)^2 + 3^2 + 2^2}$$
$$= 2\sqrt{1 + 9 + 4}$$
$$= 2\sqrt{14} \quad \text{units}$$

Example 25   ◀》 **Self Tutor**

Find the coordinates of C and D:

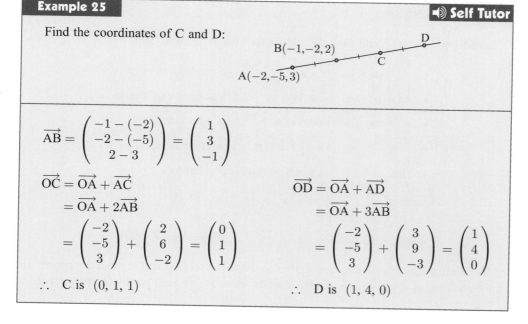

$$\overrightarrow{AB} = \begin{pmatrix} -1 - (-2) \\ -2 - (-5) \\ 2 - 3 \end{pmatrix} = \begin{pmatrix} 1 \\ 3 \\ -1 \end{pmatrix}$$

$\overrightarrow{OC} = \overrightarrow{OA} + \overrightarrow{AC}$	$\overrightarrow{OD} = \overrightarrow{OA} + \overrightarrow{AD}$
$= \overrightarrow{OA} + 2\overrightarrow{AB}$	$= \overrightarrow{OA} + 3\overrightarrow{AB}$
$= \begin{pmatrix} -2 \\ -5 \\ 3 \end{pmatrix} + \begin{pmatrix} 2 \\ 6 \\ -2 \end{pmatrix} = \begin{pmatrix} 0 \\ 1 \\ 1 \end{pmatrix}$	$= \begin{pmatrix} -2 \\ -5 \\ 3 \end{pmatrix} + \begin{pmatrix} 3 \\ 9 \\ -3 \end{pmatrix} = \begin{pmatrix} 1 \\ 4 \\ 0 \end{pmatrix}$
$\therefore$ C is $(0, 1, 1)$	$\therefore$ D is $(1, 4, 0)$

EXERCISE 12H

1 Solve the following vector equations for **x**:

a $2\mathbf{x} = \mathbf{q}$ **b** $\tfrac{1}{2}\mathbf{x} = \mathbf{n}$ **c** $-3\mathbf{x} = \mathbf{p}$

d $\mathbf{q} + 2\mathbf{x} = \mathbf{r}$ **e** $4\mathbf{s} - 5\mathbf{x} = \mathbf{t}$ **f** $4\mathbf{m} - \tfrac{1}{3}\mathbf{x} = \mathbf{n}$

2 Suppose $\mathbf{a} = \begin{pmatrix} -1 \\ 2 \\ 3 \end{pmatrix}$ and $\mathbf{b} = \begin{pmatrix} 2 \\ -2 \\ 1 \end{pmatrix}$. Find **x** if:

a $2\mathbf{a} + \mathbf{x} = \mathbf{b}$ **b** $3\mathbf{x} - \mathbf{a} = 2\mathbf{b}$ **c** $2\mathbf{b} - 2\mathbf{x} = -\mathbf{a}$

3 If $\overrightarrow{OA} = \begin{pmatrix} -2 \\ -1 \\ 1 \end{pmatrix}$ and $\overrightarrow{OB} = \begin{pmatrix} 1 \\ 3 \\ -1 \end{pmatrix}$, find $\overrightarrow{AB}$ and hence the distance from A to B.

4 For $A(-1, 3, 2)$ and $B(3, -2, 1)$ find:

    a $\overrightarrow{AB}$ in terms of $\mathbf{i}$, $\mathbf{j}$, and $\mathbf{k}$ **b** the magnitude of $\overrightarrow{AB}$

5 If $\mathbf{a} = \begin{pmatrix} 1 \\ 0 \\ 3 \end{pmatrix}$ and $\mathbf{b} = \begin{pmatrix} -2 \\ 1 \\ 1 \end{pmatrix}$, find:

    a $|\mathbf{a}|$ **b** $|\mathbf{b}|$ **c** $2|\mathbf{a}|$ **d** $|2\mathbf{a}|$

    e $-3|\mathbf{b}|$ **f** $|-3\mathbf{b}|$ **g** $|\mathbf{a} + \mathbf{b}|$ **h** $|\mathbf{a} - \mathbf{b}|$

6 If $\overrightarrow{AB} = \mathbf{i} - \mathbf{j} + \mathbf{k}$ and $\overrightarrow{BC} = -2\mathbf{i} + \mathbf{j} - 3\mathbf{k}$ find $\overrightarrow{AC}$ in terms of $\mathbf{i}$, $\mathbf{j}$, and $\mathbf{k}$.

7 Consider the points $A(2, 1, -2)$, $B(0, 3, -4)$, $C(1, -2, 1)$, and $D(-2, -3, 2)$.
    Deduce that $\overrightarrow{BD} = 2\overrightarrow{AC}$.

8 Find the coordinates of C, D, and E.

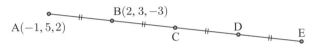

9 Use vectors to determine whether ABCD is a parallelogram:

    a $A(3, -1)$, $B(4, 2)$, $C(-1, 4)$, and $D(-2, 1)$

    b $A(5, 0, 3)$, $B(-1, 2, 4)$, $C(4, -3, 6)$, and $D(10, -5, 5)$

    c $A(2, -3, 2)$, $B(1, 4, -1)$, $C(-2, 6, -2)$, and $D(-1, -1, 2)$.

10 Use vector methods to find the remaining vertex of:

    a   **b**   **c**

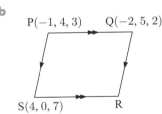
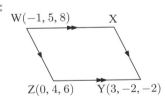

11

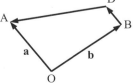

In the given figure [BD] is parallel to [OA] and half its length. Find, in terms of $\mathbf{a}$ and $\mathbf{b}$, vector expressions for:

    a $\overrightarrow{BD}$ **b** $\overrightarrow{AB}$ **c** $\overrightarrow{BA}$

    d $\overrightarrow{OD}$ **e** $\overrightarrow{AD}$ **f** $\overrightarrow{DA}$

12 If $\overrightarrow{AB} = \begin{pmatrix} -1 \\ 3 \\ 2 \end{pmatrix}$, $\overrightarrow{AC} = \begin{pmatrix} 2 \\ -1 \\ 4 \end{pmatrix}$, and $\overrightarrow{BD} = \begin{pmatrix} 0 \\ 2 \\ -3 \end{pmatrix}$, find:

    a $\overrightarrow{AD}$ **b** $\overrightarrow{CB}$ **c** $\overrightarrow{CD}$

13 For $\mathbf{a} = \begin{pmatrix} 2 \\ -1 \\ 1 \end{pmatrix}$, $\mathbf{b} = \begin{pmatrix} 1 \\ 2 \\ -3 \end{pmatrix}$, and $\mathbf{c} = \begin{pmatrix} 0 \\ 1 \\ -3 \end{pmatrix}$, find:

    a $\mathbf{a} + \mathbf{b}$ **b** $\mathbf{a} - \mathbf{b}$ **c** $\mathbf{b} + 2\mathbf{c}$

    d $\mathbf{c} - \frac{1}{2}\mathbf{a}$ **e** $\mathbf{a} - \mathbf{b} - \mathbf{c}$ **f** $2\mathbf{b} - \mathbf{c} + \mathbf{a}$

14 If $\mathbf{a} = \begin{pmatrix} -1 \\ 1 \\ 3 \end{pmatrix}$, $\mathbf{b} = \begin{pmatrix} 1 \\ -3 \\ 2 \end{pmatrix}$, and $\mathbf{c} = \begin{pmatrix} -2 \\ 2 \\ 4 \end{pmatrix}$, find:

    a $|\mathbf{a}|$ **b** $|\mathbf{b}|$ **c** $|\mathbf{b} + \mathbf{c}|$

    d $|\mathbf{a} - \mathbf{c}|$ **e** $|\mathbf{a}|\mathbf{b}$ **f** $\dfrac{1}{|\mathbf{a}|}\mathbf{a}$

15 Find scalars a, b, and c:

    a $2\begin{pmatrix} 1 \\ 0 \\ 3a \end{pmatrix} = \begin{pmatrix} b \\ c-1 \\ 2 \end{pmatrix}$ **b** $a\begin{pmatrix} 1 \\ 1 \\ 0 \end{pmatrix} + b\begin{pmatrix} 2 \\ 0 \\ -1 \end{pmatrix} + c\begin{pmatrix} 0 \\ 1 \\ 1 \end{pmatrix} = \begin{pmatrix} -1 \\ 3 \\ 3 \end{pmatrix}$

    c $a\begin{pmatrix} 2 \\ -3 \\ 1 \end{pmatrix} + b\begin{pmatrix} 1 \\ 7 \\ 2 \end{pmatrix} = \begin{pmatrix} 7 \\ -19 \\ 2 \end{pmatrix}$

I   PARALLELISM

            $\mathbf{a}$ $2\mathbf{a}$ $\frac{1}{3}\mathbf{a}$ are parallel vectors of different length.

Two non-zero vectors are **parallel** if and only if one is a scalar multiple of the other.

Given any non-zero vector $\mathbf{v}$ and non-zero scalar k, the vector $k\mathbf{v}$ is parallel to $\mathbf{v}$.

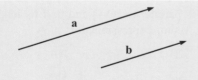

- If $\mathbf{a}$ is parallel to $\mathbf{b}$, then there exists a scalar k such that $\mathbf{a} = k\mathbf{b}$.
- If $\mathbf{a} = k\mathbf{b}$ for some scalar k, then
  - $\mathbf{a}$ is parallel to $\mathbf{b}$, and
  - $|\mathbf{a}| = |k||\mathbf{b}|$.

$|k|$ reads the modulus of k, whereas $|\mathbf{a}|$ is the length of vector $\mathbf{a}$.

Example 26 🔊 **Self Tutor**

Find r and s given that $\mathbf{a} = \begin{pmatrix} 2 \\ -1 \\ r \end{pmatrix}$ is parallel to $\mathbf{b} = \begin{pmatrix} s \\ 2 \\ -3 \end{pmatrix}$.

Since $\mathbf{a}$ and $\mathbf{b}$ are parallel, $\mathbf{a} = k\mathbf{b}$ for some scalar k.

$$\therefore \quad \begin{pmatrix} 2 \\ -1 \\ r \end{pmatrix} = k \begin{pmatrix} s \\ 2 \\ -3 \end{pmatrix}$$

$\therefore \quad 2 = ks, \quad -1 = 2k$ and $r = -3k$

Consequently, $\quad k = -\frac{1}{2} \quad$ and $\quad \therefore \quad 2 = -\frac{1}{2}s$ and $r = -3(-\frac{1}{2})$

$$\therefore \quad r = \tfrac{3}{2} \text{ and } s = -4$$

UNIT VECTORS

Given a non-zero vector $\mathbf{v}$, its magnitude $|\mathbf{v}|$ is a scalar quantity.

If we multiply $\mathbf{v}$ by the scalar $\dfrac{1}{|\mathbf{v}|}$, we obtain the parallel vector $\dfrac{1}{|\mathbf{v}|}\mathbf{v}$.

The length of this vector is $\left|\dfrac{1}{|\mathbf{v}|}\right| |\mathbf{v}| = \dfrac{|\mathbf{v}|}{|\mathbf{v}|} = 1$, so $\dfrac{1}{|\mathbf{v}|}\mathbf{v}$ is a unit vector in the direction of $\mathbf{v}$.

- A unit vector in the direction of $\mathbf{v}$ is $\dfrac{1}{|\mathbf{v}|}\mathbf{v}$.

- A vector $\mathbf{b}$ of length k in the same direction as $\mathbf{a}$ is $\mathbf{b} = \dfrac{k}{|\mathbf{a}|}\mathbf{a}$.

- A vector $\mathbf{b}$ of length k which is *parallel to* $\mathbf{a}$ could be $\mathbf{b} = \pm\dfrac{k}{|\mathbf{a}|}\mathbf{a}$.

Example 27 🔊 **Self Tutor**

If $\mathbf{a} = 3\mathbf{i} - \mathbf{j}$ find:

  a a unit vector in the direction of $\mathbf{a}$

  b a vector of length 4 units in the direction of $\mathbf{a}$

  c vectors of length 4 units which are parallel to $\mathbf{a}$.

a $\quad |\mathbf{a}| = \sqrt{3^2 + (-1)^2}$ $\qquad\qquad \therefore$ the unit vector is $\frac{1}{\sqrt{10}}(3\mathbf{i} - \mathbf{j})$

$\qquad\qquad = \sqrt{9 + 1}$ $\qquad\qquad\qquad\qquad\qquad\qquad = \frac{3}{\sqrt{10}}\mathbf{i} - \frac{1}{\sqrt{10}}\mathbf{j}$

$\qquad\qquad = \sqrt{10}$ units

b This vector is $\quad \frac{4}{\sqrt{10}}(3\mathbf{i} - \mathbf{j})$

$\qquad\qquad\qquad = \frac{12}{\sqrt{10}}\mathbf{i} - \frac{4}{\sqrt{10}}\mathbf{j}$

c These vectors are $\quad \frac{12}{\sqrt{10}}\mathbf{i} - \frac{4}{\sqrt{10}}\mathbf{j}$ and $-\frac{12}{\sqrt{10}}\mathbf{i} + \frac{4}{\sqrt{10}}\mathbf{j}$.

Example 28   ◀)) **Self Tutor**

Find a vector **b** of length 7 in the opposite direction to the vector $\mathbf{a} = \begin{pmatrix} 2 \\ -1 \\ 1 \end{pmatrix}$.

The unit vector in the direction of **a** is $\dfrac{1}{|\mathbf{a}|}\mathbf{a} = \dfrac{1}{\sqrt{4+1+1}}\begin{pmatrix} 2 \\ -1 \\ 1 \end{pmatrix} = \dfrac{1}{\sqrt{6}}\begin{pmatrix} 2 \\ -1 \\ 1 \end{pmatrix}$.

We multiply this unit vector by -7. The negative reverses the direction and the 7 gives the required length.

Thus $\mathbf{b} = -\dfrac{7}{\sqrt{6}}\begin{pmatrix} 2 \\ -1 \\ 1 \end{pmatrix}$.

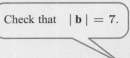

Check that $|\mathbf{b}| = 7$.

EXERCISE 12I

1 $\mathbf{a} = \begin{pmatrix} 2 \\ -1 \\ 3 \end{pmatrix}$ and $\mathbf{b} = \begin{pmatrix} -6 \\ r \\ s \end{pmatrix}$ are parallel. Find r and s.

2 Find scalars a and b given that $\begin{pmatrix} 3 \\ -1 \\ 2 \end{pmatrix}$ and $\begin{pmatrix} a \\ 2 \\ b \end{pmatrix}$ are parallel.

3 What can be deduced from the following?
    a $\overrightarrow{AB} = 3\overrightarrow{CD}$ **b** $\overrightarrow{RS} = -\tfrac{1}{2}\overrightarrow{KL}$ **c** $\overrightarrow{AB} = 2\overrightarrow{BC}$

4 The position vectors of P, Q, R, and S are $\begin{pmatrix} 3 \\ 2 \\ -1 \end{pmatrix}$, $\begin{pmatrix} 1 \\ 4 \\ -3 \end{pmatrix}$, $\begin{pmatrix} 2 \\ -1 \\ 2 \end{pmatrix}$, and $\begin{pmatrix} -1 \\ -2 \\ 3 \end{pmatrix}$ respectively.
    a Deduce that [PR] and [QS] are parallel.
    b What is the relationship between the lengths of [PR] and [QS]?

5 If $\mathbf{a} = \begin{pmatrix} 2 \\ 4 \end{pmatrix}$, write down the vector:
    a in the same direction as **a** and twice its length
    b in the opposite direction to **a** and half its length.

6 Find the unit vector in the direction of:
    a $\mathbf{i} + 2\mathbf{j}$ **b** $2\mathbf{i} - 3\mathbf{k}$ **c** $2\mathbf{i} - 2\mathbf{j} + \mathbf{k}$

7 Find a vector **v** which has:
    a the same direction as $\begin{pmatrix} 2 \\ -1 \end{pmatrix}$ and length 3 units
    b the opposite direction to $\begin{pmatrix} -1 \\ -4 \end{pmatrix}$ and length 2 units.

8 A is (3, 2) and point B is 4 units from A in the direction $\begin{pmatrix} 1 \\ -1 \end{pmatrix}$.

    a Find $\overrightarrow{AB}$.   **b** Find $\overrightarrow{OB}$ using $\overrightarrow{OB} = \overrightarrow{OA} + \overrightarrow{AB}$.

    c Hence deduce the coordinates of B.

9 **a** Find vectors of length 1 unit which are parallel to $\mathbf{a} = \begin{pmatrix} 2 \\ -1 \\ -2 \end{pmatrix}$.

    b Find vectors of length 2 units which are parallel to $\mathbf{b} = \begin{pmatrix} -2 \\ -1 \\ 2 \end{pmatrix}$.

10 Find a vector $\mathbf{b}$ in:

    a the same direction as $\begin{pmatrix} -1 \\ 4 \\ 1 \end{pmatrix}$ and with length 6 units

    b the opposite direction to $\begin{pmatrix} -1 \\ -2 \\ -2 \end{pmatrix}$ and with length 5 units.

J   THE SCALAR PRODUCT OF TWO VECTORS

For ordinary numbers a and b we can write the product of a and b as ab or $a \times b$. There is only one interpretation for this product, so we can use power notation $a^2 = a \times a$, $a^3 = a \times a \times a$, and so on as shorthand.

However, there are *two* different types of product involving two vectors. These are:

▶ The **scalar product** of 2 vectors, which results in a **scalar** answer and has the notation $\mathbf{v} \bullet \mathbf{w}$ (read "$\mathbf{v}$ dot $\mathbf{w}$").

▶ The **vector product** of 2 vectors, which results in a **vector** answer and has the notation $\mathbf{v} \times \mathbf{w}$ (read "$\mathbf{v}$ cross $\mathbf{w}$").

Consequently, for vector $\mathbf{v}$, $\mathbf{v}^2$ or $(\mathbf{v})^2$ has no meaning and is not used, as it not clear which of the vector products it would refer to.

In this course we consider only the scalar product.

SCALAR PRODUCT

The **scalar product** of two vectors is also known as the **dot product** or **inner product**.

If $\mathbf{v} = \begin{pmatrix} v_1 \\ v_2 \\ v_3 \end{pmatrix}$ and $\mathbf{w} = \begin{pmatrix} w_1 \\ w_2 \\ w_3 \end{pmatrix}$, the **scalar product** of $\mathbf{v}$ and $\mathbf{w}$ is defined as

$\mathbf{v} \bullet \mathbf{w} = v_1 w_1 + v_2 w_2 + v_3 w_3$.

ANGLE BETWEEN VECTORS

Consider the vectors  $\mathbf{v} = \begin{pmatrix} v_1 \\ v_2 \\ v_3 \end{pmatrix}$ and $\mathbf{w} = \begin{pmatrix} w_1 \\ w_2 \\ w_3 \end{pmatrix}$.

We translate one of the vectors so that they both originate from the same point.

This vector is $-\mathbf{v} + \mathbf{w} = \mathbf{w} - \mathbf{v}$
and has length $|\mathbf{w} - \mathbf{v}|$.

Using the cosine rule, $|\mathbf{w} - \mathbf{v}|^2 = |\mathbf{v}|^2 + |\mathbf{w}|^2 - 2|\mathbf{v}||\mathbf{w}|\cos\theta$

But $\mathbf{w} - \mathbf{v} = \begin{pmatrix} w_1 \\ w_2 \\ w_3 \end{pmatrix} - \begin{pmatrix} v_1 \\ v_2 \\ v_3 \end{pmatrix} = \begin{pmatrix} w_1 - v_1 \\ w_2 - v_2 \\ w_3 - v_3 \end{pmatrix}$

$\therefore\ (w_1 - v_1)^2 + (w_2 - v_2)^2 + (w_3 - v_3)^2 = v_1^2 + v_2^2 + v_3^2 + w_1^2 + w_2^2 + w_3^2 - 2|\mathbf{v}||\mathbf{w}|\cos\theta$

$\therefore\ \ v_1 w_1 + v_2 w_2 + v_3 w_3 = |\mathbf{v}||\mathbf{w}|\cos\theta$

$\therefore\ \ \mathbf{v} \bullet \mathbf{w} = |\mathbf{v}||\mathbf{w}|\cos\theta$

> The angle θ between two vectors $\mathbf{v}$ and $\mathbf{w}$ can be found using
>
> $$\cos\theta = \frac{\mathbf{v} \bullet \mathbf{w}}{|\mathbf{v}||\mathbf{w}|}$$

ALGEBRAIC PROPERTIES OF THE SCALAR PRODUCT

The scalar product has the following algebraic properties for both 2-D and 3-D vectors:

> ▶ $\mathbf{v} \bullet \mathbf{w} = \mathbf{w} \bullet \mathbf{v}$
> ▶ $\mathbf{v} \bullet \mathbf{v} = |\mathbf{v}|^2$
> ▶ $\mathbf{v} \bullet (\mathbf{w} + \mathbf{x}) = \mathbf{v} \bullet \mathbf{w} + \mathbf{v} \bullet \mathbf{x}$
> ▶ $(\mathbf{v} + \mathbf{w}) \bullet (\mathbf{x} + \mathbf{y}) = \mathbf{v} \bullet \mathbf{x} + \mathbf{v} \bullet \mathbf{y} + \mathbf{w} \bullet \mathbf{x} + \mathbf{w} \bullet \mathbf{y}$

These properties are proven by
using general vectors such as: $\mathbf{v} = \begin{pmatrix} v_1 \\ v_2 \\ v_3 \end{pmatrix}$ and $\mathbf{w} = \begin{pmatrix} w_1 \\ w_2 \\ w_3 \end{pmatrix}$.

Be careful not to confuse the **scalar product**, which is the product of two vectors to give a scalar answer, with **scalar multiplication**, which is the product of a scalar and a vector to give a parallel vector. They are quite different.

GEOMETRIC PROPERTIES OF THE SCALAR PRODUCT

▶ For non-zero vectors $\mathbf{v}$ and $\mathbf{w}$:

$\mathbf{v} \bullet \mathbf{w} = 0 \quad \Leftrightarrow \quad \mathbf{v}$ and $\mathbf{w}$ are **perpendicular** or **orthogonal**.

▶ $|\mathbf{v} \bullet \mathbf{w}| = |\mathbf{v}||\mathbf{w}| \quad \Leftrightarrow \quad \mathbf{v}$ and $\mathbf{w}$ are non-zero **parallel vectors**.

▶ If θ is the angle between vectors $\mathbf{v}$ and $\mathbf{w}$ then: $\mathbf{v} \bullet \mathbf{w} = |\mathbf{v}||\mathbf{w}| \cos \theta$

If θ is acute, $\cos \theta > 0$ and so $\mathbf{v} \bullet \mathbf{w} > 0$

If θ is obtuse, $\cos \theta < 0$ and so $\mathbf{v} \bullet \mathbf{w} < 0$.

The angle between two vectors is always taken as the angle θ such that $0° \leqslant \theta \leqslant 180°$, rather than reflex angle α.

The first two of these results can be demonstrated as follows:

If $\mathbf{v}$ is perpendicular to $\mathbf{w}$ then $\theta = 90°$.

$\therefore \quad \mathbf{v} \bullet \mathbf{w} = |\mathbf{v}||\mathbf{w}| \cos \theta$

$= |\mathbf{v}||\mathbf{w}| \cos 90°$

$= 0$

If $\mathbf{v}$ is parallel to $\mathbf{w}$ then $\theta = 0°$ or $180°$.

$\therefore \quad \mathbf{v} \bullet \mathbf{w} = |\mathbf{v}||\mathbf{w}| \cos \theta$

$= |\mathbf{v}||\mathbf{w}| \cos 0°$ or $|\mathbf{v}||\mathbf{w}| \cos 180°$

$= \pm |\mathbf{v}||\mathbf{w}|$

$\therefore \quad |\mathbf{v} \bullet \mathbf{w}| = |\mathbf{v}||\mathbf{w}|$

To formally prove these results we must also show that their converses are true.

DISCUSSION

a

Elaine has drawn a vector $\mathbf{v}$ on a *plane* which is a sheet of paper. It is therefore a 2-dimensional vector.

i How many vectors can she draw which are *perpendicular* to $\mathbf{v}$?

ii Are all of these vectors parallel?

b

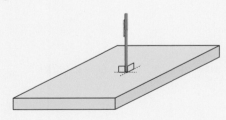

Edward is thinking about vectors in *space*. These are 3-dimensional vectors. He is holding his pen vertically on his desk to represent a vector $\mathbf{w}$.

i How many vectors are there which are *perpendicular* to $\mathbf{w}$?

ii If Edward was to draw a vector (in pencil) on his desk, would it be perpendicular to $\mathbf{w}$?

iii Are all of the vectors which are perpendicular to $\mathbf{w}$, parallel to one another?

Example 29

🔊 **Self Tutor**

If $\mathbf{p} = \begin{pmatrix} 2 \\ 3 \\ -1 \end{pmatrix}$ and $\mathbf{q} = \begin{pmatrix} -1 \\ 0 \\ 2 \end{pmatrix}$, find:

> Since $\mathbf{p} \bullet \mathbf{q} < 0$ the angle is obtuse.

a $\mathbf{p} \bullet \mathbf{q}$

b the angle between $\mathbf{p}$ and $\mathbf{q}$.

a $\mathbf{p} \bullet \mathbf{q}$

$= \begin{pmatrix} 2 \\ 3 \\ -1 \end{pmatrix} \bullet \begin{pmatrix} -1 \\ 0 \\ 2 \end{pmatrix}$

$= 2(-1) + 3(0) + (-1)2$

$= -2 + 0 - 2$

$= -4$

b $\mathbf{p} \bullet \mathbf{q} = |\mathbf{p}||\mathbf{q}| \cos \theta$

$\therefore \cos \theta = \dfrac{\mathbf{p} \bullet \mathbf{q}}{|\mathbf{p}||\mathbf{q}|}$

$= \dfrac{-4}{\sqrt{4+9+1}\sqrt{1+0+4}}$

$= \dfrac{-4}{\sqrt{70}}$

$\therefore \theta = \cos^{-1}\left(\dfrac{-4}{\sqrt{70}}\right) \approx 119°$

EXERCISE 12J

1 For $\mathbf{p} = \begin{pmatrix} 3 \\ 2 \end{pmatrix}$, $\mathbf{q} = \begin{pmatrix} -1 \\ 5 \end{pmatrix}$, and $\mathbf{r} = \begin{pmatrix} -2 \\ 4 \end{pmatrix}$, find:

a $\mathbf{q} \bullet \mathbf{p}$ **b** $\mathbf{q} \bullet \mathbf{r}$ **c** $\mathbf{q} \bullet (\mathbf{p} + \mathbf{r})$ **d** $3\mathbf{r} \bullet \mathbf{q}$

e $2\mathbf{p} \bullet 2\mathbf{p}$ **f** $\mathbf{i} \bullet \mathbf{p}$ **g** $\mathbf{q} \bullet \mathbf{j}$ **h** $\mathbf{i} \bullet \mathbf{i}$

2 For $\mathbf{a} = \begin{pmatrix} 2 \\ 1 \\ 3 \end{pmatrix}$, $\mathbf{b} = \begin{pmatrix} -1 \\ 1 \\ 1 \end{pmatrix}$, and $\mathbf{c} = \begin{pmatrix} 0 \\ -1 \\ 1 \end{pmatrix}$, find:

a $\mathbf{a} \bullet \mathbf{b}$ **b** $\mathbf{b} \bullet \mathbf{a}$ **c** $|\mathbf{a}|^2$

d $\mathbf{a} \bullet \mathbf{a}$ **e** $\mathbf{a} \bullet (\mathbf{b} + \mathbf{c})$ **f** $\mathbf{a} \bullet \mathbf{b} + \mathbf{a} \bullet \mathbf{c}$

3 If $\mathbf{p} = \begin{pmatrix} 3 \\ -1 \\ 2 \end{pmatrix}$ and $\mathbf{q} = \begin{pmatrix} -2 \\ 1 \\ 3 \end{pmatrix}$, find: **a** $\mathbf{p} \bullet \mathbf{q}$ **b** the angle between $\mathbf{p}$ and $\mathbf{q}$.

4 Find the angle between $\mathbf{m}$ and $\mathbf{n}$ if:

a $\mathbf{m} = \begin{pmatrix} 2 \\ -1 \\ -1 \end{pmatrix}$ and $\mathbf{n} = \begin{pmatrix} -1 \\ 3 \\ 2 \end{pmatrix}$ **b** $\mathbf{m} = 2\mathbf{j} - \mathbf{k}$ and $\mathbf{n} = \mathbf{i} + 2\mathbf{k}$

5 Find: **a** $(\mathbf{i} + \mathbf{j} - \mathbf{k}) \bullet (2\mathbf{j} + \mathbf{k})$ **b** $\mathbf{i} \bullet \mathbf{i}$ **c** $\mathbf{i} \bullet \mathbf{j}$

6 Find $\mathbf{p} \bullet \mathbf{q}$ if:

a $|\mathbf{p}| = 2$, $|\mathbf{q}| = 5$, $\theta = 60°$ **b** $|\mathbf{p}| = 6$, $|\mathbf{q}| = 3$, $\theta = 120°$

7 **a** Suppose $|\mathbf{v}| = 3$ and $|\mathbf{w}| = 4$. State the possible values of $\mathbf{v} \bullet \mathbf{w}$ if $\mathbf{v}$ and $\mathbf{w}$ are:

     i parallel   **ii** at 60° to each other.

b Suppose $\mathbf{a} \bullet \mathbf{b} = -12$ and $\mathbf{b}$ is a unit vector.

     i Explain why $\mathbf{a}$ and $\mathbf{b}$ are not perpendicular.

     ii Find $|\mathbf{a}|$ if $\mathbf{a}$ and $\mathbf{b}$ are parallel.

c Suppose $|\mathbf{c}| = |\mathbf{d}| = \sqrt{5}$.   What can be deduced about $\mathbf{c}$ and $\mathbf{d}$ if:

    i $\mathbf{c} \bullet \mathbf{d} = 5$ **ii** $\mathbf{c} \bullet \mathbf{d} = -5$

8 In the given figure:

  a State the coordinates of P.

  b Find $\overrightarrow{BP}$ and $\overrightarrow{AP}$.

  c Find $\overrightarrow{AP} \bullet \overrightarrow{BP}$ using **b**.

  d What property of a semi-circle has been deduced in **c**?

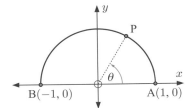

9 Use $\mathbf{a} = \begin{pmatrix} a_1 \\ a_2 \\ a_3 \end{pmatrix}$, $\mathbf{b} = \begin{pmatrix} b_1 \\ b_2 \\ b_3 \end{pmatrix}$, and $\mathbf{c} = \begin{pmatrix} c_1 \\ c_2 \\ c_3 \end{pmatrix}$ to prove that $\mathbf{a} \bullet (\mathbf{b} + \mathbf{c}) = \mathbf{a} \bullet \mathbf{b} + \mathbf{a} \bullet \mathbf{c}$.

Hence, prove that $(\mathbf{a} + \mathbf{b}) \bullet (\mathbf{c} + \mathbf{d}) = \mathbf{a} \bullet \mathbf{c} + \mathbf{a} \bullet \mathbf{d} + \mathbf{b} \bullet \mathbf{c} + \mathbf{b} \bullet \mathbf{d}$.

Example 30 🔊 **Self Tutor**

Find t such that $\mathbf{a} = \begin{pmatrix} -1 \\ 5 \end{pmatrix}$ and $\mathbf{b} = \begin{pmatrix} 2 \\ t \end{pmatrix}$ are perpendicular.

Since $\mathbf{a}$ and $\mathbf{b}$ are perpendicular, $\mathbf{a} \bullet \mathbf{b} = 0$

$$\therefore \begin{pmatrix} -1 \\ 5 \end{pmatrix} \bullet \begin{pmatrix} 2 \\ t \end{pmatrix} = 0$$

$$\therefore (-1)(2) + 5t = 0$$
$$\therefore -2 + 5t = 0$$
$$\therefore 5t = 2$$
$$\therefore t = \tfrac{2}{5}$$

*If two vectors are perpendicular then their scalar product is **zero**.*

10 Find t given that these vectors are perpendicular:

  a $\mathbf{p} = \begin{pmatrix} 3 \\ t \end{pmatrix}$ and $\mathbf{q} = \begin{pmatrix} -2 \\ 1 \end{pmatrix}$ **b** $\mathbf{r} = \begin{pmatrix} t \\ t+2 \end{pmatrix}$ and $\mathbf{s} = \begin{pmatrix} 3 \\ -4 \end{pmatrix}$

  c $\mathbf{a} = \begin{pmatrix} t \\ t+2 \end{pmatrix}$ and $\mathbf{b} = \begin{pmatrix} 2-3t \\ t \end{pmatrix}$

11 For each pair of vectors in question **10**, find the value(s) of t for which the vectors are *parallel*.

12 **a** Show that $\begin{pmatrix} 1 \\ 1 \\ 5 \end{pmatrix}$ and $\begin{pmatrix} 2 \\ 3 \\ -1 \end{pmatrix}$ are perpendicular.

Vectors are mutually perpendicular if each one is perpendicular to all the others.

  b Show that $\mathbf{a} = \begin{pmatrix} 3 \\ 1 \\ 2 \end{pmatrix}$, $\mathbf{b} = \begin{pmatrix} -1 \\ 1 \\ 1 \end{pmatrix}$, and $\mathbf{c} = \begin{pmatrix} 1 \\ 5 \\ -4 \end{pmatrix}$

    are mutually perpendicular.

  c Find t if the following vectors are perpendicular:

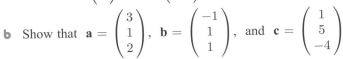

    i $\mathbf{a} = \begin{pmatrix} 3 \\ -1 \\ t \end{pmatrix}$ and $\mathbf{b} = \begin{pmatrix} 2t \\ -3 \\ -4 \end{pmatrix}$ **ii** $\begin{pmatrix} 3 \\ t \\ -2 \end{pmatrix}$ and $\begin{pmatrix} 1-t \\ -3 \\ 4 \end{pmatrix}$.

Example 31   🔊 **Self Tutor**

Consider the points A(2, 1), B(6, −1), and C(5, −3). Use a scalar product to check if triangle ABC is right angled. If it is, state the right angle.

We do not need to check $\overrightarrow{AB} \bullet \overrightarrow{AC}$ and $\overrightarrow{BC} \bullet \overrightarrow{AC}$ because a triangle cannot have more than one right angle.

$\overrightarrow{AB} = \begin{pmatrix} 4 \\ -2 \end{pmatrix}$, $\overrightarrow{BC} = \begin{pmatrix} -1 \\ -2 \end{pmatrix}$, and $\overrightarrow{AC} = \begin{pmatrix} 3 \\ -4 \end{pmatrix}$.

$\overrightarrow{AB} \bullet \overrightarrow{BC} = 4\,(-1) + (-2)\,(-2) = -4 + 4 = 0$.

∴ $\overrightarrow{AB} \perp \overrightarrow{BC}$ and so triangle ABC is right angled at B.

13 Use a scalar product to check if triangle ABC is right angled. If it is, state the right angle.

   a   A(−2, 1), B(−2, 5), and C(3, 1)   **b**   A(4, 7), B(1, 2), and C(−1, 6)

   c   A(2, −2), B(5, 7), and C(−1, −1)   **d**   A(10, 1), B(5, 2), and C(7, 4)

14 Consider triangle ABC in which A is (5, 1, 2), B is (6, −1, 0), and C is (3, 2, 0). Using scalar product only, show that the triangle is right angled.

15 A(2, 4, 2), B(−1, 2, 3), C(−3, 3, 6), and D(0, 5, 5) are vertices of a quadrilateral.

   a   Prove that ABCD is a parallelogram.

   b   Find $|\overrightarrow{AB}|$ and $|\overrightarrow{BC}|$.   What can be said about ABCD?

   c   Find $\overrightarrow{AC} \bullet \overrightarrow{BD}$.   Describe what property of ABCD you have shown.

Example 32   🔊 **Self Tutor**

Find the form of all vectors which are perpendicular to $\begin{pmatrix} 3 \\ 4 \end{pmatrix}$.

Are all of the vectors parallel?

$\begin{pmatrix} 3 \\ 4 \end{pmatrix} \bullet \begin{pmatrix} -4 \\ 3 \end{pmatrix} = -12 + 12 = 0$

So, $\begin{pmatrix} -4 \\ 3 \end{pmatrix}$ is one such vector.

The required vectors have the form $k \begin{pmatrix} -4 \\ 3 \end{pmatrix}$, $k \neq 0$.

All of these vectors are parallel.

16 Find the form of all vectors which are perpendicular to:

   a $\begin{pmatrix} 5 \\ 2 \end{pmatrix}$ **b** $\begin{pmatrix} -1 \\ -2 \end{pmatrix}$ **c** $\begin{pmatrix} 3 \\ -1 \end{pmatrix}$ **d** $\begin{pmatrix} -4 \\ 3 \end{pmatrix}$ **e** $\begin{pmatrix} 2 \\ 0 \end{pmatrix}$

17 Find any two vectors which are not parallel, but which are *both* perpendicular to $\begin{pmatrix} 1 \\ 2 \\ -1 \end{pmatrix}$.

18 Find the angle ABC of triangle ABC for A(3, 0, 1), B(−3, 1, 2), and C(−2, 1, −1).

Hint: To find the angle at B, use $\overrightarrow{BA}$ and $\overrightarrow{BC}$.

What angle is found if $\overrightarrow{BA}$ and $\overrightarrow{CB}$ are used?

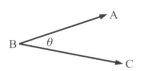

Example 33

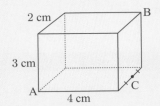

Use vector methods to determine the measure of AB̂C.

The vectors used must both be away from B (or towards B). If this is not done you will be finding the exterior angle at B.

Placing the coordinate axes as illustrated,
A is (2, 0, 0), B is (0, 4, 3), and C is (1, 4, 0).

$$\therefore \quad \overrightarrow{BA} = \begin{pmatrix} 2 \\ -4 \\ -3 \end{pmatrix} \quad \text{and} \quad \overrightarrow{BC} = \begin{pmatrix} 1 \\ 0 \\ -3 \end{pmatrix}$$

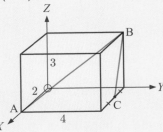

$$\cos(A\widehat{B}C) = \frac{\overrightarrow{BA} \bullet \overrightarrow{BC}}{|\overrightarrow{BA}| \, |\overrightarrow{BC}|}$$

$$= \frac{2(1) + (-4)(0) + (-3)(-3)}{\sqrt{4 + 16 + 9} \, \sqrt{1 + 0 + 9}}$$

$$= \frac{11}{\sqrt{290}}$$

$$\therefore \quad A\widehat{B}C = \cos^{-1}\left(\frac{11}{\sqrt{290}}\right) \approx 49.8°$$

---

19 The cube alongside has sides of length 2 cm. Find, using vector methods, the measure of:

   a AB̂S   **b** RB̂P   **c** PB̂S

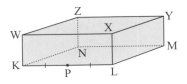

20 [KL], [LM], and [LX] are 8, 5, and 3 units long respectively. P is the midpoint of [KL]. Find, using vector methods, the measure of:

   a YN̂X   **b** YN̂P

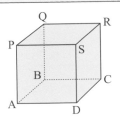

21 Consider tetrahedron ABCD.

   a Find the coordinates of M.

   b Find the measure of DM̂A.

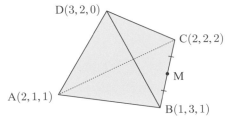

22   **a**   Find t if $2\mathbf{i} + t\mathbf{j} + (t-2)\mathbf{k}$ and $t\mathbf{i} + 3\mathbf{j} + t\mathbf{k}$ are perpendicular.

     b   Find r, s, and t if $\mathbf{a} = \begin{pmatrix} 1 \\ 2 \\ 3 \end{pmatrix}$, $\mathbf{b} = \begin{pmatrix} 2 \\ 2 \\ r \end{pmatrix}$,   and $\mathbf{c} = \begin{pmatrix} s \\ t \\ 1 \end{pmatrix}$ are mutually perpendicular.

23   Find the angle made by:

    a $\mathbf{i}$ and $\begin{pmatrix} 1 \\ 2 \\ 3 \end{pmatrix}$ **b** $\mathbf{j}$ and $\begin{pmatrix} -1 \\ 1 \\ 3 \end{pmatrix}$.

REVIEW SET 12A   NON-CALCULATOR

1   Using a scale of 1 cm represents 10 units, sketch a vector to represent:

    a   an aeroplane taking off at an angle of $8°$ to a runway with a speed of 60 m s^{-1}

    b   a displacement of 45 m in a north-easterly direction.

2   Simplify: **a** $\overrightarrow{AB} - \overrightarrow{CB}$ **b** $\overrightarrow{AB} + \overrightarrow{BC} - \overrightarrow{DC}$.

3   Construct vector   **a**   **b**
equations for:

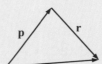 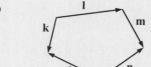

4   If $\overrightarrow{PQ} = \begin{pmatrix} -4 \\ 1 \end{pmatrix}$, $\overrightarrow{RQ} = \begin{pmatrix} -1 \\ 2 \end{pmatrix}$,   and $\overrightarrow{RS} = \begin{pmatrix} 2 \\ -3 \end{pmatrix}$,   find $\overrightarrow{SP}$.

5

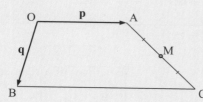

[BC] is parallel to [OA] and is twice its length.
Find, in terms of $\mathbf{p}$ and $\mathbf{q}$, vector expressions for:

    a $\overrightarrow{AC}$ **b** $\overrightarrow{OM}$.

6   Find m and n if $\begin{pmatrix} 3 \\ m \\ n \end{pmatrix}$ and $\begin{pmatrix} -12 \\ -20 \\ 2 \end{pmatrix}$ are parallel vectors.

7   If $\overrightarrow{AB} = \begin{pmatrix} 2 \\ -7 \\ 4 \end{pmatrix}$ and $\overrightarrow{AC} = \begin{pmatrix} -6 \\ 1 \\ -3 \end{pmatrix}$,   find $\overrightarrow{CB}$.

8   If $\mathbf{p} = \begin{pmatrix} 3 \\ -2 \end{pmatrix}$, $\mathbf{q} = \begin{pmatrix} -1 \\ 5 \end{pmatrix}$,   and $\mathbf{r} = \begin{pmatrix} -3 \\ 4 \end{pmatrix}$,   find: **a** $\mathbf{p} \bullet \mathbf{q}$ **b** $\mathbf{q} \bullet (\mathbf{p} - \mathbf{r})$

9   Consider points   X(−2, 5),   Y(3, 4),   W(−3, −1),   and   Z(4, 10).   Use vectors to show that WYZX is a parallelogram.

10   Consider points   A(2, 3),   B(−1, 4),   and   C(3, k).   Find k if $\widehat{BAC}$ is a right angle.

11 Find all vectors which are perpendicular to the vector $\begin{pmatrix} -4 \\ 5 \end{pmatrix}$.

12 In this question you may **not** assume any diagonal properties of parallelograms.

OABC is a parallelogram with $\overrightarrow{OA} = \mathbf{p}$ and $\overrightarrow{OC} = \mathbf{q}$. M is the midpoint of [AC].

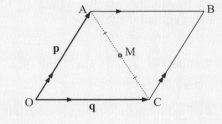

   a Find in terms of $\mathbf{p}$ and $\mathbf{q}$:

      i $\overrightarrow{OB}$ **ii** $\overrightarrow{OM}$

   b Using **a** only, show that O, M, and B are collinear, and that M is the midpoint of [OB].

13 Suppose $|\mathbf{a}| = 2$, $|\mathbf{b}| = 4$, and $|\mathbf{c}| = 5$.

   Find: **a** $\mathbf{a} \bullet \mathbf{b}$

           b $\mathbf{b} \bullet \mathbf{c}$

           c $\mathbf{a} \bullet \mathbf{c}$

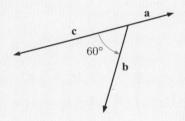

14 Find a and b if J$(-4, 1, 3)$, K$(2, -2, 0)$, and L$(a, b, 2)$ are collinear.

   Hint: Points J, K, and L are collinear $\Leftrightarrow$ $\overrightarrow{JK}$ is parallel to $\overrightarrow{KL}$.

15 [AB] and [CD] are diameters of a circle with centre O. If $\overrightarrow{OC} = \mathbf{q}$ and $\overrightarrow{OB} = \mathbf{r}$, find:

   a $\overrightarrow{DB}$ in terms of $\mathbf{q}$ and $\mathbf{r}$ **b** $\overrightarrow{AC}$ in terms of $\mathbf{q}$ and $\mathbf{r}$.

   What can be deduced about [DB] and [AC]?

16 **a** Find t given that $\begin{pmatrix} 2 - t \\ 3 \\ t \end{pmatrix}$ and $\begin{pmatrix} t \\ 4 \\ t + 1 \end{pmatrix}$ are perpendicular.

   b Show that K$(4, 3, -1)$, L$(-3, 4, 2)$, and M$(2, 1, -2)$ are vertices of a right angled triangle.

REVIEW SET 12B   CALCULATOR

1 Copy the given vectors and find geometrically:

   a $\mathbf{x} + \mathbf{y}$ **b** $\mathbf{y} - 2\mathbf{x}$

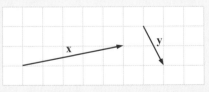

2 Show that A$(-2, -1, 3)$, B$(4, 0, -1)$, and C$(-2, 1, -4)$ are vertices of an isosceles triangle.

3 If $\mathbf{r} = \begin{pmatrix} 4 \\ 1 \end{pmatrix}$ and $\mathbf{s} = \begin{pmatrix} -3 \\ 2 \end{pmatrix}$ find: **a** $|\mathbf{s}|$ **b** $|\mathbf{r} + \mathbf{s}|$ **c** $|2\mathbf{s} - \mathbf{r}|$

4 Find scalars r and s such that $r \begin{pmatrix} -2 \\ 1 \end{pmatrix} + s \begin{pmatrix} 3 \\ -4 \end{pmatrix} = \begin{pmatrix} 13 \\ -24 \end{pmatrix}$.

5 Given P(2, 3, −1) and Q(−4, 4, 2), find:

    a $\overrightarrow{PQ}$ **b** the distance between P and Q   **c** the midpoint of [PQ].

6 If A(4, 2, −1), B(−1, 5, 2), C(3, −3, c) are vertices of triangle ABC which is right angled at B, find the value of c.

7 Suppose $\mathbf{a} = \begin{pmatrix} 2 \\ -3 \\ 1 \end{pmatrix}$ and $\mathbf{b} = \begin{pmatrix} -1 \\ 2 \\ 3 \end{pmatrix}$. Find **x** given $\mathbf{a} - 3\mathbf{x} = \mathbf{b}$.

8 Find the angle between the vectors $\mathbf{a} = 3\mathbf{i} + \mathbf{j} - 2\mathbf{k}$ and $\mathbf{b} = 2\mathbf{i} + 5\mathbf{j} + \mathbf{k}$.

9 Find two points on the Z-axis which are 6 units from P(−4, 2, 5).

10 Determine all possible values of t if $\begin{pmatrix} 3 \\ 3 - 2t \end{pmatrix}$ and $\begin{pmatrix} t^2 + t \\ -2 \end{pmatrix}$ are perpendicular.

11 If $\mathbf{u} = \begin{pmatrix} -4 \\ 2 \\ 1 \end{pmatrix}$ and $\mathbf{v} = \begin{pmatrix} -1 \\ 3 \\ -2 \end{pmatrix}$, find:

    a $\mathbf{u} \bullet \mathbf{v}$ **b** the angle between **u** and **v**.

12 [AP] and [BQ] are altitudes of triangle ABC.

Let $\overrightarrow{OA} = \mathbf{p}$, $\overrightarrow{OB} = \mathbf{q}$, and $\overrightarrow{OC} = \mathbf{r}$.

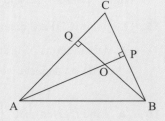

    a Find vector expressions for $\overrightarrow{AC}$ and $\overrightarrow{BC}$ in terms of **p**, **q**, and **r**.

    b Using the property $\mathbf{a} \bullet (\mathbf{b} - \mathbf{c}) = \mathbf{a} \bullet \mathbf{b} - \mathbf{a} \bullet \mathbf{c}$, deduce that $\mathbf{q} \bullet \mathbf{r} = \mathbf{p} \bullet \mathbf{q} = \mathbf{p} \bullet \mathbf{r}$.

    c Hence prove that [OC] is perpendicular to [AB].

13 Find a vector of length 4 units which is parallel to $3\mathbf{i} - 2\mathbf{j} + \mathbf{k}$.

14 Find the measure of $\widehat{DMC}$.

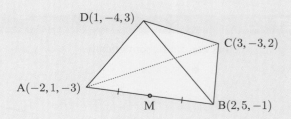

15   **a** Find k given that $\begin{pmatrix} k \\ \frac{1}{\sqrt{2}} \\ -k \end{pmatrix}$ is a unit vector.

    b Find the vector which is 5 units long and has the opposite direction to $\begin{pmatrix} 3 \\ 2 \\ -1 \end{pmatrix}$.

REVIEW SET 12C

1 Find a single vector which is equal to: **a** $\overrightarrow{PR} + \overrightarrow{RQ}$ **b** $\overrightarrow{PS} + \overrightarrow{SQ} + \overrightarrow{QR}$

2 For $\mathbf{m} = \begin{pmatrix} 6 \\ -3 \\ 1 \end{pmatrix}$, $\mathbf{n} = \begin{pmatrix} 2 \\ 3 \\ -4 \end{pmatrix}$, and $\mathbf{p} = \begin{pmatrix} -1 \\ 3 \\ 6 \end{pmatrix}$, find:

   a $\mathbf{m} - \mathbf{n} + \mathbf{p}$ **b** $2\mathbf{n} - 3\mathbf{p}$ **c** $|\mathbf{m} + \mathbf{p}|$

3 What geometrical facts can be deduced from the equations:

   a $\overrightarrow{AB} = \frac{1}{2}\overrightarrow{CD}$ **b** $\overrightarrow{AB} = 2\overrightarrow{AC}$?

4 Given $P(2, -5, 6)$ and $Q(-1, 7, 9)$, find:

   a the position vector of Q relative to P   **b** the distance from P to Q
   c the distance from P to the X-axis.

5

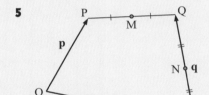

In the figure alongside, $\overrightarrow{OP} = \mathbf{p}$, $\overrightarrow{OR} = \mathbf{r}$, and $\overrightarrow{RQ} = \mathbf{q}$. M and N are the midpoints of [PQ] and [QR] respectively.

Find, in terms of $\mathbf{p}$, $\mathbf{q}$, and $\mathbf{r}$:

   a $\overrightarrow{OQ}$ **b** $\overrightarrow{PQ}$ **c** $\overrightarrow{ON}$ **d** $\overrightarrow{MN}$

6 Suppose $\mathbf{p} = \begin{pmatrix} -3 \\ 1 \\ 2 \end{pmatrix}$, $\mathbf{q} = \begin{pmatrix} 2 \\ -4 \\ 1 \end{pmatrix}$, and $\mathbf{r} = \begin{pmatrix} 3 \\ 2 \\ 0 \end{pmatrix}$. Find $\mathbf{x}$ if: **a** $\mathbf{p} - 3\mathbf{x} = \mathbf{0}$
   b $2\mathbf{q} - \mathbf{x} = \mathbf{r}$

7 Suppose $|\mathbf{v}| = 3$ and $|\mathbf{w}| = 2$. If $\mathbf{v}$ is parallel to $\mathbf{w}$, what values might $\mathbf{v} \bullet \mathbf{w}$ take?

8 Find t if $\begin{pmatrix} -4 \\ t+2 \\ t \end{pmatrix}$ and $\begin{pmatrix} t \\ 1+t \\ -3 \end{pmatrix}$ are perpendicular vectors.

9 Find all angles of the triangle with vertices $K(3, 1, 4)$, $L(-2, 1, 3)$, and $M(4, 1, 3)$.

10 Find k if the following are unit vectors: **a** $\begin{pmatrix} \frac{5}{13} \\ k \end{pmatrix}$ **b** $\begin{pmatrix} k \\ k \\ k \end{pmatrix}$

11 Use vector methods to find the measure of GÂC in the rectangular box alongside.

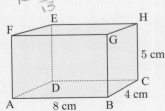

12 Using $\mathbf{p} = \begin{pmatrix} 3 \\ -2 \end{pmatrix}$, $\mathbf{q} = \begin{pmatrix} -2 \\ 5 \end{pmatrix}$, and $\mathbf{r} = \begin{pmatrix} 1 \\ -3 \end{pmatrix}$, verify that:

$\mathbf{p} \bullet (\mathbf{q} - \mathbf{r}) = \mathbf{p} \bullet \mathbf{q} - \mathbf{p} \bullet \mathbf{r}$.

13 Suppose $\overrightarrow{OM} = \begin{pmatrix} -2 \\ 4 \end{pmatrix}$, $\overrightarrow{MP} = \begin{pmatrix} 5 \\ -1 \end{pmatrix}$, $\overrightarrow{MP} \bullet \overrightarrow{PT} = 0$, and $|\overrightarrow{MP}| = |\overrightarrow{PT}|$.

Write down the two possible position vectors $\overrightarrow{OT}$.

14 Given $\mathbf{p} = 2\mathbf{i} - \mathbf{j} + 4\mathbf{k}$ and $\mathbf{q} = -\mathbf{i} - 4\mathbf{j} + 2\mathbf{k}$, find:

   a $\mathbf{p} \bullet \mathbf{q}$ **b** the angle between $\mathbf{p}$ and $\mathbf{q}$.

15 Suppose $\mathbf{u} = 2\mathbf{i} + \mathbf{j}$, $\mathbf{v} = 3\mathbf{j}$, and θ is the acute angle between $\mathbf{u}$ and $\mathbf{v}$.
Find the exact value of $\sin \theta$.

Chapter **13**

Vector applications

Syllabus reference: 4.1, 4.2, 4.3, 4.4

OPENING PROBLEM

A yacht club is situated at $(0, 0)$ and at 12:00 noon a yacht is at point $A(2, 20)$. The yacht is moving with constant speed in the straight path shown in the diagram. The grid intervals are kilometres.

At 1:00 pm the yacht is at $(6, 17)$.
At 2:00 pm it is at $(10, 14)$.

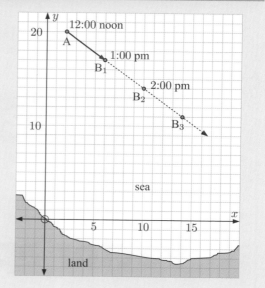

What to do:

a Find the position vectors of:

    i A   **ii** B_1 **iii** B_2

b Find $\overrightarrow{AB_1}$. Explain what it means.

c **i** How far does the yacht travel in one hour?
    ii What is its speed?

d Find $\overrightarrow{AB_2}$, $\overrightarrow{AB_3}$, and $\overrightarrow{AB_4}$. Hence write $\overrightarrow{AB_t}$ in terms of $\overrightarrow{AB_1}$.

e What is represented by the vector $\overrightarrow{OB_2}$?

A   PROBLEMS INVOLVING VECTOR OPERATIONS

When we apply vectors to problems in the real world, we often consider the combined effect when vectors are added together. This sum is called the **resultant vector**.

We have an example of vector addition when two tug boats are used to pull a ship into port. If the tugs tow with forces $\mathbf{F}_1$ and $\mathbf{F}_2$ then the resultant force is $\mathbf{F}_1 + \mathbf{F}_2$.

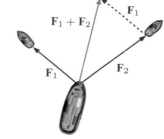

Example 1   ◀⬥)) **Self Tutor**

In still water, Jacques can swim at 1.5 m s^{-1}. Jacques is at point A on the edge of a canal, and considers point B directly opposite. A current is flowing from the left at a constant speed of 0.5 m s^{-1}.

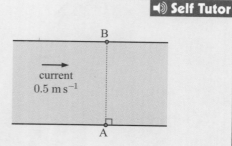

a If Jacques dives in straight towards B, and swims without allowing for the current, what will his actual speed and direction be?

b Jacques wants to swim directly across the canal to point B.

    i At what angle should Jacques *aim* to swim in order that the current will correct his direction?

    ii What will Jacques' actual speed be?

Suppose **c** is the current's velocity vector,

s is the velocity vector Jacques would have if the water was still, and

f = **c** + **s**   is Jacques' resultant velocity vector.

a   Jacques aims directly across the river, but the current takes him downstream to the right.

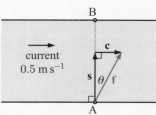

$$|\mathbf{f}|^2 = |\mathbf{c}|^2 + |\mathbf{s}|^2$$
$$= 0.5^2 + 1.5^2$$
$$= 2.5$$
$$\therefore \ |\mathbf{f}| \approx 1.58$$

$$\tan \theta = \frac{0.5}{1.5}$$
$$\therefore \ \theta \approx 18.4°$$

Jacques has an actual speed of approximately 1.58 m s^{-1} and his direction of motion is approximately 18.4° to the right of his intended line.

b   Jacques needs to aim to the left of B so the current will correct his direction.

i $\sin \phi = \dfrac{0.5}{1.5}$.

$\therefore \ \phi \approx 19.5°$

Jacques needs to aim approximately 19.5° to the left of B.

ii $|\mathbf{f}|^2 + |\mathbf{c}|^2 = |\mathbf{s}|^2$

$\therefore \ |\mathbf{f}|^2 + 0.5^2 = 1.5^2$

$\therefore \ |\mathbf{f}|^2 = 2$

$\therefore \ |\mathbf{f}| \approx 1.41$

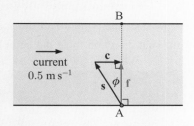

In these conditions, Jacques' actual speed towards B is approximately 1.41 m s^{-1}.

Another example of vector addition is when an aircraft is affected by wind. A pilot needs to know how to compensate for the wind, especially during take-off and landing.

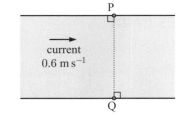

SIMULATION

EXERCISE 13A

1   An athlete can normally run with constant speed 6 m s^{-1}. Using a vector diagram to illustrate each situation, find the athlete's speed if:

   a   he is assisted by a wind of 1 m s^{-1} from directly behind him

   b   he runs into a head wind of 1 m s^{-1}.

2   In still water, Mary can swim at 1.2 m s^{-1}. She is standing at point P on the edge of a canal, directly opposite point Q. The water is flowing to the right at a constant speed of 0.6 m s^{-1}.

   a   If Mary tries to swim directly from P to Q without allowing for the current, what will her actual velocity be?

   b   Mary wants to swim directly across the canal to point Q.

      i   At what angle should she *aim* to swim in order that the current corrects her direction?

      ii   What will Mary's actual speed be?

3 A boat needs to travel south at a speed of 20 km h^{-1}. However a constant current of 6 km h^{-1} is flowing from the south-east. Use vectors to find:

  a the equivalent speed in still water for the boat to achieve the actual speed of 20 km h^{-1}

  b the direction in which the boat must head to compensate for the current.

4 As part of an endurance race, Stephanie needs to swim from X to Y across a wide river.

Stephanie swims at 1.8 m s^{-1} in still water.

The river flows with a consistent current of 0.3 m s^{-1} as shown.

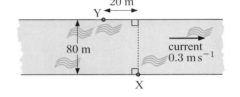

  a Find the distance from X to Y.

  b In which direction should Stephanie *aim* so that the current will push her onto a path directly towards Y?

  c Find the time Stephanie will take to cross the river.

5 An aeroplane needs to fly due east from one city to another at a speed of 400 km h^{-1}. However, a 50 km h^{-1} wind blows constantly from the north-east.

  a How does the wind affect the speed of the aeroplane?

  b In what direction must the aeroplane head to compensate for the wind?

B   LINES IN 2-D AND 3-D

In both 2-D and 3-D geometry we can determine the **equation of a line** using its **direction** and any **fixed point** on the line.

Suppose a line passes through a fixed point A with position vector **a**, and that the line is parallel to the vector **b**.

Consider a point R on the line so that $\overrightarrow{OR} = \mathbf{r}$.

By vector addition, $\overrightarrow{OR} = \overrightarrow{OA} + \overrightarrow{AR}$

$\therefore \ \ \mathbf{r} = \mathbf{a} + \overrightarrow{AR}.$

Since $\overrightarrow{AR}$ is parallel to **b**,

$\overrightarrow{AR} = t\mathbf{b}$ for some scalar $t \in \mathbb{R}$

$\therefore \ \ \mathbf{r} = \mathbf{a} + t\mathbf{b}$

DEMO

So, $\mathbf{r} = \mathbf{a} + t\mathbf{b}, \ \ t \in \mathbb{R}$ is the **vector equation** of the line.

LINES IN 2-D

- In 2-D we are dealing with a **line in a plane**.

- $\begin{pmatrix} x \\ y \end{pmatrix} = \begin{pmatrix} a_1 \\ a_2 \end{pmatrix} + t \begin{pmatrix} b_1 \\ b_2 \end{pmatrix}$ is the **vector equation** of the line

  where   R(x, y) is any point on the line,

             A(a_1, a_2) is a known fixed point on the line,

  and $\mathbf{b} = \begin{pmatrix} b_1 \\ b_2 \end{pmatrix}$ is the **direction vector** of the line.

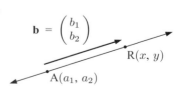

- The gradient of the line is $m = \dfrac{b_2}{b_1}$.

- Since $\begin{pmatrix} x \\ y \end{pmatrix} = \begin{pmatrix} a_1 + b_1 t \\ a_2 + b_2 t \end{pmatrix}$, we can write the **parametric equations** of the line $x = a_1 + b_1 t$

 and $y = a_2 + b_2 t$, where $t \in \mathbb{R}$ is the **parameter**.
 Each point on the line corresponds to exactly one value of t.

- We can convert these equations into Cartesian form by equating t values.

 Using $t = \dfrac{x - a_1}{b_1} = \dfrac{y - a_2}{b_2}$ we obtain $b_2 x - b_1 y = b_2 a_1 - b_1 a_2$
 which is the **Cartesian equation** of the line.

Example 2

🔊 Self Tutor

A line passes through the point $A(1, 5)$ and has direction vector $\begin{pmatrix} 3 \\ 2 \end{pmatrix}$. Describe the line using:

a a vector equation   **b** parametric equations   **c** a Cartesian equation.

a The vector equation is $\mathbf{r} = \mathbf{a} + t\mathbf{b}$ where

$\mathbf{a} = \overrightarrow{OA} = \begin{pmatrix} 1 \\ 5 \end{pmatrix}$ and $\mathbf{b} = \begin{pmatrix} 3 \\ 2 \end{pmatrix}$

$\therefore \begin{pmatrix} x \\ y \end{pmatrix} = \begin{pmatrix} 1 \\ 5 \end{pmatrix} + t \begin{pmatrix} 3 \\ 2 \end{pmatrix}$, $t \in \mathbb{R}$

b $x = 1 + 3t$ and $y = 5 + 2t$, $t \in \mathbb{R}$

c Now $t = \dfrac{x - 1}{3} = \dfrac{y - 5}{2}$

$\therefore 2x - 2 = 3y - 15$

$\therefore 2x - 3y = -13$

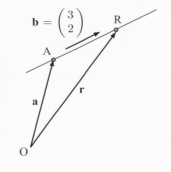

LINES IN 3-D

- In 3-D we are dealing with a **line in space**.

- $\begin{pmatrix} x \\ y \\ z \end{pmatrix} = \begin{pmatrix} a_1 \\ a_2 \\ a_3 \end{pmatrix} + t \begin{pmatrix} b_1 \\ b_2 \\ b_3 \end{pmatrix}$ is the **vector equation** of the line

 where $R(x, y, z)$ is any point on the line,
  $A(a_1, a_2, a_3)$ is the known or fixed point on the line,

 and $\mathbf{b} = \begin{pmatrix} b_1 \\ b_2 \\ b_3 \end{pmatrix}$ is the **direction vector** of the line.

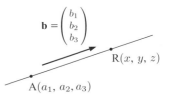

- The **parametric equations** of the line are:

 $x = a_1 + tb_1$
 $y = a_2 + tb_2$ where $t \in \mathbb{R}$ is called the **parameter**.
 $z = a_3 + tb_3$

We do not talk about the **gradient** of a line in 3-D.
We describe its direction only by its **direction vector**.

Each point on the line corresponds to exactly one value of t.

Example 3   ◀⟫ **Self Tutor**

Find a vector equation and the corresponding parametric equations of the line
through $(1, -2, 3)$ in the direction $4\mathbf{i} + 5\mathbf{j} - 6\mathbf{k}$.

The vector equation is $\mathbf{r} = \mathbf{a} + t\mathbf{b}$

$$\therefore \quad \begin{pmatrix} x \\ y \\ z \end{pmatrix} = \begin{pmatrix} 1 \\ -2 \\ 3 \end{pmatrix} + t \begin{pmatrix} 4 \\ 5 \\ -6 \end{pmatrix}, \quad t \in \mathbb{R}.$$

The parametric equations are:

$$x = 1 + 4t, \quad y = -2 + 5t, \quad z = 3 - 6t, \quad t \in \mathbb{R}.$$

NON-UNIQUENESS OF THE VECTOR EQUATION OF A LINE

Consider the line passing through $(5, 4)$ and $(7, 3)$. When
writing the equation of the line, we could use either point to
give the position vector $\mathbf{a}$.

Similarly, we could use the direction vector $\begin{pmatrix} 2 \\ -1 \end{pmatrix}$, but we

could also use $\begin{pmatrix} -2 \\ 1 \end{pmatrix}$ or indeed any non-zero scalar multiple

of these vectors.

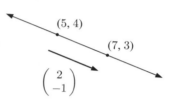

We could thus write the equation of the line as

$$\mathbf{x} = \begin{pmatrix} 5 \\ 4 \end{pmatrix} + t \begin{pmatrix} 2 \\ -1 \end{pmatrix}, \quad t \in \mathbb{R} \quad \text{or} \quad \mathbf{x} = \begin{pmatrix} 7 \\ 3 \end{pmatrix} + s \begin{pmatrix} -2 \\ 1 \end{pmatrix}, \quad s \in \mathbb{R} \quad \text{and so on.}$$

Notice how we use different parameters t and s when we write these equations. This is because the
parameters are clearly not the same: when $t = 0$, we have the point $(5, 4)$

when $s = 0$, we have the point $(7, 3)$.

In fact, the parameters are related by $s = 1 - t$.

Example 4   ◀⟫ **Self Tutor**

Find parametric equations of the line through $A(2, -1, 4)$ and $B(-1, 0, 2)$.

We require a direction vector for the line, either $\overrightarrow{AB}$ or $\overrightarrow{BA}$.

$$\overrightarrow{AB} = \begin{pmatrix} -1 - 2 \\ 0 - -1 \\ 2 - 4 \end{pmatrix} = \begin{pmatrix} -3 \\ 1 \\ -2 \end{pmatrix}$$

Using point A, the equations are: $x = 2 - 3t, \quad y = -1 + t, \quad z = 4 - 2t, \quad t \in \mathbb{R}$

or   using the point B, the equations are: $x = -1 - 3s, \quad y = s, \quad z = 2 - 2s, \quad s \in \mathbb{R}.$

EXERCISE 13B

1   Describe each of the following lines using:

      i a vector equation   **ii** parametric equations   **iii** a Cartesian equation

    a a line with direction $\begin{pmatrix} 1 \\ 4 \end{pmatrix}$ which passes through $(3, -4)$

    b a line passing through $(5, 2)$ which is perpendicular to $\begin{pmatrix} 5 \\ 2 \end{pmatrix}$

    c a line parallel to $3\mathbf{i} + 7\mathbf{j}$ which cuts the x-axis at -6

    d a line passing through $(-1, 11)$ and $(-3, 12)$.

2   A line passes through $(-1, 4)$ with direction vector $\begin{pmatrix} 2 \\ -1 \end{pmatrix}$.

    a Write parametric equations for the line using the parameter t.

    b Find the points on the line for which $t = 0, 1, 3, -1$, and -4.

3   **a** Does $(3, -2)$ lie on the line with vector equation $\mathbf{r} = \begin{pmatrix} 2 \\ 1 \end{pmatrix} + t \begin{pmatrix} 1 \\ -3 \end{pmatrix}$?

    b $(k, 4)$ lies on the line with parametric equations $x = 1 - 2t$, $y = 1 + t$.   Find k.

4   Line L has vector equation $\mathbf{r} = \begin{pmatrix} 1 \\ 5 \end{pmatrix} + t \begin{pmatrix} -1 \\ 3 \end{pmatrix}$.

    a Locate the point on the line corresponding to $t = 1$.

    b Explain why the direction of the line could also be described by $\begin{pmatrix} 1 \\ -3 \end{pmatrix}$.

    c Use your answers to **a** and **b** to write an alternative vector equation for line L.

5   Describe each of the following lines using:

      i a vector equation   **ii** parametric equations

    a a line parallel to $\begin{pmatrix} 2 \\ 1 \\ 3 \end{pmatrix}$ which passes through $(1, 3, -7)$

    b a line which passes through $(0, 1, 2)$ with direction vector $\mathbf{i} + \mathbf{j} - 2\mathbf{k}$

    c a line parallel to the X-axis which passes through $(-2, 2, 1)$

    d a line parallel to $2\mathbf{i} - \mathbf{j} + 3\mathbf{k}$ which passes through $(0, 2, -1)$.

6   Find the vector equation of the line which passes through:

    a A$(1, 2, 1)$ and B$(-1, 3, 2)$ **b** C$(0, 1, 3)$ and D$(3, 1, -1)$

    c E$(1, 2, 5)$ and F$(1, -1, 5)$ **d** G$(0, 1, -1)$ and H$(5, -1, 3)$

7   Find the coordinates of the point where the line with parametric equations $x = 1 - t$, $y = 3 + t$, and $z = 3 - 2t$ meets:

    a the XOY plane   **b** the YOZ plane   **c** the XOZ plane.

8   Find points on the line with parametric equations $x = 2 - t$, $y = 3 + 2t$, and $z = 1 + t$ which are $5\sqrt{3}$ units from the point $(1, 0, -2)$.

C   THE ANGLE BETWEEN TWO LINES

In **Chapter 12** we saw that the angle between two vectors is
measured in the range $0° \leqslant \theta \leqslant 180°$. We used the formula
$\cos \theta = \dfrac{\mathbf{b}_1 \bullet \mathbf{b}_2}{|\mathbf{b}_1| |\mathbf{b}_2|}$.

In the case of lines which continue infinitely in both directions,
we agree to talk about the *acute* angle between them. For an
acute angle, $\cos \theta > 0$, so we use the formula

$$\cos \theta = \frac{|\mathbf{b}_1 \bullet \mathbf{b}_2|}{|\mathbf{b}_1| |\mathbf{b}_2|}$$

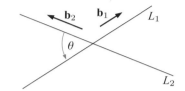

where $\mathbf{b}_1$ and $\mathbf{b}_2$ are the direction vectors of the given lines L_1
and L_2 respectively.

Example 5   ◀) Self Tutor

Find the angle between the lines L_1: $x = 2 - 3t$, $y = -1 + t$ and

$\qquad\qquad\qquad\qquad\qquad\qquad$ L_2: $x = 1 + 2s$, $y = -4 + 3s$.

$\mathbf{b}_1 = \begin{pmatrix} -3 \\ 1 \end{pmatrix}, \quad \mathbf{b}_2 = \begin{pmatrix} 2 \\ 3 \end{pmatrix}$

$\therefore \quad \cos \theta = \dfrac{|-6 + 3|}{\sqrt{10}\sqrt{13}}$

$\therefore \quad \cos \theta \approx 0.2631$

$\therefore \quad \theta \approx 74.7°$ (1.30 radians)

Consider two lines $\mathbf{r}_1 = \mathbf{a}_1 + s\mathbf{b}_1$ and $\mathbf{r}_2 = \mathbf{a}_2 + t\mathbf{b}_2$.

• $\mathbf{r}_1$ and $\mathbf{r}_2$ are **parallel** if $\mathbf{b}_1 = k\mathbf{b}_2$ for some scalar k. We write $\mathbf{r}_1 \parallel \mathbf{r}_2$.
• $\mathbf{r}_1$ and $\mathbf{r}_2$ are **perpendicular** if $\mathbf{b}_1 \bullet \mathbf{b}_2 = 0$. We write $\mathbf{r}_1 \perp \mathbf{r}_2$.

Example 6   ◀) Self Tutor

Find the angle between the lines:

$$L_1: \quad \mathbf{r}_1 = \begin{pmatrix} 2 \\ -1 \\ 4 \end{pmatrix} + s \begin{pmatrix} -3 \\ 1 \\ -2 \end{pmatrix} \quad \text{and} \quad L_2: \quad \mathbf{r}_2 = \begin{pmatrix} 1 \\ 0 \\ 2 \end{pmatrix} + t \begin{pmatrix} -3 \\ 1 \\ -2 \end{pmatrix}.$$

$\mathbf{b}_1 = \begin{pmatrix} -3 \\ 1 \\ -2 \end{pmatrix}$ and $\mathbf{b}_2 = \begin{pmatrix} -3 \\ 1 \\ -2 \end{pmatrix}$

Since $\mathbf{b}_1 = \mathbf{b}_2$, the lines are parallel and the angle between them is $0°$.

EXERCISE 13C

1 Find the angle between the lines L_1: $x = -4 + 12t$, $y = 3 + 5t$

and L_2: $x = 3s$, $y = -6 - 4s$

2 Consider the lines L_1: $x = 2 + 5p$, $y = 19 - 2p$

L_2: $x = 3 + 4r$, $y = 7 + 10r$

Show that the lines are perpendicular.

3 The line L_1 passes through $(-6, 3)$ and is parallel to $\begin{pmatrix} 4 \\ -3 \end{pmatrix}$.

The line L_2 has direction $5\mathbf{i} + 4\mathbf{j}$ and cuts the y-axis at $(0, 8)$.

Find the acute angle between the lines.

4 **a** Find the angle between the lines:

$$L_1:\ \ \mathbf{r}_1 = \begin{pmatrix} 8 \\ 9 \\ 10 \end{pmatrix} + s \begin{pmatrix} 3 \\ -16 \\ 7 \end{pmatrix} \quad \text{and} \quad L_2:\ \ \mathbf{r}_2 = \begin{pmatrix} 15 \\ 29 \\ 5 \end{pmatrix} + t \begin{pmatrix} 3 \\ 8 \\ -5 \end{pmatrix}.$$

b A third line L_3 is perpendicular to L_1 and has direction vector $\begin{pmatrix} 0 \\ -3 \\ x \end{pmatrix}$.

Find the value of x.

Example 7   ◀) **Self Tutor**

Find the measure of the acute angle between the lines $2x + y = 5$ and $3x - 2y = 8$.

$2x + y = 5$ has gradient $-\frac{2}{1}$ and $\therefore$ direction vector $\begin{pmatrix} 1 \\ -2 \end{pmatrix}$ which we call **a**.

$3x - 2y = 8$ has gradient $\frac{3}{2}$ and $\therefore$ direction vector $\begin{pmatrix} 2 \\ 3 \end{pmatrix}$ which we call **b**.

If the angle between the lines is θ, then

$$\cos \theta = \frac{|\mathbf{a} \bullet \mathbf{b}|}{|\mathbf{a}||\mathbf{b}|} = \frac{|(1 \times 2) + (-2 \times 3)|}{\sqrt{1 + 4}\sqrt{4 + 9}}$$

$$= \frac{4}{\sqrt{5}\sqrt{13}}$$

$$\therefore\ \ \theta = \cos^{-1}\left(\frac{4}{\sqrt{65}}\right) \approx 60.3°$$

If a line has gradient $\frac{b}{a}$, it has direction vector $\begin{pmatrix} a \\ b \end{pmatrix}$.

5 Find the measure of the angle between the lines:

a $x - y = 3$ and $3x + 2y = 11$

b $y = x + 2$ and $y = 1 - 3x$

c $y + x = 7$ and $x - 3y + 2 = 0$

d $y = 2 - x$ and $x - 2y = 7$

D   CONSTANT VELOCITY PROBLEMS

Consider again the yacht in the **Opening Problem**.

The **initial position** of the yacht is given by the position vector

$\mathbf{a} = \begin{pmatrix} 2 \\ 20 \end{pmatrix}.$

The direction of the yacht is given by the vector $\mathbf{b} = \begin{pmatrix} 4 \\ -3 \end{pmatrix}.$

Suppose that t hours after leaving A, the yacht is at R(x, y).

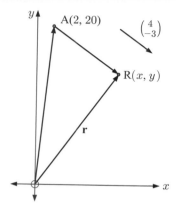

$$\overrightarrow{OR} = \overrightarrow{OA} + \overrightarrow{AR}$$

$$\therefore \quad \mathbf{r} = \begin{pmatrix} 2 \\ 20 \end{pmatrix} + t \begin{pmatrix} 4 \\ -3 \end{pmatrix} \quad \text{for } t \geqslant 0$$

$$\therefore \quad \begin{pmatrix} x \\ y \end{pmatrix} = \begin{pmatrix} 2 \\ 20 \end{pmatrix} + t \begin{pmatrix} 4 \\ -3 \end{pmatrix}$$

is the **vector equation** of the yacht's path.

> If an object has initial position vector **a** and moves with constant velocity **b**, its position at time t is given by
>
> $$\mathbf{r} = \mathbf{a} + t\mathbf{b} \quad \text{for } t \geqslant 0.$$
>
> The **speed** of the object is $|\mathbf{b}|$.

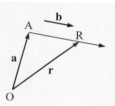

Example 8   ◀) Self Tutor

$\begin{pmatrix} x \\ y \end{pmatrix} = \begin{pmatrix} 1 \\ 9 \end{pmatrix} + t \begin{pmatrix} 3 \\ -4 \end{pmatrix}$ is the vector equation of the path of an object.

The time t is in seconds, $t \geqslant 0$. The distance units are metres.

- **a** Find the object's initial position.
- **b** Plot the path of the object for $t = 0, 1, 2, 3$.
- **c** Find the velocity vector of the object.   **d** Find the object's speed.
- **e** If the object continues in the same direction but increases its speed to 30 m s^{-1}, state its new velocity vector.

a At $t = 0$, $\begin{pmatrix} x \\ y \end{pmatrix} = \begin{pmatrix} 1 \\ 9 \end{pmatrix}$

∴ the object is at $(1, 9)$.

DEMO

b

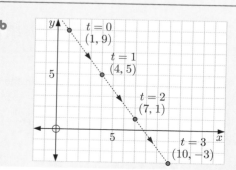

c The velocity vector is $\begin{pmatrix} 3 \\ -4 \end{pmatrix}$.

d The speed is $\left| \begin{pmatrix} 3 \\ -4 \end{pmatrix} \right| = \sqrt{3^2 + (-4)^2}$

$= 5 \text{ m s}^{-1}$.

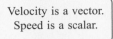

Velocity is a vector.
Speed is a scalar.

e Previously, the speed was 5 m s^{-1} and the velocity vector was $\begin{pmatrix} 3 \\ -4 \end{pmatrix}$.

$\therefore$ the new velocity vector is $6 \begin{pmatrix} 3 \\ -4 \end{pmatrix} = \begin{pmatrix} 18 \\ -24 \end{pmatrix}$.

Example 9   ◄)) **Self Tutor**

An object is initially at $(5, 10)$ and moves with velocity vector $3\mathbf{i} - \mathbf{j}$ metres per minute. Find:

a the position of the object at time t minutes

b the speed of the object

c the position of the object at $t = 3$ minutes

d the time when the object is due east of $(0, 0)$.

a

$$\mathbf{r} = \mathbf{a} + t\mathbf{b}$$

$$\therefore \begin{pmatrix} x \\ y \end{pmatrix} = \begin{pmatrix} 5 \\ 10 \end{pmatrix} + t \begin{pmatrix} 3 \\ -1 \end{pmatrix}, \quad t \in \mathbb{R}$$

$$\therefore \begin{pmatrix} x \\ y \end{pmatrix} = \begin{pmatrix} 5 + 3t \\ 10 - t \end{pmatrix}$$

After t minutes, the object is at $(5 + 3t, 10 - t)$.

b The speed of the object is $|\mathbf{b}| = \sqrt{3^2 + (-1)^2} = \sqrt{10}$ metres per minute.

c At $t = 3$ minutes, $5 + 3t = 14$ and $10 - t = 7$. The object is at $(14, 7)$.

d When the object is due east of $(0, 0)$, y must be zero.

$\therefore \quad 10 - t = 0$

$\therefore \quad t = 10$

The object is due east of $(0, 0)$ after 10 minutes.

EXERCISE 13D

1 A particle at $P(x(t), y(t))$ moves such that $x(t) = 1 + 2t$ and $y(t) = 2 - 5t$, $t \geqslant 0$. The distances are in centimetres and t is in seconds.

a Find the initial position of P.

b Illustrate the initial part of the motion of P where $t = 0, 1, 2, 3$.

c Find the velocity vector of P.

d Find the speed of P.

2 **a** Find the vector equation of a boat initially at $(2, 3)$, which travels with velocity vector $\begin{pmatrix} 4 \\ -5 \end{pmatrix}$. The grid units are kilometres and the time is in hours.

   b Locate the boat's position after 90 minutes.

   c How long will it take for the boat to reach the point $(5, -0.75)$?

3 A remote controlled toy car is initially at the point $(-3, -2)$. It moves with constant velocity $2\mathbf{i} + 4\mathbf{j}$. The distance units are centimetres, and the time is in seconds.

   a Write an expression for the position vector of the car at any time $t \geqslant 0$.

   b Hence find the position vector of the car at time $t = 2.5$.

   c Find when the car is   **i** due north   **ii** due west   of the observation point $(0, 0)$.

   d Plot the car's positions at times $t = 0, \frac{1}{2}, 1, 1\frac{1}{2}, 2, 2\frac{1}{2}, \ldots$.

4 Each of the following vector equations represents the path of a moving object. t is measured in seconds and $t \geqslant 0$. Distances are measured in metres. In each case, find:

   i the initial position   **ii** the velocity vector   **iii** the speed of the object.

   a $\begin{pmatrix} x \\ y \end{pmatrix} = \begin{pmatrix} -4 \\ 3 \end{pmatrix} + t \begin{pmatrix} 12 \\ 5 \end{pmatrix}$ **b** $x = 3 + 2t, \quad y = -t, \quad z = 4 - 2t$

5 Find the velocity vector of a speed boat moving parallel to:

   a $\begin{pmatrix} 4 \\ -3 \end{pmatrix}$ with a speed of 150 km h^{-1} **b** $2\mathbf{i} + \mathbf{j}$ with a speed of 50 km h^{-1}.

6 Find the velocity vector of a swooping eagle moving in the direction $-2\mathbf{i} + 5\mathbf{j} - 14\mathbf{k}$ with a speed of 90 km h^{-1}.

7 Yacht A moves according to $x(t) = 4 + t, \; y(t) = 5 - 2t$ where the distance units are kilometres and the time units are hours. Yacht B moves according to $x(t) = 1 + 2t, \; y(t) = -8 + t, \; t \geqslant 0$.

   a Find the initial position of each yacht.

   b Find the velocity vector of each yacht.

   c Show that the speed of each yacht is constant, and state these speeds.

   d Verify algebraically that the paths of the yachts are at right angles to each other.

8 Submarine P is at $(-5, 4)$ and fires a torpedo with velocity vector $\begin{pmatrix} 3 \\ -1 \end{pmatrix}$ at 1:34 pm.

Submarine Q is at $(15, 7)$ and a minutes later fires a torpedo with velocity vector $\begin{pmatrix} -4 \\ -3 \end{pmatrix}$.

Distances are measured in kilometres and time is in minutes.

   a Show that the position of P's torpedo can be written as $P(x_1(t), \; y_1(t))$ where $x_1(t) = -5 + 3t$ and $y_1(t) = 4 - t$.

   b What is the speed of P's torpedo?

   c Show that the position of Q's torpedo can be written as $Q(x_2(t), \; y_2(t))$ where $x_2(t) = 15 - 4(t - a)$ and $y_2(t) = 7 - 3(t - a)$.

   d Q's torpedo is successful in knocking out P's torpedo. At what time did Q fire its torpedo and at what time did the explosion occur?

9 A helicopter at A(6, 9, 3) moves with constant velocity in a straight line. 10 minutes later it is at B(3, 10, 2.5). Distances are in kilometres.

   a Find $\overrightarrow{AB}$.   **b** Find the helicopter's speed.

   c Determine the equation of the straight line path of the helicopter.

   d The helicopter is travelling directly towards its helipad, which has z-coordinate 0. Find the total time taken for the helicopter to land.

E   THE SHORTEST DISTANCE FROM A LINE TO A POINT

A ship R sails through point A in the direction **b** and continues past a port P. At what time will the ship be closest to the port?

The ship is closest when [PR] is perpendicular to [AR].

$\therefore$ $\overrightarrow{PR} \bullet \mathbf{b} = 0$

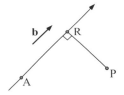

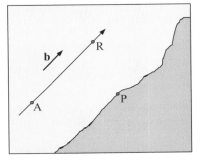

In this situation, point R is called the **foot of the perpendicular from P to the line**.

Example 10   ◀ **Self Tutor**

A line has vector equation $\begin{pmatrix} x \\ y \end{pmatrix} = \begin{pmatrix} 1 \\ 2 \end{pmatrix} + t \begin{pmatrix} 3 \\ -1 \end{pmatrix}$, $t \in \mathbb{R}$. Let P be the point $(5, -1)$.

Find exactly the shortest distance from P to the line.

Let N be the point on the line closest to P.

N has coordinates $(1 + 3t,\ 2 - t)$ for some t, and $\overrightarrow{PN}$ is $\begin{pmatrix} 1 + 3t - 5 \\ 2 - t - (-1) \end{pmatrix} = \begin{pmatrix} 3t - 4 \\ 3 - t \end{pmatrix}$.

Now $\overrightarrow{PN} \bullet \begin{pmatrix} 3 \\ -1 \end{pmatrix} = 0$ {as $\begin{pmatrix} 3 \\ -1 \end{pmatrix}$ is the direction vector of the line}

$\therefore$ $\begin{pmatrix} 3t - 4 \\ 3 - t \end{pmatrix} \bullet \begin{pmatrix} 3 \\ -1 \end{pmatrix} = 0$

$\therefore$ $3(3t - 4) - (3 - t) = 0$

$\therefore$ $9t - 12 - 3 + t = 0$

$\therefore$ $10t = 15$

$\therefore$ $t = \frac{15}{10} = \frac{3}{2}$

Thus $\overrightarrow{PN} = \begin{pmatrix} \frac{9}{2} - 4 \\ 3 - \frac{3}{2} \end{pmatrix} = \begin{pmatrix} \frac{1}{2} \\ \frac{3}{2} \end{pmatrix} = \frac{1}{2} \begin{pmatrix} 1 \\ 3 \end{pmatrix}$

and $|\overrightarrow{PN}| = \frac{1}{2} \left| \begin{pmatrix} 1 \\ 3 \end{pmatrix} \right| = \frac{1}{2} \sqrt{1^2 + 3^2} = \frac{\sqrt{10}}{2}$ units

N$(1 + 3t, 2 - t)$

$\begin{pmatrix} 3 \\ -1 \end{pmatrix}$

P$(5, -1)$

EXERCISE 13E

1 Find the shortest distance from:

a P(3, 2) to the line with parametric equations $x = 2 + t$, $y = 3 + 2t$, $t \in \mathbb{R}$

b Q(−1, 1) to the line with parametric equations $x = t$, $y = 1 − t$, $t \in \mathbb{R}$

c R(−3, −1) to the line $\begin{pmatrix} x \\ y \end{pmatrix} = \begin{pmatrix} 2 \\ 3 \end{pmatrix} + s \begin{pmatrix} 1 \\ -1 \end{pmatrix}$, $s \in \mathbb{R}$

d S(5, −2) to the line $\begin{pmatrix} x \\ y \end{pmatrix} = \begin{pmatrix} 2 \\ 5 \end{pmatrix} + t \begin{pmatrix} 3 \\ -7 \end{pmatrix}$, $t \in \mathbb{R}$.

Example 11 ◀ϩ **Self Tutor**

On the map shown, distances are measured in kilometres.

Ship R is moving in the direction $\begin{pmatrix} 3 \\ 4 \end{pmatrix}$ at 10 km h⁻¹.

a Write an expression for the position of the ship in terms of t, the number of hours after leaving port A.

b Find the time when the ship is closest to port P(10, 2).

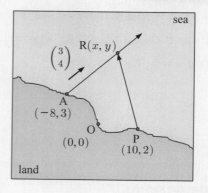

a $\left| \begin{pmatrix} 3 \\ 4 \end{pmatrix} \right| = \sqrt{3^2 + 4^2} = 5$

Since the speed is 10 km h⁻¹, the ship's velocity vector must be $2 \begin{pmatrix} 3 \\ 4 \end{pmatrix} = \begin{pmatrix} 6 \\ 8 \end{pmatrix}$.

Now $\overrightarrow{OR} = \overrightarrow{OA} + \overrightarrow{AR}$

∴ $\begin{pmatrix} x \\ y \end{pmatrix} = \begin{pmatrix} -8 \\ 3 \end{pmatrix} + t \begin{pmatrix} 6 \\ 8 \end{pmatrix}$

∴ the position of ship R is $(-8 + 6t, \ 3 + 8t)$.

b The ship is closest to P when $\overrightarrow{PR} \perp \begin{pmatrix} 3 \\ 4 \end{pmatrix}$

∴ $\overrightarrow{PR} \bullet \begin{pmatrix} 3 \\ 4 \end{pmatrix} = 0$

∴ $\begin{pmatrix} -8 + 6t - 10 \\ 3 + 8t - 2 \end{pmatrix} \bullet \begin{pmatrix} 3 \\ 4 \end{pmatrix} = 0$

∴ $3(6t - 18) + 4(1 + 8t) = 0$

∴ $18t - 54 + 4 + 32t = 0$

∴ $50t - 50 = 0$

∴ $t = 1$

So, the ship is closest to port P one hour after leaving A.

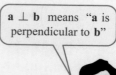 **a ⊥ b** means "**a** is perpendicular to **b**"

2 An ocean liner is at $(6, -6)$, cruising at 10 km h^{-1} in the direction $\begin{pmatrix} -3 \\ 4 \end{pmatrix}$.

A fishing boat is anchored at $(0, 0)$. Distances are in kilometres.

  a Find, in terms of **i** and **j**, the initial position vector of the liner from the fishing boat.

  b Write an expression for the position vector of the liner at any time t hours after it has sailed from $(6, -6)$.

  c When will the liner be due east of the fishing boat?

  d Find the time and position of the liner when it is nearest to the fishing boat.

3 Let **i** represent a displacement 1 km due east and **j** represent a displacement 1 km due north.
The control tower of an airport is at $(0, 0)$. Aircraft within 100 km of $(0, 0)$ are visible on the radar screen at the control tower.
At 12:00 noon an aircraft is 200 km east and 100 km north of the control tower. It is flying parallel to the vector $\mathbf{b} = -3\mathbf{i} - \mathbf{j}$ with a speed of $40\sqrt{10} \text{ km h}^{-1}$.

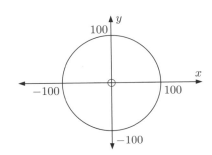

  a Write down the velocity vector of the aircraft.

  b Write a vector equation for the path of the aircraft using t to represent the time in hours that have elapsed since 12:00 noon.

  c Find the position of the aircraft at 1:00 pm.

  d Show that the aircraft first becomes visible on the radar screen at 1:00 pm.

  e Find the time when the aircraft is closest to the control tower, and find the distance between the aircraft and the control tower at this time.

  f At what time will the aircraft disappear from the radar screen?

4 The diagram shows a railway track that has equation $2x + 3y = 36$.
The axes represent two long country roads.
All distances are in kilometres.

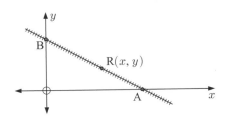

  a Find the coordinates of A and B.

  b $R(x, y)$ is a point on the railway track. Express the coordinates of point R in terms of x only.

  c Some railway workers have set up a base camp at $P(4, 0)$. Find $\overrightarrow{PR}$ and $\overrightarrow{AB}$.

  d Find the coordinates of the point on the railway track that is closest to P. Hence, find the shortest distance from the base camp to the railway track.

5 Boat A's position is given by $x(t) = 3 - t$, $y(t) = 2t - 4$, and boat B's position is given by $x(t) = 4 - 3t$, $y(t) = 3 - 2t$. The distance units are kilometres, and the time units are hours.

  a Find the initial position of each boat.

  b Find the velocity vector of each boat.

  c What is the acute angle between the paths of the boats?

  d At what time are the boats closest to each other?

Example 12   ◀◎ **Self Tutor**

Consider the point $P(-1, 2, 3)$ and the line with parametric equations $x = 1 + 2t,\ y = -4 + 3t,$ $z = 3 + t.$

   a Find the coordinates of the foot of the perpendicular from P to the line.

   b Find the shortest distance from the point to the line.

---

a The line has direction vector $\mathbf{b} = \begin{pmatrix} 2 \\ 3 \\ 1 \end{pmatrix}$.

Let $A(1 + 2t,\ -4 + 3t,\ 3 + t)$ be any point on the given line.

$$\therefore\ \ \overrightarrow{PA} = \begin{pmatrix} 1 + 2t - (-1) \\ -4 + 3t - 2 \\ 3 + t - 3 \end{pmatrix} = \begin{pmatrix} 2 + 2t \\ -6 + 3t \\ t \end{pmatrix}$$

If A is the closest point on the line to P, then $\overrightarrow{PA}$ and $\mathbf{b}$ are perpendicular.

$$\therefore\ \ \overrightarrow{PA} \bullet \mathbf{b} = 0$$

$$\therefore\ \ \begin{pmatrix} 2 + 2t \\ -6 + 3t \\ t \end{pmatrix} \bullet \begin{pmatrix} 2 \\ 3 \\ 1 \end{pmatrix} = 0$$

$$\therefore\ \ 2(2 + 2t) + 3(-6 + 3t) + 1(t) = 0$$

$$\therefore\ \ 4 + 4t - 18 + 9t + t = 0$$

$$\therefore\ \ 14t = 14$$

$$\therefore\ \ t = 1$$

Substituting $t = 1$ into the parametric equations, we obtain the foot of the perpendicular $(3, -1, 4)$.

b When $t = 1$, $\quad \overrightarrow{PA} = \begin{pmatrix} 2 + 2 \\ -6 + 3 \\ 1 \end{pmatrix} = \begin{pmatrix} 4 \\ -3 \\ 1 \end{pmatrix}$

$$\therefore\ \ PA = \sqrt{4^2 + (-3)^2 + 1^2} = \sqrt{26}\ \text{units}$$

$\therefore$ the shortest distance from P to the line is $\sqrt{26}$ units.

---

6 **a** Find the coordinates of the foot of the perpendicular from $(3, 0, -1)$ to the line with parametric equations $x = 2 + 3t,\ y = -1 + 2t,\ z = 4 + t.$

   b Find the shortest distance from the line to the point.

7 **a** Find the coordinates of the foot of the perpendicular from $(1, 1, 3)$ to the line with vector equation $\begin{pmatrix} x \\ y \\ z \end{pmatrix} = \begin{pmatrix} 1 \\ -1 \\ 2 \end{pmatrix} + t \begin{pmatrix} 2 \\ 3 \\ 1 \end{pmatrix}.$

   b Find the shortest distance from the point to the line.

F	**INTERSECTING LINES**

Vector equations of two intersecting lines can be **solved simultaneously** to find the point where the lines meet.

Example 13   ◀) **Self Tutor**

Line 1 has vector equation $\begin{pmatrix} x \\ y \end{pmatrix} = \begin{pmatrix} -2 \\ 1 \end{pmatrix} + s \begin{pmatrix} 3 \\ 2 \end{pmatrix}$ and

line 2 has vector equation $\begin{pmatrix} x \\ y \end{pmatrix} = \begin{pmatrix} 15 \\ 5 \end{pmatrix} + t \begin{pmatrix} -4 \\ 1 \end{pmatrix}$, where s and t are scalars.

Use vector methods to find where the two lines meet.

The lines meet where $\begin{pmatrix} -2 \\ 1 \end{pmatrix} + s \begin{pmatrix} 3 \\ 2 \end{pmatrix} = \begin{pmatrix} 15 \\ 5 \end{pmatrix} + t \begin{pmatrix} -4 \\ 1 \end{pmatrix}$

$\therefore$ $-2 + 3s = 15 - 4t$ and $1 + 2s = 5 + t$
$\therefore$ $3s + 4t = 17$ .... (1)   and $2s - t = 4$ .... (2)

$$
\begin{aligned}
3s + 4t &= 17 \qquad \{(1)\} \\
8s - 4t &= 16 \qquad \{(2) \times 4\} \\
\hline
\therefore \quad 11s &= 33 \\
\therefore \quad s &= 3
\end{aligned}
$$

Using (2), $2(3) - t = 4$
            $\therefore$ $t = 2$

Using line 1, $\begin{pmatrix} x \\ y \end{pmatrix} = \begin{pmatrix} -2 \\ 1 \end{pmatrix} + 3 \begin{pmatrix} 3 \\ 2 \end{pmatrix} = \begin{pmatrix} 7 \\ 7 \end{pmatrix}$

Checking in line 2, $\begin{pmatrix} x \\ y \end{pmatrix} = \begin{pmatrix} 15 \\ 5 \end{pmatrix} + 2 \begin{pmatrix} -4 \\ 1 \end{pmatrix} = \begin{pmatrix} 7 \\ 7 \end{pmatrix}$

$\therefore$ the lines meet at $(7, 7)$.

EXERCISE 13F

1 Triangle ABC is formed by three lines:

Line 1 (AB) is $\begin{pmatrix} x \\ y \end{pmatrix} = \begin{pmatrix} -1 \\ 6 \end{pmatrix} + r \begin{pmatrix} 3 \\ -2 \end{pmatrix}$,   line 2 (AC) is $\begin{pmatrix} x \\ y \end{pmatrix} = \begin{pmatrix} 0 \\ 2 \end{pmatrix} + s \begin{pmatrix} 1 \\ 1 \end{pmatrix}$

and line 3 (BC) is $\begin{pmatrix} x \\ y \end{pmatrix} = \begin{pmatrix} 10 \\ -3 \end{pmatrix} + t \begin{pmatrix} -2 \\ 3 \end{pmatrix}$ where r, s, and t are scalars.

a Draw the three lines accurately on a grid.
b Hence, find the coordinates of A, B and C.
c Prove that $\triangle$ABC is isosceles.
d Use vector methods to *check* your answers to **b**.

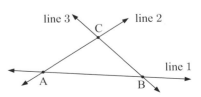

2 A parallelogram is defined by four lines as follows:

Line (AB) is $\begin{pmatrix} x \\ y \end{pmatrix} = \begin{pmatrix} -4 \\ 6 \end{pmatrix} + r \begin{pmatrix} 7 \\ 3 \end{pmatrix}$.   Line (AD) is $\begin{pmatrix} x \\ y \end{pmatrix} = \begin{pmatrix} -4 \\ 6 \end{pmatrix} + s \begin{pmatrix} 1 \\ 2 \end{pmatrix}$.

Line (CD) is $\begin{pmatrix} x \\ y \end{pmatrix} = \begin{pmatrix} 22 \\ 25 \end{pmatrix} + t \begin{pmatrix} -7 \\ -3 \end{pmatrix}$.   Line (CB) is $\begin{pmatrix} x \\ y \end{pmatrix} = \begin{pmatrix} 22 \\ 25 \end{pmatrix} + u \begin{pmatrix} -1 \\ -2 \end{pmatrix}$.

r, s, t, and u are scalars.

a Draw an accurate sketch of the four lines and the parallelogram formed by them. Label the vertices.

b From your diagram find the coordinates of A, B, C, and D.

c Use vector methods to confirm your answers to **b**.

3 An isosceles triangle ABC is formed by these lines:

(AB) is $\begin{pmatrix} x \\ y \end{pmatrix} = \begin{pmatrix} 0 \\ 2 \end{pmatrix} + r \begin{pmatrix} 2 \\ 1 \end{pmatrix}$,   (BC) is $\begin{pmatrix} x \\ y \end{pmatrix} = \begin{pmatrix} 8 \\ 6 \end{pmatrix} + s \begin{pmatrix} -1 \\ -2 \end{pmatrix}$,

and (AC) is $\begin{pmatrix} x \\ y \end{pmatrix} = \begin{pmatrix} 0 \\ 5 \end{pmatrix} + t \begin{pmatrix} 1 \\ -1 \end{pmatrix}$,   where r, s and t are scalars.

a Use vector methods to find the coordinates of A, B, and C.

b Which two sides of the triangle are equal in length? Find all side lengths.

4 (QP) is $\begin{pmatrix} x \\ y \end{pmatrix} = \begin{pmatrix} 3 \\ -1 \end{pmatrix} + r \begin{pmatrix} 14 \\ 10 \end{pmatrix}$,   (QR) is $\begin{pmatrix} x \\ y \end{pmatrix} = \begin{pmatrix} 3 \\ -1 \end{pmatrix} + s \begin{pmatrix} 17 \\ -9 \end{pmatrix}$,   and

(PR) is $\begin{pmatrix} x \\ y \end{pmatrix} = \begin{pmatrix} 0 \\ 18 \end{pmatrix} + t \begin{pmatrix} 5 \\ -7 \end{pmatrix}$,   where r, s, and t are scalars.

a Use vector methods to find the coordinates of P, Q, and R.

b Find vectors $\overrightarrow{PQ}$ and $\overrightarrow{PR}$ and evaluate $\overrightarrow{PQ} \bullet \overrightarrow{PR}$.

c Hence, find the size of $\widehat{QPR}$.

d Find the area of $\triangle PQR$.

5 Quadrilateral ABCD is formed by these lines:

(AB) is $\begin{pmatrix} x \\ y \end{pmatrix} = \begin{pmatrix} 2 \\ 5 \end{pmatrix} + r \begin{pmatrix} 4 \\ 1 \end{pmatrix}$,   (BC) is $\begin{pmatrix} x \\ y \end{pmatrix} = \begin{pmatrix} 18 \\ 9 \end{pmatrix} + s \begin{pmatrix} -8 \\ 32 \end{pmatrix}$,

(CD) is $\begin{pmatrix} x \\ y \end{pmatrix} = \begin{pmatrix} 14 \\ 25 \end{pmatrix} + t \begin{pmatrix} -8 \\ -2 \end{pmatrix}$,   and (AD) is $\begin{pmatrix} x \\ y \end{pmatrix} = \begin{pmatrix} 3 \\ 1 \end{pmatrix} + u \begin{pmatrix} -3 \\ 12 \end{pmatrix}$,

where r, s, t, and u are scalars.

a Use vector methods to find the coordinates of A, B, C, and D.

b Write down vectors $\overrightarrow{AC}$ and $\overrightarrow{DB}$ and hence find:

   i $|\overrightarrow{AC}|$ **ii** $|\overrightarrow{DB}|$ **iii** $\overrightarrow{AC} \bullet \overrightarrow{DB}$

c What do the answers to **b** tell you about quadrilateral ABCD?

THEORY OF KNOWLEDGE

In his 1827 book entitled *The Barycentric Calculus*, German mathematician August Möbius demonstrated the use of directed line segments in projective geometry. He discussed the addition and scalar multiplication of directed line segments, but he did not name them vectors.

Gauss, Hamilton, Grassmann, Laplace, and Lagrange all helped in the evolution of vectors and vector analysis as we know them today. In particular, in 1843 Sir William Hamilton defined a *quaternion* as the quotient of two directed line segments.

The American mathematician Josaiah Willard Gibbs (1839 - 1903) began teaching a course on vector analysis at Yale University in 1879. He published *Elements of Vector Analysis* in two halves, and in 1901 his work was summarised by his student Edwin Wilson in the book *Vector Analysis*.

Oliver Heaviside (1850 - 1925) developed vector analysis separately from Gibbs, receiving a copy of Gibbs' work later, in 1888. Heaviside wrote:

Sir William Hamilton

"... the invention of quaternions must be regarded as a most remarkable feat of human ingenuity. Vector analysis, without quaternions, could have been found by any mathematician by carefully examining the mechanics of the Cartesian mathematics; but to find out quaternions required a genius."

1   Are geometry and algebra two separate domains of knowledge?

2   When Gibbs and Heaviside developed vector analysis independently, who can claim to be the founder of this field?

3   Does mathematics *evolve*?

G   RELATIONSHIPS BETWEEN LINES

We have just seen how the intersection of two lines can be found by vector methods. We have also seen how to determine whether two lines are parallel.

We can now summarise the possible relationships between lines in 2 and 3 dimensions.

LINE CLASSIFICATION IN 2 DIMENSIONS

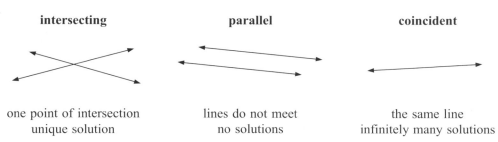

intersecting	parallel	coincident
one point of intersection unique solution	lines do not meet no solutions	the same line infinitely many solutions

LINE CLASSIFICATION IN 3 DIMENSIONS

> Lines are **coplanar** if they lie in the same plane.
> If the lines are not coplanar then they are **skew**.

- If the lines are **coplanar**, they may be intersecting, parallel, or coincident.
- If the lines are **parallel**, the angle between them is $0°$.
- If the lines are **intersecting**, the angle between them is θ, as shown.

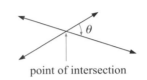

point of intersection

- If the lines are **skew**, we suppose one line is translated to intersect with the other. The angle between the original lines is defined as the angle between the intersecting lines, which is the angle θ.

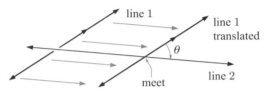

lines 1 and 2 are skew

Example 14	◀⑴ **Self Tutor**

Line 1 has equations $x = -1 + 2s$, $y = 1 - 2s$, and $z = 1 + 4s$.

Line 2 has equations $x = 1 - t$, $y = t$, and $z = 3 - 2t$.

Show that the lines are parallel but not coincident.

Line 1 is $\begin{pmatrix} x \\ y \\ z \end{pmatrix} = \begin{pmatrix} -1 \\ 1 \\ 1 \end{pmatrix} + s \begin{pmatrix} 2 \\ -2 \\ 4 \end{pmatrix}$ with direction vector $\begin{pmatrix} 2 \\ -2 \\ 4 \end{pmatrix}$.

Line 2 is $\begin{pmatrix} x \\ y \\ z \end{pmatrix} = \begin{pmatrix} 1 \\ 0 \\ 3 \end{pmatrix} + t \begin{pmatrix} -1 \\ 1 \\ -2 \end{pmatrix}$ with direction vector $\begin{pmatrix} -1 \\ 1 \\ -2 \end{pmatrix}$.

Since $\begin{pmatrix} 2 \\ -2 \\ 4 \end{pmatrix} = -2 \begin{pmatrix} -1 \\ 1 \\ -2 \end{pmatrix}$, the lines are parallel.

> If $\mathbf{a} = k\mathbf{b}$ for some scalar k, then $\mathbf{a} \parallel \mathbf{b}$.

When $s = 0$, the point on line 1 is $(-1, 1, 1)$.

For line 2, $y = t$, so the unique point on line 2 with y-coordinate 1 is the point where $t = 1$. This point is $(0, 1, 1)$.

Since $(0, 1, 1) \neq (-1, 1, 1)$, the lines are not coincident.

To help visualise the relationship between lines in 3 dimensions, click on the icon.   **3D GRAPHING**

Example 15   ◄) **Self Tutor**

Line 1 has equations $x = -1 + 2s$, $y = 1 - 2s$,   and $z = 1 + 4s$.

Line 2 has equations $x = 1 - t$, $y = t$,   and $z = 3 - 2t$.

Line 3 has equations $x = 1 + 2u$, $y = -1 - u$,   and $z = 4 + 3u$.

  a Show that line 2 and line 3 intersect and find the angle between them.

  b Show that line 1 and line 3 are skew.

a Equating x, y and z values in lines 2 and 3 gives

$$1 - t = 1 + 2u \qquad\qquad t = -1 - u \quad \text{and} \quad 3 - 2t = 4 + 3u$$
$$\therefore \ t = -2u \qquad\qquad \therefore \ t = -1 - u \quad \text{and} \quad 3u + 2t = -1 \ \ \text{.... (1)}$$

Solving these we get $-2u = -1 - u$

$$\therefore \ -u = -1$$
$$\therefore \ u = 1 \ \text{ and so } \ t = -2$$

Checking in (1): $3u + 2t = 3(1) + 2(-2) = 3 - 4 = -1$ ✓

$\therefore$ $u = 1$, $t = -2$ satisfies all three equations, a *common solution*.

Using $u = 1$, lines 2 and 3 meet at $(1 + 2(1), \ -1 - (1), \ 4 + 3(1))$ which is $(3, -2, 7)$.

Direction vectors for lines 2 and 3 are $\mathbf{a} = \begin{pmatrix} -1 \\ 1 \\ -2 \end{pmatrix}$ and $\mathbf{b} = \begin{pmatrix} 2 \\ -1 \\ 3 \end{pmatrix}$ respectively.

If θ is the acute angle between $\mathbf{a}$ and $\mathbf{b}$, then $\cos\theta = \dfrac{|\mathbf{a} \bullet \mathbf{b}|}{|\mathbf{a}||\mathbf{b}|} = \dfrac{|-2 - 1 - 6|}{\sqrt{1 + 1 + 4}\sqrt{4 + 1 + 9}}$

$$= \dfrac{9}{\sqrt{84}}$$
$$\therefore \ \theta \approx 10.89°$$

$\therefore$ the angle between lines 2 and 3 is about $10.9°$.

b Equating x, y, and z values in lines 1 and 3 gives

$$-1 + 2s = 1 + 2u \qquad\qquad 1 - 2s = -1 - u \quad \text{and} \quad 1 + 4s = 4 + 3u$$
$$\therefore \ 2s - 2u = 2 \qquad\qquad \therefore \ -2s + u = -2 \quad \text{and} \quad 4s - 3u = 3 \ \ \text{.... (2)}$$

Solving these we get $2s - 2u = 2$

$$\therefore \ -2s + u = -2$$
$$\therefore \ -u = 0 \quad \{\text{adding them}\}$$

$\therefore$ $2s = 2$ and so $s = 1$

Checking in (2), $4s - 3u = 4(1) - 3(0) = 4 \neq 3$

So, there is no simultaneous solution to all 3 equations.

$\therefore$ the lines do not intersect.

The direction vector for line 1 is $\begin{pmatrix} 2 \\ -2 \\ 4 \end{pmatrix}$ and $\begin{pmatrix} 2 \\ -2 \\ 4 \end{pmatrix} \neq k \begin{pmatrix} 2 \\ -1 \\ 3 \end{pmatrix}$ for any $k \in \mathbb{R}$.

$\therefore$ lines 1 and 3 are not parallel.

Since they do not intersect and are not parallel, they are skew.

EXERCISE 13G

1 Classify the following line pairs as either parallel, intersecting, coincident, or skew. In each case find the measure of the acute angle between them.

  a $x = 1 + 2t,\ y = 2 - t,\ z = 3 + t$ and $x = -2 + 3s,\ y = 3 - s,\ z = 1 + 2s$

  b $x = -1 + 2t,\ y = 2 - 12t,\ z = 4 + 12t$ and $x = 4s - 3,\ y = 3s + 2,\ z = -s - 1$

  c $x = 6t,\ y = 3 + 8t,\ z = -1 + 2t$ and $x = 2 + 3s,\ y = 4s,\ z = 1 + s$

  d $x = 2 - y = z + 2$ and $x = 1 + 3s,\ y = -2 - 2s,\ z = 2s + \frac{1}{2}$

  e $x = 1 + t,\ y = 2 - t,\ z = 3 + 2t$ and $x = 2 + 3s,\ y = 3 - 2s,\ z = s - 5$

  f $x = 1 - 2t,\ y = 8 + t,\ z = 5$ and $x = 2 + 4s,\ y = -1 - 2s,\ z = 3$

  g $x = 1 + 2t,\ y = -t,\ z = 1 + 3t$ and $x = 3 - 4s,\ y = -1 + 2s,\ z = 4 - 6s$

REVIEW SET 13A   NON-CALCULATOR

1 For the line that passes through $(-6, 3)$ with direction $\begin{pmatrix} 4 \\ -3 \end{pmatrix}$, write down the corresponding:

  a vector equation   b parametric equations   c Cartesian equation.

2 $(-3, m)$ lies on the line with vector equation $\begin{pmatrix} x \\ y \end{pmatrix} = \begin{pmatrix} 18 \\ -2 \end{pmatrix} + t \begin{pmatrix} -7 \\ 4 \end{pmatrix}$. Find m.

3 Line L has equation $\mathbf{r} = \begin{pmatrix} 3 \\ -3 \end{pmatrix} + t \begin{pmatrix} 2 \\ 5 \end{pmatrix}$.

  a Locate the point on the line corresponding to $t = 1$.

  b Explain why the direction of the line could also be described by $\begin{pmatrix} 4 \\ 10 \end{pmatrix}$.

  c Use your answers to a and b to write an alternative vector equation for line L.

4 $P(2, 0, 1)$, $Q(3, 4, -2)$, and $R(-1, 3, 2)$ are three points in space.

  a Find parametric equations of line (PQ).

  b Show that if $\theta = P\widehat{Q}R$, then $\cos\theta = \dfrac{20}{\sqrt{26}\sqrt{33}}$.

5 Triangle ABC is formed by three lines:

  Line (AB) is $\begin{pmatrix} x \\ y \end{pmatrix} = \begin{pmatrix} 4 \\ -1 \end{pmatrix} + t \begin{pmatrix} 1 \\ 3 \end{pmatrix}$.   Line (BC) is $\begin{pmatrix} x \\ y \end{pmatrix} = \begin{pmatrix} 7 \\ 4 \end{pmatrix} + s \begin{pmatrix} 1 \\ -1 \end{pmatrix}$.

  Line (AC) is $\begin{pmatrix} x \\ y \end{pmatrix} = \begin{pmatrix} -1 \\ 0 \end{pmatrix} + u \begin{pmatrix} 3 \\ 1 \end{pmatrix}$. s, t, and u are scalars.

  a Use vector methods to find the coordinates of A, B, and C.

  b Find $|\overrightarrow{AB}|$, $|\overrightarrow{BC}|$, and $|\overrightarrow{AC}|$.

  c Classify triangle ABC.

6 a Consider two unit vectors **a** and **b**. Prove that the vector $\mathbf{a} + \mathbf{b}$ bisects the angle between vector **a** and vector **b**.

  b Consider the points $H(9, 5, -5)$, $J(7, 3, -4)$, and $K(1, 0, 2)$.

    Find the equation of the line L that passes through J and bisects $H\widehat{J}K$.

  c Find the coordinates of the point where L meets (HK).

7 $x^2 + y^2 + z^2 = 26$ is the equation of a sphere with centre $(0, 0, 0)$ and radius $\sqrt{26}$ units. Find the point(s) where the line through $(3, -1, -2)$ and $(5, 3, -4)$ meets the sphere.

8 When an archer fires an arrow, he is suddenly aware of a breeze which pushes his shot off-target. The speed of the shot $|\mathbf{v}|$ is *not* affected by the wind, but the arrow's flight is $2°$ off-line.

   a Draw a vector diagram to represent the situation.

   b Hence explain why:

      i the breeze must be $91°$ to the intended direction of the arrow

      ii the speed of the breeze must be $2|\mathbf{v}|\sin 1°$.

REVIEW SET 13B   CALCULATOR

1 Find the vector equation of the line which cuts the y-axis at $(0, 8)$ and has direction $5\mathbf{i} + 4\mathbf{j}$.

2 A yacht is sailing with constant speed $5\sqrt{10}$ km h^{-1} in the direction $-\mathbf{i} - 3\mathbf{j}$. Initially it is at point $(-6, 10)$. A beacon is at $(0, 0)$ at the centre of a tiny atoll. Distances are in kilometres.

   a Find in terms of $\mathbf{i}$ and $\mathbf{j}$:

      i the initial position vector of the yacht

      ii the direction vector of the yacht

      iii the position vector of the yacht at any time t hours, $t \geqslant 0$.

   b Find the time when the yacht is closest to the beacon.

   c If there is a reef of radius 8 km around the atoll, will the yacht hit the reef?

3 Write down   **i** vector equation   **ii** parametric equations   for the line passing through:

   a $(2, -3)$ with direction $\begin{pmatrix} 4 \\ -1 \end{pmatrix}$ **b** $(-1, 6, 3)$ and $(5, -2, 0)$.

4 A small plane can fly at 350 km h^{-1} in still conditions. Its pilot needs to fly due north, but needs to deal with a 70 km h^{-1} wind from the east.

   a In what direction should the pilot face the plane in order that his resultant velocity is due north?

   b What will the speed of the plane be?

5 Find the angle between line L_1 passing through $(0, 3)$ and $(5, -2)$, and line L_2 passing through $(-2, 4)$ and $(-6, 7)$.

6 Submarine X23 is at $(2, 4)$. It fires a torpedo with velocity vector $\begin{pmatrix} 1 \\ -3 \end{pmatrix}$ at exactly 2:17 pm.

   Submarine Y18 is at $(11, 3)$. It fires a torpedo with velocity vector $\begin{pmatrix} -1 \\ a \end{pmatrix}$ at 2:19 pm to intercept the torpedo from X23. Distance units are kilometres. t is in minutes.

   a Find $x_1(t)$ and $y_1(t)$ for the torpedo fired from submarine X23.

   b Find $x_2(t)$ and $y_2(t)$ for the torpedo fired from submarine Y18.

   c At what time does the interception occur?

   d What was the direction and speed of the interception torpedo?

7 Classify the following line pairs as either parallel, intersecting, or skew. In each case find the measure of the acute angle between them.

   a $x = 2 + t, \ y = -1 + 2t, \ z = 3 - t$ and $x = -8 + 4s, \ y = s, \ z = 7 - 2s$

   b $x = 3 + t, \ y = 5 - 2t, \ z = -1 + 3t$ and $x = 2 - s, \ y = 1 + 3s, \ z = 4 + s$

REVIEW SET 13C

1 Find the velocity vector of an object moving in the direction $3\mathbf{i} - \mathbf{j}$ with speed 20 km h^{-1}.

2 A moving particle has coordinates $P(x(t), \, y(t))$ where $x(t) = -4 + 8t$ and $y(t) = 3 + 6t$. The distance units are metres, and $t \geqslant 0$ is the time in seconds. Find the:

   a initial position of the particle   **b** position of the particle after 4 seconds

   c particle's velocity vector   **d** speed of the particle.

3 Trapezium KLMN is formed by the following lines:

   (KL) is $\begin{pmatrix} x \\ y \end{pmatrix} = \begin{pmatrix} 2 \\ 19 \end{pmatrix} + p \begin{pmatrix} 5 \\ -2 \end{pmatrix}.$ (ML) is $\begin{pmatrix} x \\ y \end{pmatrix} = \begin{pmatrix} 33 \\ -5 \end{pmatrix} + q \begin{pmatrix} -11 \\ 16 \end{pmatrix}.$

   (NK) is $\begin{pmatrix} x \\ y \end{pmatrix} = \begin{pmatrix} 3 \\ 7 \end{pmatrix} + r \begin{pmatrix} 4 \\ 10 \end{pmatrix}.$ (MN) is $\begin{pmatrix} x \\ y \end{pmatrix} = \begin{pmatrix} 43 \\ -9 \end{pmatrix} + s \begin{pmatrix} -5 \\ 2 \end{pmatrix}.$

   $p, q, r,$ and s are scalars.

   a Which two lines are parallel? Explain your answer.

   b Which lines are perpendicular? Explain your answer.

   c Use vector methods to find the coordinates of K, L, M, and N.

   d Calculate the area of trapezium KLMN.

4 Find the angle between the lines:

      $L_1: \quad x = 1 - 4t, \quad y = 3t$ and $L_2: \quad x = 2 + 5s, \quad y = 5 - 12s.$

5 Consider $A(3, -1, 1)$ and $B(0, 2, -2)$.

   a Find $|\overrightarrow{AB}|$.

   b Show that the line passing through A and B can be described by
      $\mathbf{r} = 2\mathbf{j} - 2\mathbf{k} + \lambda(-\mathbf{i} + \mathbf{j} - \mathbf{k})$ where λ is a scalar.

   c Find the angle between (AB) and the line with vector equation $t(\mathbf{i} + \mathbf{j} + \mathbf{k})$.

6 Let $\mathbf{i}$ represent a displacement 1 km due east and $\mathbf{j}$ represent a displacement 1 km due north. Road A passes through $(-9, 2)$ and $(15, -16)$. Road B passes through $(6, -18)$ and $(21, 18)$.

   a Find a vector equation for each of the roads.

   b An injured hiker is at $(4, 11)$, and needs to travel the shortest possible distance to a road. Towards which road should he head, and how far will he need to walk to reach this road?

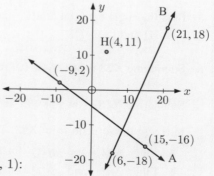

7 Given the points $A(4, 2, -1)$, $B(2, 1, 5)$, and $C(9, 4, 1)$:

   a Show that $\overrightarrow{AB}$ is perpendicular to $\overrightarrow{AC}$.

   b Find the equation of the line through: **i**   A and B   **ii**   A and C.

Chapter **14**

Introduction to differential calculus

Syllabus reference: 6.1

Contents:

OPENING PROBLEM

In a BASE jumping competition from the Petronas Towers in Kuala Lumpur, the altitude of a professional jumper in the first 3 seconds is given by $f(t) = 452 - 4.8t^2$ metres, where $0 \leqslant t \leqslant 3$ seconds.

Things to think about:

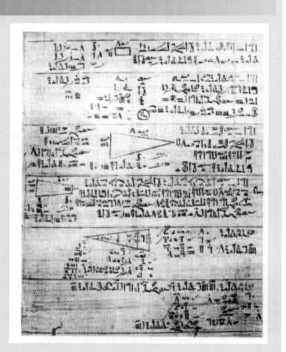

a What will a graph of the altitude of the jumper in the first 3 seconds look like?

b Does the jumper travel with constant speed?

c Can you find the speed of the jumper when:

   i $t = 0$ seconds   **ii** $t = 1$ second

   iii $t = 2$ seconds   **iv** $t = 3$ seconds?

Calculus is a major branch of mathematics which builds on algebra, trigonometry, and analytic geometry. It has widespread applications in science, engineering, and financial mathematics.

The study of calculus is divided into two fields, **differential calculus** and **integral calculus**. These fields are linked by the **Fundamental Theorem of Calculus** which we will study later in the course.

HISTORICAL NOTE

Calculus is a Latin word meaning 'pebble'. Ancient Romans used stones for counting.

The history of calculus begins with the **Egyptian Moscow papyrus** from about 1850 BC.

The Greek mathematicians **Democritus**, **Zeno of Elea**, **Antiphon**, and **Eudoxes** studied **infinitesimals**, dividing objects into an infinite number of pieces in order to calculate the area of regions, and volume of solids.

Archimedes of Syracuse was the first to find the tangent to a curve other than a circle. His methods were the foundation of modern calculus developed almost 2000 years later.

Archimedes

LIMITS

The concept of a **limit** is essential to differential calculus. We will see that calculating limits is necessary for finding the gradient of a tangent to a curve at any point on the curve.

Consider the following table of values for $f(x) = x^2$ where x is less than 2 but increasing and getting closer and closer to 2:

x	1	1.9	1.99	1.999	1.9999
$f(x)$	1	3.61	3.9601	3.996 00	3.999 60

We say that as x approaches 2 from the left, $f(x)$ approaches 4 from below.

We can construct a similar table of values where x is greater than 2 but decreasing and getting closer and closer to 2:

x	3	2.1	2.01	2.001	2.0001
$f(x)$	9	4.41	4.0401	4.004 00	4.000 40

In this case we say that as x approaches 2 from the right, $f(x)$ approaches 4 from above.

In summary, we can now say that as x approaches 2 from either direction, $f(x)$ approaches a limit of 4, and write

$$\lim_{x \to 2} x^2 = 4.$$

INFORMAL DEFINITION OF A LIMIT

The following definition of a limit is informal but adequate for the purposes of this course:

If $f(x)$ can be made as close as we like to some real number A by making x sufficiently close to (but not equal to) a, then we say that $f(x)$ has a **limit** of A as x approaches a, and we write

$$\lim_{x \to a} f(x) = A.$$

In this case, $f(x)$ is said to **converge** to A as x approaches a.

It is important to note that in defining the limit of f as x approaches a, x does *not* reach a. The limit is defined for x close to but *not equal to* a. Whether the function f is defined or not at $x = a$ is not important to the definition of the limit of f as x approaches a. What *is* important is the behaviour of the function as x gets *very close to* a.

For example, if $f(x) = \dfrac{5x + x^2}{x}$ and we wish to find the limit as $x \to 0$, it is tempting for us to simply substitute $x = 0$ into $f(x)$.

Not only do we get the meaningless value of $\frac{0}{0}$, but also we destroy the basic limit method.

Observe that if $f(x) = \dfrac{5x + x^2}{x} = \dfrac{x(5 + x)}{x}$

then $f(x) = \begin{cases} 5 + x & \text{if } x \neq 0 \\ \text{is undefined if } x = 0. \end{cases}$

The graph of $y = f(x)$ is shown alongside. It is the straight line $y = x + 5$ with the point $(0, 5)$ missing, called a **point of discontinuity** of the function.

However, even though this point is missing, the *limit* of $f(x)$ as x approaches 0 does exist. In particular, as $x \to 0$ from either direction, $y = f(x) \to 5$.

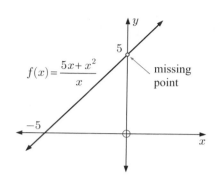

$f(x) = \dfrac{5x + x^2}{x}$

missing point

We write $\displaystyle\lim_{x \to 0} \frac{5x + x^2}{x} = 5$ which reads:

"the limit as x approaches 0, of $f(x) = \dfrac{5x + x^2}{x}$, is 5".

In practice we do not need to graph functions each time to determine limits, and most can be found algebraically.

Example 1 ◀)) **Self Tutor**

Evaluate: **a** $\displaystyle\lim_{x \to 2} x^2$ **b** $\displaystyle\lim_{x \to 0} \frac{x^2 + 3x}{x}$ **c** $\displaystyle\lim_{x \to 3} \frac{x^2 - 9}{x - 3}$

a x^2 can be made as close as we like to 4 by making x sufficiently close to 2.

$\therefore \displaystyle\lim_{x \to 2} x^2 = 4$.

b $\displaystyle\lim_{x \to 0} \frac{x^2 + 3x}{x}$

$= \displaystyle\lim_{x \to 0} \frac{x(x + 3)}{x}$

$= \displaystyle\lim_{x \to 0} (x + 3)$ since $x \neq 0$

$= 3$

c $\displaystyle\lim_{x \to 3} \frac{x^2 - 9}{x - 3}$

$= \displaystyle\lim_{x \to 3} \frac{(x + 3)(x - 3)}{x - 3}$

$= \displaystyle\lim_{x \to 3} (x + 3)$ since $x \neq 3$

$= 6$

EXERCISE 14A

1 Evaluate:

a $\displaystyle\lim_{x \to 3} (x + 4)$ **b** $\displaystyle\lim_{x \to -1} (5 - 2x)$ **c** $\displaystyle\lim_{x \to 4} (3x - 1)$

d $\displaystyle\lim_{x \to 2} (5x^2 - 3x + 2)$ **e** $\displaystyle\lim_{h \to 0} h^2(1 - h)$ **f** $\displaystyle\lim_{x \to 0} (x^2 + 5)$

2 Evaluate:

a $\displaystyle\lim_{x \to 0} 5$ **b** $\displaystyle\lim_{h \to 2} 7$ **c** $\displaystyle\lim_{x \to 0} c,$ c a constant

3 Evaluate:

a $\displaystyle\lim_{x \to 1} \frac{x^2 - 3x}{x}$ **b** $\displaystyle\lim_{h \to 2} \frac{h^2 + 5h}{h}$ **c** $\displaystyle\lim_{x \to 0} \frac{x - 1}{x + 1}$ **d** $\displaystyle\lim_{x \to 0} \frac{x}{x}$

4 Evaluate the following limits:

a $\displaystyle\lim_{x \to 0} \frac{x^2 - 3x}{x}$ **b** $\displaystyle\lim_{x \to 0} \frac{x^2 + 5x}{x}$ **c** $\displaystyle\lim_{x \to 0} \frac{2x^2 - x}{x}$

d $\displaystyle\lim_{h \to 0} \frac{2h^2 + 6h}{h}$ **e** $\displaystyle\lim_{h \to 0} \frac{3h^2 - 4h}{h}$ **f** $\displaystyle\lim_{h \to 0} \frac{h^3 - 8h}{h}$

g $\displaystyle\lim_{x \to 1} \frac{x^2 - x}{x - 1}$ **h** $\displaystyle\lim_{x \to 2} \frac{x^2 - 2x}{x - 2}$ **i** $\displaystyle\lim_{x \to 3} \frac{x^2 - x - 6}{x - 3}$

THEORY OF KNOWLEDGE

The Greek philosopher Zeno of Elea lived in what is now southern Italy, in the 5th century BC. He is most famous for his paradoxes, which were recorded in Aristotle's work *Physics*.

The arrow paradox

"If everything when it occupies an equal space is at rest, and if that which is in locomotion is always occupying such a space at any moment, the flying arrow is therefore motionless."

This argument says that if we fix an instant in time, an arrow appears motionless. Consequently, how is it that the arrow actually moves?

The dichotomy paradox

"That which is in locomotion must arrive at the half-way stage before it arrives at the goal."

If an object is to move a fixed distance then it must travel half that distance. Before it can travel a half the distance, it must travel a half *that* distance. With this process continuing indefinitely, motion is impossible.

Achilles and the tortoise

"In a race, the quickest runner can never overtake the slowest, since the pursuer must first reach the point whence the pursued started, so that the slower must always hold a lead."

According to this principle, the athlete Achilles will never be able to catch the slow tortoise!

1   A paradox is a logical argument that leads to a contradiction or a situation which defies logic or reason. Can a paradox be the truth?

2   Are Zeno's paradoxes really paradoxes?

3   Are the three paradoxes essentially the same?

4   We know from experience that things *do* move, and that Achilles *would* catch the tortoise. Does that mean that logic has failed?

5   What do Zeno's paradoxes have to do with limits?

B   LIMITS AT INFINITY

We can use the idea of limits to discuss the behaviour of functions for extreme values of x.

We write $x \to \infty$ to mean when x gets as large as we like and positive,

and $x \to -\infty$ to mean when x gets as large as we like and negative.

We read $x \to \infty$ as "x tends to plus infinity" and $x \to -\infty$ as "x tends to minus infinity".

Notice that as $x \to \infty$, $1 < x < x^2 < x^3 < ....$ and as x gets very large, the value of $\frac{1}{x}$ gets very small. In fact, we can make $\frac{1}{x}$ as close to 0 as we like by making x large enough. This means that

$$\lim_{x \to \infty} \frac{1}{x} = 0 \quad \text{even though} \quad \frac{1}{x} \text{ never actually reaches 0.}$$

Similarly, $\lim\limits_{x\to\infty}\dfrac{x}{x^2}=\lim\limits_{x\to\infty}\dfrac{1}{x}\times\dfrac{x}{x}$

$$=\lim\limits_{x\to\infty}\dfrac{1}{x}\qquad\{\text{since}\ \ x\neq0\}$$

$$=0$$

INVESTIGATION 1   LIMITS IN NUMBER SEQUENCES

The sequence $0.3,\ 0.33,\ 0.333,\ ....$ can be defined by the general term $x_n=0.333....3$ where there are n 3s after the decimal point, $n\in\mathbb{Z}^+$.

What to do:

1 Copy and complete the table alongside:

2 Consider x_{100} which contains 100 3s. In the number $(1-3x_{100})$, how many 0s are there between the decimal point and the 1?

3 In the limit as n tends to infinity, x_n contains an increasingly large number of 3s.   In the number $(1-3x_n)$, how many 0s will there be before the 1?

4 Using your answer to **3**, state $\lim\limits_{n\to\infty}1-3x_n$.

5 Hence state $\lim\limits_{n\to\infty}x_n$, which is the exact value of $0.\overline{3}$.

n	x_n	$3x_n$	$1-3x_n$
1			
2			
3			
4			
5			
10			

ASYMPTOTES

In **Chapter 2** we studied **rational functions**, and saw how they are characterised by the presence of **asymptotes**.

Consider the function $f(x)=\dfrac{2x+3}{x-4}$ which has domain $\{x\mid x\neq4,\ x\in\mathbb{R}\}$.

From the graph of $y=f(x)$, we can see the function has a vertical asymptote $x=4$, and a horizontal asymptote $y=2$.

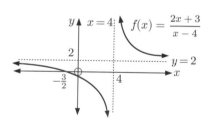

Both of these asymptotes can be described in terms of limits:

As $x\to4^-$, $f(x)\to-\infty$
As $x\to4^+$, $f(x)\to+\infty$
As $x\to-\infty$, $f(x)\to2^-$
As $x\to\infty$, $f(x)\to2^+$

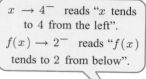

$x\to4^-$ reads "x tends to 4 from the left".

$f(x)\to2^-$ reads "$f(x)$ tends to 2 from below".

Since $f(x)$ converges to a finite value as $x\to-\infty$, we write $\lim\limits_{x\to-\infty}f(x)=2$.

Since $f(x)$ converges to a finite value as $x\to+\infty$, we write $\lim\limits_{x\to\infty}f(x)=2$.

Example 2 ◀) **Self Tutor**

a Discuss the behaviour of $f(x) = \dfrac{2-x}{1+x}$ near its asymptotes, and hence deduce their equations.

b State the values of $\displaystyle\lim_{x \to -\infty} f(x)$ and $\displaystyle\lim_{x \to \infty} f(x)$ if they exist.

a As $x \to -1^-$, $f(x) \to -\infty$
As $x \to -1^+$, $f(x) \to \infty$
As $x \to -\infty$, $f(x) \to -1^-$
As $x \to \infty$, $f(x) \to -1^+$

The vertical asymptote is $x = -1$.
The horizontal asymptote is $y = -1$.

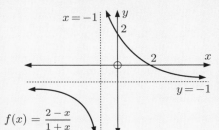

b $\displaystyle\lim_{x \to -\infty} f(x) = -1$ and $\displaystyle\lim_{x \to \infty} f(x) = -1$.

Example 3 ◀) **Self Tutor**

Find, if possible, $\displaystyle\lim_{x \to -\infty} (3 - e^{-x})$ and $\displaystyle\lim_{x \to \infty} (3 - e^{-x})$.

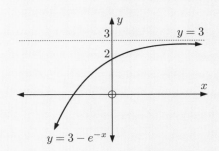

As $x \to -\infty$, $3 - e^{-x} \to -\infty$.

Since $3 - e^{-x}$ does not approach a finite value, $\displaystyle\lim_{x \to -\infty} (3 - e^{-x})$ does not exist.

As $x \to \infty$, $3 - e^{-x} \to 3^-$

$\therefore \displaystyle\lim_{x \to \infty} (3 - e^{-x}) = 3$

EXERCISE 14B

1 For each of the following functions:

    i discuss the behaviour near the asymptotes and hence deduce their equations

    ii state the values of $\displaystyle\lim_{x \to -\infty} f(x)$ and $\displaystyle\lim_{x \to \infty} f(x)$.

  a $f(x) = \dfrac{1}{x}$ **b** $f(x) = \dfrac{3x-2}{x+3}$ **c** $f(x) = \dfrac{1-2x}{3x+2}$

  d $f(x) = \dfrac{x}{1-x}$ **e** $f(x) = \dfrac{x^2-1}{x^2+1}$ **f** $f(x) = \dfrac{x}{x^2+1}$

2 **a** Sketch the graph of $y = e^x - 6$.

  b Hence discuss the value and geometric interpretation of:

    i $\displaystyle\lim_{x \to -\infty} (e^x - 6)$ **ii** $\displaystyle\lim_{x \to \infty} (e^x - 6)$

3 Find, if possible, $\displaystyle\lim_{x \to -\infty} (2e^{-x} - 3)$ and $\displaystyle\lim_{x \to \infty} (2e^{-x} - 3)$.

C   RATES OF CHANGE

A **rate** is a comparison between two quantities with different units.

We often judge performances by using rates. For example:

- Sir Donald Bradman's average batting rate at Test cricket level was 99.94 *runs per innings*.
- Michael Jordan's average basketball scoring rate was 20.0 *points per game*.
- Rangi's average typing rate is 63 *words per minute* with an error rate of 2.3 *errors per page*.

Speed is a commonly used rate. It is the rate of change in distance per unit of time. We are familiar with the formula

$$\textbf{average speed} = \frac{\textbf{distance travelled}}{\textbf{time taken}}$$

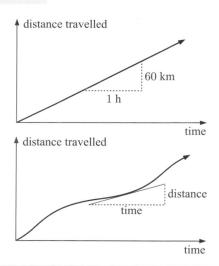

However, if a car has an average speed of 60 km h^{-1} for a journey, it does not mean that the car travels at exactly 60 km h^{-1} for the whole time.

In fact, the speed will probably vary continuously throughout the journey.

So, how can we calculate the car's speed at any particular time?

Suppose we are given a graph of the car's distance travelled against time taken. If this graph is a straight line, then we know the speed is constant and is given by the gradient of the line.

If the graph is a curve, then the car's instantaneous speed is given by the gradient of the tangent to the curve at that time.

The **instantaneous rate of change** of a dependent variable with respect to the independent variable at a particular instant, is given by the **gradient of the tangent** to the graph at that point.

HISTORICAL NOTE

The modern study of **differential calculus** originated in the 17th century with the work of **Sir Isaac Newton** and **Gottfried Wilhelm Leibniz**. They developed the necessary theory while attempting to find algebraic methods for solving problems dealing with the **gradients of tangents** to curves, and finding the **rate of change** in one variable with respect to another.

Isaac Newton 1642 – 1727

Gottfried Leibniz 1646 – 1716

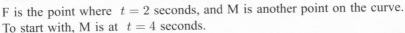

INVESTIGATION 2   **INSTANTANEOUS SPEED**

A ball bearing is dropped from the top of a tall building. The distance it has fallen after t seconds is recorded, and the following graph of distance against time obtained.

We choose a fixed point F on the curve when $t = 2$ seconds. We then choose another point M on the curve, and draw in the line segment or **chord** [FM] between the two points. To start with, we let M be the point when $t = 4$ seconds.

The *average* speed in the time interval $2 \leqslant t \leqslant 4$ is

$$= \frac{\text{distance travelled}}{\text{time taken}}$$

$$= \frac{(80 - 20) \text{ m}}{(4 - 2) \text{ s}}$$

$$= \frac{60}{2} \text{ m s}^{-1}$$

$$= 30 \text{ m s}^{-1}$$

However, this does not tell us the *instantaneous* speed at any particular time.

In this investigation we will try to measure the speed of the ball at the instant when $t = 2$ seconds.

What to do:

1   Click on the icon to start the demonstration.
    F is the point where $t = 2$ seconds, and M is another point on the curve.
    To start with, M is at $t = 4$ seconds.
    The number in the box marked *gradient* is the gradient of the chord [FM]. This is the *average speed* of the ball bearing in the interval from F to M. For M at $t = 4$ seconds, you should see the average speed is 30 m s^{-1}.

DEMO

2   Click on M and drag it slowly towards F. Copy and complete the table alongside with the gradient of the chord [FM] for M being the point on the curve at the given varying times t.

t	gradient of [FM]
3	
2.5	
2.1	
2.01	

3   Observe what happens as M reaches F. Explain why this is so.

4   For $t = 2$ seconds, what do you suspect will be the instantaneous speed of the ball bearing?

5   Move M to the origin, and then slide it towards F from the left. Copy and complete the table with the gradient of the chord [FM] for various times t.

t	gradient of [FM]
0	
1.5	
1.9	
1.99	

6   Do your results agree with those in **4**?

THE TANGENT TO A CURVE

A **chord** of a curve is a straight line segment which joins any two points on the curve.

The gradient of the chord [AB] measures the average rate of change of the function values for the given change in x-values.

A **tangent** is a straight line which *touches* a curve at a single point.

The gradient of the tangent at point A measures the instantaneous rate of change of the function at point A.

As B approaches A, the limit of the gradient of the chord [AB] will be the gradient of the tangent at A.

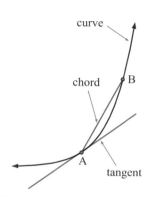

> The **gradient of the tangent** to $y = f(x)$ at $x = a$ is the instantaneous rate of change in $f(x)$ with respect to x at that point.

INVESTIGATION 3   THE GRADIENT OF A TANGENT

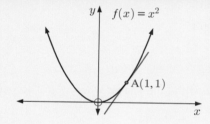

Given a curve $f(x)$, we wish to find the gradient of the tangent at the point $(a, f(a))$.

For example, the point A(1, 1) lies on the curve $f(x) = x^2$. What is the gradient of the tangent at A?

DEMO

What to do:

1 Suppose B lies on $f(x) = x^2$ and B has coordinates (x, x^2).

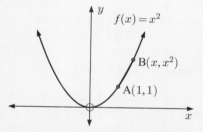

   a Show that the chord [AB] has gradient

$$\frac{f(x) - f(1)}{x - 1} \quad \text{or} \quad \frac{x^2 - 1}{x - 1}.$$

   b Copy and complete the table alongside:

   c Comment on the gradient of [AB] as x gets closer to 1.

x	Point B	gradient of [AB]
5	(5, 25)	6
3		
2		
1.5		
1.1		
1.01		
1.001		

2 Repeat the process letting x get closer to 1, but from the left of A. Use the points where $x = 0$, 0.8, 0.9, 0.99, and 0.999.

3 Click on the icon to view a demonstration of the process.

4 What do you suspect is the gradient of the tangent at A?

Fortunately we do not have to use a graph and table of values each time we wish to find the gradient of a tangent. Instead we can use an algebraic and geometric approach which involves **limits**.

From **Investigation 3**, the gradient of $[AB] = \dfrac{x^2 - 1}{x - 1}$.

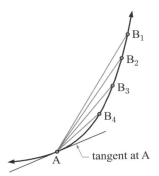

As B approaches A, $x \to 1$ and the gradient of $[AB] \to$ the gradient of the tangent at A.

So, the gradient of the tangent at the point A is

$$m_T = \lim_{x \to 1} \frac{x^2 - 1}{x - 1}$$

$$= \lim_{x \to 1} \frac{(x + 1)(x - 1)}{x - 1}$$

$$= \lim_{x \to 1} (x + 1) \quad \text{since } x \neq 1$$

$$= 2$$

As B approaches A, the gradient of $[AB]$ approaches or **converges** to 2.

EXERCISE 14C

1   Use the method in **Investigation 2** to answer the **Opening Problem** on page **344**.

2   **a**   Use the method in **Investigation 3** to find the gradient of the tangent to $y = x^2$ at the point $(2, 4)$.

   b   Evaluate $\displaystyle \lim_{x \to 2} \frac{x^2 - 4}{x - 2}$, and provide a geometric interpretation of this result.

D   THE DERIVATIVE FUNCTION

For a non-linear function with equation $y = f(x)$, the gradients of the tangents at various points are different.

Our task is to determine a **gradient function** which gives the gradient of the tangent to $y = f(x)$ at $x = a$, for any point a in the domain of f.

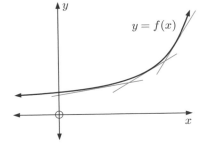

The gradient function of $y = f(x)$ is called its **derivative function** and is labelled $f'(x)$.

We read the derivative function as "eff dashed x".

The value of $f'(a)$ is the gradient of the tangent to $y = f(x)$ at the point where $x = a$.

Example 4   ◀)) **Self Tutor**

For the given graph, find $f'(4)$ and $f(4)$.

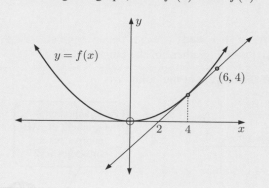

The graph shows the tangent to the curve $y = f(x)$ at the point where $x = 4$.

The tangent passes through $(2, 0)$ and $(6, 4)$,

so its gradient is $f'(4) = \dfrac{4 - 0}{6 - 2} = 1$.

The equation of the tangent is $\dfrac{y - 0}{x - 2} = 1$

$$\therefore \quad y = x - 2$$

When $x = 4$, $y = 2$, so the point of contact between the tangent and the curve is $(4, 2)$.

$$\therefore \quad f(4) = 2$$

EXERCISE 14D

1 Using the graph below, find:

   a $f(2)$ **b** $f'(2)$

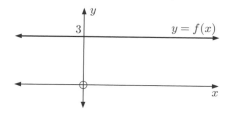

2 Using the graph below, find:

   a $f(0)$ **b** $f'(0)$

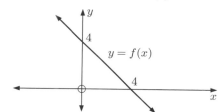

3 Consider the graph alongside.
Find $f(2)$ and $f'(2)$.

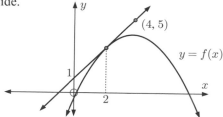

INVESTIGATION 4   GRADIENT FUNCTIONS

The software on the CD can be used to find the gradient of the function $f(x)$ at any point. By sliding the point along the graph we can observe the changing gradient of the tangent. We can hence generate the gradient function $f'(x)$.

GRADIENT FUNCTIONS

What to do:

1 Consider the functions $f(x) = 0$, $f(x) = 2$, and $f(x) = 4$.

   a For each of these functions, what is the gradient?

   b Is the gradient constant for all values of x?

2 Consider the function $f(x) = mx + c$.

   a State the gradient of the function.   **b** Is the gradient constant for all values of x?

c Use the CD software to graph the following functions and observe the gradient function $f'(x)$. Hence verify that your answer in **b** is correct.

   i $f(x) = x - 1$ **ii** $f(x) = 3x + 2$ **iii** $f(x) = -2x + 1$

3 **a** Observe the function $f(x) = x^2$ using the CD software. What *type* of function is the gradient function $f'(x)$?

  b Observe the following quadratic functions using the CD software:

    i $f(x) = x^2 + x - 2$ **ii** $f(x) = 2x^2 - 3$

    iii $f(x) = -x^2 + 2x - 1$ **iv** $f(x) = -3x^2 - 3x + 6$

  c What type of function is each of the gradient functions $f'(x)$ in **b**?

4 **a** Observe the function $f(x) = \ln x$ using the CD software.

  b What *type* of function is the gradient function $f'(x)$?

  c What is the *domain* of the gradient function $f'(x)$?

5 **a** Observe the function $f(x) = e^x$ using the CD software.

  b What is the gradient function $f'(x)$?

E   DIFFERENTIATION FROM FIRST PRINCIPLES

Consider a general function $y = f(x)$ where A is the point $(x, f(x))$ and B is the point $(x + h, f(x + h))$.

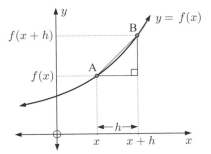

The chord [AB] has gradient $= \dfrac{f(x + h) - f(x)}{x + h - x}$

$$= \dfrac{f(x + h) - f(x)}{h}$$

If we let B approach A, then the gradient of [AB] approaches the gradient of the tangent at A.

So, the gradient of the tangent at the variable point $(x, f(x))$ is the limiting value of $\dfrac{f(x + h) - f(x)}{h}$

as h approaches 0, or $\displaystyle\lim_{h \to 0} \dfrac{f(x + h) - f(x)}{h}$.

This formula gives the gradient of the tangent to the curve $y = f(x)$ at the point $(x, f(x))$, for any value of the variable x for which this limit exists. Since there is at most one value of the gradient for each value of x, the formula is actually a function.

> The **derivative function** or simply **derivative** of $y = f(x)$ is defined as
> $$f'(x) = \lim_{h \to 0} \dfrac{f(x + h) - f(x)}{h}$$

When we evaluate this limit to find a derivative function, we say we are **differentiating from first principles**.

Example 5

◀⍾ **Self Tutor**

Use the definition of $f'(x)$ to find the gradient function of $f(x) = x^2$.

$$f'(x) = \lim_{h \to 0} \frac{f(x+h) - f(x)}{h}$$

$$= \lim_{h \to 0} \frac{(x+h)^2 - x^2}{h}$$

$$= \lim_{h \to 0} \frac{x^2 + 2hx + h^2 - x^2}{h}$$

$$= \lim_{h \to 0} \frac{\not{h}(2x+h)}{\not{h}}$$

$$= \lim_{h \to 0} (2x+h) \qquad \{\text{as } h \neq 0\}$$

$$= 2x$$

ALTERNATIVE NOTATION

If we are given a function $f(x)$ then $f'(x)$ represents the derivative function.

If we are given y in terms of x then y' or $\dfrac{dy}{dx}$ are commonly used to represent the derivative.

$\dfrac{dy}{dx}$ reads "dee y by dee x" or "the derivative of y with respect to x".

$\dfrac{dy}{dx}$ is **not a fraction**. However, the notation $\dfrac{dy}{dx}$ is a result of taking the limit of a fraction. If we replace h by δx and $f(x+h) - f(x)$ by δy, then

$$f'(x) = \lim_{h \to 0} \frac{f(x+h) - f(x)}{h} \quad \text{becomes}$$

$$f'(x) = \lim_{\delta x \to 0} \frac{\delta y}{\delta x}$$

$$= \frac{dy}{dx}.$$

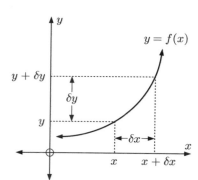

THE DERIVATIVE WHEN $x = a$

The gradient of the tangent to $y = f(x)$ at the point where $x = a$ is denoted $f'(a)$, where

$$f'(a) = \lim_{h \to 0} \frac{f(a+h) - f(a)}{h}$$

Example 6

◀⍾ **Self Tutor**

Use the first principles formula $f'(a) = \lim\limits_{h \to 0} \dfrac{f(a+h) - f(a)}{h}$ to find the instantaneous rate of change in $f(x) = x^2 + 2x$ at the point where $x = 5$.

$$f(5) = 5^2 + 2(5) = 35$$

$$\therefore \quad f'(5) = \lim_{h \to 0} \frac{f(5+h) - f(5)}{h}$$

$$= \lim_{h \to 0} \frac{(5+h)^2 + 2(5+h) - 35}{h}$$

$$\therefore \quad f'(5) = \lim_{h \to 0} \frac{25 + 10h + h^2 + \cancel{10} + 2h - \cancel{35}}{h}$$

$$= \lim_{h \to 0} \frac{h^2 + 12h}{h}$$

$$= \lim_{h \to 0} \frac{\cancel{h}(h + 12)}{\cancel{h}_1} \qquad \{\text{as } h \neq 0\}$$

$$= 12$$

$\therefore$ the instantaneous rate of change in $f(x)$ at $x = 5$ is 12.

You can also find the gradient of the tangent at a given point on a function using your graphics calculator. Instructions for doing this can be found on your CD.

GRAPHICS CALCULATOR INSTRUCTIONS

EXERCISE 14E

1 **a** Find, from first principles, the gradient function of $f(x)$ where $f(x)$ is:

     i x **ii** 5

     iii x^3 **iv** x^4

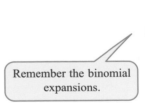

b Hence predict a formula for $f'(x)$ where $f(x) = x^n$, $n \in \mathbb{N}$.

Remember the binomial expansions.

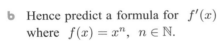

2 Find $f'(x)$ from first principles, given that $f(x)$ is:

   a $2x + 5$ **b** $x^2 - 3x$ **c** $-x^2 + 5x - 3$

3 Find $\dfrac{dy}{dx}$ from first principles given:

   a $y = 4 - x$ **b** $y = 2x^2 + x - 1$ **c** $y = x^3 - 2x^2 + 3$

4 Use the first principles formula $f'(a) = \lim_{h \to 0} \dfrac{f(a + h) - f(a)}{h}$ to find:

   a $f'(2)$ for $f(x) = x^3$ **b** $f'(3)$ for $f(x) = x^4$.

5 Use the first principles formula to find the gradient of the tangent to:

   a $f(x) = 3x + 5$ at $x = -2$ **b** $f(x) = 5 - 2x^2$ at $x = 3$

   c $f(x) = x^2 + 3x - 4$ at $x = 3$ **d** $f(x) = 5 - 2x - 3x^2$ at $x = -2$

6 **a** Given $y = x^3 - 3x$, find $\dfrac{dy}{dx}$ from first principles.

   b *Hence* find the points on the graph at which the tangent has zero gradient.

REVIEW SET 14A	**NON-CALCULATOR**

1 Evaluate:

   a $\displaystyle\lim_{x \to 1} (6x - 7)$ **b** $\displaystyle\lim_{h \to 0} \frac{2h^2 - h}{h}$ **c** $\displaystyle\lim_{x \to 4} \frac{x^2 - 16}{x - 4}$

2 Find, from first principles, the derivative of:

   a $f(x) = x^2 + 2x$ **b** $y = 4 - 3x^2$

3 Given $f(x) = 5x - x^2$, find $f'(1)$ from first principles.

4 In the **Opening Problem**, the altitude of the jumper is given by $f(t) = 452 - 4.8t^2$ metres, where $0 \leqslant t \leqslant 3$ seconds.

    a Find $f'(t) = \lim\limits_{h \to 0} \dfrac{f(t+h) - f(t)}{h}$.

    b *Hence* find the speed of the jumper when $t = 2$ seconds.

REVIEW SET 14B   CALCULATOR

1 **a** Discuss the behaviour of $y = \dfrac{x-7}{3x+2}$ near its asymptotes. Hence deduce their equations.

    b State the values of $\lim\limits_{x \to -\infty} \dfrac{x-7}{3x+2}$ and $\lim\limits_{x \to \infty} \dfrac{x-7}{3x+2}$.

2 **a** Sketch the graph of $y = e^{x-2} - 3$.

    b Hence find, if possible, $\lim\limits_{x \to -\infty} (e^{x-2} - 3)$ and $\lim\limits_{x \to \infty} (e^{x-2} - 3)$.

    c State the equation of the asymptote of $y = e^{x-2} - 3$.

3 Consider $f(x) = 2x^2$.

    a Show that $\dfrac{f(x+h) - f(x)}{h} = 4x + 2h$ provided $h \neq 0$.

    b Hence evaluate $\dfrac{f(3+h) - f(3)}{h}$ when:

        i $h = 0.1$ **ii** $h = 0.01$ **iii** in the limit as h approaches zero.

    c Give a geometric interpretation of your result from **b**.

4 The horizontal asymptote of the function $y = \dfrac{2x+3}{4-x}$ is $y = -2$.

    Justify this statement using a limit argument.

REVIEW SET 14C

1 Evaluate the limits:

    a $\lim\limits_{h \to 0} \dfrac{h^3 - 3h}{h}$ **b** $\lim\limits_{x \to 1} \dfrac{3x^2 - 3x}{x-1}$ **c** $\lim\limits_{x \to 2} \dfrac{x^2 - 3x + 2}{2-x}$

2 **a** Sketch the graph of $y = \dfrac{2+x}{x-4}$.

    b Discuss the behaviour of the graph near its asymptotes, and hence deduce their equations.

    c State the values of $\lim\limits_{x \to -\infty} \dfrac{2+x}{x-4}$ and $\lim\limits_{x \to \infty} \dfrac{2+x}{x-4}$.

3 Given $f(x) = x^4 - 2x$, find $f'(1)$ from first principles.

4 **a** Given $y = 2x^2 - 1$, find $\dfrac{dy}{dx}$ from first principles.

    b Hence state the gradient of the tangent to $y = 2x^2 - 1$ at the point where $x = 4$.

    c For what value of x is the gradient of the tangent to $y = 2x^2 - 1$ equal to -12?

Chapter 15

Rules of differentiation

OPENING PROBLEM

Consider the curve $y = x^2$.

In the previous chapter we found that the gradient function

of this curve is $\dfrac{dy}{dx} = 2x$.

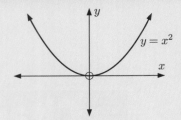

Things to think about:

a Consider the transformation of $y = x^2$ onto $y = x^2 + 3$.

   i What transformation has taken place?

   ii For a given value of x, has the gradient of the tangent to the function changed?

   iii What is the gradient function of $y = x^2 + 3$?

b Consider the transformation of $y = x^2$ onto $y = (x - 2)^2$.

   i What transformation has taken place?

   ii How does the gradient function of $y = (x - 2)^2$ relate to the gradient function of $y = x^2$?

   iii Can you write down the gradient function of $y = (x - 2)^2$?

DEMO

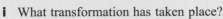

A   SIMPLE RULES OF DIFFERENTIATION

Differentiation is the process of finding a derivative or gradient function.

Given a function $f(x)$, we obtain $f'(x)$ by **differentiating with respect to** the variable x.

There are a number of rules associated with differentiation. These rules can be used to differentiate more complicated functions without having to resort to the sometimes lengthy method of first principles.

INVESTIGATION 1   SIMPLE RULES OF DIFFERENTIATION

In this investigation we attempt to differentiate functions of the form x^n, cx^n where c is a constant, and functions which are a sum or difference of polynomial terms of the form cx^n.

What to do:

1 Differentiate from first principles: **a** x^2 **b** x^3 **c** x^4

2 Consider the binomial expansion:

$$(x + h)^n = \binom{n}{0} x^n + \binom{n}{1} x^{n-1}h + \binom{n}{2} x^{n-2}h^2 + \dots + \binom{n}{n} h^n$$

$$= x^n + nx^{n-1}h + \binom{n}{2} x^{n-2}h^2 + \dots + h^n$$

Use the first principles formula $f'(x) = \lim\limits_{h \to 0} \dfrac{f(x + h) - f(x)}{h}$ to find the derivative of $f(x) = x^n$ for $x \in \mathbb{N}$.

3 Find, from first principles, the derivatives of: **a** $4x^2$ **b** $2x^3$

By comparison with **1**, copy and complete: "If $f(x) = cx^n$, then $f'(x) = \dots$"

4 Use first principles to find $f'(x)$ for:

    a $f(x) = x^2 + 3x$ **b** $f(x) = x^3 - 2x^2$

5 Copy and complete: "If $f(x) = u(x) + v(x)$ then $f'(x) = $ ......"

The rules you found in the **Investigation** are much more general than the cases you just considered.

For example, if $f(x) = x^n$ then $f'(x) = nx^{n-1}$ is true not just for all $n \in \mathbb{N}$, but actually for all $n \in \mathbb{R}$.

We can summarise the following rules:

$f(x)$	$f'(x)$	Name of rule
c (a constant)	0	**differentiating a constant**
x^n	nx^{n-1}	**differentiating x^n**
$c\,u(x)$	$c\,u'(x)$	**constant times a function**
$u(x) + v(x)$	$u'(x) + v'(x)$	**addition rule**

The last two rules can be proved using the first principles definition of $f'(x)$.

- If $f(x) = c\,u(x)$ where c is a constant then $f'(x) = c\,u'(x)$.

    Proof:
$$\begin{aligned}
f'(x) &= \lim_{h \to 0} \frac{f(x+h) - f(x)}{h} \\
&= \lim_{h \to 0} \frac{c\,u(x+h) - c\,u(x)}{h} \\
&= \lim_{h \to 0} c\left[\frac{u(x+h) - u(x)}{h}\right] \\
&= c \lim_{h \to 0} \frac{u(x+h) - u(x)}{h} \\
&= c\,u'(x)
\end{aligned}$$

- If $f(x) = u(x) + v(x)$ then $f'(x) = u'(x) + v'(x)$.

    Proof:
$$\begin{aligned}
f'(x) &= \lim_{h \to 0} \frac{f(x+h) - f(x)}{h} \\
&= \lim_{h \to 0} \left(\frac{u(x+h) + v(x+h) - [u(x) + v(x)]}{h}\right) \\
&= \lim_{h \to 0} \left(\frac{u(x+h) - u(x) + v(x+h) - v(x)}{h}\right) \\
&= \lim_{h \to 0} \frac{u(x+h) - u(x)}{h} + \lim_{h \to 0} \frac{v(x+h) - v(x)}{h} \\
&= u'(x) + v'(x)
\end{aligned}$$

Using the rules we have now developed we can differentiate sums of powers of x.

For example,   if $f(x) = 3x^4 + 2x^3 - 5x^2 + 7x + 6$ then
$$\begin{aligned}
f'(x) &= 3(4x^3) + 2(3x^2) - 5(2x) + 7(1) + 0 \\
&= 12x^3 + 6x^2 - 10x + 7
\end{aligned}$$

Example 1

◀) **Self Tutor**

If $y = 3x^2 - 4x$, find $\dfrac{dy}{dx}$ and interpret its meaning.

As $y = 3x^2 - 4x$, $\dfrac{dy}{dx} = 6x - 4$.

$\dfrac{dy}{dx}$ is:
- the gradient function or derivative of $y = 3x^2 - 4x$ from which the gradient of the tangent at any point can be found
- the instantaneous rate of change of y with respect to x.

Example 2

◀) **Self Tutor**

Find $f'(x)$ for $f(x)$ equal to: **a** $5x^3 + 6x^2 - 3x + 2$ **b** $7x - \dfrac{4}{x} + \dfrac{3}{x^3}$

a $f(x) = 5x^3 + 6x^2 - 3x + 2$
$\therefore\ f'(x) = 5(3x^2) + 6(2x) - 3(1)$
$\qquad\quad = 15x^2 + 12x - 3$

b $f(x) = 7x - \dfrac{4}{x} + \dfrac{3}{x^3}$
$\qquad\quad = 7x - 4x^{-1} + 3x^{-3}$
$\therefore\ f'(x) = 7(1) - 4(-1x^{-2}) + 3(-3x^{-4})$
$\qquad\quad = 7 + 4x^{-2} - 9x^{-4}$
$\qquad\quad = 7 + \dfrac{4}{x^2} - \dfrac{9}{x^4}$

Remember that $\dfrac{1}{x^n} = x^{-n}$.

Example 3

◀) **Self Tutor**

Find the gradient function of $y = x^2 - \dfrac{4}{x}$ and hence find the gradient of the tangent to the function at the point where $x = 2$.

$y = x^2 - \dfrac{4}{x}$ $\qquad \therefore\ \dfrac{dy}{dx} = 2x - 4(-1x^{-2})$
$\quad = x^2 - 4x^{-1}$ $\qquad\qquad\quad = 2x + 4x^{-2}$
$\qquad\qquad\qquad\qquad\qquad = 2x + \dfrac{4}{x^2}$

When $x = 2$, $\dfrac{dy}{dx} = 4 + 1 = 5$.

So, the tangent has gradient 5.

You can also use your graphics calculator to evaluate the gradient of the tangent to a function at a given point.

GRAPHICS CALCULATOR INSTRUCTIONS

Example 4   ◀) **Self Tutor**

Find the gradient function for each of the following:

   a $f(x) = 3\sqrt{x} + \dfrac{2}{x}$ **b** $g(x) = x^2 - \dfrac{4}{\sqrt{x}}$

a $f(x) = 3\sqrt{x} + \dfrac{2}{x}$

$\qquad\quad = 3x^{\frac{1}{2}} + 2x^{-1}$

$\therefore\ f'(x) = 3(\tfrac{1}{2}x^{-\frac{1}{2}}) + 2(-1x^{-2})$

$\qquad\quad = \tfrac{3}{2}x^{-\frac{1}{2}} - 2x^{-2}$

$\qquad\quad = \dfrac{3}{2\sqrt{x}} - \dfrac{2}{x^2}$

b $g(x) = x^2 - \dfrac{4}{\sqrt{x}}$

$\qquad\quad = x^2 - 4x^{-\frac{1}{2}}$

$\therefore\ g'(x) = 2x - 4(-\tfrac{1}{2}x^{-\frac{3}{2}})$

$\qquad\quad = 2x + 2x^{-\frac{3}{2}}$

$\qquad\quad = 2x + \dfrac{2}{x\sqrt{x}}$

EXERCISE 15A

1 Find $f'(x)$ given that $f(x)$ is:

  a x^3 **b** $2x^3$ **c** $7x^2$ **d** $6\sqrt{x}$

  e $3\sqrt[3]{x}$ **f** $x^2 + x$ **g** $4 - 2x^2$ **h** $x^2 + 3x - 5$

  i $\tfrac{1}{2}x^4 - 6x^2$ **j** $\dfrac{3x - 6}{x}$ **k** $\dfrac{2x - 3}{x^2}$ **l** $\dfrac{x^3 + 5}{x}$

  m $\dfrac{x^3 + x - 3}{x}$ **n** $\dfrac{1}{\sqrt{x}}$ **o** $(2x - 1)^2$ **p** $(x + 2)^3$

2 Find $\dfrac{dy}{dx}$ for:

  a $y = 2.5x^3 - 1.4x^2 - 1.3$ **b** $y = \pi x^2$ **c** $y = \dfrac{1}{5x^2}$

  d $y = 100x$ **e** $y = 10(x + 1)$ **f** $y = 4\pi x^3$

3 Differentiate with respect to x:

  a $6x + 2$ **b** $x\sqrt{x}$ **c** $(5 - x)^2$ **d** $\dfrac{6x^2 - 9x^4}{3x}$

  e $(x + 1)(x - 2)$ **f** $\dfrac{1}{x^2} + 6\sqrt{x}$ **g** $4x - \dfrac{1}{4x}$ **h** $x(x + 1)(2x - 5)$

4 Find the gradient of the tangent to:

  a $y = x^2$ at $x = 2$ **b** $y = \dfrac{8}{x^2}$ at the point $(9, \tfrac{8}{81})$

  c $y = 2x^2 - 3x + 7$ at $x = -1$ **d** $y = \dfrac{2x^2 - 5}{x}$ at the point $(2, \tfrac{3}{2})$

  e $y = \dfrac{x^2 - 4}{x^2}$ at the point $(4, \tfrac{3}{4})$ **f** $y = \dfrac{x^3 - 4x - 8}{x^2}$ at $x = -1$

  Check your answers using technology.

5 Suppose $f(x) = x^2 + (b + 1)x + 2c$, $f(2) = 4$,   and $f'(-1) = 2$.
    Find the constants b and c.

6 Find the gradient function of $f(x)$ where $f(x)$ is:

a $4\sqrt{x} + x$

b $\sqrt[3]{x}$

c $-\dfrac{2}{\sqrt{x}}$

d $2x - \sqrt{x}$

e $\dfrac{4}{\sqrt{x}} - 5$

f $3x^2 - x\sqrt{x}$

g $\dfrac{5}{x^2\sqrt{x}}$

h $2x - \dfrac{3}{x\sqrt{x}}$

7 a If $y = 4x - \dfrac{3}{x}$, find $\dfrac{dy}{dx}$ and interpret its meaning.

b The position of a car moving along a straight road is given by $S = 2t^2 + 4t$ metres where t is the time in seconds. Find $\dfrac{dS}{dt}$ and interpret its meaning.

c The cost of producing x toasters each week is given by $C = 1785 + 3x + 0.002x^2$ dollars. Find $\dfrac{dC}{dx}$ and interpret its meaning.

B   THE CHAIN RULE

In **Chapter 2** we defined the **composite** of two functions g and f as $(g \circ f)(x)$ or $g(f(x))$.

We can often write complicated functions as the composite of two or more simpler functions.

For example $y = (x^2 + 3x)^4$ could be rewritten as $y = u^4$ where $u = x^2 + 3x$, or as $y = g(f(x))$ where $g(x) = x^4$ and $f(x) = x^2 + 3x$.

Example 5	◀) Self Tutor

Find: a $g(f(x))$ if $g(x) = \sqrt{x}$ and $f(x) = 2 - 3x$

b $g(x)$ and $f(x)$ such that $g(f(x)) = \dfrac{1}{x - x^2}$.

There are several possible answers for **b**.

a $g(f(x))$
$= g(2 - 3x)$
$= \sqrt{2 - 3x}$

b $g(f(x)) = \dfrac{1}{x - x^2} = \dfrac{1}{f(x)}$

$\therefore$ $g(x) = \dfrac{1}{x}$ and $f(x) = x - x^2$

EXERCISE 15B.1

1 Find $g(f(x))$ if:

a $g(x) = x^2$ and $f(x) = 2x + 7$

b $g(x) = 2x + 7$ and $f(x) = x^2$

c $g(x) = \sqrt{x}$ and $f(x) = 3 - 4x$

d $g(x) = 3 - 4x$ and $f(x) = \sqrt{x}$

e $g(x) = \dfrac{2}{x}$ and $f(x) = x^2 + 3$

f $g(x) = x^2 + 3$ and $f(x) = \dfrac{2}{x}$

2 Find $g(x)$ and $f(x)$ such that $g(f(x))$ is:

a $(3x + 10)^3$

b $\dfrac{1}{2x + 4}$

c $\sqrt{x^2 - 3x}$

d $\dfrac{10}{(3x - x^2)^3}$

DERIVATIVES OF COMPOSITE FUNCTIONS

The reason we are interested in writing complicated functions as composite functions is to make finding derivatives easier.

INVESTIGATION 2   DIFFERENTIATING COMPOSITE FUNCTIONS

The purpose of this investigation is to gain insight into how we can differentiate composite functions.

Based on the rule "if $y = x^n$ then $\dfrac{dy}{dx} = nx^{n-1}$", we might suspect that if $y = (2x + 1)^2$ then $\dfrac{dy}{dx} = 2(2x + 1)^1$. But is this so?

What to do:

1 Expand $y = (2x + 1)^2$ and hence find $\dfrac{dy}{dx}$. How does this compare with $2(2x + 1)^1$?

2 Expand $y = (3x + 1)^2$ and hence find $\dfrac{dy}{dx}$. How does this compare with $2(3x + 1)^1$?

3 Expand $y = (ax + 1)^2$ where a is a constant, and hence find $\dfrac{dy}{dx}$. How does this compare with $2(ax + 1)^1$?

4 Suppose $y = u^2$.

   a Find $\dfrac{dy}{du}$.

   b Now suppose $u = ax + 1$, so $y = (ax + 1)^2$.

      i Find $\dfrac{du}{dx}$.   ii Write $\dfrac{dy}{du}$ from **a** in terms of x.

      iii *Hence* find $\dfrac{dy}{du} \times \dfrac{du}{dx}$.   iv Compare your answer to the result in **3**.

   c If $y = u^2$ where u is a function of x, what do you suspect $\dfrac{dy}{dx}$ will be equal to?

5 Expand $y = (x^2 + 3x)^2$ and hence find $\dfrac{dy}{dx}$.

   Does your answer agree with the rule you suggested in **4 c**?

6 Consider $y = (2x + 1)^3$.

   a Expand the brackets and then find $\dfrac{dy}{dx}$.

   b If we let $u = 2x + 1$, then $y = u^3$.

      i Find $\dfrac{du}{dx}$.   ii Find $\dfrac{dy}{du}$, and write it in terms of x.

      iii Hence find $\dfrac{dy}{du} \times \dfrac{du}{dx}$.   iv Compare your answer to the result in **a**.

7 Copy and complete: "If y is a function of u, and u is a function of x, then $\dfrac{dy}{dx} = \ldots\ldots$"

THE CHAIN RULE

If $y = g(u)$ where $u = f(x)$ then $\dfrac{dy}{dx} = \dfrac{dy}{du}\dfrac{du}{dx}$.

This rule is extremely important and enables us to differentiate complicated functions much faster.

For example, for any function $f(x)$:

If $y = [f(x)]^n$ then $\dfrac{dy}{dx} = n[f(x)]^{n-1} \times f'(x)$.

Example 6   ◀) **Self Tutor**

Find $\dfrac{dy}{dx}$ if:

a $y = (x^2 - 2x)^4$

b $y = \dfrac{4}{\sqrt{1-2x}}$

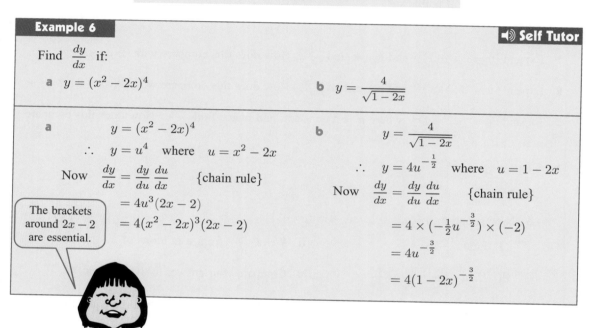

a $y = (x^2 - 2x)^4$

$\therefore \quad y = u^4$ where $u = x^2 - 2x$

Now $\dfrac{dy}{dx} = \dfrac{dy}{du}\dfrac{du}{dx}$ {chain rule}

$= 4u^3(2x - 2)$

$= 4(x^2 - 2x)^3(2x - 2)$

> The brackets around $2x - 2$ are essential.

b $y = \dfrac{4}{\sqrt{1-2x}}$

$\therefore \quad y = 4u^{-\frac{1}{2}}$ where $u = 1 - 2x$

Now $\dfrac{dy}{dx} = \dfrac{dy}{du}\dfrac{du}{dx}$ {chain rule}

$= 4 \times (-\tfrac{1}{2}u^{-\frac{3}{2}}) \times (-2)$

$= 4u^{-\frac{3}{2}}$

$= 4(1 - 2x)^{-\frac{3}{2}}$

EXERCISE 15B.2

1 Write in the form au^n, clearly stating what u is:

a $\dfrac{1}{(2x-1)^2}$

b $\sqrt{x^2 - 3x}$

c $\dfrac{2}{\sqrt{2-x^2}}$

d $\sqrt[3]{x^3 - x^2}$

e $\dfrac{4}{(3-x)^3}$

f $\dfrac{10}{x^2 - 3}$

2 Find the gradient function $\dfrac{dy}{dx}$ for:

a $y = (4x - 5)^2$

b $y = \dfrac{1}{5-2x}$

c $y = \sqrt{3x - x^2}$

d $y = (1 - 3x)^4$

e $y = 6(5 - x)^3$

f $y = \sqrt[3]{2x^3 - x^2}$

g $y = \dfrac{6}{(5x-4)^2}$

h $y = \dfrac{4}{3x - x^2}$

i $y = 2\left(x^2 - \dfrac{2}{x}\right)^3$

3 Find the gradient of the tangent to:

a $y = \sqrt{1 - x^2}$ at $x = \frac{1}{2}$

b $y = (3x + 2)^6$ at $x = -1$

c $y = \dfrac{1}{(2x - 1)^4}$ at $x = 1$

d $y = 6 \times \sqrt[3]{1 - 2x}$ at $x = 0$

e $y = \dfrac{4}{x + 2\sqrt{x}}$ at $x = 4$

f $y = \left(x + \dfrac{1}{x}\right)^3$ at $x = 1$

Check your answers using technology.

4 The gradient function of $f(x) = (2x - b)^a$ is $f'(x) = 24x^2 - 24x + 6$.
   Find the constants a and b.

5 Supppose $y = \dfrac{a}{\sqrt{1 + bx}}$ where a and b are constants.

   Find a and b given that when $x = 3$, $y = 1$ and $\dfrac{dy}{dx} = -\frac{1}{8}$.

6 If $y = x^3$ then $x = y^{\frac{1}{3}}$.

   a Find $\dfrac{dy}{dx}$ and $\dfrac{dx}{dy}$ and hence show that $\dfrac{dy}{dx} \times \dfrac{dx}{dy} = 1$.

   b Explain why $\dfrac{dy}{dx} \times \dfrac{dx}{dy} = 1$ whenever these derivatives exist for any general function $y = f(x)$.

C   THE PRODUCT RULE

We have seen the addition rule:

$$\text{If} \quad f(x) = u(x) + v(x) \quad \text{then} \quad f'(x) = u'(x) + v'(x).$$

We now consider the case $f(x) = u(x)\,v(x)$. Is $f'(x) = u'(x)\,v'(x)$?

In other words, does the derivative of a product of two functions equal the product of the derivatives of the two functions?

INVESTIGATION 3   THE PRODUCT RULE

Suppose $u(x)$ and $v(x)$ are two functions of x, and that $f(x) = u(x)\,v(x)$ is the product of these functions.

The purpose of this investigation is to find a rule for determining $f'(x)$.

What to do:

1 Suppose $u(x) = x$ and $v(x) = x$, so $f(x) = x^2$.

   a Find $f'(x)$ by direct differentiation.

   b Find $u'(x)$ and $v'(x)$.

   c Does $f'(x) = u'(x)\,v'(x)$?

2 Suppose $u(x) = x$ and $v(x) = \sqrt{x}$, so $f(x) = x\sqrt{x} = x^{\frac{3}{2}}$.

   a Find $f'(x)$ by direct differentiation.

   b Find $u'(x)$ and $v'(x)$.

   c Does $f'(x) = u'(x)\,v'(x)$?

3 Copy and complete the following table, finding $f'(x)$ by direct differentiation.

$f(x)$	$f'(x)$	$u(x)$	$v(x)$	$u'(x)$	$v'(x)$	$u'(x)\,v(x) + u(x)\,v'(x)$
x^2		x	x			
$x^{\frac{3}{2}}$		x	$\sqrt{x}$			
$x(x+1)$		x	$x+1$			
$(x-1)(2-x^2)$		$x-1$	$2-x^2$			

4 Copy and complete:

"If $u(x)$ and $v(x)$ are two functions of x and $f(x) = u(x)\,v(x)$, then $f'(x) = \ldots\ldots$"

THE PRODUCT RULE

If $u(x)$ and $v(x)$ are two functions of x and $f(x) = u(x)\,v(x)$, then
$$f'(x) = u'(x)\,v(x) + u(x)\,v'(x).$$

Alternatively if $y = uv$ then $\dfrac{dy}{dx} = \dfrac{du}{dx}\,v + u\,\dfrac{dv}{dx}$.

Example 7   ◀) **Self Tutor**

Find $\dfrac{dy}{dx}$ if:

a $y = \sqrt{x}(2x+1)^3$

b $y = x^2(x^2 - 2x)^4$

a $y = \sqrt{x}(2x+1)^3$ is the product of $u = x^{\frac{1}{2}}$ and $v = (2x+1)^3$

$\therefore\ u' = \frac{1}{2}x^{-\frac{1}{2}}$ and $v' = 3(2x+1)^2 \times 2$ {chain rule}
$$= 6(2x+1)^2$$

Now $\dfrac{dy}{dx} = u'v + uv'$ {product rule}

$$= \tfrac{1}{2}x^{-\frac{1}{2}}(2x+1)^3 + x^{\frac{1}{2}} \times 6(2x+1)^2$$
$$= \tfrac{1}{2}x^{-\frac{1}{2}}(2x+1)^3 + 6x^{\frac{1}{2}}(2x+1)^2$$

b $y = x^2(x^2 - 2x)^4$ is the product of $u = x^2$ and $v = (x^2 - 2x)^4$
$\therefore\ u' = 2x$ and $v' = 4(x^2 - 2x)^3(2x - 2)$ {chain rule}

Now $\dfrac{dy}{dx} = u'v + uv'$ {product rule}

$$= 2x(x^2 - 2x)^4 + x^2 \times 4(x^2 - 2x)^3(2x - 2)$$
$$= 2x(x^2 - 2x)^4 + 4x^2(x^2 - 2x)^3(2x - 2)$$

EXERCISE 15C

1 Use the product rule to differentiate:

    a $f(x) = x(x - 1)$ **b** $f(x) = 2x(x + 1)$ **c** $f(x) = x^2\sqrt{x + 1}$

2 Find $\dfrac{dy}{dx}$ using the product rule:

    a $y = x^2(2x - 1)$ **b** $y = 4x(2x + 1)^3$ **c** $y = x^2\sqrt{3 - x}$

    d $y = \sqrt{x}(x - 3)^2$ **e** $y = 5x^2(3x^2 - 1)^2$ **f** $y = \sqrt{x}(x - x^2)^3$

3 Find the gradient of the tangent to:

    a $y = x^4(1 - 2x)^2$ at $x = -1$ **b** $y = \sqrt{x}(x^2 - x + 1)^2$ at $x = 4$

    c $y = x\sqrt{1 - 2x}$ at $x = -4$ **d** $y = x^3\sqrt{5 - x^2}$ at $x = 1$

    Check your answers using technology.

4 Consider $y = \sqrt{x}(3 - x)^2$.

    a Show that $\dfrac{dy}{dx} = \dfrac{(3 - x)(3 - 5x)}{2\sqrt{x}}$.

    b Find the x-coordinates of all points on $y = \sqrt{x}(3 - x)^2$ where the tangent is horizontal.

    c For what values of x is $\dfrac{dy}{dx}$ undefined?

    d Are there any values of x for which y is defined but $\dfrac{dy}{dx}$ is not?

    e What is the graphical significance of your answer in **d**?

5 Suppose $y = -2x^2(x + 4)$. For what values of x does $\dfrac{dy}{dx} = 10$?

D   THE QUOTIENT RULE

Expressions like $\dfrac{x^2 + 1}{2x - 5}$, $\dfrac{\sqrt{x}}{1 - 3x}$, and $\dfrac{x^3}{(x - x^2)^4}$ are called **quotients** because they represent the division of one function by another.

Quotient functions have the form $Q(x) = \dfrac{u(x)}{v(x)}$.

        Notice that $u(x) = Q(x)\, v(x)$

and by the product rule $u'(x) = Q'(x)\, v(x) + Q(x)\, v'(x)$

$\therefore\quad u'(x) - Q(x)\, v'(x) = Q'(x)\, v(x)$

$\therefore\quad Q'(x)\, v(x) = u'(x) - \dfrac{u(x)}{v(x)}\, v'(x)$

$\therefore\quad Q'(x)\, v(x) = \dfrac{u'(x)\, v(x) - u(x)\, v'(x)}{v(x)}$

$\therefore\quad Q'(x) = \dfrac{u'(x)\, v(x) - u(x)\, v'(x)}{[v(x)]^2}$ when this exists.

THE QUOTIENT RULE

If $\quad Q(x) = \dfrac{u(x)}{v(x)} \quad$ then $\quad Q'(x) = \dfrac{u'(x)\,v(x) - u(x)\,v'(x)}{[v(x)]^2}$

or if $\quad y = \dfrac{u}{v} \quad$ where u and v are functions of x then $\quad \dfrac{dy}{dx} = \dfrac{u'v - uv'}{v^2}.$

Example 8   ◀) **Self Tutor**

Use the quotient rule to find $\dfrac{dy}{dx}$ if: **a** $y = \dfrac{1 + 3x}{x^2 + 1}$ **b** $y = \dfrac{\sqrt{x}}{(1 - 2x)^2}$

a $y = \dfrac{1 + 3x}{x^2 + 1}$ is a quotient with $\quad u = 1 + 3x \quad$ and $\quad v = x^2 + 1$

$$\therefore \quad u' = 3 \qquad\qquad \text{and} \quad v' = 2x$$

Now $\quad \dfrac{dy}{dx} = \dfrac{u'v - uv'}{v^2} \qquad$ {quotient rule}

$$= \dfrac{3(x^2 + 1) - (1 + 3x)2x}{(x^2 + 1)^2}$$

$$= \dfrac{3x^2 + 3 - 2x - 6x^2}{(x^2 + 1)^2}$$

$$= \dfrac{3 - 2x - 3x^2}{(x^2 + 1)^2}$$

b $y = \dfrac{\sqrt{x}}{(1 - 2x)^2}$ is a quotient with $\quad u = x^{\frac{1}{2}} \quad$ and $\quad v = (1 - 2x)^2$

$$\therefore \quad u' = \tfrac{1}{2}x^{-\frac{1}{2}} \quad \text{and} \quad v' = 2(1 - 2x)^1 \times (-2) \quad \text{\{chain rule\}}$$
$$= -4(1 - 2x)$$

Now $\quad \dfrac{dy}{dx} = \dfrac{u'v - uv'}{v^2} \qquad$ {quotient rule}

$$= \dfrac{\tfrac{1}{2}x^{-\frac{1}{2}}(1 - 2x)^2 - x^{\frac{1}{2}} \times (-4(1 - 2x))}{(1 - 2x)^4}$$

$$= \dfrac{\tfrac{1}{2}x^{-\frac{1}{2}}(1 - 2x)^2 + 4x^{\frac{1}{2}}(1 - 2x)}{(1 - 2x)^4}$$

$$= \dfrac{\cancel{(1 - 2x)}\left[\frac{1 - 2x}{2\sqrt{x}} + 4\sqrt{x}\left(\frac{2\sqrt{x}}{2\sqrt{x}}\right)\right]}{(1 - 2x)^{\cancel{4}\,3}} \qquad \text{\{look for common factors\}}$$

$$= \dfrac{1 - 2x + 8x}{2\sqrt{x}(1 - 2x)^3}$$

$$= \dfrac{6x + 1}{2\sqrt{x}(1 - 2x)^3}$$

Note: Simplification of $\dfrac{dy}{dx}$ as in the above example is often time consuming and unnecessary, especially if you simply want to find the gradient of a tangent at a given point. In such cases you can substitute a value for x without simplifying the derivative function first.

EXERCISE 15D

1 Use the quotient rule to find $\dfrac{dy}{dx}$ if:

    a $y = \dfrac{1 + 3x}{2 - x}$ **b** $y = \dfrac{x^2}{2x + 1}$ **c** $y = \dfrac{x}{x^2 - 3}$

    d $y = \dfrac{\sqrt{x}}{1 - 2x}$ **e** $y = \dfrac{x^2 - 3}{3x - x^2}$ **f** $y = \dfrac{x}{\sqrt{1 - 3x}}$

2 Find the gradient of the tangent to:

    a $y = \dfrac{x}{1 - 2x}$ at $x = 1$ **b** $y = \dfrac{x^3}{x^2 + 1}$ at $x = -1$

    c $y = \dfrac{\sqrt{x}}{2x + 1}$ at $x = 4$ **d** $y = \dfrac{x^2}{\sqrt{x^2 + 5}}$ at $x = -2$

    Check your answers using technology.

3 **a** If $y = \dfrac{2\sqrt{x}}{1 - x}$, show that $\dfrac{dy}{dx} = \dfrac{x + 1}{\sqrt{x}(1 - x)^2}$.

    b For what values of x is $\dfrac{dy}{dx}$ **i** zero   **ii** undefined?

4 **a** If $y = \dfrac{x^2 - 3x + 1}{x + 2}$, show that $\dfrac{dy}{dx} = \dfrac{x^2 + 4x - 7}{(x + 2)^2}$.

    b For what values of x is $\dfrac{dy}{dx}$ **i** zero   **ii** undefined?

    c What is the graphical significance of your answers in **b**?

E   DERIVATIVES OF EXPONENTIAL FUNCTIONS

In **Chapter 3** we saw that the simplest **exponential functions** have the form $f(x) = b^x$ where b is any positive constant, $b \neq 1$.

The graphs of all members of the exponential family $f(x) = b^x$ have the following properties:

For example:

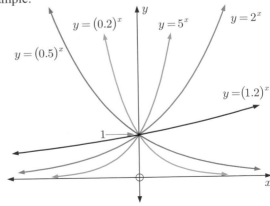

- pass through the point $(0, 1)$
- asymptotic to the x-axis at one end
- lie above the x-axis for all x.

INVESTIGATION 4   THE DERIVATIVE OF $y = b^x$

This investigation could be done by using a **graphics calculator** or by clicking on the icon.

The purpose of this investigation is to observe the nature of the derivatives of $f(x) = b^x$ for various values of b.

What to do:

1 Use your graphics calculator or the software provided to help fill in the table for $y = 2^x$:

x	y	$\dfrac{dy}{dx}$	$\dfrac{dy}{dx} \div y$
0			
0.5			
1			
1.5			
2			

CALCULUS DEMO

2 Repeat **1** for the following functions:

   a $y = 3^x$ **b** $y = 5^x$ **c** $y = (0.5)^x$

3 Use your observations from **1** and **2** to write a statement about the derivative of the general exponential $y = b^x$ for $b > 0$, $b \neq 1$.

From the **Investigation** you should have discovered that:

> If $f(x) = b^x$ then $f'(x) = kb^x$ where k is a constant equal to $f'(0)$.

Proof:

If $f(x) = b^x$,

then $f'(x) = \lim\limits_{h \to 0} \dfrac{b^{x+h} - b^x}{h}$ {first principles definition of the derivative}

$= \lim\limits_{h \to 0} \dfrac{b^x(b^h - 1)}{h}$

$= b^x \times \left(\lim\limits_{h \to 0} \dfrac{b^h - 1}{h} \right)$ {as b^x is independent of h}

But $f'(0) = \lim\limits_{h \to 0} \dfrac{f(0 + h) - f(0)}{h}$

$= \lim\limits_{h \to 0} \dfrac{b^h - 1}{h}$

$\therefore \;\; f'(x) = b^x f'(0)$

gradient is $f'(0)$

$y = b^x$

Given this result, if we can find a value of b such that $f'(0) = 1$, then we will have found *a function which is its own derivative*!

INVESTIGATION 5   SOLVING FOR b IF $f(x) = b^x$ AND $f'(x) = b^x$

Click on the icon to graph $f(x) = b^x$ and its derivative function $y = f'(x)$.

DEMO

Experiment with different values of b until the graphs of $f(x) = b^x$ and $y = f'(x)$ appear the same.

Estimate the corresponding value of b to 3 decimal places.

You should have discovered that $f(x) = f'(x) = b^x$ when $b \approx 2.718$.

To find this value of b more accurately we return to the algebraic approach:

We have already shown that if $f(x) = b^x$ then $f'(x) = b^x \left(\lim\limits_{h \to 0} \dfrac{b^h - 1}{h} \right)$.

So if $f'(x) = b^x$ then we require $\lim\limits_{h \to 0} \dfrac{b^h - 1}{h} = 1$.

$$\therefore \quad \lim_{h \to 0} b^h = \lim_{h \to 0} (1 + h)$$

Letting $h = \dfrac{1}{n}$, we notice that $\dfrac{1}{n} \to 0$ if $n \to \infty$

$$\therefore \quad \lim_{n \to \infty} b^{\frac{1}{n}} = \lim_{n \to \infty} \left(1 + \dfrac{1}{n} \right)$$

$$\therefore \quad b = \lim_{n \to \infty} \left(1 + \dfrac{1}{n} \right)^n \quad \text{if this limit exists}$$

We have in fact already seen this limit in **Chapter 3 Investigation 2** on page **102**.

We found that as $\quad n \to \infty$,

$$\left(1 + \dfrac{1}{n} \right)^n \to 2.718\,281\,828\,459\,045\,235 \ldots$$

and this irrational number is the natural exponential e.

e^x is sometimes written as $\exp(x)$.
For example,
$\exp(1 - x) = e^{1-x}$.

We now have: If $f(x) = e^x$ then $f'(x) = e^x$.

PROPERTIES OF $y = e^x$

$\dfrac{dy}{dx} = e^x = y$

As $x \to \infty$, $y \to \infty$ very rapidly,

and so $\dfrac{dy}{dx} \to \infty$.

This means that the gradient of the curve is very large for large values of x. The curve increases in steepness as x gets larger.

As $x \to -\infty$, $y \to 0$ but never reaches 0, and so $\dfrac{dy}{dx} \to 0$ also.

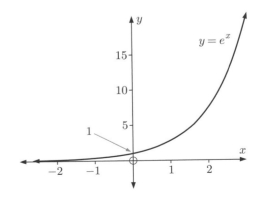

For large negative x, $f(x) = e^x$ approaches the asymptote $y = 0$.

$e^x > 0$ for all x, so the range of $f(x) = e^x$ is $\mathbb{R}^+$.

THE DERIVATIVE OF $e^{f(x)}$

The functions e^{-x}, e^{2x+3}, and e^{-x^2} are all of the form $e^{f(x)}$. Such functions are often used in problem solving.

$e^{f(x)} > 0$ for all x, no matter what the function $f(x)$.

Suppose $y = e^{f(x)} = e^u$ where $u = f(x)$.

Now $\dfrac{dy}{dx} = \dfrac{dy}{du}\dfrac{du}{dx}$ {chain rule}

$= e^u \dfrac{du}{dx}$

$= e^{f(x)} \times f'(x)$

Function	Derivative
e^x	e^x
$e^{f(x)}$	$e^{f(x)} \times f'(x)$

Example 9
◀) Self Tutor

Find the gradient function for y equal to:

a $2e^x + e^{-3x}$

b $x^2 e^{-x}$

c $\dfrac{e^{2x}}{x}$

a If $y = 2e^x + e^{-3x}$ then $\dfrac{dy}{dx} = 2e^x + e^{-3x}(-3)$

$= 2e^x - 3e^{-3x}$

b If $y = x^2 e^{-x}$ then $\dfrac{dy}{dx} = 2xe^{-x} + x^2 e^{-x}(-1)$ {product rule}

$= 2xe^{-x} - x^2 e^{-x}$

c If $y = \dfrac{e^{2x}}{x}$ then $\dfrac{dy}{dx} = \dfrac{e^{2x}(2)x - e^{2x}(1)}{x^2}$ {quotient rule}

$= \dfrac{e^{2x}(2x - 1)}{x^2}$

Example 10
◀) Self Tutor

Find the gradient function for y equal to: **a** $(e^x - 1)^3$ **b** $\dfrac{1}{\sqrt{2e^{-x} + 1}}$

a $y = (e^x - 1)^3$

$= u^3$ where $u = e^x - 1$

$\dfrac{dy}{dx} = \dfrac{dy}{du}\dfrac{du}{dx}$ {chain rule}

$= 3u^2 \dfrac{du}{dx}$

$= 3(e^x - 1)^2 \times e^x$

$= 3e^x(e^x - 1)^2$

b $y = (2e^{-x} + 1)^{-\frac{1}{2}}$

$= u^{-\frac{1}{2}}$ where $u = 2e^{-x} + 1$

$\dfrac{dy}{dx} = \dfrac{dy}{du}\dfrac{du}{dx}$ {chain rule}

$= -\tfrac{1}{2}u^{-\frac{3}{2}} \dfrac{du}{dx}$

$= -\tfrac{1}{2}(2e^{-x} + 1)^{-\frac{3}{2}} \times 2e^{-x}(-1)$

$= e^{-x}(2e^{-x} + 1)^{-\frac{3}{2}}$

EXERCISE 15E

1 Find the gradient function for $f(x)$ equal to:

    a e^{4x}
    b $e^x + 3$
    c $\exp(-2x)$
    d $e^{\frac{x}{2}}$

    e $2e^{-\frac{x}{2}}$
    f $1 - 2e^{-x}$
    g $4e^{\frac{x}{2}} - 3e^{-x}$
    h $\dfrac{e^x + e^{-x}}{2}$

    i e^{-x^2}
    j $e^{\frac{1}{x}}$
    k $10(1 + e^{2x})$
    l $20(1 - e^{-2x})$

    m e^{2x+1}
    n $e^{\frac{x}{4}}$
    o e^{1-2x^2}
    p $e^{-0.02x}$

2 Find the derivative of:

    a xe^x
    b $x^3 e^{-x}$
    c $\dfrac{e^x}{x}$
    d $\dfrac{x}{e^x}$

    e $x^2 e^{3x}$
    f $\dfrac{e^x}{\sqrt{x}}$
    g $\sqrt{x}\,e^{-x}$
    h $\dfrac{e^x + 2}{e^{-x} + 1}$

3 Find the gradient of the tangent to:

    a $y = (e^x + 2)^4$ at $x = 0$
        b $y = \dfrac{1}{2 - e^{-x}}$ at $x = 0$

    c $y = \sqrt{e^{2x} + 10}$ at $x = \ln 3$

Check your answers using technology.

4 Given $f(x) = e^{kx} + x$ and $f'(0) = -8$, find k.

5   **a** By substituting $e^{\ln 2}$ for 2 in $y = 2^x$, find $\dfrac{dy}{dx}$.

    b Show that if $y = b^x$ where $b > 0$, $b \neq 1$, then $\dfrac{dy}{dx} = b^x \times \ln b$.

6 The tangent to $f(x) = x^2 e^{-x}$ at point P is horizontal. Find the possible coordinates of P.

F   DERIVATIVES OF LOGARITHMIC FUNCTIONS

INVESTIGATION 6   THE DERIVATIVE OF $\ln x$

If $y = \ln x$, what is the gradient function?

CALCULUS DEMO

What to do:

1 Click on the icon to see the graph of $y = \ln x$. Observe the gradient function being drawn as the point moves from left to right along the graph.

2 What do you think the formula of the gradient function is?

3 Find the gradient at $x = 0.25$, $x = 0.5$, $x = 1$, $x = 2$, $x = 3$, $x = 4$, $x = 5$. Do your results confirm your prediction in **2**?

From the **Investigation** you should have observed:

$$\text{If} \quad y = \ln x \quad \text{then} \quad \frac{dy}{dx} = \frac{1}{x}.$$

The proof of this result is beyond the scope of this course.

THE DERIVATIVE OF $\ln f(x)$

Suppose $y = \ln f(x)$

$$\therefore \quad y = \ln u \quad \text{where} \quad u = f(x).$$

Now $\dfrac{dy}{dx} = \dfrac{dy}{du}\dfrac{du}{dx}$ {chain rule}

$$\therefore \quad \frac{dy}{dx} = \frac{1}{u}\frac{du}{dx}$$

$$= \frac{f'(x)}{f(x)}$$

Function	Derivative
$\ln x$	$\dfrac{1}{x}$
$\ln f(x)$	$\dfrac{f'(x)}{f(x)}$

Example 11   ◄» Self Tutor

Find the gradient function of:

a $y = \ln(kx)$, k a constant   **b** $y = \ln(1 - 3x)$ **c** $y = x^3 \ln x$

a $y = \ln(kx)$

$$\therefore \quad \frac{dy}{dx} = \frac{k}{kx}$$

$$= \frac{1}{x}$$

b $y = \ln(1 - 3x)$

$$\therefore \quad \frac{dy}{dx} = \frac{-3}{1 - 3x}$$

$$= \frac{3}{3x - 1}$$

c $y = x^3 \ln x$

$$\therefore \quad \frac{dy}{dx} = 3x^2 \ln x + x^3 \left(\frac{1}{x}\right)$$

$$\{\text{product rule}\}$$

$$= 3x^2 \ln x + x^2$$

$$= x^2(3\ln x + 1)$$

$\ln(kx) = \ln k + \ln x$

$\qquad = \ln x + \text{constant}$

so $\ln(kx)$ and $\ln x$

both have derivative $\dfrac{1}{x}$.

The laws of logarithms can help us to differentiate some logarithmic functions more easily.

For $a > 0$, $b > 0$, $n \in \mathbb{R}$: $\ln(ab) = \ln a + \ln b$

$$\ln\left(\frac{a}{b}\right) = \ln a - \ln b$$

$$\ln(a^n) = n \ln a$$

Example 12   ◀)) **Self Tutor**

Differentiate with respect to x:

a $y = \ln(xe^{-x})$

b $y = \ln\left[\dfrac{x^2}{(x+2)(x-3)}\right]$

a $y = \ln(xe^{-x})$

$\qquad = \ln x + \ln e^{-x} \qquad \{\ln(ab) = \ln a + \ln b\}$

$\qquad = \ln x - x \qquad\qquad \{\ln e^a = a\}$

$\therefore \quad \dfrac{dy}{dx} = \dfrac{1}{x} - 1$

A derivative function will only be valid on *at most* the domain of the original function.

b $y = \ln\left[\dfrac{x^2}{(x+2)(x-3)}\right]$

$\qquad = \ln x^2 - \ln[(x+2)(x-3)]$

$\qquad = 2\ln x - [\ln(x+2) + \ln(x-3)]$

$\qquad = 2\ln x - \ln(x+2) - \ln(x-3)$

$\therefore \quad \dfrac{dy}{dx} = \dfrac{2}{x} - \dfrac{1}{x+2} - \dfrac{1}{x-3}$

EXERCISE 15F

1 Find the gradient function of:

  a $\;y = \ln(7x)$

  b $\;y = \ln(2x + 1)$

  c $\;y = \ln(x - x^2)$

  d $\;y = 3 - 2\ln x$

  e $\;y = x^2 \ln x$

  f $\;y = \dfrac{\ln x}{2x}$

  g $\;y = e^x \ln x$

  h $\;y = (\ln x)^2$

  i $\;y = \sqrt{\ln x}$

  j $\;y = e^{-x} \ln x$

  k $\;y = \sqrt{x}\,\ln(2x)$

  l $\;y = \dfrac{2\sqrt{x}}{\ln x}$

  m $\;y = 3 - 4\ln(1 - x)$

  n $\;y = x\ln(x^2 + 1)$

2 Find $\dfrac{dy}{dx}$ for:

  a $\;y = x\ln 5$

  b $\;y = \ln(x^3)$

  c $\;y = \ln(x^4 + x)$

  d $\;y = \ln(10 - 5x)$

  e $\;y = [\ln(2x + 1)]^3$

  f $\;y = \dfrac{\ln(4x)}{x}$

  g $\;y = \ln\left(\dfrac{1}{x}\right)$

  h $\;y = \ln(\ln x)$

  i $\;y = \dfrac{1}{\ln x}$

3 Use the logarithm laws to help differentiate with respect to x:

  a $\;y = \ln\sqrt{1 - 2x}$

  b $\;y = \ln\left(\dfrac{1}{2x + 3}\right)$

  c $\;y = \ln\left(e^x \sqrt{x}\right)$

  d $\;y = \ln\left(x\sqrt{2 - x}\right)$

  e $\;y = \ln\left(\dfrac{x + 3}{x - 1}\right)$

  f $\;y = \ln\left(\dfrac{x^2}{3 - x}\right)$

  g $\;f(x) = \ln\left((3x - 4)^3\right)$

  h $\;f(x) = \ln\left(x(x^2 + 1)\right)$

  i $\;f(x) = \ln\left(\dfrac{x^2 + 2x}{x - 5}\right)$

4 Find the gradient of the tangent to $y = x \ln x$ at the point where $x = e$.

5 Suppose $f(x) = a \ln(2x + b)$ where $f(e) = 3$ and $f'(e) = \dfrac{6}{e}$. Find the constants a and b.

G | DERIVATIVES OF TRIGONOMETRIC FUNCTIONS

In **Chapter 10** we saw that sine and cosine curves arise naturally from motion in a circle.

Click on the icon to observe the motion of point P around the unit circle. Observe the graphs of P's height relative to the x-axis, and then P's horizontal displacement from the y-axis. The resulting graphs are those of $y = \sin t$ and $y = \cos t$.

Suppose P moves anticlockwise around the unit circle with constant linear speed of 1 unit per second.

DEMO

After 2π seconds, P will travel 2π units which is one full revolution, and thus through 2π radians.

So, after t seconds P will travel through t radians, and at time t, P is at $(\cos t,\ \sin t)$.

> The **angular velocity** of P is the rate of change of $\widehat{AOP}$ with respect to time.

Angular velocity is only meaningful in motion along a circular or elliptical arc.

For the example above, the angular velocity of P is $\dfrac{d\theta}{dt}$ and $\dfrac{d\theta}{dt} = 1$ radian per second.

> If we let l be the arc length AP, the **linear speed** of P is $\dfrac{dl}{dt}$,
> the rate of change of l with respect to time.

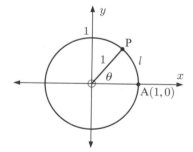

For the example above, $l = \theta r = \theta \times 1 = \theta$ and $\dfrac{dl}{dt} = 1$ unit per second.

INVESTIGATION 7   DERIVATIVES OF $\sin x$ AND $\cos x$

Our aim is to use a computer demonstration to investigate the derivatives of $\sin x$ and $\cos x$.

What to do:

1 Click on the icon to observe the graph of $y = \sin x$. A tangent with x-step of length 1 unit moves across the curve, and its y-step is translated onto the gradient graph. Predict the derivative of the function $y = \sin x$.

DERIVATIVES DEMO

2 Repeat the process in **1** for the graph of $y = \cos x$. Hence predict the derivative of the function $y = \cos x$.

From the **Investigation** you should have deduced that:

> For x in radians: If $f(x) = \sin x$ then $f'(x) = \cos x$
>
> If $f(x) = \cos x$ then $f'(x) = -\sin x$.

THE DERIVATIVE OF $\tan x$

Consider $y = \tan x = \dfrac{\sin x}{\cos x}$

DERIVATIVE
DEMO

We let $u = \sin x$ and $v = \cos x$

$\therefore \quad \dfrac{du}{dx} = \cos x$ and $\dfrac{dv}{dx} = -\sin x$

$\therefore \quad \dfrac{dy}{dx} = \dfrac{u'v - uv'}{v^2}$ {quotient rule}

$\qquad = \dfrac{\cos x \cos x - \sin x(-\sin x)}{[\cos x]^2}$

$\qquad = \dfrac{\cos^2 x + \sin^2 x}{\cos^2 x}$

$\qquad = \dfrac{1}{\cos^2 x}$ {since $\sin^2 x + \cos^2 x = 1$}

> $\dfrac{1}{\cos x}$ is often called secant x or $\sec x$, so $\dfrac{d}{dx}(\tan x) = \sec^2 x$.

Summary:

Function	Derivative
$\sin x$	$\cos x$
$\cos x$	$-\sin x$
$\tan x$	$\dfrac{1}{\cos^2 x}$

THE DERIVATIVES OF $\sin[f(x)]$, $\cos[f(x)]$, AND $\tan[f(x)]$

Suppose $y = \sin[f(x)]$

If we let $u = f(x)$, then $y = \sin u$.

But $\dfrac{dy}{dx} = \dfrac{dy}{du}\dfrac{du}{dx}$ {chain rule}

$\therefore \quad \dfrac{dy}{dx} = \cos u \times f'(x)$

$\qquad = \cos[f(x)] \times f'(x)$

We can perform the same procedure for $\cos[f(x)]$ and $\tan[f(x)]$, giving the following results:

Function	Derivative
$\sin[f(x)]$	$\cos[f(x)]\, f'(x)$
$\cos[f(x)]$	$-\sin[f(x)]\, f'(x)$
$\tan[f(x)]$	$\dfrac{f'(x)}{\cos^2[f(x)]}$

Example 13   ◀) **Self Tutor**

Differentiate with respect to x:

a $x \sin x$

b $4 \tan^2(3x)$

a   If $y = x \sin x$

then by the product rule

$\dfrac{dy}{dx} = (1) \sin x + (x) \cos x$

$= \sin x + x \cos x$

b   If $y = 4 \tan^2(3x)$

$= 4[\tan(3x)]^2$

$= 4u^2$ where $u = \tan(3x)$

$\dfrac{dy}{dx} = \dfrac{dy}{du} \dfrac{du}{dx}$ {chain rule}

$\therefore \ \dfrac{dy}{dx} = 8u \times \dfrac{du}{dx}$

$= 8 \tan(3x) \times \dfrac{3}{\cos^2(3x)}$

$= \dfrac{24 \sin(3x)}{\cos^3(3x)}$

EXERCISE 15G

1   Find $\dfrac{dy}{dx}$ for:

a $y = \sin(2x)$

b $y = \sin x + \cos x$

c $y = \cos(3x) - \sin x$

d $y = \sin(x + 1)$

e $y = \cos(3 - 2x)$

f $y = \tan(5x)$

g $y = \sin(\frac{x}{2}) - 3 \cos x$

h $y = 3 \tan(\pi x)$

i $y = 4 \sin x - \cos(2x)$

2   Differentiate with respect to x:

a $x^2 + \cos x$

b $\tan x - 3 \sin x$

c $e^x \cos x$

d $e^{-x} \sin x$

e $\ln(\sin x)$

f $e^{2x} \tan x$

g $\sin(3x)$

h $\cos(\frac{x}{2})$

i $3 \tan(2x)$

j $x \cos x$

k $\dfrac{\sin x}{x}$

l $x \tan x$

3   Differentiate with respect to x:

a $\sin(x^2)$

b $\cos(\sqrt{x})$

c $\sqrt{\cos x}$

d $\sin^2 x$

e $\cos^3 x$

f $\cos x \sin(2x)$

g $\cos(\cos x)$

h $\cos^3(4x)$

i $\dfrac{1}{\sin x}$

j $\dfrac{1}{\cos(2x)}$

k $\dfrac{2}{\sin^2(2x)}$

l $\dfrac{8}{\tan^3(\frac{x}{2})}$

4   Find the gradient of the tangent to:

a $f(x) = \sin^3 x$ at the point where $x = \frac{2\pi}{3}$

b $f(x) = \cos x \sin x$ at the point where $x = \frac{\pi}{4}$.

H   SECOND AND HIGHER DERIVATIVES

Given a function $f(x)$, the derivative $f'(x)$ is known as the **first derivative**.

The **second derivative** of $f(x)$ is the derivative of $f'(x)$, or **the derivative of the first derivative**.

We use $f''(x)$ or y'' or $\dfrac{d^2y}{dx^2}$ to represent the second derivative.

$f''(x)$ reads "*f double dashed x*".

$\dfrac{d^2y}{dx^2} = \dfrac{d}{dx}\left(\dfrac{dy}{dx}\right)$ reads "*dee two y by dee x squared*".

Example 14   ◀)) Self Tutor

Find $f''(x)$ given that $f(x) = x^3 - \dfrac{3}{x}$.

Now $f(x) = x^3 - 3x^{-1}$

$\therefore\ f'(x) = 3x^2 + 3x^{-2}$

$\therefore\ f''(x) = 6x - 6x^{-3}$

$\qquad\qquad = 6x - \dfrac{6}{x^3}$

We can continue to differentiate to obtain higher derivatives.

The ***n*th derivative of y with respect to x** is obtained by differentiating $y = f(x)$ n times.

We use the notation $f^{(n)}(x)$ or $\dfrac{d^ny}{dx^n}$ for the nth derivative.

Example 15   ◀)) Self Tutor

Given $f(x) = \cos 2x$, show that $f^{(3)}(\frac{\pi}{8}) = 4\sqrt{2}$.

$$f(x) = \cos 2x$$

$$\therefore\ f'(x) = -2\sin 2x$$

$$\therefore\ f''(x) = -4\cos 2x$$

$$\therefore\ f^{(3)}(x) = 8\sin 2x$$

$$\therefore\ f^{(3)}(\tfrac{\pi}{8}) = 8\sin(2 \times \tfrac{\pi}{8})$$

$$= 8\sin\tfrac{\pi}{4}$$

$$= 8 \times \tfrac{1}{\sqrt{2}}$$

$$= 4\sqrt{2}$$

EXERCISE 15H

1 Find $f''(x)$ given that:

    a $f(x) = 3x^2 - 6x + 2$ **b** $f(x) = \dfrac{2}{\sqrt{x}} - 1$ **c** $f(x) = 2x^3 - 3x^2 - x + 5$

    d $f(x) = \dfrac{2 - 3x}{x^2}$ **e** $f(x) = (1 - 2x)^3$ **f** $f(x) = \dfrac{x + 2}{2x - 1}$

2 Find $\dfrac{d^2y}{dx^2}$ given that:

    a $y = x - x^3$ **b** $y = x^2 - \dfrac{5}{x^2}$ **c** $y = 2 - \dfrac{3}{\sqrt{x}}$

    d $y = \dfrac{4 - x}{x}$ **e** $y = (x^2 - 3x)^3$ **f** $y = x^2 - x + \dfrac{1}{1 - x}$

3 Given $f(x) = x^3 - 2x + 5$, find:

    a $f(2)$ **b** $f'(2)$ **c** $f''(2)$ **d** $f^{(3)}(2)$

4 Suppose $y = Ae^{kx}$ where A and k are constants.

    Show that: **a** $\dfrac{dy}{dx} = ky$ **b** $\dfrac{d^2y}{dx^2} = k^2 y$ **c** $\dfrac{d^3y}{dx^3} = k^3 y$

5 Find x when $f''(x) = 0$ for:

    a $f(x) = 2x^3 - 6x^2 + 5x + 1$ **b** $f(x) = \dfrac{x}{x^2 + 2}$

6 Consider the function $f(x) = 2x^3 - x$.

Complete the following table by indicating whether $f(x)$, $f'(x)$, and $f''(x)$ are positive $(+)$, negative $(-)$, or zero (0) at the given values of x.

x	-1	0	1
$f(x)$	$-$		
$f'(x)$			
$f''(x)$			

7 Given $f(x) = \frac{2}{3} \sin 3x$, show that $f^{(3)}(\frac{2\pi}{9}) = 9$.

8 Suppose $f(x) = 2\sin^3 x - 3\sin x$.

    a Show that $f'(x) = -3\cos x \cos 2x$.   **b** Find $f''(x)$.

9 Find $\dfrac{d^2y}{dx^2}$ given:

    a $y = -\ln x$ **b** $y = x \ln x$ **c** $y = (\ln x)^2$

10 Given $f(x) = x^2 - \dfrac{1}{x}$, find: **a** $f(1)$ **b** $f'(1)$ **c** $f''(1)$ **d** $f^{(3)}(1)$

11 If $y = 2e^{3x} + 5e^{4x}$, show that $\dfrac{d^2y}{dx^2} - 7\dfrac{dy}{dx} + 12y = 0$.

12 If $y = \sin(2x + 3)$, show that $\dfrac{d^2y}{dx^2} + 4y = 0$.

13 If $y = \sin x$, show that $\dfrac{d^4y}{dx^4} = y$.

14 If $y = 2\sin x + 3\cos x$, show that $y'' + y = 0$ where y'' represents $\dfrac{d^2y}{dx^2}$.

REVIEW SET 15A   NON-CALCULATOR

1 If $f(x) = 7 + x - 3x^2$, find: **a** $f(3)$ **b** $f'(3)$ **c** $f''(3)$.

2 Find $\dfrac{dy}{dx}$ for: **a** $y = 3x^2 - x^4$ **b** $y = \dfrac{x^3 - x}{x^2}$

3 At what point on the curve $f(x) = \dfrac{x}{\sqrt{x^2 + 1}}$ does the tangent have gradient 1?

4 Find $\dfrac{dy}{dx}$ if: **a** $y = e^{x^3 + 2}$ **b** $y = \ln\left(\dfrac{x + 3}{x^2}\right)$

5 Given $y = 3e^x - e^{-x}$, show that $\dfrac{d^2y}{dx^2} = y$.

6 Differentiate with respect to x:

   a $\sin(5x)\ln(x)$ **b** $\sin(x)\cos(2x)$ **c** $e^{-2x}\tan x$

7 Find the gradient of the tangent to $y = \sin^2 x$ at the point where $x = \frac{\pi}{3}$.

8 Determine the derivative with respect to x of:

   a $f(x) = (x^2 + 3)^4$ **b** $g(x) = \dfrac{\sqrt{x + 5}}{x^2}$

9 Find $f''(2)$ for: **a** $f(x) = 3x^2 - \dfrac{1}{x}$ **b** $f(x) = \sqrt{x}$

10 Given $y = (1 - \frac{1}{3}x)^3$, show that $\dfrac{d^3y}{dx^3} = -\frac{2}{9}$.

REVIEW SET 15B   CALCULATOR

1 Differentiate with respect to x:

   a $5x - 3x^{-1}$ **b** $(3x^2 + x)^4$ **c** $(x^2 + 1)(1 - x^2)^3$

2 Find all points on the curve $y = 2x^3 + 3x^2 - 10x + 3$ where the gradient of the tangent is 2.

3 If $y = \sqrt{5 - 4x}$, find: **a** $\dfrac{dy}{dx}$ **b** $\dfrac{d^2y}{dx^2}$

4 Consider the curves $y = e^{x-1} + 1$ and $y = 3 - e^{1-x}$.
   a Sketch the curves on the same set of axes.
   b Find the point of intersection of the two curves.
   c Show that the tangents to each curve at this point have the same gradient.
   d Comment on the significance of this result.

5 Find $\dfrac{dy}{dx}$ if: **a** $y = \ln(x^3 - 3x)$ **b** $y = \dfrac{e^x}{x^2}$

6 Find x if $f''(x) = 0$ and $f(x) = 2x^4 - 4x^3 - 9x^2 + 4x + 7$.

7 If $f(x) = x - \cos x$, find
   a $f(\pi)$ **b** $f'(\frac{\pi}{2})$ **c** $f''(\frac{3\pi}{4})$

8   Given that a and b are constants, differentiate $y = 3\sin bx - a\cos 2x$ with respect to x.

Find a and b if $y + \dfrac{d^2y}{dx^2} = 6\cos 2x$.

9   Differentiate with respect to x:

a $10x - \sin(10x)$ **b** $\ln\left(\dfrac{1}{\cos x}\right)$ **c** $\sin(5x)\ln(2x)$

REVIEW SET 15C

1   Differentiate with respect to x: **a** $y = x^3\sqrt{1 - x^2}$ **b** $y = \dfrac{x^2 - 3x}{\sqrt{x + 1}}$

2   Find $\dfrac{d^2y}{dx^2}$ for: **a** $y = 3x^4 - \dfrac{2}{x}$ **b** $y = x^3 - x + \dfrac{1}{\sqrt{x}}$

3   Find all points on the curve $y = xe^x$ where the gradient of the tangent is $2e$.

4   Differentiate with respect to x: **a** $f(x) = \ln(e^x + 3)$ **b** $f(x) = \ln\left[\dfrac{(x + 2)^3}{x}\right]$

5   Given $y = \left(x - \dfrac{1}{x}\right)^4$,   find $\dfrac{dy}{dx}$ when $x = 1$.

6   **a**   Find $f'(x)$ and $f''(x)$ for $f(x) = \sqrt{x}\cos(4x)$.

  b   Hence find $f'\left(\frac{\pi}{16}\right)$ and $f''\left(\frac{\pi}{8}\right)$.

7   Suppose $y = 3\sin 2x + 2\cos 2x$.   Show that $4y + \dfrac{d^2y}{dx^2} = 0$.

8   Consider $f(x) = \dfrac{6x}{3 + x^2}$.   Find the value(s) of x when:

  a $f(x) = -\frac{1}{2}$ **b** $f'(x) = 0$ **c** $f''(x) = 0$

9   The function f is defined by $f : x \mapsto -10\sin 2x\cos 2x,\ \ 0 \leqslant x \leqslant \pi$.

  a   Write down an expression for $f(x)$ in the form $k\sin 4x$.

  b   Solve $f'(x) = 0$,   giving exact answers.

Chapter 16

Properties of curves

OPENING PROBLEM

The curve $y = x^3 - 4x$ is shown on the graph alongside.

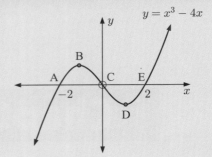

Things to think about:

a At which points is the tangent to the curve horizontal?

b On which intervals is the curve:

  i increasing   **ii** decreasing?

c At which point does the curve change its *shape*? How can we use calculus to find this point?

In the previous chapter we saw how to differentiate many types of functions. In this chapter we will learn how to use derivatives to find:

- tangents and normals to curves
- intervals where a function is increasing or decreasing
- turning points which are local minima and maxima
- points where a function changes its shape.

A   TANGENTS AND NORMALS

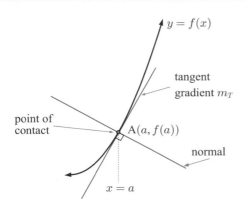

Consider a curve $y = f(x)$.

If A is the point with x-coordinate a, then the gradient of the tangent to the curve at this point is $f'(a) = m_T$.

The equation of the tangent is

$$\frac{y - f(a)}{x - a} = f'(a)$$

$$or \quad y - f(a) = f'(a)(x - a).$$

A **normal** to a curve is a line which is perpendicular to the tangent at the point of contact.

The gradients of perpendicular lines are negative reciprocals of each other, so:

The gradient of the **normal** to the curve at $x = a$ is $m_N = -\dfrac{1}{f'(a)}$.

For example:

If $f(x) = x^2$ then $f'(x) = 2x$.

At $x = 2$, $m_T = f'(2) = 4$ and $m_N = -\dfrac{1}{f'(2)} = -\dfrac{1}{4}$.

So, at $x = 2$ the tangent has gradient 4 and the normal has gradient $-\frac{1}{4}$.

Since $f(2) = 4$, the tangent has equation $y - 4 = 4(x - 2)$ or $y = 4x - 4$

and the normal has equation $y - 4 = -\frac{1}{4}(x - 2)$ or $y = -\frac{1}{4}x + \frac{9}{2}$.

Reminder: If a line has gradient $\frac{4}{5}$ say, and passes through $(2, -3)$ say, another quick way to write down its equation is $4x - 5y = 4(2) - 5(-3)$ or $4x - 5y = 23$.

If the gradient was $-\frac{4}{5}$, we would have:
$$4x + 5y = 4(2) + 5(-3) \quad \text{or} \quad 4x + 5y = -7.$$

You can also find the equations of tangents at a given point using your graphics calculator.

GRAPHICS CALCULATOR INSTRUCTIONS

Example 1   ◀) **Self Tutor**

Find the equation of the tangent to $f(x) = x^2 + 1$ at the point where $x = 1$.

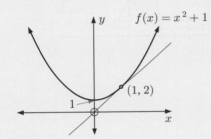

Since $f(1) = 1 + 1 = 2$, the point of contact is $(1, 2)$.

Now $f'(x) = 2x$,   so $m_T = f'(1) = 2$

∴ the tangent has equation $\dfrac{y - 2}{x - 1} = 2$

which is $y - 2 = 2x - 2$

or $y = 2x$.

EXERCISE 16A

1   Find the equation of the tangent to:

a $y = x - 2x^2 + 3$ at $x = 2$

b $y = \sqrt{x} + 1$ at $x = 4$

c $y = x^3 - 5x$ at $x = 1$

d $y = \dfrac{4}{\sqrt{x}}$ at $(1, 4)$

e $y = \dfrac{3}{x} - \dfrac{1}{x^2}$ at $(-1, -4)$

f $y = 3x^2 - \dfrac{1}{x}$ at $x = -1$.

Check your answers using technology.

Example 2   ◀) **Self Tutor**

Find the equation of the normal to $y = \dfrac{8}{\sqrt{x}}$ at the point where $x = 4$.

When $x = 4$, $y = \dfrac{8}{\sqrt{4}} = \dfrac{8}{2} = 4$.   So, the point of contact is $(4, 4)$.

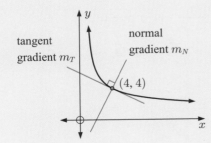

Now as $y = 8x^{-\frac{1}{2}}$, $\dfrac{dy}{dx} = -4x^{-\frac{3}{2}}$

∴ when $x = 4$, $m_T = -4 \times 4^{-\frac{3}{2}} = -\frac{1}{2}$

∴ the normal at $(4, 4)$ has gradient $m_N = \frac{2}{1}$.

∴ the equation of the normal is
$$2x - 1y = 2(4) - 1(4)$$
or $2x - y = 4$

2 Find the equation of the normal to:

 a $y = x^2$ at the point $(3, 9)$

 b $y = x^3 - 5x + 2$ at $x = -2$

 c $y = \dfrac{5}{\sqrt{x}} - \sqrt{x}$ at the point $(1, 4)$

 d $y = 8\sqrt{x} - \dfrac{1}{x^2}$ at $x = 1$.

Example 3   ◄⑴ **Self Tutor**

Find the equations of any horizontal tangents to $y = x^3 - 12x + 2$.

Since $y = x^3 - 12x + 2$, $\dfrac{dy}{dx} = 3x^2 - 12$

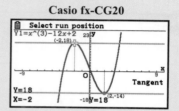

Casio fx-CG20

Horizontal tangents have gradient 0,

 so $3x^2 - 12 = 0$

 $\therefore\ 3(x^2 - 4) = 0$

$\therefore\ 3(x + 2)(x - 2) = 0$

 $\therefore\ x = -2$ or 2

When $x = 2$, $y = 8 - 24 + 2 = -14$

When $x = -2$, $y = -8 + 24 + 2 = 18$

$\therefore$ the points of contact are $(2, -14)$ and $(-2, 18)$

$\therefore$ the tangents are $y = -14$ and $y = 18$.

---

3 a Find the equations of the horizontal tangents to $y = 2x^3 + 3x^2 - 12x + 1$.

 b Find the points of contact where horizontal tangents meet the curve $y = 2\sqrt{x} + \dfrac{1}{\sqrt{x}}$.

 c Find k if the tangent to $y = 2x^3 + kx^2 - 3$ at the point where $x = 2$ has gradient 4.

 d Find the equation of the other tangent to $y = 1 - 3x + 12x^2 - 8x^3$ which is parallel to the tangent at $(1, 2)$.

4 a Consider the curve $y = x^2 + ax + b$ where a and b are constants. The tangent to this curve at the point where $x = 1$ is $2x + y = 6$. Find the values of a and b.

 b Consider the curve $y = a\sqrt{x} + \dfrac{b}{\sqrt{x}}$ where a and b are constants. The normal to this curve at the point where $x = 4$ is $4x + y = 22$. Find the values of a and b.

 c Show that the equation of the tangent to $y = 2x^2 - 1$ at the point where $x = a$, is $4ax - y = 2a^2 + 1$.

5 Find the equation of the tangent to:

 a $y = \sqrt{2x + 1}$ at $x = 4$

 b $y = \dfrac{1}{2 - x}$ at $x = -1$

 c $f(x) = \dfrac{x}{1 - 3x}$ at $(-1, -\frac{1}{4})$

 d $f(x) = \dfrac{x^2}{1 - x}$ at $(2, -4)$.

6 Find the equation of the normal to:

 a $y = \dfrac{1}{(x^2 + 1)^2}$ at $(1, \frac{1}{4})$

 b $y = \dfrac{1}{\sqrt{3 - 2x}}$ at $x = -3$

 c $f(x) = \sqrt{x}(1 - x)^2$ at $x = 4$

 d $f(x) = \dfrac{x^2 - 1}{2x + 3}$ at $x = -1$.

7 The curve $y = a\sqrt{1 - bx}$ where a and b are constants, has a tangent with equation $3x + y = 5$ at the point where $x = -1$. Find a and b.

Example 4 ◀⟩ **Self Tutor**

Show that the equation of the tangent to $y = \ln x$ at the point where $y = -1$ is $y = ex - 2$.

When $y = -1$, $\ln x = -1$

$$\therefore \quad x = e^{-1} = \tfrac{1}{e}$$

$\therefore$ the point of contact is $\left(\tfrac{1}{e}, -1\right)$.

Now $f(x) = \ln x$ has derivative $f'(x) = \dfrac{1}{x}$

$\therefore$ the tangent at $\left(\tfrac{1}{e}, -1\right)$ has gradient $\dfrac{1}{\frac{1}{e}} = e$

$\therefore$ the tangent has equation $\dfrac{y - -1}{x - \frac{1}{e}} = e$

which is $y + 1 = e\left(x - \tfrac{1}{e}\right)$

or $y = ex - 2$

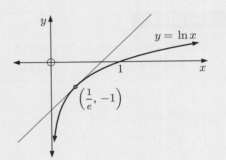

8 Find the equation of:

   a the tangent to the function $f : x \mapsto e^{-x}$ at the point where $x = 1$

   b the tangent to $y = \ln(2 - x)$ at the point where $x = -1$

   c the normal to $y = \ln \sqrt{x}$ at the point where $y = -1$.

Example 5 ◀⟩ **Self Tutor**

Find the equation of the tangent to $y = \tan x$ at the point where $x = \tfrac{\pi}{4}$.

When $x = \tfrac{\pi}{4}$, $y = \tan \tfrac{\pi}{4} = 1$

$\therefore$ the point of contact is $\left(\tfrac{\pi}{4}, 1\right)$.

Now $f(x) = \tan x$ has derivative $f'(x) = \dfrac{1}{\cos^2 x}$

$\therefore$ the tangent at $\left(\tfrac{\pi}{4}, 1\right)$ has gradient $\dfrac{1}{\cos^2 \frac{\pi}{4}} = \dfrac{1}{\left(\frac{1}{\sqrt{2}}\right)^2} = 2$

$\therefore$ the tangent has equation $\dfrac{y - 1}{x - \frac{\pi}{4}} = 2$

which is $y - 1 = 2x - \tfrac{\pi}{2}$

or $y = 2x + \left(1 - \tfrac{\pi}{2}\right)$

9 Show that the curve with equation $y = \dfrac{\cos x}{1 + \sin x}$ does not have any horizontal tangents.

10 Find the equation of:

    a the tangent to $y = \sin x$ at the origin

    b the tangent to $y = \tan x$ at the origin

    c the normal to $y = \cos x$ at the point where $x = \frac{\pi}{6}$

    d the normal to $y = \dfrac{1}{\sin(2x)}$ at the point $x = \frac{\pi}{4}$.

Example 6 ◀ⁿ **Self Tutor**

Find the coordinates of the point(s) where the tangent to $y = x^3 + x + 2$ at $(1, 4)$ meets the curve again.

Let $f(x) = x^3 + x + 2$

$\therefore\ f'(x) = 3x^2 + 1$

$\therefore\ f'(1) = 3 + 1 = 4$

$\therefore\quad$ the equation of the tangent at $(1, 4)$ is $\quad 4x - y = 4(1) - 4$

$$\text{or}\quad y = 4x.$$

Casio fx-CG20   **TI-84 Plus**   **TI-*n*spire**

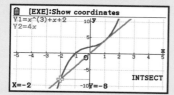 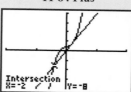 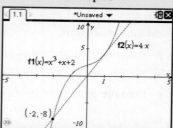

Using technology, $y = 4x$ meets $y = x^3 + x + 2$ at $(-2, -8)$.

---

11   **a** Find where the tangent to the curve $y = x^3$ at the point where $x = 2$, meets the curve again.

    b Find where the tangent to the curve $y = -x^3 + 2x^2 + 1$ at the point where $x = -1$, meets the curve again.

12 Consider the function $f(x) = x^2 + \dfrac{4}{x^2}$.

    a Find $f'(x)$.

    b Find the values of x at which the tangent to the curve is horizontal.

    c Show that the tangents at these points are the same line.

13 The tangent to $y = x^2 e^x$ at $x = 1$ cuts the x and y-axes at A and B respectively. Find the coordinates of A and B.

Example 7 ◀ɴ) **Self Tutor**

Find the equations of the tangents to $y = x^2$ from the external point $(2, 3)$.

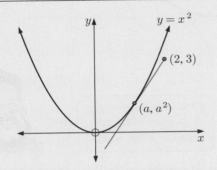

Let (a, a^2) be a general point on $f(x) = x^2$.

Now $f'(x) = 2x$, so $f'(a) = 2a$

∴ the equation of the tangent at (a, a^2) is

$$\frac{y - a^2}{x - a} = 2a$$

or $y - a^2 = 2ax - 2a^2$

or $y = 2ax - a^2$

Thus the tangents which pass through $(2, 3)$ satisfy

$$3 = 2a(2) - a^2$$
$$\therefore \quad a^2 - 4a + 3 = 0$$
$$\therefore \quad (a - 1)(a - 3) = 0$$
$$\therefore \quad a = 1 \text{ or } 3$$

∴ exactly two tangents pass through the external point $(2, 3)$.

If $a = 1$, the tangent has equation $y = 2x - 1$ with point of contact $(1, 1)$.

If $a = 3$, the tangent has equation $y = 6x - 9$ with point of contact $(3, 9)$.

14 **a** Find the equation of the tangent to $y = x^2 - x + 9$ at the point where $x = a$. Hence, find the equations of the two tangents from $(0, 0)$ to the curve. State the coordinates of the points of contact.

  b Find the equations of the tangents to $y = x^3$ from the external point $(-2, 0)$.

  c Find the equation of the normal to $y = \sqrt{x}$ from the external point $(4, 0)$.
  Hint: There is no normal at the point where $x = 0$, as this is the endpoint of the function.

15 Find the equation of the tangent to $y = e^x$ at the point where $x = a$.
Hence, find the equation of the tangent to $y = e^x$ which passes through the origin.

16 Consider $f(x) = \dfrac{8}{x^2}$.

  a Sketch the graph of the function.

  b Find the equation of the tangent at the point where $x = a$.

  c If the tangent in **b** cuts the x-axis at A and the y-axis at B, find the coordinates of A and B.

  d Find the area of triangle OAB and discuss the area of the triangle as $a \to \infty$.

17 Find, correct to 2 decimal places, the angle between the tangents to $y = 3e^{-x}$ and $y = 2 + e^x$ at their point of intersection.

18 A quadratic of the form $y = ax^2$, $a > 0$, touches the logarithmic function $y = \ln x$ as shown.

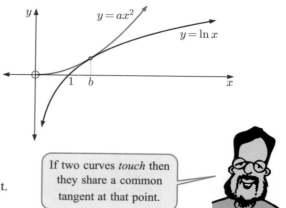

a If the x-coordinate of the point of contact is b, explain why $ab^2 = \ln b$ and $2ab = \dfrac{1}{b}$.

b Deduce that the point of contact is $(\sqrt{e}, \frac{1}{2})$.

c Find the value of a.

d Find the equation of the common tangent.

> If two curves *touch* then they share a common tangent at that point.

B   INCREASING AND DECREASING FUNCTIONS

The concepts of increasing and decreasing are closely linked to **intervals** or subsets of a function's domain.

We commonly use the algebraic notation shown in the table to describe subsets of the real numbers corresponding to intervals of the real number line.

Algebraic form	Geometric form		
$x \geqslant 2$		2	x
$x > 2$		2	x
$x \leqslant 4$		4	x
$x < 4$		4	x
$2 \leqslant x \leqslant 4$	2	4	x
$2 \leqslant x < 4$	2	4	x

Suppose S is an interval in the domain of $f(x)$, so $f(x)$ is defined for all x in S.

- $f(x)$ is **increasing** on S $\Leftrightarrow$ $f(a) \leqslant f(b)$ for all $a, b \in S$ such that $a < b$.
- $f(x)$ is **decreasing** on S $\Leftrightarrow$ $f(a) \geqslant f(b)$ for all $a, b \in S$ such that $a < b$.

For example:

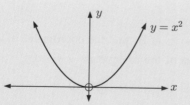

$y = x^2$ is decreasing for $x \leqslant 0$ and increasing for $x \geqslant 0$.

People often get confused about the point $x = 0$. They wonder how the curve can be both increasing and decreasing at the same point when it is clear that the tangent is horizontal. The answer is that increasing and decreasing are associated with *intervals*, not particular values for x. We must clearly state that $y = x^2$ is decreasing *on the interval* $x \leqslant 0$ and increasing *on the interval* $x \geqslant 0$.

We can determine intervals where a curve is increasing or decreasing by considering $f'(x)$ on the interval in question. For most functions that we deal with in this course:

- $f(x)$ is **increasing** on S $\Leftrightarrow$ $f'(x) \geqslant 0$ for all x in S
- $f(x)$ is **strictly increasing** on S $\Leftrightarrow$ $f'(x) > 0$ for all x in S
- $f(x)$ is **decreasing** on S $\Leftrightarrow$ $f'(x) \leqslant 0$ for all x in S
- $f(x)$ is **strictly decreasing** on S $\Leftrightarrow$ $f'(x) < 0$ for all x in S.

MONOTONICITY

Many functions are either increasing or decreasing for all $x \in \mathbb{R}$. We say these functions are **monotone increasing** or **monotone decreasing**.

For example:

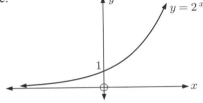

$y = 2^x$ is strictly increasing for all x.

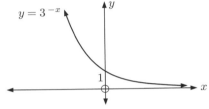

$y = 3^{-x}$ is strictly decreasing for all x.

The word "strictly" is not required for this course, but it is useful for understanding. It allows us to make statements like:

- for a **strictly increasing** function, an increase in x produces an increase in y
- for a **strictly decreasing** function, an increase in x produces a decrease in y.

Example 8   ◀) Self Tutor

Find intervals where $f(x)$ is:

a increasing

b decreasing.

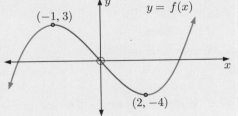

a $f(x)$ is increasing for $x \leqslant -1$ and for $x \geqslant 2$ since $f'(x) \geqslant 0$ on these intervals.

b $f(x)$ is decreasing for $-1 \leqslant x \leqslant 2$.

Sign diagrams for the derivative are extremely useful for determining intervals where a function is increasing or decreasing. Consider the following examples:

- $f(x) = x^2$

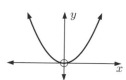

  DEMO

  $f'(x) = 2x$ which has sign diagram

  $$\xleftarrow{\hspace{2cm}} \underset{\substack{\text{decreasing} \\ 0}}{-} \Big| \underset{\text{increasing}}{+} \xrightarrow{\hspace{2cm}} x$$

  $\therefore\ f(x) = x^2$ is $\begin{cases} \text{decreasing for } x \leqslant 0 \\ \text{increasing for } x \geqslant 0. \end{cases}$

- $f(x) = -x^2$

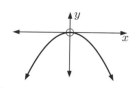

  DEMO

  $f'(x) = -2x$ which has sign diagram

  $$\xleftarrow{\hspace{2cm}} \underset{\text{increasing}}{+} \underset{0}{\Big|} \underset{\text{decreasing}}{-} \xrightarrow{\hspace{2cm}} x$$

  $\therefore\ f(x) = -x^2$ is $\begin{cases} \text{increasing for } x \leqslant 0 \\ \text{decreasing for } x \geqslant 0. \end{cases}$

- $f(x) = x^3$

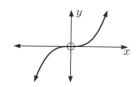

  DEMO

  $f'(x) = 3x^2$ which has sign diagram

  $$\xleftarrow{\hspace{2cm}} \underset{0}{+} \Big| + \xrightarrow{\hspace{2cm}} x$$
  increasing for all x
  (never negative)

  $\therefore\ f(x)$ is monotone increasing.

- $f(x) = x^3 - 3x + 4$

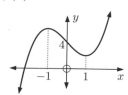

  DEMO

  $\begin{aligned} f'(x) &= 3x^2 - 3 \\ &= 3(x^2 - 1) \\ &= 3(x + 1)(x - 1) \end{aligned}$

  which has sign diagram

  $$\xleftarrow{\hspace{2cm}} + \underset{-1}{\Big|} - \underset{1}{\Big|} + \xrightarrow{\hspace{2cm}} x$$
  increasing   decreasing   increasing

  $\therefore\ f(x)$ is $\begin{cases} \text{increasing for } x \leqslant -1 \text{ and for } x \geqslant 1 \\ \text{decreasing for } -1 \leqslant x \leqslant 1. \end{cases}$

Example 9   ◀)) **Self Tutor**

Find the intervals where the following functions are increasing or decreasing:

a $f(x) = -x^3 + 3x^2 + 5$ **b** $f(x) = 3x^4 - 8x^3 + 2$

a $f(x) = -x^3 + 3x^2 + 5$ **TI-84 Plus**

$\therefore\ f'(x) = -3x^2 + 6x$

$ = -3x(x - 2)$

which has sign diagram

$$\xleftarrow{\hspace{1.5cm}} \underset{0}{-} \Big| \underset{}{+} \underset{2}{\Big|} - \xrightarrow{\hspace{1.5cm}} x$$

So, $f(x)$ is decreasing for $x \leqslant 0$ and for $x \geqslant 2$, and increasing for $0 \leqslant x \leqslant 2$.

b $f(x) = 3x^4 - 8x^3 + 2$

$\therefore \ \ f'(x) = 12x^3 - 24x^2$

$\qquad \qquad = 12x^2(x - 2)$

which has sign diagram

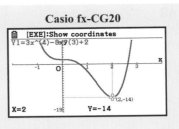

Casio fx-CG20

So, $f(x)$ is decreasing for $x \leqslant 2$, and increasing for $x \geqslant 2$.

Remember that $f(x)$ must be defined for all x on an interval before we can classify the function as increasing or decreasing on that interval. We need to take care with vertical asymptotes and other values for x where the function is not defined.

◀) **Self Tutor**

Consider $f(x) = \dfrac{2x - 3}{x^2 + 2x - 3}$.

a Show that $f'(x) = \dfrac{-2x(x - 3)}{(x + 3)^2(x - 1)^2}$ and draw its sign diagram.

b Hence, find the intervals where $y = f(x)$ is increasing or decreasing.

a $f(x) = \dfrac{2x - 3}{x^2 + 2x - 3}$

$\therefore \ \ f'(x) = \dfrac{2(x^2 + 2x - 3) - (2x - 3)(2x + 2)}{(x^2 + 2x - 3)^2}$ {quotient rule}

$\qquad = \dfrac{2x^2 + 4x - 6 - [4x^2 - 2x - 6]}{((x - 1)(x + 3))^2}$

$\qquad = \dfrac{-2x^2 + 6x}{(x - 1)^2(x + 3)^2}$

$\qquad = \dfrac{-2x(x - 3)}{(x - 1)^2(x + 3)^2}$ which has sign diagram:

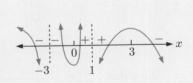

b $f(x)$ is increasing for $0 \leqslant x < 1$

$\qquad$ and for $1 < x \leqslant 3$.

$f(x)$ is decreasing for $x < -3$

$\qquad$ and for $-3 < x \leqslant 0$

$\qquad$ and for $x \geqslant 3$.

TI-nspire

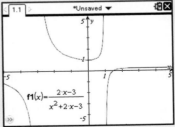

EXERCISE 16B

1 Write down the intervals where the graphs are: **i** increasing   **ii** decreasing.

a
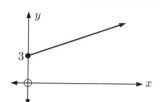

b
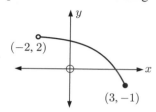

c
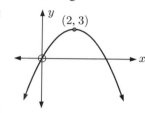

d
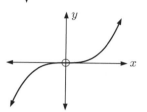

e
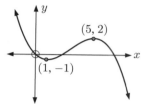

f
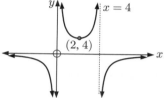

2 Find the intervals where $f(x)$ is increasing or decreasing:

 a $f(x) = x^2$

 c $f(x) = 2x^2 + 3x - 4$

 e $f(x) = \dfrac{2}{\sqrt{x}}$

 g $f(x) = e^x$

 i $f(x) = -2x^3 + 4x$

 k $f(x) = 3 + e^{-x}$

 m $f(x) = 3x^4 - 16x^3 + 24x^2 - 2$

 o $f(x) = x^3 - 6x^2 + 3x - 1$

 b $f(x) = -x^3$

 d $f(x) = \sqrt{x}$

 f $f(x) = x^3 - 6x^2$

 h $f(x) = \ln x$

 j $f(x) = -4x^3 + 15x^2 + 18x + 3$

 l $f(x) = xe^x$

 n $f(x) = 2x^3 + 9x^2 + 6x - 7$

 p $f(x) = x - 2\sqrt{x}$

3 Consider $f(x) = \dfrac{4x}{x^2 + 1}$.

 a Show that $f'(x) = \dfrac{-4(x + 1)(x - 1)}{(x^2 + 1)^2}$ and draw its sign diagram.

 b Hence, find intervals where $y = f(x)$ is increasing or decreasing.

4 Consider $f(x) = \dfrac{4x}{(x - 1)^2}$.

 a Show that $f'(x) = \dfrac{-4(x + 1)}{(x - 1)^3}$ and draw its sign diagram.

 b Hence, find intervals where $y = f(x)$ is increasing or decreasing.

5 Consider $f(x) = \dfrac{-x^2 + 4x - 7}{x - 1}$.

 a Show that $f'(x) = \dfrac{-(x + 1)(x - 3)}{(x - 1)^2}$ and draw its sign diagram.

 b Hence, find intervals where $y = f(x)$ is increasing or decreasing.

6 Find intervals where $f(x)$ is increasing or decreasing if:

a $f(x) = \dfrac{x^3}{x^2 - 1}$

b $f(x) = e^{-x^2}$

c $f(x) = x^2 + \dfrac{4}{x - 1}$

d $f(x) = \dfrac{e^{-x}}{x}$

C   STATIONARY POINTS

> A **stationary point** of a function is a point where $f'(x) = 0$.
>
> It could be a local maximum, local minimum, or stationary inflection.

TURNING POINTS (MAXIMA AND MINIMA)

Consider the following graph which has a restricted domain of $-5 \leqslant x \leqslant 6$.

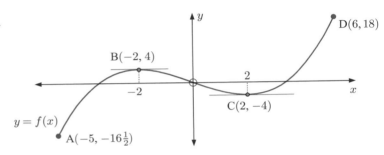

A is a **global minimum** as it has the minimum value of y on the entire domain.

B is a **local maximum** as it is a turning point where the curve has shape ⌢ and $f'(x) = 0$ at that point.

C is a **local minimum** as it is a turning point where the curve has shape ⌣ and $f'(x) = 0$ at that point.

D is a **global maximum** as it is the maximum value of y on the entire domain.

For many functions, a local maximum or minimum is also the global maximum or minimum.

For example, for $y = x^2$ the point $(0, 0)$ is a local minimum and is also the global minimum.

STATIONARY POINTS OF INFLECTION

It is not always true that whenever we find a value of x where $f'(x) = 0$, we have a local maximum or minimum.

For example, $f(x) = x^3$ has $f'(x) = 3x^2$
and $f'(x) = 0$ when $x = 0$.

The x-axis is a tangent to the curve which actually crosses over the curve at $O(0, 0)$. This tangent is horizontal but $O(0, 0)$ is neither a local maximum nor a local minimum.

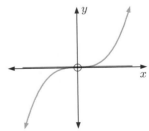

It is called a **stationary inflection** (or **inflexion**) as the curve changes its curvature or shape.

SIGN DIAGRAMS

Consider the graph alongside.

The sign diagram of its gradient function is shown directly beneath it.

We can use the sign diagram to describe the stationary points of the function.

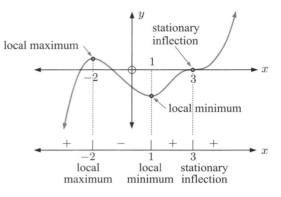

Stationary point where $f'(a) = 0$	Sign diagram of $f'(x)$ near $x = a$	Shape of curve near $x = a$
local maximum	$+ \mid -$ at a	$x = a$
local minimum	$- \mid +$ at a	$x = a$
stationary inflection	$+ \mid +$ at a or $- \mid -$ at a	$x = a$ or $x = a$

Example 11   ◀)) **Self Tutor**

Find and classify all stationary points of $f(x) = x^3 - 3x^2 - 9x + 5$.

$f(x) = x^3 - 3x^2 - 9x + 5$

$\therefore \quad f'(x) = 3x^2 - 6x - 9$

$\qquad = 3(x^2 - 2x - 3)$

$\qquad = 3(x - 3)(x + 1)$ which has sign diagram:

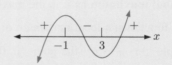

So, we have a local maximum at $x = -1$ and a local minimum at $x = 3$.

$f(-1) = (-1)^3 - 3(-1)^2 - 9(-1) + 5$
$\qquad = 10$

$f(3) = 3^3 - 3 \times 3^2 - 9 \times 3 + 5$
$\qquad = -22$

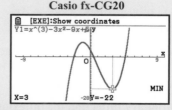

TI-84 Plus

There is a local maximum at $(-1, 10)$.

Casio fx-CG20

There is a local minimum at $(3, -22)$.

Example 12   ◀) **Self Tutor**

Find the exact position and nature of the stationary points of $y = (x - 2)e^{-x}$.

$\dfrac{dy}{dx} = (1)e^{-x} + (x - 2)e^{-x}(-1)$ {product rule}

$\quad = e^{-x}(1 - (x - 2))$

$\quad = \dfrac{3 - x}{e^x}$ where e^x is positive for all x.

So, $\dfrac{dy}{dx} = 0$ when $x = 3$.

The sign diagram of $\dfrac{dy}{dx}$ is:

$\therefore$ at $x = 3$ we have a local maximum.

But when $x = 3$, $y = (1)e^{-3} = \dfrac{1}{e^3}$

$\therefore$ the local maximum is at $\left(3, \dfrac{1}{e^3}\right)$.

If we are asked to find the greatest or least value of a function on an interval, then we must also check the value of the function at the endpoints. We seek the *global* maximum or minimum on the given domain.

Example 13   ◀) **Self Tutor**

Find the greatest and least value of $y = x^3 - 6x^2 + 5$ on the interval $-2 \leqslant x \leqslant 5$.

Now $\dfrac{dy}{dx} = 3x^2 - 12x$

$\quad = 3x(x - 4)$

$\therefore \dfrac{dy}{dx} = 0$ when $x = 0$ or 4.

The sign diagram of $\dfrac{dy}{dx}$ is:

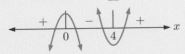

$\therefore$ there is a local maximum at $x = 0$, and a local minimum at $x = 4$.

Critical value (x)	$f(x)$
-2 (end point)	-27
0 (local max)	5
4 (local min)	-27
5 (end point)	-20

The greatest of these values is 5 when $x = 0$.

The least of these values is -27 when $x = -2$ and when $x = 4$.

EXERCISE 16C

1 The tangents at points A, B and C are horizontal.

    a Classify points A, B and C.

    b Draw a sign diagram for the gradient function $f'(x)$ for all x.

    c State intervals where $y = f(x)$ is:

        i increasing   **ii** decreasing.

    d Draw a sign diagram for $f(x)$ for all x.

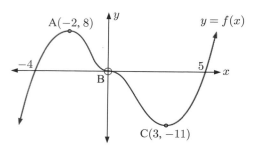

2 For each of the following functions, find and classify any stationary points. Sketch the function, showing all important features.

    a $f(x) = x^2 - 2$

    b $f(x) = x^3 + 1$

    c $f(x) = x^3 - 3x + 2$

    d $f(x) = x^4 - 2x^2$

    e $f(x) = x^3 - 6x^2 + 12x + 1$

    f $f(x) = \sqrt{x} + 2$

    g $f(x) = x - \sqrt{x}$

    h $f(x) = x^4 - 6x^2 + 8x - 3$

    i $f(x) = 1 - x\sqrt{x}$

    j $f(x) = x^4 - 2x^2 - 8$

3 At what value of x does the quadratic function $f(x) = ax^2 + bx + c$, $a \neq 0$, have a stationary point? Under what conditions is the stationary point a local maximum or a local minimum?

4 Find the position and nature of the stationary point(s) of:

    a $y = xe^{-x}$

    b $y = x^2 e^x$

    c $y = \dfrac{e^x}{x}$

    d $y = e^{-x}(x + 2)$

5 $f(x) = 2x^3 + ax^2 - 24x + 1$ has a local maximum at $x = -4$. Find a.

6 $f(x) = x^3 + ax + b$ has a stationary point at $(-2,\ 3)$.

    a Find the values of a and b.

    b Find the position and nature of all stationary points.

7 Consider $f(x) = x \ln x$.

    a For what values of x is $f(x)$ defined?

    b Show that the global minimum value of $f(x)$ is $-\dfrac{1}{e}$.

8 For each of the following, determine the position and nature of the stationary points on the interval $0 \leqslant x \leqslant 2\pi$, then show them on a graph of the function.

    a $f(x) = \sin x$

    b $f(x) = \cos(2x)$

    c $f(x) = \sin^2 x$

    d $f(x) = e^{\sin x}$

    e $f(x) = \sin(2x) + 2\cos x$

9 The cubic polynomial $P(x) = ax^3 + bx^2 + cx + d$ touches the line with equation $y = 9x + 2$ at the point $(0,\ 2)$, and has a stationary point at $(-1,\ -7)$. Find $P(x)$.

10 Find the greatest and least value of:

    a $x^3 - 12x - 2$ for $-3 \leqslant x \leqslant 5$

    b $4 - 3x^2 + x^3$ for $-2 \leqslant x \leqslant 3$

11 Show that $y = 4e^{-x} \sin x$ has a local maximum when $x = \frac{\pi}{4}$.

12 Prove that $\dfrac{\ln x}{x} \leqslant \dfrac{1}{e}$ for all $x > 0$.

  Hint: Let $f(x) = \dfrac{\ln x}{x}$ and find its greatest value.

13 Consider the function $f(x) = x - \ln x$.

 a Show that the graph of $y = f(x)$ has a local minimum and that this is the only turning point.

 b Hence prove that $\ln x \leqslant x - 1$ for all $x > 0$.

D INFLECTIONS AND SHAPE

When a curve, or part of a curve, has shape:

we say that the shape is **concave downwards**

we say that the shape is **concave upwards**.

TEST FOR SHAPE

Consider the **concave downwards** curve:

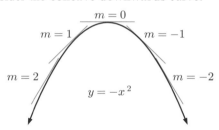

Wherever we are on the curve, as x increases, the gradient of the tangent decreases.

$\therefore$ $f'(x)$ is decreasing

$\therefore$ its derivative is negative,

   which means $f''(x) < 0$.

Likewise, if the curve is **concave upwards**:

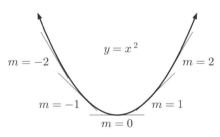

Wherever we are on the curve, as x increases, the gradient of the tangent increases.

$\therefore$ $f'(x)$ is increasing

$\therefore$ its derivative is positive,

   which means $f''(x) > 0$.

POINTS OF INFLECTION (INFLEXION)

A **point of inflection** is a point on a curve at which there is a change of **curvature** or shape.

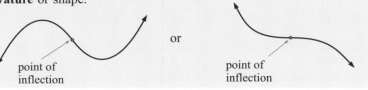

or

DEMO

If the tangent at a point of inflection is horizontal then this point is a **horizontal** or **stationary inflection**.

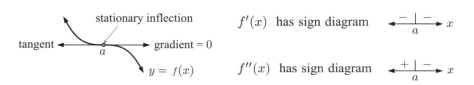

$f'(x)$ has sign diagram

$f''(x)$ has sign diagram

If the tangent at a point of inflection is not horizontal, we have a **non-horizontal** or **non-stationary inflection**.

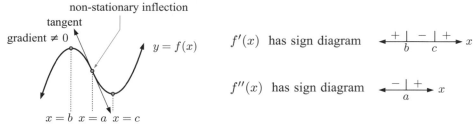

$f'(x)$ has sign diagram

$f''(x)$ has sign diagram

The tangent at the point of inflection, also called the **inflecting tangent**, crosses the curve at that point.

> There is a **point of inflection** at $x = a$ if $f''(a) = 0$ **and** the sign of $f''(x)$ changes at $x = a$.
>
> The point of inflection corresponds to a change in curvature.
>
> In the vicinity of a, $f''(x)$ has sign diagram either ⟵ $+$ | $-$ → x or ⟵ $-$ | $+$ → x

Observe that if $f(x) = x^4$ then

$f'(x) = 4x^3$ and $f''(x) = 12x^2$ and $f''(x)$ has sign diagram

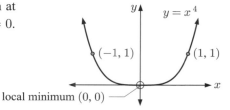

Although $f''(0) = 0$ we do not have a point of inflection at $(0, 0)$ because the sign of $f''(x)$ does not change at $x = 0$. In fact, the graph of $f(x) = x^4$ is:

SUMMARY

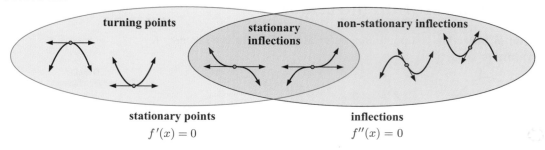

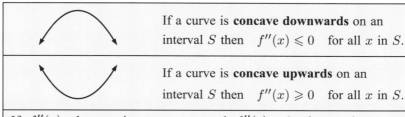

| | If a curve is **concave downwards** on an interval S then $f''(x) \leqslant 0$ for all x in S. |

| | If a curve is **concave upwards** on an interval S then $f''(x) \geqslant 0$ for all x in S. |

If $f''(x)$ changes sign at $x = a$, and $f''(a) = 0$, then we have a

- **stationary inflection** if $f'(a) = 0$
- **non-stationary inflection** if $f'(a) \neq 0$.

Click on the demo icon to examine some standard functions for turning points, points of inflection, and intervals where the function is increasing, decreasing, and concave up or down.

DEMO

Example 14   ◀) Self Tutor

Find and classify all points of inflection of $f(x) = x^4 - 4x^3 + 5$.

$f(x) = x^4 - 4x^3 + 5$

$\therefore f'(x) = 4x^3 - 12x^2 = 4x^2(x - 3)$

$\therefore f''(x) = 12x^2 - 24x$

$\quad = 12x(x - 2)$

$\therefore f''(x) = 0$ when $x = 0$ or 2

Since the signs of $f''(x)$ change about $x = 0$ and $x = 2$, these two points are points of inflection.

Also $f'(0) = 0$, $f'(2) = 32 - 48 \neq 0$

and $f(0) = 5$, $f(2) = 16 - 32 + 5 = -11$

Thus $(0, 5)$ is a stationary inflection, and $(2, -11)$ is a non-stationary inflection.

EXERCISE 16D.1

1 **a** In the diagram shown, B and D are stationary points, and C is a point of inflection. Complete the table by indicating whether each value is zero, positive, or negative:

Point	$f(x)$	$f'(x)$	$f''(x)$
A	+		
B			
C			
D		0	
E			

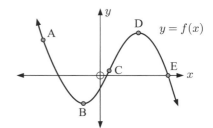

b Describe the turning points of $y = f(x)$.

c Describe the inflection point of $y = f(x)$.

2 Find and classify all points of inflection of:

a $f(x) = x^2 + 3$

b $f(x) = 2 - x^3$

c $f(x) = x^3 - 6x^2 + 9x + 1$

d $f(x) = x^3 + 6x^2 + 12x + 5$

e $f(x) = -3x^4 - 8x^3 + 2$

f $f(x) = 3 - \dfrac{1}{\sqrt{x}}$

Example 15   ◀) **Self Tutor**

Consider $f(x) = 3x^4 - 16x^3 + 24x^2 - 9$.

a Find and classify all points where $f'(x) = 0$.

b Find and classify all points of inflection.

c Find intervals where the function is increasing or decreasing.

d Find intervals where the function is concave up or down.

e Sketch the function showing the features you have found.

---

a $f(x) = 3x^4 - 16x^3 + 24x^2 - 9$

$\therefore \quad f'(x) = 12x^3 - 48x^2 + 48x$ $\therefore \quad f'(x)$ has sign diagram:

$\qquad = 12x(x^2 - 4x + 4)$

$\qquad = 12x(x - 2)^2$

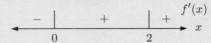

Now $f(0) = -9$ and $f(2) = 7$

$\therefore \quad (0, -9)$ is a local minimum and $(2, 7)$ is a stationary inflection.

b $f''(x) = 36x^2 - 96x + 48$ $\therefore \quad f''(x)$ has sign diagram:

$\qquad = 12(3x^2 - 8x + 4)$

$\qquad = 12(x - 2)(3x - 2)$

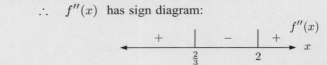

Now $f(\tfrac{2}{3}) \approx -2.48$

$\therefore \quad (2, 7)$ is a stationary inflection and $(\tfrac{2}{3}, -2.48)$ is a non-stationary inflection.

c $f(x)$ is decreasing for $x \leqslant 0$
   $f(x)$ is increasing for $x \geqslant 0$.

e

d $f(x)$ is concave up for $x \leqslant \tfrac{2}{3}$ and $x \geqslant 2$
   $f(x)$ is concave down for $\tfrac{2}{3} \leqslant x \leqslant 2$.

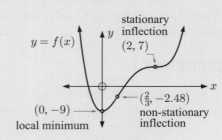

---

3 For each of the following functions:

i Find and classify all points where $f'(x) = 0$

ii Find and classify all points of inflection

iii Find intervals where the function is increasing or decreasing

iv Find intervals where the function is concave up or down

v Sketch the function showing the features you have found.

a $f(x) = x^2$

b $f(x) = x^3$

c $f(x) = \sqrt{x}$

d $f(x) = x^3 - 3x^2 - 24x + 1$

e $f(x) = 3x^4 + 4x^3 - 2$

f $f(x) = (x-1)^4$

g $f(x) = x^4 - 4x^2 + 3$

h $f(x) = 3 - \dfrac{4}{\sqrt{x}}$

Example 16   ◀⑴ **Self Tutor**

Consider the function $y = 2 - e^{-x}$.

a   Find the x-intercept.

b   Find the y-intercept.

c   Show algebraically that the function is increasing for all x.

d   Show algebraically that the function is concave down for all x.

e   Use technology to help graph $y = 2 - e^{-x}$.

f   Explain why $y = 2$ is a horizontal asymptote.

---

a   The x-intercept occurs when $y = 0$

$\therefore \quad e^{-x} = 2$

$\therefore \quad -x = \ln 2$

$\therefore \quad x = -\ln 2$

$\therefore$ the x-intercept is $-\ln 2 \approx -0.693$

b   The y-intercept occurs when $x = 0$

$\therefore \quad y = 2 - e^0 = 2 - 1 = 1$

c $\dfrac{dy}{dx} = 0 - e^{-x}(-1) = e^{-x} = \dfrac{1}{e^x}$

Now $e^x > 0$ for all x,

so $\dfrac{dy}{dx} > 0$ for all x.

$\therefore$ the function is increasing for all x.

d $\dfrac{d^2y}{dx^2} = e^{-x}(-1)$

$= \dfrac{-1}{e^x}$ which is < 0 for all x.

$\therefore$ the function is concave down for all x.

e

Casio fx-CG20	TI-84 Plus	TI-*n*spire
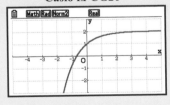	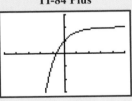	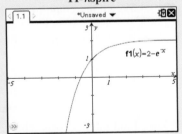

f   As $x \to \infty$, $e^x \to \infty$ and $e^{-x} \to 0$

$\therefore \quad y \to 2^-$

Hence, the horizontal asymptote is $y = 2$.

---

4   The function $f(x) = e^{2x} - 3$ cuts the x-axis at A and the y-axis at B.

a   Find the coordinates of A and B.

b   Show algebraically that the function is increasing for all x.

c   Find $f''(x)$ and hence explain why $f(x)$ is concave up for all x.

d   Use technology to help graph $y = e^{2x} - 3$.

e   Explain why $y = -3$ is a horizontal asymptote.

5 Suppose $f(x) = e^x - 3$ and $g(x) = 3 - 5e^{-x}$ where $-3 \leqslant x \leqslant 4$.

   a Find the x and y-intercepts of both functions.

   b Discuss $f(x)$ and $g(x)$ as $x \to \infty$ and as $x \to -\infty$.

   c Find algebraically the point(s) of intersection of the functions.

   d Sketch the graph of both functions on the same set of axes. Show all important features on your graph.

6 The function $y = e^x - 3e^{-x}$ cuts the x-axis at P and the y-axis at Q.

   a Determine the coordinates of P and Q.

   b Prove that the function is increasing for all x.

   c Show that $\dfrac{d^2y}{dx^2} = y$. What can be deduced about the concavity of the function above and below the x-axis?

   d Use technology to help graph $y = e^x - 3e^{-x}$.
Show the features of **a**, **b**, and **c** on the graph.

7 Consider $f(x) = \ln(2x - 1) - 3$.

   a Find the x-intercept.

   b Can $f(0)$ be found? What is the significance of this result?

   c Find the gradient of the tangent to the curve at $x = 1$.

   d Find the domain of f.

   e Find $f''(x)$ and hence explain why $f(x)$ is concave down for all x in the domain of f.

   f Graph the function, showing the features you have found.

8 Consider $f(x) = \ln x$.

   a For what values of x is $f(x)$ defined?

   b Find the signs of $f'(x)$ and $f''(x)$ and comment on the geometrical significance of each.

   c Sketch the graph of $f(x) = \ln x$ and find the equation of the normal at the point where $y = 1$.

9 Consider the function $f(x) = \dfrac{e^x}{x}$.

   a Does the graph of $y = f(x)$ have any x or y-intercepts?

   b Discuss $f(x)$ as $x \to \infty$ and as $x \to -\infty$.

   c Find and classify any stationary points of $y = f(x)$.

   d Find the intervals where $f(x)$ is: **i** concave up   **ii** concave down.

   e Sketch the graph of $y = f(x)$ showing all important features.

   f Find the equation of the tangent to $f(x) = \dfrac{e^x}{x}$ at the point where $x = -1$.

10 A function commonly used in statistics is the *normal distribution function* $f(x) = \dfrac{1}{\sqrt{2\pi}}e^{-\frac{1}{2}x^2}$.

   a Find the stationary points of the function and find the intervals where the function is increasing and decreasing.

   b Find all points of inflection.

   c Discuss $f(x)$ as $x \to \infty$ and as $x \to -\infty$.

   d Sketch the graph of $y = f(x)$ showing all important features.

ZEROS OF $f'(x)$ AND $f''(x)$

Suppose $y = f(x)$ has an inflection point at $x = a$.

$\therefore$ $f''(a) = 0$ and the derivative function $f'(x)$ has a stationary point at $x = a$.

If $f''(x)$ changes sign at $x = a$, then the stationary point of $f'(x)$ is a local maximum or local minimum.

If, in addition, $f'(a) = 0$, then the local maximum or local minimum of $f'(x)$ lies on the x-axis, and we know $y = f(x)$ has a stationary inflection point at $x = a$. Otherwise, $y = f(x)$ has a non-stationary inflection point at $x = a$.

Example 17   ◀) **Self Tutor**

Using the graph of $y = f(x)$ alongside, sketch the graphs of $y = f'(x)$ and $y = f''(x)$.

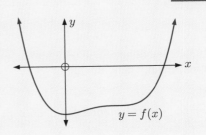

The local minimum corresponds to $f'(x) = 0$ and $f''(x) \neq 0$.

The non-stationary point of inflection corresponds to $f'(x) \neq 0$ and $f''(x) = 0$.

The stationary point of inflection corresponds to $f'(x) = 0$ and $f''(x) = 0$.

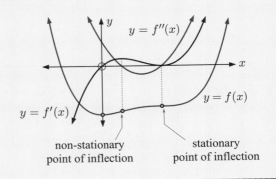

EXERCISE 16D.2

1 Using the graphs of $y = f(x)$ below, sketch the graphs of $y = f'(x)$ and $y = f''(x)$. Show clearly the axes intercepts and turning points.

a
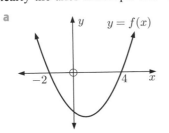

b
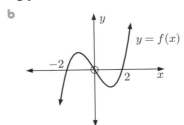

c
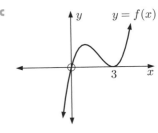

Example 18

◀) Self Tutor

The graph alongside shows a gradient function $y = f'(x)$.

Sketch a graph which could be $y = f(x)$, showing clearly the x-values corresponding to all stationary points and points of inflection.

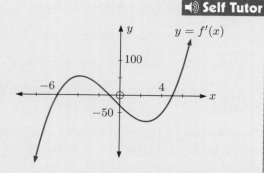

Sign diagram of $f'(x)$ is:

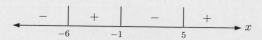

$f'(x)$ is a maximum when $x = -4$ and a minimum when $x \approx 2\frac{1}{2}$.

At these points $f''(x) = 0$ but $f'(x) \neq 0$, so they correspond to non-stationary points of inflection.

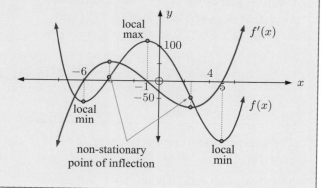

2   For the graphs of $y = f'(x)$ below, sketch a graph which could be $y = f(x)$. Show clearly the location of any stationary points and points of inflection.

a

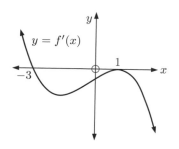

b

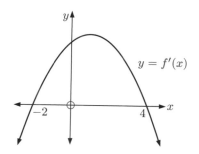

ACTIVITY

Click on the icon to run a card game on curve properties.

CARD GAME

REVIEW SET 16A   NON-CALCULATOR

1   Find the equation of the tangent to $y = -2x^2$ at the point where $x = -1$.

2   Find the equation of the normal to $y = \dfrac{1 - 2x}{x^2}$ at the point where $x = 1$.

3   Consider the function $f(x) = \dfrac{3x - 2}{x + 3}$.

  a   State the equation of the vertical asymptote.
  b   Find the axes intercepts.
  c   Find $f'(x)$ and draw its sign diagram.
  d   Does the function have any stationary points?

4   Find the equation of the normal to $y = e^{-x^2}$ at the point where $x = 1$.

5   Show that the equation of the tangent to $y = x \tan x$ at $x = \frac{\pi}{4}$ is $(2 + \pi)x - 2y = \dfrac{\pi^2}{4}$.

6   The tangent to $y = \dfrac{ax + b}{\sqrt{x}}$ at $x = 1$ is $2x - y = 1$. Find a and b.

7   Show that the equation of the tangent to $f(x) = 4\ln(2x)$ at the point $P(1, 4\ln 2)$ is given by $y = 4x + 4\ln 2 - 4$.

8   Consider the function $f(x) = \dfrac{e^x}{x - 1}$.

  a   Find the y-intercept of the function.
  b   For what values of x is $f(x)$ defined?
  c   Find the signs of $f'(x)$ and $f''(x)$ and comment on the geometrical significance of each.
  d   Sketch the graph of $y = f(x)$.
  e   Find the equation of the tangent at the point where $x = 2$.

9   The curve $y = 2x^3 + ax + b$ has a tangent with gradient 10 at the point $(-2, 33)$. Find the values of a and b.

10   The line through $A(2, 4)$ and $B(0, 8)$ is a tangent to $y = \dfrac{a}{(x + 2)^2}$. Find a.

11   Find the coordinates of P and Q if (PQ) is the tangent to $y = \dfrac{5}{\sqrt{x}}$ at $(1, 5)$.

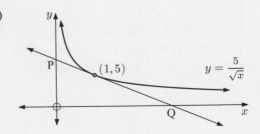

12 Given the graph of $y = f'(x)$ drawn alongside, sketch a possible curve for $y = f(x)$. Show clearly any turning points and points of inflection.

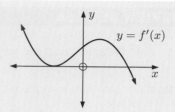

13 Find the equation of the tangent to $y = \ln(x^2 + 3)$ at the point where $x = 0$.

REVIEW SET 16B   CALCULATOR

1 Determine the equation of any horizontal tangents to the curve with equation $y = x^3 - 3x^2 - 9x + 2$.

2 The tangent to $y = x^2 \sqrt{1 - x}$ at $x = -3$ cuts the axes at points A and B. Determine the area of triangle OAB.

3 Suppose $f(x) = x^3 + ax$, $a < 0$ has a turning point when $x = \sqrt{2}$.
  a Find a.
  b Find the position and nature of all stationary points of $y = f(x)$.
  c Sketch the graph of $y = f(x)$.

4 At the point where $x = 0$, the tangent to $f(x) = e^{4x} + px + q$ has equation $y = 5x - 7$. Find p and q.

5 Find where the tangent to $y = 2x^3 + 4x - 1$ at $(1, 5)$ cuts the curve again.

6 Find a given that the tangent to $y = \dfrac{4}{(ax + 1)^2}$ at $x = 0$ passes through $(1, 0)$.

7 Consider the function $f(x) = e^x - x$.
  a Find and classify any stationary points of $y = f(x)$.
  b Discuss what happens to $f(x)$ as $x \to \infty$.
  c Find $f''(x)$ and draw its sign diagram. Give a geometrical interpretation for the sign of $f''(x)$.
  d Sketch the graph of $y = f(x)$.
  e Deduce that $e^x \geqslant x + 1$ for all x.

8 Find the equation of the normal to $y = \dfrac{x + 1}{x^2 - 2}$ at the point where $x = 1$.

9 Show that $y = 2 - \dfrac{7}{1 + 2x}$ has no horizontal tangents.

10 Find the equation of the quadratic function $g(x)$ where $y = g(x)$ is the parabola shown. Give your answer in the form $g(x) = ax^2 + bx + c$.

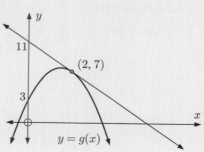

11 Consider $f(x) = \sqrt{\cos x}$ for $0 \leqslant x \leqslant 2\pi$.

    a For what values of x in this interval is $f(x)$ defined?

    b Find $f'(x)$ and hence find intervals where $f(x)$ is increasing and decreasing.

    c Sketch the graph of $y = f(x)$ on $0 \leqslant x \leqslant 2\pi$.

12 The graph of $y = f(x)$ is given.
On the same axes sketch the graph of
$y = f'(x)$.

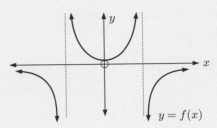

13   **a** Sketch the graph of $x \mapsto \dfrac{4}{x}$ for $x > 0$.

    b Find the equation of the tangent to the function at the point where $x = k$, $k > 0$.

    c If the tangent in **b** cuts the x-axis at A and the y-axis at B, find the coordinates of A and B.

    d What can be deduced about the area of triangle OAB?

    e Find k if the normal to the curve at $x = k$ passes through the point $(1, 1)$.

REVIEW SET 16C

1 Find the equation of the normal to $y = \dfrac{1}{\sqrt{x}}$ at the point where $x = 4$.

2 $y = f(x)$ is the parabola shown.

    a Find $f(3)$ and $f'(3)$.

    b Hence find $f(x)$ in the form
$f(x) = ax^2 + bx + c$.

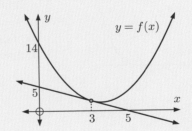

3 $y = 2x$ is a tangent to the curve $y = x^3 + ax + b$ at $x = 1$. Find a and b.

4 The tangent to $y = x^3 + ax^2 - 4x + 3$ at $x = 1$ is parallel to the line $y = 3x$.

    a Find the value of a and the equation of the tangent at $x = 1$.

    b Where does the tangent cut the curve again?

5 Find where the tangent to $y = \ln(x^4 + 3)$ at $x = 1$ cuts the y-axis.

6 Consider the function $f(x) = 2x^3 - 3x^2 - 36x + 7$.

    a Find and classify all stationary points and points of inflection.

    b Find intervals where the function is increasing and decreasing.

    c Find intervals where the function is concave up or down.

    d Sketch the graph of $y = f(x)$ showing all important features.

7 If the normal to $f(x) = \dfrac{3x}{1+x}$ at $(2, 2)$ cuts the axes at B and C, determine the length of [BC].

8 Consider the function $f(x) = x^3 - 4x^2 + 4x$.

   a Find all axes intercepts.

   b Find and classify all stationary points and points of inflection.

   c Sketch the graph of $y = f(x)$ showing features from **a** and **b**.

9 Find the equation of:

   a the tangent to $y = \dfrac{1}{\sin x}$ at the point where $x = \frac{\pi}{3}$

   b the normal to $y = \cos(\frac{x}{2})$ at the point where $x = \frac{\pi}{2}$.

10 The curve $f(x) = 3x^3 + ax^2 + b$ has tangent with gradient 0 at the point $(-2, 14)$. Find a and b and hence $f''(-2)$.

11 Show that the curves whose equations are $y = \sqrt{3x+1}$ and $y = \sqrt{5x - x^2}$ have a common tangent at their point of intersection. Find the equation of this common tangent.

12 Consider the function $f(x) = x + \ln x$.

   a Find the values of x for which $f(x)$ is defined.

   b Find the signs of $f'(x)$ and $f''(x)$ and comment on the geometrical significance of each.

   c Sketch the graph of $y = f(x)$.

   d Find the equation of the normal at the point where $x = 1$.

13

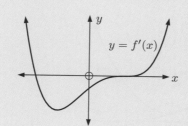

$y = f'(x)$

The graph of $y = f'(x)$ is drawn.

On the same axes clearly draw a possible graph of $y = f(x)$. Show all turning points and points of inflection.

Chapter **17**

Applications of
differential calculus

Syllabus reference: 6.3, 6.6

Contents: A   Kinematics
B   Rates of change
C   Optimisation

OPENING PROBLEM

Michael rides up a hill and down the other side to his friend's house. The dots on the graph show Michael's position at various times t.

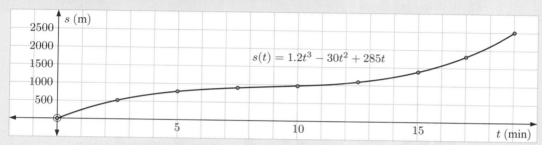

$t = 0$ $t = 5$ $t = 15$ $t = 17$ $t = 19$

Michael's place $t = 10$

friend's house

DEMO

The distance Michael has travelled at various times is given by the function
$s(t) = 1.2t^3 - 30t^2 + 285t$ metres for $0 \leqslant t \leqslant 19$ minutes.

$s(t) = 1.2t^3 - 30t^2 + 285t$

Things to think about:

a Explain why $s(t)$ should be an increasing function.

b Can you find a function for Michael's *speed* at any time t?

c Michael's *acceleration* is the rate at which his speed is changing with respect to time. How can we interpret $s''(t)$?

d Can you find Michael's speed and acceleration at the time $t = 15$ minutes?

e At what point do you think the hill was steepest? How far had Michael travelled to this point?

We saw in the previous chapter some of the curve properties that can be analysed using calculus. In this chapter we look at applying these techniques in real world problems of:

- kinematics (motion problems of displacement, velocity, and acceleration)
- rates of change
- optimisation (maxima and minima).

A   KINEMATICS

In the **Opening Problem** we are dealing with the movement of Michael riding his bicycle. We do not know the direction Michael is travelling, so we talk simply about the distance he has travelled and his speed.

For problems of **motion in a straight line**, we can include the direction the object is travelling along the line. We therefore can talk about displacement and velocity.

DISPLACEMENT

Suppose an object P moves along a straight line so that its position
s from an origin O is given as some function of time t. We write
$s = s(t)$ where $t \geqslant 0$.

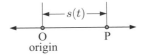

$s(t)$ is a **displacement function** and for any value of t it gives the displacement from O.

$s(t)$ is a vector quantity. Its magnitude is the distance from O, and its sign indicates the direction
from O.

> On the horizontal axis through O:
>
> - if $s(t) > 0$, P is located to the **right of O**
> - if $s(t) = 0$, P is located **at O**
> - if $s(t) < 0$, P is located to the **left of O**.

MOTION GRAPHS

Consider $s(t) = t^2 + 2t - 3$ cm.

$s(0) = -3$ cm, $s(1) = 0$ cm, $s(2) = 5$ cm, $s(3) = 12$ cm, $s(4) = 21$ cm.

To appreciate the motion of P we draw a **motion graph**. You can also view the motion by clicking on
the icon.

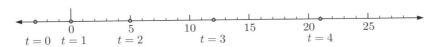

DEMO

Fully animated, we not only get a good idea of the position of P, but also of what is happening to its
velocity and acceleration.

VELOCITY

> The **average velocity** of an object moving in a straight line in the time interval from $t = t_1$ to $t = t_2$
> is the ratio of the change in displacement to the time taken.
>
> If $s(t)$ is the displacement function then **average velocity** $= \dfrac{s(t_2) - s(t_1)}{t_2 - t_1}$.

On a graph of $s(t)$ against time t for the time interval from $t = t_1$ to $t = t_2$, the average velocity is
the gradient of a chord through the points $(t_1, s(t_1))$ and $(t_2, s(t_2))$.

In **Chapter 14** we established that the instantaneous rate of change of a quantity is given by its derivative.

> If $s(t)$ is the displacement function of an object moving in a straight line, then
>
> $$v(t) = s'(t) = \lim_{h \to 0} \frac{s(t+h) - s(t)}{h} \quad \text{is the \textbf{instantaneous velocity} or}$$
>
> **velocity function** of the object at time t.

On a graph of $s(t)$ against time t, the instantaneous velocity at a particular time is the gradient of the
tangent to the graph at that point.

ACCELERATION

If an object moves in a straight line with velocity function $v(t)$ then its **average acceleration** for the time interval from $t = t_1$ to $t = t_2$ is the ratio of the change in velocity to the time taken.

$$\text{average acceleration} = \frac{v(t_2) - v(t_1)}{t_2 - t_1}.$$

If a particle moves in a straight line with velocity function $v(t)$, then the **instantaneous acceleration** at time t is $a(t) = v'(t) = \lim_{h \to 0} \frac{v(t + h) - v(t)}{h}$.

UNITS

Each time we differentiate with respect to time t, we calculate a rate per unit of time. So, for a displacement in metres and time in seconds:

- the units of velocity are m s^{-1}
- the units of acceleration are m s^{-2}.

Example 1   ◀) **Self Tutor**

A particle moves in a straight line with displacement from O given by $s(t) = 3t - t^2$ metres at time t seconds. Find:

a the average velocity for the time interval from $t = 2$ to $t = 5$ seconds

b the average velocity for the time interval from $t = 2$ to $t = 2 + h$ seconds

c $\lim_{h \to 0} \dfrac{s(2 + h) - s(2)}{h}$ and comment on its significance.

a average velocity

$= \dfrac{s(5) - s(2)}{5 - 2}$

$= \dfrac{(15 - 25) - (6 - 4)}{3}$

$= \dfrac{-10 - 2}{3}$

$= -4 \text{ m s}^{-1}$

b average velocity

$= \dfrac{s(2 + h) - s(2)}{2 + h - 2}$

$= \dfrac{3(2 + h) - (2 + h)^2 - 2}{h}$

$= \dfrac{6 + 3h - 4 - 4h - h^2 - 2}{h}$

$= \dfrac{-h - h^2}{h}$

$= -1 - h \text{ m s}^{-1}$ provided $h \neq 0$

c $\lim_{h \to 0} \dfrac{s(2 + h) - s(2)}{h}$

$= \lim_{h \to 0} (-1 - h)$ {since $h \neq 0$}

$= -1 \text{ m s}^{-1}$

This is the instantaneous velocity of the particle at time $t = 2$ seconds.

EXERCISE 17A.1

1 A particle P moves in a straight line with a displacement function of $s(t) = t^2 + 3t - 2$ metres, where $t \geqslant 0$, t in seconds.

    a Find the average velocity from $t = 1$ to $t = 3$ seconds.

    b Find the average velocity from $t = 1$ to $t = 1 + h$ seconds.

    c Find the value of $\displaystyle\lim_{h \to 0} \frac{s(1 + h) - s(1)}{h}$ and comment on its significance.

    d Find the average velocity from time t to time $t + h$ seconds and interpret $\displaystyle\lim_{h \to 0} \frac{s(t + h) - s(t)}{h}$.

2 A particle P moves in a straight line with a displacement function of $s(t) = 5 - 2t^2$ cm, where $t \geqslant 0$, t in seconds.

    a Find the average velocity from $t = 2$ to $t = 5$ seconds.

    b Find the average velocity from $t = 2$ to $t = 2 + h$ seconds.

    c Find the value of $\displaystyle\lim_{h \to 0} \frac{s(2 + h) - s(2)}{h}$ and state the meaning of this value.

    d Interpret $\displaystyle\lim_{h \to 0} \frac{s(t + h) - s(t)}{h}$.

3 A particle moves in a straight line with velocity function $v(t) = 2\sqrt{t} + 3$ cm s^{-1}, $t \geqslant 0$.

    a Find the average acceleration from $t = 1$ to $t = 4$ seconds.

    b Find the average acceleration from $t = 1$ to $t = 1 + h$ seconds.

    c Find the value of $\displaystyle\lim_{h \to 0} \frac{v(1 + h) - v(1)}{h}$. Interpret this value.

    d Interpret $\displaystyle\lim_{h \to 0} \frac{v(t + h) - v(t)}{h}$.

4 An object moves in a straight line with displacement function $s(t)$ and velocity function $v(t)$, $t \geqslant 0$. State the meaning of:

    a $\displaystyle\lim_{h \to 0} \frac{s(4 + h) - s(4)}{h}$
        b $\displaystyle\lim_{h \to 0} \frac{v(4 + h) - v(4)}{h}$

VELOCITY AND ACCELERATION FUNCTIONS

If a particle P moves in a straight line and its position is given by the displacement function $s(t)$, $t \geqslant 0$, then:

- the **velocity** of P at time t is given by $v(t) = s'(t)$
- the **acceleration** of P at time t is given by $a(t) = v'(t) = s''(t)$
- $s(0)$, $v(0)$, and $a(0)$ give us the position, velocity, and acceleration of the particle at time $t = 0$, and these are called the **initial conditions**.

$$\boxed{\begin{array}{c} s(t) \\ \text{displacement} \end{array}} \xrightarrow{\text{differentiate}} \boxed{\begin{array}{c} v(t) = \dfrac{ds}{dt} \\ \text{velocity} \end{array}} \xrightarrow{\text{differentiate}} \boxed{\begin{array}{c} a(t) = \dfrac{dv}{dt} = \dfrac{d^2 s}{dt^2} \\ \text{acceleration} \end{array}}$$

SIGN INTERPRETATION

Suppose a particle P moves in a straight line with displacement function $s(t)$ relative to an origin O. Its velocity function is $v(t)$ and its acceleration function is $a(t)$.

We can use **sign diagrams** to interpret:

- where the particle is located relative to O
- the direction of motion and where a change of direction occurs
- when the particle's velocity is increasing or decreasing.

SIGNS OF $s(t)$:

$s(t)$	Interpretation
$= 0$	P is at O
> 0	P is located to the right of O
< 0	P is located to the left of O

$$v(t) = \lim_{h \to 0} \frac{s(t+h) - s(t)}{h}$$

SIGNS OF $v(t)$:

If $v(t) > 0$ then $s(t+h) - s(t) > 0$

$$\therefore \quad s(t+h) > s(t)$$

$v(t)$	Interpretation
$= 0$	P is instantaneously at rest
> 0	P is moving to the right
< 0	P is moving to the left

$\therefore$ P is moving to the right.

SIGNS OF $a(t)$:

$a(t)$	Interpretation
> 0	velocity is increasing
< 0	velocity is decreasing
$= 0$	velocity may be a maximum or minimum or possibly constant

A useful table:

Phrase used in a question	t	s	v	a
initial conditions	0			
at the origin		0		
stationary			0	
reverses			0	
maximum or minimum displacement			0	
constant velocity				0
maximum or minimum velocity				0

When a particle reverses direction, its velocity must change sign.
This corresponds to a local maximum or local minimum distance from the origin O.

We need a sign diagram of a to determine if the velocity of the point is a local maximum or minimum.

SPEED

As we have seen, velocities have size (magnitude) and sign (direction). In contrast, speed simply measures *how fast* something is travelling, regardless of the direction of travel. Speed is a *scalar* quantity which has size but no sign. Speed cannot be negative.

> The **speed** at any instant is the magnitude of the object's velocity.
>
> If $S(t)$ represents speed then we write $S = |v|$.

Be careful not to confuse speed $S(t)$ with displacement $s(t)$.

To determine when the speed $S(t)$ of an object P with displacement $s(t)$ is increasing or decreasing, we need to employ a **sign test**.

- If the signs of $v(t)$ and $a(t)$ are the same (both positive or both negative), then the speed of P is increasing.
- If the signs of $v(t)$ and $a(t)$ are opposite, then the speed of P is decreasing.

We prove *the first* of these as follows:

Proof: Let $S = |v|$ be the speed of P at any instant, so $S = \begin{cases} v & \text{if } v \geqslant 0 \\ -v & \text{if } v < 0. \end{cases}$

Case 1: If $v > 0$, $S = v$ and $\therefore$ $\dfrac{dS}{dt} = \dfrac{dv}{dt} = a(t)$

If $a(t) > 0$ then $\dfrac{dS}{dt} > 0$ which implies that S is increasing.

Case 2: If $v < 0$, $S = -v$ and $\therefore$ $\dfrac{dS}{dt} = -\dfrac{dv}{dt} = -a(t)$

If $a(t) < 0$ then $\dfrac{dS}{dt} > 0$ which also implies that S is increasing.

Thus if $v(t)$ and $a(t)$ have the same sign then the speed of P is increasing.

INVESTIGATION   DISPLACEMENT, VELOCITY, AND ACCELERATION GRAPHS

In this investigation we examine the motion of a projectile which is fired in a vertical direction. The projectile is affected by gravity, which is responsible for the projectile's constant acceleration.

MOTION DEMO

We then extend the investigation to consider other cases of motion in a straight line.

What to do:

1 Click on the icon to examine vertical projectile motion in a straight line.
  Observe first the displacement along the line, then look at the velocity or rate of change in displacement. When is the velocity positive and when is it negative?

2 Examine the following graphs and comment on their shapes:

  - *displacement* v *time*
  - *velocity* v *time*
  - *acceleration* v *time*

3 Pick from the menu or construct functions of your own choosing to investigate the relationship between displacement, velocity, and acceleration.

You are encouraged to use the motion demo above to help answer questions in the following exercise.

Example 2 　　　　　　　　　　　　　　　　　　　　　◀) **Self Tutor**

A particle moves in a straight line with position relative to O given by $s(t) = t^3 - 3t + 1$ cm, where t is the time in seconds, $t \geqslant 0$.

a Find expressions for the particle's velocity and acceleration, and draw sign diagrams for each of them.

b Find the initial conditions and hence describe the motion at this instant.

c Describe the motion of the particle at $t = 2$ seconds.

d Find the position of the particle when changes in direction occur.

e Draw a motion diagram for the particle.

f For what time interval is the particle's speed increasing?

g What is the total distance travelled in the time from $t = 0$ to $t = 2$ seconds?

a 　　$s(t) = t^3 - 3t + 1$ cm
　　∴ $v(t) = 3t^2 - 3$ 　　　{as $v(t) = s'(t)$}
　　　　$= 3(t^2 - 1)$
　　　　$= 3(t+1)(t-1)$ cm s^{-1}
　　which has sign diagram

and $a(t) = 6t$ cm s^{-2} 　　{as $a(t) = v'(t)$}
　　which has sign diagram

b When $t = 0$, $s(0) = 1$ cm
　　　　　　$v(0) = -3$ cm s^{-1}
　　　　　　$a(0) = 0$ cm s^{-2}

∴ the particle is 1 cm to the right of O, moving to the left at a speed of 3 cm s^{-1}.

c When $t = 2$, $s(2) = 8 - 6 + 1 = 3$ cm
　　　　　　$v(2) = 12 - 3 = 9$ cm s^{-1}
　　　　　　$a(2) = 12$ cm s^{-2}

∴ the particle is 3 cm to the right of O, moving to the right at a speed of 9 cm s^{-1}.
Since a and v have the same sign, the speed of the particle is increasing.

d Since $v(t)$ changes sign when $t = 1$, a change of direction occurs at this instant.
　$s(1) = 1 - 3 + 1 = -1$,   so the particle changes direction when it is 1 cm to the left of O.

e

The motion is actually **on the line**, not above it as shown.

As $t \to \infty$, $s(t) \to \infty$ and $v(t) \to \infty$.

f Speed is increasing when $v(t)$ and $a(t)$ have the same sign. This is for $t \geqslant 1$.

g Total distance travelled $= 2 + 4 = 6$ cm.

In later chapters on integral calculus we will see another technique for finding the distances travelled and displacement over time.

EXERCISE 17A.2

1   An object moves in a straight line with position given by $s(t) = t^2 - 4t + 3$ cm from O, where t is in seconds, $t \geqslant 0$.

   a   Find expressions for the object's velocity and acceleration, and draw sign diagrams for each function.

   b   Find the initial conditions and explain what is happening to the object at that instant.

   c   Describe the motion of the object at time $t = 2$ seconds.

   d   At what time(s) does the object reverse direction? Find the position of the object at these instants.

   e   Draw a motion diagram for the object.

   f   For what time intervals is the speed of the object decreasing?

2   A stone is projected vertically so that its position above ground level after t seconds is given by $s(t) = 98t - 4.9t^2$ metres, $t \geqslant 0$.

   a   Find the velocity and acceleration functions for the stone and draw sign diagrams for each function.

   b   Find the initial position and velocity of the stone.

   c   Describe the stone's motion at times $t = 5$ and $t = 12$ seconds.

   d   Find the maximum height reached by the stone.

   e   Find the time taken for the stone to hit the ground.

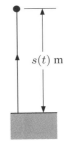

3   When a ball is thrown, its height above the ground is given by $s(t) = 1.2 + 28.1t - 4.9t^2$ metres where t is the time in seconds.

   a   From what distance above the ground was the ball released?

   b   Find $s'(t)$ and state what it represents.

   c   Find t when $s'(t) = 0$. What is the significance of this result?

   d   What is the maximum height reached by the ball?

   e   Find the ball's speed: i   when released   ii   at $t = 2$ s   iii   at $t = 5$ s.
       State the significance of the sign of the derivative $s'(t)$.

   f   How long will it take for the ball to hit the ground?

   g   What is the significance of $s''(t)$?

4   A shell is accidentally fired vertically from a mortar at ground level and reaches the ground again after 14.2 seconds.   Its height above the ground at time t seconds is given by $s(t) = bt - 4.9t^2$ metres where b is constant.

   a   Show that the initial velocity of the shell is b m s^{-1} upwards.

   b   Find the initial velocity of the shell.

5 A particle moves in a straight line with displacement function $s(t) = 12t - 2t^3 - 1$ centimetres where t is in seconds, $t \geqslant 0$.

    a Find velocity and acceleration functions for the particle's motion.

    b Find the initial conditions and interpret their meaning.

    c Find the times and positions when the particle reverses direction.

    d At what times is the particle's: **i** speed increasing   **ii** velocity increasing?

6 The position of a particle moving along the x-axis is given by $x(t) = t^3 - 9t^2 + 24t$ metres where t is in seconds, $t \geqslant 0$.

When finding the total distance travelled, always look for direction reversals first.

    a Draw sign diagrams for the particle's velocity and acceleration functions.

    b Find the position of the particle at the times when it reverses direction, and hence draw a motion diagram for the particle.

    c At what times is the particle's:

        i speed decreasing   **ii** velocity decreasing?

    d Find the total distance travelled by the particle in the first 5 seconds of motion.

7 A particle P moves in a straight line.   Its displacement from the origin O is given by $s(t) = 100t + 200e^{-\frac{t}{5}}$ cm   where t is the time in seconds, $t \geqslant 0$.

    a Find the velocity and acceleration functions.

    b Find the initial position, velocity, and acceleration of P.

    c Discuss the velocity of P as $t \to \infty$.

    d Sketch the graph of the velocity function.

    e Find when the velocity of P is 80 cm per second.

8 A particle P moves along the x-axis with position given by $x(t) = 1 - 2\cos t$ cm   where t is the time in seconds.

    a State the initial position, velocity and acceleration of P.

    b Describe the motion when $t = \frac{\pi}{4}$ seconds.

    c Find the times when the particle reverses direction on $0 < t < 2\pi$ and find the position of the particle at these instants.

    d When is the particle's speed increasing on $0 \leqslant t \leqslant 2\pi$?

9 In an experiment, an object is fired vertically from the earth's surface. From the results, a two-dimensional graph of the position $s(t)$ metres above the earth's surface is plotted, where t is the time in seconds. It is noted that the graph is *parabolic*.

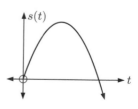

Assuming a constant gravitational acceleration g and an initial velocity of $v(0)$, show that:

    a $v(t) = v(0) + gt$ **b** $s(t) = v(0) \times t + \frac{1}{2}gt^2$.

Hint: Assume that $s(t) = at^2 + bt + c$.

B   RATES OF CHANGE

We have seen previously that if $s(t)$ is a displacement function then $s'(t)$ or $\dfrac{ds}{dt}$ is the instantaneous rate of change in displacement with respect to time, which we call velocity.

There are countless examples in the real world where quantities vary with time, or with respect to some other variable.

For example:
- temperature varies continuously
- the height of a tree varies as it grows
- the prices of stocks and shares vary with each day's trading.

We have already seen that if $y = f(x)$ then $f'(x)$ or $\dfrac{dy}{dx}$ is the gradient of the tangent to $y = f(x)$ at the given point.

> $\dfrac{dy}{dx}$ gives the **rate of change in y with respect to x**.

We can therefore use the derivative of a function to tell us the **rate** at which something is happening.

For example:

- $\dfrac{dH}{dt}$ or $H'(t)$ could be the instantaneous rate of ascent of the person in the Ferris wheel.
  It might also have units metres per second or $\mathrm{m\,s^{-1}}$.

- $\dfrac{dC}{dt}$ or $C'(t)$ could be a person's instantaneous rate of change in lung capacity.
  It might have units litres per second or $\mathrm{L\,s^{-1}}$.

Example 3   ◀) Self Tutor

According to a psychologist, the ability of a person to understand spatial concepts is given by $A = \frac{1}{3}\sqrt{t}$ where t is the age in years, $5 \leqslant t \leqslant 18$.

  a Find the rate of improvement in ability to understand spatial concepts when a person is:

      i 9 years old   **ii** 16 years old.

  b Explain why $\dfrac{dA}{dt} > 0$ for $5 \leqslant t \leqslant 18$.   Comment on the significance of this result.

  c Explain why $\dfrac{d^2A}{dt^2} < 0$ for $5 \leqslant t \leqslant 18$.   Comment on the significance of this result.

---

  a $A = \frac{1}{3}\sqrt{t} = \frac{1}{3}t^{\frac{1}{2}}$ $\therefore$ $\dfrac{dA}{dt} = \frac{1}{6}t^{-\frac{1}{2}} = \dfrac{1}{6\sqrt{t}}$

    i When $t = 9$, $\dfrac{dA}{dt} = \frac{1}{18}$ **ii** When $t = 16$, $\dfrac{dA}{dt} = \frac{1}{24}$

      $\therefore$ the rate of improvement is $\therefore$ the rate of improvement is

      $\frac{1}{18}$ units per year for a 9 year old. $\frac{1}{24}$ units per year for a 16 year old.

  b Since $\sqrt{t}$ is never negative, $\dfrac{1}{6\sqrt{t}}$ is never negative

    $\therefore$ $\dfrac{dA}{dt} > 0$ for all $5 \leqslant t \leqslant 18$.

  This means that the ability to understand spatial concepts increases with age.

> **c** $\dfrac{dA}{dt} = \frac{1}{6}t^{-\frac{1}{2}}$
>
> $\therefore \quad \dfrac{d^2A}{dt^2} = -\frac{1}{12}t^{-\frac{3}{2}} = -\dfrac{1}{12t\sqrt{t}}$
>
> $\therefore \quad \dfrac{d^2A}{dt^2} < 0 \quad$ for all $\ 5 \leqslant t \leqslant 18$.
>
> This means that while the ability to understand spatial concepts increases with time, the rate of increase slows down with age.

You are encouraged to use technology to graph each function you need to consider. This is often useful in interpreting results.

EXERCISE 17B

1   The estimated future profits of a small business are given by $P(t) = 2t^2 - 12t + 118$ thousand dollars, where t is the time in years from now.

     a   What is the current annual profit?   **b**   Find $\dfrac{dP}{dt}$ and state its units.

     c   What is the significance of $\dfrac{dP}{dt}$?

     d   For what values of t will the profit:

         i   decrease   **ii**   increase   on the previous year?

     e   What is the minimum profit and when does it occur?

     f   Find $\dfrac{dP}{dt}$ when $t = 4$, 10 and 25. What do these figures represent?

2   Water is draining from a swimming pool. The remaining volume of water after t minutes is $V = 200(50 - t)^2$ m^3. Find:

     a   the average rate at which the water leaves the pool in the first 5 minutes

     b   the instantaneous rate at which the water is leaving at $t = 5$ minutes.

3   The quantity of a chemical in human skin which is responsible for its 'elasticity' is given by $Q = 100 - 10\sqrt{t}$ where t is the age of a person in years.

     a   Find Q at: **i** $t = 0$ **ii** $t = 25$ **iii** $t = 100$ years.

     b   At what rate is the quantity of the chemical changing at the age of:

         i   25 years   **ii**   50 years?

     c   Show that the rate at which the skin loses the chemical is decreasing for all $t > 0$.

4   The height of *pinus radiata*, grown in ideal conditions, is given by $H = 20 - \dfrac{97.5}{t + 5}$ metres, where t is the number of years after the tree was planted from an established seedling.

     a   How high was the tree at the time of its planting?

     b   Find the height of the tree at $t = 4$, $t = 8$, and $t = 12$ years.

     c   Find the rate at which the tree is growing at $t = 0$, 5, and 10 years.

     d   Show that $\dfrac{dH}{dt} > 0$ for all $t \geqslant 0$. What is the significance of this result?

Example 4
◄》 **Self Tutor**

The cost in dollars of producing x items in a factory each day is given by

$$C(x) = \underbrace{0.000\,13x^3 + 0.002x^2}_{\text{labour}} + \underbrace{5x}_{\text{raw materials}} + \underbrace{2200}_{\text{fixed costs}}$$

a Find $C'(x)$, which is called the marginal cost function.

b Find the marginal cost when 150 items are produced. Interpret this result.

c Find $C(151) - C(150)$. Compare this with the answer in **b**.

a The marginal cost function is
$C'(x) = 0.000\,39x^2 + 0.004x + 5$ dollars per item.

b $C'(150) = \$14.38$

This is the rate at which the costs are increasing with respect to the production level x when 150 items are made per day.

It gives an estimate of the cost increase in total cost from making the 151st item.

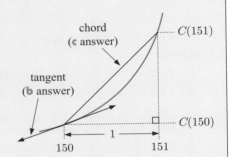

c $C(151) - C(150) \approx \$3448.19 - \$3433.75$
$\approx \$14.44$

This is the actual increase in total cost from making the 151st item each day, so the answer in **b** gives a good estimate.

---

5 Seablue make denim jeans. The cost model for making x pairs per day is
$$C(x) = 0.0003x^3 + 0.02x^2 + 4x + 2250 \text{ dollars.}$$

a Find the marginal cost function $C'(x)$.

b Find $C'(220)$. What does it estimate?

c Find $C(221) - C(220)$. What does this represent?

d Find $C''(x)$ and the value of x when $C''(x) = 0$. What is the significance of this point?

6 The total cost of running a train from Paris to Marseille is given by $C(v) = \frac{1}{5}v^2 + \dfrac{200\,000}{v}$ euros
where v is the average speed of the train in $\text{km}\,\text{h}^{-1}$.

a Find the total cost of the journey if the average speed is:

   i 50 $\text{km}\,\text{h}^{-1}$ **ii** 100 $\text{km}\,\text{h}^{-1}$.

b Find the rate of change in the cost of running the train at speeds of:

   i 30 $\text{km}\,\text{h}^{-1}$ **ii** 90 $\text{km}\,\text{h}^{-1}$.

c At what speed will the cost be a minimum?

7 A tank contains 50 000 litres of water. The tap is left fully on and all the water drains from the tank in 80 minutes. The volume of water remaining in the tank after t minutes is given by

$$V = 50\,000 \left(1 - \frac{t}{80}\right)^2 \text{ litres where } 0 \leqslant t \leqslant 80.$$

a Find $\dfrac{dV}{dt}$ and draw the graph of $\dfrac{dV}{dt}$ against t.

b At what time was the outflow fastest?

c Show that $\dfrac{d^2V}{dt^2}$ is always constant and positive. Interpret this result.

8

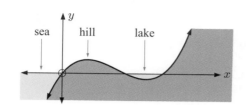

sea   hill   lake

Alongside is a land and sea profile where the x-axis is sea level. The function $y = \frac{1}{10}x(x-2)(x-3)$ km gives the height of the land or sea bed relative to sea level at distance x km from the shore line.

a Find where the lake is located relative to the shore line of the sea.

b Find $\dfrac{dy}{dx}$ and interpret its value when $x = \frac{1}{2}$ and when $x = 1\frac{1}{2}$ km.

c Find the deepest point of the lake and the depth at this point.

9 A radioactive substance decays according to the formula $W = 20e^{-kt}$ grams where t is the time in hours.

a Find k given that after 50 hours the weight is 10 grams.

b Find the weight of radioactive substance present at:

   i $t = 0$ hours   **ii** $t = 24$ hours   **iii** $t = 1$ week.

c How long will it take for the weight to reach 1 gram?

d Find the rate of radioactive decay at: **i** $t = 100$ hours   **ii** $t = 1000$ hours.

e Show that $\dfrac{dW}{dt}$ is proportional to the weight of substance remaining.

10 The temperature of a liquid after being placed in a refrigerator is given by $T = 5 + 95e^{-kt}$ °C where k is a positive constant and t is the time in minutes.

a Find k if the temperature of the liquid is 20°C after 15 minutes.

b What was the temperature of the liquid when it was first placed in the refrigerator?

c Show that $\dfrac{dT}{dt} = c(T - 5)$ for some constant c. Find the value of c.

d At what rate is the temperature changing at:

   i $t = 0$ mins   **ii** $t = 10$ mins   **iii** $t = 20$ mins?

11 The height of a certain species of shrub t years after it is planted is given by $H(t) = 20\ln(3t + 2) + 30$ cm, $t \geqslant 0$.

a How high was the shrub when it was planted?

b How long will it take for the shrub to reach a height of 1 m?

c At what rate is the shrub's height changing:

   i 3 years after being planted   **ii** 10 years after being planted?

12 In the conversion of sugar solution to alcohol, the chemical reaction obeys the law $A = s(1 - e^{-kt})$, $t \geqslant 0$ where t is the number of hours after the reaction commenced, s is the original sugar concentration (%), and A is the alcohol produced, in litres.

a Find A when $t = 0$.

b If $s = 10$ and $A = 5$ after 3 hours:

   i find k **ii** find the speed of the reaction at time 5 hours.

c Show that the speed of the reaction is proportional to $A - s$.

Example 5 ◄)) **Self Tutor**

Find the rate of change in the area of triangle ABC as θ changes, at the time when $\theta = 60°$.

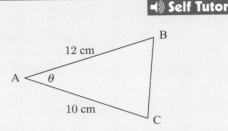

Area $A = \frac{1}{2} \times 10 \times 12 \times \sin \theta$ $\{Area = \frac{1}{2}bc \sin A\}$

$\therefore$ $A = 60 \sin \theta$ cm^2

$\therefore$ $\dfrac{dA}{d\theta} = 60 \cos \theta$

When $\theta = \frac{\pi}{3}$, $\cos \theta = \frac{1}{2}$

$\therefore$ $\dfrac{dA}{d\theta} = 30$ cm^2 per radian

θ must be in **radians** so the dimensions are correct.

13   Find exactly the rate of change in the area of triangle PQR as θ changes, at the time when $\theta = 45°$.

14   On the Indonesian coast, the depth of water at time t hours after midnight is given by $d = 9.3 + 6.8 \cos(0.507t)$ metres.

a   What is the rate of change in the depth of water at 8:00 am?

b   Is the tide rising or falling at this time?

15   The voltage in a circuit is given by $V(t) = 340 \sin(100\pi t)$ where t is the time in seconds. At what rate is the voltage changing:

a   when $t = 0.01$ b   when $V(t)$ is a maximum?

16   A piston is operated by rod [AP] attached to a flywheel of radius 1 m. AP = 2 m. P has coordinates $(\cos t, \sin t)$ and point A is $(-x, 0)$.

a   Show that $x = \sqrt{4 - \sin^2 t} - \cos t$.

b   Find the rate at which x is changing at the instant when:

i $t = 0$ ii $t = \frac{\pi}{2}$ iii $t = \frac{2\pi}{3}$

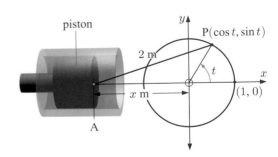

C | OPTIMISATION

There are many problems for which we need to find the **maximum** or **minimum** value of a function. The solution is often referred to as the **optimum** solution and the process is called **optimisation**.

We can find optimum solutions in several ways:

- using technology to graph the function and search for the maximum or minimum value
- using analytical methods such as the formula $x = -\dfrac{b}{2a}$ for the vertex of a parabola
- using differential calculus to locate the turning points of a function.

These last two methods are useful especially when exact solutions are required.

WARNING

The maximum or minimum value does not always occur when the first derivative is zero. It is essential to also examine the values of the function at the endpoint(s) of the interval under consideration for global maxima and minima.

For example:

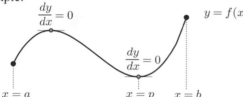

The maximum value of y occurs at the endpoint $x = b$. The minimum value of y occurs at the local minimum $x = p$.

TESTING OPTIMAL SOLUTIONS

If one is trying to optimise a function $f(x)$ and we find values of x such that $f'(x) = 0$, there are several tests we can use to see whether we have a maximum or a minimum solution:

SIGN DIAGRAM TEST

If, near to $x = a$ where $f'(a) = 0$ the sign diagram is:

- we have a **local maximum**
- we have a **local minimum**.

SECOND DERIVATIVE TEST

At $x = a$ where $f'(a) = 0$:

- If $\dfrac{d^2y}{dx^2} < 0$ we have ⌢ shape, which indicates we have a **local maximum**.
- If $\dfrac{d^2y}{dx^2} > 0$ we have ⌣ shape, which indicates we have a **local minimum**.

GRAPHICAL TEST

If the graph of $y = f(x)$ shows:

- ⌢ we have a **local maximum**
- ⌣ we have a **local minimum**.

OPTIMISATION PROBLEM SOLVING METHOD

Step 1:   Draw a large, clear diagram of the situation.

Step 2:   Construct a formula with the variable to be **optimised** as the subject. It should be written in terms of **one** convenient **variable**, for example x. You should write down what domain restrictions there are on x.

Step 3:   Find the **first derivative** and find the values of x which make the first derivative **zero**.

Step 4:   For a restricted domain such as $a \leqslant x \leqslant b$, the maximum or minimum may occur either when the derivative is zero, at an endpoint, or at a point where the derivative is not defined. Show using the **sign diagram test**, the **second derivative test**, or the **graphical test**, that you have a maximum or a minimum.

Step 5:   Write your answer in a sentence, making sure you specifically answer the question.

Example 6   ◀)) Self Tutor

A rectangular cake dish is made by cutting out squares from the corners of a 25 cm by 40 cm rectangle of tin-plate, and then folding the metal to form the container.

What size squares must be cut out to produce the cake dish of maximum volume?

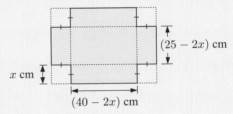

Step 1:   Let x cm be the side lengths of the squares that are cut out.

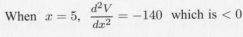

Step 2:   Volume = length × width × depth
$$= (40 - 2x)(25 - 2x)x$$
$$= (1000 - 80x - 50x + 4x^2)x$$
$$= 1000x - 130x^2 + 4x^3 \text{ cm}^3$$

Since the side lengths must be positive, $x > 0$ and $25 - 2x > 0$.

∴ $0 < x < 12.5$

Step 3: $\dfrac{dV}{dx} = 12x^2 - 260x + 1000$
$$= 4(3x^2 - 65x + 250)$$
$$= 4(3x - 50)(x - 5)$$

∴ $\dfrac{dV}{dx} = 0$ when $x = \frac{50}{3} = 16\frac{2}{3}$ or $x = 5$

DEMO

Step 4:   **Sign diagram test**   *or*   **Second derivative test**

$\dfrac{dV}{dx}$ has sign diagram:

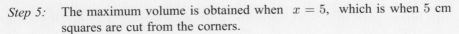

$\dfrac{d^2V}{dx^2} = 24x - 260$

When $x = 5$, $\dfrac{d^2V}{dx^2} = -140$ which is < 0

∴   the shape is ⌒ and we have a local maximum.

Step 5:   The maximum volume is obtained when $x = 5$, which is when 5 cm squares are cut from the corners.

Example 7   ◀) **Self Tutor**

A 4 litre container must have a square base, vertical sides, and an open top. Find the most economical shape which minimises the surface area of material needed.

open
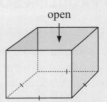

Step 1:

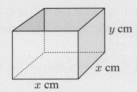

y cm

x cm

x cm

Let the base lengths be x cm and the depth be y cm.

The volume $V = \text{length} \times \text{width} \times \text{depth}$

$\therefore \ V = x^2 y$

$\therefore \ 4000 = x^2 y$ .... (1)   {1 litre $\equiv 1000$ cm^3}

Step 2:   The total surface area

$A = \text{area of base} + 4(\text{area of one side})$

$\quad = x^2 + 4xy$

$\quad = x^2 + 4x\left(\dfrac{4000}{x^2}\right)$ {using (1)}

$\therefore \ A(x) = x^2 + 16\,000x^{-1}$ where $x > 0$

TI-84 Plus

Step 3: $A'(x) = 2x - 16\,000x^{-2}$

$\therefore \ A'(x) = 0$ when $2x = \dfrac{16\,000}{x^2}$

$\therefore \ 2x^3 = 16\,000$

$\therefore \ x = \sqrt[3]{8000} = 20$

Step 4:   **Sign diagram test**   *or*   **Second derivative test**

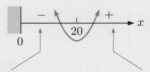

$A''(x) = 2 + 32\,000x^{-3}$

$= 2 + \dfrac{32\,000}{x^3}$

which is always positive as $x^3 > 0$ for all $x > 0$.

If $x = 10$,
$A'(10) = 20 - \frac{16\,000}{100}$
$= 20 - 160$
$= -140$

If $x = 30$,
$A'(30) = 60 - \frac{16\,000}{900}$
$\approx 60 - 17.8$
≈ 42.2

The minimum material is used to make the container when $x = 20$ and $y = \dfrac{4000}{20^2} = 10$.

Step 5:   The most economical shape has a square base 20 cm $\times$ 20 cm, and height 10 cm.

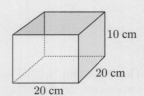

10 cm

20 cm

20 cm

Sometimes the variable to be optimised is in the form of a single square root function. In these situations it is convenient to square the function and use the fact that if $A(x) > 0$ for all x in the interval under consideration, then the optimum value of $A(x)$ occurs at the same value of x as the optimum value of $[A(x)]^2$.

Example 8

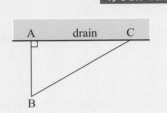

An animal enclosure is a right angled triangle with one side being a drain. The farmer has 300 m of fencing available for the other two sides, [AB] and [BC].

a If $AB = x$ m, show that $AC = \sqrt{90\,000 - 600x}$.

b Find the maximum possible area of the triangular enclosure.

---

a $(AC)^2 + x^2 = (300 - x)^2$ {Pythagoras}

$\therefore \ (AC)^2 = 90\,000 - 600x + x^2 - x^2$

$= 90\,000 - 600x$

$\therefore \ AC = \sqrt{90\,000 - 600x}, \quad 0 < x < 300$

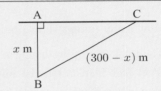

b The area of triangle ABC is

$A(x) = \frac{1}{2}(\text{base} \times \text{altitude})$

$= \frac{1}{2}(AC \times x)$

$= \frac{1}{2}x\sqrt{90\,000 - 600x}$

$\therefore \ [A(x)]^2 = \frac{x^2}{4}(90\,000 - 600x)$

$= 22\,500x^2 - 150x^3$

$\therefore \ \dfrac{d}{dx}[A(x)]^2 = 45\,000x - 450x^2$

$= 450x(100 - x)$

$\therefore \ \dfrac{d}{dx}[A(x)]^2$ has sign diagram:

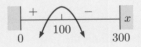

$A(x)$ is maximised when $x = 100$

$\therefore \ A_{\max} = \frac{1}{2}(100)\sqrt{90\,000 - 60\,000}$

$\approx 8660 \text{ m}^2$

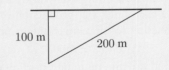

The maximum area is about 8660 m^2 when the enclosure has the side lengths shown.

Use **calculus techniques** to answer the following problems.

GRAPHING PACKAGE

In cases where finding the zeros of the derivatives is difficult you may use a **graphics calculator** or **graphing package** to help you.

EXERCISE 17C

1 When a manufacturer makes x items per day, the cost function is $C(x) = 720 + 4x + 0.02x^2$ dollars and the price function is $p(x) = 15 - 0.002x$ dollars per item. Find the production level that will maximise profits.

2 A duck farmer wishes to build a rectangular enclosure of area 100 m². The farmer must purchase wire netting for three of the sides as the fourth side is an existing fence. Naturally, the farmer wishes to minimise the length (and therefore cost) of fencing required to complete the job.

    a If the shorter sides have length x m, show that the required length of wire netting to be purchased

       is $L = 2x + \dfrac{100}{x}$.

    b Use *technology* to help you sketch the graph of $y = 2x + \dfrac{100}{x}$.

    c Find the minimum value of L and the corresponding value of x when this occurs.

    d Sketch the optimum situation showing all dimensions.

3 A manufacturer can produce x fittings per day where $0 \leqslant x \leqslant 10\,000$. The production costs are:

    • €1000 per day for the workers   • €2 per day per fitting

    • €$\dfrac{5000}{x}$ per day for running costs and maintenance.

    How many fittings should be produced daily to minimise the total production costs?

4 The total cost of producing x blankets per day is $\frac{1}{4}x^2 + 8x + 20$ dollars, and for this production level each blanket may be sold for $(23 - \frac{1}{2}x)$ dollars.

    How many blankets should be produced per day to maximise the total profit?

5 The cost of running a boat is $£\left(\dfrac{v^2}{10} + 22\right)$ per hour, where v km h^{-1} is the speed of the boat.

    Find the speed which will minimise the total cost per kilometre.

6 A psychologist claims that the ability A to memorise simple facts during infancy years can be calculated using the formula $A(t) = t \ln t + 1$ where $0 < t \leqslant 5$, t being the age of the child in years.

    a At what age is the child's memorising ability a minimum?

    b Sketch the graph of $A(t)$ for $0 < t \leqslant 5$.

7 A manufacturing company makes door hinges. They have a standing order filled by producing 50 each hour, but production of more than 150 per hour is useless as they will not sell. The cost function for making x hinges per hour is:

        $C(x) = 0.0007x^3 - 0.1796x^2 + 14.663x + 160$ dollars where $50 \leqslant x \leqslant 150$.

    Find the minimum and maximum hourly costs, and the production levels when each occurs.

8 Radioactive waste is to be disposed of in fully enclosed lead boxes of inner volume 200 cm³. The base of the box has dimensions in the ratio 2 : 1.

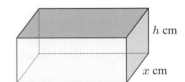

    a What is the inner length of the box?

    b Explain why $x^2 h = 100$.

    c Explain why the inner surface area of the box is given

       by $A(x) = 4x^2 + \dfrac{600}{x}$ cm².

    d Use *technology* to help sketch the graph of $y = 4x^2 + \dfrac{600}{x}$.

    e Find the minimum inner surface area of the box and the corresponding value of x.

    f Sketch the optimum box shape showing all dimensions.

9 A manufacturer of electric kettles performs a cost control study. They discover that to produce x kettles per day, the cost per kettle $C(x)$ is given by

$$C(x) = 4\ln x + \left(\frac{30 - x}{10}\right)^2 \quad \text{dollars}$$

with a minimum production capacity of 10 kettles per day.
How many kettles should be manufactured to keep the cost per kettle to a minimum?

10 Infinitely many rectangles which sit on the x-axis can be inscribed under the curve $y = e^{-x^2}$.
Determine the coordinates of C such that rectangle ABCD has maximum area.

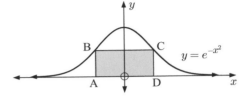

11 Consider the manufacture of cylindrical tin cans of 1 L capacity where the cost of the metal used is to be minimised. This means that the surface area must be as small as possible.

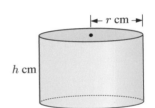

  a Explain why the height h is given by $h = \dfrac{1000}{\pi r^2}$ cm.

  b Show that the total surface area A is given by

$$A = 2\pi r^2 + \frac{2000}{r} \quad \text{cm}^2.$$

  c Use *technology* to help you sketch the graph of A against r.

  d Find the value of r which makes A as small as possible.

  e Sketch the can of smallest surface area.

12 A circular piece of tinplate of radius 10 cm has 3 segments removed as illustrated. The angle θ is measured in radians.

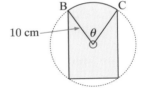

  a Show that the remaining area is given by
  $A = 50(\theta + 3\sin\theta)$ cm^2.

  b Hence, find θ such that the area A is a maximum. Find the maximum area A.

13 Sam has sheets of metal which are 36 cm by 36 cm square. He wants to cut out identical squares which are x cm by x cm from the corners of each sheet. He will then bend the sheets along the dashed lines to form an open container.

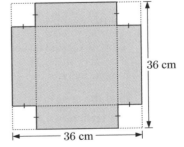

  a Show that the capacity of the container is given by
  $V(x) = x(36 - 2x)^2$ cm^3.

  b What sized squares should be cut out to produce the container of greatest capacity?

14 An athletics track has two 'straights' of length l m and two semicircular ends of radius x m. The perimeter of the track is 400 m.

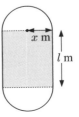

  a Show that $l = 200 - \pi x$ and hence write down the possible values that x may have.

  b What values of l and x maximise the shaded rectangle inside the track? What is this maximum area?

15 A small population of wasps is observed.   After t weeks the population is modelled by

$P(t) = \dfrac{50\,000}{1 + 1000e^{-0.5t}}$ wasps, where $0 \leqslant t \leqslant 25$.

Find when the wasp population is growing fastest.

16 When a new pain killing injection is administered, the effect is modelled by $E(t) = 750te^{-1.5t}$ units, where $t \geqslant 0$ is the time in hours after the injection.

At what time is the drug most effective?

17 A right angled triangular pen is made from 24 m of fencing, all used for sides [AB] and [BC]. Side [AC] is an existing brick wall.

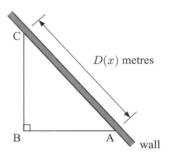

a If $AB = x$ m, find $D(x)$ in terms of x.

b Find $\dfrac{d[D(x)]^2}{dx}$ and hence draw its sign diagram.

c Find the smallest possible value of $D(x)$ and the design of the pen in this case.

18 A symmetrical gutter is made from a sheet of metal 30 cm wide by bending it twice as shown.

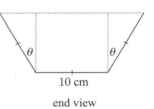

end view

a Deduce that the cross-sectional area is given by
$A = 100\cos\theta(1 + \sin\theta)$.

b Show that $\dfrac{dA}{d\theta} = 0$ when $\sin\theta = \frac{1}{2}$ or -1.

c For what value of θ does the gutter have maximum carrying capacity? Find this maximum capacity.

19 A sector of radius 10 cm and angle $\theta°$ is bent to form a conical cup as shown.

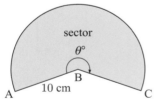

becomes

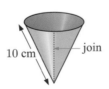

when edges [AB] and [CB] are joined with tape.

Suppose the resulting cone has base radius r cm and height h cm.

a Show using the sector that arc $AC = \dfrac{\theta\pi}{18}$.

b Explain why $r = \dfrac{\theta}{36}$.   c Show that $h = \sqrt{100 - \left(\frac{\theta}{36}\right)^2}$.

d Find the cone's capacity V in terms of θ only.

e Use technology to sketch the graph of $V(\theta)$.

f Find θ when $V(\theta)$ is a maximum.

20 At 1:00 pm a ship A leaves port P. It sails in the direction 030° at 12 km h^{-1}. At the same time, ship B is 100 km due east of P, and is sailing at 8 km h^{-1} towards P.

a Show that the distance $D(t)$ between the two ships is given by
$D(t) = \sqrt{304t^2 - 2800t + 10\,000}$ km, where t is the number of hours after 1:00 pm.

b Find the minimum value of $[D(t)]^2$ for all $t \geqslant 0$.

c At what time, to the nearest minute, are the ships closest?

21 Hieu can row a boat across a circular lake of radius 2 km at 3 km h^{-1}. He can walk around the edge of the lake at 5 km h^{-1}.

What is the longest possible time Hieu could take to get from P to R by rowing from P to Q and then walking from Q to R?

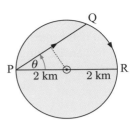

Example 9   ◀)) **Self Tutor**

Two corridors meet at right angles and are 2 m and 3 m wide respectively. θ is the angle marked on the given figure. [AB] is a thin metal tube which must be kept horizontal and cannot be bent as it moves around the corner from one corridor to the other.

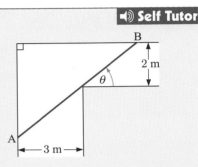

a Show that the length AB is given by $L = \dfrac{3}{\cos\theta} + \dfrac{2}{\sin\theta}$.

b Show that $\dfrac{dL}{d\theta} = 0$ when $\theta = \tan^{-1}\left(\sqrt[3]{\tfrac{2}{3}}\right) \approx 41.1°$.

DEMO

c Find L when $\theta = \tan^{-1}\left(\sqrt[3]{\tfrac{2}{3}}\right)$ and comment on the significance of this value.

---

a $\cos\theta = \dfrac{3}{a}$ and $\sin\theta = \dfrac{2}{b}$

$\therefore$ $a = \dfrac{3}{\cos\theta}$ and $b = \dfrac{2}{\sin\theta}$

$\therefore$ $L = a + b = \dfrac{3}{\cos\theta} + \dfrac{2}{\sin\theta}$

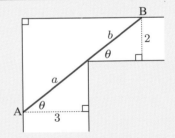

b $L = 3[\cos\theta]^{-1} + 2[\sin\theta]^{-1}$

$\therefore$ $\dfrac{dL}{d\theta} = -3[\cos\theta]^{-2}(-\sin\theta) - 2[\sin\theta]^{-2}\cos\theta$

$= \dfrac{3\sin\theta}{\cos^2\theta} - \dfrac{2\cos\theta}{\sin^2\theta}$

$= \dfrac{3\sin^3\theta - 2\cos^3\theta}{\cos^2\theta \sin^2\theta}$

Thus $\dfrac{dL}{d\theta} = 0$ when $3\sin^3\theta = 2\cos^3\theta$

$\therefore$ $\tan^3\theta = \tfrac{2}{3}$

$\therefore$ $\tan\theta = \sqrt[3]{\tfrac{2}{3}}$

$\therefore$ $\theta = \tan^{-1}\left(\sqrt[3]{\tfrac{2}{3}}\right) \approx 41.1°$

c   *Sign diagram* of $\dfrac{dL}{d\theta}$:

When $\theta = 30°$, $\dfrac{dL}{d\theta} \approx -4.93 < 0$

When $\theta = 60°$, $\dfrac{dL}{d\theta} \approx 9.06 > 0$

Thus, AB is minimised when $\theta \approx 41.1°$. At this time $L \approx 7.02$ metres. Ignoring the width of the rod, the greatest length of rod able to be horizontally carried around the corner is 7.02 m.

22 In a hospital, two corridors 4 m wide and 3 m wide meet at right angles. What is the maximum possible length of an X-ray screen which can be carried upright around the corner?

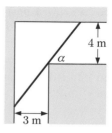

THEORY OF KNOWLEDGE

"Aristotle is recognized as the inventor of scientific method because of his refined analysis of logical implications contained in demonstrative discourse, which goes well beyond natural logic and does not owe anything to the ones who philosophized before him."

– Riccardo Pozzo

A **scientific method** of inquiry for investigating phenomena has been applied in varying degrees throughout the course of history. The first formal statement of such a method was made by René Descartes in his *Discourse on the Method* published in 1637. This work is perhaps best known for Descartes' quote, *"Je pense, donc je suis"* which means "I think, therefore I am". In 1644 in his *Principles of Philosophy* he published the same quote in Latin: *"Cogito ergo sum"*.

The scientific method involves a series of steps:

Step 1:   asking a question (how, when, why, ...)

Step 2:   conducting appropriate research

Step 3:   constructing a hypothesis, or possible explanation why things are so

Step 4:   testing the hypothesis by a fair experiment

Step 5:   analysing the results

Step 6:   drawing a conclusion

Step 7:   communicating your findings

Snell's law states the relationship between the angles of incidence and refraction when a ray of light passes from one homogeneous medium to another.

It was first discovered in 984 AD by the Persian scientist Ibn Sahl, who was studying the shape of lenses. However, it is named after Willebrord Snellius, one of those who rediscovered the law in the Renaissance. The law was published by Descartes in the *Discourse on the Method*.

In the figure alongside, a ray passes from A to B via point X. The refractive indices of the two media are n and m. The angle of incidence is α and the angle of refraction is β.

Snell's law is: $n \sin \alpha = m \sin \beta$.

The law follows from Fermat's principle of least time. It gives the path of least time for the ray travelling from A to B.

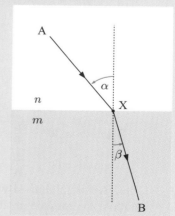

1 Is optimisation unique to mathematics?

2 How does mathematics fit into the scientific method?

3 Does mathematics have a prescribed method of its own?

4 Is mathematics a science?

1 A particle P moves in a straight line with position relative to the origin O given by $s(t) = 2t^3 - 9t^2 + 12t - 5$ cm, where t is the time in seconds, $t \geqslant 0$.

   a Find expressions for the particle's velocity and acceleration and draw sign diagrams for each of them.

   b Find the initial conditions.

   c Describe the motion of the particle at time $t = 2$ seconds.

   d Find the times and positions where the particle changes direction.

   e Draw a diagram to illustrate the motion of P.

   f Determine the time intervals when the particle's speed is increasing.

2 Rectangle ABCD is inscribed within the parabola $y = k - x^2$ and the x-axis, as shown.

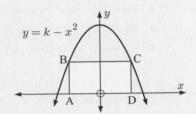

   a If OD $= x$, show that the rectangle ABCD has area function $A(x) = 2kx - 2x^3$.

   b If the area of ABCD is a maximum when AD $= 2\sqrt{3}$, find k.

3 A particle moves in a straight line along the x-axis with position given by $x(t) = 3 + \sin(2t)$ cm after t seconds.

   a Find the initial position, velocity, and acceleration of the particle.

   b Find the times when the particle changes direction during $0 \leqslant t \leqslant \pi$ seconds.

   c Find the total distance travelled by the particle in the first π seconds.

4 A rectangular gutter is formed by bending a 24 cm wide sheet of metal as shown. Where must the bends be made in order to maximise the capacity of the gutter?

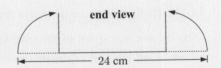

5 A particle moves in a straight line with position relative to O given by $s(t) = 2t - \dfrac{4}{t+1}$ cm, where $t \geqslant 0$ is the time in seconds.

   a Find velocity and acceleration functions for the particle's motion and draw sign diagrams for each of them.

   b Describe the motion of the particle at $t = 1$ second.

   c Does the particle ever change direction? If so, where and when does it do this?

   d Draw a diagram to illustrate the motion of the particle.

   e Find the time intervals when the:

   i velocity is increasing   **ii** speed is increasing.

6 A rectangular sheet of tin-plate is $2k$ cm by k cm. Four squares, each with sides x cm, are cut from its corners. The remainder is bent into the shape of an open rectangular container. Find the value of x which will maximise the capacity of the container.

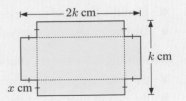

7 A cork bobs up and down in a bucket of water such that the distance from the centre of the cork to the bottom of the bucket is given by $s(t) = 30 + \cos(\pi t)$ cm, $t \geqslant 0$ seconds.

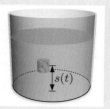

   a Find the cork's velocity at times $t = 0, \frac{1}{2}, 1, 1\frac{1}{2}, 2$ s.

   b Find the time intervals when the cork is falling.

REVIEW SET 17B   CALCULATOR

1 The height of a tree t years after it was planted is given by $H(t) = 60 + 40\ln(2t + 1)$ cm, $t \geqslant 0$.

   a How high was the tree when it was planted?

   b How long does it take for the tree to reach: **i** 150 cm   **ii** 300 cm?

   c At what rate is the tree's height increasing after: **i** 2 years   **ii** 20 years?

2 A particle P moves in a straight line with position given by $s(t) = 80e^{-\frac{t}{10}} - 40t$ m where t is the time in seconds, $t \geqslant 0$.

   a Find the velocity and acceleration functions.

   b Find the initial position, velocity, and acceleration of P.

   c Discuss the velocity of P as $t \to \infty$.

   d Sketch the graph of the velocity function.

   e Find the exact time when the velocity is -44 m s^{-1}.

3 The cost per hour of running a freight train is given by $C(v) = \dfrac{v^2}{30} + \dfrac{9000}{v}$ dollars where v is the average speed of the train in km h^{-1}.

   a Find the cost of running the train for:

      i two hours at 45 km h^{-1} **ii** 5 hours at 64 km h^{-1}.

   b Find the rate of change in the hourly cost of running the train at speeds of:

      i 50 km h^{-1} **ii** 66 km h^{-1}.

   c At what speed will the cost per hour be a minimum?

4 A particle moves along the x-axis with position relative to origin O given by $x(t) = 3t - \sqrt{t + 1}$ cm, where t is the time in seconds, $t \geqslant 0$.

   a Find expressions for the particle's velocity and acceleration at any time t, and draw sign diagrams for each function.

   b Find the initial conditions and hence describe the motion at that instant.

   c Describe the motion of the particle at $t = 8$ seconds.

   d Find the time and position when the particle reverses direction.

   e Determine the time interval when the particle's speed is decreasing.

5 The value of a car t years after its purchase is given by $V = 20\,000e^{-0.4t}$ dollars. Calculate:

   a the purchase price of the car

   b the rate of decrease of the value of the car 10 years after it was purchased.

6 When a shirt maker sells x shirts per day, their income is given by

$$I(x) = 200 \ln \left(1 + \frac{x}{100}\right) + 1000 \text{ dollars.}$$

The manufacturing costs are determined by the cost function

$$C(x) = (x - 100)^2 + 200 \text{ dollars.}$$

How many shirts should be sold daily to maximise profits? What is the maximum daily profit?

7 A 200 m fence is placed around a lawn which has the shape of a rectangle with a semi-circle on one of its sides.

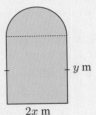

   a Using the dimensions shown on the figure, show that $y = 100 - x - \frac{\pi}{2}x$.

   b Find the area of the lawn A in terms of x only.

   c Find the dimensions of the lawn if it has the maximum possible area.

y m

$2x$ m

REVIEW SET 17C

1 A manufacturer of open steel boxes has to make one with a square base and a capacity of 1 m³. The steel costs $2 per square metre.

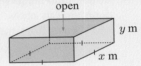

open

y m

x m

   a If the base measures x m by x m and the height is y m, find y in terms of x.

   b Hence, show that the total cost of the steel is $C(x) = 2x^2 + \frac{8}{x}$ dollars.

   c Find the dimensions of the box which would cost the least in steel to make.

2 A particle P moves in a straight line with position from O given by $s(t) = 15t - \dfrac{60}{(t+1)^2}$ cm,

where t is the time in seconds, $t \geqslant 0$.

   a Find velocity and acceleration functions for P's motion.

   b Describe the motion of P at $t = 3$ seconds.

   c For what values of t is the particle's speed increasing?

3 Infinitely many rectangles can be inscribed under the curve $y = e^{-2x}$ as shown.
Determine the coordinates of A such that the rectangle OBAC has maximum area.

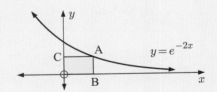

$y = e^{-2x}$

4 The height of a tree t years after it is planted is given by $H(t) = 6\left(1 - \dfrac{2}{t+3}\right)$ metres,

$t \geqslant 0$.

   a How high was the tree when it was planted?

   b Determine the height of the tree after $t = 3$, 6 and 9 years.

   c Find the rate at which the tree is growing at $t = 0$, 3, 6 and 9 years.

   d Show that $H'(t) > 0$ and explain the significance of this result.

   e Sketch the graph of $H(t)$ against t.

5 A particle P moves in a straight line with position given by $s(t) = 25t - 10\ln t$ cm, $t \geqslant 1$, where t is the time in minutes.

   a Find the velocity and acceleration functions.

   b Find the position, velocity, and acceleration when $t = e$ minutes.

   c Discuss the velocity as $t \to \infty$.

   d Sketch the graph of the velocity function.

   e Find when the velocity of P is 20 cm per minute.

6 A triangular pen is enclosed by two fences [AB] and [BC], each of length 50 m, with the river being the third side.

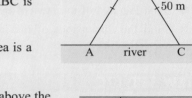

   a If $AC = 2x$ m, show that the area of triangle ABC is
$$A(x) = x\sqrt{2500 - x^2} \text{ m}^2.$$

   b Find $\dfrac{d[A(x)]^2}{dx}$ and hence find x such that the area is a maximum.

7 A light bulb hangs from the ceiling at height h metres above the floor, directly above point N. At any point A on the floor which is x metres from the light bulb, the illumination I is given by
$$I = \frac{\sqrt{8}\cos\theta}{x^2} \text{ units.}$$

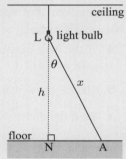

   a If $NA = 1$ metre, show that at A, $I = \sqrt{8}\cos\theta\sin^2\theta$.

   b The light bulb may be lifted or lowered to change the intensity at A. Assuming $NA = 1$ metre, find the height the bulb should be above the floor for greatest illumination at A.

Chapter **18**

Integration

OPENING PROBLEM

The function $f(x) = x^2 + 1$ lies above the x-axis for all $x \in \mathbb{R}$.

Things to think about:

a How can we calculate the shaded area A, which is the area under the curve for $1 \leqslant x \leqslant 4$?

b What function has $x^2 + 1$ as its derivative?

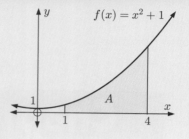

In the previous chapters we used differential calculus to find the derivatives of many types of functions. We also used it in problem solving, in particular to find the gradients of graphs and rates of changes, and to solve optimisation problems.

In this chapter we consider **integral calculus**. This involves **antidifferentiation** which is the reverse process of differentiation. Integral calculus also has many useful applications, including:

- finding areas where curved boundaries are involved
- finding volumes of revolution
- finding distances travelled from velocity functions
- solving problems in economics and biology
- solving problems in statistics
- solving differential equations.

A   THE AREA UNDER A CURVE

Finding the area under a curve has been important to mathematicians for thousands of years. In the history of mathematics it was fundamental to the development of integral calculus. We will therefore begin our study by calculating the area under a curve using the same methods as the ancient mathematicians.

UPPER AND LOWER RECTANGLES

Consider the function $f(x) = x^2 + 1$.

We wish to estimate the area A enclosed by $y = f(x)$, the x-axis, and the vertical lines $x = 1$ and $x = 4$.

Suppose we divide the interval $1 \leqslant x \leqslant 4$ into three strips of width 1 unit as shown. We obtain three sub-intervals of equal width.

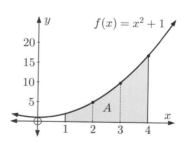

The diagram alongside shows **upper rectangles**, which are rectangles with top edges at the maximum value of the curve on that subinterval.

The area of the upper rectangles,

$A_U = 1 \times f(2) + 1 \times f(3) + 1 \times f(4)$
$\quad = 5 + 10 + 17$
$\quad = 32$ units^2

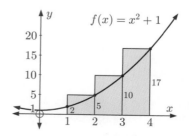

The next diagram shows **lower rectangles**, which are rectangles with top edges at the minimum value of the curve on that subinterval.

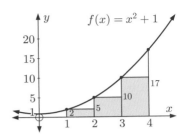

The area of the lower rectangles,

$$A_L = 1 \times f(1) + 1 \times f(2) + 1 \times f(3)$$
$$= 2 + 5 + 10$$
$$= 17 \text{ units}^2$$

Now clearly $A_L < A < A_U$, so the area A lies between 17 units^2 and 32 units^2.

If the interval $1 \leqslant x \leqslant 4$ was divided into 6 subintervals, each of width $\frac{1}{2}$, then

$$A_U = \tfrac{1}{2}f(1\tfrac{1}{2}) + \tfrac{1}{2}f(2) + \tfrac{1}{2}f(2\tfrac{1}{2}) + \tfrac{1}{2}f(3) + \tfrac{1}{2}f(3\tfrac{1}{2}) + \tfrac{1}{2}f(4)$$
$$= \tfrac{1}{2}(\tfrac{13}{4} + 5 + \tfrac{29}{4} + 10 + \tfrac{53}{4} + 17)$$
$$= 27.875 \text{ units}^2$$

and $A_L = \tfrac{1}{2}f(1) + \tfrac{1}{2}f(1\tfrac{1}{2}) + \tfrac{1}{2}f(2) + \tfrac{1}{2}f(2\tfrac{1}{2}) + \tfrac{1}{2}f(3) + \tfrac{1}{2}f(3\tfrac{1}{2})$

$$= \tfrac{1}{2}(2 + \tfrac{13}{4} + 5 + \tfrac{29}{4} + 10 + \tfrac{53}{4})$$
$$= 20.375 \text{ units}^2$$

From this refinement we conclude that the area A lies between 20.375 and 27.875 units^2.

As we create more subdivisions, the estimates A_L and A_U will become more and more accurate. In fact, as the subdivision width is reduced further and further, both A_L and A_U will **converge** to A.

We illustrate this process by estimating the area A between the graph of $y = x^2$ and the x-axis for $0 \leqslant x \leqslant 1$.

This example is of historical interest. **Archimedes** (287 - 212 BC) found the exact area. In an article that contains 24 propositions, he developed the essential theory of what is now known as integral calculus.

Consider $f(x) = x^2$ and divide the interval $0 \leqslant x \leqslant 1$ into 4 subintervals of equal width.

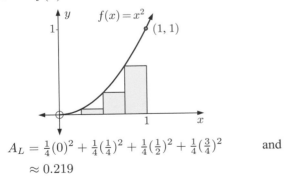

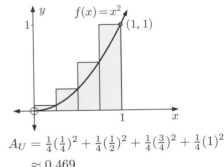

$A_L = \tfrac{1}{4}(0)^2 + \tfrac{1}{4}(\tfrac{1}{4})^2 + \tfrac{1}{4}(\tfrac{1}{2})^2 + \tfrac{1}{4}(\tfrac{3}{4})^2$ and $A_U = \tfrac{1}{4}(\tfrac{1}{4})^2 + \tfrac{1}{4}(\tfrac{1}{2})^2 + \tfrac{1}{4}(\tfrac{3}{4})^2 + \tfrac{1}{4}(1)^2$

≈ 0.219 ≈ 0.469

Now suppose there are n subintervals between $x = 0$ and $x = 1$, each of width $\dfrac{1}{n}$.

We can use technology to help calculate A_L and A_U for large values of n.

Click on the appropriate icon to access our **area finder** software or instructions for the procedure on a **graphics calculator**.

AREA FINDER

GRAPHICS CALCULATOR INSTRUCTIONS

The table alongside summarises the results you should obtain for $n = 4$, 10, 25, and 50.

The exact value of A is in fact $\frac{1}{3}$, as we will find later in the chapter. Notice how both A_L and A_U are converging to this value as n increases.

n	A_L	A_U	Average
4	0.218 75	0.468 75	0.343 75
10	0.285 00	0.385 00	0.335 00
25	0.313 60	0.353 60	0.333 60
50	0.323 40	0.343 40	0.333 40

EXERCISE 18A.1

1 Consider the area between $y = x$ and the x-axis from $x = 0$ to $x = 1$.

   a Divide the interval into 5 strips of equal width, then estimate the area using:

      i upper rectangles   **ii** lower rectangles.

   b Calculate the actual area and compare it with your answers in **a**.

2 Consider the area between $y = \dfrac{1}{x}$ and the x-axis from $x = 2$ to $x = 4$. Divide the interval into 6 strips of equal width, then estimate the area using:

   a upper rectangles   **b** lower rectangles.

3 Use rectangles to find lower and upper sums for the area between the graph of $y = x^2$ and the x-axis for $1 \leqslant x \leqslant 2$. Use $n = 10$, 25, 50, 100, and 500.

Give your answers to 4 decimal places.

As n gets larger, both A_L and A_U converge to the same number which is a simple fraction. What is it?

4   **a** Use rectangles to find lower and upper sums for the areas between the graphs of each of the following functions and the x-axis for $0 \leqslant x \leqslant 1$.

      Use values of $n = 5$, 10, 50, 100, 500, 1000, and 10 000.

      Give your answer to 5 decimal places in each case.

      i $y = x^3$ **ii** $y = x$ **iii** $y = x^{\frac{1}{2}}$ **iv** $y = x^{\frac{1}{3}}$

   b For each case in **a**, A_L and A_U converge to the same number which is a simple fraction. What fractions are they?

   c On the basis of your answer to **b**, predict the area between the graph of $y = x^a$ and the x-axis for $0 \leqslant x \leqslant 1$ and any number $a > 0$.

5 Consider the quarter circle of centre $(0, 0)$ and radius 2 units illustrated.

Its area is $\frac{1}{4}$(full circle of radius 2)

        $= \frac{1}{4} \times \pi \times 2^2$

        $= \pi$ units^2

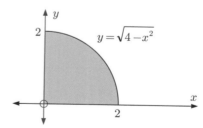

   a Estimate the area using lower and upper rectangles for $n = 10$, 50, 100, 200, 1000, and 10 000. Hence, find rational bounds for π.

   b Archimedes found the famous approximation $3\frac{10}{71} < \pi < 3\frac{1}{7}$.

      For what value of n is your estimate for π better than that of Archimedes?

THE DEFINITE INTEGRAL

Consider the lower and upper rectangle sums for a function which is positive and increasing on the interval $a \leqslant x \leqslant b$.

We divide the interval into n subintervals, each of width $w = \dfrac{b-a}{n}$.

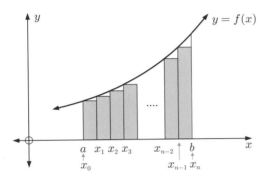 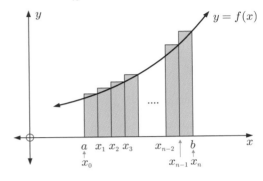

Since the function is increasing,

$$A_L = w\,f(x_0) + w\,f(x_1) + w\,f(x_2) + \ldots + w\,f(x_{n-2}) + w\,f(x_{n-1}) = w\sum_{i=0}^{n-1} f(x_i)$$

and $\quad A_U = w\,f(x_1) + w\,f(x_2) + w\,f(x_3) + \ldots + w\,f(x_{n-1}) + w\,f(x_n) \quad = w\sum_{i=1}^{n} f(x_i)$

Notice that $\quad A_U - A_L = w\,(f(x_n) - f(x_0))$

$$= \frac{1}{n}(b-a)\,(f(b) - f(a))$$

$\therefore \quad \displaystyle\lim_{n\to\infty} (A_U - A_L) = 0 \qquad \text{\{since } \displaystyle\lim_{n\to\infty}\frac{1}{n} = 0\}$

$\therefore \quad \displaystyle\lim_{n\to\infty} A_L = \lim_{n\to\infty} A_U \quad \text{\{when both limits exist\}}$

$\therefore \quad$ since $A_L < A < A_U$, for all values of n, it follows that $\quad \displaystyle\lim_{n\to\infty} A_L = A = \lim_{n\to\infty} A_U$

This fact is true for all positive continuous functions on an interval $a \leqslant x \leqslant b$.

The value A is known as the "**definite integral** of $f(x)$ from a to b", written $\quad A = \displaystyle\int_a^b f(x)\,dx$.

If $\quad f(x) \geqslant 0 \quad$ for all $a \leqslant x \leqslant b$, then

$$\int_a^b f(x)\,dx \quad \text{is equal to the shaded area.}$$

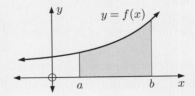

HISTORICAL NOTE

The word **integration** means "*to put together into a whole*". An **integral** is the "whole" produced from integration, since the areas $f(x_i) \times w$ of the thin rectangular strips are put together into one whole area.

The symbol $\int$ is called an **integral sign**. In the time of **Newton** and **Leibniz** it was the stretched out letter s, but it is no longer part of the alphabet.

Example 1   ◀) **Self Tutor**

a Sketch the graph of $y = x^4$ for $0 \leqslant x \leqslant 1$. Shade the area described by $\int_0^1 x^4 \, dx$.

b Use technology to calculate the lower and upper rectangle sums for n equal subdivisions where $n = 5, 10, 50, 100,$ and 500.

AREA FINDER

c Hence find $\int_0^1 x^4 \, dx$ to 2 significant figures.

a
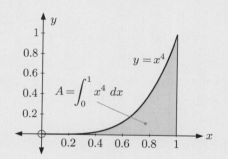

b

n	A_L	A_U
5	0.1133	0.3133
10	0.1533	0.2533
50	0.1901	0.2101
100	0.1950	0.2050
500	0.1990	0.2010

c When $n = 500$, $A_L \approx A_U \approx 0.20$, to 2 significant figures.

$\therefore$ since $A_L < \int_0^1 x^4 \, dx < A_U$, $\int_0^1 x^4 \, dx \approx 0.20$

EXERCISE 18A.2

1 a Sketch the graph of $y = \sqrt{x}$ for $0 \leqslant x \leqslant 1$.

   Shade the area described by $\int_0^1 \sqrt{x} \, dx$.

   b Find the lower and upper rectangle sums for $n = 5, 10, 50, 100,$ and 500.

   c Use the information in **b** to find $\int_0^1 \sqrt{x} \, dx$ to 2 significant figures.

2 a Sketch the graph of $y = \sqrt{1 + x^3}$ and the x-axis for $0 \leqslant x \leqslant 2$.

   b Write expressions for the lower and upper rectangle sums using n subintervals, $n \in \mathbb{N}$.

   c Find the lower and upper rectangle sums for $n = 50, 100,$ and 500.

   d What is your best estimate for $\int_0^2 \sqrt{1 + x^3} \, dx$?

Example 2   ◀) **Self Tutor**

Use graphical evidence and   **a** $\int_0^2 (2x+1)\, dx$ **b** $\int_0^1 \sqrt{1-x^2}\, dx$
known area facts to find:

a

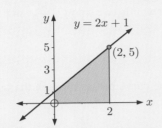

$$\int_0^2 (2x+1)\, dx$$

= shaded area

$= \left(\frac{1+5}{2}\right) \times 2$

$= 6$

b If $y = \sqrt{1-x^2}$ then $y^2 = 1 - x^2$ and so $x^2 + y^2 = 1$ which is the equation of the unit circle. $y = \sqrt{1-x^2}$ is the upper half.

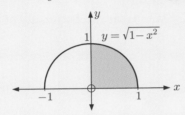

$$\int_0^1 \sqrt{1-x^2}\, dx$$

= shaded area

$= \frac{1}{4}(\pi r^2)$ where $r = 1$

$= \frac{\pi}{4}$

3 Use graphical evidence and known area facts to find:

a $\int_1^3 (1+4x)\, dx$ **b** $\int_{-1}^2 (2-x)\, dx$ **c** $\int_{-2}^2 \sqrt{4-x^2}\, dx$

INVESTIGATION 1   **ESTIMATING** $\int_{-3}^3 e^{-\frac{x^2}{2}}\, dx$

The integral $\int_{-3}^3 e^{-\frac{x^2}{2}}\, dx$ is of considerable interest to statisticians.

In this investigation we shall estimate the value of this integral using upper and lower rectangular sums for $n = 4500$. We will perform the integration in sections.

What to do:

1 Sketch the graph of $y = e^{-\frac{x^2}{2}}$ for $-3 \leqslant x \leqslant 3$.

2 Calculate the upper and lower rectangular sums for the interval $0 \leqslant x \leqslant 3$ using $n = 2250$.

GRAPHICS CALCULATOR INSTRUCTIONS

3 Use the fact that the function $y = e^{-\frac{x^2}{2}}$ is symmetric to find upper and lower rectangular sums for $-3 \leqslant x \leqslant 0$ for $n = 2250$.

4 Use your results of **2** and **3** to estimate $\int_{-3}^3 e^{-\frac{x^2}{2}}\, dx$.

AREA FINDER

How accurate is your estimate compared with $\sqrt{2\pi}$?

B ANTIDIFFERENTIATION

In many problems in calculus we know the rate of change of one variable with respect to another, but we do not have a formula which relates the variables. In other words, we know $\dfrac{dy}{dx}$, but we need to know y in terms of x.

Examples of problems we need to solve include:

- The gradient function $f'(x)$ of a curve is $2x + 3$ and the curve passes through the origin. What is the function $y = f(x)$?

- The rate of change in temperature is $\dfrac{dT}{dt} = 10e^{-t}$ °C per minute where $t \geqslant 0$. What is the temperature function given that initially the temperature was 11°C?

> The process of finding y from $\dfrac{dy}{dx}$, or $f(x)$ from $f'(x)$, is the reverse process of differentiation. We call it **antidifferentiation**.

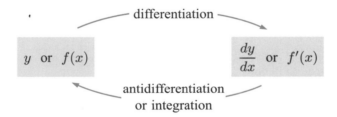

Consider $\dfrac{dy}{dx} = x^2$.

From our work on differentiation, we know that when we differentiate power functions the index reduces by 1. We hence know that y must involve x^3.

Now if $y = x^3$ then $\dfrac{dy}{dx} = 3x^2$, so if we start with $y = \frac{1}{3}x^3$ then $\dfrac{dy}{dx} = x^2$.

However, in all of the cases $y = \frac{1}{3}x^3 + 2$, $y = \frac{1}{3}x^3 + 100$, and $y = \frac{1}{3}x^3 - 7$ we find $\dfrac{dy}{dx} = x^2$.

In fact, there are infinitely many functions of the form $y = \frac{1}{3}x^3 + c$ where c is an arbitrary constant which will give $\dfrac{dy}{dx} = x^2$. Ignoring the arbitrary constant, we say that $\frac{1}{3}x^3$ is the **antiderivative** of x^2. It is the simplest function which, when differentiated, gives x^2.

> If $F(x)$ is a function where $F'(x) = f(x)$ we say that:
> - the **derivative** of $F(x)$ is $f(x)$ and
> - the **antiderivative** of $f(x)$ is $F(x)$.

Example 3 ◀) **Self Tutor**

Find the antiderivative of: **a** x^3 **b** e^{2x} **c** $\dfrac{1}{\sqrt{x}}$

a $\dfrac{d}{dx}\left(x^4\right) = 4x^3$

$\therefore \quad \dfrac{d}{dx}\left(\tfrac{1}{4}x^4\right) = x^3$

$\therefore$ the antiderivative of x^3 is $\tfrac{1}{4}x^4$.

b $\dfrac{d}{dx}\left(e^{2x}\right) = e^{2x} \times 2$

$\therefore \quad \dfrac{d}{dx}\left(\tfrac{1}{2}e^{2x}\right) = \tfrac{1}{2} \times e^{2x} \times 2 = e^{2x}$

$\therefore$ the antiderivative of e^{2x} is $\tfrac{1}{2}e^{2x}$.

c $\dfrac{1}{\sqrt{x}} = x^{-\frac{1}{2}}$

Now $\dfrac{d}{dx}\left(x^{\frac{1}{2}}\right) = \tfrac{1}{2}x^{-\frac{1}{2}}$

$\therefore \quad \dfrac{d}{dx}\left(2x^{\frac{1}{2}}\right) = 2(\tfrac{1}{2})x^{-\frac{1}{2}} = x^{-\frac{1}{2}}$

$\therefore$ the antiderivative of $\dfrac{1}{\sqrt{x}}$ is $2\sqrt{x}$.

EXERCISE 18B

1 **a** Find the antiderivative of:

     i x **ii** x^2 **iii** x^5 **iv** x^{-2} **v** x^{-4} **vi** $x^{\frac{1}{3}}$ **vii** $x^{-\frac{1}{2}}$

     b From your answers in **a**, predict a general rule for the antiderivative of x^n, for $n \neq -1$.

2 **a** Find the antiderivative of:

     i e^{2x} **ii** e^{5x} **iii** $e^{\frac{1}{2}x}$ **iv** $e^{0.01x}$ **v** $e^{\pi x}$ **vi** $e^{\frac{x}{3}}$

     b From your answers in **a**, predict a general rule for the antiderivative of e^{kx} where k is a constant.

3 Find the antiderivative of:

     a $6x^2 + 4x$ by first differentiating $x^3 + x^2$ **b** e^{3x+1} by first differentiating e^{3x+1}

     c $\sqrt{x}$ by first differentiating $x\sqrt{x}$ **d** $(2x+1)^3$ by first differentiating $(2x+1)^4$

C   THE FUNDAMENTAL THEOREM OF CALCULUS

Sir Isaac Newton and **Gottfried Wilhelm Leibniz** showed the link between differential calculus and the definite integral or limit of an area sum we saw in **Section A**. This link is called the **fundamental theorem of calculus**. The beauty of this theorem is that it enables us to evaluate complicated summations.

We have already observed that:

If $f(x)$ is a continuous positive function on an interval $a \leqslant x \leqslant b$ then the area under the curve between $x = a$ and $x = b$ is $\displaystyle\int_a^b f(x)\,dx$.

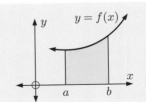

INVESTIGATION 2   THE AREA FUNCTION

Consider the constant function $f(x) = 5$.

We wish to find an **area function** which will give the area under the function between $x = a$ and some other value of x which we will call t.

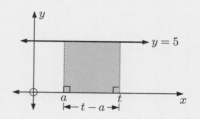

The area function is $A(t) = \displaystyle\int_a^t 5\ dx$

$\quad\quad\quad\quad\quad\quad = $ shaded area in graph

$\quad\quad\quad\quad\quad\quad = (t - a)5$

$\quad\quad\quad\quad\quad\quad = 5t - 5a$

$\therefore$ we can write $A(t)$ in the form $F(t) - F(a)$ where $F(t) = 5t$ or equivalently, $F(x) = 5x$.

What to do:

1 What is the derivative $F'(x)$ of the function $F(x) = 5x$? How does this relate to the function $f(x)$?

2 Consider the simplest linear function $f(x) = x$.
The corresponding area function is

$$A(t) = \int_a^t x\ dx$$

$\quad\quad\quad = $ shaded area in graph

$\quad\quad\quad = \left(\dfrac{t+a}{2}\right)(t-a)$

a Can you write $A(t)$ in the form $F(t) - F(a)$?

b If so, what is the derivative $F'(x)$? How does it relate to the function $f(x)$?

3 Consider $f(x) = 2x + 3$.   The corresponding area function is

$$A(t) = \int_a^t (2x + 3)\ dx$$

$\quad\quad\quad = $ shaded area in graph

$\quad\quad\quad = \left(\dfrac{2t + 3 + 2a + 3}{2}\right)(t - a)$

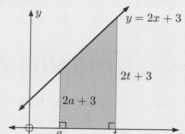

a Can you write $A(t)$ in the form $F(t) - F(a)$?

b If so, what is the derivative $F'(x)$?
How does it relate to the function $f(x)$?

4 Repeat the procedure in **2** and **3** for finding the area functions of:

a $f(x) = \frac{1}{2}x + 3$ **b** $f(x) = 5 - 2x$

Do your results fit with your earlier observations?

5 If $f(x) = 3x^2 + 4x + 5$,   predict what $F(x)$ would be without performing the algebraic procedure.

From the **Investigation** you should have discovered that, for $f(x) \geqslant 0$,

$$\int_a^t f(x)\,dx = F(t) - F(a) \quad \text{where} \quad F'(x) = f(x). \quad F(x) \text{ is the \textbf{antiderivative} of } f(x).$$

The following argument shows why this is true for all functions $f(x) \geqslant 0$.

Consider a function $y = f(x)$ which has antiderivative $F(x)$ and an area function $A(t) = \int_a^t f(x)\,dx$ which is the area from $x = a$ to $x = t$.

$A(t)$ is clearly an increasing function and
$A(a) = 0$ .... (1)

Consider the narrow strip between $x = t$ and $x = t + h$. The area of this strip is $A(t + h) - A(t)$, but we also know it must lie between a lower and upper rectangle on the interval $t \leqslant x \leqslant t + h$ of width h.

$$\begin{array}{c} \text{area of smaller} \\ \text{rectangle} \end{array} \leqslant A(t + h) - A(t) \leqslant \begin{array}{c} \text{area of larger} \\ \text{rectangle} \end{array}$$

If $f(x)$ is increasing on this interval then

$$hf(t) \leqslant A(t + h) - A(t) \leqslant hf(t + h)$$

$$\therefore \quad f(t) \leqslant \frac{A(t + h) - A(t)}{h} \leqslant f(t + h)$$

Equivalently, if $f(x)$ is decreasing on this interval then $f(t + h) \leqslant \dfrac{A(t + h) - A(t)}{h} \leqslant f(t)$.

Taking the limit as $h \to 0$ gives $f(t) \leqslant A'(t) \leqslant f(t)$
$$\therefore \quad A'(t) = f(t)$$

The area function $A(t)$ must only differ from the antiderivative of $f(t)$ by a constant.

$$\therefore \quad A(t) = F(t) + c$$

Letting $t = a$, $A(a) = F(a) + c$

But from (1), $A(a) = 0$, so $c = -F(a)$

$$\therefore \quad A(t) = F(t) - F(a)$$

Letting $t = b$, $\displaystyle\int_a^b f(x)\,dx = F(b) - F(a)$

This result is in fact true for all continuous functions $f(x)$.

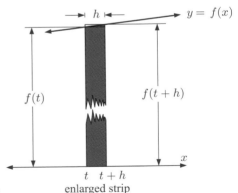

enlarged strip

THE FUNDAMENTAL THEOREM OF CALCULUS

For a continuous function $f(x)$ with antiderivative $F(x)$, $\displaystyle\int_a^b f(x)\,dx = F(b) - F(a)$.

Instructions for evaluating definite integrals on your calculator can be found by clicking on the icon.

**GRAPHICS
CALCULATOR
INSTRUCTIONS**

PROPERTIES OF DEFINITE INTEGRALS

The following properties of definite integrals can all be deduced from the fundamental theorem of calculus:

- $\displaystyle\int_a^a f(x)\,dx = 0$

- $\displaystyle\int_a^b c\,dx = c(b-a)$ $\{c$ is a constant$\}$

- $\displaystyle\int_b^a f(x)\,dx = -\int_a^b f(x)\,dx$

- $\displaystyle\int_a^b c\,f(x)\,dx = c\int_a^b f(x)\,dx$

- $\displaystyle\int_a^b f(x)\,dx + \int_b^c f(x)\,dx = \int_a^c f(x)\,dx$

- $\displaystyle\int_a^b [f(x)\pm g(x)]dx = \int_a^b f(x)\,dx \pm \int_a^b g(x)\,dx$

Example proof:

$$\int_a^b f(x)\,dx + \int_b^c f(x)\,dx$$
$$= F(b) - F(a) + F(c) - F(b)$$
$$= F(c) - F(a)$$
$$= \int_a^c f(x)\,dx$$

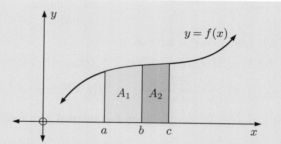

For the case where $a \leqslant b \leqslant c$ and $f(x) \geqslant 0$ for $a \leqslant x \leqslant c$,

$$\int_a^b f(x)\,dx + \int_b^c f(x)\,dx = A_1 + A_2 = \int_a^c f(x)\,dx$$

Example 4   ◀) **Self Tutor**

Use the fundamental theorem of calculus to find the area between:
a   the x-axis and $y = x^2$ from $x = 0$ to $x = 1$
b   the x-axis and $y = \sqrt{x}$ from $x = 1$ to $x = 9$.

a
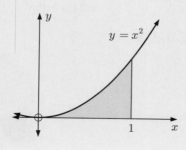

$f(x) = x^2$ has antiderivative $F(x) = \dfrac{x^3}{3}$

$\therefore$ the area $= \displaystyle\int_0^1 x^2\,dx$

$= F(1) - F(0)$

$= \tfrac{1}{3} - 0$

$= \tfrac{1}{3}$ units^2

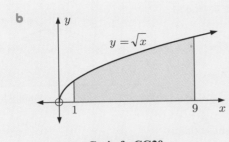

b

$f(x) = \sqrt{x} = x^{\frac{1}{2}}$ has antiderivative

$$F(x) = \frac{x^{\frac{3}{2}}}{\frac{3}{2}} = \frac{2}{3}x\sqrt{x}$$

$\therefore$ the area $= \displaystyle\int_1^9 x^{\frac{1}{2}}\, dx$

$= F(9) - F(1)$

$= \frac{2}{3} \times 27 - \frac{2}{3} \times 1$

$= 17\frac{1}{3}$ units^2

Casio fx-CG20

$\displaystyle\int_1^9 \sqrt{x}\, dx$

17.33333333

EXERCISE 18C

1 Use the fundamental theorem of calculus to find the area between:

   a the x-axis and $y = x^3$ from $x = 0$ to $x = 1$

   b the x-axis and $y = x^2$ from $x = 1$ to $x = 2$

   c the x-axis and $y = \sqrt{x}$ from $x = 0$ to $x = 1$.

   Check your answers using technology.

2 Use the fundamental theorem of calculus to show that:

   a $\displaystyle\int_a^a f(x)\, dx = 0$ and explain the result graphically

   b $\displaystyle\int_a^b c\, dx = c(b - a)$ where c is a constant

   c $\displaystyle\int_b^a f(x)\, dx = -\int_a^b f(x)\, dx$

   d $\displaystyle\int_a^b c\, f(x)\, dx = c\int_a^b f(x)\, dx$ where c is a constant

   e $\displaystyle\int_a^b [f(x) + g(x)]\, dx = \int_a^b f(x)\, dx + \int_a^b g(x)\, dx$

3 Use the fundamental theorem of calculus to find the area between the x-axis and:

   a $y = x^3$ from $x = 1$ to $x = 2$

   b $y = x^2 + 3x + 2$ from $x = 1$ to $x = 3$

   c $y = \sqrt{x}$ from $x = 1$ to $x = 2$

   d $y = e^x$ from $x = 0$ to $x = 1.5$

   e $y = \dfrac{1}{\sqrt{x}}$ from $x = 1$ to $x = 4$

   f $y = x^3 + 2x^2 + 7x + 4$ from $x = 1$ to $x = 1.25$

Check each answer using technology.

4 Use technology to find the area between the x-axis and $y = \sqrt{9 - x^2}$ from $x = 0$ to $x = 3$.

Check your answer by direct calculation of the area.

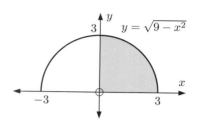

5   **a** Use the fundamental theorem of calculus to show that

$$\int_a^b (-f(x)) \, dx = -\int_a^b f(x) \, dx$$

b Hence show that if $f(x) \leqslant 0$ for all x on

$a \leqslant x \leqslant b$ then the shaded area $= -\displaystyle\int_a^b f(x) \, dx$.

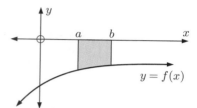

c Calculate the following integrals, and give graphical interpretations of your answers:

i $\displaystyle\int_0^1 (-x^2) \, dx$ **ii** $\displaystyle\int_0^1 (x^2 - x) \, dx$ **iii** $\displaystyle\int_{-2}^0 3x \, dx$

d Use graphical evidence and known area facts to find $\displaystyle\int_0^2 \left(-\sqrt{4 - x^2}\right) \, dx$.

D   INTEGRATION

Earlier we showed that the **antiderivative** of x^2 is $\frac{1}{3}x^3$.

We showed that any function of the form $\frac{1}{3}x^3 + c$ where c is a constant, has derivative x^2.

We say that the **indefinite integral** or **integral** of x^2 is $\frac{1}{3}x^3 + c$, and write $\displaystyle\int x^2 \, dx = \frac{1}{3}x^3 + c$.

We read this as "the integral of x^2 with respect to x is $\frac{1}{3}x^3 + c$, where c is a constant".

$$\text{If} \quad F'(x) = f(x) \quad \text{then} \quad \int f(x) \, dx = F(x) + c.$$

This process is known as **indefinite integration**. It is indefinite because it is not being applied to a particular interval.

DISCOVERING INTEGRALS

Since integration is the reverse process of differentiation we can sometimes discover integrals by differentiation. For example:

- if $F(x) = x^4$ then $F'(x) = 4x^3$

$$\therefore \int 4x^3 \, dx = x^4 + c$$

- if $F(x) = \sqrt{x} = x^{\frac{1}{2}}$ then $F'(x) = \frac{1}{2}x^{-\frac{1}{2}} = \frac{1}{2\sqrt{x}}$

$$\therefore \int \frac{1}{2\sqrt{x}} \, dx = \sqrt{x} + c$$

The following rules may prove useful:

- Any constant may be written in front of the integral sign.

$$\int k\,f(x)\,dx = k\int f(x)\,dx, \quad k \text{ is a constant}$$

Proof: Consider differentiating $kF(x)$ where $F'(x) = f(x)$.

$$\frac{d}{dx}(k\,F(x)) = k\,F'(x) = k\,f(x)$$

$$\therefore \int k\,f(x)\,dx = k\,F(x)$$

$$= k\int f(x)\,dx$$

- The integral of a sum is the sum of the separate integrals. This rule enables us to integrate term by term.

$$\int [f(x) + g(x)]\,dx = \int f(x)\,dx + \int g(x)\,dx$$

Example 5   ◀ᴺ **Self Tutor**

If $y = x^4 + 2x^3$, find $\dfrac{dy}{dx}$.   Hence find $\displaystyle\int (2x^3 + 3x^2)\,dx$.

If $y = x^4 + 2x^3$ then $\dfrac{dy}{dx} = 4x^3 + 6x^2$

$$\therefore \int 4x^3 + 6x^2\,dx = x^4 + 2x^3 + c$$

$$\therefore \int 2(2x^3 + 3x^2)\,dx = x^4 + 2x^3 + c$$

$$\therefore 2\int (2x^3 + 3x^2)\,dx = x^4 + 2x^3 + c$$

$$\therefore \int (2x^3 + 3x^2)\,dx = \tfrac{1}{2}x^4 + x^3 + c$$

> c represents a general constant, so is simply any value $c \in \mathbb{R}$. Instead of writing $\frac{c}{2}$, we can therefore still write just c.

EXERCISE 18D

1   If $y = x^7$, find $\dfrac{dy}{dx}$.   Hence find $\displaystyle\int x^6\,dx$.

2   If $y = x^3 + x^2$, find $\dfrac{dy}{dx}$.   Hence find $\displaystyle\int (3x^2 + 2x)\,dx$.

3   If $y = e^{2x+1}$, find $\dfrac{dy}{dx}$.   Hence find $\displaystyle\int e^{2x+1}\,dx$.

4   If $y = (2x + 1)^4$ find $\dfrac{dy}{dx}$.   Hence find $\displaystyle\int (2x + 1)^3\,dx$.

Example 6   ◀) **Self Tutor**

Suppose $y = \sqrt{5x - 1}$.

a Find $\dfrac{dy}{dx}$.   **b** Hence find $\displaystyle\int \frac{1}{\sqrt{5x - 1}}\, dx$.

a $y = \sqrt{5x - 1}$

$\quad = (5x - 1)^{\frac{1}{2}}$

$\therefore \quad \dfrac{dy}{dx} = \tfrac{1}{2}(5x - 1)^{-\frac{1}{2}}(5)$ {chain rule}

$\quad = \dfrac{5}{2\sqrt{5x - 1}}$

b Using **a**, $\displaystyle\int \frac{5}{2\sqrt{5x - 1}}\, dx = \sqrt{5x - 1} + c$

$\therefore \quad \tfrac{5}{2}\displaystyle\int \frac{1}{\sqrt{5x - 1}}\, dx = \sqrt{5x - 1} + c$

$\therefore \quad \displaystyle\int \frac{1}{\sqrt{5x - 1}}\, dx = \tfrac{2}{5}\sqrt{5x - 1} + c$

5 If $y = x\sqrt{x}$, find $\dfrac{dy}{dx}$. Hence find $\displaystyle\int \sqrt{x}\, dx$.

6 If $y = \dfrac{1}{\sqrt{x}}$, find $\dfrac{dy}{dx}$. Hence find $\displaystyle\int \frac{1}{x\sqrt{x}}\, dx$.

7 If $y = \cos 2x$, find $\dfrac{dy}{dx}$. Hence find $\displaystyle\int \sin 2x\, dx$.

8 If $y = \sin(1 - 5x)$, find $\dfrac{dy}{dx}$. Hence find $\displaystyle\int \cos(1 - 5x)\, dx$.

9 By considering $\dfrac{d}{dx}(x^2 - x)^3$, find $\displaystyle\int (2x - 1)(x^2 - x)^2\, dx$.

10 Prove the rule $\displaystyle\int [f(x) + g(x)]\, dx = \int f(x)\, dx + \int g(x)\, dx$.

11 Find $\dfrac{dy}{dx}$ if $y = \sqrt{1 - 4x}$. Hence find $\displaystyle\int \frac{1}{\sqrt{1 - 4x}}\, dx$.

12 By considering $\dfrac{d}{dx}\ln(5 - 3x + x^2)$, find $\displaystyle\int \frac{4x - 6}{5 - 3x + x^2}\, dx$.

We can check that an integral is correct by differentiating the answer. It should give us the **integrand**, the function we originally integrated.

E   RULES FOR INTEGRATION

In earlier chapters we developed rules to help us differentiate functions more efficiently:

Function	Derivative	Name
c, a constant	0	
$mx + c$, m and c are constants	m	
x^n	nx^{n-1}	**power rule**
$cu(x)$	$cu'(x)$	
$u(x) + v(x)$	$u'(x) + v'(x)$	**addition rule**
$u(x)v(x)$	$u'(x)v(x) + u(x)v'(x)$	**product rule**
$\dfrac{u(x)}{v(x)}$	$\dfrac{u'(x)v(x) - u(x)v'(x)}{[v(x)]^2}$	**quotient rule**
$y = f(u)$ where $u = u(x)$	$\dfrac{dy}{dx} = \dfrac{dy}{du}\dfrac{du}{dx}$	**chain rule**
e^x	e^x	
$e^{f(x)}$	$e^{f(x)} f'(x)$	
$\ln x$	$\dfrac{1}{x}$	
$\ln f(x)$	$\dfrac{f'(x)}{f(x)}$	
$[f(x)]^n$	$n[f(x)]^{n-1} f'(x)$	
$\sin x$	$\cos x$	
$\cos x$	$-\sin x$	
$\tan x$	$\dfrac{1}{\cos^2 x}$	

These rules or combinations of them can be used to differentiate almost all functions we consider in this course.

However, the task of finding **antiderivatives** is not so easy and cannot be written as a simple list of rules as we did above. In fact, huge books of different types of functions and their integrals have been written. Fortunately our course is restricted to a few special cases.

RULES FOR INTEGRATION

For k a constant, $\dfrac{d}{dx}(kx + c) = k$ $\qquad \therefore \quad \displaystyle\int k\,dx = kx + c$

If $n \neq -1$, $\dfrac{d}{dx}\left(\dfrac{x^{n+1}}{n+1} + c\right) = \dfrac{(n+1)x^n}{n+1} = x^n$ $\quad \therefore \quad \displaystyle\int x^n\,dx = \dfrac{x^{n+1}}{n+1} + c, \ n \neq -1$

$$\frac{d}{dx}(e^x + c) = e^x \qquad \therefore \quad \int e^x \, dx = e^x + c$$

If $x > 0$, $\frac{d}{dx}(\ln x + c) = \frac{1}{x}$

If $x < 0$, $\frac{d}{dx}(\ln(-x) + c) = \frac{-1}{-x} = \frac{1}{x}$

$$\left.\begin{array}{l}\end{array}\right\} \qquad \therefore \quad \int \frac{1}{x} \, dx = \ln|x| + c$$

$|x|$ is the modulus or size of x.

$$\frac{d}{dx}(\sin x + c) = \cos x \qquad \therefore \quad \int \cos x \, dx = \sin x + c$$

$$\frac{d}{dx}(-\cos x + c) = \sin x + c \qquad \therefore \quad \int \sin x \, dx = -\cos x + c$$

Function	Integral
k, a constant	$kx + c$
x^n	$\dfrac{x^{n+1}}{n+1} + c, \ n \neq -1$
e^x	$e^x + c$
$\dfrac{1}{x}$	$\ln|x| + c$
$\cos x$	$\sin x + c$
$\sin x$	$-\cos x + c$

In each case, c is an arbitrary constant called the **constant of integration** or **integrating constant**.

Remember that you can always check your integration by differentiating the resulting function.

Example 7   ◄》 **Self Tutor**

Find: **a** $\displaystyle\int (x^3 - 2x^2 + 5) \, dx$ **b** $\displaystyle\int \left(\frac{1}{x^3} - \sqrt{x}\right) dx$

a $\displaystyle\int (x^3 - 2x^2 + 5) \, dx$

$= \dfrac{x^4}{4} - \dfrac{2x^3}{3} + 5x + c$

b $\displaystyle\int \left(\frac{1}{x^3} - \sqrt{x}\right) dx$

$= \displaystyle\int (x^{-3} - x^{\frac{1}{2}}) \, dx$

$= \dfrac{x^{-2}}{-2} - \dfrac{x^{\frac{3}{2}}}{\frac{3}{2}} + c$

$= -\dfrac{1}{2x^2} - \dfrac{2}{3}x^{\frac{3}{2}} + c$

Example 8   🔊 **Self Tutor**

Integrate with respect to x:

a $2\sin x - \cos x$

b $-\dfrac{2}{x} + 3e^x$

a $\displaystyle\int (2\sin x - \cos x)\, dx$

$= 2(-\cos x) - \sin x + c$

$= -2\cos x - \sin x + c$

b $\displaystyle\int \left(-\dfrac{2}{x} + 3e^x\right) dx$

$= -2\ln|x| + 3e^x + c$

There is no product or quotient rule for integration. Consequently we often have to carry out multiplication or division before we integrate.

Example 9   🔊 **Self Tutor**

Find: **a** $\displaystyle\int \left(3x + \dfrac{2}{x}\right)^2 dx$ **b** $\displaystyle\int \left(\dfrac{x^2 - 2}{\sqrt{x}}\right) dx$

a $\displaystyle\int \left(3x + \dfrac{2}{x}\right)^2 dx$

$= \displaystyle\int \left(9x^2 + 12 + \dfrac{4}{x^2}\right) dx$

$= \displaystyle\int (9x^2 + 12 + 4x^{-2})\, dx$

$= \dfrac{9x^3}{3} + 12x + \dfrac{4x^{-1}}{-1} + c$

$= 3x^3 + 12x - \dfrac{4}{x} + c$

We expand the brackets and simplify to a form that can be integrated.

b $\displaystyle\int \left(\dfrac{x^2 - 2}{\sqrt{x}}\right) dx$

$= \displaystyle\int \left(\dfrac{x^2}{\sqrt{x}} - \dfrac{2}{\sqrt{x}}\right) dx$

$= \displaystyle\int (x^{\frac{3}{2}} - 2x^{-\frac{1}{2}})\, dx$

$= \dfrac{x^{\frac{5}{2}}}{\frac{5}{2}} - \dfrac{2x^{\frac{1}{2}}}{\frac{1}{2}} + c$

$= \tfrac{2}{5}x^2\sqrt{x} - 4\sqrt{x} + c$

EXERCISE 18E.1

1 Find:

a $\displaystyle\int (x^4 - x^2 - x + 2)\, dx$

b $\displaystyle\int (\sqrt{x} + e^x)\, dx$

c $\displaystyle\int \left(3e^x - \dfrac{1}{x}\right) dx$

d $\displaystyle\int \left(x\sqrt{x} - \dfrac{2}{x}\right) dx$

e $\displaystyle\int \left(\dfrac{1}{x\sqrt{x}} + \dfrac{4}{x}\right) dx$

f $\displaystyle\int \left(\tfrac{1}{2}x^3 - x^4 + x^{\frac{1}{3}}\right) dx$

g $\displaystyle\int \left(x^2 + \dfrac{3}{x}\right) dx$

h $\displaystyle\int \left(\dfrac{1}{2x} + x^2 - e^x\right) dx$

i $\displaystyle\int \left(5e^x + \tfrac{1}{3}x^3 - \dfrac{4}{x}\right) dx$

2 Integrate with respect to x:

a $3\sin x - 2$

b $4x - 2\cos x$

c $\sin x - 2\cos x + e^x$

d $x^2\sqrt{x} - 10\sin x$

e $\dfrac{x(x-1)}{3} + \cos x$

f $-\sin x + 2\sqrt{x}$

3 Find:

a $\displaystyle\int (x^2 + 3x - 2)\, dx$

b $\displaystyle\int \left(\sqrt{x} - \dfrac{1}{\sqrt{x}}\right) dx$

c $\displaystyle\int \left(2e^x - \dfrac{1}{x^2}\right) dx$

d $\displaystyle\int \dfrac{1 - 4x}{x\sqrt{x}}\, dx$

e $\displaystyle\int (2x + 1)^2\, dx$

f $\displaystyle\int \dfrac{x^2 + x - 3}{x}\, dx$

g $\displaystyle\int \dfrac{2x - 1}{\sqrt{x}}\, dx$

h $\displaystyle\int \dfrac{x^2 - 4x + 10}{x^2\sqrt{x}}\, dx$

i $\displaystyle\int (x + 1)^3\, dx$

4 Find:

a $\displaystyle\int \left(\sqrt{x} + \tfrac{1}{2}\cos x\right) dx$

b $\displaystyle\int \left(2e^t - 4\sin t\right) dt$

c $\displaystyle\int \left(3\cos t - \dfrac{1}{t}\right) dt$

5 Find y if:

a $\dfrac{dy}{dx} = 6$

b $\dfrac{dy}{dx} = 4x^2$

c $\dfrac{dy}{dx} = 5\sqrt{x} - x^2$

d $\dfrac{dy}{dx} = \dfrac{1}{x^2}$

e $\dfrac{dy}{dx} = 2e^x - 5$

f $\dfrac{dy}{dx} = 4x^3 + 3x^2$

6 Find y if:

a $\dfrac{dy}{dx} = (1 - 2x)^2$

b $\dfrac{dy}{dx} = \sqrt{x} - \dfrac{2}{\sqrt{x}}$

c $\dfrac{dy}{dx} = \dfrac{x^2 + 2x - 5}{x^2}$

7 Find $f(x)$ if:

a $f'(x) = x^3 - 5\sqrt{x} + 3$

b $f'(x) = 2\sqrt{x}(1 - 3x)$

c $f'(x) = 3e^x - \dfrac{4}{x}$

PARTICULAR VALUES

We can find the constant of integration c if we are given a particular value of the function.

Example 10 ◀) **Self Tutor**

Find $f(x)$ given that $f'(x) = x^3 - 2x^2 + 3$ and $f(0) = 2$.

Since $f'(x) = x^3 - 2x^2 + 3$,

$$f(x) = \int (x^3 - 2x^2 + 3)\, dx$$

$\therefore \quad f(x) = \dfrac{x^4}{4} - \dfrac{2x^3}{3} + 3x + c$

But $f(0) = 2$, so $0 - 0 + 0 + c = 2$ and hence $c = 2$

Thus $f(x) = \dfrac{x^4}{4} - \dfrac{2x^3}{3} + 3x + 2$

Example 11   ◀) **Self Tutor**

Find $f(x)$ given that $f'(x) = 2\sin x - \sqrt{x}$ and $f(0) = 4$.

$$f(x) = \int \left(2\sin x - x^{\frac{1}{2}} \right) \, dx$$

$$\therefore \quad f(x) = 2 \times (-\cos x) - \frac{x^{\frac{3}{2}}}{\frac{3}{2}} + c$$

$$\therefore \quad f(x) = -2\cos x - \tfrac{2}{3}x^{\frac{3}{2}} + c$$

But $f(0) = 4$, so $-2\cos 0 - 0 + c = 4$

and hence $c = 6$

Thus $f(x) = -2\cos x - \tfrac{2}{3}x^{\frac{3}{2}} + 6$.

If we are given the second derivative we need to integrate twice to find the function. This creates two integrating constants, so we need two other facts about the curve in order to determine these constants.

Example 12   ◀) **Self Tutor**

Find $f(x)$ given that $f''(x) = 12x^2 - 4$, $f'(0) = -1$, and $f(1) = 4$.

If $f''(x) = 12x^2 - 4$

then $f'(x) = \dfrac{12x^3}{3} - 4x + c$ {integrating with respect to x}

$\therefore \quad f'(x) = 4x^3 - 4x + c$

But $f'(0) = -1$, so $0 - 0 + c = -1$ and hence $c = -1$

Thus $f'(x) = 4x^3 - 4x - 1$

$\therefore \quad f(x) = \dfrac{4x^4}{4} - \dfrac{4x^2}{2} - x + d$ {integrating again}

$\therefore \quad f(x) = x^4 - 2x^2 - x + d$

But $f(1) = 4$, so $1 - 2 - 1 + d = 4$ and hence $d = 6$

Thus $f(x) = x^4 - 2x^2 - x + 6$

EXERCISE 18E.2

1 Find $f(x)$ given that:

    a $f'(x) = 2x - 1$ and $f(0) = 3$

    b $f'(x) = 3x^2 + 2x$ and $f(2) = 5$

    c $f'(x) = e^x + \dfrac{1}{\sqrt{x}}$ and $f(1) = 1$

    d $f'(x) = x - \dfrac{2}{\sqrt{x}}$ and $f(1) = 2$

2 Find $f(x)$ given that:

    a $f'(x) = x^2 - 4\cos x$ and $f(0) = 3$

    b $f'(x) = 2\cos x - 3\sin x$ and $f\left(\tfrac{\pi}{4}\right) = \tfrac{1}{\sqrt{2}}$

3 Find $f(x)$ given that:

a $f''(x) = 2x + 1$, $f'(1) = 3$, and $f(2) = 7$

b $f''(x) = 15\sqrt{x} + \dfrac{3}{\sqrt{x}}$, $f'(1) = 12$, and $f(0) = 5$

c $f''(x) = \cos x$, $f'(\frac{\pi}{2}) = 0$, and $f(0) = 3$

d $f''(x) = 2x$ and the points $(1,\ 0)$ and $(0,\ 5)$ lie on the curve.

F   INTEGRATING $f(ax + b)$

In this section we deal with integrals of functions which are composite with the linear function $ax + b$.

Notice that $\dfrac{d}{dx}\left(\dfrac{1}{a} e^{ax+b}\right) = \dfrac{1}{a} e^{ax+b} \times a = e^{ax+b}$

$$\therefore \quad \int e^{ax+b}\,dx = \dfrac{1}{a} e^{ax+b} + c \quad \text{for } a \neq 0$$

Likewise if $n \neq -1$,

$$\dfrac{d}{dx}\left(\dfrac{1}{a(n+1)}(ax+b)^{n+1}\right) = \dfrac{1}{a(n+1)}(n+1)(ax+b)^n \times a,$$
$$= (ax+b)^n$$

$$\therefore \quad \int (ax+b)^n\,dx = \dfrac{1}{a}\dfrac{(ax+b)^{n+1}}{(n+1)} + c \quad \text{for } n \neq -1$$

Also, $\dfrac{d}{dx}\left(\dfrac{1}{a}\ln(ax+b)\right) = \dfrac{1}{a}\left(\dfrac{a}{ax+b}\right) = \dfrac{1}{ax+b}$ for $ax+b > 0$, $a \neq 0$

$$\therefore \quad \int \dfrac{1}{ax+b}\,dx = \dfrac{1}{a}\ln(ax+b) + c \quad \text{for } ax+b > 0, \ a \neq 0$$

In fact, $$\int \dfrac{1}{ax+b}\,dx = \dfrac{1}{a}\ln|ax+b| + c \quad \text{for } a \neq 0.$$

We can perform the same process for the circular functions:

$$\dfrac{d}{dx}(\sin(ax+b)) = a\cos(ax+b)$$

$$\therefore \quad \int a\cos(ax+b)\,dx = \sin(ax+b) + c$$

$$\therefore \quad a\int \cos(ax+b)\,dx = \sin(ax+b) + c$$

So, $$\int \cos(ax+b)\,dx = \dfrac{1}{a}\sin(ax+b) + c \quad \text{for } a \neq 0.$$

Likewise we can show $$\int \sin(ax+b)\,dx = -\dfrac{1}{a}\cos(ax+b) + c \quad \text{for } a \neq 0.$$

For a, b constants with $a \neq 0$, we have:

Function	Integral
e^{ax+b}	$\dfrac{1}{a} e^{ax+b} + c$
$(ax+b)^n$	$\dfrac{1}{a} \dfrac{(ax+b)^{n+1}}{n+1} + c, \quad n \neq -1$
$\dfrac{1}{ax+b}$	$\dfrac{1}{a} \ln|ax+b| + c$
$\cos(ax+b)$	$\dfrac{1}{a} \sin(ax+b) + c$
$\sin(ax+b)$	$-\dfrac{1}{a} \cos(ax+b) + c$

Example 13   ◀) Self Tutor

Find: **a** $\displaystyle\int (2x+3)^4 \, dx$ **b** $\displaystyle\int \frac{1}{\sqrt{1-2x}} \, dx$

a $\displaystyle\int (2x+3)^4 \, dx$

$= \frac{1}{2} \times \dfrac{(2x+3)^5}{5} + c$

$= \frac{1}{10}(2x+3)^5 + c$

b $\displaystyle\int \frac{1}{\sqrt{1-2x}} \, dx$

$= \displaystyle\int (1-2x)^{-\frac{1}{2}} \, dx$

$= \dfrac{1}{-2} \times \dfrac{(1-2x)^{\frac{1}{2}}}{\frac{1}{2}} + c$

$= -\sqrt{1-2x} + c$

Example 14   ◀) Self Tutor

Find: **a** $\displaystyle\int (2e^{2x} - e^{-3x}) \, dx$ **b** $\displaystyle\int \frac{4}{1-2x} \, dx$

a $\displaystyle\int (2e^{2x} - e^{-3x}) \, dx$

$= 2(\frac{1}{2})e^{2x} - (\frac{1}{-3})e^{-3x} + c$

$= e^{2x} + \frac{1}{3}e^{-3x} + c$

b $\displaystyle\int \frac{4}{1-2x} \, dx$

$= 4 \displaystyle\int \frac{1}{1-2x} \, dx$

$= 4 \left(\frac{1}{-2}\right) \ln|1-2x| + c$

$= -2\ln|1-2x| + c$

Example 15   ◀) Self Tutor

Integrate with respect to x:

$2\sin(3x) + \cos(4x+\pi)$

$\displaystyle\int (2\sin(3x) + \cos(4x+\pi)) \, dx$

$= 2 \times \frac{1}{3}(-\cos(3x)) + \frac{1}{4}\sin(4x+\pi) + c$

$= -\frac{2}{3}\cos(3x) + \frac{1}{4}\sin(4x+\pi) + c$

Example 16

◀) **Self Tutor**

Integrate $(2 - \sin x)^2$ with respect to x, using the identity $\sin^2 x = \frac{1}{2} - \frac{1}{2}\cos(2x)$.

$$\int (2 - \sin x)^2 \, dx$$
$$= \int (4 - 4\sin x + \sin^2 x) \, dx$$
$$= \int \left(4 - 4\sin x + \frac{1}{2} - \frac{1}{2}\cos(2x)\right) dx$$
$$= \int \left(\frac{9}{2} - 4\sin x - \frac{1}{2}\cos(2x)\right) dx$$
$$= \frac{9}{2}x + 4\cos x - \frac{1}{2} \times \frac{1}{2}\sin(2x) + c$$
$$= \frac{9}{2}x + 4\cos x - \frac{1}{4}\sin(2x) + c$$

EXERCISE 18F

1 Find:

a $\displaystyle\int (2x + 5)^3 \, dx$

b $\displaystyle\int \frac{1}{(3 - 2x)^2} \, dx$

c $\displaystyle\int \frac{4}{(2x - 1)^4} \, dx$

d $\displaystyle\int (4x - 3)^7 \, dx$

e $\displaystyle\int \sqrt{3x - 4} \, dx$

f $\displaystyle\int \frac{10}{\sqrt{1 - 5x}} \, dx$

g $\displaystyle\int 3(1 - x)^4 \, dx$

h $\displaystyle\int \frac{4}{\sqrt{3 - 4x}} \, dx$

2 Integrate with respect to x:

a $\sin(3x)$

b $2\cos(-4x) + 1$

c $3\cos\left(\frac{x}{2}\right)$

d $3\sin(2x) - e^{-x}$

e $2\sin\left(2x + \frac{\pi}{6}\right)$

f $-3\cos\left(\frac{\pi}{4} - x\right)$

g $\cos(2x) + \sin(2x)$

h $2\sin(3x) + 5\cos(4x)$

i $\frac{1}{2}\cos(8x) - 3\sin x$

3 a Find $y = f(x)$ given $\dfrac{dy}{dx} = \sqrt{2x - 7}$ and that $y = 11$ when $x = 8$.

b The function $f(x)$ has gradient function $f'(x) = \dfrac{4}{\sqrt{1 - x}}$, and the curve $y = f(x)$ passes through the point $(-3, -11)$.

Find the point on the graph of $y = f(x)$ with x-coordinate -8.

4 Using the identities $\cos^2 x = \frac{1}{2} + \frac{1}{2}\cos(2x)$ and $\sin^2 x = \frac{1}{2} - \frac{1}{2}\cos(2x)$ to help you, integrate with respect to x:

a $\cos^2 x$

b $\sin^2 x$

c $1 + \cos^2(2x)$

d $3 - \sin^2(3x)$

e $\frac{1}{2}\cos^2(4x)$

f $(1 + \cos x)^2$

5 Find:

a $\displaystyle\int 3(2x - 1)^2 \, dx$

b $\displaystyle\int (x^2 - x)^2 \, dx$

c $\displaystyle\int (1 - 3x)^3 \, dx$

d $\displaystyle\int (1 - x^2)^2 \, dx$

e $\displaystyle\int 4\sqrt{5 - x} \, dx$

f $\displaystyle\int (x^2 + 1)^3 \, dx$

6 Find:

a $\displaystyle\int \left(2e^x + 5e^{2x}\right)\, dx$

b $\displaystyle\int \left(3e^{5x-2}\right)\, dx$

c $\displaystyle\int \left(e^{7-3x}\right)\, dx$

d $\displaystyle\int \frac{1}{2x-1}\, dx$

e $\displaystyle\int \frac{5}{1-3x}\, dx$

f $\displaystyle\int \left(e^{-x} - \frac{4}{2x+1}\right)\, dx$

g $\displaystyle\int (e^x + e^{-x})^2\, dx$

h $\displaystyle\int (e^{-x} + 2)^2\, dx$

i $\displaystyle\int \left(x - \frac{5}{1-x}\right)\, dx$

7 Find y given that:

a $\dfrac{dy}{dx} = (1 - e^x)^2$

b $\dfrac{dy}{dx} = 1 - 2x + \dfrac{3}{x+2}$

c $\dfrac{dy}{dx} = e^{-2x} + \dfrac{4}{2x-1}$

8 To find $\displaystyle\int \frac{1}{4x}\, dx$, where $x > 0$, Tracy's answer was $\displaystyle\int \frac{1}{4x}\, dx = \frac{1}{4}\ln(4x) + c, \ x > 0$

and Nadine's answer was $\displaystyle\int \frac{1}{4x}\, dx = \frac{1}{4}\int \frac{1}{x}\, dx = \frac{1}{4}\ln x + c, \ x > 0.$

Which of them has found the correct answer?   Prove your statement.

9 Suppose $f'(x) = p\sin\left(\frac{1}{2}x\right)$ where p is a constant. $f(0) = 1$ and $f(2\pi) = 0$. Find p and hence $f(x)$.

10 Consider a function g such that $g''(x) = -\sin 2x$.

Show that the gradients of the tangents to $y = g(x)$ when $x = \pi$ and $x = -\pi$ are equal.

11 a Find $f(x)$ given $f'(x) = 2e^{-2x}$ and $f(0) = 3$.

b Find $f(x)$ given $f'(x) = 2x - \dfrac{2}{1-x}$ and $f(-1) = 3$.

c A curve has gradient function $\sqrt{x} + \frac{1}{2}e^{-4x}$ and passes through $(1,\, 0)$. Find the equation of the function.

12 Show that $(\sin x + \cos x)^2 = 1 + \sin 2x$ and hence determine $\displaystyle\int (\sin x + \cos x)^2\, dx$.

13 Show that $(\cos x + 1)^2 = \frac{1}{2}\cos 2x + 2\cos x + \frac{3}{2}$ and hence determine $\displaystyle\int (\cos x + 1)^2\, dx$.

G INTEGRATION BY SUBSTITUTION

Consider the integral $\displaystyle\int (x^2 + 3x)^4(2x + 3)\, dx$.

The function we are integrating is the product of two expressions:

- The first expression is $(x^2 + 3x)^4$, which has the form $f(u(x))$ where $f(u) = u^4$ and $u(x) = x^2 + 3x$.

- The second expression is $2x + 3$, and we notice that this is also $u'(x)$.

So, we can write the integral in the form $\displaystyle\int f(u(x))\, u'(x)\, dx$ where $f(u) = u^4$ and $u(x) = x^2 + 3x$.

We can integrate functions of this form using the theorem

$$\int f(u)\,\frac{du}{dx}\,dx = \int f(u)\,du$$

Proof: Suppose $F(u)$ is the antiderivative of $f(u)$, so $\dfrac{dF}{du} = f(u)$

$$\therefore \quad \int f(u)\,du = F(u) + c \quad .... \;(1)$$

$$\text{But} \quad \frac{dF}{dx} = \frac{dF}{du}\,\frac{du}{dx} \qquad \{\text{chain rule}\}$$

$$= f(u)\,\frac{du}{dx}$$

$$\therefore \quad \int f(u)\,\frac{du}{dx}\,dx = F(u) + c$$

$$= \int f(u)\,du \quad \{\text{from } (1)\}$$

Using the theorem,

$$\int (x^2 + 3x)^4 (2x + 3)\,dx$$

$$= \int u^4\,\frac{du}{dx}\,dx \qquad\qquad \{u = x^2 + 3x, \quad \frac{du}{dx} = 2x + 3\}$$

$$= \int u^4\,du \qquad\qquad \{\text{replacing } \frac{du}{dx}\,dx \text{ by } du\}$$

$$= \frac{u^5}{5} + c$$

$$= \tfrac{1}{5}(x^2 + 3x)^5 + c$$

> We use $u\,(x)$ in our solution, but we give our answer in terms of x, since the original integral was with respect to x.

Example 17   ◀ **Self Tutor**

Use substitution to find: $\displaystyle\int \sqrt{x^3 + 2x}\,(3x^2 + 2)\,dx$

$$\int \sqrt{x^3 + 2x}\,(3x^2 + 2)\,dx$$

$$= \int \sqrt{u}\,\frac{du}{dx}\,dx \qquad \{u = x^3 + 2x, \quad \frac{du}{dx} = 3x^2 + 2\}$$

$$= \int u^{\frac{1}{2}}\,du$$

$$= \frac{u^{\frac{3}{2}}}{\frac{3}{2}} + c$$

$$= \tfrac{2}{3}(x^3 + 2x)^{\frac{3}{2}} + c$$

Example 18   🔊 **Self Tutor**

Use substitution to find: **a** $\int \dfrac{3x^2 + 2}{x^3 + 2x}\, dx$ **b** $\int xe^{1-x^2}\, dx$

a $\displaystyle\int \dfrac{3x^2 + 2}{x^3 + 2x}\, dx$

$= \displaystyle\int \dfrac{1}{x^3 + 2x}\,(3x^2 + 2)\, dx$

$= \displaystyle\int \dfrac{1}{u}\,\dfrac{du}{dx}\, dx$ $\{u = x^3 + 2x,$

$= \displaystyle\int \dfrac{1}{u}\, du$ $\qquad\qquad\dfrac{du}{dx} = 3x^2 + 2\}$

$= \ln|u| + c$

$= \ln\left|x^3 + 2x\right| + c$

b $\displaystyle\int xe^{1-x^2}\, dx$

$= -\tfrac{1}{2} \displaystyle\int (-2x)e^{1-x^2}\, dx$

$= -\tfrac{1}{2} \displaystyle\int e^u \dfrac{du}{dx}\, dx$ $\{u = 1 - x^2,$

$= -\tfrac{1}{2} \displaystyle\int e^u\, du$ $\qquad\qquad\dfrac{du}{dx} = -2x\}$

$= -\tfrac{1}{2}e^u + c$

$= -\tfrac{1}{2}e^{1-x^2} + c$

Example 19   🔊 **Self Tutor**

Integrate with respect to x: **a** $\cos^3 x \sin x$ **b** $\dfrac{\cos x}{\sin x}$

a $\displaystyle\int \cos^3 x \sin x\, dx$

$= \displaystyle\int (\cos x)^3 \sin x\, dx$

$= \displaystyle\int u^3 \left(-\dfrac{du}{dx}\right) dx$ $\{u = \cos x,$

$= -\displaystyle\int u^3\, du$ $\qquad\qquad\dfrac{du}{dx} = -\sin x\}$

$= -\dfrac{u^4}{4} + c$

$= -\tfrac{1}{4}\cos^4 x + c$

b $\displaystyle\int \dfrac{\cos x}{\sin x}\, dx$

$= \displaystyle\int \dfrac{1}{u}\,\dfrac{du}{dx}\, dx$ $\{u = \sin x, \dfrac{du}{dx} = \cos x\}$

$= \displaystyle\int \dfrac{1}{u}\, du$

$= \ln|u| + c$

$= \ln|\sin x| + c$

Note: The substitutions we make need to be chosen with care.

For example, in **Example 19** part **b**, if we let $u = \cos x$, $\dfrac{du}{dx} = -\sin x$ then we obtain

$\displaystyle\int \dfrac{\cos x}{\sin x}\, dx = \int \dfrac{u}{-\frac{du}{dx}}\, dx$.   This is not in the correct form to apply our theorem, which tells us

we have made the wrong substitution and we need to try another.

EXERCISE 18G

1   Use the substitutions given to perform the integration:

a $\displaystyle\int 3x^2(x^3 + 1)^4\, dx$ using $u(x) = x^3 + 1$ **b** $\displaystyle\int x^2 e^{x^3+1}\, dx$ using $u(x) = x^3 + 1$

c $\displaystyle\int \sin^4 x \cos x\, dx$ using $u(x) = \sin x$

2 Integrate by substitution:

  a $4x^3(2+x^4)^3$ **b** $\dfrac{2x}{\sqrt{x^2+3}}$ **c** $\dfrac{x}{(1-x^2)^5}$ **d** $\sqrt{x^3+x}\,(3x^2+1)$

3 Find:

  a $\displaystyle\int -2e^{1-2x}\,dx$ **b** $\displaystyle\int 2xe^{x^2}\,dx$ **c** $\displaystyle\int \dfrac{e^{\sqrt{x}}}{\sqrt{x}}\,dx$ **d** $\displaystyle\int (2x-1)e^{x-x^2}\,dx$

4 Find:

  a $\displaystyle\int \dfrac{2x}{x^2+1}\,dx$ **b** $\displaystyle\int \dfrac{x}{2-x^2}\,dx$ **c** $\displaystyle\int \dfrac{2x-3}{x^2-3x}\,dx$ **d** $\displaystyle\int \dfrac{6x^2-2}{x^3-x}\,dx$

5 Integrate by substitution:

  a $\dfrac{\sin x}{\sqrt{\cos x}}$ **b** $\tan x$ **c** $\sqrt{\sin x}\,\cos x$ **d** $x\sin(x^2)$

H   DEFINITE INTEGRALS

Earlier we saw the **fundamental theorem of calculus**:

If $F(x)$ is the antiderivative of $f(x)$ where $f(x)$ is continuous on the interval $a \leqslant x \leqslant b$, then the **definite integral** of $f(x)$ on this interval is $\displaystyle\int_a^b f(x)\,dx = F(b) - F(a)$.

$\displaystyle\int_a^b f(x)\,dx$ reads "the integral from $x=a$ to $x=b$ of $f(x)$ with respect to x"
     or "the integral from a to b of $f(x)$ with respect to x".

It is called a **definite** integral because there are lower and upper limits for the integration, and it therefore results in a numerical answer.

When calculating definite integrals we can omit the constant of integration c as this will always cancel out in the subtraction process.

It is common to write $F(b)-F(a)$ as $[F(x)]_a^b$, and so $\displaystyle\int_a^b f(x)\,dx = [F(x)]_a^b = F(b) - F(a)$

Earlier in the chapter we proved the following properties of definite integrals using the fundamental theorem of calculus:

- $\displaystyle\int_a^b f(x)\,dx = -\int_b^a f(x)\,dx$

- $\displaystyle\int_a^b cf(x)\,dx = c\int_a^b f(x)\,dx,\quad c$ is any constant

- $\displaystyle\int_a^b f(x)\,dx + \int_b^c f(x)\,dx = \int_a^c f(x)\,dx$

- $\displaystyle\int_a^b [f(x)+g(x)]\,dx = \int_a^b f(x)\,dx + \int_a^b g(x)\,dx$

Example 20   ◀️) **Self Tutor**

Find $\displaystyle\int_1^3 (x^2 + 2)\, dx$.

$\displaystyle\int_1^3 (x^2 + 2)\, dx$

$= \left[\dfrac{x^3}{3} + 2x \right]_1^3$

$= \left(\dfrac{3^3}{3} + 2(3) \right) - \left(\dfrac{1^3}{3} + 2(1) \right)$

$= (9 + 6) - (\tfrac{1}{3} + 2)$

$= 12\tfrac{2}{3}$

Example 21   ◀️) **Self Tutor**

Evaluate: **a** $\displaystyle\int_0^{\frac{\pi}{3}} \sin x\, dx$ **b** $\displaystyle\int_1^4 \left(2x + \dfrac{3}{x} \right) dx$

a $\displaystyle\int_0^{\frac{\pi}{3}} \sin x\, dx$

$= \left[-\cos x \right]_0^{\frac{\pi}{3}}$

$= (-\cos \tfrac{\pi}{3}) - (-\cos 0)$

$= -\tfrac{1}{2} + 1$

$= \tfrac{1}{2}$

b $\displaystyle\int_1^4 \left(2x + \dfrac{3}{x} \right) dx$

$= \left[x^2 + 3\ln x \right]_1^4$ {since $x > 0$}

$= (16 + 3\ln 4) - (1 + 3\ln 1)$

$= 15 + 6\ln 2$

Some definite integrals are difficult or even impossible to evaluate analytically. In these cases you are expected to use a graphics calculator to evaluate the integral.

GRAPHICS CALCULATOR INSTRUCTIONS

Example 22   ◀️) **Self Tutor**

Evaluate $\displaystyle\int_2^5 xe^x\, dx$ to an accuracy of 4 significant figures.

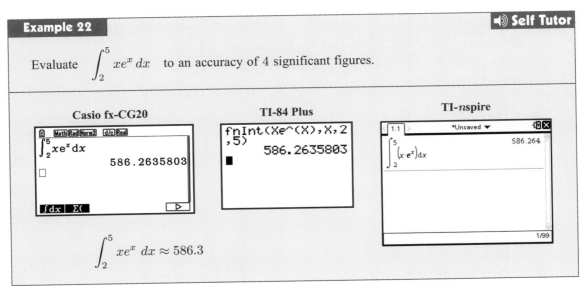

Casio fx-CG20

$\displaystyle\int_2^5 xe^x dx$

$\qquad\qquad 586.2635803$

TI-84 Plus

fnInt(Xe^(X),X,2
,5)
          586.2635803

TI-nspire

$\displaystyle\int_2^5 (x \cdot e^x)dx$ 586.264

$\displaystyle\int_2^5 xe^x\, dx \approx 586.3$

EXERCISE 18H

Use questions **1** to **4** to check the properties of definite integrals.

1 Find:
a $\displaystyle\int_1^4 \sqrt{x}\, dx$ and $\displaystyle\int_1^4 (-\sqrt{x})\, dx$
b $\displaystyle\int_0^1 x^7\, dx$ and $\displaystyle\int_0^1 (-x^7)\, dx$

2 Find:
a $\displaystyle\int_0^1 x^2\, dx$
b $\displaystyle\int_1^2 x^2\, dx$
c $\displaystyle\int_0^2 x^2\, dx$
d $\displaystyle\int_0^1 3x^2\, dx$

3 Find:
a $\displaystyle\int_0^2 (x^3 - 4x)\, dx$
b $\displaystyle\int_2^3 (x^3 - 4x)\, dx$
c $\displaystyle\int_0^3 (x^3 - 4x)\, dx$

4 Find:
a $\displaystyle\int_0^1 x^2\, dx$
b $\displaystyle\int_0^1 \sqrt{x}\, dx$
c $\displaystyle\int_0^1 (x^2 + \sqrt{x})\, dx$

5 Evaluate the following and check with your graphics calculator:

a $\displaystyle\int_0^1 x^3\, dx$
b $\displaystyle\int_0^2 (x^2 - x)\, dx$
c $\displaystyle\int_0^1 e^x\, dx$

d $\displaystyle\int_0^{\frac{\pi}{6}} \cos x\, dx$
e $\displaystyle\int_1^4 \left(x - \frac{3}{\sqrt{x}}\right) dx$
f $\displaystyle\int_4^9 \frac{x - 3}{\sqrt{x}}\, dx$

g $\displaystyle\int_1^3 \frac{1}{x}\, dx$
h $\displaystyle\int_{\frac{\pi}{3}}^{\frac{\pi}{2}} \sin x\, dx$
i $\displaystyle\int_1^2 (e^{-x} + 1)^2\, dx$

j $\displaystyle\int_2^6 \frac{1}{\sqrt{2x - 3}}\, dx$
k $\displaystyle\int_0^1 e^{1-x}\, dx$
l $\displaystyle\int_0^{\frac{\pi}{6}} \sin(3x)\, dx$

6 Use the identity $\cos^2 x = \frac{1}{2} + \frac{1}{2}\cos(2x)$ to help evaluate $\displaystyle\int_0^{\frac{\pi}{4}} \cos^2 x\, dx$.

7 Use the identity $\sin^2 x = \frac{1}{2} - \frac{1}{2}\cos(2x)$ to help evaluate $\displaystyle\int_0^{\frac{\pi}{2}} \sin^2 x\, dx$.

8 Evaluate using technology:

a $\displaystyle\int_1^3 \ln x\, dx$
b $\displaystyle\int_{-1}^1 e^{-x^2}\, dx$
c $\displaystyle\int_{\frac{\pi}{4}}^{\frac{\pi}{6}} \sin(\sqrt{x})\, dx$

9 Show that $\dfrac{4x + 1}{x - 1}$ may be written in the form $4 + \dfrac{5}{x - 1}$.

Hence show that $\displaystyle\int_3^5 \frac{4x + 1}{x - 1}\, dx = 8 + 5\ln 2$.

10 Find m such that:

a $\displaystyle\int_m^{-2} \frac{1}{4 - x}\, dx = \ln \frac{3}{2}$
b $\displaystyle\int_m^{2m} (2x - 1)\, dx = 4$

11 Evaluate the following integrals using area interpretation:

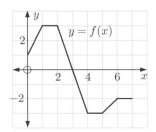

    a $\displaystyle\int_0^3 f(x)\,dx$ **b** $\displaystyle\int_3^7 f(x)\,dx$

    c $\displaystyle\int_2^4 f(x)\,dx$ **d** $\displaystyle\int_0^7 f(x)\,dx$

12 Evaluate the following integrals using area interpretation:

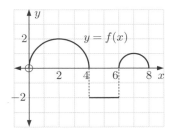

    a $\displaystyle\int_0^4 f(x)\,dx$ **b** $\displaystyle\int_4^6 f(x)\,dx$

    c $\displaystyle\int_6^8 f(x)\,dx$ **d** $\displaystyle\int_0^8 f(x)\,dx$

13 Write as a single integral:

    a $\displaystyle\int_2^4 f(x)\,dx + \int_4^7 f(x)\,dx$ **b** $\displaystyle\int_1^3 g(x)\,dx + \int_3^8 g(x)\,dx + \int_8^9 g(x)\,dx$

14   **a** If $\displaystyle\int_1^3 f(x)\,dx = 2$ and $\displaystyle\int_1^6 f(x)\,dx = -3$, find $\displaystyle\int_3^6 f(x)\,dx$.

    b If $\displaystyle\int_0^2 f(x)\,dx = 5$, $\displaystyle\int_4^6 f(x)\,dx = -2$, and $\displaystyle\int_0^6 f(x)\,dx = 7$, find $\displaystyle\int_2^4 f(x)\,dx$.

15 Given that $\displaystyle\int_{-1}^1 f(x)\,dx = -4$, determine the value of:

    a $\displaystyle\int_1^{-1} f(x)\,dx$ **b** $\displaystyle\int_{-1}^1 (2 + f(x))\,dx$ **c** $\displaystyle\int_{-1}^1 2f(x)\,dx$

    d k such that $\displaystyle\int_{-1}^1 kf(x)\,dx = 7$

16 If $g(2) = 4$ and $g(3) = 5$, calculate $\displaystyle\int_2^3 \big(g'(x) - 1\big)\,dx$.

HISTORICAL NOTE

Following the work of Newton and Leibniz, integration was rigorously formalised using limits by the German mathematician **Bernhard Riemann** (1826 - 1866).

If $f(x) \geqslant 0$ on the interval $a \leqslant x \leqslant b$, we have seen that the area under the curve is $A = \displaystyle\int_a^b f(x)\,dx$.

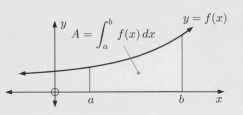

This is known as the **Riemann integral**.

Bernhard Riemann

REVIEW SET 18A   NON-CALCULATOR

1 The graph of $y = f(x)$ is illustrated:
Evaluate the following using area interpretation:

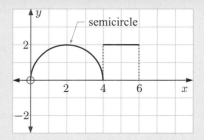

   a $\displaystyle\int_0^4 f(x)\, dx$ **b** $\displaystyle\int_4^6 f(x)\, dx$

2 Integrate with respect to x:

   a $\dfrac{4}{\sqrt{x}}$ **b** $\dfrac{3}{1-2x}$ **c** $\sin(4x-5)$ **d** e^{4-3x}

3 Find the exact value of: **a** $\displaystyle\int_{-5}^{-1} \sqrt{1-3x}\, dx$ **b** $\displaystyle\int_0^{\frac{\pi}{2}} \cos\left(\tfrac{x}{2}\right) dx$

4 By differentiating $y = \sqrt{x^2 - 4}$, find $\displaystyle\int \dfrac{x}{\sqrt{x^2-4}}\, dx$.

5 Find the values of b such that $\displaystyle\int_0^b \cos x\, dx = \dfrac{1}{\sqrt{2}}, \quad 0 < b < \pi$.

6 Use the identity $\cos^2 x = \tfrac{1}{2} + \tfrac{1}{2}\cos(2x)$ to help find $\displaystyle\int (2-\cos x)^2\, dx$.

7 By differentiating $(3x^2 + x)^3$, find $\displaystyle\int (3x^2 + x)^2 (6x+1)\, dx$.

8 If $\displaystyle\int_1^4 f(x)\, dx = 3$, determine:

   a $\displaystyle\int_1^4 (f(x) + 1)\, dx$ **b** $\displaystyle\int_1^2 f(x)\, dx - \int_4^2 f(x)\, dx$

9 Find $\displaystyle\int e^{\sin x} \cos x\, dx$ using the substitution $u(x) = \sin x$.

10 Given that $f''(x) = 2\sin(2x)$, $f'(\tfrac{\pi}{2}) = 0$, and $f(0) = 3$, find the exact value of $f(\tfrac{\pi}{2})$.

11 Use the identity $\sin^2 x = \tfrac{1}{2} - \tfrac{1}{2}\cos(2x)$ to help evaluate $\displaystyle\int_0^{\frac{\pi}{6}} \sin^2\left(\tfrac{x}{2}\right) dx$.

12 **a** Find $\displaystyle\int 2x(x^2+1)^3\, dx$ using the substitution $u(x) = x^2 + 1$.

   b *Hence* evaluate:

     i $\displaystyle\int_0^1 2x(x^2+1)^3\, dx$ **ii** $\displaystyle\int_{-1}^2 -x(1+x^2)^3\, dx$

REVIEW SET 18B   CALCULATOR

1 **a** Sketch the region between the curve $y = \dfrac{4}{1 + x^2}$ and the x-axis for $0 \leqslant x \leqslant 1$.

Divide the interval into 5 equal parts and display the 5 upper and lower rectangles.

  b Find the lower and upper rectangle sums for $n = 5,\ 50,\ 100,$ and 500.

  c Give your best estimate for $\displaystyle\int_0^1 \dfrac{4}{1 + x^2}\,dx$ and compare this answer with π.

2 Find y if: **a** $\dfrac{dy}{dx} = (x^2 - 1)^2$ **b** $\dfrac{dy}{dx} = 400 - 20e^{-\frac{x}{2}}$

3 Evaluate correct to 4 significant figures:

  a $\displaystyle\int_{-2}^{0} 4e^{-x^2}\,dx$ **b** $\displaystyle\int_0^1 \dfrac{10x}{\sqrt{3x + 1}}\,dx$

4 Find $\dfrac{d}{dx}(\ln x)^2$ and hence find $\displaystyle\int \dfrac{\ln x}{x}\,dx$.

5 A curve $y = f(x)$ has $f''(x) = 18x + 10$. Find $f(x)$ if $f(0) = -1$ and $f(1) = 13$.

6 If $\displaystyle\int_0^a e^{1-2x}\,dx = \dfrac{e}{4}$, find a in the form $\ln k$.

7 Evaluate the following correct to 6 significant figures:

  a $\displaystyle\int_3^4 \dfrac{x}{\sqrt{2x + 1}}\,dx$ **b** $\displaystyle\int_0^1 x^2 e^{x+1}\,dx$

8 Suppose $f''(x) = 3x^2 + 2x$ and $f(0) = f(2) = 3$. Find:

  a $f(x)$ **b** the equation of the normal to $y = f(x)$ at $x = 2$.

9 **a** Find $(e^x + 2)^3$ using the binomial expansion.

  b Hence find the exact value of $\displaystyle\int_0^1 (e^x + 2)^3\,dx$.

  c Check your answer to **b** using technology.

10 Integrate by substitution: $\displaystyle\int_{\frac{\pi}{4}}^{\frac{\pi}{3}} \sin^5 x \cos x\,dx$. Check your answer using technology.

REVIEW SET 18C

1 Find:

  a $\displaystyle\int \left(2e^{-x} - \dfrac{1}{x} + 3\right)dx$ **b** $\displaystyle\int \left(\sqrt{x} - \dfrac{1}{\sqrt{x}}\right)^2 dx$ **c** $\displaystyle\int \left(3 + e^{2x-1}\right)^2 dx$

2 Given that $f'(x) = x^2 - 3x + 2$ and $f(1) = 3$, find $f(x)$.

3 Find the exact value of $\displaystyle\int_2^3 \dfrac{1}{\sqrt{3x - 4}}\,dx$.

4 Use the identity $\cos^2 x = \frac{1}{2} + \frac{1}{2}\cos(2x)$ to help evaluate $\displaystyle\int_0^{\frac{\pi}{3}} \cos^2\left(\frac{x}{2}\right)\, dx$.

5 Find $\dfrac{d}{dx}(e^{-2x}\sin x)$ and hence find $\displaystyle\int_0^{\frac{\pi}{2}} \left[e^{-2x}(\cos x - 2\sin x)\right]\, dx$

6 Find $\displaystyle\int (2x+3)^n\, dx$ for all integers n.

7 A function has gradient function $2\sqrt{x} + \dfrac{a}{\sqrt{x}}$ and passes through the points $(0,\ 2)$ and $(1,\ 4)$. Find a and hence explain why the function $y = f(x)$ has no stationary points.

8 $\displaystyle\int_a^{2a} (x^2 + ax + 2)\, dx = \dfrac{73a}{2}$.   Find a.

9

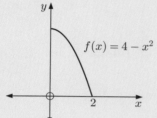

a Use *four* upper and lower rectangles to find rational numbers A and B such that:
$$A < \int_0^2 (4 - x^2)\, dx < B.$$

b Hence, find a good estimate for
$$\int_0^2 (4 - x^2)\, dx.$$

10 Integrate by substitution:

a $\displaystyle\int \dfrac{2x}{\sqrt{x^2 - 5}}\, dx$

b $\displaystyle\int_1^2 3x^2\sqrt{x^3 - 1}\, dx$

Chapter 19

Applications of integration

Syllabus reference: 6.5, 6.6

Contents:

OPENING PROBLEM

A wooden bowl is made in the shape of a *paraboloid*.

We start with the curve $y = 4\sqrt{x}$ for $0 \leqslant x \leqslant 4$, then rotate this curve through $360°$ around the x-axis.

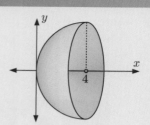

Things to think about:

a   If we take a vertical slice of the bowl, what shape do we obtain?

b   Can you explain why the capacity of the bowl is given by $\displaystyle\int_0^4 \pi(4\sqrt{x})^2 \, dx$?

c   Hence find the capacity of the bowl.

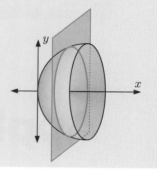

We have already seen how definite integrals can be related to the areas between functions and the x-axis. In this chapter we explore this relationship further, and consider other applications of integral calculus such as kinematics and volumes of solids of revolution.

A   THE AREA UNDER A CURVE

We have already established in **Chapter 18** that:

If $f(x)$ is positive and continuous on the interval $a \leqslant x \leqslant b$, then the area bounded by $y = f(x)$, the x-axis, and the vertical lines $x = a$ and $x = b$ is given by $\displaystyle A = \int_a^b f(x) \, dx$ or $\displaystyle\int_a^b y \, dx$.

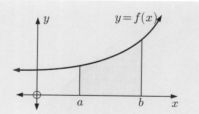

Example 1
◀)) **Self Tutor**

Find the area of the region enclosed by $y = 2x$, the x-axis, $x = 0$, and $x = 4$ by using:

a   a geometric argument

b   integration.

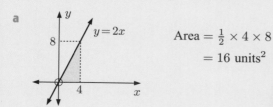

a

$\text{Area} = \frac{1}{2} \times 4 \times 8$

$= 16 \text{ units}^2$

b $\text{Area} = \displaystyle\int_0^4 2x \, dx$

$= \left[x^2\right]_0^4$

$= 4^2 - 0^2$

$= 16 \text{ units}^2$

Example 2 ◄) **Self Tutor**

Find the area of the region enclosed by $y = x^2 + 1$, the x-axis, $x = 1$, and $x = 2$.

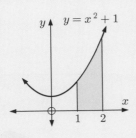

$$\text{Area} = \int_1^2 (x^2 + 1)\, dx$$

$$= \left[\frac{x^3}{3} + x \right]_1^2$$

$$= \left(\frac{8}{3} + 2 \right) - \left(\frac{1}{3} + 1 \right)$$

$$= 3\tfrac{1}{3} \text{ units}^2$$

It is helpful to sketch the region.

We can check this result using a graphics calculator or graphing package.

GRAPHICS CALCULATOR INSTRUCTIONS

GRAPHING PACKAGE

TI-*n*spire

Casio fx-CG20

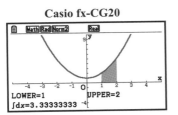

TI-84 Plus

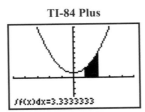

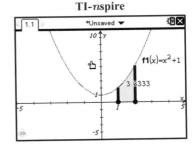

Example 3 ◄) **Self Tutor**

Find the area enclosed by one arch of the curve $y = \sin 2x$ and the x-axis.

The period of $y = \sin 2x$ is $\frac{2\pi}{2} = \pi$, so the first positive x-intercept is $\frac{\pi}{2}$.

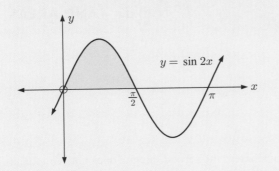

The required area $= \displaystyle\int_0^{\frac{\pi}{2}} \sin 2x\, dx$

$$= \left[\tfrac{1}{2}(-\cos 2x) \right]_0^{\frac{\pi}{2}}$$

$$= -\tfrac{1}{2} \left[\cos 2x \right]_0^{\frac{\pi}{2}}$$

$$= -\tfrac{1}{2}(\cos \pi - \cos 0)$$

$$= 1 \text{ unit}^2$$

EXERCISE 19A

1 Find the area of each of the regions described below by using:

    i a geometric argument   **ii** integration

  a $y = 5$, the x-axis, $x = -6$, and $x = 0$

  b $y = x$, the x-axis, $x = 4$, and $x = 5$

  c $y = -3x$, the x-axis, $x = -3$, and $x = 0$

  d $y = -x$, the x-axis, $x = 0$, and $x = 2$

2 Find the exact value of the area of the region bounded by:

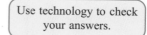
Use technology to check
your answers.

  a $y = x^2$, the x-axis, and $x = 1$

  b $y = \sin x$, the x-axis, $x = 0$, and $x = \pi$

  c $y = x^3$, the x-axis, $x = 1$, and $x = 4$

  d $y = e^x$, the x-axis, the y-axis, and $x = 1$

  e the x-axis and the part of $y = 6 + x - x^2$ above the x-axis

  f the axes and $y = \sqrt{9 - x}$

  g $y = \dfrac{1}{x}$, the x-axis, $x = 1$, and $x = 4$

  h $y = \dfrac{1}{x}$, the x-axis, $x = 1$, and $x = 3$

  i $y = 2 - \dfrac{1}{\sqrt{x}}$, the x-axis, and $x = 4$

  j $y = e^x + e^{-x}$, the x-axis, $x = -1$, and $x = 1$

3 Find the area enclosed by one arch of the curve $y = \cos 3x$ and the x-axis.

4 Write down an expression for the area of each region described by the following boundaries. Use technology to calculate the area.

  a $y = \ln x$, the x-axis, $x = 1$, and $x = 4$

  b $y = x \sin x$, the x-axis, $x = 1$, and $x = \frac{\pi}{2}$

  c $y = x^2 e^{-x}$, the x-axis, $x = 0$, and $x = 2.8$.

INVESTIGATION $\displaystyle\int_a^b f(x)\,dx$ **AND AREAS**

Does $\displaystyle\int_a^b f(x)\,dx$ always give us an area?

What to do:

1 Find $\displaystyle\int_0^1 x^3\,dx$ and $\displaystyle\int_{-1}^1 x^3\,dx$.

2 Explain why the first integral in **1** gives an area, whereas the second integral does not. Graphical evidence is essential.

3 Find $\displaystyle\int_{-1}^0 x^3\,dx$ and explain why the answer is negative.

4 Check that $\displaystyle\int_{-1}^{0} x^3 \, dx + \int_{0}^{1} x^3 \, dx = \int_{-1}^{1} x^3 \, dx.$

5 Find $\displaystyle\int_{0}^{-1} x^3 \, dx$ and interpret its meaning.

6 Suppose $f(x)$ is a function such that $f(x) \leqslant 0$ for all $a \leqslant x \leqslant b$. Can you suggest an expression for the area between the curve and the function for $a \leqslant x \leqslant b$?

<h1>B   THE AREA BETWEEN TWO FUNCTIONS</h1>

If two functions $f(x)$ and $g(x)$ intersect at $x = a$ and $x = b$, and $f(x) \geqslant g(x)$ for all $a \leqslant x \leqslant b$, then the area of the shaded region between their points of intersection is given by

$$A = \int_{a}^{b} [f(x) - g(x)] \, dx.$$

Alternatively, if the upper and lower functions are $y = y_U$ and $y = y_L$ respectively, then the area is

$$A = \int_{a}^{b} [y_U - y_L] \, dx.$$

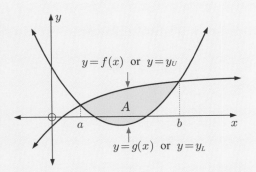

Proof: If we translate each curve vertically through $\begin{pmatrix} 0 \\ k \end{pmatrix}$ until it is completely above the x-axis, the area does not change.

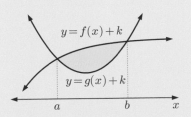

Area of shaded region

$$= \int_{a}^{b} [f(x) + k] \, dx - \int_{a}^{b} [g(x) + k] \, dx$$

$$= \int_{a}^{b} [f(x) - g(x)] \, dx$$

We can see immediately that if $y = f(x) = 0$ then the enclosed area is $\displaystyle\int_{a}^{b} [-g(x)] \, dx$

or $-\displaystyle\int_{a}^{b} g(x) \, dx.$

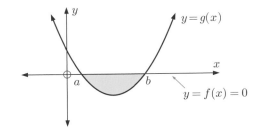

Example 4   ◀⑴ **Self Tutor**

Use $\displaystyle\int_a^b [y_U - y_L]\,dx$ to find the area bounded by the x-axis and $y = x^2 - 2x$.

The curve cuts the x-axis when $y = 0$

$\therefore \quad x^2 - 2x = 0$

$\therefore \quad x(x - 2) = 0$

$\qquad \therefore \quad x = 0$ or 2

$\therefore$ the x-intercepts are 0 and 2.

Area $= \displaystyle\int_0^2 [y_U - y_L]\,dx$

$= \displaystyle\int_0^2 [0 - (x^2 - 2x)]\,dx$

$= \displaystyle\int_0^2 (2x - x^2)\,dx$

$= \left[x^2 - \dfrac{x^3}{3} \right]_0^2$

$= \left(4 - \tfrac{8}{3} \right) - (0)$

$\therefore$ the area is $\tfrac{4}{3}$ units^2.

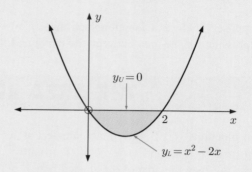

$y_U = 0$

$y_L = x^2 - 2x$

Example 5   ◀⑴ **Self Tutor**

Find the area of the region enclosed by $y = x + 2$ and $y = x^2 + x - 2$.

$y = x + 2$ meets $y = x^2 + x - 2$

where $x^2 + x - 2 = x + 2$

$\therefore \quad x^2 - 4 = 0$

$\therefore \quad (x + 2)(x - 2) = 0$

$\qquad \therefore \quad x = \pm 2$

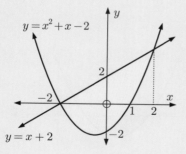

$y = x^2 + x - 2$

$y = x + 2$

Area $= \displaystyle\int_{-2}^2 [y_U - y_L]\,dx$

$= \displaystyle\int_{-2}^2 [(x + 2) - (x^2 + x - 2)]\,dx$

$= \displaystyle\int_{-2}^2 (4 - x^2)\,dx$

$= \left[4x - \dfrac{x^3}{3} \right]_{-2}^2$

$= \left(8 - \tfrac{8}{3} \right) - \left(-8 + \tfrac{8}{3} \right)$

$= 10\tfrac{2}{3}$ units^2

$\therefore$ the area is $10\tfrac{2}{3}$ units^2.

Example 6

◀) **Self Tutor**

Find the total area of the regions contained by $y = f(x)$ and the x-axis for $f(x) = x^3 + 2x^2 - 3x$.

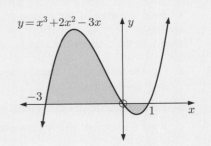

$$f(x) = x^3 + 2x^2 - 3x$$
$$= x(x^2 + 2x - 3)$$
$$= x(x - 1)(x + 3)$$
$$\therefore \quad y = f(x) \quad \text{cuts the } x\text{-axis at } 0, 1, \text{ and } -3.$$

Total area

$$= \int_{-3}^{0} (x^3 + 2x^2 - 3x)\, dx - \int_{0}^{1} (x^3 + 2x^2 - 3x)\, dx$$

$$= \left[\frac{x^4}{4} + \frac{2x^3}{3} - \frac{3x^2}{2} \right]_{-3}^{0} - \left[\frac{x^4}{4} + \frac{2x^3}{3} - \frac{3x^2}{2} \right]_{0}^{1}$$

$$= \left(0 - -11\tfrac{1}{4} \right) - \left(-\tfrac{7}{12} - 0 \right)$$

$$= 11\tfrac{5}{6} \text{ units}^2$$

The area between the functions $f(x)$ and $g(x)$ on the interval $a \leqslant x \leqslant b$ is
$$A = \int_{a}^{b} |f(x) - g(x)|\, dx.$$

The modulus ensures the two components of the area are added together.

For example, the area in **Example 6** may be found using technology using

GRAPHICS CALCULATOR INSTRUCTIONS

area $= \displaystyle\int_{-3}^{1} \left| x^3 + 2x^2 - 3x \right|\, dx$.

TI-nspire

Casio fx-CG20

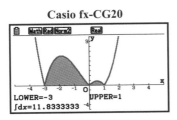

TI-84 Plus

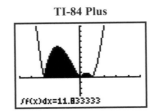

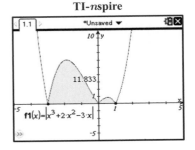

EXERCISE 19B

1 Find the exact value of the area bounded by:

a the x-axis and $y = x^2 + x - 2$

b the x-axis, $y = e^{-x} - 1$, and $x = 2$

c the x-axis and the part of $y = 3x^2 - 8x + 4$ below the x-axis

d $y = \cos x$, the x-axis, $x = \frac{\pi}{2}$, and $x = \frac{3\pi}{2}$

e $y = x^3 - 4x$, the x-axis, $x = 1$, and $x = 2$

f $y = \sin x - 1$, the x-axis, $x = 0$, and $x = \frac{\pi}{2}$

g one arch of $y = \sin^2 x$ and the x-axis.

2 Find the area of the region enclosed by $y = x^2 - 2x$ and $y = 3$.

3 Consider the graphs of $y = x - 3$ and $y = x^2 - 3x$.

    a Sketch the graphs on the same set of axes.

    b Find the coordinates of the points where the graphs meet.

    c Find the area of the region enclosed by the two graphs.

4 Determine the area of the region enclosed by $y = \sqrt{x}$ and $y = x^2$.

5   **a** On the same set of axes, graph $y = e^x - 1$ and $y = 2 - 2e^{-x}$, showing axes intercepts and asymptotes.

    b Find algebraically the points of intersection of $y = e^x - 1$ and $y = 2 - 2e^{-x}$.

    c Find the area of the region enclosed by the two curves.

6 Determine exactly the area of the region bounded by $y = 2e^x$, $y = e^{2x}$, and $x = 0$.

7 On the same set of axes, draw the graphs of the functions $y = 2x$ and $y = 4x^2$. Determine exactly the area of the region enclosed by these functions.

8 Sketch the circle with equation $x^2 + y^2 = 9$.

    a Explain why the upper half of the circle has equation $y = \sqrt{9 - x^2}$.

    b Hence, determine $\displaystyle\int_0^3 \sqrt{9 - x^2}\, dx$ without actually integrating the function.

    c Check your answer using technology.

9 Find the area enclosed by the function $y = f(x)$ and the x-axis for:

    a $f(x) = x^3 - 9x$ **b** $f(x) = -x(x - 2)(x - 4)$ **c** $f(x) = x^4 - 5x^2 + 4$.

10 The illustrated curves are those of $y = \sin x$ and $y = \sin(2x)$.

    a Identify each curve.

    b Find algebraically the coordinates of A.

    c Find the total area enclosed by C_1 and C_2 for $0 \leqslant x \leqslant \pi$.

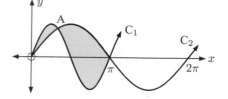

11   **a** Explain why the total area shaded is *not* equal to $\displaystyle\int_1^7 f(x)\, dx$.

    b Write an expression for the total shaded area in terms of integrals.

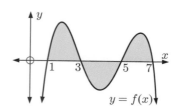

12

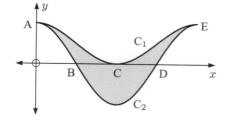

The illustrated curves are $y = \cos(2x)$ and $y = \cos^2 x$.

    a Identify each curve as C_1 or C_2.

    b Determine the coordinates of A, B, C, D, and E.

    c Show that the area of the shaded region is $\frac{\pi}{2}$ units^2.

13 Find, correct to 3 significant figures, the areas of the regions enclosed by the curves:

   a $y = e^{-x^2}$ and $y = x^2 - 1$ **b** $y = x^x$ and $y = 4x - \frac{1}{10}x^4$

14 The shaded area is 0.2 units^2.
Find k, correct to 4 decimal places.

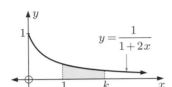

15 The shaded area is 1 unit^2.
Find b, correct to 4 decimal places.

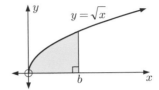

16 The shaded area is $6a$ units^2.
Find the exact value of a.

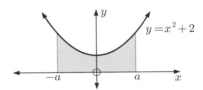

C   KINEMATICS

DISTANCES FROM VELOCITY GRAPHS

Suppose a car travels at a constant positive velocity of 60 km h^{-1} for 15 minutes.

We know the distance travelled $=$ speed $\times$ time
$$= 60 \text{ km h}^{-1} \times \tfrac{1}{4} \text{ h}$$
$$= 15 \text{ km.}$$

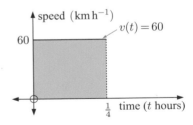

When we graph *speed* against *time*, the graph is a horizontal line, and we can see that the distance travelled is the area shaded.

So, the distance travelled can also be found by the definite integral $\displaystyle\int_0^{\frac{1}{4}} 60 \, dt = 15$ km.

Now suppose the speed decreases at a constant rate so that the car, initially travelling at 60 km h^{-1}, stops in 6 minutes or $\frac{1}{10}$ hour.

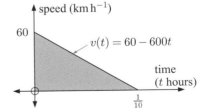

In this case the *average* speed is 30 km h^{-1}, so the distance travelled $= 30$ km h$^{-1} \times \frac{1}{10}$ h
$$= 3 \text{ km}$$

But the triangle has area $= \frac{1}{2} \times$ base $\times$ altitude
$$= \frac{1}{2} \times \frac{1}{10} \times 60 = 3$$

So, once again the shaded area gives us the distance travelled, and we can find it using the definite integral $\displaystyle\int_0^{\frac{1}{10}} (60 - 600t)\, dt = 3$.

These results suggest that   distance travelled $= \displaystyle\int_{t_1}^{t_2} v(t)\, dt$ provided we do not change direction.

If we have a change of direction within the time interval then the velocity will change sign. We therefore need to add the components of area above and below the t-axis to find the total distance travelled.

For a velocity-time function $v(t)$ where $v(t) \geqslant 0$ on the interval $t_1 \leqslant t \leqslant t_2$,

$$\text{distance travelled} = \int_{t_1}^{t_2} \boldsymbol{v(t)\, dt}.$$

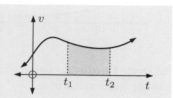

For a velocity-time function $v(t)$ where $v(t) \leqslant 0$ on the interval $t_1 \leqslant t \leqslant t_2$,

$$\text{distance travelled} = -\int_{t_1}^{t_2} \boldsymbol{v(t)\, dt}.$$

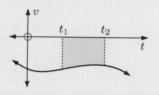

Example 7   ◀) **Self Tutor**

The velocity-time graph for a train journey is illustrated in the graph alongside. Find the total distance travelled by the train.

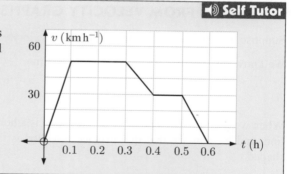

Total distance travelled

$=$ total area under the graph

$=$ area A $+$ area B $+$ area C $+$ area D $+$ area E

$= \frac{1}{2}(0.1)50 + (0.2)50 + \left(\frac{50+30}{2}\right)(0.1) + (0.1)30$
$\qquad + \frac{1}{2}(0.1)30$

$= 2.5 + 10 + 4 + 3 + 1.5$

$= 21$ km

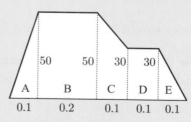

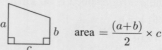

EXERCISE 19C.1

1 A runner has the velocity-time graph shown. Find the total distance travelled by the runner.

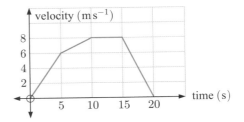

2

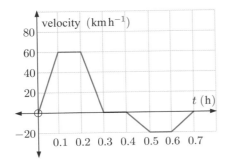

A car travels along a straight road with the velocity-time function illustrated.

a What is the significance of the graph:

   i above the t-axis

   ii below the t-axis?

b Find the total distance travelled by the car.

c Find the final displacement of the car from its starting point.

3 A cyclist rides off from rest, accelerating at a constant rate for 3 minutes until she reaches 40 km h^{-1}. She then maintains a constant speed for 4 minutes until reaching a hill. She slows down at a constant rate over one minute to 30 km h^{-1}, then continues at this rate for 10 minutes. At the top of the hill she reduces her speed uniformly and is stationary 2 minutes later.

a Draw a graph to show the cyclist's motion.

b How far has the cyclist travelled?

DISPLACEMENT AND VELOCITY FUNCTIONS

In this section we are concerned with **motion in a straight line**, or **linear motion**.

For some displacement function $s(t)$, the velocity function is $v(t) = s'(t)$.

So, given a velocity function we can determine the displacement function by the integral

$$s(t) = \int v(t) \, dt$$

The constant of integration determines where on the line the object begins, called the **initial position**.

Using the displacement function we can quickly determine the change in displacement in a time interval $t_1 \leqslant t \leqslant t_2$.

$$\text{Displacement} = s(t_2) - s(t_1) = \int_{t_1}^{t_2} v(t) \, dt$$

TOTAL DISTANCE TRAVELLED

To determine the total distance travelled in a time interval $t_1 \leqslant t \leqslant t_2$, we need to account for any changes of direction in the motion.

To find the total distance travelled given a velocity function $v(t) = s'(t)$ on $t_1 \leqslant t \leqslant t_2$:

- Draw a sign diagram for $v(t)$ so we can determine any changes of direction.
- Determine $s(t)$ by integration, including a constant of integration.
- Find $s(t_1)$ and $s(t_2)$. Also find $s(t)$ at each time the direction changes.
- Draw a motion diagram.
- Determine the total distance travelled from the motion diagram.

Using technology, we can simply use

$$\text{total distance travelled from } t = t_1 \text{ to } t = t_2 = \int_{t_1}^{t_2} |v(t)| \, dt$$

VELOCITY AND ACCELERATION FUNCTIONS

We know that the acceleration function is the derivative of the velocity function, so $a(t) = v'(t)$.

So, given an acceleration function, we can determine the velocity function by integration:

$$v(t) = \int a(t) \, dt.$$

SUMMARY

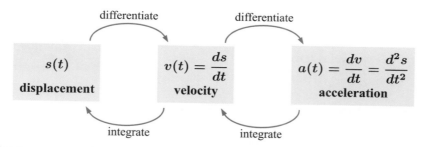

differentiate   differentiate

$s(t)$ $v(t) = \dfrac{ds}{dt}$ $a(t) = \dfrac{dv}{dt} = \dfrac{d^2s}{dt^2}$

displacement   **velocity**   **acceleration**

integrate   integrate

Example 8   🔊 **Self Tutor**

A particle P moves in a straight line with velocity function $v(t) = t^2 - 3t + 2$ ms^{-1}.
Answer the following without using a calculator:

a How far does P travel in the first 4 seconds of motion?
b Find the displacement of P after 4 seconds.

---

a $v(t) = s'(t) = t^2 - 3t + 2$ ∴   the sign diagram of v is:
$ = (t - 1)(t - 2)$

Since the signs change, P reverses direction at $t = 1$ and $t = 2$ seconds.

Now $s(t) = \displaystyle\int (t^2 - 3t + 2) \, dt = \dfrac{t^3}{3} - \dfrac{3t^2}{2} + 2t + c$

Hence $s(0) = c$ $s(1) = \frac{1}{3} - \frac{3}{2} + 2 + c = c + \frac{5}{6}$

$s(2) = \frac{8}{3} - 6 + 4 + c = c + \frac{2}{3}$ $s(4) = \frac{64}{3} - 24 + 8 + c = c + 5\frac{1}{3}$

Motion diagram:

$\therefore$ total distance travelled $= (c + \frac{5}{6} - c) + (c + \frac{5}{6} - [c + \frac{2}{3}]) + (c + 5\frac{1}{3} - [c + \frac{2}{3}])$

$= \frac{5}{6} + \frac{5}{6} - \frac{2}{3} + 5\frac{1}{3} - \frac{2}{3}$

$= 5\frac{2}{3}$ m

b Displacement $=$ final position $-$ original position

$= s(4) - s(0)$

$= c + 5\frac{1}{3} - c$

$= 5\frac{1}{3}$ m

So, the displacement is $5\frac{1}{3}$ m to the right.

EXERCISE 19C.2

1 A particle has velocity function $v(t) = 1 - 2t$ cm s^{-1} as it moves in a straight line. The particle is initially 2 cm to the right of O.

   a Write a formula for the displacement function $s(t)$.

   b Find the total distance travelled in the first second of motion.

   c Find the displacement of the particle at the end of one second.

2 Particle P is initially at the origin O. It moves with the velocity function $v(t) = t^2 - t - 2$ cm s^{-1}.

   a Write a formula for the displacement function $s(t)$.

   b Find the total distance travelled in the first 3 seconds of motion.

   c Find the displacement of the particle at the end of three seconds.

3 The velocity of a moving object is given by $v(t) = 32 + 4t$ m s^{-1}.

   a If $s = 16$ m when $t = 0$ seconds, find the displacement function.

   b Explain why the displacement of the object and its total distance travelled in the interval

     $0 \leqslant t \leqslant t_1$, can both be represented by the definite integral $\displaystyle\int_0^{t_1} (32 + 4t)\, dt$.

   c Show that the object is travelling with constant acceleration.

4 An object has velocity function $v(t) = \cos(2t)$ m s^{-1}. If $s(\frac{\pi}{4}) = 1$ m, determine $s(\frac{\pi}{3})$ exactly.

5 A particle moves along the x-axis with velocity function $x'(t) = 16t - 4t^3$ units per second. Find the total distance travelled in the time interval:

   a $0 \leqslant t \leqslant 3$ seconds   **b** $1 \leqslant t \leqslant 3$ seconds.

6 A particle moves in a straight line with velocity function $v(t) = \cos t$ m s^{-1}.

   a Show that the particle oscillates between two points.

   b Find the distance between the two points in **a**.

7 The velocity of a particle travelling in a straight line is given by $v(t) = 50 - 10e^{-0.5t}$ m s^{-1}, where $t \geqslant 0$, t in seconds.

   a State the initial velocity of the particle.

   b Find the velocity of the particle after 3 seconds.

   c How long will it take for the particle's velocity to increase to 45 m s^{-1}?

   d Discuss $v(t)$ as $t \to \infty$.

   e Show that the particle's acceleration is always positive.

   f Draw the graph of $v(t)$ against t.

   g Find the total distance travelled by the particle in the first 3 seconds of motion.

Example 9   ◄》 **Self Tutor**

A particle is initially at the origin and moving to the right at 5 cm s^{-1}. It accelerates with time according to $a(t) = 4 - 2t$ cm s^{-2}. Answer the following without using a calculator:

   a Find the velocity function of the particle, and sketch its graph for $0 \leqslant t \leqslant 6$ s.

   b For the first 6 seconds of motion, determine the:

      i displacement of the particle   **ii** total distance travelled.

a $v(t) = \displaystyle\int a(t)\, dt = \int (4 - 2t)\, dt$

$\qquad\qquad = 4t - t^2 + c$

But $v(0) = 5$, so $c = 5$

$\therefore\ v(t) = -t^2 + 4t + 5$ cm s^{-1}

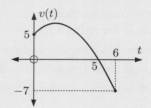

b $s(t) = \displaystyle\int v(t)\, dt = \int (-t^2 + 4t + 5)\, dt$

$\qquad\qquad = -\tfrac{1}{3}t^3 + 2t^2 + 5t + c$ cm

But $s(0) = 0$, so $c = 0$

$\therefore\ s(t) = -\tfrac{1}{3}t^3 + 2t^2 + 5t$ cm

   i Displacement $= s(6) - s(0)$

$\qquad\qquad\qquad = -\tfrac{1}{3}(6)^3 + 2(6)^2 + 5(6)$

$\qquad\qquad\qquad = 30$ cm

   ii The particle changes direction when $t = 5$ s.

Now $s(5) = -\tfrac{1}{3}(5)^3 + 2(5)^2 + 5(5)$

$\qquad\qquad = 33\tfrac{1}{3}$ cm

Motion diagram:

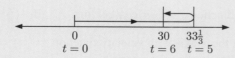

$\therefore$ the total distance travelled $= 33\tfrac{1}{3} + 3\tfrac{1}{3}$

$\qquad\qquad\qquad\qquad\qquad\qquad = 36\tfrac{2}{3}$ cm

Using technology, we can check that $\displaystyle\int_0^6 \left| -t^2 + 4t + 5 \right|\, dt = 36\tfrac{2}{3}$

8 A particle is initially at the origin, and is stationary. It accelerates according to the function $a(t) = \dfrac{-1}{(t+1)^2}$ m s^{-2}.

    a Find the velocity function $v(t)$ for the particle.

    b Find the displacement function $s(t)$ for the particle.

    c Describe the motion of the particle at the time $t = 2$ seconds.

9 A train moves along a straight track with acceleration $\frac{t}{10} - 3$ m s^{-2}. The initial velocity of the train is 45 m s^{-1}.

    a Determine the velocity function $v(t)$.

    b Evaluate $\displaystyle\int_0^{60} v(t)\, dt$ and explain what this value represents.

10 An object has initial velocity 20 m s^{-1} as it moves in a straight line with acceleration function $4e^{-\frac{t}{20}}$ m s^{-2}.

    a Show that as t increases the object approaches a limiting velocity.

    b Find the total distance travelled in the first 10 seconds of motion.

D   SOLIDS OF REVOLUTION

Consider the curve $y = f(x)$ for $a \leqslant x \leqslant b$.

If the shaded area below is **revolved about the x-axis** through $360°$ or 2π, a 3-dimensional solid will be formed. Such a solid is called a **solid of revolution**.

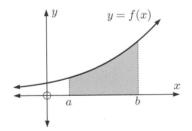
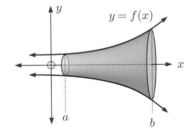

VOLUME OF REVOLUTION

We can use integration to find volumes of revolution between $x = a$ and $x = b$.

The solid can be thought to be made up of an infinite number of thin cylindrical discs.

Since the volume of a cylinder $= \pi r^2 h$:

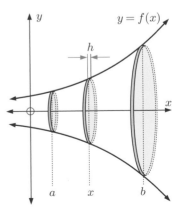

- the left-most disc has approximate volume $\pi[f(a)]^2 h$
- the right-most disc has approximate volume $\pi[f(b)]^2 h$
- the middle disc has approximate volume $\pi[f(x)]^2 h$.

As there are infinitely many discs, we let $h \to 0$.

We obtain $\quad V = \displaystyle\lim_{h \to 0} \sum_{x=a}^{x=b} \pi[f(x)]^2\, h = \int_a^b \pi[f(x)]^2\, dx = \pi \int_a^b y^2\, dx.$

When the region enclosed by $y = f(x)$, the x-axis, and the vertical lines $x = a$ and $x = b$ is revolved through 2π about the x-axis to generate a solid, the volume of the solid is given by

Volume of revolution $= \pi \displaystyle\int_a^b y^2 \, dx$.

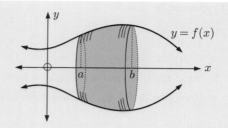

Example 10
🔊 **Self Tutor**

Use integration to find the volume of the solid generated when the line $y = x$ for $1 \leqslant x \leqslant 4$ is revolved through 2π around the x-axis.

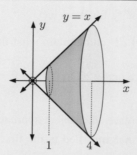

Volume of revolution $= \pi \displaystyle\int_a^b y^2 \, dx$

$\qquad = \pi \displaystyle\int_1^4 x^2 \, dx$

$\qquad = \pi \left[\dfrac{x^3}{3} \right]_1^4$

$\qquad = \pi \left(\dfrac{64}{3} - \dfrac{1}{3} \right)$

$\qquad = 21\pi$ cubic units

The volume of a cone of height h and base radius r is

$V_{\text{cone}} = \frac{1}{3}\pi r^2 h$

So, in this example

$V = \frac{1}{3}\pi 4^2 (4) - \frac{1}{3}\pi 1^2 (1)$

$\quad = \dfrac{64\pi}{3} - \dfrac{\pi}{3}$

$\quad = 21\pi \quad \checkmark$

Example 11
🔊 **Self Tutor**

Find the volume of the solid formed when the graph of the function $y = x^2$ for $0 \leqslant x \leqslant 5$ is revolved through 2π about the x-axis.

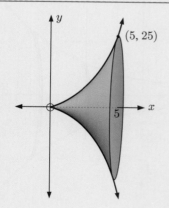

Volume of revolution $= \pi \displaystyle\int_a^b y^2 \, dx$

$\qquad = \pi \displaystyle\int_0^5 (x^2)^2 \, dx$

$\qquad = \pi \displaystyle\int_0^5 x^4 \, dx$

$\qquad = \pi \left[\dfrac{x^5}{5} \right]_0^5$

$\qquad = \pi (625 - 0)$

$\qquad = 625\pi$ cubic units

**GRAPHICS
CALCULATOR
INSTRUCTIONS**

EXERCISE 19D.1

1 Find the volume of the solid formed when the following are revolved through 2π about the x-axis:

a $y = 2x$ for $0 \leqslant x \leqslant 3$

b $y = \sqrt{x}$ for $0 \leqslant x \leqslant 4$

c $y = x^3$ for $1 \leqslant x \leqslant 2$

d $y = x^{\frac{3}{2}}$ for $1 \leqslant x \leqslant 4$

e $y = x^2$ for $2 \leqslant x \leqslant 4$

f $y = \sqrt{25 - x^2}$ for $0 \leqslant x \leqslant 5$

g $y = \dfrac{1}{x - 1}$ for $2 \leqslant x \leqslant 3$

h $y = x + \dfrac{1}{x}$ for $1 \leqslant x \leqslant 3$

2 Use technology to find, correct to 3 significant figures, the volume of the solid of revolution formed when these functions are rotated through $360°$ about the x-axis:

a $y = \dfrac{x^3}{x^2 + 1}$ for $1 \leqslant x \leqslant 3$

b $y = e^{\sin x}$ for $0 \leqslant x \leqslant 2$.

3 Find the volume of revolution when the shaded region is revolved through 2π about the x-axis.

a
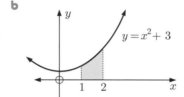

b

c

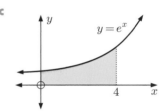

4 Answer the **Opening Problem** on page **476**.

5

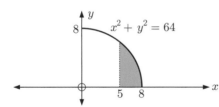

The shaded region is rotated through $360°$ about the x-axis.

a Find the volume of revolution.

b A hemispherical bowl of radius 8 cm contains water to a depth of 3 cm.
What is the volume of water?

6 **a** What is the name of the solid of revolution when the shaded region is revolved about the x-axis?

b Find the equation of the line segment [AB] in the form $y = ax + b$.

c Find a formula for the volume of the solid using

$$\pi \int_a^b y^2 \, dx.$$

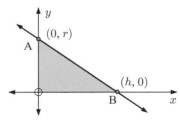

7

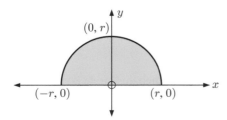

A circle with centre $(0, 0)$ and radius r units has equation $x^2 + y^2 = r^2$.

a If the shaded region is revolved about the x-axis, what solid is formed?

b Use integration to show that the volume of revolution is $\frac{4}{3}\pi r^3$.

Example 12

◀) **Self Tutor**

One arch of $y = \sin x$ is rotated through $360°$ about the x-axis.

Using the identity $\sin^2 x = \frac{1}{2} - \frac{1}{2}\cos(2x)$ to help you, find the volume of revolution.

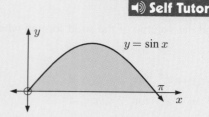

$$\text{Volume} = \pi \int_a^b y^2 \, dx$$

$$= \pi \int_0^\pi \sin^2 x \, dx$$

$$= \pi \int_0^\pi \left[\tfrac{1}{2} - \tfrac{1}{2}\cos(2x)\right] \, dx$$

$$= \pi \left[\frac{x}{2} - \frac{1}{2}\left(\tfrac{1}{2}\right)\sin(2x)\right]_0^\pi$$

$$= \pi \left[\left(\tfrac{\pi}{2} - \tfrac{1}{4}\sin(2\pi)\right) - \left(0 - \tfrac{1}{4}\sin 0\right)\right]$$

$$= \pi \times \tfrac{\pi}{2}$$

$$= \tfrac{\pi^2}{2} \text{ units}^3$$

8   Find the volume of revolution when the following regions are rotated through 2π about the x-axis. You may use the identity $\cos^2 x = \frac{1}{2} + \frac{1}{2}\cos(2x)$.

    a $y = \sqrt{\cos x}$ for $0 \leqslant x \leqslant \frac{\pi}{2}$
          b $y = \cos x$ for $0 \leqslant x \leqslant \frac{\pi}{4}$

9   **a**   Sketch the graph of $y = \sin x + \cos x$ for $0 \leqslant x \leqslant \frac{\pi}{2}$.

    b   Hence, find the volume of revolution of the shape bounded by $y = \sin x + \cos x$,   the x-axis, $x = 0$,   and $x = \frac{\pi}{4}$ when it is rotated through 2π about the x-axis.

VOLUMES FOR TWO DEFINING FUNCTIONS (EXTENSION)

Consider the circle with centre $(0, 3)$ and radius 1 unit.

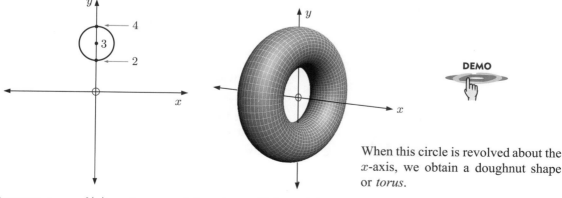

When this circle is revolved about the x-axis, we obtain a doughnut shape or *torus*.

Suppose $y_U = f(x)$ and $y_L = g(x)$,   where $f(x) \geqslant g(x)$ for all $a \leqslant x \leqslant b$.

If the region bounded by the upper function $y_U = f(x)$ and the lower function $y_L = g(x)$, and the lines $x = a$, $x = b$ is revolved about the x-axis, then its volume of revolution is given by:

$$V = \pi \int_a^b \left([f(x)]^2 - [g(x)]^2 \right) dx \quad \text{or} \quad V = \pi \int_a^b \left(y_U^{\,2} - y_L^{\,2} \right) dx$$

Rotating 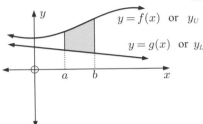 about the x-axis gives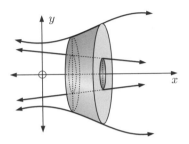

Example 13   ◀) **Self Tutor**

Find the volume of revolution generated by revolving the region between $y = x^2$ and $y = \sqrt{x}$ about the x-axis.

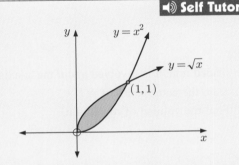

Volume $= \pi \displaystyle\int_0^1 \left(y_U^{\,2} - y_L^{\,2} \right) dx$

$= \pi \displaystyle\int_0^1 \left((\sqrt{x})^2 - (x^2)^2 \right) dx$

$= \pi \displaystyle\int_0^1 (x - x^4) \, dx$

$= \pi \left[\dfrac{x^2}{2} - \dfrac{x^5}{5} \right]_0^1$

$= \pi \left(\left(\tfrac{1}{2} - \tfrac{1}{5} \right) - (0) \right)$

$= \tfrac{3\pi}{10}$ units^3

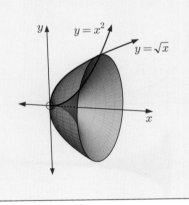

EXERCISE 19D.2

1 The shaded region between $y = 4 - x^2$ and $y = 3$ is revolved about the x-axis.

  a What are the coordinates of A and B?

  b Find the volume of revolution.

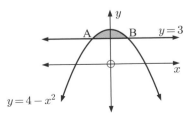

2

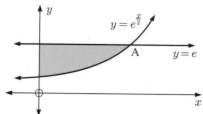

The shaded region is revolved about the x-axis.

   a Find the coordinates of A.

   b Find the volume of revolution.

3 The shaded region between $y = x$, $y = \dfrac{1}{x}$,

and $x = 2$ is revolved about the x-axis.

   a Find the coordinates of A.

   b Find the volume of revolution.

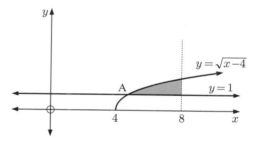

4 The shaded region is revolved about the x-axis.

   a State the coordinates of A.

   b Find the volume of revolution.

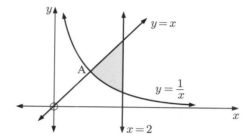

5

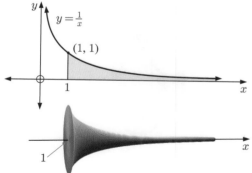

Prove that the shaded area from $x = 1$ to infinity is infinite whereas its volume of revolution is finite.

We call this a mathematical paradox.

---

1 Write an expression for the total shaded area.

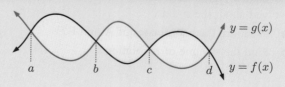

2

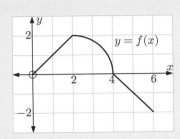

Find: **a** $\displaystyle\int_0^4 f(x)\,dx$

b $\displaystyle\int_4^6 f(x)\,dx$

c $\displaystyle\int_0^6 f(x)\,dx$

3 Does $\displaystyle\int_{-1}^3 f(x)\,dx$ represent the area of the shaded region?
Explain your answer briefly.

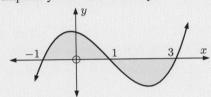

4 Determine k if the enclosed region has area $5\frac{1}{3}$ units^2.

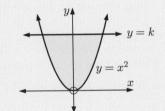

5 By appealing only to geometrical evidence, explain why

$$\int_0^1 e^x\,dx + \int_1^e \ln x\,dx = e.$$

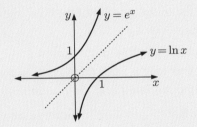

6 Find the area of the region enclosed by $y = x^2 + 4x + 1$ and $y = 3x + 3$.

7 A particle moves in a straight line with velocity $v(t) = t^2 - 6t + 8$ m s^{-1}, for $t \geqslant 0$ seconds.
   a Draw a sign diagram for $v(t)$.
   b Explain exactly what happens to the particle in the first 5 seconds of motion.
   c After 5 seconds, how far is the particle from its original position?
   d Find the total distance travelled in the first 5 seconds of motion.

8 Determine the area enclosed by the axes and $y = 4e^x - 1$.

9 Show that the volume of revolution generated by rotating the shaded region through $360°$ about the x-axis is $\frac{256}{15}\pi$ units^3.

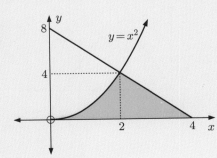

REVIEW SET 19B   CALCULATOR

1 A particle moves in a straight line with velocity $v(t) = 2t - 3t^2$ m s^{-1}, for $t \geqslant 0$ seconds.

    a Find a formula for the acceleration function $a(t)$.

    b Find a formula for the displacement function $s(t)$.

    c Find the change in displacement after two seconds.

2 Consider $f(x) = \dfrac{x}{1 + x^2}$.

    a Find the position and nature of all turning points of $y = f(x)$.

    b Discuss $f(x)$ as $x \to \infty$ and as $x \to -\infty$.

    c Sketch the graph of $y = f(x)$.

    d Find, using technology, the area enclosed by $y = f(x)$, the x-axis, and the vertical line $x = -2$.

3 A particle moves in a straight line with velocity given by $v(t) = \sin t$ m s^{-1}, where $t \geqslant 0$ seconds. Find the total distance travelled by the particle in the first 4 seconds of motion.

4 A boat travelling in a straight line has its engine turned off at time $t = 0$. Its velocity at time t seconds thereafter is given by $v(t) = \dfrac{100}{(t + 2)^2}$ m s^{-1}.

    a Find the initial velocity of the boat, and its velocity after 3 seconds.

    b Discuss $v(t)$ as $t \to \infty$.

    c Sketch the graph of $v(t)$ against t.

    d Find how long it takes for the boat to travel 30 metres from when the engine is turned off.

    e Find the acceleration of the boat at any time t.

    f Show that $\dfrac{dv}{dt} = -kv^{\frac{3}{2}}$, and find the value of the constant k.

5 The figure shows the graphs of $y = \cos(2x)$ and $y = e^{3x}$ for $-\pi \leqslant x \leqslant \frac{\pi}{2}$.

Find correct to 4 decimal places:

    a the x-coordinates of their points of intersection

    b the area of the shaded region.

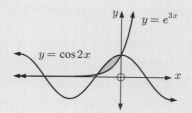

6 The shaded region has area $\frac{1}{2}$ unit^2. Find the value of m.

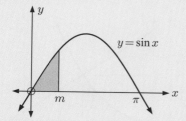

7 Find, correct to 4 decimal places:

    a the value of a

    b the area of the shaded region.

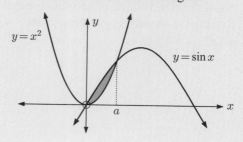

8 Find the volume of the solid of revolution formed when the shaded region is revolved about the x-axis:

a

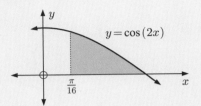

$y = \cos(2x)$

$\dfrac{\pi}{16}$

b

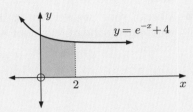

$y = e^{-x} + 4$

2

REVIEW SET 19C

1 At time $t = 0$ a particle passes through the origin with velocity 27 cm s^{-1}. Its acceleration t seconds later is $6t - 30$ cm s^{-2}.

   a Write an expression for the particle's velocity.

   b Write an integral which represents the displacement from the origin after 6 seconds. Hence calculate this displacement.

2 **a** Sketch the graphs of $y = \sin^2 x$ and $y = \sin x$ on the same set of axes for $0 \leqslant x \leqslant \pi$.

   b Find the exact value of the area enclosed by these curves for $0 \leqslant x \leqslant \frac{\pi}{2}$.

3 Find a given that the area of the region between $y = e^x$ and the x-axis from $x = 0$ to $x = a$ is 2 units^2.
Hence determine b such that the area of the region from $x = a$ to $x = b$ is also 2 units^2.

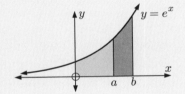

$y = e^x$

a b

4 Determine the area of the region enclosed by $y = x$, $y = \sin x$, and $x = \pi$.

5 Determine the area enclosed by $y = \frac{2}{\pi} x$ and $y = \sin x$.

6 OABC is a rectangle and the two shaded regions are equal in area. Find k.

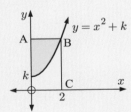

$y = x^2 + k$

A   B

k

C

2

7 Find the volume of the solid of revolution formed when the following are revolved about the x-axis:

   a $y = x$ between $x = 4$ and $x = 10$

   b $y = x + 1$ between $x = 4$ and $x = 10$

   c $y = \sqrt{\sin x}$ between $x = 0$ and $x = \pi$

   d $y = 1 - \cos x$ between $x = 0$ and $x = \frac{\pi}{2}$.

8 **a** Use $V = \frac{1}{3}\pi r^2 h$ to find the volume of this
cone.

b Check your answer to **a** by defining an
appropriate solid of revolution and calculating its
volume.

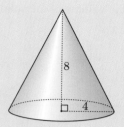

9

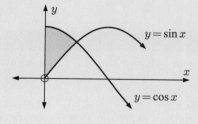

Find the volume of the solid of revolution obtained
when the shaded region is rotated through $360°$
about the x-axis:

Chapter **20**

Descriptive statistics

Syllabus reference: 5.1, 5.2, 5.3

OPENING PROBLEM

A farmer wanted to investigate the effect of a new organic fertiliser on his crops of peas. He divided a small garden into two equal plots and planted many peas in each. Both plots were treated the same except that fertiliser was used on one but not the other.

A random sample of 150 pods was harvested from each plot at the same time, and the number of peas in each pod was counted. The results were:

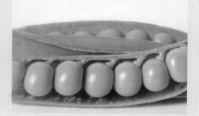

Without fertiliser

4 6 5 6 5 6 4 6 4 9 5 3 6 8 5 4 6 8 6 5 6 7 4 6 5 2 8 6 5 6 5 5 5 4 4 4 6 7 5 6 7 5 5 6
4 8 5 3 7 5 3 6 4 7 5 6 5 7 5 7 6 7 5 4 7 5 5 5 6 6 5 6 7 5 8 6 8 6 7 6 6 3 7 6 8 3 3 4
4 7 6 5 6 4 5 7 3 7 7 6 7 7 4 6 6 5 6 7 6 3 4 6 6 3 7 6 7 6 8 6 6 6 6 4 7 6 6 5 3 8 6 7
6 8 6 7 6 6 6 8 4 4 8 6 6 2 6 5 7 3

With fertiliser

6 7 7 4 9 5 5 5 8 9 8 9 7 7 5 8 7 6 6 7 9 7 7 7 8 9 3 7 4 8 5 10 8 6 7 6 7 5 6 8 7 9 4
4 9 6 8 5 8 7 7 4 7 8 10 6 10 7 7 7 9 7 7 8 6 8 6 8 7 4 8 6 8 7 3 8 7 6 9 7 6 9 7 6 8 3
9 5 7 6 8 7 9 7 8 4 8 7 7 7 6 6 8 6 3 8 5 8 7 6 7 4 9 6 6 6 8 4 7 8 9 7 7 4 7 5 7 4 7 6
4 6 7 7 6 7 8 7 6 6 7 8 6 7 10 5 13 4 7 11

Things to think about:

- Can you state clearly the problem that the farmer wants to solve?
- How has the farmer tried to make a fair comparison?
- How could the farmer make sure that his selection was random?
- What is the best way of organising this data?
- What are suitable methods of displaying the data?
- Are there any abnormally high or low results and how should they be treated?
- How can we best describe the most typical pod size?
- How can we best describe the spread of possible pod sizes?
- Can the farmer make a reasonable conclusion from his investigation?

A   KEY STATISTICAL CONCEPTS

In statistics we collect information about a group of individuals, then analyse this information to draw conclusions about those individuals.

You should already be familiar with these words which are commonly used in statistics:

- **Population** - an entire collection of individuals about which we want to draw conclusions
- **Census** - the collection of information from the **whole population**
- **Sample** - a subset of the population which should be chosen at **random** to avoid **bias** in the results
- **Survey** - the collection of information from a **sample**

- **Data** - information about individuals in a population
- **Categorical variable** - describes a particular quality or characteristic which can be divided into categories
- **Numerical variable** - describes a characteristic which has a numerical value that can be counted or measured
- **Parameter** - a numerical quantity measuring some aspect of a population
- **Statistic** - a quantity calculated from data gathered from a sample, usually used to estimate a population parameter
- **Distribution** - the pattern of variation of data, which may be described as:

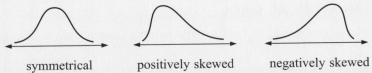

symmetrical   positively skewed   negatively skewed

- **Outliers** - data values that are either much larger or much smaller than the general body of data; they should be included in analysis *unless* they are the result of human or other known error

NUMERICAL VARIABLES

There are two types of numerical variable we will deal with in this course:

A **discrete numerical variable** takes exact number values and is often a result of **counting**.

Examples of discrete numerical variables are:

- *The number of people in a car*:   the variable could take the values 1, 2, 3, ...
- *The score out of 20 for a test*:   the variable could take the values 0, 1, 2, 3, ..., 20.

A **continuous variable** takes numerical values within a certain continuous range. It is usually a result of **measuring**.

Examples of continuous numerical variables are:

- *The height of Year 11 students*:   the variable can take any value from about 140 cm to 200 cm.
- *The speed of cars on a stretch of highway*:   the variable can take any value from 0 $km\,h^{-1}$ to the fastest speed that a car can travel, but is most likely to be in the range 60 $km\,h^{-1}$ to 160 $km\,h^{-1}$.

FREQUENCY TABLES

One of the simplest ways to organise data is using a frequency table.

For example, consider the data set:

| 1 3 1 2 4 | 2 4 1 5 3 | 1 3 2 2 4 |
| 1 3 4 1 2 | 3 2 4 1 3 | 2 1 2 5 2 |

A **tally** is used to count the number of 1s, 2s, 3s, and so on. As we read the data from left to right, we place a vertical stroke in the tally column. We use |||| to represent 5.

The **frequency** column summarises the number of each particular data value.

The **relative frequency** column measures the percentage of the total number of data values that are in each group.

Value	Tally	Frequency (f)	% relative frequency
1	⥿⥿ ⦀	8	26.7 ← $\frac{8}{30} \times 100\%$
2	⥿⥿ ⦀⦀	9	30.0
3	⥿⥿ ⎮	6	20.0
4	⥿⥿	5	16.7
5	⎮⎮	2	6.7
	Totals	30	100

DISPLAY OF NUMERICAL DATA

From previous courses you should be familiar with **column graphs** used to display **discrete** numerical variables.

When data is recorded for a **continuous** variable there are likely to be many different values. We organise the data in a frequency table by grouping it into **class intervals** of **equal width**.

A special type of graph called a **frequency histogram** or just **histogram** is used to display the data. This is similar to a column graph but, to account for the continuous nature of the variable, a number line is used for the horizontal axis and the 'columns' are joined together.

Column graphs and frequency histograms both have the following features:

- The frequency of occurrence is on the vertical axis.
- The range of scores is on the horizontal axis.
- The column widths are equal and the column height represents frequency.

The **modal class**, or class of values that appears most often, is easy to identify from the highest column of the frequency histogram.

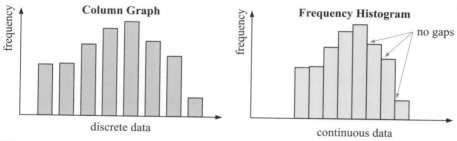

CASE STUDY

DRIVING A GOLF BALL

While attending a golf championship, I measured how far Ethan, a professional golfer, hit 30 drives on the practice fairway. The results are given below in metres:

244.6	245.1	248.0	248.8	250.0	251.1
251.2	253.9	254.5	254.6	255.9	257.0
260.6	262.8	262.9	263.1	263.2	264.3
264.4	265.0	265.5	265.6	266.5	267.4
269.7	270.5	270.7	272.9	275.6	277.5

To organise the data, we sort it into **groups** in a frequency table.

When forming groups, we find the lowest and highest values, and then choose a group width so that there are about 6 to 12 groups. In this case the lowest value is 244.6 m and the highest is 277.5 m. If we choose a group width of 5 m, we obtain eight groups of equal width between values 240 m and 280 m, which cover all of the data values.

Suppose d is the length of a drive. The first group $240 \leqslant d < 245$ includes any data value which is at least 240 m but less than 245 m. The group $260 \leqslant d < 265$ includes data which is at least 260 m but < 265 m. We use this technique to create eight groups into which all data values will fall.

Ethan's 30 drives

Distance (m)	Tally	Frequency (f)	% relative frequency	
$240 \leqslant d < 245$	|	1	3.3	$\approx \frac{1}{30} \times 100$
$245 \leqslant d < 250$	|||	3	10.0	$= \frac{3}{30} \times 100$
$250 \leqslant d < 255$	|||| |	6	20.0	
$255 \leqslant d < 260$	||	2	6.7	
$260 \leqslant d < 265$	|||| ||	7	23.3	
$265 \leqslant d < 270$	|||| |	6	20.0	
$270 \leqslant d < 275$	|||	3	10.0	
$275 \leqslant d < 280$	||	2	6.7	
	Totals	30	100.0	

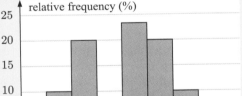

From this table we can draw both a **frequency histogram** and a **relative frequency histogram**:

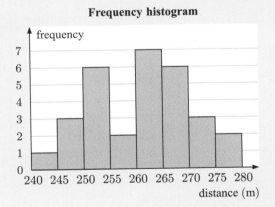

Frequency histogram — Relative frequency histogram

We can see that the modal class is $260 \leqslant d < 265$.

The advantage of the relative frequency histogram is that we can easily compare it with other distributions with different numbers of data values. Using percentages allows for a fair comparison.

Each graph should have a title and its axes should be labelled.

Example 1   ◆)) **Self Tutor**

A sample of 20 juvenile lobsters is randomly selected from a tank containing several hundred. Each lobster is measured for length (in cm) and the results are:

$$4.9, \ 5.6, \ 7.2, \ 6.7, \ 3.1, \ 4.6, \ 6.0, \ 5.0, \ 3.7, \ 7.3,$$
$$6.0, \ 5.4, \ 4.2, \ 6.6, \ 4.7, \ 5.8, \ 4.4, \ 3.6, \ 4.2, \ 5.4$$

a Organise the data using a frequency table, and hence graph the data.

b State the modal class for the data.   **c** Describe the distribution of the data.

a The variable 'the length of a lobster' is *continuous* even though lengths have been rounded to the nearest mm.

The shortest length is 3.1 cm and the longest is 7.3 cm, so we will use class intervals of length 1 cm.

Length l (cm)	Frequency
$3 \leqslant l < 4$	3
$4 \leqslant l < 5$	6
$5 \leqslant l < 6$	5
$6 \leqslant l < 7$	4
$7 \leqslant l < 8$	2

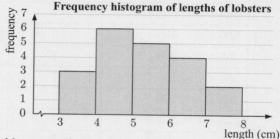

Frequency histogram of lengths of lobsters

b The modal class is $4 \leqslant l < 5$ cm as this occurred most frequently.

c The data is positively skewed.

EXERCISE 20A

1 A frequency table for the heights of a basketball squad is given alongside.

a Explain why 'height' is a continuous variable.

b Construct a frequency histogram for the data. The axes should be clearly marked and labelled, and the graph should have a title.

c What is the modal class? Explain what this means.

d Describe the distribution of the data.

Height (cm)	Frequency
$170 \leqslant H < 175$	1
$175 \leqslant H < 180$	8
$180 \leqslant H < 185$	9
$185 \leqslant H < 190$	11
$190 \leqslant H < 195$	9
$195 \leqslant H < 200$	3
$200 \leqslant H < 205$	3

2 A school has conducted a survey of 60 students to investigate the time it takes for them to travel to school. The following data gives the travel times to the nearest minute:

12	15	16	8	10	17	25	34	42	18	24	18	45	33	38
45	40	3	20	12	10	10	27	16	37	45	15	16	26	32
35	8	14	18	15	27	19	32	6	12	14	20	10	16	14
28	31	21	25	8	32	46	14	15	20	18	8	10	25	22

a Is travel time a discrete or continuous variable?

b Copy and complete the frequency table shown.

c Describe the distribution of the data.

d What is the travelling time modal class?

Time (min)	Tally	Frequency
0 - 9		
10 - 19		
20 - 29		
30 - 39		
40 - 49		

3   For the following data, state whether a frequency histogram or a column graph
    should be used, and draw the appropriate graph.

   a   The number of matches in 30 match boxes:

Number of matches per box	47	49	50	51	52	53	55
Frequency	1	1	9	12	4	2	1

   b   The heights of 25 hockey players (to the nearest cm):

Height (cm)	120 - 129	130 - 139	140 - 149	150 - 159	160 - 169
Frequency	1	2	7	14	1

4   A plant inspector takes a random sample of six month
    old seedlings from a nursery and measures their heights
    to the nearest mm.

    The results are shown in the frequency histogram.

   a   How many of the seedlings are 400 mm or more
        in height?

   b   What percentage of the seedlings are between 349
        and 400 mm?

   c   The total number of seedlings in the nursery is
        1462. Estimate the number of seedlings which
        measure:

        i   less than 400 mm
        ii   between 374 and 425 mm.

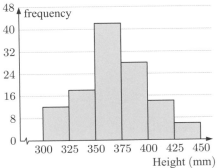

Frequency histogram of heights of seedlings

B   MEASURING THE CENTRE OF DATA

We can get a better understanding of a data set if we can locate the **middle** or **centre** of the data, and
also get an indication of its **spread** or dispersion. Knowing one of these without the other is often of
little use.

There are *three statistics* that are used to measure the **centre** of a data set. These are the **mode**, the
mean, and the **median**.

THE MODE

> For discrete numerical data, the **mode** is the most frequently occurring value in the data set.
>
> For continuous numerical data, we cannot talk about a mode in this way because no two
> data values will be *exactly* equal. Instead we talk about a **modal class**, which is the class
> or group that occurs most frequently.

THE MEAN

> The **mean** of a data set is the statistical name for the arithmetic average.
>
> $$\text{mean} = \frac{\textbf{sum of all data values}}{\textbf{the number of data values}}$$

The mean gives us a single number which indicates a centre of the data set. It is usually not a member
of the data set.

For example, a mean test mark of 73% tells us that there are several marks below 73% and several above it. 73% is at the centre, but it is not always the case that one of the students scored 73%.

Suppose x is a numerical variable. We let:

x_i be the ith data value

n be the number of data values in the sample or population

$\overline{x}$ represent the mean of a **sample**, so

'μ' reads "mu".

$$\overline{x} = \frac{x_1 + x_2 + x_3 + \ldots + x_n}{n} = \frac{\sum\limits_{i=1}^{n} x_i}{n}$$

μ represent the mean of a **population**, so $\mu = \dfrac{\sum\limits_{i=1}^{n} x_i}{n}$.

In many cases we do not have data from all of the members of a population, so the exact value of μ is often unknown.

Instead we collect data from a sample of the population, and use the mean of the sample $\overline{x}$ as an approximation for μ.

THE MEDIAN

The **median** is the *middle value* of an ordered data set.

An ordered data set is obtained by listing the data from smallest to largest value.

The median splits the data in halves. Half of the data are less than or equal to the median, and half are greater than or equal to it.

For example, if the median mark for a test is 73% then you know that half the class scored less than or equal to 73% and half scored greater than or equal to 73%.

For an **odd number** of data, the median is one of the original data values.

For an **even number** of data, the median is the average of the two middle values, and hence may not be in the original data set.

If there are n data values listed in order from smallest to largest, the median is the $\left(\dfrac{n+1}{2}\right)$th data value.

For example:

If $n = 13$, $\dfrac{13+1}{2} = 7$, so the median is the 7th ordered data value.

DEMO

If $n = 14$, $\dfrac{14+1}{2} = 7.5$, so the median is the average of the 7th and 8th ordered data values.

THE MERITS OF THE MEAN AND MEDIAN AS MEASURES OF CENTRE

The **median** is the only measure of centre that will locate the true centre regardless of the data set's features. It is unaffected by the presence of extreme values. It is called a *resistant* measure of centre.

The **mean** is an accurate measure of centre if the distribution is symmetrical or approximately symmetrical. If it is not, then unbalanced high or low values will *drag* the mean toward them and cause it to be an inaccurate measure of the centre. It is called a *non-resistant* measure of centre because it is influenced by all data values in the set. *If it is considered inaccurate, it should not be used in discussion.*

THE RELATIONSHIP BETWEEN THE MEAN AND THE MEDIAN FOR DIFFERENT DISTRIBUTIONS

For distributions that are **symmetric** about the centre, the mean and median will be approximately equal.

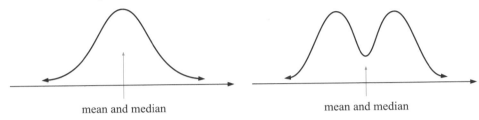

If the data set has symmetry, both the mean and the median should accurately measure the centre of the distribution.

If the data set is not symmetric, it may be positively or negatively skewed:

Notice that the mean and median are clearly different for these skewed distributions.

| INVESTIGATION 1 | MERITS OF THE MEAN AND MEDIAN |

For this investigation you can either use the software provided on the CD or your graphics calculator.

STATISTICS PACKAGE

Consider the data gained from Ethan, a professional golfer. The data was as follows:

244.6	245.1	248.0	248.8	250.0	251.1	251.2	253.9	254.5	254.6
255.9	257.0	260.6	262.8	262.9	263.1	263.2	264.3	264.4	265.0
265.5	265.6	266.5	267.4	269.7	270.5	270.7	272.9	275.6	277.5

GRAPHICS CALCULATOR INSTRUCTIONS

What to do:

1   Enter the data into your graphics calculator as a list, or use the **statistics package** supplied.

    a   Produce a frequency histogram of the data. Set the X values from 240 to 280 with an increment of 5. Set the Y values from 0 to 30.

    b   Comment on the shape of the distribution.

    c   Find the mean and median of the data.

    d   Compare the mean and the median. Is the mean an accurate measure of the centre?

2   Since we have continuous numerical data, we have a modal class rather than an individual mode.

    a   What is the modal class?

    b   What would the modal class be if our intervals were 2 m wide starting at 240 m?

3   Now suppose Ethan had hit a few very bad drives. Let us say that his three shortest drives were very short!

    a   Change the three shortest drives to 82.1 m, 103.2 m, and 111.1 m.

    b   Repeat **1 a**, **b**, **c**, and **d** but set the X values from 75 to 300 with an increment of 25 for the frequency histogram.

    c   Describe the distribution as symmetric, positively skewed, or negatively skewed.

    d   What effect have the changed values had on the mean and median as measures of the centre of the data?

4   What would have happened if Ethan had hit a few really long balls in addition to the very bad ones? Let us imagine that the longest balls he hit were very long indeed!

    a   Change the three longest drives to 403.9 m, 415.5 m, and 420.0 m.

    b   Repeat **1 a**, **b**, **c**, and **d** but set the X values from 50 to 450 with an increment of 50 for the frequency histogram.

    c   Describe the distribution as symmetric, positively skewed, or negatively skewed.

    d   What effect have the changed values had on the mean and median as measures of the centre of the data?

5   While collecting the data from Ethan, I decided I would also hit 30 golf balls with my driver. The relative frequency histogram alongside shows the results. The distribution is clearly positively skewed.

Discuss the merits of the median and mean as measures of the centre of this distribution.

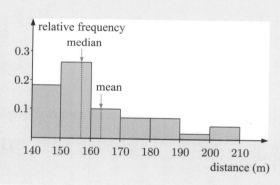

UNGROUPED DATA

Example 2

◀◉ **Self Tutor**

The number of faulty products returned to an electrical goods store over a 21 day period is:

    3   4   4   9   8   8   6   4   7   9   1   3   5   3   5   9   8   6   3   7   1

For this data set, find:

  a   the mean   **b**   the median   **c**   the mode.

a   mean $= \dfrac{3+4+4+....+3+7+1}{21}$ ⟵ sum of the data

                           21 ⟵ 21 data values

      $= \dfrac{113}{21}$

      ≈ 5.38 faulty products

b As $n = 21$, $\dfrac{n+1}{2} = 11$

The ordered data set is: ~~1~~ ~~1~~ ~~3~~ ~~3~~ ~~3~~ ~~3~~ ~~4~~ ~~4~~ ~~4~~ ~~5~~ 5 ~~6~~ ~~6~~ ~~7~~ ~~7~~ ~~8~~ ~~8~~ ~~8~~ ~~9~~ ~~9~~ ~~9~~

$$\uparrow$$
11th value

∴   median = 5 faulty products

c 3 is the score which occurs the most often, so the mode is 3 faulty products.

For the faulty products data in **Example 2**, how are the measures of the middle affected if on the 22nd day the number of faulty products was 9?

We expect the mean to rise as the new data value is greater than the old mean.

In fact, the new mean $= \dfrac{113 + 9}{22} = \dfrac{122}{22} \approx 5.55$ faulty products.

As $n = 22$, $\dfrac{n+1}{2} = 11.5$

The new ordered data set would be: 1 1 3 3 3 3 4 4 4 5 5̲ 6̲ 6 7 7 8 8 8 9 9 9 9

two middle scores

The new median $= \dfrac{5 + 6}{2} = 5.5$ faulty products.

This new data set has two modes. The modes are 3 and 9 faulty products and we say that the data set is **bimodal**.

Note: • If a data set has three or more modes, we do not use the mode as a measure of the middle or centre of the data values.

• Consider the data: 4 2 5 6 7 4 5 3 5 4 7 6 3 5 8 6 5.

The dot plot of this data is:

For this data the mean, median, and mode are all 5.

For a *symmetrical distribution* of data, the mean, mode, and median will all be equal.

However, equal or approximately equal values of the mean, mode, and median does not necessarily indicate a distribution is symmetric.

Example 3	◀⑴ **Self Tutor**

If 6 people have a mean mass of 53.7 kg, find their total mass.

$\dfrac{\text{sum of masses}}{6} = 53.7$ kg

∴   sum of masses $= 53.7 \times 6$

So the total mass $= 322.2$ kg.

EXERCISE 20B.1

1 For each of the following data sets, find the: **a** mean   **b** median   **c** mode.

    a 2, 3, 3, 3, 4, 4, 4, 5, 5, 5, 5, 6, 6, 6, 6, 6, 7, 7, 8, 8, 8, 9, 9

    b 10, 12, 12, 15, 15, 16, 16, 17, 18, 18, 18, 18, 19, 20, 21

    c 22.4, 24.6, 21.8, 26.4, 24.9, 25.0, 23.5, 26.1, 25.3, 29.5, 23.5

GRAPHICS
CALCULATOR
INSTRUCTIONS

Check your answers using the statistics features on your graphics calculator.

2 Consider the following two data sets: *Data set A*:   3, 4, 4, 5, 6, 6, 7, 7, 7, 8, 8, 9, 10

                                              Data set B: 3, 4, 4, 5, 6, 6, 7, 7, 7, 8, 8, 9, 15

    a Find the mean for both data set A and data set B.

    b Find the median of both data set A and data set B.

    c Explain why the mean of data set A is less than the mean of data set B.

    d Explain why the median of data set A is the same as the median of data set B.

3 The annual salaries of ten office workers are:

                $23 000, $46 000, $23 000, $38 000, $24 000,
                $23 000, $23 000, $38 000, $23 000, $32 000

    a Find the mean, median, and modal salaries of this group.

    b Explain why the mode is an unsatisfactory measure of the middle in this case.

    c Is the median a satisfactory measure of the middle of this data set?

4 The following raw data is the daily rainfall (to the nearest millimetre) for the month of July 2007 in the desert:

       3, 1, 0, 0, 0, 0, 0, 2, 0, 0, 3, 0, 0, 0, 7, 1, 1, 0, 3, 8, 0, 0, 0, 42, 21, 3, 0, 3, 1, 0, 0

    a Find the mean, median, and mode for the data.

    b Explain why the median is not the most suitable measure of centre for this set of data.

    c Explain why the mode is not the most suitable measure of centre for this set of data.

    d Are there any outliers in this data set?

    e On some occasions outliers are removed because they must be due to errors in observation or calculation. If the outliers in the data set were accurately found, should they be removed before finding the measures of the middle?

5 A basketball team scored 43, 55, 41, and 37 points in their first four matches.

    a Find the mean number of points scored for the first four matches.

    b What score will the team need to shoot in the next match so that they maintain the same mean score?

    c The team scores only 25 points in the fifth match.

        i Find the mean number of points scored for the five matches.

        ii The team then scores 41 points in their sixth and final match. Will this increase or decrease their previous mean score? What is the mean score for all six matches?

6 This year, the mean monthly sales for a clothing store have been $15 467. Calculate the total sales for the store for the year.

7 While on an outback safari, Bill drove an average of 262 km per day for a period of 12 days. How far did Bill drive in total while on safari?

8 Given $\bar{x} = 11.6$ and $n = 10$, calculate $\sum\limits_{i=1}^{10} x_i$.

9 Towards the end of season, a netballer had played 14 matches and had thrown an average of 16.5 goals per game. In the final two matches of the season she threw 21 goals and 24 goals. Find the netballer's average for the whole season.

10 The selling prices of the last 10 houses sold in a certain district were as follows:

    $146 400, $127 600, $211 000, $192 500,
    $256 400, $132 400, $148 000, $129 500,
    $131 400, $162 500

  a Calculate the mean and median selling prices and comment on the results.

  b Which measure would you use if you were:

    i a vendor wanting to sell your house

    ii looking to buy a house in the district?

11 Find x if   5, 9, 11, 12, 13, 14, 17, and x have a mean of 12.

12 Find a given that   3, 0, a, a, 4, a, 6, a, and 3   have a mean of 4.

13 Over the complete assessment period, Aruna averaged 35 out of a possible 40 marks for her maths tests. However, when checking her files, she could only find 7 of the 8 tests. For these she scored 29, 36, 32, 38, 35, 34, and 39. How many marks out of 40 did she score for the eighth test?

14 A sample of 10 measurements has a mean of 15.7 and a sample of 20 measurements has a mean of 14.3. Find the mean of all 30 measurements.

15 The mean and median of a set of 9 measurements are both 12. Seven of the measurements are 7, 9, 11, 13, 14, 17, and 19. Find the other two measurements.

16 Jana took seven spelling tests, each with ten words, but she could only find the results of five of them. These were 9, 5, 7, 9, and 10. She asked her teacher for the other two results and the teacher said that the mode of her scores was 9 and the mean was 8. Given that Jana remembers she only got one 10, find the two missing results.

MEASURES OF THE CENTRE FROM OTHER SOURCES

When the same data values appear several times we often summarise the data in a frequency table.

Consider the data in the given table:

We can find the measures of the centre directly from the table.

The mode

The data value 7 has the highest frequency.

The mode is therefore 7.

Data value (x)	Frequency (f)	Product (fx)
3	1	$1 \times 3 = 3$
4	1	$1 \times 4 = 4$
5	3	$3 \times 5 = 15$
6	7	$7 \times 6 = 42$
7	15	$15 \times 7 = 105$
8	8	$8 \times 8 = 64$
9	5	$5 \times 9 = 45$
Total	$\sum f = 40$	$\sum fx = 278$

The mean

Adding a 'Product' column to the table helps to add all scores.

For example, there are 15 data of value 7 and these add to $7 \times 15 = 105$.

Remembering that the mean $= \dfrac{\text{sum of all data values}}{\text{the number of data values}}$, we find

$$\overline{x} = \frac{f_1 x_1 + f_2 x_2 + f_3 x_3 + \ldots + f_k x_k}{f_1 + f_2 + f_3 + \ldots + f_k} \qquad \text{where } k \text{ is the number of } \textit{different} \text{ data values.}$$

$$= \frac{\sum\limits_{i=1}^{k} f_i x_i}{\sum\limits_{i=1}^{k} f_i}$$

This formula is often abbreviated as $\overline{x} = \dfrac{\sum f x}{\sum f}$.

In this case the mean $= \dfrac{278}{40} = 6.95$.

The median

Since $\dfrac{n+1}{2} = \dfrac{41}{2} = 20.5$, the median is the average of the 20th and 21st data values, when they are listed in order.

In the table, the blue numbers show us accumulated frequency values, or the **cumulative frequency**.

We can see that the 20th and 21st data values (in order) are both 7s.

$\therefore$ the median $= \dfrac{7+7}{2} = 7$

Data value	Frequency	Cumulative frequency
3	1	1 ⟵ one number is 3
4	1	2 ⟵ two numbers are 4 or less
5	3	5 ⟵ five numbers are 5 or less
6	7	12 ⟵ 12 numbers are 6 or less
7	15	27 ⟵ 27 numbers are 7 or less
8	8	35 ⟵ 35 numbers are 8 or less
9	5	40 ⟵ all numbers are 9 or less
Total	40	

Notice that we have a skewed distribution even though the mean, median and mode are nearly equal. So, we must be careful if we use measures of the middle to call a distribution symmetric.

The publishers acknowledge the late Mr Jim Russell, General Features for the reproduction of this cartoon.

Example 4   ◀) **Self Tutor**

The table below shows the number of aces served by tennis players in their first sets of a tournament.

Number of aces	1	2	3	4	5	6
Frequency	4	11	18	13	7	2

Determine the: **a** mean   **b** median   **c** mode   for this data.

Number of aces (x)	Frequency (f)	Product (fx)	Cumulative frequency
1	4	4	4
2	11	22	15
3	18	54	33
4	13	52	46
5	7	35	53
6	2	12	55
Total	$\sum f = 55$	$\sum fx = 179$	

a $\bar{x} = \dfrac{\sum fx}{\sum f}$

$= \dfrac{179}{55}$

≈ 3.25 aces

In this case $\dfrac{\sum fx}{\sum f}$ is short for $\dfrac{\displaystyle\sum_{i=1}^{6} f_i x_i}{\displaystyle\sum_{i=1}^{6} f_i}$.

b There are 55 data values, so $n = 55$. $\dfrac{n+1}{2} = 28$, so the median is the 28th data value.

From the cumulative frequency column, the data values 16 to 33 are 3 aces.

∴ the 28th data value is 3 aces.

∴ the median is 3 aces.

c Looking down the frequency column, the highest frequency is 18. This corresponds to 3 aces, so the mode is 3 aces.

EXERCISE 20B.2

1 The table alongside shows the results when 3 coins were tossed simultaneously 30 times.

Calculate the:

a mode   **b** median   **c** mean.

Number of heads	Frequency
0	4
1	12
2	11
3	3
Total	30

Check your answers using the statistics features of your graphics calculator.

GRAPHICS CALCULATOR INSTRUCTIONS

2 The following frequency table records the number of phone calls made in a day by 50 fifteen-year-olds.

Number of phone calls	Frequency
0	5
1	8
2	13
3	8
4	6
5	3
6	3
7	2
8	1
11	1

  a For this data, find the:
   i mean   **ii** median   **iii** mode.
  b Construct a column graph for the data and show the position of the mean, median, and mode on the horizontal axis.
  c Describe the distribution of the data.
  d Why is the mean larger than the median for this data?
  e Which measure of centre would be the most suitable for this data set?

3 A company claims that their match boxes contain, on average, 50 matches per box. On doing a survey, the Consumer Protection Society recorded the following results:

Number in a box	Frequency
47	5
48	4
49	11
50	6
51	3
52	1
Total	30

  a Calculate the:
   i mode   **ii** median   **iii** mean
  b Do the results of this survey support the company's claim?
  c In a court for 'false advertising', the company won their case against the Consumer Protection Society. Suggest how they did this.

4 Families at a school in Australia were surveyed, and the number of children in each family recorded. The results of the survey are shown alongside.

Number of children	Frequency
1	5
2	28
3	15
4	8
5	2
6	1
Total	59

  a Calculate the:
   i mean   **ii** mode   **iii** median.
  b The average Australian family has 2.2 children. How does this school compare to the national average?
  c The data set is skewed. Is the skewness positive or negative?
  d How has the skewness of the data affected the measures of the centre of the data set?

5 The frequency column graph gives the value of donations for the Heart Foundation collected in a particular street.

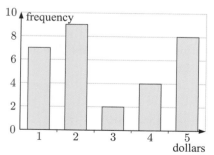

  a Construct a frequency table from the graph.
  b Determine the total number of donations.
  c Find the: **i** mean   **ii** median   **iii** mode of the donations.
  d Which of the measures of central tendency can be found easily using the graph only?

6 The table shows the IB mathematics scores for a class. A pass is considered to be a score of 4 or more.

Score	1	2	3	4	5	6	7
Number of students	0	2	3	5	x	4	1

  a Given the mean score was 4.45, find the value of x.
  b Find the percentage of students who passed.

7 Revisit the **Opening Problem** on page **500**.

    a Use a frequency table for the *Without fertiliser* data to find the:

        i mean   **ii** mode   **iii** median number of peas per pod.

    b Use a frequency table for the *With fertiliser* data to find the:

        i mean   **ii** mode   **iii** median number of peas per pod.

    c Which of the measures of the centre is appropriate to use in a report on this data?

    d Has the application of fertiliser significantly improved the number of peas per pod?

> You will need this data again, so if possible store it in your calculator.

8 The table alongside compares the mass at birth of some guinea pigs with their mass when they were two weeks old.

    a What was the mean birth mass?

    b What was the mean mass after two weeks?

    c What was the mean increase over the two weeks?

Guinea Pig	Mass (g) at birth	Mass (g) at 2 weeks
A	75	210
B	70	200
C	80	200
D	70	220
E	74	215
F	60	200
G	55	206
H	83	230

9 Out of 31 measurements, 15 are below 10 cm and 12 are above 11 cm. Find the median if the other 4 measurements are 10.1 cm, 10.4 cm, 10.7 cm, and 10.9 cm.

10 Two brands of toothpicks claim that their boxes contain an average of 50 toothpicks per box. In a survey the Consumer Protection Society (C.P.S.) recorded the following results:

Brand A

Number in a box	46	47	48	49	50	51	52	53	55
Frequency	1	2	3	7	10	20	15	3	1

Brand B

Number in a box	48	49	50	51	52	53	54
Frequency	3	17	30	7	2	1	1

    a Find the average contents of Brands A and B toothpick boxes.

    b Would it be fair for the C.P.S. to prosecute the manufacturers of either brand, based on these statistics?

11 In an office of 20 people there are only 4 salary levels paid:

      €50 000 (1 person), €42 000 (3 people), €35 000 (6 people), €28 000 (10 people).

    a Calculate: **i** the median salary   **ii** the modal salary   **iii** the mean salary.

    b Which measure of central tendency might be used by the boss who is against a pay rise for the other employees?

GROUPED DATA

When information has been gathered in groups or classes, we use the **midpoint** or **mid-interval value** to represent all scores within that interval.

We are assuming that the scores within each class are evenly distributed throughout that interval. The mean calculated is an **approximation** of the true value, and we cannot do better than this without knowing each individual data value.

INVESTIGATION 2   MID-INTERVAL VALUES

When mid-interval values are used to represent all scores within that interval, what effect will this have on estimating the mean of the grouped data?

Consider the following table which summarises the marks received by students for a physics examination out of 50. The exact results for each student have been lost.

Marks	Frequency
0 - 9	2
10 - 19	31
20 - 29	73
30 - 39	85
40 - 49	28

What to do:

1 Suppose that all of the students scored the lowest possible result in their class interval, so 2 students scored 0, 31 students scored 10, and so on.

Calculate the mean of these results, and hence complete:

"The mean score of students in the physics examination must be *at least* ...."

2 Now suppose that all of the students scored the highest possible result in their class interval. Calculate the mean of these results, and hence complete:

"The mean score of students in the physics examination must be *at most* ...."

3 We now have two extreme values between which the actual mean must lie.

Now suppose that all of the students scored the mid-interval value in their class interval. We assume that 2 students scored 4.5, 31 students scored 14.5, and so on.

a Calculate the mean of these results.

b How does this result compare with lower and upper limits found in 1 and 2?

c Copy and complete:

"The mean score of the students in the physics examination was approximately ...."

Example 5   ◄ Self Tutor

Estimate the mean of the following *ages of bus drivers* data, to the nearest year:

Age (yrs)	21 - 25	26 - 30	31 - 35	36 - 40	41 - 45	46 - 50	51 - 55
Frequency	11	14	32	27	29	17	7

Age (yrs)	Frequency (f)	Midpoint (x)	fx
21 - 25	11	23	253
26 - 30	14	28	392
31 - 35	32	33	1056
36 - 40	27	38	1026
41 - 45	29	43	1247
46 - 50	17	48	816
51 - 55	7	53	371
Total	$\sum f = 137$		$\sum fx = 5161$

$$\overline{x} = \frac{\sum fx}{\sum f}$$

$$= \frac{5161}{137}$$

$$\approx 37.7$$

∴ the mean age of the drivers is about 38 years.

EXERCISE 20B.3

1 50 students sit a mathematics test. Estimate the mean score given these results:

Score	0 - 9	10 - 19	20 - 29	30 - 39	40 - 49
Frequency	2	5	7	27	9

GRAPHICS CALCULATOR INSTRUCTIONS

Check your answers using your calculator.

2 The table shows the petrol sales in one day by a number of city service stations.

   a How many service stations were involved in the survey?
   b Estimate the total amount of petrol sold for the day by the service stations.
   c Find the approximate mean sales of petrol for the day.

Litres (L)	Frequency
$2000 < L \leqslant 3000$	4
$3000 < L \leqslant 4000$	4
$4000 < L \leqslant 5000$	9
$5000 < L \leqslant 6000$	14
$6000 < L \leqslant 7000$	23
$7000 < L \leqslant 8000$	16

3 This frequency histogram illustrates the results of an aptitude test given to a group of people seeking positions in a company.

   a How many people sat for the test?
   b Estimate the mean score for the test.
   c What fraction of the people scored less than 100 for the test?
   d What percentage of the people scored more than 130 for the test?

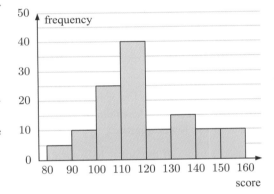

C   MEASURING THE SPREAD OF DATA

To accurately describe a distribution we need to measure both its **centre** and its **spread** or **dispersion**.

The distributions shown have the same mean, but clearly they have different spreads. The A distribution has most scores close to the mean whereas the C distribution has the greatest spread.

We will examine four different measures of spread: the **range**, the **interquartile range** (**IQR**), the **variance**, and the **standard deviation**.

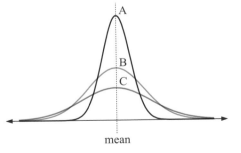

THE RANGE

The **range** is the difference between the maximum (largest) and the minimum (smallest) data value.

$$\textbf{range} = \textbf{maximum} - \textbf{minimum}$$

Example 6 ◀)) **Self Tutor**

A library surveys 20 borrowers each day from Monday to Friday, and records the number who are not satisfied with the range of reading material. The results are: 3 7 6 8 11.

The following year the library receives a grant that enables the purchase of a large number of books. The survey is then repeated and the results are: 2 3 5 4 6.

Find the range of data in each survey.

The range is the maximum minus the minimum data value.

For the first survey, the range is $11 - 3 = 8$.

For the second survey, the range is $6 - 2 = 4$.

The **range** is not considered to be a particularly reliable measure of spread as it uses only two data values. It may be influenced by data values which are extremely low or extremely high compared with the rest of the data.

THE QUARTILES AND THE INTERQUARTILE RANGE

The median divides the ordered data set into two halves and these halves are divided in half again by the **quartiles**.

The middle value of the lower half is called the **lower quartile** or **25th percentile**. One quarter or 25% of the data have values less than or equal to the lower quartile. 75% of the data have values greater than or equal to the lower quartile.

The middle value of the upper half is called the **upper quartile** or **75th percentile**. One quarter or 25% of the data have values greater than or equal to the upper quartile. 75% of the data have values less than or equal to the upper quartile.

The **interquartile range** is the range of the middle half or 50% of the data.

> **interquartile range = upper quartile − lower quartile**

The data set is thus divided into quarters by the lower quartile (Q_1), the median (Q_2), and the upper quartile (Q_3).

So, the interquartile range, $\mathbf{IQR = Q_3 - Q_1}$.

The interquartile range is not affected by extremely low or extremely high data values, as these lie outside the middle 50% of data values.

Example 7 ◀)) **Self Tutor**

For the data set: 7, 3, 1, 7, 6, 9, 3, 8, 5, 8, 6, 3, 7, 1, 9   find the:

  a median   **b** lower quartile   **c** upper quartile   **d** interquartile range

The ordered data set is: ~~1, 1,~~ 3, ~~3, 3,~~ 5, ~~6,~~ 6, ~~7, 7, 7, 8, 8, 9, 9~~ (15 of them)

  a As $n = 15$, $\dfrac{n+1}{2} = 8$ $\therefore$ the median = 8th data value = 6

b/c As the median is a data value we now ignore it and split the remaining data into two:

$$\underbrace{1\ 1\ 3\ 3\ 3\ 5\ 6}_{\text{lower}} \quad \underbrace{7\ 7\ 7\ 8\ 8\ 9\ 9}_{\text{upper}}$$

$Q_1 = $ median of lower half $= 3$

$Q_3 = $ median of upper half $= 8$

d IQR $= Q_3 - Q_1 = 8 - 3 = 5$

The data set in **Example 7** can thus be summarised:

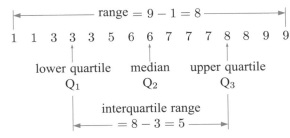

| Example 8 | ◀) **Self Tutor** |

For the data set: 6, 4, 9, 15, 5, 13, 7, 12, 8, 10, 4, 1, 13, 1, 6, 4, 5, 2, 8, 2   find:

a the median   **b** Q_1 **c** Q_3 **d** the interquartile range

The ordered data set is:

$$1\ 1\ 2\ 2\ 4\ 4\ 4\ 5\ 5\ 6\ 6\ 7\ 8\ 8\ 9\ 10\ 12\ 13\ 13\ 15 \qquad \text{(20 of them)}$$

a As $n = 20$, $\dfrac{n+1}{2} = 10.5$

$\therefore$ the median $= \dfrac{\text{10th value } + \text{ 11th value}}{2} = \dfrac{6+6}{2} = 6$

b/c As we have an even number of data values, we split the data into two:

$$\underbrace{1\ 1\ 2\ 2\ 4\ 4\ 4\ 5\ 5\ 6}_{\text{lower}} \quad \underbrace{6\ 7\ 8\ 8\ 9\ 10\ 12\ 13\ 13\ 15}_{\text{upper}}$$

$\therefore$ $Q_1 = \dfrac{4+4}{2} = 4$, $Q_3 = \dfrac{9+10}{2} = 9.5$

Some computer packages calculate quartiles differently.

d IQR $= Q_3 - Q_1$
$= 9.5 - 4$
$= 5.5$

EXERCISE 20C

1 For each of the following data sets, make sure the data is ordered and then find:

    i the median   **ii** the upper and lower quartiles

    iii the range   **iv** the interquartile range.

  a 2, 3, 3, 3, 4, 4, 4, 5, 5, 5, 5, 6, 6, 6, 6, 6, 7, 7, 8, 8, 8, 9, 9

  b 10, 12, 15, 12, 24, 18, 19, 18, 18, 15, 16, 20, 21, 17, 18, 16, 22, 14

  c 21.8, 22.4, 23.5, 23.5, 24.6, 24.9, 25, 25.3, 26.1, 26.4, 29.5

Check your answers using your graphics calculator.

GRAPHICS
CALCULATOR
INSTRUCTIONS

2 The times spent (in minutes) by 20 people waiting
in a queue at a bank for a teller were:

3.4 2.1 3.8 2.2 4.5 1.4 0   0   1.6 4.8
1.5 1.9 0   3.6 5.2 2.7 3.0 0.8 3.8 5.2

   a Find the median waiting time and the upper
and lower quartiles.

   b Find the range and interquartile range of the
waiting times.

   c Copy and complete the following statements:

      i "50% of the waiting times were greater than ...... minutes."

      ii "75% of the waiting times were less than or equal to ...... minutes."

      iii "The minimum waiting time was ...... minutes and the maximum waiting time was ......
minutes. The waiting times were spread over ...... minutes."

3 The heights of 20 ten year olds were recorded (in cm) as follows:

109 111 113 114 114 118 119 122 122 124
124 126 128 129 129 131 132 135 138 138

   a Find the:

      i median height   **ii** upper and lower quartiles of the data.

   b Copy and complete the following statements:

      i "Half of the children are no more than ...... cm tall."

      ii "75% of the children are no more than ...... cm tall."

   c Find the: **i** range   **ii** interquartile range for the height of the ten year olds.

   d Copy and complete: "The middle 50% of the children have heights spread over ...... cm."

4 A data set has the following known measures of centre and spread:

Measure	median	mode	range	interquartile range
Value	9	7	13	6

Determine the new value of each of these measures if every member of the data set is:

   a increased by 2   **b** doubled.

5 Revisit the **Opening Problem** on page **500**.

   a For the *Without fertiliser* data, find:

      i the range   **ii** the median   **iii** the lower quartile

      iv the upper quartile   **v** the interquartile range.

   b Repeat **a** for the *With fertiliser* data.

   c Consider again the questions posed in the **Opening Problem**. Amend your solutions where
appropriate.

BOXPLOTS

A **boxplot** or **box and whisker plot** is a visual display of some of the descriptive statistics of a data set. It shows:

- the minimum value
- the lower quartile (Q_1)
- the median (Q_2)
- the upper quartile (Q_3)
- the maximum value

These five numbers form the **five-number summary** of the data set.

For the data set in **Example 8** on page **519**, the five-number summary and boxplot are:

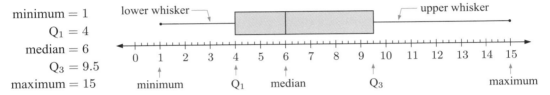

minimum $= 1$
$Q_1 = 4$
median $= 6$
$Q_3 = 9.5$
maximum $= 15$

The rectangular box represents the 'middle' half of the data set.

The lower whisker represents the 25% of the data with smallest values.

The upper whisker represents the 25% of the data with greatest values.

INTERPRETING A BOXPLOT

A set of data with a **symmetric distribution** will have a symmetric boxplot.

The whiskers of the boxplot are the same length and the median line is in the centre of the box.

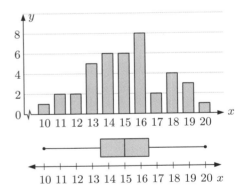

A set of data which is **positively skewed** will have a positively skewed boxplot.

The right whisker is longer than the left whisker and the median line is to the left of the box.

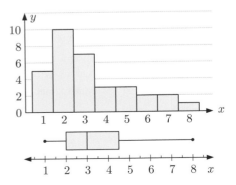

A set of data which is **negatively skewed** will have a negatively skewed boxplot.

The left whisker is longer than the right whisker and the median line is to the right of the box.

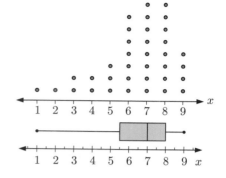

Click on the icon to explore boxplots further.

GAME

Example 9   🔊 **Self Tutor**

Consider the data set: 8 2 3 9 6 5 3 2 2 6 2 5 4 5 5 6

a Construct the five-number summary for this data.

b Draw a boxplot.

c Find the: i range   ii interquartile range of the data.

d Find the percentage of data values less than 3.

a The ordered data set is:

2 2 2 2 3 3 4 5 ⋮ 5 5 5 6 6 6 8 9   (16 of them)

$$Q_1 = 2.5 \qquad \text{median} = 5 \qquad Q_3 = 6$$

So the 5-number summary is: $\begin{cases} \text{minimum} = 2 & Q_1 = 2.5 \\ \text{median} = 5 & Q_3 = 6 \\ \text{maximum} = 9 \end{cases}$

b
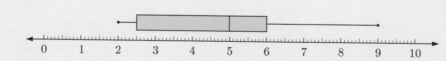

c i range = maximum − minimum

$$= 9 - 2$$
$$= 7$$

ii IQR = $Q_3 - Q_1$

$$= 6 - 2.5$$
$$= 3.5$$

d Using the ordered data set in a,
4 out of 16 data values are less than 3.
∴ 25% of the data values are less than 3.

We cannot use the boxplot to answer d because the boxplot does not tell us that all of the data values are integers.

OUTLIERS

Outliers are extraordinary data that are separated from the main body of the data.
Outliers are either much larger or much smaller than most of the data.

A commonly used test to identify outliers involves the calculation of upper and lower boundaries:

- **The upper boundary = upper quartile + 1.5 × IQR.**
  Any data larger than the upper boundary is an outlier.
- **The lower boundary = lower quartile − 1.5 × IQR.**
  Any data smaller than the lower boundary is an outlier.

Outliers are marked with an asterisk on a boxplot. There may be more than one outlier at either end.

Each whisker extends to the last value that is not an outlier.

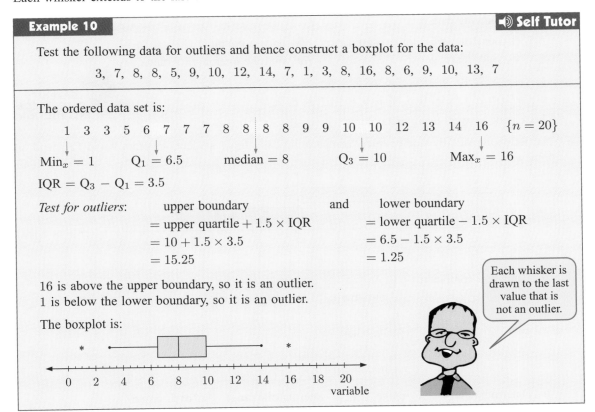

Example 10	◀)) **Self Tutor**

Test the following data for outliers and hence construct a boxplot for the data:

$$3, \ 7, \ 8, \ 8, \ 5, \ 9, \ 10, \ 12, \ 14, \ 7, \ 1, \ 3, \ 8, \ 16, \ 8, \ 6, \ 9, \ 10, \ 13, \ 7$$

The ordered data set is:

$$1 \quad 3 \quad 3 \quad 5 \quad 6 \quad 7 \quad 7 \quad 7 \quad 8 \quad 8 \mid 8 \quad 8 \quad 9 \quad 9 \quad 10 \quad 10 \quad 12 \quad 13 \quad 14 \quad 16 \quad \{n = 20\}$$

$\text{Min}_x = 1 \qquad Q_1 = 6.5 \qquad \text{median} = 8 \qquad Q_3 = 10 \qquad \text{Max}_x = 16$

$\text{IQR} = Q_3 - Q_1 = 3.5$

Test for outliers:

upper boundary	and	lower boundary
$= \text{upper quartile} + 1.5 \times \text{IQR}$		$= \text{lower quartile} - 1.5 \times \text{IQR}$
$= 10 + 1.5 \times 3.5$		$= 6.5 - 1.5 \times 3.5$
$= 15.25$		$= 1.25$

16 is above the upper boundary, so it is an outlier.
1 is below the lower boundary, so it is an outlier.

The boxplot is:

> Each whisker is drawn to the last value that is not an outlier.

EXERCISE 20D

1

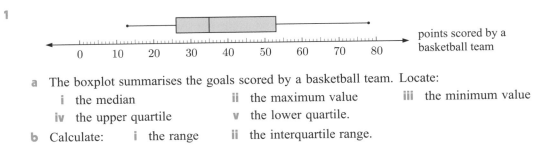

points scored by a basketball team

a The boxplot summarises the goals scored by a basketball team. Locate:
  i the median   ii the maximum value   iii the minimum value
  iv the upper quartile   v the lower quartile.

b Calculate: i the range   ii the interquartile range.

2

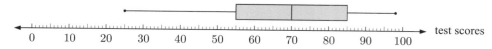

The boxplot summarises the class results for a test out of 100 marks.

a Copy and complete the following statements about the test results:

   i The highest mark scored for the test was ...., and the lowest mark was ....

   ii Half of the class scored a mark greater than or equal to ....

   iii The top 25% of the class scored at least .... marks for the test.

   iv The middle half of the class had scores between .... and .... for this test.

b Find the range of the data set.

c Find the interquartile range of the data set.

3 For the following data sets:

   i construct a 5-number summary   ii draw a boxplot

   iii find the range   iv find the interquartile range.

a 3, 5, 5, 7, 10, 9, 4, 7, 8, 6, 6, 5, 8, 6

b 3, 7, 0, 1, 4, 6, 8, 8, 8, 9, 7, 5, 6, 8, 7, 8, 8, 2, 9

GRAPHICS
CALCULATOR
INSTRUCTIONS

Check your answers using technology.

4 The following side-by-side boxplots compare the daily times students in years 9 and 12 spend on homework.

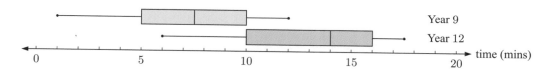

a Copy and complete:

Statistic	Year 9	Year 12
minimum		
Q_1		
median		
Q_3		
maximum		

b Determine the: i range   ii interquartile range   for each group.

c Are the following true or false, or is there not enough information to tell?

   i On average, Year 12 students spend about twice as much time on homework than Year 9 students.

   ii Over 25% of Year 9 students spend less time on homework than all Year 12 students.

5 Enid examines a new variety of bean and counts the number of beans in 33 pods. Her results were:

   5, 8, 10, 4, 2, 12, 6, 5, 7, 7, 5, 5, 5, 13, 9, 3, 4, 4, 7, 8, 9, 5, 5, 4, 3, 6, 6, 6, 6, 9, 8, 7, 6

a Find the median, lower quartile, and upper quartile of the data set.

b Find the interquartile range of the data set.

c Draw a boxplot of the data set.

6 A set of data has a lower quartile of 31.5, a median of 37, and an upper quartile of 43.5.

    a Calculate the interquartile range for this data set.

    b Calculate the boundaries that identify outliers.

    c Which of the data 22, 13.2, 60, 65 would be outliers?

7 Ranji counts the number of bolts in several boxes and tabulates the data as follows:

Number of bolts	33	34	35	36	37	38	39	40
Frequency	1	5	7	13	12	8	0	1

    a Find the five-number summary for this data set.

    b Find the **i** range **ii** IQR for this data set.

    c Draw a boxplot of the data set.

    d Are there any outliers in this data?

> An outlier is more than
> $1.5 \times$ IQR from the
> nearest quartile.

8 James goes bird watching for 25 days. The number of birds he sees each day are:

        12, 5, 13, 16, 8, 10, 12, 18, 9, 11, 14, 14, 22, 9, 10, 7, 9, 11, 13, 7, 10, 6, 13, 3, 8.

    a Find the median, lower quartile, and upper quartile of the data set.

    b Find the interquartile range of the data set.

    c Find the lower and upper boundaries for outliers.

    d Are there any outliers?

    e Draw a boxplot of the data set.

9 Match the graphs **A, B, C,** and **D** to the boxplots **I, II, III,** and **IV**.

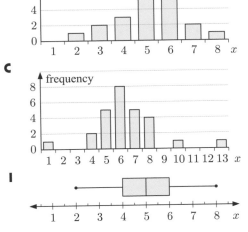

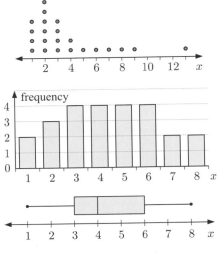

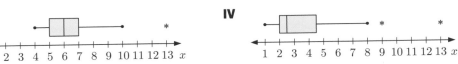

10 Shane and Brett play in the same cricket team and are fierce but friendly rivals when it comes to bowling. During a season the number of wickets taken in each innings by the bowlers were:

Shane: 1 6 2 0 3 4 1 4 2 3 0 3 2 4 3 4 3 3
         3 4 2 4 3 2 3 3 0 5 3 5 3 2 4 3 4 3

Brett: 7 2 4 8 1 3 4 2 3 0 5 3 5 2 3 1 2 0
         4 3 4 0 3 3 0 2 5 1 1 2 2 5 1 4 0 1

a Is the variable discrete or continuous?

b Enter the data into a graphics calculator or statistics package.

c Produce a vertical column graph for each data set.

d Are there any outliers?

e Describe the shape of each distribution.

f Compare the measures of the centre of each distribution.

g Compare the spreads of each distribution.

h Obtain a side-by-side boxplot.

i What conclusions can be drawn from the data?

11 A manufacturer of light globes claims that their new design has a 20% longer life than those they are presently selling. Forty of each globe are randomly selected and tested. Here are the results to the nearest hour:

Old type: 103 96 113 111 126 100 122 110   84 117 103 113 104 104
            111 87   90 121   99 114 105 121   93 109   87 118   75 111
             87 127 117 131 115 116   82 130 113   95 108 112

New type: 146 131 132 160 128 119 133 117 139 123 109 129 109 131
            191 117 132 107 141 136 146 142 123 144 145 125 164 125
            133 124 153 129 118 130 134 151 145 131 133 135

a Is the variable discrete or continuous?

b Enter the data into a graphics calculator or statistics package.

c Are there any outliers? Should they be deleted before we start to analyse the data?

d Compare the measures of centre and spread.

e Obtain a side-by-side boxplot.

f Describe the shape of each distribution.

g What conclusions, if any, can be drawn from the data?

E   CUMULATIVE FREQUENCY GRAPHS

Sometimes, in addition to finding the median, it is useful to know the number or proportion of scores that lie above or below a particular value. In such situations we can construct a **cumulative frequency distribution table** and use a graph called a **cumulative frequency graph** to represent the data.

The cumulative frequencies are plotted and the points joined by a smooth curve. This compares with an ogive or cumulative frequency polygon where two points are joined by straight lines.

PERCENTILES

A **percentile** is the score which a certain percentage of the data lies at or below.

For example:
- the 85th percentile is the score which 85% of the data lies at or below.
- If your score in a test is the 95th percentile, then 95% of the class have scored the same or less than you.

Notice that:
- the **lower quartile** (Q_1) is the 25th percentile
- the **median** (Q_2) is the 50th percentile
- the **upper quartile** (Q_3) is the 75th percentile.

A cumulative frequency graph provides a convenient way to find percentiles.

Example 11   ◀) **Self Tutor**

The data shows the results of the women's marathon at the 2008 Olympics, for all competitors who finished the race.

a Construct a cumulative frequency distribution table.

b Represent the data on a cumulative frequency graph.

c Use your graph to estimate the:

   i median finishing time

   ii number of competitors who finished in less than 2 hours 35 minutes

   iii percentage of competitors who took more than 2 hours 39 minutes to finish

   iv time taken by a competitor who finished in the top 20% of runners completing the marathon.

Finishing time t	Frequency
2 h 26 $\leqslant t <$ 2 h 28	8
2 h 28 $\leqslant t <$ 2 h 30	3
2 h 30 $\leqslant t <$ 2 h 32	9
2 h 32 $\leqslant t <$ 2 h 34	11
2 h 34 $\leqslant t <$ 2 h 36	12
2 h 36 $\leqslant t <$ 2 h 38	7
2 h 38 $\leqslant t <$ 2 h 40	5
2 h 40 $\leqslant t <$ 2 h 48	8
2 h 48 $\leqslant t <$ 2 h 56	6

a

Finishing time t	Frequency	Cumulative frequency
2 h 26 $\leqslant t <$ 2 h 28	8	8
2 h 28 $\leqslant t <$ 2 h 30	3	11
2 h 30 $\leqslant t <$ 2 h 32	9	20
2 h 32 $\leqslant t <$ 2 h 34	11	31
2 h 34 $\leqslant t <$ 2 h 36	12	43
2 h 36 $\leqslant t <$ 2 h 38	7	50
2 h 38 $\leqslant t <$ 2 h 40	5	55
2 h 40 $\leqslant t <$ 2 h 48	8	63
2 h 48 $\leqslant t <$ 2 h 56	6	69

$8 + 3 = 11$ competitors completed the marathon in less than 2 hours 30 minutes.

50 competitors completed the marathon in less than 2 hours 38 minutes.

b

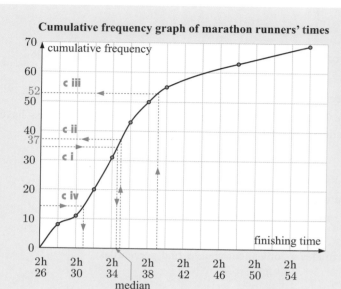

Cumulative frequency graph of marathon runners' times

The cumulative frequency gives a *progressive total* of the number of runners finishing by a given time. It is plotted at the right end boundary of the interval.

c
i The median is estimated using the 50th percentile. As 50% of 69 is 34.5, we start with the cumulative frequency of 34.5 and find the corresponding time.
The median is approximately 2 hours 34.5 min.

ii There are approximately 37 competitors who took less than 2 h 35 min to complete the race.

iii There are $69 - 52 = 17$ competitors who took more than 2 hours 39 min.
So $\frac{17}{69} \approx 26.4\%$ took more than 2 hours 39 min.

iv The time taken is estimated using the 20th percentile. As 20% of 69 is 13.8, we find the time corresponding to a cumulative frequency of approximately 14.
The top 20% of competitors took less than 2 hours 31 minutes.

Another way to calculate percentiles is to add a separate scale to a cumulative frequency graph. On the graph alongside, the cumulative frequency is read from the axis on the left side, and each value corresponds to a percentile on the right side.

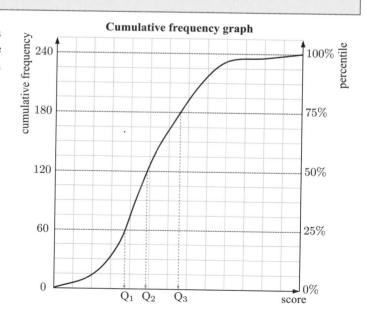

EXERCISE 20E

1 The examination scores of a group of students are shown in the table.

Draw a cumulative frequency graph for the data and use it to answer the following:

  a Find the median examination mark.

  b How many students scored 65 marks or less?

  c How many students scored at least 50 but less than 70 marks?

  d If the pass mark was 45, how many students failed?

  e If the top 16% of students were awarded credits, what was the credit mark?

Score	Frequency
$10 \leqslant x < 20$	2
$20 \leqslant x < 30$	5
$30 \leqslant x < 40$	7
$40 \leqslant x < 50$	21
$50 \leqslant x < 60$	36
$60 \leqslant x < 70$	40
$70 \leqslant x < 80$	27
$80 \leqslant x < 90$	9
$90 \leqslant x < 100$	3

2 The following data shows the lengths of 30 trout caught in a lake during a fishing competition. The measurements were *rounded down* to the next centimetre.

31	38	34	40	24	33	30	36	38	32	35	32	36	27	35
40	34	37	44	38	36	34	33	31	38	35	36	33	33	28

  a Construct a cumulative frequency table for trout lengths, x cm, using the intervals $24 \leqslant x < 27$, $27 \leqslant x < 30$, and so on.

  b Draw a cumulative frequency graph for the data.

  c Hence estimate the median length.

  d Use the original data to find its median and compare your answer with **c**. Comment on your results.

3 A botanist has measured the heights of 60 seedlings and has presented her findings on the cumulative frequency graph below.

Heights of seedlings

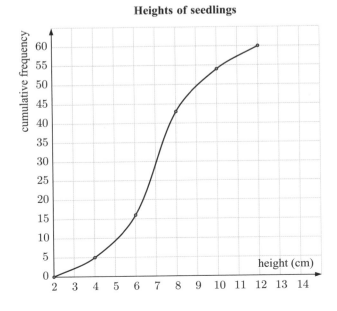

  a How many seedlings have heights of 5 cm or less?

  b What percentage of seedlings are taller than 8 cm?

  c Find the median height.

  d Find the interquartile range for the heights.

  e Find the 90th percentile for the data and explain what your answer means.

4 The following table summarises the age groups of car drivers involved in accidents in a city for a given year.

Draw a cumulative frequency graph for the data and use it to:

a find the median age of the drivers involved in accidents

b find the percentage of drivers involved in accidents who had an age of 23 or less

c estimate the probability that a driver involved in an accident is:

  i aged 27 years or less   ii aged 27 years.

Age (in years)	No. of accidents
$16 \leqslant x < 20$	59
$20 \leqslant x < 25$	82
$25 \leqslant x < 30$	43
$30 \leqslant x < 35$	21
$35 \leqslant x < 40$	19
$40 \leqslant x < 50$	11
$50 \leqslant x < 60$	24
$60 \leqslant x < 80$	41

5 The following cumulative frequency graph displays the performance of 80 competitors in a cross-country race.

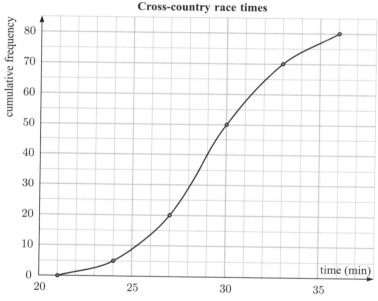

Cross-country race times

a Find the lower quartile time.

b Find the median.

c Find the upper quartile.

d Find the interquartile range.

e Estimate the 40th percentile.

f Use the cumulative frequency curve to complete the following table:

Time t (mins)	$21 \leqslant t < 24$	$24 \leqslant t < 27$	$27 \leqslant t < 30$	$30 \leqslant t < 33$	$33 \leqslant t < 36$
Number of competitors					

6 The table shows the lifetimes of a sample of electric light globes.

Draw a cumulative frequency graph for the data and use it to estimate:

a the median life of a globe

b the percentage of globes which had a life of 2700 hours or less

c the number of globes which had a life between 1500 and 2500 hours.

Life (hours)	Number of globes
$0 \leqslant l < 500$	5
$500 \leqslant l < 1000$	17
$1000 \leqslant l < 2000$	46
$2000 \leqslant l < 3000$	79
$3000 \leqslant l < 4000$	27
$4000 \leqslant l < 5000$	4

F   VARIANCE AND STANDARD DEVIATION

The problem with using the range and the IQR as measures of spread or dispersion of scores is that both of them only use two values in their calculation. Some data sets can therefore have their spread characteristics hidden when the range or IQR are quoted, and so we need a better way of describing spread.

Consider a data set of n values: $x_1, x_2, x_3, x_4, ..., x_n,$ with mean $\overline{x}$.

$x_i - \overline{x}$ measures how far x_i deviates from the mean, so one might suspect that the mean of the deviations $\frac{1}{n}\sum_{i=1}^{n}(x_i - \overline{x})$ would give a good measure of spread. However, this value turns out to always be zero.

Instead, we define:

> The **variance** of a sample of n data values is $s_n^2 = \dfrac{\sum\limits_{i=1}^{n}(x_i - \overline{x})^2}{n}.$

Notice in this formula that:

- $(x_i - \overline{x})^2$ is also a measure of how far x_i deviates from $\overline{x}$. However, the square ensures that each term in the sum is positive, which is why the sum turns out not to be zero.

- If $\sum\limits_{i=1}^{n}(x_i - \overline{x})^2$ is small, it will indicate that most of the data values are close to $\overline{x}$.

- Dividing by n gives an indication of how far, on average, the data is from the mean.

> For a data set of n values, $s_n = \sqrt{\dfrac{\sum\limits_{i=1}^{n}(x_i - \overline{x})^2}{n}}$ is called the **standard deviation**.

The square root in the standard deviation is used to correct the units.

For example, if x_i is the weight of a student in kg, s_n^2 would be in kg^2.

For this reason the standard deviation is more frequently quoted than the variance.

The standard deviation is a **non-resistant** measure of spread. This is due to its dependence on the mean of the sample and because extreme data values will give large values for $(x_i - \overline{x})^2$. It is only a useful measure if the distribution is approximately symmetrical. However, the standard deviation is particularly useful when the data from which it came is **normally distributed**. This will be discussed in detail in **Chapter 24**.

The IQR and percentiles are more appropriate tools for measuring spread if the distribution is considerably skewed.

INVESTIGATION 3   STANDARD DEVIATION

A group of 5 students is chosen from each of three schools, to test their ability to solve puzzles.

The 15 students are each given a series of puzzles and two hours to solve as many as they can individually.

The results were: School A: 7, 7, 7, 7, 7

                          School B: 5, 6, 7, 8, 9

                          School C: 3, 5, 7, 9, 11

What to do:

1. Show that the mean and median for each school is 7.

2. Given the mean $\overline{x} = 7$ for each group, complete a table like the one following, for each school:

School ....

Score (x_i)	Deviation ($x_i - \overline{x}$)	Square of deviation ($x_i - \overline{x})^2$
Sum		

3. Calculate the variance $\dfrac{\sum (x_i - \overline{x})^2}{n}$ and standard deviation $\sqrt{\dfrac{\sum (x_i - \overline{x})^2}{n}}$ for each group.

Check your results match the following table:

School	Mean	Variance	Standard deviation
A	7	0	0
B	7	2	$\sqrt{2}$
C	7	8	$\sqrt{8}$

4. Use the table above to compare the performances of the different schools.

5. A group of 5 students from a higher year level at school C are given the same test. They each score 2 more than the students in the lower year group, so their scores are: 5, 7, 9, 11, 13.

   a Find the mean, variance, and standard deviation for this set.

   b Comment on the effect of adding 2 to each member of a data set.

6. A group of 5 teachers from B decide to show their students how clever they are. They complete twice as many puzzles as each of their students, so their scores are: 10, 12, 14, 16, 18.

   a Find the mean, variance, and standard deviation for this set.

   b Comment on the effect of doubling each member of a data set.

In this course you are only expected to use technology to calculate variance and standard deviation. However, we present both methods in the following example to help you understand standard deviations better.

GRAPHICS CALCULATOR INSTRUCTIONS

Example 12 ◀) **Self Tutor**

Consider again the library surveys data from **Example 6**.

a Find the mean and standard deviation for each survey using:
  i the formula **ii** technology.

b What do these statistics tell us?

a **i** *Survey 1*

x	$x - \overline{x}$	$(x - \overline{x})^2$
3	-4	16
7	0	0
6	-1	1
8	1	1
11	4	16
35	*Total*	34

Survey 2

x	$x - \overline{x}$	$(x - \overline{x})^2$
2	-2	4
3	-1	1
5	1	1
4	0	0
6	2	4
20	*Total*	10

$$\therefore \quad \overline{x} = \frac{35}{5} \qquad s_n = \sqrt{\frac{\sum(x - \overline{x})^2}{n}}$$

$$= 7$$

$$= \sqrt{\frac{34}{5}}$$

$$\approx 2.61$$

$$\therefore \quad \overline{x} = \frac{20}{5} \qquad s_n = \sqrt{\frac{\sum(x - \overline{x})^2}{n}}$$

$$= 4$$

$$= \sqrt{\frac{10}{5}}$$

$$\approx 1.41$$

ii

Casio fx-CG20   **TI-84 Plus**   **TI-*n*spire**

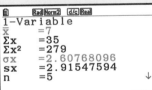

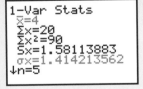

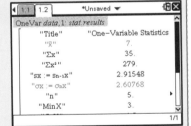

b The second survey shows that the number of dissatisfied borrowers has almost halved and there is less variability in the number of dissatisfied borrowers.

EXERCISE 20F.1

1 The column graphs show two distributions:

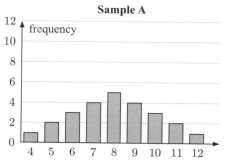

Sample A

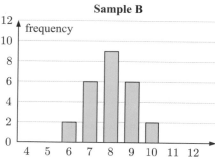

Sample B

a By looking at the graphs, which distribution appears to have wider spread?

b Find the mean of each sample.

c Find the standard deviation for each sample. Comment on your answers.

d The other measures of spread for the two samples are given alongside:

In what way does the standard deviation give a better description of how the data is distributed?

Sample	Range	IQR
A	8	3
B	4	2

2 The number of points scored by Andrew and Brad in the last 8 basketball matches are tabulated below.

Points by Andrew	23	17	31	25	25	19	28	32
Points by Brad	9	29	41	26	14	44	38	43

a Find the mean and standard deviation of the number of points scored by each player.

b Which of the two players is more consistent?

3 Two baseball coaches compare the number of runs scored by their teams in their last ten matches:

Rockets	0	10	1	9	11	0	8	5	6	7
Bullets	4	3	4	1	4	11	7	6	12	5

a Show that each team has the same mean and range of runs scored.

b Which team's performance do you suspect is more variable over the period?

c Check your answer to **b** by finding the standard deviation for each distribution.

d Does the range or the standard deviation give a better indication of variability?

4 A manufacturer of soft drinks employs a statistician for quality control. He needs to check that 375 mL of drink goes into each can, but realises the machine which fills the cans will slightly vary each delivery.

a Would you expect the standard deviation for the whole production run to be the same for one day as it is for one week? Explain your answer.

   b If samples of 125 cans are taken each day, what measure would be used to:
      i check that an average of 375 mL of drink goes into each can
      ii check the variability of the volume of drink going into each can?
   c What is the significance of a low standard deviation in this case?

5 The weights in kg of seven footballers are: 79, 64, 59, 71, 68, 68, 74.
   a Find the mean and standard deviation for this group.
   b When measured five years later, each footballer's weight had increased by exactly 10 kg. Find the new mean and standard deviation.
   c Comment on your results in general terms.

6 The weights of ten young turkeys to the nearest 0.1 kg are:
0.8, 1.1, 1.2, 0.9, 1.2, 1.2, 0.9, 0.7, 1.0, 1.1

   a Find the mean and standard deviation for the weights of the turkeys.
   b After being fed a special diet for one month, the weights of the turkeys doubled. Find the new mean and standard deviation.
   c Comment on your results.

7 The following table shows the decrease in cholesterol levels in 6 volunteers after a two week trial of special diet and exercise.

Volunteer	A	B	C	D	E	F
Decrease in cholesterol	0.8	0.6	0.7	0.8	0.4	2.8

   a Find the standard deviation of the data.
   b Recalculate the standard deviation with the outlier removed.
   c Discuss the effect of an extreme value on the standard deviation.

SAMPLING FROM A POPULATION

Populations are often huge, and gathering data from every individual is often impossible due to time constraints and cost.

Consequently, a **random sample** is taken from the population with the hope that it will truly reflect the characteristics of the population. To ensure this, the sample must be sufficiently large, and be taken in such a way that the results are unbiased.

To help distinguish between a sample and the whole population, we use different notation for the mean, variance, and standard deviation. This is shown in the table opposite.

	sample	population
mean	$\overline{x}$	μ
variance	s_n^2	σ^2
standard deviation	s_n	σ

In general, the population mean μ and standard deviation σ will be unknown.

However, given statistics from a sample, we can make **inferences** about the population using the following results which are assumed without proof:

> When a sample of size n is used to draw inference about a population:
>
> - the mean $\overline{x}$ of the sample is an unbiased estimate of μ
> - s_n is an estimate of the standard deviation σ.

Example 13

◆ **Self Tutor**

A random sample of 48 sheep was taken from a flock of over 2000 sheep. The sample mean of their weights was 48.6 kg with variance 17.5 kg².

a Find the standard deviation of the sample. Hence estimate the standard deviation of the population from which the sample was taken.

b Find an unbiased estimate of the mean weight of sheep in the flock.

a $s_n = \sqrt{\text{variance}} = \sqrt{17.5} \approx 4.18$ kg

σ is estimated by s_n, so we estimate the standard deviation to be 4.18 kg.

b μ is estimated by $\overline{x} = 48.6$ kg.

EXERCISE 20F.2

1 A random sample of 87 deer from a huge herd had a mean weight of 93.8 kg with a variance of 45.9 kg².

a Find the standard deviation of the sample. Hence estimate the standard deviation of the whole herd.

b Find an unbiased estimate of the mean of the whole herd.

2 The weights (in grams) of a random sample of sparrows are as follows:

87   75   68   69   81   89   73   66   91   77   84   83   77   74   80   76   67

a Find the mean and standard deviation of the sample.

b Estimate the mean and standard deviation of the population from which the sample was taken.

STANDARD DEVIATION FOR GROUPED DATA

Suppose there are n scores in a set of grouped data with mean $\overline{x}$.

If the different data values are x_1, x_2, ..., x_k, with corresponding frequencies f_1, f_2, ..., f_k, then the standard deviation is given by

$$s_n = \sqrt{\frac{\sum f_i(x_i - \overline{x})^2}{n}}.$$

Once again, you are expected to use technology to calculate standard deviation in this course. We use the formula in the following example to assist understanding only.

GRAPHICS CALCULATOR INSTRUCTIONS

For continuous data, or data that has been grouped in classes, we use the midpoint of the interval to represent all data in that interval.

Example 14

Find the standard deviation of the distribution using:

a the standard deviation formula

b technology.

Score	1	2	3	4	5
Frequency	1	2	4	2	1

a

x	f	fx	$x - \overline{x}$	$(x - \overline{x})^2$	$f(x - \overline{x})^2$
1	1	1	-2	4	4
2	2	4	-1	1	2
3	4	12	0	0	0
4	2	8	1	1	2
5	1	5	2	4	4
Total	10	30			12

$$\overline{x} = \frac{\sum fx}{n} = \frac{30}{10} = 3$$

$$s_n = \sqrt{\frac{\sum f(x - \overline{x})^2}{n}}$$

$$= \sqrt{\frac{12}{10}} \approx 1.10$$

b

Casio fx-CG20

```
      Rad Norm2 d/c Real
1-Variable
x̄    =3
Σx   =30
Σx²  =102
σx   =1.09544511
sx   =1.15470053
n    =10          ↓
```

TI-84 Plus

```
1-Var Stats
x̄=3
Σx=30
Σx²=102
Sx=1.154700538
σx=1.095445115
↓n=10
```

TI-nspire

```
◀ 1.1  1.2      *Unsaved ▼        ▣▣⊠
OneVar one,two: stat.results
    "Title"      "One-Variable Statistics
     "x̄"                    3.
     "Σx"                  30.
     "Σx²"                102.
  "SX := Sn-1X"          1.1547
  "σX := σnX"            1.09545
     "n"                  10.        ▶
    "MinX"                 1.
                                    1/1
```

EXERCISE 20F.3

1 Below is a sample of family sizes taken at random from people in a city.

Number of children, x	0	1	2	3	4	5	6	7
Frequency, f	14	18	13	5	3	2	2	1

a Find the sample mean and standard deviation.

b Estimate the mean and standard deviation of the population from which the sample was taken.

2 Below is a random sample of the ages of squash players at the Junior National Squash Championship.

Age	11	12	13	14	15	16	17	18
Frequency	2	1	4	5	6	4	2	1

a Find the mean and standard deviation of the ages.

b Estimate the mean and standard deviation of the population from which the sample was taken.

3 The number of toothpicks in a random sample of 48 boxes was counted and the results tabulated.

Number of toothpicks	33	35	36	37	38	39	40
Frequency	1	5	7	13	12	8	2

a Find the mean and standard deviation of the number of toothpicks in the boxes.

b Estimate the mean and standard deviation of the population from which the sample was taken.

4 The lengths of 30 randomly selected 12-day old babies were measured and the following data obtained:

  a Estimate the mean length and the standard deviation of the lengths.

  b Estimate the mean and standard deviation of the population from which the sample was taken.

Length (cm)	Frequency
$40 \leqslant L < 42$	1
$42 \leqslant L < 44$	1
$44 \leqslant L < 46$	3
$46 \leqslant L < 48$	7
$48 \leqslant L < 50$	11
$50 \leqslant L < 52$	5
$52 \leqslant L < 54$	2

5 The weekly wages (in dollars) of 200 randomly selected steel workers are given alongside:

  a Estimate the mean and the standard deviation of the wages.

  b Estimate the mean and standard deviation of the population from which the sample was taken.

Wage ($)	Number of workers
360 - 369.99	17
370 - 379.99	38
380 - 389.99	47
390 - 399.99	57
400 - 409.99	18
410 - 419.99	10
420 - 429.99	10
430 - 439.99	3

THEORY OF KNOWLEDGE

Statistics are often used to give the reader a misleading impression of what the data actually means. In some cases this happens by accident through mistakes in the statistical process. Often, however, it is done deliberately in an attempt to persuade the reader to believe something.

Even simple things like the display of data can be done so as to create a false impression. For example, the two graphs below show the profits of a company for the first four months of the year.

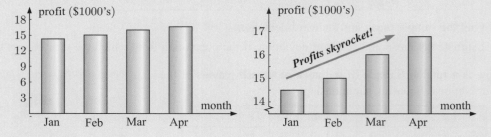

Both graphs accurately display the data, but on one graph the vertical axis has a break in its scale which can give the impression that the increase in profits is much larger than it really is. The comment 'Profits skyrocket!' encourages the reader to come to that conclusion without looking at the data more carefully.

  1 Given that the data is presented with mathematical accuracy in both graphs, would you say the author in the second case has lied?

When data is collected by sampling, the choice of a biased sample can be used to give misleading results. There is also the question of whether outliers should be considered as genuine data, or ignored and left out of statistical analysis.

2 In what other ways can statistics be used to deliberately mislead the target audience?

The use of statistics in science and medicine has been widely debated, as companies employ scientific 'experts' to back their claims. For example, in the multi-billion dollar tobacco industry, huge volumes of data have been collected which claim that smoking leads to cancer and other harmful effects. However, the industry has sponsored other studies which deny these claims.

There are many scientific articles and books which discuss the uses and misuses of statistics. For example:

- *Surgeons General's reports on smoking and cancer: uses and misuses of statistics and of science*, R J Hickey and I E Allen, Public Health Rep. 1983 Sep-Oct; **98**(5): 410-411.
- *Misusage of Statistics in Medical Researches*, I Ercan, B Yazici, Y Yang, G Ozkaya, S Cangur, B Ediz, I Kan, 2007, European Journal of General Medicine, **4**(3),127-133.
- *Sex, Drugs, and Body Counts: The Politics of Numbers in Global Crime and Conflict*, P Andreas and K M Greenhill, 2010, Cornell University Press.

3 Can we trust statistical results published in the media and in scientific journals?

4 What role does ethics have to play in mathematics?

REVIEW SET 20A   NON-CALCULATOR

1 The data supplied below is the diameter (in cm) of a number of bacteria colonies as measured by a microbiologist 12 hours after seeding.

| 0.4 | 2.1 | 3.4 | 3.9 | 4.7 | 3.7 | 0.8 | 3.6 | 4.1 | 4.9 | 2.5 | 3.1 | 1.5 | 2.6 | 4.0 |
| 1.3 | 3.5 | 0.9 | 1.5 | 4.2 | 3.5 | 2.1 | 3.0 | 1.7 | 3.6 | 2.8 | 3.7 | 2.8 | 3.2 | 3.3 |

a Find the **i** median **ii** range of the data.

b Group the data in 5 groups and display it using a frequency histogram.

c Comment on the skewness of the data.

2 The data set 4, 6, 9, a, 3, b has a mean and mode of 6. Find the values of a and b given $a > b$.

3 The histograms alongside show the times for the 100 metre freestyle recorded by members of a swimming squad.

a Copy and complete:

Distribution	Girls	Boys
shape		
median		
mean		
modal class		

b Discuss the distributions of times for the boys and girls. What conclusion can you make?

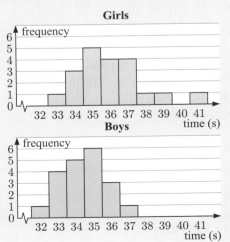

4 Draw a box and whisker plot for the following data:

   11, 12, 12, 13, 14, 14, 15, 15, 15, 16, 17, 17, 18.

5 80 senior students needed to run 400 metres in a Physical Education program. Their times were recorded and the results were used to produce the cumulative frequency graph shown.

Estimate:

   a the median

   b the interquartile range

   c the time corresponding to the top 10% of runners.

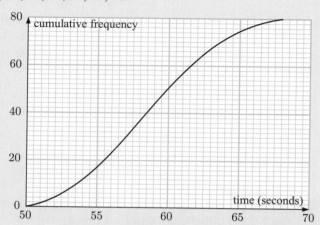

6 Consider the frequency table:

Score	Frequency	Cumulative frequency
6	2	2
7	4	m
8	7	13
9	p	25
10	5	30

   a Find the values of p and m.

   b Hence complete:

Measure	mode	median	range
Value			

   c Given that $\sum\limits_{i=1}^{5} f_i x_i = 254$, write the mean $\overline{x}$ as a fraction.

7 This cumulative frequency curve shows the times taken for 200 students to travel to school by bus.

   a Estimate how many of the students spent between 10 and 20 minutes travelling to school.

   b If 30% of the students spent more than m minutes travelling to school, estimate the value of m.

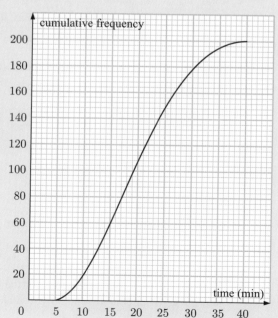

c Use the cumulative frequency curve to complete the following table:

Time t (min)	$5 \leqslant t < 10$	$10 \leqslant t < 15$	....	$35 \leqslant t < 40$
Frequency				

REVIEW SET 20B   CALCULATOR

1 The data below shows the distance in metres that Thabiso threw a baseball:

71.2 65.1 68.0 71.1 74.6 68.8 83.2 85.0 74.5 87.4
84.3 77.0 82.8 84.4 80.6 75.9 89.7 83.2 97.5 82.9
90.5 85.5 90.7 92.9 95.6 85.5 64.6 73.9 80.0 86.5

a Determine the highest and lowest value for the data set.

b Choose between 6 and 12 groups into which all the data values can be placed.

c Prepare a frequency distribution table.

d Draw a frequency histogram for the data.

e Determine:

    i the mean   **ii** the median.

2 Consider the data set: $k - 2, \ k, \ k + 3, \ k + 3$.

a Show that the mean of the data set is equal to $k + 1$.

b Suppose each number in the data set is increased by 2. Find the new mean of the data set in terms of k.

3 Consider the following distribution of continuous grouped data:

Scores	$0 \leqslant x < 10$	$10 \leqslant x < 20$	$20 \leqslant x < 30$	$30 \leqslant x < 40$	$40 \leqslant x < 50$
Frequency	1	13	27	17	2

a Construct a cumulative frequency graph for the data.

b Estimate the median of the data.   **c** Estimate the interquartile range.

d Estimate the mean and standard deviation.

4 The number of litres of petrol purchased by a random sample of motor vehicle drivers is shown alongside. Estimate the mean and standard deviation of the number of litres purchased by vehicles:

a in this sample

b in the population from which this sample was taken.

Litres	Number of vehicles
$15 \leqslant l < 20$	5
$20 \leqslant l < 25$	13
$25 \leqslant l < 30$	17
$30 \leqslant l < 35$	29
$35 \leqslant l < 40$	27
$40 \leqslant l < 45$	18
$45 \leqslant l < 50$	7

5 Katja's golf scores for her last 20 rounds were:

$$90 \quad 106 \quad 84 \quad 103 \quad 112 \quad 100 \quad 105 \quad 81 \quad 104 \quad 98$$
$$107 \quad 95 \quad 104 \quad 108 \quad 99 \quad 101 \quad 106 \quad 102 \quad 98 \quad 101$$

a Find the:

    i median   **ii** lower quartile   **iii** upper quartile.

b Find the interquartile range of the data set.

c Find the mean and standard deviation of her scores.

6 The table alongside shows the number of matches in a sample of boxes.

Number	47	48	49	50	51	52
Frequency	21	29	35	42	18	31

   a Find the mean and standard deviation for this data.

   b Does this result justify a claim that the average number of matches per box is 50?

7 Consider the data set: 120, 118, 132, 127, 135, 116, 122, 93, 128.

a Find the standard deviation for the data.

b Find the upper and lower quartiles of the data set.

c Are there any outliers in the data set?

d Draw a boxplot to display the data.

8 Katie loves cats. She visits every house in her street to find out how many cats live there. The responses are given below:

Number of cats	Frequency
0	36
1	9
2	11
3	5
4	1
5	1

a Draw a graph to display this data.

b Describe the distribution.

c Find the:

    i mode   **ii** mean   **iii** median.

d Which of the measures of centre is most appropriate for this data? Explain your answer.

REVIEW SET 20C

1 The winning margin in 100 basketball games was recorded. The results are given alongside:

Margin (points)	Frequency
1 - 10	13
11 - 20	35
21 - 30	27
31 - 40	18
41 - 50	7

a Is the winning margin discrete or continuous?

b Draw an appropriate graph to represent this information.

c Can you calculate the mean winning margin exactly? Explain your answer.

2 The following distribution has a mean score of 5.7:

    a Find the value of x.

    b Hence find the variance of the distribution.

Score	2	5	x	$x+6$
Frequency	3	2	4	1

3 The table alongside shows the number of customers visiting a supermarket on various days.

Estimate the mean number of customers per day.

Number of customers	Frequency
250 - 299	14
300 - 349	34
350 - 399	68
400 - 449	72
450 - 499	54
500 - 549	23
550 - 599	7

4 The given parallel boxplots represent the 100-metre sprint times for the members of two athletics squads.

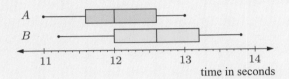

    a Determine the 5 number summaries for both A and B.

    b Determine the   **i** range   **ii** interquartile range   for each group.

    c Copy and complete:

       i We know the members of squad ...... generally ran faster because ......

      ii We know the times in squad ...... are more varied because ......

5 A random sample of the weekly supermarket bills for a number of families was observed and recorded in the table given.

    a Estimate the mean bill and the standard deviation of the bills.

    b Estimate the mean and standard deviation of the population from which the data was taken.

Bill (€)	Number of families
70 - 79.99	27
80 - 89.99	32
90 - 99.99	48
100 - 109.99	25
110 - 119.99	37
120 - 129.99	21
130 - 139.99	18
140 - 149.99	7

6 Pratik is a quality control officer for a biscuit company. He needs to check that 250 g of biscuits go into each packet, but realises that the weight in each packet will vary slightly.

    a Would you expect the standard deviation for the whole population to be the same for one day as it is for one week? Explain your answer.

    b If a sample of 100 packets is measured each day, what measure would be used to check:

       i that an average of 250 g of biscuits goes into each packet

      ii the variability of the mass going into each packet?

    c Explain the significance of a low standard deviation in this case.

7   An examination worth 100 marks was given to 800 biology students.
The cumulative frequency graph for the students' results is shown below.

a   Find the number of students who scored 45 marks or less for the test.

b   Find the median score.

c   Between what values do the middle 50% of test results lie?

d   Find the interquartile range of the data.

e   What percentage of students obtained a mark more than 55?

f   If a 'distinction' is awarded to the top 10% of students, what score is required to receive this honour?

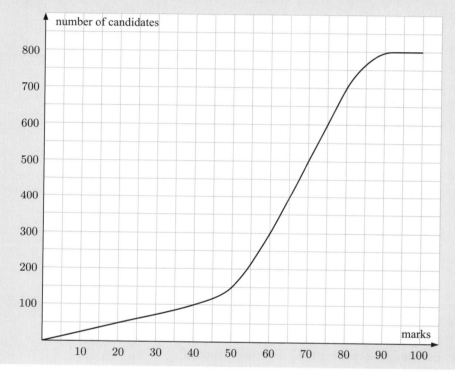

Chapter 21

Linear modelling

Syllabus reference: 5.4

OPENING PROBLEM

At a junior tournament, a group of young athletes throw a discus. The *age* and *distance thrown* are recorded for each athlete.

Athlete	A	B	C	D	E	F	G	H	I	J	K	L
Age (years)	12	16	16	18	13	19	11	10	20	17	15	13
Distance thrown (m)	20	35	23	38	27	47	18	15	50	33	22	20

Things to think about:

a Do you think the distance an athlete can throw is related to the person's age?

b How can you graph the data so we can clearly see the relationship between the variables?

c How can we *measure* the relationship between the variables?

d How can we use this data to predict the distance a 14 year old athlete can throw a discus?

Statisticians are often interested in how two variables are **related**.

For example, in the **Opening Problem**, we want to know how a change in the *age* of the athlete will affect the *distance* the athlete can throw.

We can observe the relationship between the variables by plotting the data on a **scatter diagram**.

We place the **independent variable** *age* on the horizontal axis, and the **dependent variable** *distance* on the vertical axis.

We then plot each data value as a point on the scatter diagram. For example, the red point represents athlete H, who is 10 years old and threw the discus 15 metres.

From the general shape formed by the dots, we can see that as the *age* increases, so does the *distance thrown*.

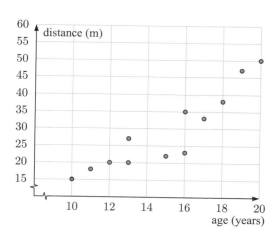

A   CORRELATION

> **Correlation** refers to the relationship or association between two variables.

There are several characteristics we consider when describing the correlation between two variables: direction, linearity, strength, outliers, and causation.

DIRECTION

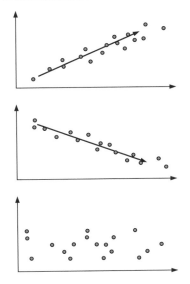

For a generally *upward* trend, we say that the correlation is **positive**. An increase in the independent variable means that the dependent variable generally increases.

For a generally *downward* trend, we say that the correlation is **negative**. An increase in the independent variable means that the dependent variable generally decreases.

For *randomly scattered* points, with no upward or downward trend, we say there is **no correlation**.

LINEARITY

We determine whether the points follow a **linear** trend, or in other words approximately form a straight line.

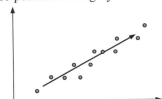

These points are roughly linear.

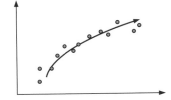

These points do not follow a linear trend.

STRENGTH

We want to know how closely the data follows a pattern or trend. The strength of correlation is usually described as either strong, moderate, or weak.

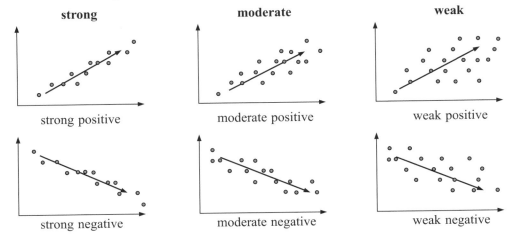

strong	**moderate**	**weak**
strong positive	moderate positive	weak positive
strong negative	moderate negative	weak negative

OUTLIERS

We observe and investigate any **outliers**, or isolated points which do not follow the trend formed by the main body of data.

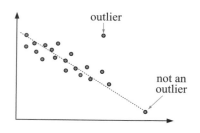

If an outlier is the result of a recording or graphing error, it should be discarded. However, if the outlier proves to be a genuine piece of data, it should be kept.

For the scatter diagram for the data in the **Opening Problem**, we can say that there is a strong positive correlation between *age* and *distance thrown*. The relationship appears to be linear, with no outliers.

CAUSATION

Correlation between two variables does not necessarily mean that one variable *causes* the other.

Consider the following:

1   The *arm length* and *running speed* of a sample of young children were measured, and a strong, positive correlation was found to exist between the variables.

Does this mean that short arms cause a reduction in running speed or that a high running speed causes your arms to grow long? This would clearly be nonsense.

Rather, the strong, positive correlation between the variables is attributed to the fact that both *arm length* and *running speed* are closely related to a third variable, *age*. Up to a certain age, both *arm length* and *running speed* increase with *age*.

2   The number of television sets sold in Ballarat and the number of stray dogs collected in Bendigo were recorded over several years and a strong positive correlation was found between the variables. Obviously the number of television sets sold in Ballarat was not influencing the number of stray dogs collected in Bendigo. Both variables have simply been increasing over the period of time that their numbers were recorded.

If a change in one variable *causes* a change in the other variable then we say that a **causal relationship** exists between them.

For example, in the **Opening Problem** there is a causal relationship in which increasing the *age* of an athlete increases the *distance thrown*.

In cases where this is not apparent, there is no justification, based on high correlation alone, to conclude that changes in one variable cause the changes in the other.

CASE STUDY   MASS ON A SPRING

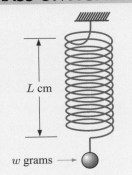

Suppose we wish to examine the relationship between the *length* of a helical spring and the *mass* that is hung from the spring.

The force of gravity on the mass causes the spring to stretch.

The length of the spring depends on the force applied, so the dependent variable is the *length*.

The following experimental results are obtained when objects of varying mass are hung from the spring:

Mass w (grams)	0	50	100	150	200	250
Length L (cm)	17.7	20.4	22.0	25.0	26.0	27.8

For each addition of 50 grams in mass, the consecutive increases in length are roughly constant.

There appears to be a strong positive correlation between the mass of the object hung from the spring, and the length of the spring. The relationship appears to be linear, with no obvious outliers.

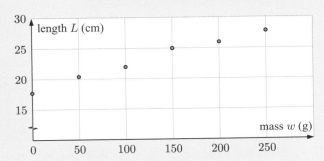

EXERCISE 21A

1 Describe what is meant by:

   a a scatter diagram   **b** correlation   **c** positive correlation

   d negative correlation   **e** an outlier.

2 For the following scatter diagrams, comment on:

   i the existence of any *pattern* (positive, negative or no correlation)

   ii the relationship *strength* (zero, weak, moderate or strong)

   iii whether the relationship is linear   **iv** whether there are any outliers.

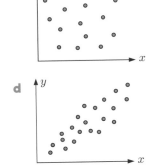

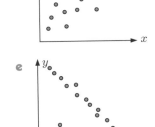

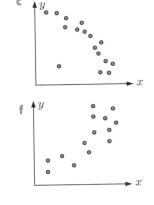

3 Ten students participated in a typing contest, where the students were given one minute to type as many words as possible. The table below shows how many words each student typed, and how many errors they made:

Student	A	B	C	D	E	F	G	H	I	J
Number of words x	40	53	20	65	35	60	85	49	35	76
Number of errors y	11	15	2	20	4	22	30	16	27	25

a Draw a scatter diagram for this data.

b Name the student who is best described as:

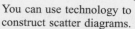

    i slow but accurate

    ii fast but inaccurate

    iii an outlier.

c Describe the direction and strength of correlation between these variables.

GRAPHICS CALCULATOR INSTRUCTIONS

d Is the data linear?

4 The scores awarded by two judges at an ice skating competition are shown in the table.

Competitor	P	Q	R	S	T	U	V	W	X	Y
Judge A	5	6.5	8	9	4	2.5	7	5	6	3
Judge B	6	7	8.5	9	5	4	7.5	5	7	4.5

a Construct a scatter diagram for this data with Judge A's scores on the horizontal axis and Judge B's scores on the vertical axis.

b Copy and complete the following comments about the scatter diagram:

There appears to be ......, ... correlation between Judge A's scores and Judge B's scores. This means that as Judge A's scores increase, Judge B's scores ......

c Would it be reasonable to conclude that an increase in Judge A's scores *causes* an increase in Judge B's scores?

B   PEARSON'S CORRELATION COEFFICIENT

In the previous section, we classified the strength of the correlation between two variables as either strong, moderate, or weak. We observed the points on a scatter diagram, and made a judgement as to how clearly the points formed a linear relationship.

However, this method can be quite inaccurate, so it is important to get a more precise measure of the strength of linear correlation between two variables. We achieve this using **Pearson's product-moment correlation coefficient** r.

For a set of n data given as ordered pairs (x_1, y_1), (x_2, y_2), (x_3, y_3), ..., (x_n, y_n),

Pearson's correlation coefficient is $r = \dfrac{\sum(x - \overline{x})(y - \overline{y})}{\sqrt{\sum(x - \overline{x})^2 \sum(y - \overline{y})^2}}$

where $\overline{x}$ and $\overline{y}$ are the means of the x and y data respectively, and $\sum$ means the sum over all the data values.

You are not required to learn this formula. Instead, we generally use technology to find the value of r.

GRAPHICS CALCULATOR INSTRUCTIONS

The values of r range from -1 to $+1$.

> The **sign** of r indicates the **direction** of the correlation.

- A positive value for r indicates the variables are **positively correlated**. An increase in one of the variables will result in an increase in the other.
- A negative value for r indicates the variables are **negatively correlated**. An increase in one of the variables will result in a decrease in the other.

> The **size** of r indicates the **strength** of the correlation.

- A value of r close to $+1$ or -1 indicates strong correlation between the variables.
- A value of r close to zero indicates weak correlation between the variables.

The following table is a guide for describing the strength of linear correlation using r.

Positive correlation			**Negative correlation**		
$r = 1$	perfect positive correlation		$r = -1$	perfect negative correlation	
$0.95 \leqslant r < 1$	very strong positive correlation		$-1 < r \leqslant -0.95$	very strong negative correlation	
$0.87 \leqslant r < 0.95$	strong positive correlation		$-0.95 < r \leqslant -0.87$	strong negative correlation	
$0.5 \leqslant r < 0.87$	moderate positive correlation		$-0.87 < r \leqslant -0.5$	moderate negative correlation	
$0.1 \leqslant r < 0.5$	weak positive correlation		$-0.5 < r \leqslant -0.1$	weak negative correlation	
$0 \leqslant r < 0.1$	no correlation		$-0.1 < r \leqslant 0$	no correlation	

Example 1   ◀) **Self Tutor**

A chemical fertiliser company wishes to determine the extent of correlation between the *quantity of compound X* used and the *lawn growth* per day.

Find and interpret the correlation coefficient between the two variables.

Lawn	Compound X (g)	Lawn growth (mm)
A	1	3
B	2	3
C	4	6
D	5	8

x	y	$x - \overline{x}$	$y - \overline{y}$	$(x - \overline{x})(y - \overline{y})$	$(x - \overline{x})^2$	$(y - \overline{y})^2$
1	3	-2	-2	4	4	4
2	3	-1	-2	2	1	4
4	6	1	1	1	1	1
5	8	2	3	6	4	9
Totals: 12	20			13	10	18

$$\therefore \quad \overline{x} = \frac{\sum x}{n} \qquad \overline{y} = \frac{\sum y}{n} \qquad r = \frac{\sum(x - \overline{x})(y - \overline{y})}{\sqrt{\sum(x - \overline{x})^2 \sum(y - \overline{y})^2}}$$

$$= \frac{12}{4} \qquad\qquad = \frac{20}{4} \qquad\qquad = \frac{13}{\sqrt{10 \times 18}}$$

$$= 3 \qquad\qquad = 5 \qquad\qquad \approx 0.969$$

There is a very strong positive correlation between the *quantity of compound X* used and *lawn growth*.

This suggests that the more of compound X used, the greater the lawn growth per day. However, care must be taken, as the small amount of data may provide a misleading result.

Example 2   ◀) **Self Tutor**

A group of adults is weighed, and their maximum speed when sprinting is measured:

Weight x (kg)	85	60	78	100	83	67	79	62	88	68
Maximum speed y (km h^{-1})	26	29	24	17	22	30	25	24	19	27

a Use technology to find r for the data.

b Describe the correlation between *weight* and *maximum speed*.

a

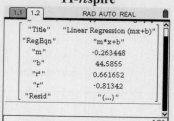

Using technology, $r \approx -0.813$.

b Since $-0.87 < r \leqslant -0.5$, there is a moderate negative correlation between *weight* and *maximum speed*.

EXERCISE 21B

1 Match each scatter diagram with the correct value of r.

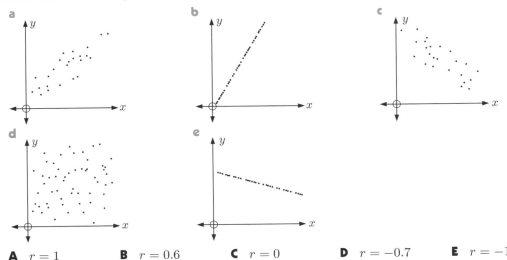

| **A** $r = 1$ | **B** $r = 0.6$ | **C** $r = 0$ | **D** $r = -0.7$ | **E** $r = -1$ |

2 Use the formula $r = \dfrac{\sum (x - \bar{x})(y - \bar{y})}{\sqrt{\sum (x - \bar{x})^2 \sum (y - \bar{y})^2}}$ to determine the correlation coefficient r in the following:

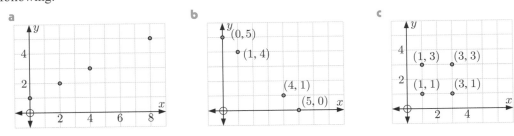

Check your answers using a calculator.

3 The table alongside shows the ages of five children, and the number of times they visited the doctor in the last year:

Age	2	5	7	5	8
Number of doctor visits	10	6	5	4	3

   a Draw a scatter diagram of the data.

   b Calculate the correlation coefficient by hand. *Check* your answer using technology.

   c Describe the correlation between *age* and *number of doctor visits*.

4 Jill hangs her clothes out to dry every Saturday, and notices that the clothes dry more quickly some days than others. She investigates the relationship between the temperature and the time her clothes take to dry:

Temperature x (°C)	25	32	27	39	35	24	30	36	29	35
Drying time y (min)	100	70	95	25	38	105	70	35	75	40

   a Draw a scatter diagram for this data.   **b** Calculate r.

   c Describe the correlation between *temperature* and *drying time*.

5 The table below shows the ticket and beverage sales for each day of a 12 day music festival:

Ticket sales ($x \times 1000$)	25	22	15	19	12	17	24	20	18	23	29	26
Beverage sales ($y \times 1000$)	9	7	4	8	3	4	8	10	7	7	9	8

   a Draw a scatter diagram for this data.   **b** Calculate r.

   c Describe the correlation between *ticket sales* and *beverage sales*.

6 A local council collected data from a number of parks in the area, recording the size of the parks and the number of trees each contained:

Size (hectares)	2.8	6.9	7.4	4.3	8.5	2.3	9.4	5.2	8.0	4.9	6.2	3.3	4.5
Number of trees	18	31	33	24	13	17	40	32	37	30	32	25	28

   a Draw a scatter diagram for this data.

   b Would you expect r to be positive or negative? Explain your answer.   **c** Calculate r.

   d Are there any outliers?   **e** Remove the outlier, and re-calculate r.

C   LINE OF BEST FIT

Consider again the data from the **Opening Problem**:

Athlete	A	B	C	D	E	F	G	H	I	J	K	L
Age (years)	12	16	16	18	13	19	11	10	20	17	15	13
Distance thrown (m)	20	35	23	38	27	47	18	15	50	33	22	20

We have seen that there is a strong positive linear correlation between *age* and *distance thrown*.

We can therefore model the data using a **line of best fit**.

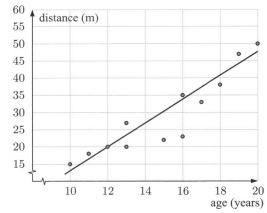

We draw a line of best fit connecting variables X and Y as follows:

Step 1:   Calculate the mean of the X values $\overline{x}$, and the mean of the Y values $\overline{y}$.

Step 2:   Mark the **mean point** $(\overline{x}, \overline{y})$ on the scatter diagram.

Step 3:   Draw a line through the mean point which fits the trend of the data, and so that about the same number of data points are above the line as below it.

The line formed is called a **line of best fit by eye**. This line will vary from person to person.

For the **Opening Problem**, the mean point is $(15, 29)$. So, we draw our line of best fit through $(15, 29)$.

We can use the line of best fit to estimate the value of y for any given value of x, and vice versa.

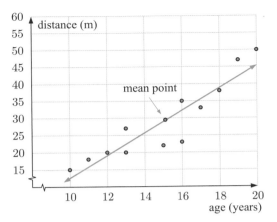

| Example 3 | ◀) **Self Tutor** |

Consider the following data for a mass on a spring:

Mass w (grams)	0	50	100	150	200	250
Length L (cm)	17.7	20.4	22.0	25.0	26.0	27.8

a Draw a scatter diagram for the data, and draw a line of best fit incorporating the mean point.

b Find the equation of the line you have drawn.

a The mean of the masses in the experiment is $\overline{w} = 125$ g.

The mean of the spring lengths is $\overline{L} = 23.15$ cm.

∴ the mean point is $(125, 23.15)$.

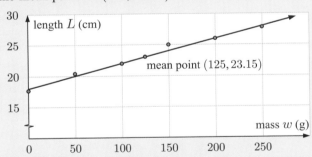

b The line of best fit above passes through $(125, 23.15)$ and $(200, 26)$.

The line has gradient $m = \dfrac{26 - 23.15}{200 - 125} \approx 0.04$.

Its equation is $\dfrac{y - 26}{x - 200} \approx 0.04$

∴ $y - 26 \approx 0.04x - 8$

∴ $y \approx 0.04x + 18$

or in this case $L \approx 0.04w + 18$

EXERCISE 21C

1 For each of the following data sets:

      i draw the scatter diagram and draw a line of best fit incorporating the mean point

      ii find the equation of the line you have drawn.

a

x	1	3	4	5	6	8
y	2	3	3	4	5	7

b

x	13	18	7	1	12	6	15	4	17	3
y	10	6	17	18	13	14	6	15	5	14

c

x	11	7	16	4	8	10	17	5	12	2	8	13	9	18	5	12
y	16	12	32	5	7	19	30	14	19	6	17	24	15	34	6	26

2 Over 10 days the *maximum temperature* and *number of car break-ins* was recorded for a city:

Maximum temperature x (°C)	22	17	14	18	24	29	33	32	26	22
Number of car break-ins y	30	18	9	20	31	38	47	40	29	25

    a Draw a scatter diagram for the data.

    b Describe the correlation between the *maximum temperature* and *number of car break-ins*.

    c Draw a line of best fit through the data.

    d Find the equation of the line of best fit.

    e Use your equation to estimate the number of car break-ins you would expect to occur on a 25°C day.

3 To investigate whether speed cameras have an impact on road safety, data was collected from several cities. The number of speed cameras in operation was recorded for each city, as well as the number of accidents over a 7 day period.

Number of speed cameras x	7	15	20	3	16	17	28	17	24	25	20	5	16	25	15	19
Number of car accidents y	48	35	31	52	40	35	28	30	34	19	29	42	31	21	37	32

    a Construct a scatter diagram to display the data.

    b Calculate r for the data.

    c Describe the relationship between the *number of speed cameras* and the *number of car accidents*.

    d Plot the mean point $(\overline{x}, \overline{y})$ on the scatter diagram, and draw a line of best fit through the mean point.

    e Where does your line cut the y-axis? Interpret what this answer means.

D · THE LEAST SQUARES REGRESSION LINE

The problem with drawing a line of best fit by eye is that the line drawn will vary from one person to another.

Instead, we use a method known as **linear regression** to find the equation of the line which best fits the data. The most common method is the method of 'least squares'.

Consider the set of points alongside.

For any line we draw to model the linear relationship between the points, we can find the vertical distances d_1, d_2, d_3, ... between each point and the line.

We can then square each of these distances, and find their sum $d_1^2 + d_2^2 + d_3^2 + ...$

If the line is a good fit for the data, most of the distances will be small, and so will the sum of their squares.

The **least squares regression line** is the line which makes this sum as small as possible.

The demonstration alongside allows you to experiment with various data sets. Use trial and error to find the least squares regression line for each set.

DEMO

In practice, rather than finding the regression line by experimentation, we use a **calculator** or **statistics package**.

GRAPHICS CALCULATOR INSTRUCTIONS

STATISTICS PACKAGE

Example 4							◀) **Self Tutor**

Use technology to find the least squares regression line for the mass on a spring data:

Mass w (grams)	0	50	100	150	200	250
Length L (cm)	17.7	20.4	22.0	25.0	26.0	27.8

Casio fx-9860G Plus	**TI-84 Plus**	**TI-nspire**

```
LinearReg(ax+b)
  a =0.04017142
  b =18.1285714
  r =0.99192816
  r²=0.98392147
  MSe=0.28842857
y=ax+b
          COPY  DRAW
```

```
LinReg
y=ax+b
a=.0401714286
b=18.12857143
r²=.9839214788
r=.9919281621
```

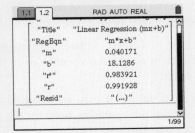

The least squares regression line is

$$y \approx 0.0402x + 18.1,$$
$$\text{or } L \approx 0.0402w + 18.1.$$

Compare this equation with the one we obtained in **Example 3**.

EXERCISE 21D

1 Use technology to find the least squares regression line for each data set in **Exercise 21C** question **1**.

2 Find the least squares regression line for the *maximum temperature* vs *number of break-ins* data in **Exercise 21C** question **2**. Hence check your prediction made in part **e**.

3 Steve wanted to see whether there was any relationship between the temperature when he leaves for work in the morning, and the time it takes to get to work.

He collected data over a 14 day period:

Temperature x (°C)	25	19	23	27	32	35	29	27	21	18	16	17	28	34
Time y (min)	35	42	49	31	37	33	31	47	42	36	45	33	48	39

a Draw a scatter diagram of the data.

b Calculate r.

c Describe the relationship between the variables.

d Is it reasonable to try to find a line of best fit for this data? Explain your answer.

4 The table below shows the price of petrol and the number of customers per hour for sixteen petrol stations.

Petrol price x (cents per litre)	105.9	106.9	109.9	104.5	104.9	111.9	110.5	112.9
Number of customers y	45	42	25	48	43	15	19	10

Petrol price x (cents per litre)	107.5	108.0	104.9	102.9	110.9	106.9	105.5	109.5
Number of customers y	30	23	42	50	12	24	32	17

a Calculate r for the data.

b Describe the relationship between the *petrol price* and the *number of customers*.

c Use technology to find the least squares regression line.

E ▐ INTERPOLATION AND EXTRAPOLATION

Suppose we have gathered data to investigate the association between two variables. We obtain the scatter diagram shown below. The data with the lowest and highest values of x are called the **poles**.

We use the least squares regression line to estimate values of one variable given a value for the other.

If we use values of x **in between** the poles, we say we are **interpolating** between the poles.

If we use values of x **outside** the poles, we say we are **extrapolating** outside the poles.

The accuracy of an interpolation depends on how linear the original data was. This can be gauged by determining the correlation coefficient and ensuring that the data is randomly scattered around the linear regression line.

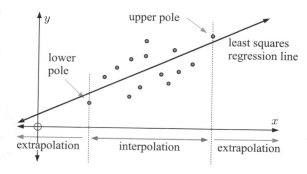

The accuracy of an extrapolation depends not only on how linear the original data was, but also on the assumption that the linear trend will continue past the poles. The validity of this assumption depends greatly on the situation we are looking at.

As a general rule, it is reasonable to interpolate between the poles, but unreliable to extrapolate outside the poles.

Example 5 ◀) **Self Tutor**

The table below shows how far a group of students live from school, and how long it takes them to travel there each day.

Distance from school x (km)	7.2	4.5	13	1.3	9.9	12.2	19.6	6.1	23.1
Time to travel to school y (min)	17	13	29	2	25	27	41	15	53

a Draw a scatter diagram of the data.
b Use technology to find: **i** r **ii** the equation of the least squares regression line.
c Pam lives 15 km from school.
   i Estimate how long it takes Pam to travel to school.
   ii Comment on the reliability of your estimate.

a
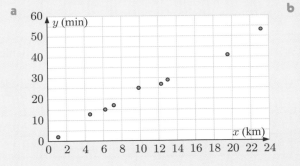

b
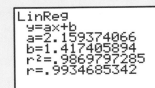

  i $r \approx 0.993$
  ii The least squares regression line is
    $y \approx 2.16x + 1.42$.

c **i** When $x = 15$, $y \approx 2.16(15) + 1.42 \approx 33.8$
    So, it will take Pam approximately 34 minutes to travel to school.
  ii The estimate is an interpolation, and the correlation coefficient indicates a very strong correlation. This suggests that the estimate is reliable.

EXERCISE 21E

1 Consider the *temperature* vs *drying time* problem on page **553**.
  a Use technology to find the equation of the least squares regression line.
  b Estimate the time it will take for Jill's clothes to dry on a 28°C day.
  c How reliable is your estimate in **b**?

2 Consider the *ticket sales* vs *beverage sales* problem on page **554**.
  a Find the equation of the least squares regression line.
  b The music festival is extended by one day, and $35 000 worth of tickets are sold.
    i Predict the beverage sales for this day.
    ii Comment on the reliability of your prediction.

3 The table below shows the amount of time a collection of families spend preparing homemade meals each week, and the amount of money they spend each week on fast food.

Time on homemade meals x (hours)	3.3	6.0	4.0	8.5	7.2	2.5	9.1	6.9	3.8	7.7
Money on fast food y ($)	85	0	60	0	27	100	15	40	59	29

  a Draw a scatter diagram for the data.
  b Calculate the value of r.
  c Use technology to find the equation of the least squares regression line.
  d Interpret the gradient and y-intercept of the least squares regression line.
  e Another family spends 5 hours per week preparing homemade meals. Estimate how much money they spend on fast food each week. Comment on the reliability of your estimate.

4 The ages and heights of children at a playground are given below:

Age x (years)	3	9	7	4	4	12	8	6	5	10	13
Height y (cm)	94	132	123	102	109	150	127	110	115	145	157

  a Draw a scatter diagram for the data.
  b Use technology to find the least squares regression line.
  c At what age would you expect children to reach a height of 140 cm?
  d Interpret the gradient of the least squares regression line.
  e Use the line to predict the height of a 20 year old. Do you think this prediction is reliable?

5 Once a balloon has been blown up, it slowly starts to deflate. A balloon's diameter was recorded at various times after it was blown up:

Time t (hours)	0	10	25	40	55	70	90	100	110
Diameter D (cm)	40.2	37.8	34.5	30.2	26.1	23.9	19.8	17.2	14.0

  a Draw a scatter diagram of the data.
  b Describe the correlation between D and t.
  c Find the equation of the least squares regression line.
  d Use this equation to predict:

  i the diameter of the balloon after 80 hours
  ii the time it took for the balloon to completely deflate.

  e Which of your predictions in **d** is more likely to be reliable?

6 The mass of bacteria in a culture is measured each day for five days.

t days	1	2	3	4	5
M grams	3.6	5.7	9.1	14.6	23.3

  a Add a row to the table for the values of $\ln M$.
  b Use technology to graph M against t and $\ln M$ against t. Which of the scatter diagrams is linear?
  c Use technology to find the linear model $Y = mX + c$ where $Y \equiv \ln M$ and $X \equiv t$.
  d Hence show that $M \approx 2.25 \times 1.60^t$.
  e Estimate the original mass of bacteria.

7 The quantity Q of a chemical responsible for skin elasticity is measured at various ages (t years). The results are shown in the table and graph.

Age t (years)	2	10	20	30	50	65	80
Chemical Q (mg)	119	98	82	70	50	40	30

a What is the effect on Q as t increases?

b Is the graph linear?

c Construct a table of values comparing Q with $\sqrt{t}$.

d Explain why $Q = m\sqrt{t} + c$ is a likely model for the original data.

e Use your calculator to find m and c.

f Find the quantity of chemical in:

   i a newly born baby   **ii** a 25 year old.

g Are the answers in **f** likely to be reliable?

8 A bird bath is filled with water. Over time, the water evaporates as shown in the table below:

Time t (hours)	3	6	9	12	15	18	21	24
Water remaining V (litres)	6.7	3.6	2	1.1	0.6	0.32	0.18	0.10

a Draw a scatter diagram of V against t.

b Draw a scatter diagram of:

   i $\ln V$ against t **ii** $\ln V$ against $\ln t$.

c Find the model connecting V and t.

d Estimate the amount of water remaining in the bird bath after 5 hours.

e Estimate the amount of water which has evaporated after 10 hours.

THEORY OF KNOWLEDGE

In the previous exercise we saw examples of data which was non-linear, but for which we could *transform* the variables so a linear model could be used.

In other situations we can use quadratic or trigonometric functions to model data.

1 Can all data be modelled by a known mathematical function?

2 How reliable is mathematics in predicting real-world phenomena?

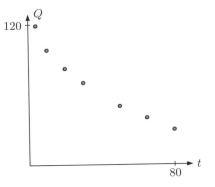

Friedrich Wilhelm Bessel (1784 - 1846) was a German mathematician and astronomer who described the Bessel functions named after him. The Bessel functions are the solutions to a particular class of **differential equation**, which is an equation involving derivative functions. They are used in both classical and quantum physics to describe the dynamics of gravitational systems.

Friedrich Wilhelm Bessel

3 Are the Bessel functions defined by nature or by man?

REVIEW SET 21A   NON-CALCULATOR

1 For the following scatter diagrams, comment on:

     i the direction and strength of correlation between the two variables

     ii whether the relationship is linear.

a

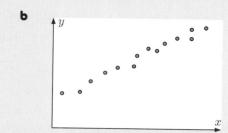

b

2 The results of a group of students for a Maths test and an Art essay are compared:

Student	A	B	C	D	E	F	G	H	I	J
Maths test	64	67	69	70	73	74	77	82	84	85
Art essay	85	82	80	82	72	71	70	71	62	66

  a Construct a scatter diagram for the data. Make the scales on both axes from 60 to 90.

  b Describe the relationship between the Mathematics and Art marks.

  c Given the mean Maths score was 74.5 and the mean Art score was 74.1, draw a line of best fit on your graph.

3 The Botanical Gardens have been trying out a new chemical to control the number of beetles infesting their plants. The results of one of their tests are shown in the table.

  a Draw a scatter diagram for the data.

  b Given the correlation coefficient $r \approx -0.859$, describe the correlation between the *quantity of chemical* and the *number of surviving beetles*.

Sample	Quantity of chemical (g)	Number of surviving beetles
A	2	11
B	5	6
C	6	4
D	3	6
E	9	3

4 A clothing store recorded the length of time customers were in the store and the amount they spent.

Time (min)	8	18	5	10	17	11	2	13	18	4	11	20	23	22	17
Money (€)	40	78	0	46	72	86	0	59	33	0	0	122	90	137	93

  a Draw a scatter diagram of the data.

  b Given the mean time ≈ 13.3 mins, and the mean amount $\approx$ €57.07, plot the mean point on your diagram and draw a line of best fit.

  c Describe the relationship between *time in the store* and the *money spent*.

5 Safety authorities advise drivers to travel three seconds behind the car in front of them. This gives the driver a greater chance of avoiding a collision if the car in front has to brake quickly or is itself involved in an accident.

A test was carried out to find out how long it would take a driver to bring a car to rest from the time a red light was flashed. The following results are for one driver in the same car under the same test conditions.

Speed v (km h^{-1})	10	20	30	40	50	60	70	80	90
Stopping time t (s)	1.23	1.54	1.88	2.20	2.52	2.83	3.15	3.45	3.83

a Produce a scatter diagram of the data.

b The least squares regression line has the equation $t = 0.03v + 0.9$. Plot this line on your scatter diagram.

c Use the equation in **b** to estimate the stopping time for a speed of:

    i 55 km h^{-1} **ii** 110 km h^{-1}

d Which of your estimates in **c** is more likely to be reliable?

REVIEW SET 21B   CALCULATOR

1 Thomas rode for an hour each day for eleven days. He recorded the number of kilometres he rode and the temperature on that day.

Temperature T ($^\circ$C)	32.9	33.9	35.2	37.1	38.9	30.3	32.5	31.7	35.7	36.3	34.7
Distance d (km)	26.5	26.7	24.4	19.8	18.5	32.6	28.7	29.4	23.8	21.2	29.7

a Construct a scatter diagram of the data.

b Find and interpret Pearson's correlation coefficient for the two variables.

c Calculate the equation of the least squares regression line.

d Using your answer to **c**, how hot must it get before Thomas does not ride at all?

2 A garden centre manager believes that during March, the number of customers is related to the temperature at noon. Over a period of a fortnight the number of customers and the noon temperature were recorded.

Temperature x ($^\circ$C)	23	25	28	30	30	27	25	28	32	31	33	29	27
Number of customers y	57	64	62	75	69	58	61	78	80	35	84	73	76

a Draw a scatter diagram of the data.

b Calculate the correlation coefficient r.

c Are there any outliers?

d Remove the outlier, and re-calculate r.

e Using your answer to **d**, describe the association between the *number of customers* and the *noon temperature* at the garden centre.

3 Fifteen students were weighed, and their pulse rates were measured:

Weight x (kg)	61	52	47	72	62	79	57	45	67	71	80	58	51	43	55
Pulse rate y (beats per min)	65	59	54	74	69	87	61	59	70	69	75	60	56	53	58

  a Draw a scatter diagram for the data.

  b Describe the relationship between *weight* and *pulse rate*.

  c Calculate the mean point $(\overline{x}, \overline{y})$.

  d Draw a line of best fit through the data.

  e Find the equation of your line of best fit.

  f Hence estimate the pulse rate of a student who weighs 65 kg.

4 Eight identical flower beds contain petunias. The different beds were watered different numbers of times each week, and the number of flowers each bed produced was recorded in the table below:

Number of waterings n	0	1	2	3	4	5	6	7
Flowers produced f	18	52	86	123	158	191	228	250

  a Which is the independent variable?

  b Find the equation of the least squares regression line.

  c Plot the least squares regression line on a scatter diagram of the data.

  d Violet has two beds of petunias. One she waters five times a fortnight ($2\frac{1}{2}$ times a week), and the other ten times a week.

    i How many flowers can she expect from each bed?

    ii Which is the more reliable estimate?

5 The yield of pumpkins on a farm depends on the quantity of fertiliser used.

Fertiliser x (g m^{-2})	4	13	20	26	30	35	50
Yield y (kg)	1.8	2.9	3.8	4.2	4.7	5.7	4.4

  a Draw a scatter diagram of the data and identify the outlier.

  b Calculate the correlation coefficient:

    i with the outlier included   **ii** without the outlier.

  c Calculate the equation of the least squares regression line:

    i with the outlier included   **ii** without the outlier.

  d If you wish to estimate the yield when 15 g m^{-2} of fertiliser is used, which regression line from **c** should be used?

  e Attempt to explain what may have caused the outlier.

REVIEW SET 21C

1 The scatter diagram alongside shows the marks obtained by students in a test out of 50 marks, plotted against the number of hours each student studied for the test.

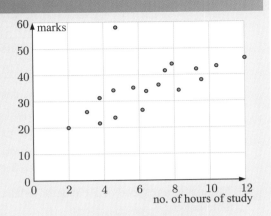

a Describe the correlation between the variables.

b How should the outlier be treated? Explain your answer.

2 A sample of 8 tyres was taken to examine the association between the *tread depth* and the *number of kilometres travelled*.

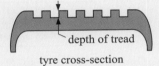

depth of tread

tyre cross-section

Kilometres x ($\times 1000$)	14	17	24	34	35	37	38	39
Tread depth y (mm)	5.7	6.5	4.0	3.0	1.9	2.7	1.9	2.3

a Draw a scatter diagram of the data.

b Calculate the correlation coefficient r.

c Describe the correlation between the *tread depth* and the *number of kilometres travelled*.

3 The trunk widths and heights of the trees in a garden were recorded:

Trunk width x (cm)	35	47	72	40	15	87	20	66	57	24	32
Height y (m)	11	18	24	12	3	30	22	21	17	5	10

a Draw a scatter diagram of the data.

b Which of the points is an outlier?

c How would you describe the tree represented by the outlier?

d Calculate the mean point $(\overline{x}, \overline{y})$.

e Draw a line of best fit through the data.

f Find the equation of the line of best fit.

g Estimate the height of a tree with trunk width 120 cm. How reliable is this estimate?

4 A drinks vendor varies the price of Supa-fizz on a daily basis. He records the number of drinks sold in the following table:

Price p	$2.50	$1.90	$1.60	$2.10	$2.20	$1.40	$1.70	$1.85
Sales s	389	450	448	386	381	458	597	431

a Produce a scatter diagram for the data.

b Are there any outliers? If so, should they be included in the analysis?

c Find the equation of the least squares regression line.

d Do you think the least squares regression line would give an accurate prediction of sales if Supa-fizz was priced at 50 cents? Explain your answer.

5 The maximum speed of a canoe on a lake with different numbers of rowers is recorded in the table below:

Number of rowers r	4	6	10	14	18
Maximum speed S ($km\,h^{-1}$)	8.7	10.3	12.6	14.2	15.9

a Draw a scatter diagram of S against r.

b Draw a scatter diagram of $\ln S$ against $\ln r$.

c Find the model connecting r and S.

d Predict the maximum speed of the canoe if there are 8 rowers.

Chapter 22

Probability

Syllabus reference: 5.5, 5.6

OPENING PROBLEM

In the late 17th century, English mathematicians compiled and analysed mortality tables which showed the number of people who died at different ages. From these tables they could estimate the probability that a person would be alive at a future date. This led to the establishment of the first life-insurance company in 1699.

Life Insurance Companies use statistics on **life expectancy** and **death rates** to work out the premiums to charge people who insure with them.

The **life table** shown is from Australia. It shows the number of people out of 100 000 births who survive to different ages, and the expected years of remaining life at each age.

For example, we can see that out of 100 000 births, 98 052 males are expected to survive to the age of 20, and from that age the survivors are expected to live a further 54.35 years.

LIFE TABLE					
Male			**Female**		
Age	Number surviving	Expected remaining life	Age	Number surviving	Expected remaining life
0	100 000	73.03	0	100 000	79.46
5	98 809	68.90	5	99 307	75.15
10	98 698	63.97	10	99 125	70.22
15	98 555	59.06	15	98 956	65.27
20	98 052	54.35	20	98 758	60.40
25	97 325	49.74	25	98 516	55.54
30	96 688	45.05	30	98 278	50.67
35	96 080	40.32	35	98 002	45.80
40	95 366	35.60	40	97 615	40.97
45	94 323	30.95	45	96 997	36.22
50	92 709	26.45	50	95 945	31.59
55	89 891	22.20	55	94 285	27.10
60	85 198	18.27	60	91 774	22.76
65	78 123	14.69	65	87 923	18.64
70	67 798	11.52	70	81 924	14.81
75	53 942	8.82	75	72 656	11.36
80	37 532	6.56	80	58 966	8.38
85	20 998	4.79	85	40 842	5.97
90	8416	3.49	90	21 404	4.12
95	2098	2.68	95	7004	3.00
99	482	2.23	99	1953	2.36

Things to think about:

a Can you use the life table to estimate how many years you can expect to live?

b Can you estimate the chance that a new-born boy or girl reaches the age of 15?

c Can the table be used to estimate the chance that:
   i a 15 year old boy *will* reach age 75
   ii a 15 year old girl *will not* reach age 75?

d An insurance company sells policies to people to insure them against death over a 30-year period. If the person dies during this period, the beneficiaries receive the agreed payout figure. Why are such policies cheaper to take out for a 20 year old than for a 50 year old?

e How many of your classmates would you expect to be alive and able to attend a 30 year class reunion?

In the field of **probability theory** we use mathematics to describe the **chance** or **likelihood** of an event happening.

We apply probability theory in physical and biological sciences, economics, politics, sport, life insurance, quality control, production planning, and a host of other areas.

We assign to every event a number which lies between 0 and 1 inclusive. We call this number a **probability**.

An **impossible** event which has 0% chance of happening is assigned a probability of 0.

A **certain** event which has 100% chance of happening is assigned a probability of 1.

All other events can be assigned a probability between 0 and 1.

The number line below shows how we could interpret different probabilities:

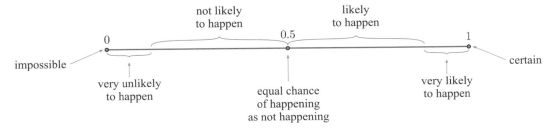

The assigning of probabilities is usually based on either:

- observing the results of an experiment (experimental probability),   or
- using arguments of symmetry (theoretical probability).

A   EXPERIMENTAL PROBABILITY

In experiments involving chance we use the following terms to talk about what we are doing and the results we obtain:

- The **number of trials** is the total number of times the experiment is repeated.
- The **outcomes** are the different results possible for one trial of the experiment.
- The **frequency** of a particular outcome is the number of times that this outcome is observed.
- The **relative frequency** of an outcome is the frequency of that outcome expressed as a fraction or percentage of the total number of trials.

For example, when a small plastic cone was tossed into the air 279 times it fell on its *side* 183 times and on its *base* 96 times.

We say:

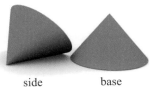

- the number of trials is 279
- the outcomes are *side* and *base*
- the frequencies of *side* and *base* are 183 and 96 respectively
- the relative frequencies of *side* and *base* are $\frac{183}{279} \approx 0.656$ and $\frac{96}{279} \approx 0.344$ respectively.

  In the absence of any further data, the relative frequency of each event is our best estimate of the probability of that event occurring.

Experimental probability $=$ relative frequency.

In this case, we write

Experimental P(side) = the experimental probability the cone will land on its side when tossed
≈ 0.656

Experimental P(base) = the experimental probability the cone will land on its base when tossed
≈ 0.344

The larger the number of trials, the more confident we are that the estimated probability will be accurate.

INVESTIGATION 1   TOSSING DRAWING PINS

If a drawing pin tossed in the air finishes we say it has finished on its *back*. If it

finishes we say it has finished on its *side*.

If two drawing pins are tossed simultaneously, the possible results are:

two backs

back and side

two sides

What to do:

1   Obtain two drawing pins of the same shape and size. Toss the pair 80 times and record the outcomes in a table.

2   Obtain relative frequencies (experimental probabilities) for each of the three outcomes.

3   Pool your results with four other people and so obtain experimental probabilities from 400 tosses. The other people must have pins with the same shape.

4   Which gives the more reliable probability estimates, your results or the whole group's? Explain your answer.

5   Keep your results as they may be useful later in this chapter.

In some situations, for example in the **Investigation** above, experimentation is the only way of obtaining probabilities.

EXERCISE 22A

1   When a batch of 145 paper clips was dropped onto 6 cm by 6 cm squared paper, it was observed that 113 fell completely inside squares and 32 finished up on the grid lines. Find, to 2 decimal places, the experimental probability of a clip falling:

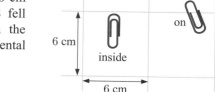

   a   inside a square   b   on a line.

2
Length	Frequency
0 - 19	17
20 - 39	38
40 - 59	19
60+	4

Jose surveyed the length of TV commercials (in seconds). Find, to 3 decimal places, the experimental probability that a randomly chosen TV commercial will last:

   a   20 to 39 seconds   b   more than a minute

   c   between 20 and 59 seconds (inclusive).

3 Betul records the number of phone calls she receives over a period of consecutive days.

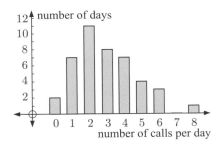

  a For how many days did the survey last?

  b Estimate Betul's chance of receiving:

   i no phone calls in a day

   ii 5 or more phone calls in a day

   iii less than 3 phone calls in a day.

4 Pat does a lot of travelling in her car, and she keeps records on how often she fills her car with petrol. The table alongside shows the frequencies of the number of days between refills. Estimate the likelihood that:

  a there is a four day gap between refills

  b there is at least a four day gap between refills.

Days between refills	Frequency
1	37
2	81
3	48
4	17
5	6
6	1

INVESTIGATION 2   COIN TOSSING EXPERIMENTS

The coins of most currencies have two distinct faces, usually referred to as 'heads' and 'tails'. When we toss a coin in the air, we expect it to finish on a head or tail with equal likelihood.

In this investigation the coins do not have to be all the same type.

What to do:

1 Toss *one coin* 40 times. Record the number of heads in each trial, in a table:

Result	Tally	Frequency	Relative frequency
1 head			
no heads			

2 Toss *two coins* 60 times. Record the number of heads in each trial, in a table:

Result	Tally	Frequency	Relative frequency
2 heads			
1 head			
no heads			

3 Toss *three coins* 80 times. Record the number of heads in each trial, in a table:

Result	Tally	Frequency	Relative frequency
3 heads			
2 heads			
1 head			
no heads			

4 Share your results to **1**, **2**, and **3** with several other students. Comment on any similarities and differences.

5 Pool your results and find new relative frequencies for tossing one coin, two coins, and three coins.

6 Click on the icon to examine a coin tossing simulation.

Set it to toss one coin 10 000 times.

Run the simulation ten times, each time recording the relative frequency for each possible result. Comment on these results. Do your results agree with what you expected?

COIN TOSSING

7 Experiment with the simulation for *two coins* and then *three coins*.

From the previous **Investigation** you should have observed that, when tossing two coins, there are roughly twice as many 'one head' results as there are 'no heads' or 'two heads'.

The explanation for this is best seen using two different coins where you could get:

     two heads   one head   one head   no heads

We should expect the ratio two heads : one head : no heads to be $1 : 2 : 1$. However, due to chance, there will be variations from this when we look at experimental results.

INVESTIGATION 3   DICE ROLLING EXPERIMENTS

You will need: At least one normal six-sided die with numbers 1 to 6 on its faces. Several dice would be useful to speed up the experimentation.

WORKSHEET

What to do:

1 List the possible outcomes for the uppermost face when the die is rolled.

2 Suppose the die is rolled 60 times.

Copy and complete the following table of your **expected results**:

Outcomes	Expected frequency	Expected relative frequency
1		
2		
⋮		
6		

3 Roll the die 60 times. Record the results in a table like the one shown:

Outcome	Tally	Frequency	Relative frequency
1			
2			
⋮			
6			
	Total	60	1

4 Pool as much data as you can with other students.

    a Look at similarities and differences from one set to another.

    b Summarise the overall pooled data in one table.

    c Compare your results with your expectation in **2**.

5 Use the die rolling simulation on the CD to roll the die 10 000 times. Repeat this 10 times. On each occasion, record your results in a table like that in **3**. Do your results further confirm your expected results?

    SIMULATION

6 The different possible outcomes when a pair of dice is rolled are shown alongside.

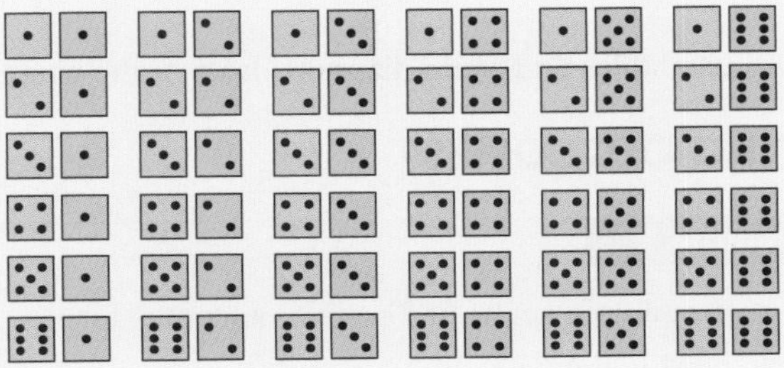

    There are 36 possible outcomes.

    Notice that the three outcomes $\{1, 3\}$, $\{2, 2\}$, and $\{3, 1\}$, give a sum of 4.

    We observe that the possible sums of the dice are 2, 3, ..., 12.

Using the illustration above, copy and complete the table of **expected results**:

Sum of dice	2	3	4	5	6	7	8	9	10	11	12
Fraction of possible outcomes with this sum			$\frac{3}{36}$								
Fraction as decimal			0.083								

7 If a pair of dice is rolled 360 times, how many of each result (2, 3, 4, ..., 12) would you expect to get? Extend the table in **6** by adding another row and writing your **expected frequencies** within it.

8 Toss two dice 360 times. Record the *sum of the two numbers* for each toss in a table.

    WORKSHEET

Sum	Tally	Frequency	Relative frequency
2			
3			
4			
⋮			
12			
	Total	360	1

9 Pool as much data as you can with other students and find the overall relative frequency of each sum.

10 Use the two dice simulation on the CD to roll the pair of dice 10 000 times. Repeat this 10 times and on each occasion record your results in a table like that in **8**. Are your results consistent with your expectations?

    SIMULATION

B   SAMPLE SPACE

> A **sample space** U is the set of all possible outcomes of an experiment. It is also referred to as the **universal set** U.

There are a variety of ways of representing or illustrating sample spaces, including:

- lists
- tables of outcomes
- 2-dimensional grids
- Venn diagrams
- tree diagrams

We will use tables and Venn diagrams later in the chapter.

LISTING OUTCOMES

Example 1	◀) Self Tutor

List the sample space of possible outcomes for:

   a   tossing a coin   **b**   rolling a normal die.

   a   When a coin is tossed, there are two possible outcomes.
        $\therefore$ sample space $= \{H, T\}$

   b   When a die is rolled, there are 6 possible outcomes.
        $\therefore$ sample space $= \{1, 2, 3, 4, 5, 6\}$

2-DIMENSIONAL GRIDS

When an experiment involves more than one operation we can still use listing to illustrate the sample space. However, a grid is often more efficient.

Example 2	◀) Self Tutor

Use a 2-dimensional grid to illustrate the possible outcomes when 2 coins are tossed.

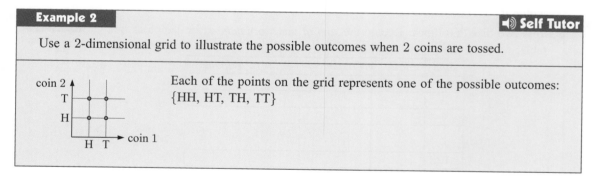

Each of the points on the grid represents one of the possible outcomes:
$\{HH, HT, TH, TT\}$

TREE DIAGRAMS

The sample space in **Example 2** could also be represented by a tree diagram. The advantage of tree diagrams is that they can be used when more than two operations are involved.

Example 3	◀) Self Tutor

Illustrate, using a tree diagram, the possible outcomes when:

   a   tossing two coins

   b   drawing two marbles from a bag containing many red, green, and yellow marbles.

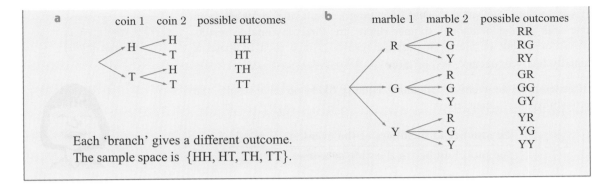

a   coin 1   coin 2   possible outcomes

		HH
H	H	HH
	T	HT
T	H	TH
	T	TT

b   marble 1   marble 2   possible outcomes

Each 'branch' gives a different outcome.
The sample space is {HH, HT, TH, TT}.

EXERCISE 22B

1 List the sample space for the following:

a twirling a square spinner labelled A, B, C, D

b the sexes of a 2-child family

c the order in which 4 blocks A, B, C and D can be lined up

d the 8 different 3-child families.

2 Illustrate on a 2-dimensional grid the sample space for:

a rolling a die and tossing a coin simultaneously

b rolling two dice

c rolling a die and spinning a spinner with sides A, B, C, D

d twirling two square spinners, one labelled A, B, C, D and the other 1, 2, 3, 4.

3 Illustrate on a tree diagram the sample space for:

a tossing a 5-cent and a 10-cent coin simultaneously

b tossing a coin and twirling an equilateral triangular spinner labelled A, B, and C

c twirling two equilateral triangular spinners labelled 1, 2, and 3, and X, Y, and Z

d drawing two tickets from a hat containing a large number of pink, blue, and white tickets.

C   THEORETICAL PROBABILITY

Consider the **octagonal spinner** alongside.

Since the spinner is symmetrical, when it is spun the arrowed marker could finish with equal likelihood on each of the sections marked 1 to 8.

The likelihood of obtaining the outcome 4 would be:

1 chance in 8, $\frac{1}{8}$, $12\frac{1}{2}\%$,   or   0.125.

This is a **mathematical** or **theoretical** probability and is based on what we theoretically expect to occur. It is the chance of that event occurring in any trial of the experiment.

If we are interested in the event of getting a result of *6 or more* from one spin of the octagonal spinner, there are three favourable results (6, 7, or 8) out of the eight possible results. Since each of these is equally likely to occur, P(6 or more) $= \frac{3}{8}$.

We read $\frac{3}{8}$ as "3 chances in 8".

In general, for an event A containing **equally likely** possible results, the probability of A occurring is

$$P(A) = \frac{\text{the number of members of the event } A}{\text{the total number of possible outcomes}} = \frac{n(A)}{n(U)}.$$

Example 4

🔊 **Self Tutor**

A ticket is *randomly selected* from a basket containing 3 green, 4 yellow, and 5 blue tickets. Determine the probability of getting:

a a green ticket

b a green or yellow ticket

c an orange ticket

d a green, yellow, or blue ticket.

There are $3 + 4 + 5 = 12$ tickets which could be selected with equal chance.

a P(G)

$= \frac{3}{12}$

$= \frac{1}{4}$

b P(G or Y)

$= \frac{3+4}{12}$

$= \frac{7}{12}$

c P(O)

$= \frac{0}{12}$

$= 0$

d P(G, Y, or B)

$= \frac{3+4+5}{12}$

$= 1$

From **Example 4**, notice that:

- In **c** an orange result cannot occur. The calculated probability is 0 because the event has *no chance of occurring*.
- In **d** the outcome of a green, yellow, or blue is certain to occur. It is 100% likely so the theoretical probability is 1.

Events which have *no chance of occurring* or probability 0, or are *certain to occur* or probability 1, are two extremes.

For any event A, the probability $P(A)$ of A occurring satisfies $0 \leqslant P(A) \leqslant 1$.

Example 5

🔊 **Self Tutor**

An ordinary 6-sided die is rolled once. Determine the chance of:

a getting a 6   **b** not getting a 6   **c** getting a 1 or 2   **d** not getting a 1 or 2

The sample space of possible outcomes is $\{1, 2, 3, 4, 5, 6\}$.

a P(6)

$= \frac{1}{6}$

b P(not a 6)

$= $ P(1, 2, 3, 4, or 5)

$= \frac{5}{6}$

c P(1 or 2)

$= \frac{2}{6}$

$= \frac{1}{3}$

d P(not a 1 or 2)

$= $ P(3, 4, 5, or 6)

$= \frac{4}{6}$

$= \frac{2}{3}$

COMPLEMENTARY EVENTS

In **Example 5** notice that $\qquad$ P(6) + P(not a 6) = 1 $\quad$ and that

$$P(1 \text{ or } 2) + P(\text{not a 1 or 2}) = 1.$$

This is no surprise as *a* 6 and *not a* 6 are **complementary events**. It is certain that one of the events will occur, and impossible for both of them to occur at the same time.

> Two events are **complementary** if exactly one of the events *must* occur.
> If A is an event, then A' is the complementary event of A, or 'not A'.
>
> $$\mathbf{P}(A) + \mathbf{P}(A') = 1$$

EXERCISE 22C.1

1   A marble is randomly selected from a box containing 5 green, 3 red, and 7 blue marbles. Determine the probability that the marble is:

    a   red   b   green   c   blue

    d   not red   e   neither green nor blue   f   green or red.

2   A carton of a dozen eggs contains eight brown eggs.
    The rest are white.

    a   How many white eggs are there in the carton?

    b   Find the probability that an egg selected at random is:

        i   brown   ii   white.

3   A dart board has 36 sectors labelled 1 to 36. Determine the probability that a dart thrown at the centre of the board will hit a sector labelled with:

    a   a multiple of 4

    b   a number between 6 and 9 inclusive

    c   a number greater than 20

    d   9   e   a multiple of 13

    f   an odd number that is a multiple of 3

    g   a multiple of both 4 and 6

    h   a multiple of 4 or 6, or both.

4   What is the probability that a randomly chosen person has his or her next birthday:

    a   on a Tuesday   b   on a weekend   c   in July   d   in January or February?

5   a   List the six different orders in which Antti, Kai, and Neda may sit in a row.

    b   If the three of them sit randomly in a row, determine the probability that:

        i   Antti sits in the middle   ii   Antti sits at the left end

        iii   Antti does not sit at the right end iv   Kai and Neda are seated together.

6   a   List the 8 possible 3-child families according to the gender of the children. For example, GGB means "*the first is a girl, the second is a girl, the third is a boy*".

    b   Assuming that each of these is equally likely to occur, determine the probability that a randomly selected 3-child family consists of:

        i   all boys   ii   all girls   iii   boy then girl then girl

        iv   two girls and a boy   v   a girl for the eldest   vi   at least one boy.

7 a List, in systematic order, the 24 different orders in which four people A, B, C, and D may sit in a row.

b Determine the probability that when the four people sit at random in a row:

   i A sits on one of the end seats

   ii B sits on one of the two middle seats

   iii A and B are seated together

   iv A, B, and C are seated together, not necessarily in that order.

USING GRIDS TO FIND PROBABILITIES

Two-dimensional grids can give us excellent visual displays of sample spaces. We can use them to count favourable outcomes and so calculate probabilities.

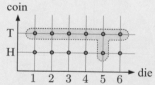

This point represents 'a tail from coin A' and 'a tail from coin B'.

This point represents 'a tail from coin A' and 'a head from coin B'.

There are four members of the sample space.

Example 6   ◀)) Self Tutor

Use a two-dimensional grid to illustrate the sample space for tossing a coin and rolling a die simultaneously. From this grid determine the probability of:

a tossing a head   **b** getting a tail and a 5   **c** getting a tail or a 5.

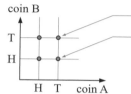

There are 12 members in the sample space.

a $P(\text{head}) = \frac{6}{12} = \frac{1}{2}$

b $P(\text{tail and a '5'}) = \frac{1}{12}$

c $P(\text{tail or a '5'}) = \frac{7}{12}$ {the enclosed points}

In probability, we take "a tail or a 5" to mean "a tail or a 5 or both".

EXERCISE 22C.2

1 Draw the grid of the sample space when a 5-cent and a 10-cent coin are tossed simultaneously. Hence determine the probability of getting:

  a two heads   **b** two tails   **c** exactly one head   **d** at least one head.

2 A coin and a pentagonal spinner with sectors 1, 2, 3, 4, and 5 are tossed and spun respectively.

  a Draw a grid to illustrate the sample space of possible outcomes.

  b How many outcomes are possible?

c Use your grid to determine the chance of getting:

    i a tail and a 3

    ii a head and an even number

    iii an odd number

    iv a head or a 5.

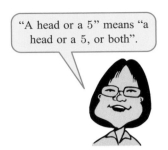

"A head or a 5" means "a head or a 5, or both".

3 A pair of dice is rolled. The 36 different possible results are illustrated in the 2-dimensional grid.

Use the grid to determine the probability of getting:

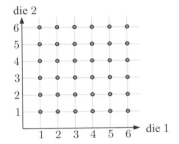

a two 3s

b a 5 and a 6

c a 5 or a 6 (or both)

d at least one 6

e exactly one 6

f no sixes

g a sum of 7

h a sum greater than 8

i a sum of 7 or 11

j a sum of no more than 8.

DISCUSSION

Three children have been experimenting with a coin, tossing it in the air and recording the outcomes. They have done this 10 times and have recorded 10 tails. Before the next toss they make the following statements:

Jackson: "It's got to be a head next time!"

Sally: "No, it always has an equal chance of being a head or a tail. The coin cannot remember what the outcomes have been."

Amy: "Actually, I think it will probably be a tail again, because I think the coin must be biased. It might be weighted so it is more likely to give a tail."

Discuss the statements of each child. Who do you think is correct?

D   TABLES OF OUTCOMES

Tables of outcomes are tables which compare two categorical variables. They usually result from a survey.

For example, a group of teachers were asked which mode of transport they used to travel to school. Their responses are summarised in the table below. The variables are *gender* and *mode of transport*.

	Car	Bicycle	Bus
Male	37	10	10
Female	30	5	13

—— 13 female teachers catch the bus to school.

In the following example we will see how these tables can be used to estimate probabilities. To help us, we extend the table to include totals in each row and column.

Example 7 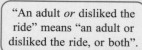 ◀) **Self Tutor**

People exiting a new ride at a theme park were asked whether they liked or disliked the ride. The results are shown in the table alongside.

	Child	Adult
Liked the ride	55	28
Disliked the ride	17	30

Use this table to estimate the probability that a randomly selected person who went on the ride:

a   liked the ride

b   is a child *and* disliked the ride

c   is an adult *or* disliked the ride

d   liked the ride, given that he or she is a child

e   is an adult, given that he or she disliked the ride.

We extend the table to include totals:

	Child	Adult	Total
Liked the ride	55	28	83
Disliked the ride	17	30	47
Total	72	58	130

a   83 out of the 130 people surveyed liked the ride.

∴   P(liked the ride) $\approx \frac{83}{130} \approx 0.638$

b   17 of the 130 people surveyed are children who disliked the ride.

∴   P(child *and* disliked the ride) $\approx \frac{17}{130} \approx 0.131$

c $28 + 30 + 17 = 75$ of the 130 people are adults or disliked the ride.

∴   P(adults *or* disliked the ride) $\approx \frac{75}{130} \approx 0.577$

> "An adult *or* disliked the ride" means "an adult or disliked the ride, or both".

d   Of the 72 children, 55 liked the ride.

∴   P(liked the ride given that he or she is a child) $\approx \frac{55}{72} \approx 0.764$

e   Of the 47 people who disliked the ride, 30 were adults.

∴   P(adult given that he or she disliked the ride) $\approx \frac{30}{47} \approx 0.638$

EXERCISE 22D

1   A sample of adults in a suburb were surveyed about their current employment status and their level of education. The results are summarised in the table below.

	Employed	Unemployed
Attended university	225	34
Did not attend university	197	81

Estimate the probability that the next randomly chosen adult:

a   attended university

b   did not attend university and is currently employed

c   is unemployed

d   is employed, given that they attended university

e   attended university, given that they are unemployed.

2 The types of ticket used to gain access to a basketball match were recorded as people entered the stadium. The results are shown alongside.

	Adult	Child
Season ticket holder	1824	779
Not a season ticket holder	3247	1660

   a What was the total attendance for the match?

   b One person is randomly selected to sit on the home team's bench. Find the probability that the person selected:

     i is a child   **ii** is not a season ticket holder

     iii is an adult season ticket holder.

3 A small hotel in London has kept a record of all the room bookings made for the year, categorised by season and booking type. Find the probability that a randomly selected booking was:

	Single	Double	Family
Peak season	125	220	98
Off-peak season	248	192	152

   a in the peak season   **b** a single room in the off-peak season

   c a single or a double room   **d** a family room, given that it was in the off-peak season

   e in the peak season, given that it was not a single room.

E   COMPOUND EVENTS

Suppose box X contains 2 blue and 2 green balls, and box Y contains 1 white and 3 red balls. A ball is randomly selected from each of the boxes. Determine the probability of getting "a blue ball from X *and* a red ball from Y".

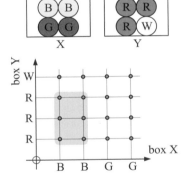

By illustrating the sample space on the two-dimensional grid shown, we can see that 6 of the 16 possibilities are blue from X and red from Y. Each of the outcomes is equally likely, so

$$P(\text{blue from X } \textbf{and} \text{ red from Y}) = \tfrac{6}{16}.$$

In this section we look for a quicker method for finding the probability in such a situation.

INVESTIGATION 4   PROBABILITIES OF COMPOUND EVENTS

Suppose a coin is tossed and a die is rolled at the same time. The result of the coin toss will be called outcome A, and the result of the die roll will be outcome B.

What to do:

1 Copy and complete, using a 2-dimensional grid if necessary:

	$P(A \text{ and } B)$	$P(A)$	$P(B)$
P(a head and a 4)			
P(a head and an odd number)			
P(a tail and a number larger than 1)			
P(a tail and a number less than 3)			

2 What is the connection between $P(A \text{ and } B)$, $P(A)$, and $P(B)$?

INVESTIGATION 5   REVISITING DRAWING PINS

We cannot find by theoretical argument the probability that a drawing pin will land on its back ⊥ . We can only find this probability by experimentation.

When tossing *two* drawing pins, can we still use the rule for compound events:

$$P(\text{back and back}) = P(\text{back}) \times P(\text{back})?$$

What to do:

1 From **Investigation 1** on page **570**, what is your estimate of P(back *and* back)?

2 a Count the number of drawing pins in a full packet. They must be identical to each other and the same ones that you used in **Investigation 1**.

   b Drop the whole packet onto a solid surface and count the number of *backs* and *sides*. Repeat this several times. Pool results with others and finally estimate P(back).

   c Hence find   P(back) × P(back)   using **2 b**.

3 Is   P(back *and* back) ≈ P(back) × P(back)?

From **Investigations 4** and **5**, it seems that if A and B are two events for which the occurrence of each one does not affect the occurrence of the other, then $P(A \text{ and } B) = P(A) \times P(B)$.

Before we can formalise this as a rule, however, we need to distinguish between **independent** and **dependent** events.

INDEPENDENT EVENTS

Events are **independent** if the occurrence of either of them does not affect the probability that the others occur.

Consider again the example on the previous page. Suppose we happen to choose a blue ball from box X. This does not affect the outcome when we choose a ball from box Y. The probability of selecting a red ball from box Y is $\frac{3}{4}$ regardless of which colour ball is selected from box X.

So, the two events "a blue ball from X" and "a red ball from Y" are independent.

> If A and B are **independent events** then $P(A \text{ and } B) = P(A) \times P(B)$.

This rule can be extended for any number of independent events.

For example: If A, B, and C are all **independent events**, then
$P(A \text{ and } B \text{ and } C) = P(A) \times P(B) \times P(C)$.

Example 8	◀ Self Tutor

A coin and a die are tossed simultaneously. Determine the probability of getting a head and a 3 without using a grid.

P(a head and a 3) = P(H) × P(3)   {events are independent}

$$= \tfrac{1}{2} \times \tfrac{1}{6} = \tfrac{1}{12}$$

EXERCISE 22E.1

1 At a mountain village in Papua New Guinea it rains on average 6 days a week. Determine the probability that it rains on:

   a   any one day   b   two successive days   c   three successive days.

2 A coin is tossed 3 times. Determine the probability of getting the following sequences of results:

   a   head then head then head   b   tail then head then tail.

3 A school has two photocopiers. On any one day, machine A has an 8% chance of malfunctioning and machine B has a 12% chance of malfunctioning. Determine the probability that on any one day both machines will:

   a   malfunction   b   work effectively.

4 A couple would like 4 children, none of whom will be adopted. They will be disappointed if the children are not born in the order boy, girl, boy, girl. Determine the probability that they will be:

   a   happy with the order of arrival   b   unhappy with the order of arrival.

5 Two marksmen fire at a target simultaneously. Jiri hits the target 70% of the time and Benita hits it 80% of the time. Determine the probability that:

   a   they both hit the target

   b   they both miss the target

   c   Jiri hits but Benita misses

   d   Benita hits but Jiri misses.

6  An archer always hits a circular target with each arrow fired, and hits the bullseye on average 2 out of every 5 shots. If 3 arrows are fired at the target, determine the probability that the bullseye is hit:

   a   every time

   b   the first two times, but not on the third shot

   c   on no occasion.

DEPENDENT EVENTS

Suppose a hat contains 5 red and 3 blue tickets. One ticket is randomly chosen, its colour is noted, and it is then put aside and so *not* put back in the hat. A second ticket is then randomly selected. What is the chance that it is red?

If the first ticket was red,   P(second is red) $= \frac{4}{7}$ ————— 4 reds remaining
                                                  ————— 7 to choose from

If the first ticket was blue,   P(second is red) $= \frac{5}{7}$ ————— 5 reds remaining
                                                  ————— 7 to choose from

So, the probability of the second ticket being red *depends* on what colour the first ticket was. We therefore have **dependent events**.

Two or more events are **dependent** if they are **not independent**.

Events are **dependent** if the occurrence of one of the events *does affect* the occurrence of the other event.

If A and B are dependent events then

$$P(A \textbf{ then } B) = P(A) \times P(B \text{ given that } A \text{ has occurred}).$$

Example 9   ◄)) Self Tutor

A box contains 4 red and 2 yellow tickets. Two tickets are randomly selected from the box one by one *without* replacement. Find the probability that:

a both are red

b the first is red and the second is yellow.

a   P(both red)

= P(first selected is red *and* second is red)

= P(first selected is red) $\times$ P(second is red given that the first is red)

= $\frac{4}{6} \times \frac{3}{5}$ ◄——— If a red is drawn first, 3 reds remain out of a total of 5.

= $\frac{2}{5}$ ———— 4 reds out of a total of 6 tickets

b   P(first is red *and* second is yellow)

= P(first is red) $\times$ P(second is yellow given that the first is red)

= $\frac{4}{6} \times \frac{2}{5}$ ◄——— If a red is drawn first, 2 yellows remain out of a total of 5.

= $\frac{4}{15}$ ———— 4 reds out of a total of 6 tickets

Example 10   ◄)) Self Tutor

A hat contains 20 tickets numbered 1, 2, 3, ..., 20. If 3 tickets are drawn from the hat without replacement, determine the probability that they are all prime numbers.

> In each fraction the numerator is the number of outcomes in the event. The denominator is the total number of possible outcomes.

$\{2, 3, 5, 7, 11, 13, 17, 19\}$ are primes.

∴ there are 20 numbers of which 8 are primes.

∴   P(3 primes)

= P(1st drawn is prime *and* 2nd is prime *and* 3rd is prime)

= $\frac{8}{20}$ ◄———— 8 primes out of 20 numbers

$\times \frac{7}{19}$ ◄———— 7 primes out of 19 numbers after a successful first draw

$\times \frac{6}{18}$ ◄— 6 primes out of 18 numbers after two successful draws

≈ 0.0491

EXERCISE 22E.2

1   A bin contains 12 identically shaped chocolates of which 8 are strawberry creams. If 3 chocolates are selected simultaneously from the bin, determine the probability that:

    a   they are all strawberry creams

    b   none of them are strawberry creams.

Drawing three chocolates *simultaneously* implies there is no replacement.

2   A box contains 7 red and 3 green balls. Two balls are drawn one after another from the box without replacement. Determine the probability that:

    a   both are red

    b   the first is green and the second is red

    c   a green and a red are obtained.

3   A lottery has 100 tickets which are placed in a barrel. Three tickets are drawn at random from the barrel, without replacement, to decide 3 prizes. If John has 3 tickets in the lottery, determine his probability of winning:

    a   first prize   b   first and second prize   c   all 3 prizes   d   none of the prizes.

4   A hat contains 7 names of players in a tennis squad including the captain and the vice captain. If a team of 3 is chosen at random by drawing the names from the hat, determine the probability that it does *not* contain:

    a   the captain   b   the captain or the vice captain.

5   Two students are chosen at random from a group of two girls and five boys, all of different ages. Find the probability that the two students chosen will be:

    a   two boys   b   the eldest two students.

F   TREE DIAGRAMS

Tree diagrams can be used to illustrate sample spaces if the possible outcomes are not too numerous. Once the sample space is illustrated, the tree diagram can be used for determining probabilities.

Consider two archers firing simultaneously at a target. These are independent events.

Li has probability $\frac{3}{4}$ of hitting a target and Yuka has probability $\frac{4}{5}$.

The tree diagram for this information is:

H = hit   M = miss

Li's results

Yuka's results

	outcome	probability
H	H and H	$\frac{3}{4} \times \frac{4}{5} = \frac{12}{20}$
M	H and M	$\frac{3}{4} \times \frac{1}{5} = \frac{3}{20}$
H	M and H	$\frac{1}{4} \times \frac{4}{5} = \frac{4}{20}$
M	M and M	$\frac{1}{4} \times \frac{1}{5} = \frac{1}{20}$
	total	1

$\frac{3}{4}$ H $\frac{4}{5}$ $\frac{1}{5}$

$\frac{1}{4}$ M $\frac{4}{5}$ $\frac{1}{5}$

Notice that:

• The probabilities for hitting and missing are marked on the branches.

• There are *four* alternative branches, each showing a particular outcome.

• All outcomes are represented.

• The probability of each outcome is obtained by **multiplying** the probabilities along its branch.

Example 11   ◀) **Self Tutor**

Carl is not having much luck lately. His car will only start 80% of the time and his motorbike will only start 60% of the time.

> **a** Draw a tree diagram to illustrate this situation.
>
> **b** Use the tree diagram to determine the chance that:
>
> **i** both will start   **ii** Carl can only use his car.

a

C = car starts
M = motorbike starts
∴ C' = complementary
event of C
= car does not start
and M' = motorbike does
not start

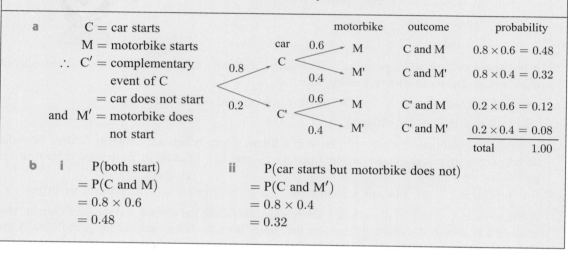

motorbike	outcome	probability
M	C and M	$0.8 \times 0.6 = 0.48$
M'	C and M'	$0.8 \times 0.4 = 0.32$
M	C' and M	$0.2 \times 0.6 = 0.12$
M'	C' and M'	$0.2 \times 0.4 = 0.08$
	total	1.00

b **i**   P(both start)
= P(C and M)
$= 0.8 \times 0.6$
$= 0.48$

ii   P(car starts but motorbike does not)
= P(C and M')
$= 0.8 \times 0.4$
$= 0.32$

If there is more than one outcome that results in an event occurring, then we need to **add** the probabilities of these outcomes.

Example 12   ◀) **Self Tutor**

Two boxes each contain 6 petunia plants that are not yet flowering. Box A contains 2 plants that will have purple flowers and 4 plants that will have white flowers. Box B contains 5 plants that will have purple flowers and 1 plant that will have white flowers. A box is selected by tossing a coin, and one plant is removed at random from it. Determine the probability that it will have purple flowers.

Box A   Box B

P	W	W
W	P	W

P	P	P
W	P	P

P(purple flowers)
$= P(A \text{ and } P) + P(B \text{ and } P)$
$= \frac{1}{2} \times \frac{2}{6} + \frac{1}{2} \times \frac{5}{6}$ {branches marked ✓}
$= \frac{7}{12}$

EXERCISE 22F

1   Of the students in a class playing musical instruments, 60%
    are female. 20% of the females and 30% of the males play
    the violin.

    a   Copy and complete the tree diagram.

    b   What is the probability that a randomly selected
        student:

        i   is male and does not play the violin

        ii plays the violin?

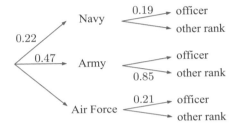

2   a   Copy and complete this tree diagram about
        people in the armed forces.

    b   What is the probability that a member of the
        armed forces:

        i   is an officer

        ii is not an officer in the navy

        iii is not an army or air force officer?

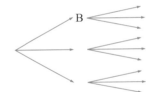

3   Suppose this spinner
    is spun twice.

    a   Copy and complete the branches on the tree
        diagram shown.

    b   Find the probability that black appears on both spins.

    c   Find the probability that yellow appears on both spins.

    d   Find the probability that different colours appear on the two spins.

    e   Find the probability that black appears on either spin.

4   The probability of rain tomorrow is estimated to be $\frac{1}{5}$. If it does rain, Mudlark will start favourite in
    the horse race, with probability $\frac{1}{2}$ of winning. If it is fine, he only has a 1 in 20 chance of winning.
    Display the sample space of possible results of the horse race on a tree diagram. Hence determine
    the probability that Mudlark will win tomorrow.

5   Machine A makes 40% of the bottles produced at a factory. Machine B makes the rest. Machine
    A spoils 5% of its product, while Machine B spoils only 2%. Using an appropriate tree diagram,
    determine the probability that the next bottle inspected at this factory is spoiled.

6   Jar A contains 2 white and 3 red discs. Jar B contains 3 white and 1 red disc. A jar is chosen at
    random by the flip of a coin, and one disc is taken at random from it. Determine the probability
    that the disc is red.

7   The English Premier League consists of 20 teams. Tottenham is currently in 8th place on the table.
    It has 20% chance of winning and 50% chance of losing against any team placed above it. If a team
    is placed below it, Tottenham has a 50% chance of winning and a 30% chance of losing. Find the
    probability that Tottenham will draw its next game.

8 Three bags contain different numbers of blue and red marbles.

A bag is selected using a die which has three A faces, two B faces, and one C face. One marble is then selected randomly from the bag.

Determine the probability that the marble is:

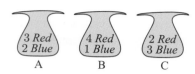

a blue   **b** red.

G SAMPLING WITH AND WITHOUT REPLACEMENT

Suppose we have a large group of objects. If we select one of the objects at random and inspect it for particular features, then this process is known as **sampling**.

If the object is put back in the group before an object is chosen again, we call it **sampling with replacement**.

If the object is put to one side, we call it **sampling without replacement**.

Sampling is commonly used in the quality control of industrial processes.

Sometimes the inspection process makes it impossible to return the object to the large group. For example:

- To see if a chocolate is hard or soft-centred, we need to bite it or squeeze it.
- To see if an egg contains one or two yolks, we need to break it open.
- To see if an object is correctly made, we may need to pull it apart.

Consider a box containing 3 red, 2 blue, and 1 yellow marble. If we sample two marbles, we can do this either:

- **with replacement** of the first before the second is drawn, or
- **without replacement** of the first before the second is drawn.

Examine how the tree diagrams differ:

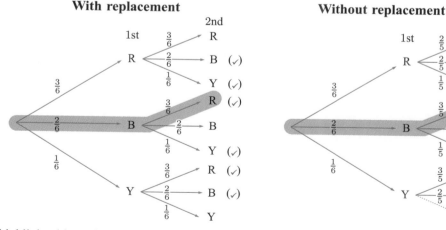

The highlighted branch represents a blue marble with the first draw and a red marble with the second draw. We write this as BR.

Notice that:

- with replacement (independent events), $P(\text{two reds}) = \frac{3}{6} \times \frac{3}{6} = \frac{1}{4}$
- without replacement (dependent events), $P(\text{two reds}) = \frac{3}{6} \times \frac{2}{5} = \frac{1}{5}$

Example 13   ◀) **Self Tutor**

A box contains 3 red, 2 blue and 1 yellow marble. Find the probability of getting two different colours:

  a if replacement occurs   **b** if replacement does not occur.

To answer this question we use the tree diagram on page **588**.

a   P(two different colours)

= P(RB or RY or BR or BY or YR or YB)   {ticked ones ✓}

= $\frac{3}{6} \times \frac{2}{6} + \frac{3}{6} \times \frac{1}{6} + \frac{2}{6} \times \frac{3}{6} + \frac{2}{6} \times \frac{1}{6} + \frac{1}{6} \times \frac{3}{6} + \frac{1}{6} \times \frac{2}{6}$

= $\frac{11}{18}$

b   P(two different colours)

= P(RB or RY or BR or BY or YR or YB)   {crossed ones ✗}

= $\frac{3}{6} \times \frac{2}{5} + \frac{3}{6} \times \frac{1}{5} + \frac{2}{6} \times \frac{3}{5} + \frac{2}{6} \times \frac{1}{5} + \frac{1}{6} \times \frac{3}{5} + \frac{1}{6} \times \frac{2}{5}$

= $\frac{11}{15}$

In **b**, "2 different colours" and "2 same colours" are complementary events.

∴ P(2 different colours)

= 1 − P(2 the same)

= 1 − P(RR or BB)

= $1 - (\frac{3}{6} \times \frac{2}{5} + \frac{2}{6} \times \frac{1}{5})$

= $\frac{11}{15}$

Example 14   ◀) **Self Tutor**

A bag contains 5 red and 3 blue marbles. Two marbles are drawn simultaneously from the bag. Determine the probability that at least one is red.

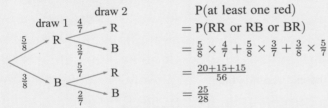

P(at least one red)

= P(RR or RB or BR)

= $\frac{5}{8} \times \frac{4}{7} + \frac{5}{8} \times \frac{3}{7} + \frac{3}{8} \times \frac{5}{7}$

= $\frac{20+15+15}{56}$

= $\frac{25}{28}$

Drawing *simultaneously* is the same as sampling *without* replacement.

Alternatively,   P(at least one red)

= 1 − P(no reds)   {complementary events}

= 1 − P(BB)   and so on.

EXERCISE 22G

1 Two marbles are drawn in succession from a box containing 2 purple and 5 green marbles. Determine the probability that the two marbles are different colours if:

  a the first is replaced   **b** the first is *not* replaced.

2 5 tickets numbered 1, 2, 3, 4, and 5 are placed in a bag. Two are taken from the bag without replacement.

  a Complete the tree diagram by writing the probabilities on the branches.

  b Determine the probability that:

    i both are odd

    ii both are even

    iii one is odd and the other even.

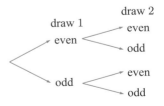

3 A die has 4 faces showing A, and 2 faces showing B. Jar A contains 3 red and 2 green tickets. Jar B contains 3 red and 7 green tickets.

A roll of the die is used to select either jar A or jar B. Once a jar has been selected, two tickets are randomly selected from it without replacement. Determine the probability that:

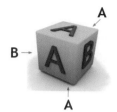

   a both are green
   b they are different in colour.

4 Marie has a bag of sweets which are all identical in shape. The bag contains 6 orange drops and 4 lemon drops. She selects one sweet at random, eats it, and then takes another at random.

   a Determine the probability that:

      i both sweets are orange drops

      ii both sweets are lemon drops

      iii the first is an orange drop and the second is a lemon drop

      iv the first is a lemon drop and the second is an orange drop.

   b Add your answers in **a**. Explain why the total must be 1.

5 A board game uses the spinner shown. If the first spin is red, then the spinner is spun a second time.

   a Complete the tree diagram by labelling each branch with its probability.

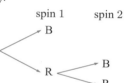

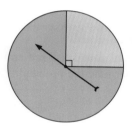

   b Calculate the probability that the end result is blue.

6 A bag contains four red and two blue marbles. Three marbles are selected simultaneously. Determine the probablity that:

   a all are red
   b only two are red
   c at least two are red.

7 Bag A contains 3 red and 2 white marbles. Bag B contains 4 red and 3 white marbles. One marble is randomly selected from A and its colour noted. If it is red, 2 reds are added to bag B. If it is white, 2 whites are added to bag B. A marble is then selected from bag B. What is the chance that the marble selected is white?

8 A man holds two tickets in a 100-ticket lottery in which there are two winning tickets chosen. If no replacement occurs, determine the probability that he will win:

   a both prizes
   b neither prize
   c at least one prize.

9 A container holds 3 red, 7 white, and 2 black balls. A ball is chosen at random from the container and is not replaced. A second ball is then chosen. Find the probability of choosing one white and one black ball in any order.

10 A bag contains 7 yellow and n blue markers.

Two markers are selected at random, without replacement. The probability that both markers are yellow is $\frac{3}{13}$. How many blue markers are there in the bag?

H   SETS AND VENN DIAGRAMS

Venn diagrams are a useful way of representing the events in a sample space. These diagrams usually consist of a rectangle which represents the complete sample space U, and circles within it which represent particular events.

Venn diagrams can be used to solve certain types of probability questions and also to establish a number of probability laws.

When we roll an ordinary die, the sample space or universal set is $U = \{1, 2, 3, 4, 5, 6\}$.

If the event A is *"a number less than 3"*, then there are two outcomes which satisfy event A. We can write $A = \{1, 2\}$.

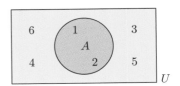

The Venn diagram alongside illustrates the event A within the universal set U.

$n(U) = 6$ and $n(A) = 2$, so $\mathrm{P}(A) = \dfrac{n(A)}{n(U)} = \dfrac{2}{6} = \dfrac{1}{3}$.

SET NOTATION

-

  The **universal set** or **sample space** U is represented by a rectangle.
  A set within the universal set is usually represented by a circle.

-

  A' (shaded green) is the **complement** of A (shaded purple).
  A' represents the non-occurrence of A, so $\mathrm{P}(A) + \mathrm{P}(A') = 1$.

  If $U = \{1, 2, 3, 4, 5, 6, 7\}$ and $A = \{2, 4, 6\}$ then $A' = \{1, 3, 5, 7\}$.

- $x \in A$ reads 'x is in A' and means that x is an element of the set A.

- $n(A)$ reads 'the number of elements in set A'.

- $A \cap B$ denotes the **intersection** of sets A and B. This set contains all elements common to **both** sets.

  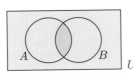

  $A \cap B$ is shaded in purple.

  $$A \cap B = \{x \mid x \in A \textbf{ and } x \in B\}$$

- $A \cup B$ denotes the **union** of sets A and B. This set contains all elements belonging to A **or** B **or both** A and B.

  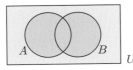

  $A \cup B$ is shaded in purple.

  $$A \cup B = \{x \mid x \in A \textbf{ or } x \in B \textbf{ or } x \in A \cap B\}$$

- **Disjoint sets** are sets which do not have elements in common.

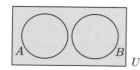

These two sets are disjoint.

$A \cap B = \varnothing$ where $\varnothing$ denotes the **empty set**.

A and B are said to be **mutually exclusive**.

Example 15   ◀) **Self Tutor**

Suppose A is the set of all factors of 24 and B is the set of all factors of 28.
$U = \{x \mid 1 \leqslant x \leqslant 28, \ x \in \mathbb{Z}\}$

  a Find $A \cap B$.   **b** Illustrate A and B on a Venn diagram.   **c** Find $A \cup B$.

$A = \{1, 2, 3, 4, 6, 8, 12, 24\}$ and $B = \{1, 2, 4, 7, 14, 28\}$

a $A \cap B =$ the set of factors common to both 24 **and** 28 $= \{1, 2, 4\}$

b
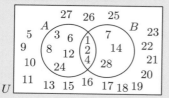

c $A \cup B$
    = the set of factors of 24 **or** 28 (or both)
    = $\{1, 2, 3, 4, 6, 7, 8, 12, 14, 24, 28\}$

Example 16   ◀) **Self Tutor**

On separate Venn diagrams containing two events A and B that intersect, shade the region representing:

  a in A but not in B **b** neither in A nor B.

Shading is shown in green.

a
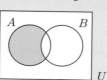

b
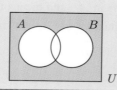

To practise shading the regions represented by various subsets, click on the icon.

DEMO

EXERCISE 22H.1

1 Let A be the set of all factors of 6, B be the set of all positive even integers < 11, and
   $U = \{x \mid 1 \leqslant x \leqslant 10, \ x \in \mathbb{Z}\}$

  a Describe A and B using set notation.

  b Illustrate A and B on a Venn diagram.

  c Find: **i** $n(A)$ **ii** $A \cup B$ **iii** $A \cap B$.

2 On separate Venn diagrams containing two events A and B that intersect, shade the region representing:

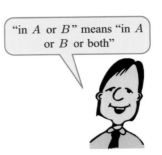

"in A or B" means "in A or B or both"

   a in A **b** in B

   c in both A and B **d** in A or B

   e in B but not in A **f** in exactly one of A or B.

3 If A and B are two non-disjoint sets, shade the region of a Venn diagram representing:

   a A' **b** $A' \cap B$ **c** $A \cup B'$ **d** $A' \cap B'$

4 The diagram alongside is the most general case for three events in the same sample space U.

On separate Venn diagram sketches, shade:

   a A **b** B' **c** $B \cap C$

   d $A \cup C$ **e** $A \cap B \cap C$ **f** $(A \cup B) \cap C$

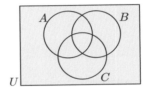

Example 17	🔊 **Self Tutor**

If the Venn diagram alongside illustrates the number of people in a sporting club who play tennis (T) and hockey (H), determine the number of people:

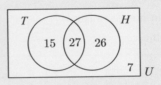

   a in the club   **b** who play hockey

   c who play both sports   **d** who play neither sport

   e who play at least one sport.

   a Number in the club   **b** Number who play hockey

      $= 15 + 27 + 26 + 7 = 75$ $= 27 + 26 = 53$

   c Number who play both sports $= 27$ **d** Number who play neither sport $= 7$

   e Number who play at least one sport

      $= 15 + 27 + 26 = 68$

---

5 The Venn diagram alongside illustrates the number of students in a particular class who study Chemistry (C) and History (H). Determine the number of students:

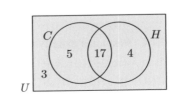

   a in the class   **b** who study both subjects

   c who study at least one of the subjects

   d who only study Chemistry.

Example 18

◀) Self Tutor

The Venn diagram alongside represents the set U of all children in a class. Each dot represents a student. The event E shows all those students with blue eyes. Determine the probability that a randomly selected child:

a   has blue eyes

b   does not have blue eyes.

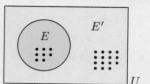

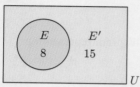

$n(U) = 23, \quad n(E) = 8$

a $P(\text{blue eyes}) = \dfrac{n(E)}{n(U)} = \dfrac{8}{23}$

b $P(\text{not blue eyes}) = \dfrac{n(E')}{n(U)} = \dfrac{15}{23}$

   or $P(\text{not blue}) = 1 - P(\text{blue eyes})$

   $= 1 - \dfrac{8}{23} = \dfrac{15}{23}$

Example 19

◀) Self Tutor

In a class of 30 students, 19 study Physics, 17 study Chemistry, and 15 study both of these subjects. Display this information on a Venn diagram and hence determine the probability that a randomly selected class member studies:

a   both subjects

b   at least one of the subjects

c   Physics but not Chemistry

d   exactly one of the subjects

e   neither subject

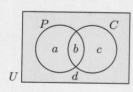

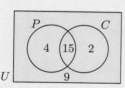

Let P represent the event of 'studying Physics' and C represent the event of 'studying Chemistry'.

Now $a + b = 19$ {as 19 study Physics}

$b + c = 17$ {as 17 study Chemistry}

$b = 15$ {as 15 study both}

$a + b + c + d = 30$ {as there are 30 in the class}

$\therefore \quad b = 15, \quad a = 4, \quad c = 2, \quad d = 9.$

a $P(\text{studies both})$
$= \dfrac{15}{30}$ or $\dfrac{1}{2}$

b $P(\text{studies at least one subject})$
$= \dfrac{4+15+2}{30}$
$= \dfrac{7}{10}$

c $P(P \text{ but not } C)$
$= \dfrac{4}{30}$
$= \dfrac{2}{15}$

d $P(\text{studies exactly one})$
$= \dfrac{4+2}{30}$
$= \dfrac{1}{5}$

e $P(\text{studies neither})$
$= \dfrac{9}{30}$
$= \dfrac{3}{10}$

6 In a survey at an alpine resort, people were asked whether they liked skiing (S) or snowboarding (B). Use the Venn diagram to determine the number of people:

   a in the survey

   b who liked both activities

   c who liked neither activity

   d who liked exactly one activity.

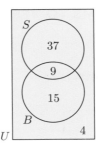

7 For two events A and B we are given that $n(A \cap B) = 5$, $n(A) = 11$, $n(A \cup B) = 12$, and $n(B') = 8$.

   a Complete the Venn diagram:

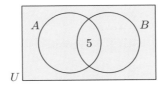

   b Hence find:

   i $P(A \cup B)$ **ii** $P(A')$

8 In a class of 40 students, 19 play tennis, 20 play netball, and 8 play neither of these sports. A student is randomly chosen from the class. Determine the probability that the student:

   a plays tennis   **b** does not play netball

   c plays at least one of the sports   **d** plays one and only one of the sports

   e plays netball but not tennis.

9 50 married men were asked whether they gave their wife flowers or chocolates for her last birthday. The results were: 31 gave chocolates, 12 gave flowers, and 5 gave both chocolates and flowers. If one of the married men was chosen at random, determine the probability that he gave his wife:

   a chocolates or flowers   **b** chocolates but not flowers

   c neither chocolates nor flowers.

10 The medical records for a class of 30 children showed that 24 had previously had measles, 12 had previously had measles and mumps, and 26 had previously had at least one of measles or mumps. If one child from the class is selected at random, determine the probability that he or she has had:

   a mumps   **b** mumps but not measles   **c** neither mumps nor measles.

11 The Venn diagram opposite indicates the types of program a group of 40 individuals watched on television last night.

   M represents movies, S represents sport, and D represents drama.

   a Given that 10 people watched a movie last night, calculate a and b.

   b Find the probability that one of these individuals, selected at random, watched:

   i sport   **ii** drama and sport   **iii** a movie but not sport

   iv drama but not a movie   **v** drama or a movie.

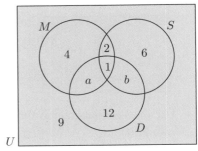

USING VENN DIAGRAMS TO VERIFY SET IDENTITIES

Example 20   ◀ Self Tutor

Verify that $(A \cup B)' = A' \cap B'$.

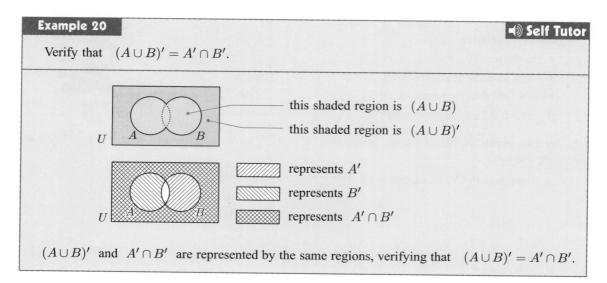

this shaded region is $(A \cup B)$

this shaded region is $(A \cup B)'$

▨▨▨ represents A'

▭ represents B'

▨ represents $A' \cap B'$

$(A \cup B)'$ and $A' \cap B'$ are represented by the same regions, verifying that $(A \cup B)' = A' \cap B'$.

EXERCISE 22H.2

1 By drawing appropriate Venn diagrams, verify that:

   a $(A \cap B)' = A' \cup B'$

   b $A \cup (B \cap C) = (A \cup B) \cap (A \cup C)$

   c $A \cap (B \cup C) = (A \cap B) \cup (A \cap C)$

2 Suppose $S = \{x \mid x \text{ is a positive integer} < 100\}$.

   Let $A = \{\text{multiples of 7 in } S\}$ and $B = \{\text{multiples of 5 in } S\}$.

   a How many elements are there in: **i** A **ii** B **iii** $A \cap B$ **iv** $A \cup B$?

   b If $n(E)$ represents the number of elements in set E, verify that
      $n(A \cup B) = n(A) + n(B) - n(A \cap B)$.

   c Use the figure alongside to establish that
      $n(A \cup B) = n(A) + n(B) - n(A \cap B)$
      for all sets A and B in a universal set U.

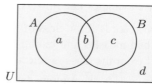

3

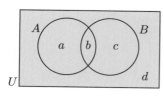

From the Venn diagram, $P(A) = \dfrac{a+b}{a+b+c+d}$.

   a Use the Venn diagram to find:

      i $P(B)$ **ii** $P(A \cap B)$ **iii** $P(A \cup B)$ **iv** $P(A) + P(B) - P(A \cap B)$

   b What is the connection between $P(A \cup B)$ and $P(A) + P(B) - P(A \cap B)$?

LAWS OF PROBABILITY

THE ADDITION LAW

In the previous exercise we demonstrated the **addition law of probability**:

For two events A and B, $\qquad P(A \cup B) = P(A) + P(B) - P(A \cap B)$

which means: $\qquad P(\textbf{either } A \textbf{ or } B \textbf{ or both}) = P(A) + P(B) - P(\textbf{both } A \textbf{ and } B).$

Example 21 🔊 Self Tutor

If $P(A) = 0.6$, $P(A \cup B) = 0.7$, and $P(A \cap B) = 0.3$, find $P(B)$.

$P(A \cup B) = P(A) + P(B) - P(A \cap B)$
$\therefore \quad 0.7 = 0.6 + P(B) - 0.3$
$\therefore \quad P(B) = 0.4$

or

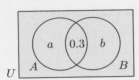

Using a Venn diagram with the probabilities on it,

$a + 0.3 = 0.6 \qquad$ and $\qquad a + b + 0.3 = 0.7$
$\therefore \quad a = 0.3 \qquad\qquad\qquad \therefore \quad a + b = 0.4$
$\qquad\qquad\qquad\qquad\qquad\qquad \therefore \quad 0.3 + b = 0.4$
$\qquad\qquad\qquad\qquad\qquad\qquad\qquad \therefore \quad b = 0.1$

$\therefore \quad P(B) = 0.3 + b = 0.4$

MUTUALLY EXCLUSIVE OR DISJOINT EVENTS

If A and B are **mutually exclusive** events then $\quad P(A \cap B) = 0$

and so the addition law becomes $\quad P(A \cup B) = P(A) + P(B)$.

Example 22 🔊 Self Tutor

A chocolate is randomly selected from a box which contains 6 chocolates with hard centres and 12 chocolates with soft centres.

Let H be the event that a randomly selected chocolate from the box has a hard centre, and S be the event that a randomly selected chocolate from the box has a soft centre.

a Are the events H and S mutually exclusive?

b Find: i $P(H)$ ii $P(S)$ iii $P(H \cap S)$ iv $P(H \cup S)$.

a Chocolates cannot have both a hard and a soft centre.
$\quad \therefore \quad H$ and S are mutually exclusive.

b i $P(H) = \frac{6}{18} = \frac{1}{3}$ $\qquad\qquad\qquad\qquad$ ii $P(S) = \frac{12}{18} = \frac{2}{3}$

iii $P(H \cap S) = 0 \qquad\qquad$ {a chocolate cannot have a hard *and* a soft centre}

iv $P(H \cup S) = \frac{18}{18} = 1 \qquad$ {a chocolate must have a hard *or* a soft centre}

CONDITIONAL PROBABILITY

Given two events A and B, the **conditional probability of A given B** is the probability that A occurs given that B has already occurred.

The conditional probability is written $A \mid B$ and read as "A given B".

Example 23   ◀) **Self Tutor**

In a class of 25 students, 14 like pizza and 16 like iced coffee. One student likes neither and 6 students like both. One student is randomly selected from the class. What is the probability that the student:

   a likes pizza   **b** likes pizza given that he or she likes iced coffee?

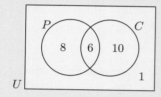

The Venn diagram of the situation is shown.

a Of the 25 students, 14 like pizza.

$$\therefore \quad P(\text{pizza}) = \tfrac{14}{25}$$

b Of the 16 who like iced coffee, 6 like pizza.

$$\therefore \quad P(\text{pizza} \mid \text{iced coffee}) = \tfrac{6}{16}$$

If A and B are events then $\quad P(A \mid B) = \dfrac{P(A \cap B)}{P(B)}$.

Proof:

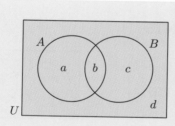

$$P(A \mid B) = \frac{b}{b + c} \qquad \{\text{Venn diagram}\}$$

$$= \frac{\frac{b}{(a+b+c+d)}}{\frac{b+c}{(a+b+c+d)}}$$

$$= \frac{P(A \cap B)}{P(B)}$$

It follows that:

$$P(A \cap B) = P(A \mid B)\, P(B)$$

$$P(A \cap B) = P(B \mid A)\, P(A).$$

EXERCISE 22I

1 If $P(A) = 0.4$, $P(A \cup B) = 0.9$, and $P(A \cap B) = 0.1$, find $P(B)$.

2 If $P(X) = 0.6$, $P(Y) = 0.5$, and $P(X \cup Y) = 0.9$, find $P(X \cap Y)$.

3 A and B are mutually exclusive events.

If $P(B) = 0.45$ and $P(A \cup B) = 0.8$, find $P(A)$.

Example 24   ◀) **Self Tutor**

In a class of 40 students, 34 like bananas, 22 like pineapple, and 2 dislike both fruits. A student is randomly selected. Find the probability that the student:

   a likes both fruits   **b** likes at least one fruit

   c likes bananas given that he or she likes pineapple

   d dislikes pineapple given that he or she likes bananas.

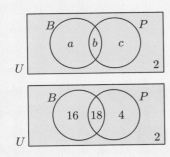

B represents students who like bananas.
P represents students who like pineapple.

We are given that $a + b = 34$
$$b + c = 22$$
$$a + b + c = 38$$

$\therefore$ $c = 38 - 34 = 4$ and so $b = 18$
and $a = 16$

  a P(likes both)   **b** P(likes at least one)   **c** $P(B \mid P)$ **d** $P(P' \mid B)$

    $= \frac{18}{40}$ $= \frac{38}{40}$ $= \frac{18}{22}$ $= \frac{16}{34}$

    $= \frac{9}{20}$ $= \frac{19}{20}$ $= \frac{9}{11}$ $= \frac{8}{17}$

Example 25   ◀) **Self Tutor**

The top shelf in a cupboard contains 3 cans of pumpkin soup and 2 cans of chicken soup. The bottom shelf contains 4 cans of pumpkin soup and 1 can of chicken soup.

Lukas is twice as likely to take a can from the bottom shelf as he is from the top shelf. Suppose Lukas takes one can of soup without looking at the label. Determine the probability that it:

   a is chicken   **b** was taken from top shelf given that it is chicken.

T represents the top shelf.
B represents the bottom shelf.
P represents the pumpkin soup.
C represents the chicken soup.

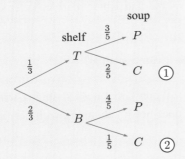

  a P(soup is chicken)

    $= \frac{1}{3} \times \frac{2}{5} + \frac{2}{3} \times \frac{1}{5}$ {paths ① and ②}

    $= \frac{4}{15}$

  b P(top shelf | chicken)

    $= \dfrac{\text{P(top shelf and chicken)}}{\text{P(chicken)}}$

    $= \dfrac{\frac{1}{3} \times \frac{2}{5}}{\frac{4}{15}}$ ⟵ path ①

               ⟵ from a

    $= \frac{1}{2}$

4 In a group of 50 students, 40 study Mathematics, 32 study Physics, and each student studies at least one of these subjects.

   a Use a Venn diagram to find how many students study both subjects.

   b If a student from this group is randomly selected, find the probability that he or she:

     i studies Mathematics but not Physics

     ii studies Physics given that he or she studies Mathematics.

5 In a group of 40 boys, 23 have dark hair, 18 have brown eyes, and 26 have dark hair, brown eyes, or both. One of the boys is selected at random. Determine the probability that he has:

   a dark hair and brown eyes

   b neither dark hair nor brown eyes

   c dark hair but not brown eyes

   d brown eyes given that he has dark hair.

6 50 students went bushwalking. 23 were sunburnt, 22 were bitten by ants, and 5 were both sunburnt and bitten by ants. Determine the probability that a randomly selected student:

   a escaped being bitten

   b was bitten or sunburnt (or both)

   c was neither bitten nor sunburnt

   d was bitten, given that he or she was sunburnt

   e was sunburnt, given that he or she was not bitten.

7 400 families were surveyed. It was found that 90% had a TV set and 60% had a computer. Every family had at least one of these items. One of these families is randomly selected, and it is found that it has a computer. Find the probability that it also has a TV set.

8 In a certain town three newspapers are published. 20% of the population read A, 16% read B, 14% read C, 8% read A and B, 5% read A and C, 4% read B and C, and 2% read all 3 newspapers. A person is selected at random. Use a Venn diagram to help determine the probability that the person reads:

   a none of the papers

   b at least one of the papers

   c exactly one of the papers

   d A or B (or both)

   e A, given that the person reads at least one paper

   f C, given that the person reads either A or B or both.

9 Urn A contains 2 red and 3 blue marbles, and urn B contains 4 red and 1 blue marble. Peter selects an urn by tossing a coin, and takes a marble from that urn.

   a Determine the probability that it is red.

   b Given that the marble is red, what is the probability that it came from B?

10 The probability that Greta's mother takes her shopping is $\frac{2}{5}$. When Greta goes shopping with her mother she gets an icecream 70% of the time. When Greta does not go shopping with her mother she gets an icecream 30% of the time.

Determine the probability that:

   a Greta's mother buys her an icecream when shopping

   b Greta went shopping with her mother, given that her mother buys her an icecream.

11 On a given day, machine A has a 10% chance of malfunctioning and machine B has a 7% chance of the same. Given that at least one of the machines malfunctioned today, what is the chance that machine B malfunctioned?

12 On any day, the probability that a boy eats his prepared lunch is 0.5. The probability that his sister eats her lunch is 0.6. The probability that the girl eats her lunch given that the boy eats his is 0.9. Determine the probability that:

   a both eat their lunch   **b** the boy eats his lunch given that the girl eats hers

   c at least one of them eats their lunch.

13 The probability that a randomly selected person has cancer is 0.02. The probability that he or she reacts positively to a test which detects cancer is 0.95 if he or she has cancer, and 0.03 if he or she does not. Determine the probability that a randomly tested person:

   a reacts positively   **b** has cancer given that he or she reacts positively.

14 A double-headed, a double-tailed, and an ordinary coin are placed in a tin can. One of the coins is randomly chosen without identifying it. The coin is tossed and falls "heads". Determine the probability that the coin is the "double-header".

J   INDEPENDENT EVENTS

A and B are **independent events** if the occurrence of each one of them does not affect the probability that the other occurs.

This means that $P(A \mid B) = P(A \mid B') = P(A)$.

$\Leftrightarrow$ means 'if and only if'.

Using $P(A \cap B) = P(A \mid B)P(B)$ we see that

A and B are **independent events** $\Leftrightarrow$ $P(A \cap B) = P(A)P(B)$

which is the result we saw earlier.

Example 26   ◀》 **Self Tutor**

When two coins are tossed, A is the event of getting 2 heads. When a die is rolled, B is the event of getting a 5 or 6. Show that A and B are independent events.

$P(A) = \frac{1}{4}$ and $P(B) = \frac{2}{6}$.

Therefore, $P(A)\,P(B) = \frac{1}{4} \times \frac{2}{6} = \frac{1}{12}$

$P(A \cap B)$

$= P(2 \text{ heads } \textbf{and} \text{ a 5 or a 6})$

$= \frac{2}{24}$

$= \frac{1}{12}$

Since $P(A \cap B) = P(A)P(B)$, the events A and B are independent.

Example 27   ◀ⁱ) **Self Tutor**

Suppose $P(A) = \frac{1}{2}$, $P(B) = \frac{1}{3}$, and $P(A \cup B) = p$. Find p if:

  a A and B are mutually exclusive   **b** A and B are independent.

  a If A and B are mutually exclusive, $A \cap B = \varnothing$ and so $P(A \cap B) = 0$

      But $P(A \cup B) = P(A) + P(B) - P(A \cap B)$

          $\therefore$ $p = \frac{1}{2} + \frac{1}{3} - 0 = \frac{5}{6}$

  b If A and B are independent, $P(A \cap B) = P(A)\,P(B) = \frac{1}{2} \times \frac{1}{3} = \frac{1}{6}$

    $\therefore$ $P(A \cup B) = \frac{1}{2} + \frac{1}{3} - \frac{1}{6}$

        $\therefore$ $p = \frac{2}{3}$

Example 28   ◀ⁱ) **Self Tutor**

Suppose $P(A) = \frac{2}{5}$, $P(B \mid A) = \frac{1}{3}$, and $P(B \mid A') = \frac{1}{4}$. Find: **a** $P(B)$ **b** $P(A \cap B')$

$P(B \mid A) = \dfrac{P(B \cap A)}{P(A)}$ so $P(B \cap A) = P(B \mid A)\,P(A) = \frac{1}{3} \times \frac{2}{5} = \frac{2}{15}$

Similarly, $P(B \cap A') = P(B \mid A')\,P(A') = \frac{1}{4} \times \frac{3}{5} = \frac{3}{20}$

$\therefore$ the Venn
diagram is:

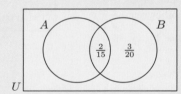

  a $P(B) = \frac{2}{15} + \frac{3}{20} = \frac{17}{60}$

  b $P(A \cap B') = P(A) - P(A \cap B)$

             $= \frac{2}{5} - \frac{2}{15}$

             $= \frac{4}{15}$

EXERCISE 22J

1 If $P(R) = 0.4$, $P(S) = 0.5$, and $P(R \cup S) = 0.7$, are R and S independent events?

2 If $P(A) = \frac{2}{5}$, $P(B) = \frac{1}{3}$, and $P(A \cup B) = \frac{1}{2}$, find:

  a $P(A \cap B)$ **b** $P(B \mid A)$ **c** $P(A \mid B)$

  Are A and B independent events?

3 If $P(X) = 0.5$, $P(Y) = 0.7$, and X and Y are independent events, determine the probability of the occurrence of:

  a both X and Y **b** X or Y or both   **c** neither X nor Y

  d X but not Y **e** X given that Y occurs.

4 The probabilities that students A, B, and C can solve a particular problem are $\frac{3}{5}$, $\frac{2}{3}$, and $\frac{1}{2}$ respectively. If they all try, determine the probability that at least one of the group solves the problem.

5 **a** Find the probability of getting at least one six when a die is rolled 3 times.

  b Find the smallest n such that $P(\text{at least one 6 in } n \text{ rolls of a die}) > 99\%$.

6 A and B are independent events. Prove that A' and B' are also independent events.

7   Suppose $P(A \cap B) = 0.1$ and $P(A \cap B') = 0.4$. Find $P(A \cup B')$ given that A and B are independent.

8   Suppose $P(C) = \frac{9}{20}$, $P(C \mid D') = \frac{3}{7}$, and $P(C \mid D) = \frac{6}{13}$.

    a   Find: **i** $P(D)$ **ii** $P(C' \cup D')$

    b   Are C and D independent events? Give a reason for your answer.

THEORY OF KNOWLEDGE

Modern probability theory began in 1653 when gambler Chevalier de Mere contacted mathematician **Blaise Pascal** with a problem on how to divide the stakes when a gambling game is interrupted during play. Pascal involved **Pierre de Fermat**, a lawyer and amateur mathematician, and together they solved the problem. In the process they laid the foundations upon which the laws of probability were formed.

Blaise Pascal   *Pierre de Fermat*

Agner Krarup Erlang

Applications of probability are now found from quantum physics to medicine and industry.

The first research paper on **queueing theory** was published in 1909 by the Danish engineer **Agner Krarup Erlang** who worked for the Copenhagen Telephone Exchange. In the last hundred years this theory has become an integral part of the huge global telecommunications industry, but it is equally applicable to modelling car traffic right down to queues at your local supermarket.

Statistics and probability are used extensively to predict the behaviour of the global stock market. For example, American mathematician **Edward Oakley Thorp** developed and applied hedge fund techniques for the financial markets in the 1960s.

On the level of an individual investor, money is put into the stock market if there is a good probability that the value of the shares will increase. This investment has risk, however, as witnessed recently with the Global Financial Crisis of 2008-2009.

   1   In what ways can mathematics model the world without using functions?

   2   How does a knowledge of probability theory affect decisions we make?

   3   Do ethics play a role in the use of mathematics?

REVIEW SET 22A   NON-CALCULATOR

1 List the different orders in which 4 people A, B, C, and D could line up. If they line up at random, determine the probability that:

    a A is next to C   **b** there is exactly one person between A and C.

2 Given $P(A) = m$ is the probability of event A occurring in any given trial:

    a Write $P(A')$ in terms of m.

    b State the range of possible values of m.

    c Suppose two trials are performed independently. Find, in terms of m, the probability of A occurring:

        i exactly once   **ii** at least once.

3 A coin is tossed and a square spinner labelled A, B, C, D, is twirled. Determine the probability of obtaining:

    a a head and consonant   **b** a tail and C   **c** a tail or a vowel or both.

4 The probability that a man will be alive in 25 years is $\frac{3}{5}$, and the probability that his wife will be alive is $\frac{2}{3}$. Determine the probability that in 25 years:

    a both will be alive   **b** at least one will be alive   **c** only the wife will be alive.

5 Given $P(Y) = 0.35$ and $P(X \cup Y) = 0.8$, and that X and Y are mutually exclusive events, find:

    a $P(X \cap Y)$ **b** $P(X)$

    c the probability that X occurs or Y occurs, but not both X and Y.

6 What is meant by: **a** independent events   **b** mutually exclusive events?

7 Graph the sample space of all possible outcomes when a pair of dice is rolled. Hence determine the probability of getting:

    a a sum of 7 or 11   **b** a sum of at least 8.

8 In a group of 40 students, 22 study Economics, 25 study Law, and 3 study neither of these subjects. Determine the probability that a randomly chosen student studies:

    a both Economics and Law   **b** at least one of these subjects

    c Economics given that he or she studies Law.

9 The probability that a particular salesman will leave his sunglasses behind in any store is $\frac{1}{5}$. Suppose the salesman visits two stores in succession and leaves his sunglasses behind in one of them. What is the probability that the salesman left his sunglasses in the first store?

REVIEW SET 22B   CALCULATOR

1 Niklas and Rolf play tennis with the winner being the first to win two sets. Niklas has a 40% chance of beating Rolf in any set. Draw a tree diagram showing the possible outcomes and hence determine the probability that Niklas will win the match.

2 If I buy 4 tickets in a 500 ticket lottery, and the prizes are drawn without replacement, determine the probability that I will win:

    a the first 3 prizes   **b** at least one of the first 3 prizes.

3 The students in a school are all vaccinated against measles. 48% of the students are males, of whom 16% have an allergic reaction to the vaccine. 35% of the girls also have an allergic reaction. A student is randomly chosen from the school. Find the probability that the student:

    a has an allergic reaction

    b is female given that a reaction occurs.

4 On any one day it could rain with 25% chance and be windy with 36% chance.

    a Draw a tree diagram showing the possibilities with regard to wind and rain on a particular day.

    b Hence determine the probability that on a particular day there will be:

        i rain and wind   **ii** rain or wind or both.

    c What assumption have you made in your answers?

5 A, B, and C have 10%, 20%, and 30% chance of independently solving a certain maths problem. If they all try independently of one another, what is the probability that at least one of them will solve the problem?

6 Two events are defined such that $P(A) = 0.11$ and $P(B) = 0.7$. $n(B) = 14$.

    a Calculate: **i** $P(A')$ **ii** $n(U)$

    b If A and B are independent events, find: **i** $P(A \cap B)$ **ii** $P(A \mid B)$

    c If instead, A and B are mutually exclusive events, find $P(A \cup B)$.

7 A survey of 200 people included 90 females. It found that 60 people smoked, 40 of whom were male.

    a Use the given information to complete the table:

    b A person is selected at random. Find the probability that this person is:

	Female	Male	Total
Smoker			
Non-smoker			
Total			

        i a female non-smoker

        ii a male given the person was a non-smoker.

    c If two people from the survey are selected at random, calculate the probability that:

        i both of them are non-smoking females

        ii one is a smoker and the other is a non-smoker.

8 Let C be the event that "a person has a cat" and D be the event that "a person has a dog". $P(C) = \frac{3}{7}$, $P(D \mid C') = \frac{2}{5}$, and $P(D' \mid C) = \frac{3}{4}$.

    a Complete the tree diagram by marking a probability on each branch.

    b If a person is chosen at random, find the probability that the person has:

        i a cat and a dog

        ii at least one pet (cat or dog).

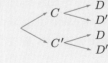

REVIEW SET 22C

1 Systematically list the possible sexes of a 4-child family. Hence determine the probability that a randomly selected 4-child family has two children of each sex.

2 A bag contains 3 red, 4 yellow and 5 blue marbles. Two marbles are randomly selected from the bag without replacement. What is the probability that:

    a both are blue

    b they have the same colour

    c at least one is red

    d exactly one is yellow?

3 A class contains 25 students. 13 play tennis, 14 play volleyball, and 1 plays neither of these sports.

    a A student is randomly selected from the class. Determine the probability that the student:

        i plays both tennis and volleyball

        ii plays at least one of these sports

        iii plays volleyball given that he or she does not play tennis.

    b Three students are randomly selected from the class. Determine the probability that:

        i none of these students play tennis

        ii at least one of these students plays tennis.

4 An urn contains three red balls and six blue balls.

    a A ball is drawn at random and found to be blue. What is the probability that a second draw with no replacement will also produce a blue ball?

    b Two balls are drawn without replacement and the second is found to be red. What is the probability that the first ball was also red?

5 A school photocopier has a 95% chance of working on any particular day. Find the probability that it will be working on at least one of the next two days.

6 Jon goes cycling on three random mornings of each week. When he goes cycling he has eggs for breakfast 70% of the time. When he does not go cycling he has eggs for breakfast 25% of the time. Determine the probability that Jon:

    a has eggs for breakfast

    b goes cycling given that he has eggs for breakfast.

7 A survey of 50 men and 50 women was conducted to see how many people prefer coffee or tea. It was found that 15 men and 24 women prefer tea.

    a Display this information in a two-way table.

    b Let C represent the people who prefer coffee and M represent the men. Hence complete the Venn diagram:

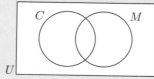

    c Calculate: **i** $P(C')$ **ii** $P(M \mid C)$

8 T and M are events such that $n(U) = 30$, $n(T) = 10$, $n(M) = 17$, and $n((T \cup M)') = 5$.

    a Draw a Venn diagram to display this information.

    b Hence find: **i** $P(T \cap M)$ **ii** $P((T \cap M) \mid M)$

9 Answer the questions in the **Opening Problem** on page **568**.

Chapter **23**

Discrete random variables

Syllabus reference: 5.7, 5.8

OPENING PROBLEM

It is known that 3.2% of the pens manufactured in a factory are faulty.

The factory quality controller randomly tests 120 pens, checking them one at a time, and replacing them into the batch before the next one is chosen.

Things to think about:

a What will the probability be that:

   i all are faulty   **ii** none are faulty?

b How can we find the probability that:

   i less than 2 are faulty   **ii** between 5 and 10 (inclusive) are faulty?

A   DISCRETE RANDOM VARIABLES

RANDOM VARIABLES

In previous work on probability we have often described events by using words. However, if possible, it is far more convenient to use numbers.

> A **random variable** represents in number form the possible outcomes which could occur for some random experiment.

A **discrete random variable** X has a set of distinct possible values. In this course you will consider only a finite number of outcomes, so we label them $x_1, x_2, x_3, ..., x_n$.

For example, X could be:

- the number of houses in your suburb which have a 'power safety switch'
- the number of new bicycles sold each year by a bicycle store
- the number of defective light bulbs in the purchase order of a city store.

To determine the value of a discrete random variable we need to **count**.

A **continuous random variable** X could take possible values in some interval on the number line.

For example, X could be:

- the heights of men, which would all lie in the interval $50 < X < 250$ cm
- the volume of water in a rainwater tank, which could lie in the interval $0 < X < 100$ m^3.

To determine the value of a continuous random variable we need to **measure**.

PROBABILITY DISTRIBUTIONS

For any random variable there is a corresponding **probability distribution** which describes the probability that the variable will take any particular value.

The probability that the variable X takes value x is denoted $P(X = x)$.

For example, when tossing two coins, the random variable X could be 0 heads, 1 head, or 2 heads, so $X = 0$, 1, or 2. The associated probability distribution is $P(X = 0) = \frac{1}{4}$, $P(X = 1) = \frac{1}{2}$, and $P(X = 2) = \frac{1}{4}$.

Spike graph

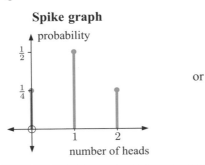

Probability column graph

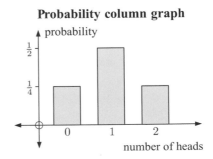

or

Example 1   ◄ᴺ **Self Tutor**

A supermarket has three checkout points A, B, and C. A government inspector checks the weighing scales for accuracy at each checkout. If a weighing scale is accurate then Y is recorded, and if not, N is recorded. Suppose the random variable X is the number of accurate weighing scales at the supermarket.

a List the possible outcomes.

b Describe, using X, the events of there being:

  i one accurate scale   ii at least one accurate scale.

a Possible outcomes:

A	B	C	X
N	N	N	0
Y	N	N	1
N	Y	N	1
N	N	Y	1
N	Y	Y	2
Y	N	Y	2
Y	Y	N	2
Y	Y	Y	3

b i $X = 1$

  ii $X = 1$, 2, or 3

EXERCISE 23A

1 Classify the following random variables as continuous or discrete:

  a the quantity of fat in a sausage

  b the mark out of 50 for a geography test

  c the weight of a seventeen year old student

  d the volume of water in a cup of coffee

  e the number of trout in a lake

  f the number of hairs on a cat

  g the length of hairs on a horse

  h the height of a sky-scraper.

2 For each of the following:

  i   identify the random variable being considered
  ii give possible values for the random variable
  iii indicate whether the variable is continuous or discrete.

  a To measure the rainfall over a 24-hour period in Singapore, the height of water collected in a rain gauge (up to 400 mm) is used.

  b To investigate the stopping distance for a tyre with a new tread pattern, a braking experiment is carried out.

  c To check the reliability of a new type of light switch, switches are repeatedly turned off and on until they fail.

3 A supermarket has four checkouts A, B, C, and D. Management checks the weighing devices at each checkout. If a weighing device is accurate a Y is recorded; otherwise, N is recorded. The random variable being considered is the number of weighing devices which are accurate.

  a Suppose X is the random variable. What values can X have?

  b Tabulate the possible outcomes and the corresponding values for X.

  c Describe, using X, the events of:

  i   exactly two devices being accurate   **ii** at least two devices being accurate.

4 Consider tossing three coins simultaneously. The random variable under consideration is the number of heads that could result.

  a List the possible values of X.

  b Tabulate the possible outcomes and the corresponding values of X.

  c Find the values of $P(X = x)$, the probability of each x value occurring.

  d Graph the probability distribution $P(X = x)$ against x as a probability column graph.

B   DISCRETE PROBABILITY DISTRIBUTIONS

We saw in **Chapter 22** that probabilities may be assigned to events in a number of ways.

For example:

- we can conduct experiments where we perform trials many times over until a pattern emerges
- we can use symmetry to say the chances of a coin being a head or a tail are both $\frac{1}{2}$, or an ordinary die showing a particular number is $\frac{1}{6}$
- we can evaluate the form of tennis players to predict their chances in an upcoming match.

However, probabilities are assigned, they must satisfy the following rule:

If X is a random variable with sample space $\{x_1, x_2, x_3, ..., x_n\}$ and corresponding probabilities $\{p_1, p_2, p_3, ..., p_n\}$ so that $P(X = x_i) = p_i$, $i = 1, ..., n$, then:

- $0 \leqslant p_i \leqslant 1$ for all $i = 1$ to n

- $\displaystyle\sum_{i=1}^{n} p_i = p_1 + p_2 + p_3 + ... + p_n = 1$

- $\{p_1, ..., p_n\}$ describes the **probability distribution** of X.

For example, when a coin is tossed twice, the number of heads X has sample space $\{0, 1, 2\}$ with corresponding probabilities $\{\frac{1}{4}, \frac{1}{2}, \frac{1}{4}\}$. We see that $0 \leqslant p_i \leqslant 1$ for each value of i, and that the probabilities add up to 1.

The **probability distribution** of a **discrete random variable** can be given:

- in table form
- in graphical form
- in function form as a **probability distribution function** or **probability mass function**
  $P(x) = P(X = x)$.
  The domain of the probability mass function is the set of possible values of the variable, and the range is the set of values in the probability distribution of the variable.

When we consider discrete random variables, we often look at intervals of values which the variable may take. We need to be careful about whether the end points of an interval are included. For example, consider these intervals:

Notation	Statement
$P(X = 3)$	the probability that X equals 3
$P(X < 3)$	the probability that X is less than 3
$P(X \leqslant 3)$	the probability that X is at most 3
$P(X > 3)$	the probability that X is more than 3
$P(X \geqslant 3)$	the probability that X is at least 3
$P(3 < X < 7)$	the probability that X is between 3 and 7
$P(3 \leqslant X \leqslant 7)$	the probability that X is at least 3 but no more than 7
$P(3 < X \leqslant 7)$	the probability that X is more than 3 but no more than 7
$P(3 \leqslant X < 7)$	the probability that X is at least 3 but less than 7

Example 2 ◄ᴺ) Self Tutor

A magazine store recorded the number of magazines purchased by its customers in one week. 23% purchased one magazine, 38% purchased two, 21% purchased three, 13% purchased four, and 5% purchased five.

a What is the random variable?

b Make a probability table for the random variable.

c Graph the probability distribution using a spike graph.

a The random variable X is the number of magazines sold.

So, $X = 1, 2, 3, 4,$ or 5.

b

x	1	2	3	4	5
$P(X = x)$	0.23	0.38	0.21	0.13	0.05

c

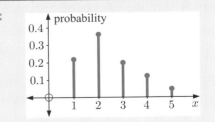

Example 3   ◄⑤ **Self Tutor**

Show that the following are probability distribution functions:

a $P(x) = \dfrac{x^2 + 1}{34}, \quad x = 1, 2, 3, 4$

b $P(x) = \binom{3}{x}(0.6)^x(0.4)^{3-x}, \quad x = 0, 1, 2, 3$

---

a $P(1) = \frac{2}{34} \qquad P(2) = \frac{5}{34} \qquad P(3) = \frac{10}{34} \qquad P(4) = \frac{17}{34}$

All of these obey $0 \leqslant P(x_i) \leqslant 1$, and $\sum P(x_i) = \frac{2}{34} + \frac{5}{34} + \frac{10}{34} + \frac{17}{34} = 1$

∴ $P(x)$ is a probability distribution function.

b For $P(x) = \binom{3}{x}(0.6)^x(0.4)^{3-x}$,

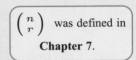

$$P(0) = \binom{3}{0}(0.6)^0(0.4)^3 \quad = 1 \times 1 \times (0.4)^3 \quad = 0.064$$
$$P(1) = \binom{3}{1}(0.6)^1(0.4)^2 \quad = 3 \times (0.6) \times (0.4)^2 \quad = 0.288$$
$$P(2) = \binom{3}{2}(0.6)^2(0.4)^1 \quad = 3 \times (0.6)^2 \times (0.4) \quad = 0.432$$
$$P(3) = \binom{3}{3}(0.6)^3(0.4)^0 \quad = 1 \times (0.6)^3 \times 1 \quad = 0.216$$

$$\text{Total} \qquad \overline{1.000}$$

$\binom{n}{r}$ was defined in **Chapter 7**.

All probabilities lie between 0 and 1, and $\sum P(x_i) = 1$.

∴ $P(x)$ is a probability distribution function.

EXERCISE 23B

1 Find k in these probability distributions:

a

x	0	1	2
P($X = x$)	0.3	k	0.5

b

x	0	1	2	3
P($X = x$)	k	$2k$	$3k$	k

2 The probabilities of Jason scoring home runs in each game during his baseball career are given in the following table. X is the number of home runs per game.

x	0	1	2	3	4	5
$P(x)$	a	0.3333	0.1088	0.0084	0.0007	0.0000

a State the value of $P(2)$.

b What is the value of a? Explain what this number means.

c What is the value of $P(1) + P(2) + P(3) + P(4) + P(5)$? Explain what this means.

d Draw a probability distribution spike graph of $P(x)$ against x.

3 Explain why the following are not valid probability distribution functions:

a

x	0	1	2	3
$P(x)$	0.2	0.3	0.4	0.2

b

x	2	3	4	5
$P(x)$	0.3	0.4	0.5	-0.2

4 Sally's number of hits in each softball match has the following probability distribution:

x	0	1	2	3	4	5
$P(X=x)$	0.07	0.14	k	0.46	0.08	0.02

 a State clearly what the random variable represents.

 b Find k.

 c Find: **i** $P(X \geqslant 2)$ **ii** $P(1 \leqslant X \leqslant 3)$

5 A die is rolled twice.

 a Draw a grid which shows the sample space.

 b Suppose X denotes the sum of the results for the two rolls. Find the probability distribution of X.

 c Draw a probability distribution column graph for this situation.

6 Find k for the following probability distributions:

 a $P(x) = k(x+2)$ for $x = 1, 2, 3$ **b** $P(x) = \dfrac{k}{x+1}$ for $x = 0, 1, 2, 3$

7 A discrete random variable X has probability distribution given by $P(X=x) = k\left(\frac{1}{3}\right)^x \left(\frac{2}{3}\right)^{4-x}$ where $x = 0, 1, 2, 3, 4$.

 a Find $P(X=x)$ for $x = 0, 1, 2, 3$ and 4.   **b** Find k and hence find $P(X \geqslant 2)$.

Example 4   ◀） **Self Tutor**

A bag contains 4 red and 2 blue marbles. Two marbles are randomly selected without replacement. If X denotes the number of reds selected:

 a find the probability distribution of X

 b illustrate the distribution using a spike graph.

 a 1st selection   2nd selection

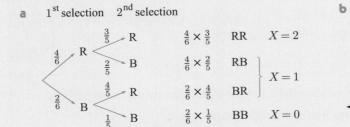

x	0	1	2
$P(X=x)$	$\frac{2}{30}$	$\frac{16}{30}$	$\frac{12}{30}$

 b

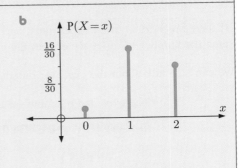

---

8 Electrical components are produced and packed into boxes of 10. It is known that 4% of the components produced are faulty. The random variable X denotes the number of faulty items in the box, and has probability distribution function

$$P(X=x) = \binom{10}{x} (0.04)^x (0.96)^{10-x}, \quad x = 0, 1, 2, \ldots., 10.$$

 a Find the probability that a randomly selected box will not contain a faulty component.

 b Find the probability that a randomly selected box will contain at least one faulty component.

9 A bag contains 5 blue and 3 green tickets and a number of tickets are randomly selected without replacement. We let X denote the number of blue tickets selected.

Find the probability distribution of X if:

   a two tickets are randomly selected   **b** three tickets are randomly selected.

10 When a pair of dice is rolled, D denotes the sum of the top faces.

   a Display the possible results in a table.   **b** Find $P(D = 7)$.

   c Find the probability distribution of D.   **d** Find $P(D \geqslant 8 \mid D \geqslant 6)$.

11 When a pair of dice is rolled, N denotes the difference between the numbers on the top faces.

   a Display the possible results in a table.

   b Construct a probability distribution table for the possible values of N.

   c Find $P(N = 3)$.

   d Find $P(N \geqslant 3 \mid N \geqslant 1)$.

C   EXPECTATION

Consider the following problem:

   A die is to be rolled 120 times. On how many occasions should we *expect* the result to be a "six"?

In order to answer this question we must first consider all possible outcomes of rolling the die. The possibilities are 1, 2, 3, 4, 5, and 6, and each of these is equally likely to occur.

Therefore, we would expect $\frac{1}{6}$ of them to be a "six".

$\frac{1}{6}$ of 120 is 20, so we expect 20 of the 120 rolls of the die to yield a "six".

However, this does not mean that we *will* get 20 sixes when we roll a die 120 times.

If there are n trials of an experiment, and an event has probability p of occurring in each of the trials, then the number of times we **expect** the event to occur is np.

We can also talk about the *expected* outcome from one trial of an experiment.

> The expected outcome for the random variable X is the **mean** result μ.
>
> In general, the **expectation** of the random variable X is
>
> $$E(X) = \mu = \sum_{i=1}^{n} x_i p_i \quad \text{or} \quad \sum_{i=1}^{n} x_i \, P(X = x_i)$$

Example 5   ◀)) Self Tutor

Each time a footballer kicks for goal he has a $\frac{3}{4}$ chance of being successful.

In a particular game he has 12 kicks for goal. How many goals would you expect him to kick?

$p = P(\text{goal}) = \frac{3}{4}$ $\therefore$ the expected number of goals is $E = np$

$\qquad\qquad\qquad\qquad\qquad\qquad\qquad\qquad\qquad\qquad\quad = 12 \times \frac{3}{4}$

$\qquad\qquad\qquad\qquad\qquad\qquad\qquad\qquad\qquad\qquad\quad = 9$

Example 6

Self Tutor

Find the mean of the magazine store data in **Example 2**. Explain what it means.

The probability table is:

x_i	1	2	3	4	5
p_i	0.23	0.38	0.21	0.13	0.05

Now $\mu = \sum x_i p_i$
$$= 1(0.23) + 2(0.38) + 3(0.21) + 4(0.13) + 5(0.05)$$
$$= 2.39$$

In the long run, the average number of magazines purchased per customer is 2.39.

FAIR GAMES

In gambling, we say that the **expected gain** of the player from each game is the expected return or payout from the game, less the amount it cost them to play.

The game will be **fair** if the expected gain is zero.

> Suppose X represents the gain of a player from each game.
> The game is **fair** if $E(X) = 0$.

Example 7

Self Tutor

In a game of chance, a player spins a square spinner labelled 1, 2, 3, 4. The player wins the amount of money shown in the table alongside, depending on which number comes up.

Number	1	2	3	4
Winnings	\$1	\$2	\$5	\$8

Determine:

a the expected return for one spin of the spinner

b the expected *gain* of the player if it costs \$5 to play each game

c whether you would recommend playing this game.

a Let Y denote the return or payout from each spin.
As each outcome is equally likely, the probability for each outcome is $\frac{1}{4}$
$\therefore$ expected return $= E(Y) = \frac{1}{4} \times 1 + \frac{1}{4} \times 2 + \frac{1}{4} \times 5 + \frac{1}{4} \times 8 = \$4$.

b Let X denote the *gain* of the player from each game.
Since it costs \$5 to play the game, the expected gain $= E(X) = E(Y) - \$5$
$$= \$4 - \$5$$
$$= -\$1$$

c Since $E(X) \neq 0$, the game is not fair. In particular, since $E(X) = -\$1$, we expect the player to lose \$1 on average with each spin. We would not recommend that a person play the game.

EXERCISE 23C

1 In a particular region, the probability that it will rain on any one day is 0.28. On how many days of the year would you expect it to rain?

2 **a** If 3 coins are tossed, what is the chance that they all fall heads?

    b If the 3 coins are tossed 200 times, on how many occasions would you expect them all to fall heads?

3 If two dice are rolled simultaneously 180 times, on how many occasions would you expect to get a double?

4 A single coin is tossed once. If a head appears you win $2, and if a tail appears you lose $1. How much would you expect to win when playing this game three times?

5 During the snow season there is a $\frac{3}{7}$ probability of snow falling on any particular day. If Udo skis for five weeks, on how many days could he expect to see snow falling?

6

A goalkeeper has probability $\frac{3}{10}$ of saving a penalty attempt. How many goals would he expect to save from 90 attempts?

7 In a random survey of her electorate, politician A discovered the residents' voting intentions in relation to herself and her two opponents B and C. The results are indicated alongside:

A	B	C
165	87	48

    a Estimate the probability that a randomly chosen voter in the electorate will vote for:

      i A   **ii** B   **iii** C.

    b If there are 7500 people in the electorate, how many of these would you expect to vote for:

      i A   **ii** B   **iii** C?

8 A charity fundraiser gets a licence to run the following gambling game: A die is rolled and the returns to the player are given in the 'pay table' alongside. To play the game costs $4. A result of getting a 6 wins $10, so in fact you are ahead by $6 if you get a 6 on the first roll.

Result	Wins
6	$10
4, 5	$4
1, 2, 3	$1

    a What are your chances of playing one game and winning:

      i $10   **ii** $4   **iii** $1?

    b Your expected return from throwing a 6 is $\frac{1}{6} \times$ $10. What is your expected return from throwing:

      i a 4 or 5   **ii** a 1, 2, or 3   **iii** a 1, 2, 3, 4, 5, or 6?

    c What is your overall expected result at the end of one game?

    d What is your overall expected result at the end of 100 games?

9 A person rolls a normal six-sided die and wins the number of euros shown on the face.

    a Find the expected return from one roll of the die.

    b Find the expected *gain* of the player if it costs €4 to play the game. Would you advise the person to play several games?

    c Suppose it costs €k to play the game. What value(s) of k will result in:

        i a fair game   **ii** a profit being made by the vendor?

10 A person plays a game with a pair of coins. If two heads appear then £10 is won. If a head and a tail appear then £3 is won. If two tails appear then £5 is lost.

    a How much would a person expect to win playing this game once?

    b If the organiser of the game wishes to make an average of £1 per game, how much should the organiser charge people per game to play?

11 A country exports crayfish to overseas markets. The buyers are prepared to pay high prices when the crayfish arrive still alive.

If X is the number of deaths per dozen crayfish, the probability distribution for X is given by:

x	0	1	2	3	4	5	> 5
$P(X = x)$	0.54	0.26	0.15	k	0.01	0.01	0.00

    a Find k.

    b Over a long period, what is the mean number of deaths per dozen crayfish?

12 A random variable X has probability distribution given by $P(X = x) = \dfrac{x^2 + x}{20}$ for $x = 1, 2, 3$.

Calculate the mean μ for this distribution.

13 A pair of dice is rolled and the random variable M is the larger of the two numbers that are shown uppermost, or the value of a single die if a double is thrown.

    a In table form, obtain the probability distribution of M.

    b Find the mean of the M-distribution.

14 At a charity event there is a money-raising game involving a pair of ordinary dice. The game costs $\$a$ to play. When the two dice are rolled, their sum is described by the variable X. The organisers decide that a sum which is less than 4 or between 7 and 9 inclusive is a loss of $\$\frac{a}{3}$, a result between 4 and 6 inclusive gives a return of $7, and a result of 10 or more gives a return of $21.

    a Determine $P(X \leqslant 3)$, $P(4 \leqslant X \leqslant 6)$, $P(7 \leqslant X \leqslant 9)$, and $P(X \geqslant 10)$.

    b Show that the expected gain of a player is given by $\frac{1}{6}(35 - 7a)$ dollars.

    c What value would a need to have for the game to be 'fair'?

    d Explain why the organisers would not let a be 4.

    e If the organisers let a be 6 and the game was played 2406 times, estimate the amount of money raised by this game.

D   THE BINOMIAL DISTRIBUTION

Thus far in the chapter we have considered properties of general discrete random variables.

We now examine a special type of discrete random variable which is applied to **sampling with replacement**. The probability distribution associated with this variable is the **binomial probability distribution**.

For sampling without replacement the hypergeometric probability distribution is the model used, but that distribution is not part of this course.

BINOMIAL EXPERIMENTS

Consider an experiment for which there are two possible results: **success** if some event occurs, or **failure** if the event does not occur.

If we repeat this experiment in a number of **independent trials**, we call it a **binomial experiment**.

The probability of a success p must be constant for all trials. Since success and failure are complementary events, the probability of a failure is $1 - p$ and is constant for all trials.

The random variable X is the total number of successes in n trials.

INVESTIGATION 1   SAMPLING SIMULATION

When balls enter the 'sorting' chamber shown they hit a metal rod and may go left or right. This movement continues as the balls fall from one level of rods to the next. The balls finally come to rest in collection chambers at the bottom of the sorter.

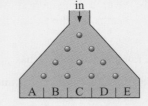

This sorter looks very much like a tree diagram rotated through $90°$.

Click on the icon to open the simulation. Notice that the sliding bar will alter the probabilities of balls going to the left or right at each rod.

What to do:

1   To simulate the results of tossing two coins, set the bar to 50% and the sorter as shown.
    Run the simulation 200 times and repeat this four more times. Record each set of results.
    What do you notice about the results?

2   A bag contains 7 blue and 3 red marbles. Two marbles are randomly selected from the bag, the first being *replaced* before the second is drawn.
    Since $P(\text{blue}) = \frac{7}{10} = 70\%$,   set the bar to 70%.

    a   Run the simulation a large number of times. Hence estimate the probability of getting:
        i two blues   **ii** one blue   **iii** no blues.
    b   The following tree diagram shows the theoretical probabilities for the different outcomes:

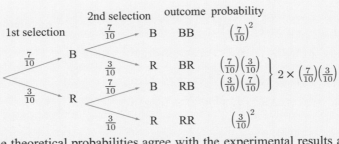

i Do the theoretical probabilities agree with the experimental results above?

ii Write down the algebraic expansion of $(a + b)^2$.

iii Substitute $a = \frac{7}{10}$ and $b = \frac{3}{10}$ in the $(a+b)^2$ expansion. What do you notice?

3 From the bag of 7 blue and 3 red marbles, *three* marbles are randomly selected *with replacement*. Set the sorter to 3 levels and the bar to 70%.

   a Run the simulation many times to obtain experimental probabilities of getting:

      i three blues   **ii** two blues   **iii** one blue   **iv** no blues.

   b Use a tree diagram showing 1st selection, 2nd selection, and 3rd selection to find theoretical probabilities for this experiment.

   c Show that $(a + b)^3 = a^3 + 3a^2b + 3ab^2 + b^3$. Substitute $a = \frac{7}{10}$ and $b = \frac{3}{10}$ and compare your results with **a** and **b**.

THE BINOMIAL PROBABILITY DISTRIBUTION

Suppose a spinner has three blue edges and one white edge. Clearly, for each spin we will get either a blue or a white.

The chance of finishing on blue is $\frac{3}{4}$ and on white is $\frac{1}{4}$.

If we call a blue result a 'success' and a white result a 'failure', then we have a binomial experiment.

We let p be the probability of getting a blue, so $p = \frac{3}{4}$. The probability of getting a white is $1 - p = \frac{1}{4}$.

Consider twirling the spinner $n = 3$ times.

Let the random variable X be the number of 'successes' or blue results, so $X = 0$, 1, 2, or 3.

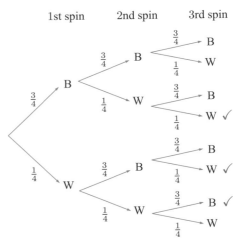

$P(X = 0) = P(\text{none are blue})$
$= \frac{1}{4} \times \frac{1}{4} \times \frac{1}{4}$
$= \left(\frac{1}{4}\right)^3$

$P(X = 1) = P(\text{1 blue and 2 white})$
$= P(\text{BWW or WBW or WWB})$
$= \left(\frac{3}{4}\right) \left(\frac{1}{4}\right)^2 \times 3$ {the 3 branches ✓}

$P(X = 2) = P(\text{2 blue and 1 white})$
$= P(\text{BBW or BWB or WBB})$
$= \left(\frac{3}{4}\right)^2 \left(\frac{1}{4}\right) \times 3$

$P(X = 3) = P(\text{3 blues})$
$= \left(\frac{3}{4}\right)^3$

The coloured factor $\boxed{3}$ is the number of ways of getting one success in three trials, which is $\binom{3}{1}$.

Notice that:

$$P(X = 0) = \left(\tfrac{1}{4}\right)^3 \qquad = \binom{3}{0}\left(\tfrac{3}{4}\right)^0 \left(\tfrac{1}{4}\right)^3 \approx 0.0156$$

$$P(X = 1) = 3\left(\tfrac{1}{4}\right)^2 \left(\tfrac{3}{4}\right)^1 = \binom{3}{1}\left(\tfrac{3}{4}\right)^1 \left(\tfrac{1}{4}\right)^2 \approx 0.1406$$

$$P(X = 2) = 3\left(\tfrac{1}{4}\right)^1 \left(\tfrac{3}{4}\right)^2 = \binom{3}{2}\left(\tfrac{3}{4}\right)^2 \left(\tfrac{1}{4}\right)^1 \approx 0.4219$$

$$P(X = 3) = \left(\tfrac{3}{4}\right)^3 \qquad = \binom{3}{3}\left(\tfrac{3}{4}\right)^3 \left(\tfrac{1}{4}\right)^0 \approx 0.4219$$

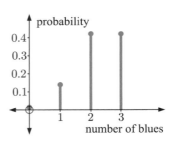

This suggests that $P(X = x) = \binom{3}{x}\left(\tfrac{3}{4}\right)^x \left(\tfrac{1}{4}\right)^{3-x}$ where $x = 0,\ 1,\ 2,\ 3.$

The sum of the probabilities $P(X = 0) + P(X = 1) + P(X = 2) + P(X = 3)$

$$= \left(\tfrac{1}{4}\right)^3 + 3\left(\tfrac{1}{4}\right)^2 \left(\tfrac{3}{4}\right) + 3\left(\tfrac{1}{4}\right)\left(\tfrac{3}{4}\right)^2 + \left(\tfrac{3}{4}\right)^3$$

which is the binomial expansion for $\left(\tfrac{1}{4} + \tfrac{3}{4}\right)^3$, and $\left(\tfrac{1}{4} + \tfrac{3}{4}\right)^3 = 1^3 = 1.$

Example 8   ◀ŭ **Self Tutor**

a Expand $\left(\tfrac{9}{10} + \tfrac{1}{10}\right)^5.$

b An archer has a 90% chance of hitting a target with each arrow. If 5 arrows are fired, determine the chance of hitting the target:

    i twice only   **ii** at most 3 times.

---

a $\left(\tfrac{9}{10} + \tfrac{1}{10}\right)^5$

$= \left(\tfrac{9}{10}\right)^5 + 5\left(\tfrac{9}{10}\right)^4 \left(\tfrac{1}{10}\right) + 10\left(\tfrac{9}{10}\right)^3 \left(\tfrac{1}{10}\right)^2 + 10\left(\tfrac{9}{10}\right)^2 \left(\tfrac{1}{10}\right)^3 + 5\left(\tfrac{9}{10}\right)\left(\tfrac{1}{10}\right)^4 + \left(\tfrac{1}{10}\right)^5$

b The probability of success with each arrow is $p = \tfrac{9}{10}.$

Let X be the number of arrows that hit the target.

The expansion in **a** gives the probability distribution for X.

$$\underset{\substack{P(X = 5)\\ 5 \text{ hits}}}{\left(\tfrac{9}{10}\right)^5} + \underset{\substack{P(X = 4)\\ 4 \text{ hits}\\ 1 \text{ miss}}}{5\left(\tfrac{9}{10}\right)^4 \left(\tfrac{1}{10}\right)} + \underset{\substack{P(X = 3)\\ 3 \text{ hits}\\ 2 \text{ misses}}}{10\left(\tfrac{9}{10}\right)^3 \left(\tfrac{1}{10}\right)^2} + \underset{\substack{P(X = 2)\\ 2 \text{ hits}\\ 3 \text{ misses}}}{10\left(\tfrac{9}{10}\right)^2 \left(\tfrac{1}{10}\right)^3} + \underset{\substack{P(X = 1)\\ 1 \text{ hit}\\ 4 \text{ misses}}}{5\left(\tfrac{9}{10}\right)\left(\tfrac{1}{10}\right)^4} + \underset{\substack{P(X = 0)\\ 5 \text{ misses}}}{\left(\tfrac{1}{10}\right)^5}$$

   i   P(hits twice only)

     $= P(X = 2)$

     $= 10\left(\tfrac{9}{10}\right)^2 \left(\tfrac{1}{10}\right)^3$

     $= 0.0081$

   ii   P(hits at most 3 times)

     $= P(X \leqslant 3)$

     $= P(X = 0) + P(X = 1) + P(X = 2) + P(X = 3)$

     $= \left(\tfrac{1}{10}\right)^5 + 5\left(\tfrac{9}{10}\right)\left(\tfrac{1}{10}\right)^4 + 10\left(\tfrac{9}{10}\right)^2 \left(\tfrac{1}{10}\right)^3 + 10\left(\tfrac{9}{10}\right)^3 \left(\tfrac{1}{10}\right)^2$

     ≈ 0.0815

EXERCISE 23D.1

1 **a** Expand $(p+q)^4$.

   b If a coin is tossed *four* times, what is the probability of getting 3 heads?

2 **a** Expand $(p+q)^5$.

   b If *five* coins are tossed simultaneously, what is the probability of getting:

   i 4 heads and 1 tail in any order   **ii** 2 heads and 3 tails in any order

   iii 4 heads and 1 tail in that order?

3 **a** Expand $\left(\frac{2}{3} + \frac{1}{3}\right)^4$.

   b Four chocolates are selected at random, with replacement, from a box which contains strawberry creams and almond centres in the ratio 2 : 1. Find the probability of getting:

   i all strawberry creams   **ii** two of each type   **iii** at least 2 strawberry creams.

4 **a** Expand $\left(\frac{3}{4} + \frac{1}{4}\right)^5$.

   b In New Zealand in 1946 there were two different coins of value two shillings. These were 'normal' kiwis and 'flat back' kiwis, in the ratio 3 : 1. From a very large batch of 1946 two shilling coins, five were selected at random with replacement. Find the probability that:

   i two were 'flat backs'   **ii** at least 3 were 'flat backs'

   iii at most 3 were 'normal' kiwis.

5 When rifle shooter Huy fires a shot, he hits the target 80% of the time. If Huy fires 4 shots at the target, determine the probability that he has:

   a 2 hits and 2 misses in any order   **b** at least 2 hits.

THE BINOMIAL PROBABILITY DISTRIBUTION FUNCTION

Consider a binomial experiment for which p is the probability of a *success* and $1-p$ is the probability of a *failure*.

If there are n independent trials then the probability that there are r *successes* and $n-r$ *failures* is

$P(X=r) = \binom{n}{r} p^r (1-p)^{n-r}$ where $r = 0, 1, 2, 3, 4, \ldots, n$.

$P(X=r)$ is the **binomial probability distribution function**.

The **expected** or **mean** outcome of the experiment is $\mu = E(X) = np$.

If X is the random variable of a binomial experiment with parameters n and p, then we write $X \sim B(n, p)$ where $\sim$ reads *"is distributed as"*.

We can quickly calculate binomial probabilities using a graphics calculator.

For example:

GRAPHICS CALCULATOR INSTRUCTIONS

- To find the probability $P(X=r)$ that the variable takes the value r, we use the **binomial probability distribution function**.

- To find the probability that the variable takes a *range* of values, such as $P(X \leqslant r)$ or $P(X \geqslant r)$, we use the **binomial cumulative distribution function**.

Some calculator models, such as the **TI-84 Plus**, only allow you to calculate $P(X \leqslant r)$. To find the probability $P(X \geqslant r)$ for these models, it is often easiest to find the complement $P(X \leqslant r-1)$ and use $P(X \geqslant r) = 1 - P(X \leqslant r-1)$.

Example 9   ◀◉ **Self Tutor**

72% of union members are in favour of a certain change to their conditions of employment. A random sample of five members is taken. Find:

a the probability that three members are in favour of the change in conditions

b the probability that at least three members are in favour of the changed conditions

c the expected number of members in the sample that are in favour of the change.

Let X denote the number of members in the sample in favour of the changes.

$n = 5$, so $X = 0, 1, 2, 3, 4,$ or $5,$ and $p = 72\% = 0.72$

$\therefore \quad X \sim B(5, 0.72)$.

a $P(X = 3)$

$= \binom{5}{3} (0.72)^3 (0.28)^2$

≈ 0.293

Casio fx-CG20	TI-84 Plus	TI-nspire
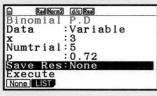	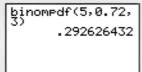	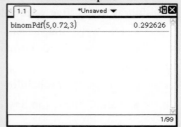

b $P(X \geqslant 3)$

≈ 0.862

Casio fx-CG20	TI-84 Plus	TI-nspire
		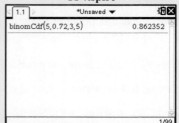

c $E(X) = np = 5 \times 0.72 = 3.6$ members

EXERCISE 23D.2

1 For which of these probability experiments does the binomial distribution apply? Justify your answers, using a full sentence.

   a A coin is thrown 100 times. The variable is the number of heads.

   b One hundred coins are each thrown once. The variable is the number of heads.

   c A box contains 5 blue and 3 red marbles. I draw out 5 marbles, replacing the marble each time. The variable is the number of red marbles drawn.

d A box contains 5 blue and 3 red marbles. I draw out 5 marbles without replacement. The variable is the number of red marbles drawn.

e A large bin contains ten thousand bolts, 1% of which are faulty. I draw a sample of 10 bolts from the bin. The variable is the number of faulty bolts.

2 5% of electric light bulbs are defective at manufacture. If 6 bulbs are tested at random with each one being replaced before the next is chosen, determine the probability that:

   a two are defective   **b** at least one is defective.

3 In a multiple choice test there are 10 questions. Each question has 5 choices, one of which is correct. If 70% is the pass mark and Raj, who knows absolutely nothing about the subject, guesses each answer at random, determine the probability that he will pass.

4 At a manufacturing plant, 35% of the employees work night-shift. If 7 employees are each selected from the entire group at random, find the probability that:

   a exactly 3 of them work night-shift   **b** less than 4 of them work night-shift

   c at least 4 of them work night-shift.

5 Records show that 6% of the items assembled on a production line are faulty.
A random sample of 12 items is selected with replacement. Find the probability that:

   a none will be faulty   **b** at most one will be faulty

   c at least two will be faulty   **d** less than four will be faulty.

6 There is a 5% chance that any apple in a crate will have a blemish. If a random sample of 25 apples is taken with replacement, find:

   a the probability that exactly 2 of these have blemishes

   b the probability that at least one has a blemish

   c the expected number of apples that will have a blemish.

7 The local bus service does not have a good reputation. The 8 am bus will run late on average two days out of every five. For any week of the year taken at random, find the probability of the 8 am bus being on time:

   a all 7 days   **b** only on Monday   **c** on any 6 days   **d** on at least 4 days.

8 An infectious flu virus is spreading through a school. The probability of a randomly selected student having the flu next week is 0.3.

   a Mr C has a class of 25 students.

      i Calculate the probability that 2 or more students will have the flu next week.

      ii If more than 20% of the students have the flu next week, a class test will have to be cancelled. What is the probability that the test will be cancelled?

   b If the school has 350 students, find the expected number that will have the flu next week.

9 During a season, a basketball player has a 94% success rate in shooting from the free throw line. In one match the basketballer has 20 shots from the free throw line.

   a Find the probability that the basketballer is successful on:

      i all 20 throws   **ii** at least 18 throws.

   b Find the expected number of successful throws for the match.

10 Martina beats Jelena in 2 games out of 3 at tennis. What is the probability that Jelena wins a set of tennis 6 games to 4?

Hint: What is the score after 9 games?

11 How many ordinary dice are needed for there to be a better than an even chance of at least one six when they are thrown together?

12 If a fair coin is tossed 200 times, find the probability that:

    a between 90 and 110 (inclusive) heads turn up

    b more than 95 but less than 105 heads turn up.

13 A new drug has 75% probability of curing a patient within one week. If 38 patients are treated using this drug, what is the probability that between 24 and 31 patients (inclusive) will be cured within a week?

THE MEAN AND STANDARD DEVIATION OF A BINOMIAL DISTRIBUTION

We have already seen that the expected outcome for a binomial experiment is the mean value $\mu = np$.

INVESTIGATION 2   THE MEAN AND STANDARD DEVIATION OF A BINOMIAL DISTRIBUTION

In this investigation we use a calculator to calculate the mean and standard deviation of a number of binomial distributions. A spreadsheet can also be used to speed up the process and handle a larger number of examples.

We will first calculate the mean and standard deviation for the variable $X \sim B(30, 0.25)$.

GRAPHICS
CALCULATOR
INSTRUCTIONS

What to do:

1 Enter the possible values for X from $x = 0$ to $x = 30$ into **List 1**, and their corresponding binomial probabilities $P(X = x)$ into **List 2**.

2 Draw the scatter diagram of **List 1** against **List 2**.

3 Calculate the descriptive statistics for the distribution.

```
1-Var Stats
μ →  x̄=7.5
     Σx=7.5
     Σx²=61.875
     Sx=
σ →  σx=2.371708245
     ↓n=1
```

4 Copy and complete the following table by repeating steps **1** to **3** for the remaining values of n and p.

	$p = 0.1$	$p = 0.25$	$p = 0.5$	$p = 0.7$
$n = 10$				
$n = 30$		$\mu = 7.5$ $\sigma \approx 2.3717$		
$n = 50$				

5 Compare your values with the formulae $\mu = np$ and $\sigma = \sqrt{np(1-p)}$.

From this **Investigation** you should have observed the following results which are true in general:

> Suppose X is a binomial random variable with parameters n and p, so $X \sim B(n, p)$.
>
> - The **mean** of X is $\mu = np$.
> - The **standard deviation** of X is $\sigma = \sqrt{np(1 - p)}$.
> - The **variance** of X is $\sigma^2 = np(1 - p)$.

Example 10 ◀) Self Tutor

A fair die is rolled twelve times and X is the number of sixes that could result.
Find the mean and standard deviation of the X-distribution.

This is a binomial distribution with $n = 12$ and $p = \frac{1}{6}$, so $X \sim B(12, \frac{1}{6})$.

So, $\mu = np$ and $\sigma = \sqrt{np(1 - p)}$
$\quad = 12 \times \frac{1}{6}$ $\quad = \sqrt{12 \times \frac{1}{6} \times \frac{5}{6}}$
$\quad = 2$ $\quad \approx 1.291$

We expect a six to be rolled 2 times, with standard deviation 1.291.

Example 11 ◀) Self Tutor

5% of a batch of batteries are defective. A random sample of 80 batteries is taken with replacement.
Find the mean and standard deviation of the number of defective batteries in the sample.

This is a binomial sampling situation with $n = 80$, $p = 5\% = \frac{1}{20}$.

If X is the random variable for the number of defectives, then $X \sim B(80, \frac{1}{20})$.

So, $\mu = np$ and $\sigma = \sqrt{np(1 - p)}$
$\quad = 80 \times \frac{1}{20}$ $\quad = \sqrt{80 \times \frac{1}{20} \times \frac{19}{20}}$
$\quad = 4$ $\quad \approx 1.949$

We expect a defective battery 4 times, with standard deviation 1.949.

EXERCISE 23D.3

1 Suppose $X \sim B(6, p)$.   For each of the following cases:

    i   find the mean and standard deviation of the X-distribution
    ii   graph the distribution using a column graph
    iii   comment on the shape of the distribution.

   a $p = 0.5$ **b** $p = 0.2$ **c** $p = 0.8$

2 A coin is tossed 10 times and X is the number of heads which occur. Find the mean and variance of the X-distribution.

3 Bolts produced by a machine vary in quality. The probability that a given bolt is defective is 0.04. Random samples of 30 bolts are taken from the week's production.

    a If X is the number of defective bolts in a sample, find the mean and standard deviation of the X-distribution.

    b If Y is the number of non-defective bolts in a sample, find the mean and standard deviation of the Y-distribution.

4 A city restaurant knows that 13% of reservations are not honoured, which means the group does not arrive. Suppose the restaurant receives 30 reservations. Let X be the random variable of the number of groups that do not arrive. Find the mean and standard deviation of the X-distribution.

<hr>

REVIEW SET 23A   **NON-CALCULATOR**

1 $P(X = x) = \dfrac{a}{x^2 + 1}$, $x = 0, 1, 2, 3$ is a probability distribution function.

    a Find a.   **b** Find $P(X \geqslant 1)$.

2 A random sample of 120 toothbrushes is taken with replacement from a very large batch where 4% are known to be defective. Find the mean number of defectives in the sample.

3 A random variable X has the probability distribution function $P(x)$ described in the table.

x	0	1	2	3	4
$P(x)$	0.10	0.30	0.45	0.10	k

    a Find k.   **b** Find $P(X \geqslant 3)$.

    c Find the expectation $E(X)$ for the distribution.

4   **a** Expand $\left(\frac{3}{5} + \frac{2}{5}\right)^4$.

    b A tin contains 20 pens of which 12 have blue ink. Four pens are randomly selected, with replacement, from the tin. Find the probability that:

        i two of them have blue ink   **ii** at most two have blue ink.

5 Three green balls and two yellow balls are placed in a hat. Two balls are randomly drawn without replacement. Let X be the number of green balls drawn.

    a Find the probability that: **i** $X = 0$ **ii** $X = 1$ **iii** $X = 2$

    b Find $E(X)$.

6 Lakshmi rolls a normal six-sided die. She wins twice the number of pounds as the number shown on the face.

    a How much does Lakshmi expect to win from one roll of the die?

    b If it costs £8 to play the game, would you advise Lakshmi to play several games? Explain your answer.

7 A binomial distribution has probability distribution function $P(X = x) = k \left(\frac{1}{3}\right)^x \left(\frac{2}{3}\right)^{7-x}$ where $x = 0, 1, 2, 3, ..., 7$.

    a Write k in the form $\binom{n}{r}$.   **b** Find the mean and variance of the distribution.

8 A pentagonal and a square spinner are illustrated. The pentagonal spinner has 3 red and 2 green sections.

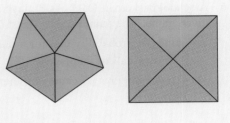

a Copy and complete the tree diagram which shows all possible results when then two are spun together.

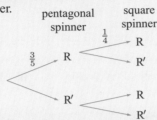

b Calculate the probability that exactly one red will occur.

c The pair of spinners is now spun 10 times and X is the number of times that exactly one red occurs.

  i Write down expressions for $P(X = 1)$ and $P(X = 9)$.

  ii Hence determine which of these outcomes is more likely.

REVIEW SET 23B   CALCULATOR

1 A binomial random variable X has probability distribution function $P(x) = k \left(\frac{3}{4}\right)^x \left(\frac{1}{4}\right)^{3-x}$ where $x = 0, 1, 2, 3$ and k is a constant. Find:

  a k **b** $P(X \geqslant 1)$ **c** $E(X)$

  d the standard deviation of the distribution.

2 A manufacturer finds that 18% of the items produced from its assembly lines are defective. During a floor inspection, the manufacturer randomly selects ten items with replacement. Find the probability that the manufacturer finds:

  a one defective   **b** two defective   **c** at least two defective items.

3 From data over the last fifteen years it is known that the chance of a netballer with a knee injury needing major knee surgery in any one season is 0.0132. In 2007 there were 487 knee injuries in netball games throughout the country. Find the expected number of major knee surgeries required.

4 An X-ray has probability of 0.96 of showing a fracture in the arm. If four different X-rays are taken of a particular fracture, find the probability that:

  a all four show the fracture

  b the fracture does not show up

  c at least three X-rays show the fracture

  d only one X-ray shows the fracture.

5 24% of visitors to a museum make voluntary donations. On a certain day the museum has 175 visitors. Find:

  a the expected number of donations

  b the probability that less than 40 visitors make a donation.

6 A school basketball team has 8 players, each of whom has a 75% chance of turning up for any given game. The team needs at least 5 players to avoid forfeiting the game.

    a Find the probability that for a randomly chosen game, the team will:

        i have all of its players   **ii** have to forfeit the game.

    b The team plays 30 games for the season. How many games would you expect the team to forfeit?

7 The binomial distribution $X \sim \mathrm{B}(n,\, p)$ has mean 30 and variance 22.5.

    a Find n and p.

    b Hence find: **i** $\mathrm{P}(X = 25)$ **ii** $\mathrm{P}(X \geqslant 25)$ **iii** $\mathrm{P}(15 \leqslant X \leqslant 25)$

REVIEW SET 23C

1 Find k for the following probability distribution functions:

    a $\mathrm{P}(X = x) = \dfrac{k}{2x}, \quad x = 1,\, 2,\, 3$ **b**

x	0	1	2	3
$P(x)$	$\frac{k}{2}$	0.2	k^2	0.3

2 A random variable X has probability distribution function $\mathrm{P}(X = x) = \binom{4}{x}\left(\frac{1}{2}\right)^{x}\left(\frac{1}{2}\right)^{4-x}$ for $x = 0,\, 1,\, 2,\, 3,\, 4$.

    a Find $\mathrm{P}(X = x)$ for $x = 0,\, 1,\, 2,\, 3,\, 4$.   **b** Find the mean μ for the distribution.

    c Find the standard deviation σ for the distribution.

3   **a** Expand $\left(\frac{4}{5} + \frac{1}{5}\right)^{5}$.

    b With every attempt, Jack has an 80% chance of kicking a goal. In one quarter of a match he has 5 kicks for goal.

    Determine the probability that he scores:

        i 3 goals then misses twice

        ii 3 goals and misses twice.

4 A die is biased such that the probability of obtaining a 6 is $\frac{2}{5}$. The die is rolled 1200 times. Let X be the number of sixes obtained. Find the mean and standard deviation of X.

5 Only 40% of young trees that are planted will survive the first year. The Botanical Gardens buys five young trees. Assuming independence, find the probability that during the first year:

    a exactly one tree will survive   **b** at most one tree will survive

    c at least one tree will survive.

6 In a game, the numbers from 1 to 20 are written on tickets and placed in a bag. A player draws out a number at random. He or she wins $3 if the number is even, $6 if the number is a square number, and $9 if the number is both even and square.

    a Calculate the probability that the player wins: **i** $3   **ii** $6   **iii** $9

    b How much should be charged to play the game so that it is a fair game?

7 A fair die is rolled 360 times. Find the probability that:

    a less than 50 results are a 6   **b** between 55 and 65 results (inclusive) are a 6.

Chapter 24

The normal distribution

OPENING PROBLEM

A salmon breeder catches hundreds of adult fish. He records their weights in a frequency table with class intervals $3 \leqslant w < 3.1$ kg, $3.1 \leqslant w < 3.2$ kg, $3.2 \leqslant w < 3.3$ kg, and so on.

The mean weight is 4.73 kg, and the standard deviation is 0.53 kg.

A frequency histogram of the data is bell-shaped and symmetric about the mean.

Things to think about:

a Can we use the mean and standard deviation only to find the proportion of salmon whose weight is:

   i greater than 6 kg   **ii** between 4 kg and 6 kg?

b How can we find the weight:

   i which 90% of salmon weigh less than   **ii** which 25% of salmon weigh more than?

In the previous chapter we looked at discrete random variables and examined binomial probability distributions where the random variable X could take the non-negative integer values $x = 0, 1, 2,$ $3, 4, ..., n$ for some finite $n \in \mathbb{N}$.

For a **continuous random variable** X, x can take any real value.

We use a function called a **probability density function** to define the probability distribution.

Probabilities are found by calculating areas under the probability density function curve for a particular interval.

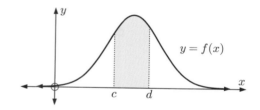

For a continuous random variable X, the **probability density function** is a function $f(x)$ such that $f(x) \geqslant 0$ on its entire domain.

If the domain of the function is $a \leqslant x \leqslant b$, then $\displaystyle\int_a^b f(x)\, dx = 1$.

The probability that X lies in the interval $c \leqslant X \leqslant d$ is $\mathbf{P}(c \leqslant X \leqslant d) = \displaystyle\int_c^d f(x)\, dx$.

For a continuous variable X, the probability that X is *exactly* equal to a particular value is zero. So, $\mathbf{P}(X = x) = 0$ for all x.

For example, the probability that an egg will weigh *exactly* 72.9 g is zero.

If you were to weigh an egg on scales that weigh to the nearest 0.1 g, a reading of 72.9 g means the weight lies somewhere between 72.85 g and 72.95 g. No matter how accurate your scales are, you can only ever know the weight of an egg within a range.

So, for a continuous variable we can only talk about the probability that an event lies in an **interval**.

A consequence of this is that $\mathbf{P}(c \leqslant X \leqslant d) = \mathbf{P}(c < X \leqslant d) = \mathbf{P}(c \leqslant X < d) = \mathbf{P}(c < X < d)$.

This would not be true if X was discrete.

A

THE NORMAL DISTRIBUTION

The normal distribution is the most important distribution for a continuous random variable. Many naturally occurring phenomena have a distribution that is normal, or approximately normal. Some examples are:

- physical attributes of a population such as height, weight, and arm length
- crop yields
- scores for tests taken by a large population

Once a normal model has been established, we can use it to make predictions about a distribution and to answer other relevant questions.

HOW A NORMAL DISTRIBUTION ARISES

Consider the oranges picked from an orange tree. They do not all have the same weight. The variation may be due to several factors, including:

- genetics
- different times when the flowers were fertilised
- different amounts of sunlight reaching the leaves and fruit
- different weather conditions such as the prevailing winds.

The result is that most of the fruit will have weights close to the mean, while fewer oranges will be *much* heavier or *much* lighter.

This results in a **bell-shaped distribution** for the weight of oranges in a crop, which is symmetric about the mean.

A TYPICAL NORMAL DISTRIBUTION

A large sample of cockle shells was collected and the maximum width of each shell was measured. Click on the video clip icon to see how a histogram of the data is built up. Then click on the demo icon to observe the effect of changing the class interval lengths for normally distributed data.

VIDEO CLIP

DEMO

THE NORMAL PROBABILITY DENSITY FUNCTION

If X is **normally distributed** then its **probability density function** is

$\sim$ is read "is distributed as"

$$f(x) = \frac{1}{\sigma\sqrt{2\pi}} e^{-\frac{1}{2}\left(\frac{x-\mu}{\sigma}\right)^2} \quad \text{for} \quad -\infty < x < \infty$$

where μ is the mean and σ^2 is the variance of the distribution.

We write $X \sim N(\mu, \sigma^2)$.

- The curve $y = f(x)$, which is called a **normal curve**, is symmetrical about the vertical line $x = \mu$.

- As $x \to \pm \infty$ the normal curve approaches its asymptote, the x-axis.

- $f(x) > 0$ for all x.

- Since the total probability must be 1, $\int_{-\infty}^{\infty} f(x)\, dx = 1$.

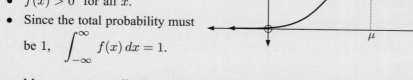

- More scores are distributed closer to the mean than further away. This results in the typical **bell shape**.

Click on the icon to explore the normal probability density function and how it changes when μ and σ are altered.

DEMO

THE GEOMETRIC SIGNIFICANCE OF μ AND σ

Differentiating $f(x) = \dfrac{1}{\sigma\sqrt{2\pi}}\, e^{-\frac{1}{2}\left(\frac{x-\mu}{\sigma}\right)^2}$

we obtain $f'(x) = \dfrac{-1}{\sigma^2\sqrt{2\pi}}\left(\dfrac{x-\mu}{\sigma}\right) e^{-\frac{1}{2}\left(\frac{x-\mu}{\sigma}\right)^2}$

$\therefore$ $f'(x) = 0$ only when $x = \mu$, and this corresponds to the point on the graph when $f(x)$ is a maximum.

Differentiating again, we obtain $f''(x) = \dfrac{-1}{\sigma^2\sqrt{2\pi}}\, e^{-\frac{1}{2}\left(\frac{x-\mu}{\sigma}\right)^2}\left[\dfrac{1}{\sigma} - \dfrac{(x-\mu)^2}{\sigma^3}\right]$

$\therefore$ $f''(x) = 0$ when $\dfrac{(x-\mu)^2}{\sigma^3} = \dfrac{1}{\sigma}$

$\therefore$ $(x-\mu)^2 = \sigma^2$

$\therefore$ $x - \mu = \pm\sigma$

$\therefore$ $x = \mu \pm \sigma$

So, the points of inflection are at
$x = \mu + \sigma$ and $x = \mu - \sigma$.

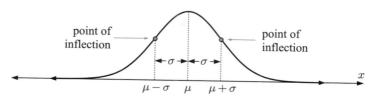

For a normal curve, the standard deviation is uniquely determined as the horizontal distance from the line of symmetry $x = \mu$ to a point of inflection.

INVESTIGATION 1   STANDARD DEVIATION

The purpose of this investigation is to find the proportions of normal distribution data which lie within σ, 2σ, and 3σ of the mean.

What to do:

1 Click on the icon to start the demonstration in Microsoft$^{\circledR}$ Excel.

DEMO

2 Take a random sample of size $n = 1000$ from a normal distribution.

3 Find the sample mean $\overline{x}$ and standard deviation s.

4 Find:

   a $\overline{x} - s$ and $\overline{x} + s$ **b** $\overline{x} - 2s$ and $\overline{x} + 2s$ **c** $\overline{x} - 3s$ and $\overline{x} + 3s$

5 Count all values between:

   a $\overline{x} - s$ and $\overline{x} + s$ **b** $\overline{x} - 2s$ and $\overline{x} + 2s$ **c** $\overline{x} - 3s$ and $\overline{x} + 3s$

6 Determine the percentage of data values in these intervals.

7 Repeat the procedure several times. Hence suggest the proportions of normal distribution data which lie within:

   a σ **b** 2σ **c** 3σ from the mean.

For a normal distribution with mean μ and standard deviation σ, the percentage breakdown of where the random variable could lie is shown below.

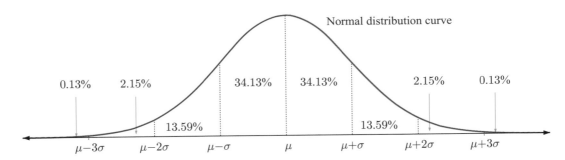

Notice that: • $\approx 68.26\%$ of values lie between $\mu - \sigma$ and $\mu + \sigma$
   • $\approx 95.44\%$ of values lie between $\mu - 2\sigma$ and $\mu + 2\sigma$
   • $\approx 99.74\%$ of values lie between $\mu - 3\sigma$ and $\mu + 3\sigma$.

HISTORICAL NOTE

The normal distribution was first characterised by **Carl Friedrich Gauss** in 1809 as a way to rationalize his **method of least squares** for linear regression.

Marquis de Laplace was the first to calculate $\displaystyle\int_{-\infty}^{\infty} e^{-x^2} \, dx = \sqrt{\pi}$. This led to the correct

normalization constant $\dfrac{1}{\sigma\sqrt{2\pi}}$ being used for the normal distribution, ensuring $\displaystyle\int_{-\infty}^{\infty} f(x) \, dx = 1$.

Example 1   ◀)) **Self Tutor**

The chest measurements of 18 year old male footballers are normally distributed with a mean of 95 cm and a standard deviation of 8 cm.

a Find the percentage of footballers with chest measurements between:

   i 87 cm and 103 cm   **ii** 103 cm and 111 cm

b Find the probability that the chest measurement of a randomly chosen footballer is between 87 cm and 111 cm.

c Find the value of k such that approximately 16% of chest measurements are below k cm.

a   **i** We need the percentage between
$\mu - \sigma$ and $\mu + \sigma$.

∴ about 68.3% of footballers have a chest measurement between 87 cm and 103 cm.

  ii We need the percentage between
$\mu + \sigma$ and $\mu + 2\sigma$.

∴ about 13.6% of footballers have a chest measurement between 103 cm and 111 cm.

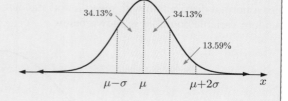

b We need the percentage between
$\mu - \sigma$ and $\mu + 2\sigma$.

This is $\quad 2(34.13\%) + 13.59\%$

$\quad\quad \approx 81.9\%.$

So, the probability is ≈ 0.819.

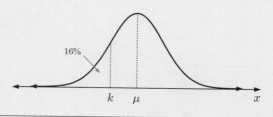

c Approximately 16% of data lies more than one standard deviation lower than the mean.

∴ k is σ below the mean μ

∴ $k = 95 - 8$

$\quad = 87$ cm

EXERCISE 24A

1 Draw each of the following normal distributions accurately on one set of axes.

Distribution	Mean (mL)	Standard deviation (mL)
A	25	5
B	30	2
C	21	10

2 Explain why it is likely that the distributions of the following variables will be normal:

  a the volume of soft drink in cans

  b the diameter of bolts immediately after manufacture.

3   State the probability that a randomly selected, normally distributed value lies between:

   a σ below the mean and σ above the mean

   b   the mean and the value 2σ above the mean.

4   The mean height of players in a basketball competition is 184 cm. If the standard deviation is 5 cm, what percentage of them are likely to be:

   a   taller than 189 cm

   b   taller than 179 cm

   c   between 174 cm and 199 cm

   d   over 199 cm tall?

5   The mean average rainfall of Claudona for August is 48 mm with a standard deviation of 6 mm. Over a 20 year period, how many times would you expect there to be less than 42 mm of rainfall during August in Claudona?

6   Two hundred lifesavers competed in a swimming race. The mean time was 10 minutes 30 seconds, and the standard deviation was 15 seconds. Estimate the number of competitors who:

   a   took longer than 11 minutes

   b   took less than 10 minutes 15 seconds

   c   completed the race in a time between 10 min 15 s and 10 min 45 s.

7   The weights of babies born at Prince Louis Maternity Hospital last year averaged 3.0 kg with a standard deviation of 200 grams. If there were 545 babies born at this hospital last year, estimate the number that weighed:

   a   less than 3.2 kg

   b   between 2.8 kg and 3.4 kg.

8   Given $X \sim N(3, 0.1^2)$, find:

   a   the probability that a randomly selected value lies within 2 standard deviations of the mean

   b   the value of X which is 1 standard deviation below the mean.

9   The weights of Jason's oranges are normally distributed. 84% of the crop weigh more than 152 grams and 16% weigh more than 200 grams.

   a   Find μ and σ for the crop.

   b   What percentage of the oranges weigh between 152 grams and 224 grams?

10   The height of male students in a university is normally distributed with mean 170 cm and standard deviation 8 cm.

   a   Find the percentage of male students whose height is:

      i   between 162 cm and 170 cm

      ii   between 170 cm and 186 cm.

   b   Find the probability that a randomly chosen student from this group has a height:

      i   between 178 cm and 186 cm

      ii   less than 162 cm

      iii   less than 154 cm

      iv   greater than 162 cm.

   c   Find the value of k such that 16% of the students are taller than k cm.

11   The heights of 13 year old boys are normally distributed. 97.72% of them are above 131 cm and 2.28% are above 179 cm.

   a   Find μ and σ for the height distribution.

   b   A 13 year old boy is randomly chosen. What is the probability that his height lies between 143 cm and 191 cm?

12 When a specific variety of radish is grown without fertiliser, the weights of the radishes produced are normally distributed with mean 40 g and standard deviation 10 g.

When the same variety of radish is grown in the same way but with fertiliser added, the weights of the radishes produced are also normally distributed, but with mean 140 g and standard deviation 40 g.

Determine the proportion of radishes grown:

  a without fertiliser with weights less than 50 grams

  b with fertiliser with weights less than 60 grams

  c **i** with and   **ii** without fertiliser, which have weights between 20 and 60 g

  d **i** with and   **ii** without fertiliser, which have weights greater than 60 g.

13 A bottle filling machine fills an average of 20 000 bottles a day with a standard deviation of 2000. Assuming that production is normally distributed and the year comprises 260 working days, calculate the approximate number of working days on which:

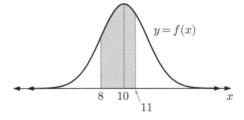

  a under 18 000 bottles are filled

  b over 16 000 bottles are filled

  c between 18 000 and 24 000 bottles (inclusive) are filled.

B   PROBABILITIES USING A CALCULATOR

Using the properties of the normal probability density function, we have considered probabilities in regions of width σ either side of the mean.

To find probabilities more generally we use technology.

Suppose $X \sim N(10,\ 2.3^2)$, so X is normally distributed with mean 10 and standard deviation 2.3.

To find $P(8 \leqslant X \leqslant 11)$, we need to calculate

$\int_{8}^{11} f(x)\,dx$, where $f(x)$ is the probability density

function of the normal curve.

Click on the icon to find instructions for these processes.

GRAPHICS
CALCULATOR
INSTRUCTIONS

Example 2   ◄) **Self Tutor**

If $X \sim N(10,\ 2.3^2)$, find these probabilities:

  a $P(8 \leqslant X \leqslant 11)$ **b** $P(X \leqslant 12)$ **c** $P(X > 9)$. Illustrate your results.

X is normally distributed with mean 10 and standard deviation 2.3 .

Using technology:

a

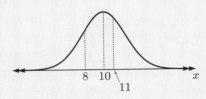

$P(8 \leqslant X \leqslant 11) \approx 0.476$

b

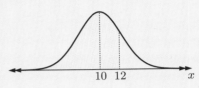

$P(X \leqslant 12) \approx 0.808$

c

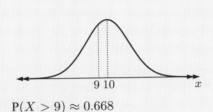

$P(X > 9) \approx 0.668$

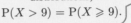
For continuous distributions,
$P(X > 9) = P(X \geqslant 9)$.

Example 3   ◄)) **Self Tutor**

In 1972 the heights of rugby players were approximately normally distributed with mean 179 cm and standard deviation 7 cm. Find the probability that a randomly selected player in 1972 was:

  a at least 175 cm tall
          b between 170 cm and 190 cm.

If X is the height of a player then X is normally distributed with $\mu = 179$, $\sigma = 7$.

Using technology:

a

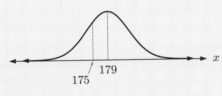

$P(X \geqslant 175) \approx 0.716$

b

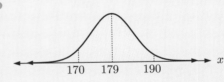

$P(170 < X < 190) \approx 0.843$

EXERCISE 24B

It is helpful to sketch the normal distribution and shade the area of interest.

1 X is a random variable that is distributed normally with mean 70 and standard deviation 4. Find:

  a $P(70 \leqslant X \leqslant 74)$ **b** $P(68 \leqslant X \leqslant 72)$ **c** $P(X \leqslant 65)$

2 X is a random variable that is distributed normally with mean 60 and standard deviation 5. Find:

  a $P(60 \leqslant X \leqslant 65)$ **b** $P(62 \leqslant X \leqslant 67)$

  c $P(X \geqslant 64)$ **d** $P(X \leqslant 68)$

  e $P(X \leqslant 61)$ **f** $P(57.5 \leqslant X \leqslant 62.5)$

3 A machine produces metal bolts. The lengths of these bolts have a normal distribution with mean 19.8 cm and standard deviation 0.3 cm. If a bolt is selected at random from the machine, find the probability that it will have a length between 19.7 cm and 20 cm.

4 Max's customers put money for charity into a collection box on the front counter of his shop. The average weekly collection is approximately normally distributed with mean $40 and standard deviation $6. What proportion of weeks would he expect to collect:

  a between $30.00 and $50.00   **b** at least $50.00?

5 Eels are washed onto a beach after a storm. Their lengths have a normal distribution with mean 41 cm and variance 11 cm^2.

  a If an eel is randomly selected, find the probability that it is at least 50 cm long.

  b Find the proportion of eels measuring between 40 cm and 50 cm long.

  c How many eels from a sample of 200 would you expect to measure at least 45 cm in length?

6 The speed of cars passing the supermarket is normally distributed with mean 56.3 km h^{-1} and standard deviation 7.4 km h^{-1}. Find the probability that a randomly selected car has speed:

  a between 60 and 75 km h^{-1} **b** at most 70 km h^{-1}

  c at least 60 km h^{-1}.

Example 4 ◀⁾ **Self Tutor**

The time taken by students to complete a puzzle is normally distributed with mean 28.3 minutes and standard deviation 3.6 minutes. Calculate the probability that:

  a a randomly selected student took at least 30 minutes to complete the puzzle

  b out of 10 randomly selected students, at most half of them took at least 30 minutes to complete the puzzle.

  a Let X denote the time for a student to complete the puzzle.

    $X \sim N(28.3, 3.6^2)$

    $\therefore$ $P(X \geqslant 30) \approx 0.318\,38$ {using technology}

               ≈ 0.318

  b Let Y denote the number of students who took at least 30 minutes to complete the puzzle.

    Then $Y \sim B(10, 0.318\,38)$

    $\therefore$ $P(Y \leqslant 5) \approx 0.938$ {using technology}

7 Apples from a grower's crop were normally distributed with mean 173 grams and standard deviation 34 grams. Apples weighing less than 130 grams were too small to sell.

   a Find the proportion of apples from this crop which were too small to sell.

   b Find the probability that in a picker's basket of 100 apples, up to 10 apples were too small to sell.

8 People found to have high blood pressure are started on a course of tablets and have their blood pressure checked at the end of 4 weeks. The drop in blood pressure over the period is normally distributed with mean 5.9 units and standard deviation 1.9 units.

   a Find the proportion of people who show a drop of more than 4 units.

   b Eight people from the large population taking the course of tablets are selected at random. Find the probability that more than five of them will show a drop in blood pressure of more than 4 units.

C   THE STANDARD NORMAL DISTRIBUTION (Z-DISTRIBUTION)

Every normal X-distribution can be **transformed** into the **standard normal distribution** or Z-**distribution** using the transformation $\quad z = \dfrac{x - \mu}{\sigma}$.

INVESTIGATION 2   PROPERTIES OF $z = \dfrac{x - \mu}{\sigma}$

Suppose a random variable X is **normally distributed** with mean μ and standard deviation σ.

For each value of x we can calculate a **z-score** using the algebraic transformation $\quad z = \dfrac{x - \mu}{\sigma}$.

What to do:

1 Consider the x-values: 1, 2, 2, 3, 3, 3, 3, 4, 4, 4, 4, 4, 5, 5, 5, 5, 6, 6, 7.

   a Draw a graph of the distribution to check that it is approximately normal.

   b Find the mean μ and standard deviation σ for the distribution of x-values.

   c Use the transformation $z = \dfrac{x - \mu}{\sigma}$ to convert each x-value into a z-value.

   d Find the mean and standard deviation for the distribution of z-values.

2 Click on the icon to load a large sample drawn from a normal population. By clicking appropriately we can repeat the four steps in **1**.

         DEMO

3 Summarise your findings.

> The Z-distribution has mean 0 and standard deviation 1.
>
> In fact, $Z \sim N(0, 1)$.

No matter what the parameters μ and σ of the X-distribution are, we always end up with the same Z-distribution $Z \sim N(0, 1)$.

THE Z-TRANSFORMATION

To explain how this works, remember that a normal X-distribution with mean μ and standard deviation σ has probability density function

$$f(x) = \frac{1}{\sigma\sqrt{2\pi}} \, e^{-\frac{1}{2}(\frac{x-\mu}{\sigma})^2}.$$

Consider first the normal distribution $N(0, 1)$ with $\mu = 0$, $\sigma = 1$, and probability density function

$$f(x) = \frac{1}{\sqrt{2\pi}} \, e^{-\frac{1}{2}x^2}.$$

With $\mu = 0$ and $\sigma = 1$, the transformation $z = \frac{x-\mu}{\sigma}$ is simply $z = x$.

So, the distribution $N(0, 1)$ is unchanged under the transformation, and the probability density function for the Z-distribution is

$$f(z) = \frac{1}{\sqrt{2\pi}} \, e^{-\frac{1}{2}z^2}.$$

So what happens with other X-distributions?

$N(0, 1)$ is symmetric about the mean $x = 0$, with points of inflection at $x = \pm 1$.

To transform $N(0, 1)$ into $N(\mu, \sigma^2)$ we need:

- a horizontal stretch with scale factor σ to shift the inflection points to $x = \pm\sigma$
- a horizontal translation μ units to the right to shift the mean to $x = \mu$.

This gives us $f(\frac{x-\mu}{\sigma}) = \frac{1}{\sqrt{2\pi}} \, e^{-\frac{1}{2}(\frac{x-\mu}{\sigma})^2}.$

However, when we made the horizontal stretch, we changed the area under the curve. We know this needs to be 1 for a probability density function. We therefore also need:

- a vertical stretch with scale factor $\frac{1}{\sigma}$ to ensure that $\displaystyle\int_{-\infty}^{\infty} f(x)\,dx = 1.$

DEMO

We now have the probability density function $f(x) = \frac{1}{\sigma\sqrt{2\pi}} \, e^{-\frac{1}{2}(\frac{x-\mu}{\sigma})^2}.$

The Z-transformation does this in reverse, so no matter what normal distribution we start with, we end up with the standard normal distribution function $f(z)$.

THE SIGNIFICANCE OF THE Z-DISTRIBUTION

The **probability density function** for the Z-distribution is $f(z) = \frac{1}{\sqrt{2\pi}} e^{-\frac{1}{2}z^2}$, $-\infty < z < \infty$.

If x is an observation from a normal distribution with mean μ and standard deviation σ, the **z-score** of x, $z = \frac{x - \mu}{\sigma}$, is the number of standard deviations x is from the mean.

For example:

- if $z = 1.84$, then x is 1.84 standard deviations to the right of the mean
- if $z = -0.273$, then x is 0.273 standard deviations to the left of the mean.

This diagram shows how the z-score is related to a general normal curve:

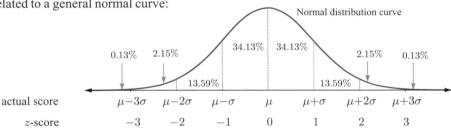

This means that for $X \sim N(\mu, \sigma^2)$ and $Z \sim N(0, 1^2)$ and for any $x_1, x_2 \in \mathbb{R}$, $x_1 < x_2$, with corresponding z-values $z_1 = \frac{x_1 - \mu}{\sigma}$ and $z_2 = \frac{x_2 - \mu}{\sigma}$, then:

- $P(X \geqslant x_1) = P(Z \geqslant z_1)$

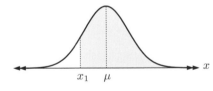 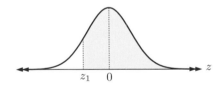

- $P(X \leqslant x_1) = P(Z \leqslant z_1)$

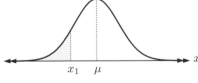 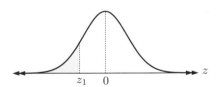

- $P(x_1 \leqslant X \leqslant x_2) = P(z_1 \leqslant Z \leqslant z_2)$

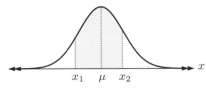 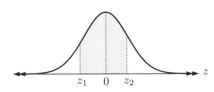

z-scores are particularly useful when comparing two populations with different μ and σ. However, these comparisons will only be reasonable if both distributions are approximately normal.

Example 5
🔊 Self Tutor

Kelly scored 73% in History where the class mean was 68% and the standard deviation was 10.2%. In Mathematics she scored 66%, where the class mean was 62% and the standard deviation was 6.8%.

In which subject did Kelly perform better compared with the rest of her class?

Assume the scores for both subjects were normally distributed.

Kelly's z-score for History $= \dfrac{73 - 68}{10.2} \approx 0.490$

Kelly's z-score for Mathematics $= \dfrac{66 - 62}{6.8} \approx 0.588$

So, Kelly's result in Mathematics was 0.588 standard deviations above the mean, whereas her result in History was 0.490 standard deviations above the mean.

∴ Kelly's result in Mathematics was better compared to her class, even though her percentage was lower.

EXERCISE 24C

1   The table shows Emma's midyear exam results. The exam results for each subject are normally distributed with the mean μ and standard deviation σ shown in the table.

   a Find the z-score for each of Emma's subjects.

   b Arrange Emma's subjects from 'best' to 'worst' in terms of the z-scores.

Subject	Emma's score	μ	σ
English	48	40	4.4
Mandarin	81	60	9
Geography	84	55	18
Biology	68	50	20
Maths	84	50	15

2   The table alongside shows Sergio's results in his final examinations, along with the class means and standard deviations.

   a Find Sergio's Z-value for each subject.

   b Arrange Sergio's performances in each subject in order from 'best' to 'worst'.

	Sergio	μ	σ
Physics	73%	78%	10.8%
Chemistry	77%	72%	11.6%
Mathematics	76%	74%	10.1%
German	91%	86%	9.6%
Biology	58%	62%	5.2%

3   Consider the normal distribution probabilities:

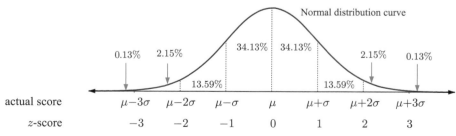

Use the diagram to calculate the following probabilities. In each case sketch the Z-distribution and shade in the region of interest.

   a $P(-1 < Z < 1)$

   b $P(-1 \leqslant Z \leqslant 3)$

   c $P(-1 < Z < 0)$

   d $P(Z < 2)$

   e $P(-1 < Z)$

   f $P(Z \geqslant 1)$

4   Given $X \sim N(\mu, \sigma^2)$ and $Z \sim N(0, 1)$, determine the values of a and b such that:

   a $P(\mu - \sigma < X < \mu + 2\sigma) = P(a < Z < b)$

   b $P(\mu - 0.5\sigma < X < \mu) = P(a < Z < b)$

   c $P(0 \leqslant Z \leqslant 3) = P(\mu - a\sigma \leqslant X \leqslant \mu + b\sigma)$

Example 6   ◀) **Self Tutor**

Use technology to illustrate and calculate:

   a $P(-0.41 \leqslant Z \leqslant 0.67)$ b $P(Z \leqslant 1.5)$ c $P(Z > 0.84)$

$Z \sim N(0, 1)$

a

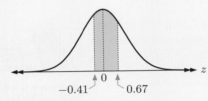

$P(-0.41 \leqslant Z \leqslant 0.67) \approx 0.408$

b

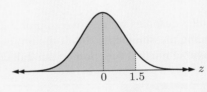

$P(Z \leqslant 1.5) \approx 0.933$

c

$P(Z > 0.84) \approx 0.200$

---

5   If Z is the standard normal distribution, find the following probabilities using technology. In each case sketch the regions.

   a $P(-0.86 \leqslant Z \leqslant 0.32)$ b $P(-2.3 \leqslant Z \leqslant 1.5)$ c $P(Z \leqslant 1.2)$

   d $P(Z \leqslant -0.53)$ e $P(Z \geqslant 1.3)$ f $P(Z \geqslant -1.4)$

   g $P(Z > 4)$

6   Suppose the variable X is normally distributed with mean $\mu = 58.3$ and standard deviation $\sigma = 8.96$.

   a   Let the z-score of $x = 50.6$ be z_1 and the z-score of $x = 68.9$ be z_2.

      i   Calculate z_1 and z_2.   ii   Find $P(z_1 \leqslant Z \leqslant z_2)$.

   b   Check your answer by calculating $P(50.6 \leqslant X \leqslant 68.9)$ directly from your calculator.

D QUANTILES OR k-VALUES

Consider a population of crabs where the length of a shell, X mm, is normally distributed with mean 70 mm and standard deviation 10 mm.

A biologist wants to protect the population by allowing only the largest 5% of crabs to be harvested. He therefore asks the question: "95% of the crabs have lengths less than what?".

To answer this question we need to find k such that $P(X \leqslant k) = 0.95$.

The number k is known as a **quantile**, and in this case the 95% quantile.

When finding quantiles we are given a probability and are asked to calculate the corresponding measurement. This is the *inverse* of finding probabilities, and we use the **inverse normal function** on our calculator.

GRAPHICS
CALCULATOR
INSTRUCTIONS

Example 7 ◀)) **Self Tutor**

If $X \sim N(23.6, 3.1^2)$, find k for which $P(X < k) = 0.95$.

X has mean 23.6 and standard deviation 3.1.

If $P(X < k) = 0.95$ then
$$k \approx 28.7$$

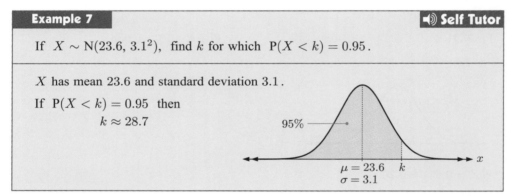

Example 8 ◀)) **Self Tutor**

If Z is the standard normal distribution, find k such that $P(Z > k) = 0.73$. Interpret your result.

If $P(Z > k) = 0.73$ then
$\quad P(Z \leqslant k) = 0.27$
$\quad \therefore \ k \approx -0.613$

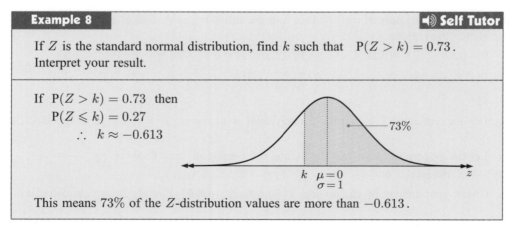

This means 73% of the Z-distribution values are more than -0.613.

EXERCISE 24D.1

1 Suppose Z is the standard normal distribution. Illustrate with a sketch and find k such that:

   a $P(Z \leqslant k) = 0.81$ **b** $P(Z \leqslant k) = 0.58$ **c** $P(Z \leqslant k) = 0.17$

2 $X \sim N(20, 3^2)$. Illustrate with a sketch and find k such that:

    a $P(X \leqslant k) = 0.348$ **b** $P(X \leqslant k) = 0.878$ **c** $P(X \leqslant k) = 0.5$

3 Suppose $X \sim N(38.7, 8.2^2)$. Illustrate with a sketch and find k such that:

    a $P(X \leqslant k) = 0.9$ **b** $P(X \geqslant k) = 0.8$

4 Given that $X \sim N(23, 5^2)$, find a such that:

    a $P(X < a) = 0.378$ **b** $P(X \geqslant a) = 0.592$ **c** $P(23 - a < X < 23 + a) = 0.427$

Example 9   ◄)) Self Tutor

A university professor determines that no more than 80% of this year's History candidates should pass the final examination. The examination results were approximately normally distributed with mean 62 and standard deviation 13. Find the lowest score necessary to pass the examination.

Let X denote the final examination result, so $X \sim N(62, 13^2)$.

We need to find k such that

    $P(X \geqslant k) = 0.8$

$\therefore$ $P(X < k) = 0.2$

    $\therefore$ $k \approx 51.059$

So, the minimum pass mark is 52.

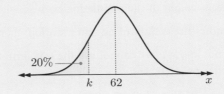

5 The students of Class X sat a Physics test. The average score was 46 with a standard deviation of 25. The teacher decided to award an A to the top 7% of the students in the class. Assuming that the scores were normally distributed, find the lowest score that would achieve an A.

6 The length of fish from a particular species is normally distributed with mean 35 cm and standard deviation 8 cm. The fisheries department has decided that the smallest 10% of the fish are not to be harvested. What is the size of the smallest fish that can be harvested?

7 The length of a screw produced by a machine is normally distributed with mean 75 mm and standard deviation 0.1 mm. If a screw is too long it is automatically rejected. If 1% of screws are rejected, what is the length of the smallest screw to be rejected?

8 Pedro is studying Algebra and Geometry. He sits for the mid-year exams in each subject.

Pedro's Algebra mark is 56%, and the class mean and standard deviation are 50.2% and 15.8% respectively.

In Geometry he is told that the class mean and standard deviation are 58.7% and 18.7% respectively.

What percentage does Pedro need to have scored in Geometry, to have an equivalent result to his Algebra mark?

9 The volume of cool drink in a bottle filled by a machine is normally distributed with mean 503 mL and standard deviation 0.5 mL. 1% of the bottles are rejected because they are underfilled, and 2% are rejected because they are overfilled; otherwise they are kept for retail. What range of volumes is in the bottles that are kept?

THE IMPORTANCE OF QUANTILES

For some questions we **must** convert to z-scores in order to find the answer.

> We always need to convert to z-scores if we are trying to find an unknown mean μ or standard deviation σ.

Example 10   ◀)) **Self Tutor**

An adult scallop population is known to be normally distributed with a standard deviation of 5.9 g. If 15% of scallops weigh less than 58.2 g, find the mean weight of the population.

Let the mean weight of the population be μ g.

If X g denotes the weight of an adult scallop, then $X \sim N(\mu, 5.9^2)$.

As we do not know μ we cannot use the invNorm directly, but we can convert to z-scores and use the properties of $N(0, 1^2)$.

Now $\quad P(X \leqslant 58.2) = 0.15$

$\therefore \ P\left(Z \leqslant \dfrac{58.2 - \mu}{5.9}\right) = 0.15$

Using invNorm for $N(0, 1^2)$,

$\dfrac{58.2 - \mu}{5.9} \approx -1.0364$

$\therefore \ 58.2 - \mu \approx -6.1$

$\mu \approx 64.3$

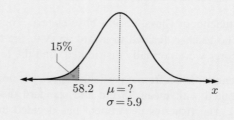

So, the mean weight is 64.3 g.

EXERCISE 24D.2

1 The IQs of students at school are normally distributed with a standard deviation of 15. If 20% of students have an IQ higher than 125, find the mean IQ of students at school.

2 The distances an athlete jumps are normally distributed with mean 5.2 m. If 15% of the jumps by this athlete are less than 5 m, what is the standard deviation?

3 The weekly income of a bakery is normally distributed with a mean of $6100. If 85% of the time the weekly income exceeds $6000, what is the standard deviation?

4 The arrival times of buses at a depot are normally distributed with standard deviation 5 minutes. If 10% of the buses arrive before 3:55 pm, find the mean arrival time of buses at the depot.

Example 11   🔊 **Self Tutor**

Find the mean and standard deviation of a normally distributed random variable X if
$P(X \leqslant 20) = 0.1$ and $P(X \geqslant 29) = 0.15$.

$X \sim N(\mu, \sigma^2)$ where we have to find μ and σ.

We start by finding z_1 and z_2 which correspond to $x_1 = 20$ and $x_2 = 29$.

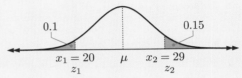

Now $P(X \leqslant x_1) = 0.1$

$\therefore$ $P(Z \leqslant \dfrac{20 - \mu}{\sigma}) = 0.1$

$\therefore$ $z_1 = \dfrac{20 - \mu}{\sigma} \approx -1.282$

$\therefore$ $20 - \mu \approx -1.282\sigma$ .... (1)

and $P(X \leqslant x_2) = 0.85$

$\therefore$ $P(Z \leqslant \dfrac{29 - \mu}{\sigma}) = 0.85$

$\therefore$ $z_2 = \dfrac{29 - \mu}{\sigma} \approx 1.036$

$\therefore$ $29 - \mu \approx 1.036\sigma$ .... (2)

Solving (1) and (2) simultaneously we get $\mu \approx 25.0$ and $\sigma \approx 3.88$.

---

5   **a**   Find the mean and standard deviation of a normally distributed random variable X, given that
$P(X \geqslant 80) = 0.1$ and $P(X \leqslant 30) = 0.15$.

   b   In a Mathematics examination it was found that 10% of the students scored at least 80, and no more than 15% scored under 30. Assuming the scores are normally distributed, what proportion of students scored more than 50?

6   The diameters of pistons manufactured by a company are normally distributed. Only those pistons whose diameters lie between 3.994 cm and 4.006 cm are acceptable.

   a   Find the mean and the standard deviation of the distribution if 4% of the pistons are rejected as being too small, and 5% are rejected as being too large.

   b   Determine the probability that the diameter of a randomly chosen piston lies between 3.997 cm and 4.003 cm.

7   Circular metal tokens are used to operate a washing machine in a laundromat. The diameters of the tokens are normally distributed, and only tokens with diameters between 1.94 and 2.06 cm will operate the machine.

   a   Find the mean and standard deviation of the distribution given that 2% of the tokens are too small, and 3% are too large.

   b   Find the probability that at most one token out of a randomly selected sample of 20 will not operate the machine.

ACTIVITY

Click on the icon to obtain a card game for the normal distribution.   **CARD GAME**

REVIEW SET 24A   NON-CALCULATOR

1 The average height of 17 year old boys is normally distributed with mean 179 cm and standard deviation 8 cm. Calculate the percentage of 17 year old boys whose heights are:

   a more than 195 cm   **b** between 163 cm and 195 cm

   c between 171 cm and 187 cm.

2 The contents of cans of a certain brand of soft drink are normally distributed with mean 377 mL and standard deviation 4.2 mL.

   a Find the percentage of cans with contents:

      i less than 368.6 mL   **ii** between 372.8 mL and 389.6 mL.

   b Find the probability that a randomly selected can contains between 377 mL and 381.2 mL.

3 The edible part of a batch of Coffin Bay oysters is normally distributed with mean 38.6 grams and standard deviation 6.3 grams.

Let the random variable X be the mass of a Coffin Bay oyster.

   a Find a if $P(38.6 - a \leqslant X \leqslant 38.6 + a) = 0.6826$.

   b Find b if $P(X \geqslant b) = 0.8413$.

4 The results of a test are normally distributed. Harri gained a z-score equal to -2.

   a Interpret this z-score with regard to the mean and standard deviation of the test scores.

   b What proportion of students obtained a better score than Harri?

   c The mean test score was 151 and Harri's actual score was 117. Find the standard deviation of the test scores.

5 The continuous random variable Z is distributed such that $Z \sim N(0, 1)$.

Find the value of k if $P(-k \leqslant Z \leqslant k) = 0.95$.

6 The distance that a 15 year old boy can throw a tennis ball is normally distributed with mean 35 m and standard deviation 4 m.

The distance that a 10 year old boy can throw a tennis ball is normally distributed with mean 25 m and standard deviation 3 m.

Jarrod is 15 years old and can throw a tennis ball 41 m. How far does his 10 year old brother Paul need to throw a tennis ball to perform as well as Jarrod?

7 State the probability that a randomly selected, normally distributed value lies between:

   a σ above the mean and 2σ above the mean

   b the mean and σ above the mean.

8

A bottle shop sells on average 2500 bottles per day with a standard deviation of 300 bottles. Assuming that the number of bottles sold per day is normally distributed, calculate the percentage of days when:

   a less than 1900 bottles are sold

   b more than 2200 bottles are sold

   c between 2200 and 3100 bottles are sold.

1 The mean and standard deviation of a normal distribution are 150 and 12 respectively. What percentage of values lie between:

    a 138 and 162   **b** 126 and 174   **c** 126 and 162   **d** 162 and 174?

2 The arm lengths of 18 year old females are normally distributed with mean 64 cm and standard deviation 4 cm.

    a Find the percentage of 18 year old females whose arm lengths are:

        i between 60 cm and 72 cm   **ii** greater than 60 cm.

    b Find the probability that a randomly chosen 18 year old female has an arm length in the range 56 cm to 64 cm.

    c The arm lengths of 70% of the 18 year old females are more than x cm. Find the value of x.

3 The length of steel rods produced by a machine is normally distributed with a standard deviation of 3 mm. It is found that 2% of all rods are less than 25 mm long. Find the mean length of rods produced by the machine.

4 The distribution curve shown corresponds to $X \sim N(\mu, \sigma^2)$.

Area A = Area $B = 0.2$.

    a Find μ and σ.

    b Calculate:

        i $P(X \leqslant 35)$ **ii** $P(23 \leqslant X \leqslant 30)$

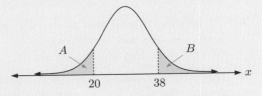

5 Let X be the weight in grams of bags of sugar filled by a machine. Bags less than 500 grams are considered underweight.

Suppose that $X \sim N(503, 2^2)$.

    a What proportion of bags are underweight?

    b If a quality inspector randomly selects 20 bags, what is the probability that at most 2 bags are underweight?

6 The marks of 2376 candidates in an IB examination are normally distributed with mean 49 marks and variance 225.

    a If the pass mark is 45, estimate the number of candidates who passed the examination.

    b If the top 7% of the candidates are awarded a '7', find the minimum mark required to obtain a '7'.

7 The life of a Xenon-brand battery is normally distributed with mean 33.2 weeks and standard deviation 2.8 weeks.

    a Find the probability that a randomly selected battery will last at least 35 weeks.

    b For how many weeks can the manufacturer expect the batteries to last before 8% of them fail?

8 The random variable X is normally distributed with $P(X \leqslant 30) = 0.0832$ and $P(X \geqslant 90) = 0.101$.

    a Find the mean μ and standard deviation σ.

    b Hence find $P(-7 \leqslant X - \mu \leqslant 7)$.

9 Kerry's marks for an English essay and a Chemistry test were 26 out of 40, and 82% respectively.

    a Explain briefly why the information given is not sufficient to determine whether Kerry's results are better in English than in Chemistry.

    b Suppose that the marks of all students in the English essay and the Chemistry test were normally distributed as $N(22, 4^2)$ and $N(75, 7^2)$ respectively. Use this information to determine which of Kerry's two marks is better.

REVIEW SET 24C

1 The middle 68% of a normal distribution lies between 16.2 and 21.4.

    a What is the mean and standard deviation of the distribution?

    b Over what range of values would you expect the middle 95% of the data to spread?

2 A random variable X is normally distributed with mean 20.5 and standard deviation 4.3. Find:

    a $P(X \geqslant 22)$ **b** $P(18 \leqslant X \leqslant 22)$ **c** k such that $P(X \leqslant k) = 0.3$.

3 X is a continuous random variable where $X \sim N(\mu, 2^2)$.

    Find $P(-0.524 < X - \mu < 0.524)$.

4 The lengths of metal rods produced in a manufacturing process are normally distributed with mean μ cm and standard deviation 6 cm. 5.63% of the rods have length greater than 89.52 cm. Find the mean length of the metal rods.

5 The curve shown is the probability density function for a normally distributed random variable X. Its mean is 50, and $P(X < 90) \approx 0.975$.

    Find the shaded area.

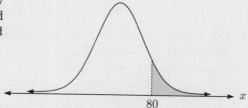

6 The weight of an apple in an apple harvest is normally distributed with mean 300 grams and standard deviation 50 grams. Only apples with weights between 250 and 350 grams are considered fit for sale.

    a Find the proportion of apples fit for sale.

    b In a sample of 100 apples, what is the probability that at least 75 are fit for sale?

7 A factory has a machine designed to fill bottles of drink with volume 375 mL of liquid. It is found that the average amount of drink in each bottle is 376 mL, and that 2.3% of the drink bottles have a volume smaller than 375 mL. Assuming that the amount of drink in each bottle is normally distributed, find the standard deviation.

8 The height of an 18 year old boy is normally distributed with mean 187 cm. Fifteen percent of 18 year old boys have heights greater than 193 cm. Find the probability that two 18 year old boys, chosen at random, will have heights greater than 185 cm.

Chapter 25

Miscellaneous questions

A   NON-CALCULATOR QUESTIONS

EXERCISE 25A

1 A geometric sequence has $S_1 = 2$ and $S_2 = 8$. Find:

    a the common ratio r **b** the twentieth term u_{20}.

2 Show that the sum of the first forty terms of the series $\ln 2 + \ln 4 + \ln 8 + \ln 16 + ...$ is $820 \ln 2$.

3 Suppose $f(x) = be^x$ and $g(x) = \ln(bx)$. Find:

    a $(f \circ g)(x)$ **b** $(g \circ f)(x)$

    c an expression for x^*, in terms of b, such that $(f \circ g)(x^*) = (g \circ f)(x^*)$.

4 Consider $f(x) = -2(x - b)^2 + 2$.

    a State the coordinates of the vertex.

    b Find the axes intercepts.

    c The graph of function g is obtained by translating the graph of f vertically through b units. For what values of b will the graph of g:

        i have exactly one x-intercept   **ii** have no x-intercepts

        iii pass through the origin?

5   **a** Expand $(x - 2)^3$.

    b Hence, find the coefficient of x^3 in $(3x^2 - 7)(x - 2)^3$.

6 Consider $f(x) = \sqrt{1 - 2x}$. Find:

    a $f(0)$ **b** $f(-4)$ **c** the domain of f **d** the range of f.

7 Let $a = \sin 20°$ and $b = \tan 50°$. In terms of a and b, write expressions for:

    a $\sin 160°$ **b** $\tan(-50°)$ **c** $\cos 70°$ **d** $\tan 20°$

8 Suppose $f(x) = \cos x$ and $g(x) = 2x$.

    Solve the following equations on the domain $0 \leqslant x \leqslant 2\pi$:

    a $(f \circ g)(x) = 1$ **b** $(g \circ f)(x) = 1$

9 Consider the graphs illustrated.

Copy and complete the following table by indicating whether each constant is positive, negative, or zero:

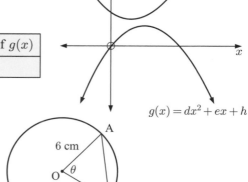

$f(x) = ax^2 + bx + c$

$g(x) = dx^2 + ex + h$

Constant	a	b	c	d	e	h	Δ of $f(x)$	Δ of $g(x)$
Sign								

10 In the given figure, the perimeter of sector AB is $(12 + 2\pi)$ cm.

    a Find the value of θ.

    b Hence state the length of chord AB.

11 Let $f(x) = x^2 + 6$.

   a Can you solve $f(x) = 3$?   **b** What does this tell us about the range of $f(x)$?

12 Consider $\mathbf{u} = \mathbf{i} - 2\mathbf{j} + \mathbf{k}$ and $\mathbf{v} = 3\mathbf{i} + p\mathbf{j} - \mathbf{k}$.

   a Find p if $\mathbf{u}$ is perpendicular to $\mathbf{v}$.   **b** Evaluate $|\mathbf{u}|\,|\mathbf{v}|$.

   c Show that no value of p exists such that $\mathbf{v} - \mathbf{u}$ and $\mathbf{u}$ are parallel.

13 Consider the parallelogram ABCD illustrated.

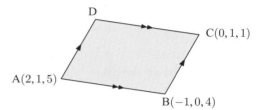

   a Find $\overrightarrow{BA}$ and $\overrightarrow{BC}$.

   b Hence find $|\overrightarrow{BA}|$ and $|\overrightarrow{BC}|$.

   c What can be deduced about parallelogram ABCD?

   d Calculate:

     i $\cos(\widehat{CBA})$ **ii** $\sin(\widehat{CBA})$ **iii** the area of ABCD.

14 a, b, c, d, e, f, g, h, i, j, k, l, and m are 13 data values which have been arranged in *ascending* order.

   a Which variable represents the median?

   b Write down an algebraic expression for:

     i the range   **ii** the interquartile range.

15 For the data set $\{a, b, c\}$, the mean is 17.5 and the standard deviation is 3.2.

   Copy and complete the following table by finding the mean and standard deviation of each new data set:

	New data set	Mean	Standard deviation
a	$\{2a,\ 2b,\ 2c\}$		
b	$\{a+2,\ b+2,\ c+2\}$		
c	$\{3a+5,\ 3b+5,\ 3c+5\}$		

16 A dart is thrown at the dartboard shown. It is equally likely to land anywhere on the board.

   Given that the dart lands on the board, show that the probability of it landing on the shaded region is exactly

$$1 - \frac{5}{2\pi}\sin\left(\frac{2\pi}{5}\right).$$

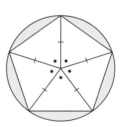

17 For the function $y = f(x)$ with graph shown, sketch the graphs of:

   a $y = f'(x)$ **b** $y = f''(x)$

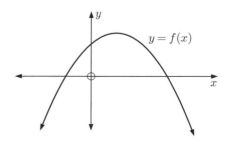

18 Consider $g(x) = 3 - 2\cos(2x)$.

   a Find $g'(x)$.

   b Sketch $y = g'(x)$ for $-\pi \leqslant x \leqslant \pi$.

   c Write down the number of solutions to $g'(x) = 0$ for $-\pi \leqslant x \leqslant \pi$.

   d Mark a point M on the sketch in **b** where $g'(x) = 0$ *and* $g''(x) > 0$.

19 A and B are mutually exclusive events where $P(A) = x$ and $P(B') = 0.43$.

   a Write $P(A \cup B)$ in terms of x.   **b** Find x given that $P(A \cup B) = 0.73$.

20 For the function $g(x)$, the sign diagrams for $g'(x)$ and $g''(x)$ are shown alongside.

The points $A(0, 2)$, $B(2, 0)$, and $C(4, -2)$ all lie on $y = g(x)$.

Sketch $y = g(x)$, labelling the stationary points.

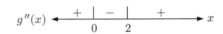

21 Consider $f(x) = xe^{1-2x}$.

   a Show that $f'(x) = e^{1-2x}(1 - 2x)$.

   b Find the point on the graph of $y = f(x)$ where the tangent is horizontal.

   c Find values of x for which:

     i $f(x) > 0$ **ii** $f'(x) > 0$

22 A particle moves in a straight line so that its position s at time t seconds is given by $s(t) = 3 - 4e^{2t} + kt$ metres, where k is a constant.

   a Find the velocity function $v(t)$ in terms of k.

   b Determine the value of k, given the particle is stationary when $t = \ln 3$ seconds.

23 Solve for x:

   a $\log_3 27 = x$ **b** $e^{5-2x} = 8$ **c** $\ln(x^2 - 3) - \ln(2x) = 0$

24 The graph shows the velocity v m s^{-1} of an object at time t seconds, $t \geqslant 0$. Find and interpret:

   a $v(0)$ **b** $v'(2)$ **c** $\displaystyle\int_1^3 v(t)\, dt$.

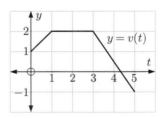

25 Suppose $\displaystyle\int_{-1}^2 f(x)\, dx = 10$. Find the value of:

   a $\displaystyle\int_{-1}^2 (f(x) - 6)\, dx$ **b** k if $\displaystyle\int_2^{-1} k\,f(x)\, dx = -5$.

26 **a** Show that $(\sin\theta - \cos\theta)^2 = 1 - \sin 2\theta$.

   b Hence calculate $\displaystyle\int_0^{\frac{\pi}{4}} (\sin\theta - \cos\theta)^2\, d\theta$.

27   The following table shows the probability distribution for a discrete random variable X.

x	-2	-1	0	1	2
$P(X = x)$	0.1	a	0.25	b	0.15

Find a and b given that $E(X) = 0$.

28   Consider the infinite geometric sequence: $e, \dfrac{1}{e}, \dfrac{1}{e^3}, \dfrac{1}{e^5}, ...$ Find, in terms of e:

    a   the common ratio   **b**   the 101st term

    c   the sum of the corresponding infinite series.

29   **a**   Use the formula $\dbinom{n}{r} = \dfrac{n!}{r!\,(n-r)!}$ to evaluate $\dbinom{6}{2}$.

    b   Hence state the value of $\dbinom{6}{4}$.

    c   Given that $\dbinom{6}{3} = 20$,   write down the expansion of $(x-2)^6$.   Simplify your answer.

30   The random variable X is normally distributed with mean μ and standard deviation σ.
Let k be such that $P(X < k) = 0.7$.

    a   Copy the normal distribution curve and mark on it μ and k.

    b   On the graph shade the region which illustrates $P(X < k) = 0.7$.

    c   Find:

       i $P(X > k)$ **ii** $P(\mu < X < k)$ **iii** $P(\mu - \sigma < X < k)$

    d   If $P(X \geqslant t) = 0.2$,   find $P(k \leqslant X \leqslant t)$.

31

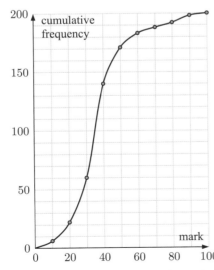

The examination marks for 200 students are displayed on the cumulative frequency graph shown. The pass mark for the examination was 30.

    a   What percentage of the students passed the examination?

    b   A boxplot for the examination data is:

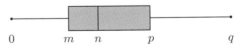

From the graph, estimate:

       i m **ii** n **iii** p **iv** q

32   The line L has equation $y = \left(\tan \frac{\pi}{3}\right) x$.

    a   Find p given that the point $A(10, p)$ lies on L.

    b   Find the equation of the line which passes through A and is perpendicular to L.
Write your answer in the form $ax + by = c$.

33 The acceleration of an object moving in a straight line is given by

$a(t) = 1 - 3\cos\left(2t + \frac{\pi}{2}\right)$ cm s^{-2},   where t is the time in seconds.

The object's initial velocity is 5 cm s^{-1}.

   a Find an expression for the object's velocity v in terms of t.

   b Find the velocity of the object at $t = \frac{\pi}{4}$ seconds.

34 Consider $f(x) = e^{3x-4} + 1$.

   a Show that $f^{-1}(x) = \dfrac{\ln(x-1) + 4}{3}$.

   b Calculate $f^{-1}(8) - f^{-1}(3)$. Give your answer in the form $a \ln b$ where $a, b \in \mathbb{Q}^+$.

35 Given that $\sin A = \frac{2}{5}$ and $\frac{\pi}{2} \leqslant A \leqslant \pi$, find:

   a $\cos A$ **b** $\tan A$ **c** $\sin 2A$

36 Consider the infinite geometric sequence $160, 80\sqrt{2}, 80, 40\sqrt{2}, \ldots$.

   a Write the 12th term of the sequence in the form $k\sqrt{2}$ where $k \in \mathbb{Q}$.

   b Find exactly the following sums for the corresponding geometric series. Give your answer in the form $a + b\sqrt{2}$ where $a, b \in \mathbb{Z}$:

      i the partial sum S_{10} **ii** the sum S of the infinite series.

37 A particle is initially located at P(3, 1, −2). It moves with fixed velocity in a straight line, and after 2 seconds the particle is at Q(1, 3, 4). Find:

   a $\overrightarrow{PQ}$ **b** the particle's speed   **c** the equation of the straight line.

38 A journalist is investigating the consistency of online reviews for electrical items. She compares the scores given to two different camera models by 6 different reviewers, recording the results in the table shown.

Camera A	8.5	8	9	7	8.5	7.5
Camera B	7	6	7.5	9	7.5	6

   a Draw a scatter diagram of the data.   **b** Are there any outliers?

   c What can the journalist report about the consistency of online reviews for these cameras?

39 Suppose $g(x) = e^{\frac{x}{4}}$ where $0 \leqslant x \leqslant 4$.

   a Sketch $y = g(x)$ on the given domain.   **b** Find the range of $g(x)$.

   c On the same set of axes used in **a**, sketch $y = g^{-1}(x)$.

   d State the domain and range of $g^{-1}(x)$.   **e** Find $g^{-1}(x)$ algebraically.

40 [QS] is a diagonal of quadrilateral PQRS where PQ = 3 cm, QR = 7 cm, PS = 5 cm, and $Q\widehat{R}S = 30°$.

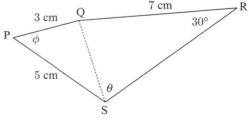

   a Show that if $S\widehat{P}Q = \phi$, then QS = $\sqrt{34 - 30\cos\phi}$ cm.

   b If $\phi = 60°$ and $Q\widehat{S}R = \theta$:

      i show that $\sin\theta = \dfrac{7}{2\sqrt{19}}$

      ii find the *exact* length of [RS], given that θ is acute

      iii hence, find the exact perimeter and area of PQRS.

41 Suppose $f(x) = -\frac{1}{4}x^2 + 3x + 4$.

    a Find $f'(x)$ in simplest form.

    b **i** Find the equation of the normal to $y = f(x)$
            at the point $(2, \, 9)$.

       ii Find the coordinates of the point where this
           normal meets $y = f(x)$ again.

    c The graph of $y = f(x)$ is shown alongside.

       i Write down an expression for the area of the
          shaded region R.

      ii Calculate the exact area of R.

     iii Suppose the region R is revolved about the
          x-axis through one revolution.   Find an
          expression for the volume of the solid formed.

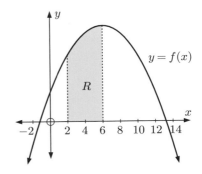

42 **a** Consider the geometric sequence: $4, \; -12, \; 36, \; -108, \; ....$

       i Write down the common ratio.   **ii** Find the 14th term.

    b Suppose the sequence $x, \; x - 2, \; 2x - 7, \; ....$ is geometric.

       i Find x.

      ii Does the sum of the corresponding geometric series converge? Explain your answer.

    c Suppose the sequence $x, \; x - 2, \; 2x - 7, \; ....$ is arithmetic. Find:

       i its 30th term   **ii** the sum of its first 50 terms.

43 Suppose A has position vector $3\mathbf{i} + 2\mathbf{j} - \mathbf{k}$,   B has position vector $2\mathbf{i} - \mathbf{j} - 8\mathbf{k}$,   and C has
position vector $\mathbf{i} + \mathbf{j} + a\mathbf{k}$.

    a Find $\overrightarrow{AB}$.

    b Find the unit vector $\mathbf{u}$ in the direction of $\overrightarrow{BA}$.

    c Is $\mathbf{u}$ perpendicular to $\overrightarrow{OA}$?

    d Find a given that $\overrightarrow{OC}$ is perpendicular to $a\mathbf{i} - \mathbf{j} + 4\mathbf{k}$.

    e Find the position vector of M, the midpoint of [AB].

    f Line L_1 passes through M and is parallel to $\overrightarrow{OA}$.
       Write down the vector equation $\mathbf{r}_1$ of line L_1.

    g Suppose line L_2 has vector equation $\mathbf{r}_2 = (m\mathbf{i} + \mathbf{j} - \mathbf{k}) + s(2\mathbf{i} - 3\mathbf{j} + \mathbf{k})$.

       i Explain why L_1 is not parallel to L_2.

      ii Find m if L_1 and L_2 intersect.

     iii Find the position vector of P, the point of intersection of L_1 and L_2.

44 Consider the functions $f(x) = \frac{1}{2}x - 1$ and $g(x) = \sqrt{3}x$.
Find exactly the angle between the straight line and the positive x-axis for:

    a $y = f(x)$ **b** $y = (f \circ g)x$.

45 **a** Consider the quadratic function $y = -x^2 + 12x - 20$.

 i Explain why this quadratic has a maximum value.

 ii What value of x gives this maximum value?

 iii What is the maximum value?

b

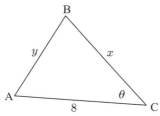

In $\triangle ABC$, $AB = y$, $BC = x$, and $AC = 8$.
The perimeter of $\triangle ABC$ is 20.

 i Write y in terms of x.

 ii Use the cosine rule to write y^2 in terms of x and $\cos\theta$.

 iii Hence, show that $\cos\theta = \dfrac{3x - 10}{2x}$.

 iv If the area of the triangle is A, show that $A^2 = 16x^2\sin^2\theta$.

 v Show that $A^2 = 20(-x^2 + 12x - 20)$.

 vi Hence, find the maximum area of $\triangle ABC$.

 vii Comment on the shape of the triangle when it has maximum area.

46 Suppose $f(x) = 4x - 3$ and $g(x) = x + 2$.

 a Find $f^{-1}(x)$ and $g^{-1}(x)$, the inverse functions of f and g.

 b Find $(f \circ g^{-1})(x)$.

 c Find the value of x such that $(f \circ g^{-1})(x) = f^{-1}(x)$.

 d Suppose $H(x) = \dfrac{f(x)}{g(x)}$.

  i Sketch the graph of $y = H(x)$. Include its asymptotes and their equations.

  ii Find constants A and B such that $\dfrac{4x - 3}{x + 2} = A + \dfrac{B}{x + 2}$.

  iii Calculate the exact value of $\displaystyle\int_{-1}^{2} H(x)\,dx$.

  iv On your sketch in **i**, shade the region whose area is given by $\displaystyle\int_{1}^{3} H(x)\,dx$.

47 Hannah, Heidi, and Holly have different sets of cards, but each set contains cards with the numbers 0, 1, 2, 3, or 4, one per card.

 a Hannah wrongly states that the probability distribution of her set of cards is:

Why is Hannah wrong?

x	0	1	2	3	4
$P(X = x)$	0.1	0.3	0.3	0.2	0.2

 b Heidi correctly states that her probability distribution is:

What can be deduced about a and b?

x	0	1	2	3	4
$P(X = x)$	0.2	a	0.3	b	0.2

 c Holly correctly states that the probability distribution for her set of cards is

$$P(X = x) = \frac{x(x + 2)}{50}.$$

If one card is randomly chosen from Holly's set, find the probability that it is:

  i a 2   **ii** not a 2.

48 Bag C contains 4 blue and 1 yellow ticket. Bag D contains 2 blue and 3 yellow tickets.
An ordinary 6-sided die is used to select one of the two bags.
If a 1 or 2 is rolled, bag C is chosen. Otherwise, bag D is chosen.
A ticket is drawn at random from that bag.

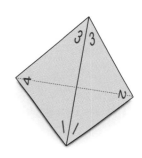

  a Copy and complete the tree diagram, showing all probabilities.

  b Find the probability that a yellow ticket is drawn from bag D.

  c Find the probability of drawing a yellow ticket from either bag.

  d If a blue ticket is chosen, find the probability that it came from bag D.

  e In a gambling game, a player wins $6 for getting a blue ticket and $9 for getting a yellow one.
Find the player's expected return.

49 Two identical tetrahedral dice are rolled. Their four vertices are clearly labelled 1, 2, 3, and 4.

The result when one die comes to rest is the number on the uppermost vertex. This is 3 in the diagram.

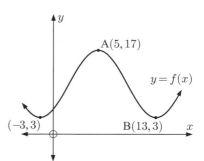

  a Illustrate the sample space of 16 possible results when the two dice are rolled.

  b Let X be the sum of the scores on the two dice.
What are the possible values of X?

  c Find: **i** $P(X = 4)$ **ii** $P(X > 4)$

  d When Mimi uses the two dice to play a fair game, she:
  - wins €5 if the sum is 4
  - wins €1 if the sum is greater than 4
  - loses €d if the sum is less than 4.

Find the value of d.

50 A particle moves in a straight line such that at time t seconds, $t \geqslant 0$, the acceleration is $a(t) = 3t - \sin t$ cm s^{-2}.

  a Find the particle's acceleration at times $t = 0$ and $t = \frac{\pi}{2}$ seconds.

  b If the initial velocity of the particle is 3 cm s^{-1}, find its velocity function $v(t)$.

  c Find $\displaystyle\int_{0}^{\frac{\pi}{2}} v(t)\, dt$ and explain why the result is positive.

  d Interpret the result in **c** with regard to the particle's motion.

51 The graph of $f(x) = a \sin b(x - c) + d$ is illustrated.
A is a local maximum and B is a local minimum.

  a Find the values of a, b, c, and d.

  b The function $g(x)$ is obtained from $f(x)$ by a translation of $\begin{pmatrix} 2 \\ -3 \end{pmatrix}$ followed by a vertical stretch with scale factor 2.

    i Find the coordinates of A$'$, the image of A under T.

    ii Find $g(x)$ in the form $g(x) = p \sin q(x - r) + s$.

    iii Describe fully the transformation which maps g back to f.

52 **a** Factorise $4^x - 2^x - 20$ in the form $(2^x + a)(2^x - b)$ where $a, b \in \mathbb{Z}^+$.

    b Hence, find the exact solution of $2^x(2^x - 1) = 20$.

    c Suppose $p = \log_5 2$.

        i Write the solution to **b** in terms of p.

        ii Find the solution to $8^x = 5^{1-x}$ in terms of p only.

53 Suppose $f(x) = a \cos 2x + b \sin^2 x$ where $b < 2a, \ 0 \leqslant x \leqslant 2\pi$.

    a Show that $f'(x) = (b - 2a) \sin 2x$.

    b Find the maximum value of $f'(x)$ and when this maximum occurs.

    c Find the turning points of $y = f(x)$ on $0 \leqslant x \leqslant 2\pi$.

54 Suppose $S(x) = \frac{1}{2}(e^x - e^{-x})$ and $C(x) = \frac{1}{2}(e^x + e^{-x})$.

    a Show that $[C(x)]^2 - [S(x)]^2 = 1$.   **b** Show that $\dfrac{d}{dx}[S(x)] = C(x)$.

    c Find $\dfrac{d}{dx}[C(x)]$ in terms of $S(x)$.

    d If $T(x) = \dfrac{S(x)}{C(x)}$, find $\dfrac{d}{dx}[T(x)]$ in terms of $C(x)$.

55 The size of a population at time t years is given by $P(t) = 60\,000 \left(1 + 2e^{-\frac{t}{4}}\right)^{-1}$, $t \geqslant 0$.

    a Find $P(0)$.   **b** Find $P'(t)$.

    c Show that $P'(t) > 0$ for all $t \geqslant 0$. Explain what this means.

    d Find $P''(t)$.

    e Find the maximum growth rate of the population, and the exact time when this occurs.

    f Discuss $P(t)$ as $t \to \infty$.

    g Sketch the population function, showing the information you have found.

56 **a** Find $\displaystyle\int x^2 e^{1-x^3} \, dx$ using the substitution $u(x) = 1 - x^3$.

    b Hence show that $\displaystyle\int_0^1 x^2 e^{1-x^3} \, dx = \dfrac{e - 1}{3}$.

57 Suppose $f(x)$ is defined by $f : x \mapsto \cos^3 x$.

    a State the range of f.

    b For the interval $0 \leqslant x \leqslant 2\pi$, how many solutions does $8 \cos^3 x = 1$ have?

    c Find $f'(x)$.

    d $h(x) = \sqrt{3} \cos x \sqrt{\sin x}$ is defined on $0 \leqslant x \leqslant \frac{\pi}{2}$.

    When $h(x)$ is revolved about the x-axis through one revolution, a solid is generated. Find the volume of this solid.

58

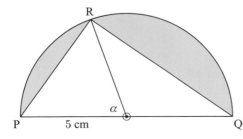

[PQ] is the diameter of a semi-circle with centre O and radius 5 cm.

    a Find the area of triangle PQR.

    b Hence, find the shaded area A in terms of the angle α.

    c Find the maximum and minimum values of the area A, and the values of α when they occur.

59 The graph of the function $f(x) = a(x-h)^2 + k$ is shown alongside. It has x-intercepts 1 and 7, and a maximum value of 18.

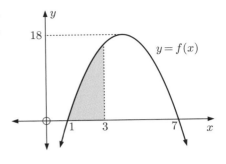

a Find the value of:

     i h ii k iii a

b Find the shaded area.

60 a Find the exact value of x for which:

     i $2^{1-2x} = 0.5$ ii $\log_x 7 = 5$

b Solve for x: $25^x - 6(5^x) + 5 = 0$.

c If $2^x = 3^{1-x}$, show that $x = \log_6 3$.

61 a Suppose $\dfrac{1 - \cos 2\theta}{\sin 2\theta} = \sqrt{3}$ where $0 < \theta < \frac{\pi}{2}$.

     i Show that $\tan \theta = \sqrt{3}$ also.   ii Find θ.

b If $\cos 2x = 2\cos x$, find the value of $\cos x$.

62 The sum of the first n terms of a series is given by $S_n = n^3 + 2n - 1$. Find u_n, the nth term of the series.

63 Find the *exact* values of x for which $\sin^2 x + \sin x - 2 = 0$ and $-2\pi \leqslant x \leqslant 2\pi$.

64 If $f : x \mapsto \ln x$ and $g : x \mapsto 3 + x$, find:

a $f^{-1}(2) \times g^{-1}(2)$ b $(f \circ g)^{-1}(2)$.

65 The equation of line L is $\mathbf{r} = 2\mathbf{i} - 3\mathbf{j} + \mathbf{k} + t(-\mathbf{i} + \mathbf{j} - \mathbf{k})$, $t \in \mathbb{R}$. Find the coordinates of the point on L that is nearest to the origin.

66 For the function $f(x)$, $f'(x) > 0$ and $f''(x) < 0$ for all $x \in \mathbb{R}$, $f(2) = 1$, and $f'(2) = 2$.

a Find the equation of the tangent to $f(x)$ where $x = 2$.

b On the same set of axes, sketch $y = f(x)$ and the tangent to the curve where $x = 2$.

c Explain why $f(x)$ has exactly one zero.

d Estimate an interval in which the zero of $f(x)$ lies.

67 In a team of 30 judo players, 13 have won a match by throwing (T), 12 have won by hold-down (H), and 13 have won by points decision (P). 2 have won matches by all three methods. 5 have won matches by throwing and hold-down. 4 have won matches by hold-down and points decision. 3 have won matches by throwing and points decision.

a Draw a Venn diagram to display this information.

b Find:

     i $P(T \cap H)$ ii $P(P)$ iii $P(H \cap P')$

     iv $P(T \cup P)$ v $P(T \cap H' \cap P)$

68 Use the figure alongside to show that $\cos 36° = \dfrac{1+\sqrt{5}}{4}$.

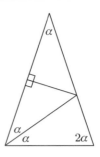

69

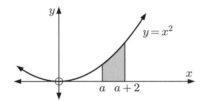

Find a given that the shaded region has area $5\frac{1}{6}$ units².

70 What can be deduced if $A \cap B$ and $A \cup B$ are independent events?

71 Solve $\sin\theta\cos\theta = \frac{1}{4}$ on the domain $-\pi \leqslant \theta \leqslant \pi$.

72 f is defined by $x \mapsto \ln(x(x-2))$.

   a State the domain of $f(x)$.   **b** Find $f'(x)$.

   c Find the equation of the tangent to $y = f(x)$ at the point where $x = 3$.

73 Hat 1 contains three green and four blue tickets. Hat 2 contains four green and three blue tickets. One ticket is randomly selected from each hat.

   a Find the probability that the tickets are the same colour.

   b Given that the tickets are different colours, what is the probability that the green ticket came from Hat 2?

74 A normally distributed random variable X has a mean of 90.

The probability $P(X < 85) \approx 0.1587$.

   a Find $P(90 < X < 95)$.

   b *Estimate* the standard deviation for the random variable X.

75 The discrete random variable X has probability function $P(X = x) = a\left(\frac{2}{5}\right)^x$, $x = 0, 1, 2, 3, \ldots$. Find the value of a.

76 Given $x = \log_3 y^2$,   express $\log_y 81$ in terms of x.

77 Matt has noticed that his pet rat Pug does not always eat the same amount of food each day. He wonders whether this is connected to the temperature, so he decides to collect some data.

Temperature (°C)	10	16	12	19	20
Food eaten (grams)	15	12	13	9	11

   a Draw a scatter diagram for this data.

   b Hence describe the correlation between *temperature* and *food eaten*.

   c Find the mean point for the data.

   d Hence draw the line of best fit on your scatter diagram.

   e Determine the equation of your line of best fit.

   f Hence estimate the amount of food Pug would eat on a 5°C day.

   g Comment on the reliability of your prediction.

78 The point A$(-2,\ 3)$ lies on the graph of $y = f(x)$. Give the coordinates of the point that A moves to under the transformation:

    a $y = f(x - 2) + 1$ **b** $y = 2f(x - 2)$ **c** $y = f(2x) - 3$ **d** $y = f^{-1}(x)$

79 Find a trigonometric equation in the form $y = a\sin(b(x - c)) + d$ which represents the following information:

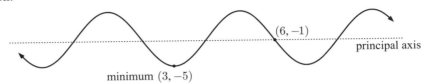

minimum $(3, -5)$

80 A and B are events for which $P(A) = 0.3 + x$, $P(B) = 0.2 + x$, and $P(A \cap B) = x$.

    a Find x if A and B are mutually exclusive events.

    b Calculate the possible values of x if A and B are independent events.

81 Simplify: **a** $9^{\log_3 11}$ **b** $\log_m n \times \log_n m^2$

82

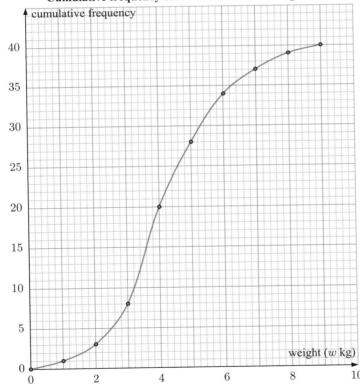

Cumulative frequency curve of watermelon weight data

The graph describes the weight of 40 watermelons.

    a Estimate the:

        i median weight

        ii IQR

    for the weight of the watermelons.

    b Construct a frequency table corresponding to the data.

    c Estimate the mean weight of the watermelons.

83 If $f : x \mapsto 2x + 1$ and $g : x \mapsto \dfrac{x + 1}{x - 2}$, find: **a** $(f \circ g)(x)$ **b** $g^{-1}(x)$.

84 A and B are two events such that $P(A) = \frac{1}{3}$ and $P(B) = \frac{2}{7}$.

    Find $P(A \cup B)$ if A and B are: **a** mutually exclusive   **b** independent.

85 Find x in terms of a if $a > 1$ and $\log_a(x + 2) = \log_a x + 2$.

86 Consider the expansion $(a+b)^5 = a^5 + 5a^4b + 10a^3b^2 + 10a^2b^3 + 5ab^4 + b^5$.

   a Write down the binomial expansion for $(a-b)^5$.

   b Simplify $(0.4)^5 + 5(0.4)^4(0.6) + 10(0.4)^3(0.6)^2 + 10(0.4)^2(0.6)^3 + 5(0.4)(0.6)^4 + (0.6)^5$.

   c Write $\left(2x + \dfrac{1}{x}\right)^5$ in simplified expanded form.

87 If $x + \dfrac{1}{x} = a$, find in terms of a:

   a $x^2 + \dfrac{1}{x^2}$
             b $x^3 + \dfrac{1}{x^3}$

88 The illustrated ellipse has equation

$$\frac{x^2}{16} + \frac{y^2}{4} = 1.$$

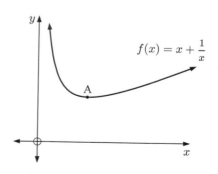

   a Find the coordinates of points:

      i A and B
            ii C and D.

   b State the equation of the top half BCA of the ellipse.

   c Write a definite integral for the area of the ellipse.

   d If the ellipse is rotated through 2π about the x-axis, a solid of revolution is generated. Find the exact volume of this solid.

89 Consider $f(x) = \sin^2 x$.

   a Copy and complete the table of values:

x	0	$\frac{\pi}{4}$	$\frac{\pi}{2}$	$\frac{3\pi}{4}$	π	$\frac{5\pi}{4}$	$\frac{3\pi}{2}$	$\frac{7\pi}{4}$	2π
$f(x)$	0	$\frac{1}{2}$			0			$\frac{1}{2}$	

   b Sketch the graph of $f(x) = \sin^2 x$ on the domain $0 \leqslant x \leqslant 2\pi$.

   c Check your graph by plotting the point where $x = \frac{\pi}{6}$.

   d State the range of $f(x)$.

   e Using $\sin^2 x = \frac{1}{2} - \frac{1}{2}\cos 2x$, find the area enclosed by $y = f(x)$ and the x-axis for $0 \leqslant x \leqslant \pi$.

   f Find the equation of the tangent to $y = f(x)$ at the point $\left(\frac{\pi}{4}, \frac{1}{2}\right)$.

90 The graph of $f(x) = x + \dfrac{1}{x}$, $x > 0$ is shown.

   a Find $f'(x)$ and solve the equation $f'(x) = 0$.

   b Find the coordinates of the local minimum A.

   c Copy and complete:

      "the sum of a positive number and its reciprocal is at least ......"

   d How many positive solutions would these equations have?

      i $x + \dfrac{1}{x} = 1$
      ii $x + \dfrac{1}{x} = 2$
      iii $x + \dfrac{1}{x} = 3$
      Give reasons for your answers.

91 A straight line passes through A$(2, 0, -3)$ and has direction vector $\mathbf{i} - \mathbf{j} + 2\mathbf{k}$.

    a Write down the vector equation of the line.

    b Write down parametric equations for the line.

    c What is represented by P$(2 + t, -t, -3 + 2t)$?

    d Find $\overrightarrow{BP}$ given the point B$(-1, 3, 5)$.

    e Find $\overrightarrow{BP} \bullet (\mathbf{i} - \mathbf{j} + 2\mathbf{k})$.

    f Hence find the value of t when [BP] is perpendicular to the original line.

    g What point on the original line is closest to B?

92 A cumulative frequency graph for the continuous random variable X is given alongside.

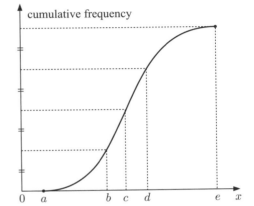

    a What is represented by:

        i a **ii** b **iii** c

        iv d **v** e?

    b What do these measure?

        i $e - a$ **ii** $d - b$

    c Determine:

        i $P(b < X \leqslant d)$ **ii** $P(X > b)$.

    d Draw an accurate boxplot for the data set.

B   CALCULATOR QUESTIONS

EXERCISE 25B

1 Find n given that $\displaystyle\sum_{k=1}^{n}(2k - 31) = 0$.

2 Consider the function $f(x) = 5\ln(x - 4) + 2$.

    a Graph the function $y = f(x)$. Clearly label the axes intercepts and asymptotes.

    b Solve the equation $f(x) = 1$.

    c Graph the function $y = f^{-1}(x)$ on the same set of axes. Clearly label the axes intercepts and asymptotes.

    d Find the equation of the normal to the curve $y = f(x)$ at the point where $x = 5$.

3 Find the constant term in the expansion of $\left(x - \dfrac{1}{5x^2}\right)^9$.

4 The value of a cash investment after t years is given by $V = 7500 \times 2^{0.09t}$ dollars.

    a Find the initial value of the cash investment.

    b Find the value of the investment after:

        i 5 years   **ii** 15 years.

    c What was the percentage increase in the investment in the first five years?

    d How many years will it take for the investment to double in value?

5 Consider the arithmetic sequence: $-900, -750, -600, -450, ...$

    a Find the 20th term of the sequence.   **b** Find the sum of its first 20 terms.

6 Functions f and g are defined by $f : x \longmapsto 2x$ and $g : x \longmapsto 1 - 5x^2$.   Solve:

    a $(f \circ g)(x) = -8$ **b** $(g \circ f)(x) = -8$ **c** $f'(x) = g'(x)$ **d** $f^{-1}(x) = g(x)$

7

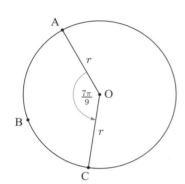

The perimeter of sector OABC is 50π cm.

    a Find r.

    b Find the area of sector OABC.

    c Calculate the side length of an equilateral triangle which has the same area as sector OABC.

8 Dora notices that the number of cups of coffee she drinks in a day varies depending on how much sleep she gets the previous night. She records the following data:

Time sleeping (hours)	6	8	6.5	5	9	5.5	7.5	6	8	8.5	7
Number of cups of coffee	3	1	2	4	0	4	2	4	0	1	2

    a Draw a scatter diagram for this data.

    b Calculate Pearson's product-moment correlation coefficient r for the data.

    c Hence describe the correlation between these two variables.

9 **a** Draw a scatter diagram for the following data:

x	0	5	10	15	20	25	30	35	40	45	50	55	60
y	1	1.5	1.9	2	1.9	1.5	1	0.5	0.1	0	0.1	0.5	1

  b Estimate:

    i the equation of the principal axis   **ii** the maximum value

    iii the period   **iv** the amplitude.

  c Hence find an equation of the form $y = a \sin bx + c$ that models the data.

10 The graph shown is a function of the form
$f(x) = m \cos(n(x - p)) + r$.

It has a maximum turning point at A(1, 12) and a minimum turning point at B(5, 4).

    a Determine the values of m, n, p, and r.

    b Find $f(6)$.

    c Find the smallest positive value of x such that $f(x) = 10$.

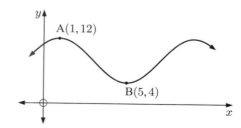

11 The lines L_1 and L_2 have equations

$$\mathbf{r}_1 = \begin{pmatrix} -2 \\ 1 \\ 4 \end{pmatrix} + t \begin{pmatrix} 4 \\ -1 \\ 3 \end{pmatrix} \quad \text{and} \quad \mathbf{r}_2 = \begin{pmatrix} -5 \\ 0 \\ 7 \end{pmatrix} + s \begin{pmatrix} 6 \\ -5 \\ 15 \end{pmatrix} \quad \text{respectively.}$$

a Determine the acute angle between L_1 and L_2.

b Show that the point $P(-10, 3, -2)$ lies on L_1.

c Does P lie on L_2? Give evidence for your answer.

d Find the point of intersection of L_1 and L_2.

e A third line L_3 has direction vector $\begin{pmatrix} a \\ 2 \\ 8 \end{pmatrix}$ and is perpendicular to L_1. Find a.

12 Consider the function $f(x) = (x+1)(x-\beta)$ where $\beta > 0$. A sketch of the function is shown alongside.

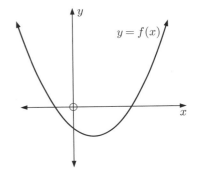

a Determine the axes intercepts of the graph of $y = f(x)$.

b Sketch the graphs of $f(x)$ and $g(x) = -f(x - 1)$ on the same set of axes.

c Hence, determine and label the axes intercepts of $y = g(x)$.

13

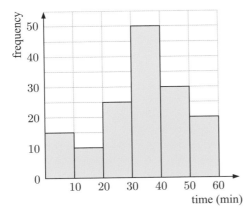

The frequency histogram illustrates the times taken by a group of people to solve a puzzle.

a Construct a cumulative frequency graph for the data.

b Hence estimate:

   i the median time taken to solve the puzzle

   ii the interquartile range of the data

   iii the probability that a randomly selected person was able to complete the puzzle within 35 minutes.

14 A theatre has 30 rows of seats. There are 16 seats in the first row and each subsequent row has 2 more seats than the previous row. Seats are allocated randomly to all theatre patrons. Calculate the probability that a randomly chosen patron will be seated in the last row of the theatre.

15 Argentina's success rate at penalty shots is 86%. In a match against Brazil, Argentina takes 5 penalty shots.

a Determine the probability that Argentina succeeds with all five of their penalty shots.

b Max said that the probability of Argentina scoring *exactly* three of their 5 shots taken is $(0.86)^3(0.14)^2$. Is Max correct? Explain your answer.

16 One of the terms from the expansion of $(1 + 3x)^7$ is chosen at random. Calculate the probability that the coefficient of this term is greater than 1000.

17 In a particular race, Carl Lewis ran the 100 m in a time of 9.99 seconds. The mean time for all athletes in the race was 10.20 seconds and the standard deviation was 0.113 seconds.

In another race Carl ran the 200 m in a time of 17.30 seconds. The mean time for this race was 18.50 seconds and the standard deviation was 0.706 seconds.

  a Assuming the times in each race were normally distributed, calculate Carl's z-scores for each event.

  b Based on the results of **a**, in which event did he perform better?

18 Let $f(x) = \sin(x^3)$ for $0 \leqslant x \leqslant \frac{\pi}{2}$.

  a Find the x-intercepts of the graph of f.

  b Sketch the graph of $y = f(x)$.

  c Find the equation of the tangent to $y = f(x)$ at the point where $x = \frac{\pi}{4}$.

  d There exists a point $P(x, y)$ on the interval $0 \leqslant x \leqslant \frac{\pi}{2}$ such that $f(x) > 0$, $f'(x) > 0$, and $f''(x) = 0$. Find the coordinates of P.

19 A comprehensive study of a new drug for treating epilepsy was conducted during 2006-2007. The results of the treatment are shown for two age groups in the table opposite.

Treatment	Under 35	Over 35
successful	951	257
unsuccessful	174	415

  a A patient from the study is selected at random. Calculate the probability that:

    i the patient was successfully treated

    ii the patient was over 35 given that his or her treatment was unsuccessful.

  b Ten patients from the study are selected at random. To calculate the probability that exactly 8 of them were successfully treated, Harry used a binomial probability distribution. Was Harry's method valid? Explain your answer.

20 Consider $f(x) = 3e^{1-4x}$. Find:

  a $f'(x)$ **b** $\displaystyle\int f(x)\,dx$ **c** $\displaystyle\int_0^2 f(x)\,dx$ to 3 significant figures.

21 The graph shows $y = (\ln x)\sin x$ for $0 < x \leqslant \frac{3\pi}{2}$. The graph crosses the x-axis at A and B, and has a local maximum at C.

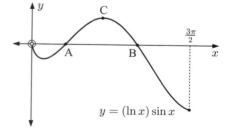

  a Write down exactly the x-coordinates of A and B.

  b Find the coordinates of C, correct to 3 decimal places.

  c Find the coordinates of the point at which the gradient of the tangent takes the largest positive value. Give your answer correct to 3 decimal places.

  d What name is given to the point in **c**?

22 Mr O'Farrell deposits $2000 into an account that pays interest at a rate of 4.5% p.a. compounded monthly. Calculate how long it will take for Mr O'Farrell's investment value to:

  a double   **b** quadruple.

23   **a** Find the remaining *three* terms of the expansion $(x^2 + 2)^5 = x^{10} + 10x^8 + 40x^6 + \dots.$

    b Hence, find $\displaystyle\int (x^2 + 2)^5 \, dx$.

24   The diagram shows the graphs of the quadratic functions
$y = f(x)$ and $g(x) = (x-1)^2$.

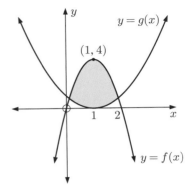

   a   The graph of f has vertex $(1, 4)$ and x-intercepts 0
and 2.
Determine the equation of f.

   b   Determine the x-coordinates of the points where
$y = f(x)$ and $y = g(x)$ intersect.

   c   Let A be the area of the region enclosed by f and g.
   i   Write down an expression for A.
   ii   Calculate A.

25   Events A and B are independent with $P(B) = 3\,P(A)$ and $P(A \cup B) = 0.68$.

   a   Show that $[P(B)]^2 - 4\,P(B) + 2.04 = 0$.
   b   Hence, calculate $P(B)$ and $P(A)$.

26   The weights in kilograms of twelve students are:
$$63 \quad 76 \quad 99 \quad 65 \quad 63 \quad 51 \quad 52 \quad 95 \quad 63 \quad 71 \quad 65 \quad 83$$

   a   Calculate the mean weight of the students.

   b   When one student leaves the class, the mean weight of the remaining 11 students is 70 kg.
Find the weight of the student who left.

   c   **i**   Calculate the standard deviation of the 11 remaining students.
   ii   Hence, find the number of standard deviations that the heaviest student is from the mean.

27   In a mathematics quiz there are 30 multiple choice questions. There are 5 choices for each question,
only one of which is correct. Assuming that you randomly guess an answer for every question, find
the probability of obtaining:

   a   exactly 10 correct answers   **b**   no more than 10 correct answers.

28   It is observed that 3% of all batteries produced by a company are defective.

   a   For a random sample of 20 batteries, calculate the probability that:
   i   none are defective   **ii**   at least one is defective.

   b   Let X be the number of defectives in a random sample of n batteries.
   i   Write down an expression for $P(X = 0)$.
   ii   Calculate the smallest value of n such that $P(X \geqslant 1) \geqslant 0.3$.

29   **a**   Bag A contains 10 white and 5 green marbles. When
a marble is randomly selected from the bag, W is the
event that a white marble is selected, and G is the
event that a green marble is selected. Two marbles
are selected without replacement from Bag A.

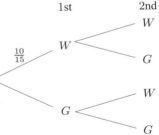

   i   Copy and complete the tree diagram.
   ii   Calculate the probability that marbles of the same
colour are selected.

   b   Bag B contains 5 white and n green marbles.
Two marbles are selected from Bag B without replacement. If the probability that both marbles
are white is $\frac{2}{11}$, find n.

30 The mass of a sea lion on a particular island is normally distributed with mean μ and standard deviation σ. 10% of the sea lions have mass greater than 900 kg, and 15% of them have mass less than 500 kg. Find μ and σ.

31 A group of horses contract a virus at a race meeting. They are then transported back to their stable. If the virus is not detected it will spread according to the formula $H = 4 \times e^{0.3442d}$, where H is the number of horses infected after d days.

   a How many horses were initially infected?

   b The stable is home to 200 horses (including the ones initially infected). How long will it take for every horse to be infected with the virus?

32 A and B are two events such that $\mathrm{P}(A \mid B) = 0.5$, $\mathrm{P}(A \cup B) = 0.9$, and $\mathrm{P}(A') = 0.2$.

For the Venn diagram given, find the probabilities:

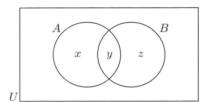

   a z **b** y **c** x.

33 Let $f(x) = \dfrac{1}{x}$, $x \neq 0$.

   a The graph $y = f(x)$ and the line $y = x + 2$ intersect at $m = \pm\sqrt{n}$ where $m, n \in \mathbb{Z}$. Find m and n.

   b The graph $y = f(x)$ is transformed to the graph $y = g(x)$ by a translation of $\begin{pmatrix} -2 \\ 0 \end{pmatrix}$ followed by a reflection in the x-axis.

     i Find an expression for $g(x)$.

     ii Write down the equations of the asymptotes of $y = g(x)$.

     iii Find the y-intercept of $y = g(x)$.

     iv Sketch $y = g(x)$ showing the features you have found.

34 The position vector of a moving object is $\mathbf{r}_1 = \begin{pmatrix} -1 \\ 3 \end{pmatrix} + t \begin{pmatrix} 4 \\ 2 \end{pmatrix}$ where t is the time in seconds, $t \geqslant 0$.

A second object has a position vector $\mathbf{r}_2 = \begin{pmatrix} 0 \\ 4 \end{pmatrix} + t \begin{pmatrix} 9 \\ 4 \end{pmatrix}$.

All distances are in metres.

   a For the first object, determine:

     i the initial position   **ii** the position after 10 seconds.

   b Hence, find the distance the first object travels in the first 10 seconds.

   c Show that the second object passes through the point $(9, 8)$.

   d Determine whether the objects collide at the point $(9, 8)$.

35 Consider the function $f(x) = -x^3 + 2x^2 + 5x - 6$ shown.

$x = k$ is a vertical line, where $k < 0$.

Given that the area of A equals the area of B, find the value of k.

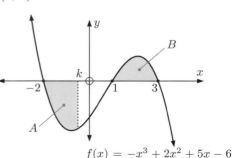

$$f(x) = -x^3 + 2x^2 + 5x - 6$$

36 The graph of $y = e^{-x^2}$ is illustrated.

a State the exact coordinates of points A and B.

b Find the area of the shaded region.

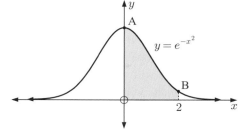

37 When a biased coin is tossed twice, the probability of getting two heads is 0.64.

a What is the probability of tossing a head with a single toss?

b If the coin is tossed 10 times, determine the probability of obtaining:

i exactly 6 heads ii at least 6 heads.

38 The height of a maize plant two months after planting is normally distributed with mean μ cm and standard deviation 6.8 cm. 75% of a crop of maize plants are less than 45 cm high. Suppose X describes the height of a maize plant.

a Find the mean height μ cm. b Find $P(X < 25)$.

c Find a such that $P(X < 25) = P(X > a)$.

39 a On the same set of axes, graph $y = 3e^{-x}$ and $y = e^{2x} + 1$.

b Hence solve $e^{2x} + 1 = 3e^{-x}$ for x. Give your answer correct to 4 decimal places.

40 Let $f(x) = x\sin(2x)$, $0 < x < 3$.

a Sketch the graph of $y = f(x)$.

b Find the range of $f(x)$.

c Find the x-intercept b of the graph of $y = f(x)$ on the given domain.

d The region enclosed by $y = f(x)$ and the x-axis from $x = 0$ to $x = b$, has area A units^2. Find A correct to 3 decimal places.

41 Consider $f(x) = e^{-3x}\sin x$, $-\frac{1}{2} \leqslant x \leqslant 3$.

a Show that $f'(x) = e^{-3x}(\cos x - 3\sin x)$.

b Find the equation of the tangent to the curve $y = f(x)$ at the point $P(\frac{\pi}{2}, e^{-\frac{3\pi}{2}})$.

c Find the area between the curve and the x-axis from $x = 0$ to $x = 1$.

42 Consider $f(x) = \dfrac{\sin x}{\cos x} + \dfrac{\cos x}{\sin x}$, $0 \leqslant x \leqslant \frac{\pi}{2}$.

a Show that $f(x) = \dfrac{2}{\sin 2x}$.

b Solve the equation $\sin 2x = 0$ and hence state the equations of any asymptote of $y = f(x)$ on $0 \leqslant x \leqslant \frac{\pi}{2}$.

c Without using calculus, find the least value of $f(x)$ and the corresponding value of x.

d If $\sin \alpha = \frac{1}{3}$, find $f(2a)$ correct to 4 significant figures.

43 On an ostrich farm the weights of the birds are found to be normally distributed. The weights of the females have mean 78.6 kg and standard deviation 5.03 kg. The weights of the males have mean 91.3 kg and standard deviation 6.29 kg.

    a Find the probability that a randomly selected:

        i male will weigh less than 80 kg   **ii** female will weigh less than 80 kg

        iii female will weigh between 70 and 80 kg.

    b 20% of females weigh less than k kg. Find k.

    c The middle 90% of the males weigh between a kg and b kg. Find the values of a and b.

    d In one field there are 82% females and 18% males. One of these ostriches is selected at random. Calculate the probability that the ostrich weighs less than 80 kg.

44 The solid figure shown is a parallelepiped. All six of its faces are parallelograms.

A is $(3, 2, -1)$, B is $(1, -1, 4)$, and C is $(2, 0, 7)$.

    a Find $\overrightarrow{BA}$ and $|\overrightarrow{BA}|$.

    b Find the coordinates of D.

    c If $\overrightarrow{BF} = \begin{pmatrix} 6 \\ -3 \\ -6 \end{pmatrix}$, find the coordinates of F.

    d Calculate $\overrightarrow{BA} \bullet \overrightarrow{BF}$ and hence find $\cos A\widehat{B}F$.

    e Hence, find the exact area of parallelogram ABFE.

45 A discrete random variable Y has the probability distribution shown:

y	1	2	3	4	5
$P(Y = y)$	$\frac{1}{10}$	$2t$	$\frac{3}{20}$	$2t^2$	$\frac{t}{2}$

    a Find t.

    b Find the expected value of the random variable Y.

    c Explain the significance of your result in **b**.

46 Consider $f(x) = 5x + e^{1-x^2} - 2$ for $-1 \leqslant x \leqslant 2$.

    a Find the y-intercept of f.   **b** Sketch the graph of $y = f(x)$.

    c Find any x-intercepts of f.

    d Find the gradient of the tangent to $y = f(x)$ at the point where $x = 1$.

47 The length of a zucchini is normally distributed with mean 24.3 cm and standard deviation 6.83 cm. A supermarket buying zucchinis in bulk finds that 15% of them are too small and 20% of them are too large for sale. The remainder, with lengths between a cm and b cm, are able to be sold.

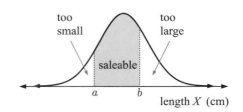

    a Find the values of a and b.

    b A zucchini is chosen at random. Find the probability that:

        i it is of saleable length   **ii** its length lies between 20 and 26 cm

        iii its length is less than 24.3 cm.

48   **a**   Sketch the graph of $y = \dfrac{6 - 2x}{x + 3}$.

   b   Discuss the behaviour of the graph near its asymptotes, and hence deduce their equations.

   c   State the values of $\displaystyle\lim_{x \to -\infty} \dfrac{6 - 2x}{x + 3}$ and $\displaystyle\lim_{x \to \infty} \dfrac{6 - 2x}{x + 3}$.

49   Line L_1 has vector equation $\mathbf{r}_1 = \begin{pmatrix} 2 \\ -1 \\ 3 \end{pmatrix} + s \begin{pmatrix} 1 \\ -1 \\ 1 \end{pmatrix}$.

   Line L_2 has vector equation $\mathbf{r}_2 = \begin{pmatrix} 6 \\ -3 \\ 4 \end{pmatrix} + t \begin{pmatrix} 2 \\ 0 \\ -1 \end{pmatrix}$.

   a   Point A lies on L_1 and has z-coordinate -2. Find the coordinates of A.

   b   Do lines L_1 and L_2 intersect? If they do, where do they meet?

   c   Find, correct to one decimal place, the angle between L_1 and L_2.

50   The graph of $f(x) = e^x(x^2 - 3x + 2)$ is shown.

   a   Find the coordinates of points A, B, and C.

   b   Write down the equations of any asymptotes of $y = f(x)$.

   c   Show that $f'(x) = e^x(x^2 - x - 1)$.

   d   Find the x-coordinates of the local maximum and local minimum.

   e   Show that the normal to the curve at A has equation $x - ey = 1$.

   f   Find the x-coordinate of D correct to 3 significant figures.

   g   Hence estimate the area of the shaded region.

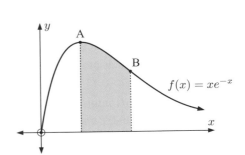

51   The graph of $f(x) = xe^{-x}, \ x \geqslant 0$ is shown.

   a   Find the y-intercept of f.

   b   Find $f'(x)$ and hence find the coordinates of the local maximum A.

   c   Find exactly the x-coordinate of the point of inflection B.

   d   Find the area of the shaded region.

52   When a pair of normal dice are rolled, E is the event of rolling *at least one* 6.

   a   Display the possible results on a 2-dimensional grid.

   b   Determine $P(E)$.

   c   The two dice are rolled 10 times. Determine the probability that event E occurs:

   i   exactly 2 times   **ii**   at most 3 times.

53 Points A and B have coordinates $(2, -1, 3)$ and $(-2, 4, -1)$ respectively.

  a Show that the line L_1 which passes through A and B has vector equation
$$\mathbf{r}_1 = (2 - 4t)\mathbf{i} + (5t - 1)\mathbf{j} + (3 - 4t)\mathbf{k}.$$

  b $C(4, a, b)$ lies on the line through A and B. Find a and b.

  c L_2 has equation $\mathbf{r}_2 = (3s - 5)\mathbf{i} + (s - 16)\mathbf{j} + (16 - s)\mathbf{k}.$
    Find the coordinates of the point where L_1 and L_2 intersect.

54

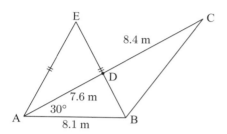

Consider the figure shown.

  a Find the lengths of [DB] and [BC].

  b Calculate the measures of $A\widehat{B}E$ and $D\widehat{B}C$.

  c Find the area of $\triangle BCD$.

  d Calculate the length of [AE].

55 The graph of $f(x) = a + \dfrac{3}{(x - 1)(x + b)}$
where $a, b \in \mathbb{Z}$ is shown.

  a State the values of a and b.

  b Find the y-intercept.

  c Find exactly the x-intercepts.

  d Show that $f'(x) = \dfrac{-3(2x + 1)}{(x^2 + x - 2)^2}$ and
    hence find the coordinates of the local
    maximum D.

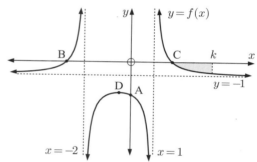

  e **i** Write down an expression for the shaded area as an integral.

    ii Find the shaded area for $k = 3$.

56 G is the event of a customer buying a goldfish from a pet shop and T is the event of a customer buying a tortoise from a pet shop.

  a At one particular pet shop, $P(G) = 0.3$, $P(T) = 0.4$, and $P(\text{neither } G \text{ nor } T) = 0.42$.

    i Find $P(G \cap T)$. Explain what this result means.

    ii Show this information on a Venn diagram.

    iii Are G and T independent events? Give reasons for your answer.

  b The probabilities at a second pet shop are represented
    in the Venn diagram.
    $P(T)$ is twice $P(G)$, $P(\text{neither } G \text{ nor } T) = 0.42$,
    and G and T are independent.

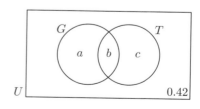

    i Show that $2a + b = c$.

    ii Show that $a = \sqrt{\dfrac{b}{2}} - b$.

    iii Hence, find b and then a.

    iv Determine $P(G)$.

57 The weight of DDT in a pile of contaminated soil is given by $W_t = 1800 \times (0.95)^t$ grams, where t is the number of years since the soil was contaminated.

   a Find the initial quantity of DDT which contaminated the soil.

   b Find the quantity of DDT remaining after:

      i $7\frac{1}{2}$ years   **ii** 40 years.

   c Sketch the graph of W_t against t.

   d The *half-life* of DDT is the time it takes for the quantity of DDT to decrease to half of the initial amount.

      Use your graph in **c** to estimate the half-life of DDT.

   e Find the time required until 100 g of DDT remains in the soil.

58 Two semi-circles touch each other within a quarter circle as shown. This means that P, Q, and R are collinear. The radius of the quarter circle is 12 cm.

   a Use the theorem of Pythagoras to show that the radius of the smaller semi-circle is 4 cm.

   b Calculate, in radians, the measure of:

      i $\widehat{TPR}$ **ii** $\widehat{PRT}$

   c Hence calculate the area of:

      i A **ii** B

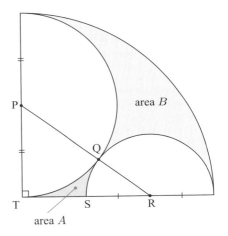

59 Solve the following equations:

   a $\log_2(x^2 - 2x + 1) = 1 + \log_2(x - 1)$ **b** $3^{2x+1} = 5(3^x) + 2$

60 A zoo's population of pygmy shrews is weighed during the annual veterinary health check.

Length (mm)	95	83	91	82	75	62	79	63	81	69	94	88	72	77
Weight (g)	5.4	4.5	5.0	4.1	3.7	2.6	4.5	3.1	4.7	3.7	5.1	4.8	3.6	4.2

   a Draw a scatter diagram for this data.

   b Calculate Pearson's product-moment correlation coefficient r for the data.

   c Hence describe the correlation between these two variables.

   d Find the equation of the least squares regression line.

   e Hence predict the weight of a pygmy shrew with length:

      i 110 mm   **ii** 70 mm

   f Which of your predictions in **e** is more likely to be reliable? Explain your answer.

61 The diagram shows a simple electrical network.

Each symbol ——•——•—— represents a switch.

All four switches operate independently, and the probability of each one of them being closed is p.

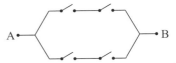

   a In terms of p, find the probability that the current flows from A to B.

   b Find the least value of p for which the probability of current flow is at least 0.5.

62 In triangle ABC, the angle at A is double the angle at B. AC $= 5$ cm and BC $= 6$ cm.

    a Find the cosine of the angle at B.

    b Find the length of [AB] using the sine rule.

    c If the cosine rule was used to find the length of [AB], how many solutions would it give?

63 ABC is an equilateral triangle with sides 10 cm long. P is a point within the triangle which is 5 cm from A and 6 cm from B. How far is P from C?

64 A company manufactures computer chips. It is known that 3% of them are faulty. In a batch of 500 chips, find the probability that between 1 and 2 percent (inclusive) of the chips are faulty.

65 A random variable X is normally distributed with standard deviation 2.83. Find the probability that a randomly selected score from X will differ from the mean by less than 4.

66 The Ferris wheel at the Royal Show turns one full circle every minute. The lowest point is 1 metre from the ground, and the highest point is 25 metres above the ground.

    a When riding on the Ferris wheel, your height above ground level after t seconds is given by the model $h(t) = a + b\sin(c(t - d))$.   Find the values of a, b, c, and d given that you start your ride at the lowest point.

    b If the motor driving the Ferris wheel breaks down after 91 seconds, how high up would you be while waiting to be rescued?

67 Consider the graph of $y = \tan ax + b$ shown.

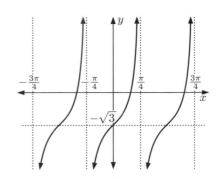

    a Find the values of a and b.

    b Hence, find the x-intercepts of the function, for $-\frac{3\pi}{4} \leqslant x \leqslant \frac{3\pi}{4}$.

68 The function f is defined by $f : x \mapsto e^{\sin^2 x},\ 0 \leqslant x \leqslant \pi$.

    a Use calculus to find the exact value(s) of x at which $f(x)$ has a maximum turning point.

    b Find $f''(x)$.

    c Find any points of inflection in the given domain.

69 The sum of an infinite geometric series is 49. The second term of the series is 10. Find the possible values for the sum of the first three terms of the series.

70 Let $f(x) = xe^{1-2x^2}$.

    a Find $f'(x)$ and $f''(x)$.

    b Find the exact coordinates of the stationary points of the function and determine their nature.

    c Find exactly the x-coordinates of the points of inflection of the function.

    d Discuss the behaviour of the function as $x \to \pm\infty$.

    e Sketch the function, showing the information you have found.

71 Consider the grouped data in the table. Estimate:

  a the mean value of X

  b the standard deviation of the X-distribution.

Score	Frequency
$9 \leqslant X < 11$	2
$11 \leqslant X < 13$	7
$13 \leqslant X < 15$	6
$15 \leqslant X < 17$	21
$17 \leqslant X < 19$	17
$19 \leqslant X < 21$	5

72 Consider the vectors $\mathbf{a} = \begin{pmatrix} \cos\theta \\ \sin\theta \\ \cos\theta \end{pmatrix}$ and $\mathbf{b} = \begin{pmatrix} \sin\theta \\ -\sin\theta \\ \cos\theta \end{pmatrix}$.

  a Show that $|\mathbf{a}| = \sqrt{1 + \cos^2\theta}$.

  b Explain why $1 \leqslant |\mathbf{a}| \leqslant \sqrt{2}$ for all θ.

  c Find all values of θ in the interval $0 \leqslant \theta \leqslant 2\pi$ such that $\mathbf{a}$ and $\mathbf{b}$ are perpendicular.

73 Solve for x on the domain $0 \leqslant x \leqslant 2\pi$:

  a $3 + 2\sin x = 0$

  b $3\cos\left(\dfrac{x}{2}\right) + 1 = 0$

74 A random variable X has the discrete probability density function $P(X = x) = \dfrac{x^2 + kx}{50}$ for $x = 0,\ 1,\ 2,\ 3,\ 4$.

  a Find k.

  b Find μ, the mean of the distribution of X.

  c Find $P(X \geqslant 2)$.

75 Consider $f(x) = \sin x \cos(2x)$ for $0 \leqslant x \leqslant \pi$.

  a Find $f'(x)$ in terms of $\cos x$ only.

  b Show that $f'(x) = 0$ when $\cos x = 0$ or $\pm\sqrt{\frac{5}{6}}$.

  c Hence, find the position and nature of the turning points of $y = f(x)$.

  d Graph $y = f(x)$, showing the features you have found.

76 An experiment was conducted to measure the shelf life of bottles of milk stored at different temperatures:

Temperature T (°C)	1	4	10	12	15	21	27
Shelf life D (days)	19	11.5	4	3	1.5	0.5	0.25

  a Draw scatter diagrams of:

    i D against T **ii** $\ln D$ against T **iii** $\ln D$ against $\ln T$

  b Determine which of the diagrams illustrates a linear relationship, and find the equation of the least squares regression line in this case.

  c Hence determine a formula for D in terms of T.

  d Estimate the shelf life of a bottle of milk stored at 7°C.

ANSWERS

EXERCISE 1A.1

1   a $x = 0, -\frac{7}{4}$ b $x = 0, -\frac{1}{3}$ c $x = 0, \frac{7}{3}$

   d $x = 0, \frac{11}{2}$ e $x = 0, \frac{8}{3}$ f $x = 0, \frac{3}{2}$

   g $x = 3, 2$ h $x = 4, -2$ i $x = 3, 7$

   j $x = 3$ k $x = -4, 3$ l $x = -11, 3$

2   a $x = \frac{2}{3}$ b $x = -\frac{1}{2}, 7$ c $x = -\frac{2}{3}, 6$

   d $x = \frac{1}{3}, -2$ e $x = \frac{3}{2}, 1$ f $x = -\frac{2}{3}, -2$

   g $x = -\frac{2}{3}, 4$ h $x = \frac{1}{2}, -\frac{3}{2}$ i $x = -\frac{1}{4}, 3$

   j $x = -\frac{3}{4}, \frac{5}{3}$ k $x = \frac{1}{7}, -1$ l $x = -2, \frac{28}{15}$

3   a $x = 2, 5$ b $x = -3, 2$ c $x = 0, -\frac{3}{2}$

   d $x = 1, 2$ e $x = \frac{1}{2}, -1$ f $x = 3$

EXERCISE 1A.2

1   a $x = -5 \pm \sqrt{2}$ b   no real solns.   c $x = 4 \pm 2\sqrt{2}$

   d $x = 8 \pm \sqrt{7}$ e $x = -3 \pm \sqrt{5}$ f $x = 2 \pm \sqrt{6}$

   g $x = -1 \pm \sqrt{10}$ h $x = -\frac{1}{2} \pm \frac{1}{2}\sqrt{3}$ i $x = \frac{1}{3} \pm \frac{\sqrt{7}}{3}$

2   a $x = 2 \pm \sqrt{3}$ b $x = -3 \pm \sqrt{7}$ c $x = 7 \pm \sqrt{3}$

   d $x = 2 \pm \sqrt{7}$ e $x = -3 \pm \sqrt{2}$ f $x = 1 \pm \sqrt{7}$

   g $x = -3 \pm \sqrt{11}$ h $x = 4 \pm \sqrt{6}$ i   no real solns.

3   a $x = -1 \pm \frac{1}{\sqrt{2}}$ b $x = \frac{5}{2} \pm \frac{\sqrt{19}}{2}$ c $x = -2 \pm \sqrt{\frac{7}{3}}$

   d $x = 1 \pm \sqrt{\frac{7}{3}}$ e $x = \frac{3}{2} \pm \sqrt{\frac{37}{20}}$ f $x = -\frac{1}{2} \pm \frac{\sqrt{6}}{2}$

EXERCISE 1A.3

1   a $x = 2 \pm \sqrt{7}$ b $x = -3 \pm \sqrt{2}$ c $x = 2 \pm \sqrt{3}$

   d $x = -2 \pm \sqrt{5}$ e $x = 2 \pm \sqrt{2}$ f $x = \frac{1}{2} \pm \frac{1}{2}\sqrt{7}$

   g $x = -\frac{4}{9} \pm \frac{\sqrt{7}}{9}$ h $x = -\frac{7}{4} \pm \frac{\sqrt{97}}{4}$

2   a $x = -2 \pm 2\sqrt{2}$ b $x = -\frac{5}{8} \pm \frac{\sqrt{57}}{8}$ c $x = \frac{5}{2} \pm \frac{\sqrt{13}}{2}$

   d $x = \frac{1}{2} \pm \frac{1}{2}\sqrt{7}$ e $x = \frac{1}{2} \pm \frac{\sqrt{5}}{2}$ f $x = \frac{3}{4} \pm \frac{\sqrt{17}}{4}$

EXERCISE 1B

1   a   2 real distinct roots   b   2 real distinct roots

   c   2 real distinct roots   d   2 real distinct roots

   e   no real roots   f   a repeated root

2   a, c, d, f

3   a $\Delta = 16 - 4m$

    i $m = 4$ ii $m < 4$ iii $m > 4$

   b $\Delta = 9 - 8m$

    i $m = \frac{9}{8}$ ii $m < \frac{9}{8}$ iii $m > \frac{9}{8}$

   c $\Delta = 9 - 4m$

    i $m = \frac{9}{4}$ ii $m < \frac{9}{4}$ iii $m > \frac{9}{4}$

4   a $\Delta = k^2 + 8k$

    i $k < -8$ or $k > 0$ ii $k \leqslant -8$ or $k \geqslant 0$

    iii $k = -8$ or 0 iv $-8 < k < 0$

   b $\Delta = 4 - 4k^2$

    i $-1 < k < 1$ ii $-1 \leqslant k \leqslant 1$

    iii $k = \pm 1$ iv $k < -1$ or $k > 1$

   c $\Delta = k^2 + 4k - 12$

    i $k < -6$ or $k > 2$ ii $k \leqslant -6$ or $k \geqslant 2$

    iii $k = -6$ or 2 iv $-6 < k < 2$

   d $\Delta = k^2 - 4k - 12$

    i $k < -2$ or $k > 6$ ii $k \leqslant -2$ or $k \geqslant 6$

    iii $k = 6$ or -2 iv $-2 < k < 6$

   e $\Delta = 9k^2 - 14k - 39$

    i $k < -\frac{13}{9}$ or $k > 3$ ii $k \leqslant -\frac{13}{9}$ or $k \geqslant 3$

    iii $k = -\frac{13}{9}$ or 3 iv $-\frac{13}{9} < k < 3$

   f $\Delta = -3k^2 - 4k$

    i $-\frac{4}{3} < k < 0$ ii $-\frac{4}{3} \leqslant k \leqslant 0$

    iii $k = -\frac{4}{3}$ or 0 iv $k < -\frac{4}{3}$ or $k > 0$

EXERCISE 1C.1

1   a $y = (x - 4)(x + 2)$ b $y = -(x - 4)(x + 2)$

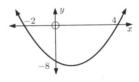

   c $y = 2(x + 3)(x + 5)$ d $y = -3x(x + 4)$

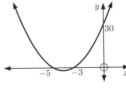

   e $y = 2(x + 3)^2$ f $y = -\frac{1}{4}(x + 2)^2$

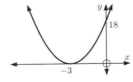

2   a $x = 1$ b $x = 1$ c $x = -4$

   d $x = -2$ e $x = -3$ f $x = -2$

3   a **C**   b **E**   c **B**   d **F**   e **G**   f **H**   g **A**   h **D**

4 a

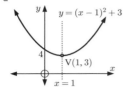

$y = (x-1)^2 + 3$
V(1, 3)
$x = 1$
4

b

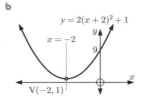

$y = 2(x+2)^2 + 1$
$x = -2$
9
V(−2, 1)

c

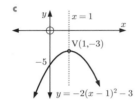

$x = 1$
V(1, −3)
−5
$y = -2(x-1)^2 - 3$

d

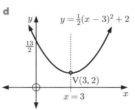

$y = \frac{1}{2}(x-3)^2 + 2$
$\frac{13}{2}$
V(3, 2)
$x = 3$

e

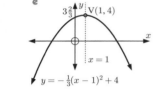

$3\frac{2}{3}$ V(1, 4)
$x = 1$
$y = -\frac{1}{3}(x-1)^2 + 4$

f

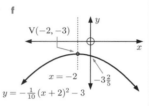

V(−2, −3)
$x = -2$
$-3\frac{2}{5}$
$y = -\frac{1}{10}(x+2)^2 - 3$

e i $x = \frac{2}{3}$
  ii $(\frac{2}{3}, \frac{1}{3})$
  iii x-intercepts $\frac{1}{3}$, 1, y-intercept −1
  iv

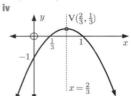

V($\frac{2}{3}, \frac{1}{3}$)
$\frac{1}{3}$ 1
−1
$x = \frac{2}{3}$

f i $x = \frac{1}{4}$
  ii $(\frac{1}{4}, \frac{9}{8})$
  iii x-intercepts $-\frac{1}{2}$, 1, y-intercept 1
  iv

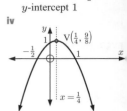

V($\frac{1}{4}, \frac{9}{8}$)
1
$-\frac{1}{2}$ 1
$x = \frac{1}{4}$

5 a G   b A   c E   d B   e I
f C   g D   h F   i H

6 a $(2, -2)$ **b** $(-1, -4)$ **c** $(0, 4)$
  d $(0, 1)$ **e** $(-2, -15)$ **f** $(-2, -5)$
  g $(-\frac{3}{2}, -\frac{11}{2})$ **h** $(\frac{5}{2}, -\frac{19}{2})$ **i** $(1, -\frac{9}{2})$

7 a ± 3 **b** $\pm\sqrt{3}$ **c** −5 and −2
  d 3 and −4   **e** 0 and 4   **f** −4 and −2
  g −1 (touching)   **h** 3 (touching)   **i** $2 \pm \sqrt{3}$
  j $-2 \pm \sqrt{7}$ **k** $3 \pm \sqrt{11}$ **l** $-4 \pm \sqrt{5}$

8 a i $x = 1$
    ii $(1, 4)$
    iii no x-intercept, y-intercept 5
    iv

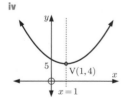

5 V(1, 4)
$x = 1$

b i $x = -2$
    ii $(-2, -5)$
    iii x-int. $-2 \pm \sqrt{5}$, y-intercept −1
    iv

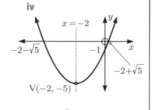

$x = -2$
$-2-\sqrt{5}$ −1
$-2+\sqrt{5}$
V(−2, −5)

g i $x = 3$
  ii $(3, 9)$
  iii x-intercepts 0, 6, y-intercept 0
  iv

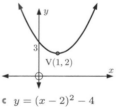

V(3, 9)
6
$x = 3$

h i $x = -3$
  ii $(-3, 1)$
  iii x-int. −2, −4, y-intercept −8
  iv

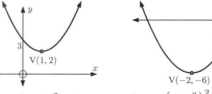

V(−3, 1)
−4   −2
−8
$x = -3$

i i $x = 4$
  ii $(4, 5)$
  iii x-int. $4 \pm 2\sqrt{5}$, y-intercept 1
  iv

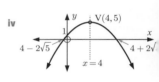

V(4, 5)
1
$4 - 2\sqrt{5}$ $4 + 2\sqrt{ }$
$x = 4$

c i $x = \frac{5}{4}$
  ii $(\frac{5}{4}, -\frac{9}{8})$
  iii x-intercepts $\frac{1}{2}$, 2, y-intercept 2
  iv

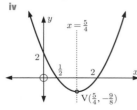

$x = \frac{5}{4}$
2
$\frac{1}{2}$ 2
V($\frac{5}{4}, -\frac{9}{8}$)

d i $x = \frac{3}{2}$
  ii $(\frac{3}{2}, \frac{1}{4})$
  iii x-intercepts 1, 2, y-intercept −2
  iv

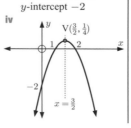

V($\frac{3}{2}, \frac{1}{4}$)
1   2
−2
$x = \frac{3}{2}$

EXERCISE 1C.2

1 a $y = (x-1)^2 + 2$

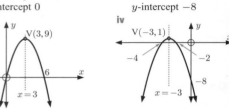

3
V(1, 2)

b $y = (x+2)^2 - 6$

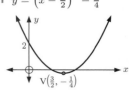

−2
V(−2, −6)

c $y = (x-2)^2 - 4$

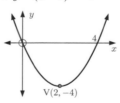

4
V(2, −4)

d $y = \left(x + \frac{3}{2}\right)^2 - \frac{9}{4}$

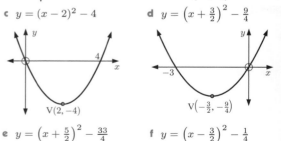

−3
V($-\frac{3}{2}, -\frac{9}{4}$)

e $y = \left(x + \frac{5}{2}\right)^2 - \frac{33}{4}$

−2
V($-\frac{5}{2}, -\frac{33}{4}$)

f $y = \left(x - \frac{3}{2}\right)^2 - \frac{1}{4}$

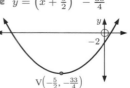

2
V($\frac{3}{2}, -\frac{1}{4}$)

g $y = (x-3)^2 - 4$

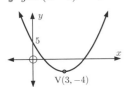

V(3, −4)

h $y = (x+4)^2 - 18$

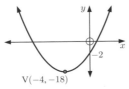

V(−4, −18)

i $y = \left(x - \frac{5}{2}\right)^2 - 5\frac{1}{4}$

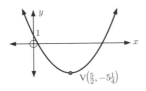

V$\left(\frac{5}{2}, -5\frac{1}{4}\right)$

2 a i $y = 2(x+1)^2 + 3$
   ii $(-1, 3)$ **iii** 5
   iv

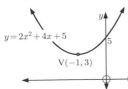

$y = 2x^2 + 4x + 5$
V(−1, 3)

b i $y = 2(x-2)^2 - 5$
   ii $(2, -5)$ **iii** 3
   iv

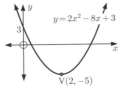

$y = 2x^2 - 8x + 3$
V(2, −5)

c i $y = 2\left(x - \frac{3}{2}\right)^2 - \frac{7}{2}$
   ii $\left(\frac{3}{2}, -\frac{7}{2}\right)$ **iii** 1
   iv

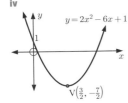

$y = 2x^2 - 6x + 1$
V$\left(\frac{3}{2}, -\frac{7}{2}\right)$

d i $y = 3(x-1)^2 + 2$
   ii $(1, 2)$ **iii** 5
   iv

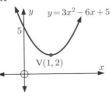

$y = 3x^2 - 6x + 5$
V(1, 2)

e i $y = -(x-2)^2 + 6$
   ii $(2, 6)$ **iii** 2
   iv

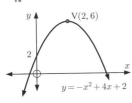

V(2, 6)
$y = -x^2 + 4x + 2$

f i $y = -2\left(x + \frac{5}{4}\right)^2 + \frac{49}{8}$
   ii $\left(-\frac{5}{4}, \frac{49}{8}\right)$ **iii** 3
   iv

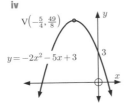

V$\left(-\frac{5}{4}, \frac{49}{8}\right)$
$y = -2x^2 - 5x + 3$

3 a $y = (x-2)^2 + 3$ **b** $y = (x+3)^2 - 6$
  c $y = -(x-2)^2 + 9$ **d** $y = 2\left(x + \frac{3}{2}\right)^2 - \frac{17}{2}$
  e $y = -2\left(x + \frac{5}{2}\right)^2 + \frac{27}{2}$ **f** $y = 3\left(x - \frac{3}{2}\right)^2 - \frac{47}{4}$

EXERCISE 1C.3

1 a cuts x-axis twice, concave up
  b cuts x-axis twice, concave up
  c lies entirely below the x-axis, concave down, negative definite
  d cuts x-axis twice, concave up
  e touches x-axis, concave up

f cuts x-axis twice, concave down
g cuts x-axis twice, concave up
h cuts x-axis twice, concave down
i touches x-axis, concave up

2 a $a = 1$ which is > 0 and $\Delta = -15$ which is < 0 so is entirely above the x-axis.
  b $a = -1$ which is < 0 and $\Delta = -8$ which is < 0 so is entirely below the x-axis.
  c $a = 2$ which is > 0 and $\Delta = -40$ which is < 0 so is entirely above the x-axis.
  d $a = -2$ which is < 0 and $\Delta = -23$ which is < 0 so is entirely below the x-axis.

3 $a = 3$ which is > 0 and $\Delta = k^2 + 12$ which is always > 0 {as $k^2 \geqslant 0$ for all k} $\therefore$ always cuts x-axis twice.

4 $-4 < k < 4$

EXERCISE 1D

1 a $y = 2(x-1)(x-2)$ **b** $y = 2(x-2)^2$
  c $y = (x-1)(x-3)$ **d** $y = -(x-3)(x+1)$
  e $y = -3(x-1)^2$ **f** $y = -2(x+2)(x-3)$

2 a $y = \frac{3}{2}(x-2)(x-4)$ **b** $y = -\frac{1}{2}(x+4)(x-2)$
  c $y = -\frac{4}{3}(x+3)^2$

3 a $y = 3x^2 - 18x + 15$ **b** $y = -4x^2 + 6x + 4$
  c $y = -x^2 + 6x - 9$ **d** $y = 4x^2 + 16x + 16$
  e $y = \frac{3}{2}x^2 - 6x + \frac{9}{2}$ **f** $y = -\frac{1}{3}x^2 + \frac{2}{3}x + 5$

4 a $y = -(x-2)^2 + 4$ **b** $y = 2(x-2)^2 - 1$
  c $y = -2(x-3)^2 + 8$ **d** $y = \frac{2}{3}(x-4)^2 - 6$
  e $y = -2(x-2)^2 + 3$ **f** $y = 2(x - \frac{1}{2})^2 - \frac{3}{2}$

EXERCISE 1E

1 a $(1, 7)$ and $(2, 8)$ **b** $(4, 5)$ and $(-3, -9)$
  c $(3, 0)$ (touching)   **d** graphs do not meet

2 a $(0.586, 5.59)$ and $(3.41, 8.41)$ **b** $(3, -4)$ touching
  c graphs do not meet **d** $(-2.56, -18.8)$ and $(1.56, 1.81)$

3 a i $(-1, 1)$ and $(2, 4)$ **ii** $x < -1$ or $x > 2$
  b i $(-2, -3)$ and $(1, 0)$ **ii** $x < -2$ or $x > 1$
  c i $(1, 4)$ **ii** $x \in \mathbb{R}$, $x \neq 1$
  d i $(-4, -1)$ and $(1, 4)$ **ii** $x < -4$ or $x > 1$

4 $c = -9$

5 $m = 0$ or -8

6 -1 or 11

7 a $c < -9$
  b example: $c = -10$

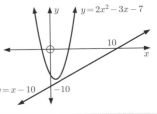

$y = 2x^2 - 3x - 7$
$y = x - 10$

EXERCISE 1F

1 7 and -5 or -7 and 5   **2** 5 or $\frac{1}{5}$ **3** 14
4 18 and 20 or -18 and -20 **5** 15 and 17 or -15 and -17
6 15 sides   **7** 3.48 cm
8 b 6 cm by 6 cm by 7 cm   **9** 11.2 cm square   **10** no
12 61.8 km h^{-1} **13** 32
14 b The graph is a parabola.   **c** 21.25 m
   d $f(x) = -0.05x^2 + 2x + 1.25$ **e** yes
15 a $y = -\frac{8}{9}x^2 - 8$

b No, as the tunnel is only 4.44 m high when it is the same width as the truck.

EXERCISE 1G

1 **a** min. -1, when $x = 1$ **b** max. 8, when $x = -1$
c max. $8\frac{1}{3}$, when $x = \frac{1}{3}$ **d** min. $-1\frac{1}{8}$, when $x = -\frac{1}{4}$
e min. $4\frac{15}{16}$, when $x = \frac{1}{8}$ **f** max. $6\frac{1}{8}$, when $x = \frac{7}{4}$

2 **a** 40 refrigerators **b** \$4000

4 500 m by 250 m **5** **c** 100 m by 112.5 m

6 **a** $41\frac{2}{3}$ m by $41\frac{2}{3}$ m **b** 50 m by $31\frac{1}{4}$ m

7 **b** $3\frac{1}{8}$ units **8** **a** $y = 6 - \frac{3}{4}x$ **b** 3 cm by 4 cm

REVIEW SET 1A

1 **a** $-2, 1$ **e**
b $x = -\frac{1}{2}$
c 4
d $\left(-\frac{1}{2}, \frac{9}{2}\right)$

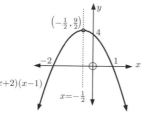

2 **a** $x = 0$ or 4 **b** $x = -\frac{5}{3}$ or 2 **c** $x = 15$ or -4

3 **a** $x = \frac{-5 \pm \sqrt{13}}{2}$ **b** $x = \frac{-11 \pm \sqrt{145}}{6}$

4 $x = -\frac{7}{2} \pm \frac{\sqrt{65}}{2}$

5 **a** **b**

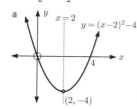

6 **a** $y = 3x^2 - 24x + 48$ **b** $y = \frac{2}{5}x^2 + \frac{16}{5}x + \frac{37}{5}$

7 $a = -2$ which is < 0 $\therefore$ a max.
max. $= 5$ when $x = 1$

8 $(4, 4)$ and $(-3, 18)$ **9** $k < -3\frac{1}{8}$

10 **a** $m = \frac{9}{8}$ **b** $m < \frac{9}{8}$ **c** $m > \frac{9}{8}$ **11** $\frac{6}{5}$ or $\frac{5}{6}$

12 **Hint:** Let the line have equation $y = mx + 10$.

13 **a** $m = -2$, $n = 4$ **b** $k = 7$

REVIEW SET 1B

1 **a** $y = 2\left(x + \frac{3}{2}\right)^2 - \frac{15}{2}$ **d**
b $\left(-\frac{3}{2}, -\frac{15}{2}\right)$
c -3

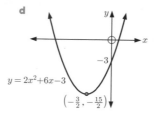

2 **a** $x \approx 0.586$ or 3.41 **b** $x \approx -0.186$ or 2.69

3

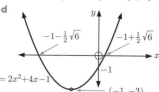

4 $x = \frac{4}{3}$, $V\left(\frac{4}{3}, 12\frac{1}{3}\right)$
5 **a** two distinct rational solns
b a repeated solution

6 **a** $c > -6$ **b** example: $c = -2$, $(-1, -5)$ and $(3, 7)$
7 **a** $x = -1$ **d**
b $(-1, -3)$
c y-intercept -1,
x-ints. $-1 \pm \frac{1}{2}\sqrt{6}$

8 13.5 cm by 13.5 cm
9 **a** $x = -2$ **b** $x \in \mathbb{R}$, $x \neq -2$
10 **a** min. $= 5\frac{2}{3}$ when $x = -\frac{2}{3}$
b max. $= 5\frac{1}{8}$ when $x = -\frac{5}{4}$
11 **b** $37\frac{1}{2}$ m by $33\frac{1}{3}$ m **c** 1250 m²
12 **a** $k = -12$ or 12 **b** $(0, 4)$

REVIEW SET 1C

1 **a** $x = 2$ **d**
b $(2, -4)$
c -2

2 **a** $x = \frac{5}{2} \pm \frac{\sqrt{37}}{2}$
b $x = \frac{7}{4} \pm \frac{\sqrt{73}}{4}$
3 **a** $x = \frac{7}{2} \pm \frac{\sqrt{37}}{2}$
b no real roots
4 **a** $y = \frac{20}{9}(x - 2)^2 - 20$
b $y = -\frac{2}{7}(x - 1)(x - 7)$
c $y = \frac{2}{9}(x + 3)^2$

5 **a** graph cuts
x-axis twice
b graph cuts
x-axis twice

6 **a** $a < 0$, $\Delta > 0$, neither
b $a > 0$, $\Delta < 0$, positive definite
7 $y = -6(x - 2)^2 + 25$ **8** $\frac{1}{2}$ **9** $k < 1$
10 $y = -4x^2 + 4x + 24$ **11** $m = -5$ or 19
12 **a** **i** $A(-m, 0)$, $B(-n, 0)$ **ii** $x = \frac{-m - n}{2}$
b **i** positive **ii** negative
13 **a** **i** $y = 3x^2 - 27$ **ii** $y = 9x - 27$ **b** $0 \leqslant x \leqslant 3$

EXERCISE 2A

1 a, d, e **2** a, b, c, e, g, i **3** No, for example $x = 1$
4 No, for example $(0, 3)$ and $(0, -3)$ satisfy the relation.

EXERCISE 2B

1 **a** 2 **b** 8 **c** -1 **d** -13 **e** 1
2 **a** 2 **b** 2 **c** -16 **d** -68 **e** $\frac{17}{4}$
3 **a** -3 **b** 3 **c** 3 **d** -3 **e** $\frac{15}{2}$

4 **a** $7 - 3a$ **b** $7 + 3a$ **c** $-3a - 2$ **d** $10 - 3b$
e $1 - 3x$ **f** $7 - 3x - 3h$

5 **a** $2x^2 + 19x + 43$ **b** $2x^2 - 11x + 13$
c $2x^2 - 3x - 1$ **d** $2x^4 + 3x^2 - 1$
e $2x^4 - x^2 - 2$ **f** $2x^2 + (4h + 3)x + 2h^2 + 3h - 1$

6 **a** **i** $-\frac{7}{2}$ **ii** $-\frac{3}{4}$ **iii** $-\frac{4}{9}$

b $x = 4$ **c** $\dfrac{2x + 7}{x - 2}$ **d** $x = \frac{9}{5}$

7 f is the function which converts x into $f(x)$ whereas $f(x)$ is the value of the function at any value of x.

8 **a** 6210 euros, value after 4 years
b $t = 4.5$ years, the time for the photocopier to reach a value of 5780 euros.
c 9650 euros

9

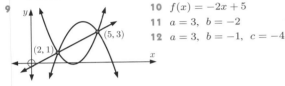

(2, 1)   (5, 3)

10 $f(x) = -2x + 5$
11 $a = 3,\ b = -2$
12 $a = 3,\ b = -1,\ c = -4$

EXERCISE 2C

1 **a** Domain $= \{x \mid x \geqslant -1\}$, Range $= \{y \mid y \leqslant 3\}$
b Domain $= \{x \mid -1 < x \leqslant 5\}$, Range $= \{y \mid 1 < y \leqslant 3\}$
c Domain $= \{x \mid x \neq 2\}$, Range $= \{y \mid y \neq -1\}$
d Domain $= \{x \mid x \in \mathbb{R}\}$, Range $= \{y \mid 0 < y \leqslant 2\}$
e Domain $= \{x \mid x \in \mathbb{R}\}$, Range $= \{y \mid y \geqslant -1\}$
f Domain $= \{x \mid x \in \mathbb{R}\}$, Range $= \{y \mid y \leqslant \frac{25}{4}\}$
g Domain $= \{x \mid x \geqslant -4\}$, Range $= \{y \mid y \geqslant -3\}$
h Domain $= \{x \mid x \in \mathbb{R}\}$, Range $= \{y \mid y > -2\}$
i Domain $= \{x \mid x \neq \pm 2\}$,
Range $= \{y \mid y \leqslant -1 \text{ or } y > 0\}$

2 **a** $f(x)$ defined for $x \geqslant -6$, Domain $= \{x \mid x \geqslant -6\}$
b $f(x)$ defined for $x \neq 0$, Domain $= \{x \mid x \neq 0\}$
c $f(x)$ defined for $x < \frac{3}{2}$, Domain $= \{x \mid x < \frac{3}{2}\}$

3 **a** Domain $= \{x \mid x \in \mathbb{R}\}$, Range $= \{y \mid y \in \mathbb{R}\}$
b Domain $= \{x \mid x \in \mathbb{R}\}$, Range $= \{3\}$
c Domain $= \{x \mid x \geqslant 0\}$, Range $= \{y \mid y \geqslant 0\}$
d Domain $= \{x \mid x \neq -1\}$, Range $= \{y \mid y \neq 0\}$
e Domain $= \{x \mid x > 0\}$, Range $= \{y \mid y < 0\}$
f Domain $= \{x \mid x \neq 3\}$, Range $= \{y \mid y \neq 0\}$

4 **a** Domain $= \{x \mid x \geqslant 2\}$, Range $= \{y \mid y \geqslant 0\}$
b Domain $= \{x \mid x \neq 0\}$, Range $= \{y \mid y > 0\}$
c Domain $= \{x \mid x \leqslant 4\}$, Range $= \{y \mid y \geqslant 0\}$
d Domain $= \{x \mid x \in \mathbb{R}\}$, Range $= \{y \mid y \geqslant -2\frac{1}{4}\}$
e Domain $= \{x \mid x \in \mathbb{R}\}$, Range $= \{y \mid y \geqslant 2\}$
f Domain $= \{x \mid x \leqslant -2 \text{ or } x \geqslant 2\}$, Range $= \{y \mid y \geqslant 0\}$
g Domain $= \{x \mid x \in \mathbb{R}\}$, Range $= \{y \mid y \leqslant \frac{25}{12}\}$
h Domain $= \{x \mid x \neq 0\}$, Range $= \{y \mid y \leqslant -2 \text{ or } y \geqslant 2\}$
i Domain $= \{x \mid x \neq 2\}$, Range $= \{y \mid y \neq 1\}$
j Domain $= \{x \mid x \in \mathbb{R}\}$, Range $= \{y \mid y \in \mathbb{R}\}$
k Domain $= \{x \mid x \neq -1, \text{ and } x \neq 2\}$,
Range $= \{y \mid y \leqslant \frac{1}{3} \text{ or } y \geqslant 3\}$
l Domain $= \{x \mid x \neq 0\}$, Range $= \{y \mid y \geqslant 2\}$
m Domain $= \{x \mid x \neq 0\}$, Range $= \{y \mid y \leqslant -2 \text{ or } y \geqslant 2\}$
n Domain $= \{x \mid x \in \mathbb{R}\}$, Range $= \{y \mid y \geqslant -8\}$

EXERCISE 2D

1 **a** $5 - 2x$ **b** $-2x - 2$ **c** 11
2 **a** $4 + x$ **b** $5 - x$ **c** $1 - x$
3 **a** $25x - 42$ **b** $\sqrt{8}$ **c** -7
4 $f(g(x)) = (2 - x)^2$, $g(f(x)) = 2 - x^2$,
Domain $= \{x \mid x \in \mathbb{R}\}$,   Domain $= \{x \mid x \in \mathbb{R}\}$,
Range $= \{y \mid y \geqslant 0\}$ Range $= \{y \mid y \leqslant 2\}$

5 **a** **i** $x^2 - 6x + 10$ **ii** $2 - x^2$ **b** $x = \pm\frac{1}{\sqrt{2}}$

6 **a** Let $x = 0$, $\therefore$ $b = d$ and so
$ax + b = cx + b$
$\therefore$ $ax = cx$ for all x
Let $x = 1$, $\therefore$ $a = c$
b $(f \circ g)(x) = [2a]x + [2b + 3] = 1x + 0$ for all x
$\therefore$ $2a = 1$ and $2b + 3 = 0$
c Yes, $\{(g \circ f)(x) = [2a]x + [3a + b]\}$

7 **a** $(f \circ g)(x) = \sqrt{1 - x^2}$
b Domain $= \{x \mid -1 \leqslant x \leqslant 1\}$, Range $= \{y \mid 0 \leqslant y \leqslant 1\}$

EXERCISE 2E

1 **a** (number line: $-$ $+$ at 2)   **b** (number line: $-$ $+$ $-$ at -1, 3)

c (number line: $+$ $-$ $+$ at 0, 2)   **d** (number line: $+$ $+$ at 1)

e (number line: $-$ $-$ at -2)   **f** (number line: $+$ $-$ $+$ $-$ at -2, 0, 2)

g (number line: $-$ $+$ at 0)   **h** (number line: $+$ $+$ $+$ at -1, 2)

i (number line: $-$ $+$ $+$ $-$ at -3, 0, 4)   **j** (number line: $+$ $-$ $+$ at 1, 2)

k (number line: $-$ $+$ $-$ $+$ at -1, 0, 3)   **l** (number line: $-$ $+$ $-$ $+$ $-$ at -2, -1, 1, 2)

2 **a** (number line: $+$ $-$ $+$ at -4, 2)   **b** (number line: $+$ $-$ $+$ at 0, 3)

c (number line: $+$ $-$ $+$ at -2, 0)   **d** (number line: $-$ $+$ $-$ at -1, 3)

e (number line: $-$ $+$ $-$ at $\frac{1}{2}$, 3)   **f** (number line: $+$ $-$ $+$ at $\frac{1}{2}$, 5)

g (number line: $+$ $-$ $+$ at -3, 3)   **h** (number line: $-$ $+$ $-$ at -2, 2)

i (number line: $-$ $+$ $-$ at 0, 5)   **j** (number line: $+$ $-$ $+$ at 1, 2)

k (number line: $-$ $+$ $-$ at $-\frac{1}{2}$, $\frac{1}{2}$)   **l** (number line: $+$ $-$ $+$ at $-\frac{2}{3}$, $\frac{1}{2}$)

m (number line: $-$ $+$ $-$ at -3, $\frac{1}{3}$)   **n** (number line: $-$ $+$ $-$ at $-\frac{1}{2}$, 5)

o (number line: $-$ $+$ $-$ at $-\frac{2}{5}$, $\frac{1}{3}$)

3 a

```
  +      +
←——————————→ x
    -2
```

b
```
  +      +
←——————————→ x
      3
```

c
```
  -      -
←——————————→ x
    -2
```

d
```
  -      -
←——————————→ x
      4
```

e
```
  +      +
←——————————→ x
      1
```

f
```
  -      -
←——————————→ x
      2
```

g
```
  +      +
←——————————→ x
     ½
```

h
```
  -      -
←——————————→ x
     -3
```

i
```
  -      -
←——————————→ x
     3/2
```

4 a
```
  +  |  -  |  +
←——————————————→ x
   -2     1
```

b
```
  +  |  -  |  +
←——————————————→ x
   -3     0
```

c
```
  -  |  +  |  -
←——————————————→ x
  -3/2    4
```

d
```
  -  |  +  |  -
←——————————————→ x
   ¼     2
```

e
```
  +  |  -  |  +
←——————————————→ x
   0     2
```

f
```
  +  |  -  |  +
←——————————————→ x
   0     3
```

g
```
  -  |  +  |  +
←——————————————→ x
   0     1
```

h
```
  -  |  -  |  +
←——————————————→ x
  -1     0
```

i
```
  +  |  -  |  +  |  -
←——————————————————→ x
  -2   1   3
```

j
```
  +  |  -  |  +  |  -
←——————————————————→ x
   0   1   2
```

k
```
  +  |  -  |  +  |  -
←——————————————————→ x
  -2   0   2
```

l
```
  +  |  -  |  +  |  -
←——————————————————→ x
 -3/2  2   3
```

EXERCISE 2F

1 a i vertical asymptote $x = 2$, horizontal asymptote $y = 0$
ii Domain $= \{x \mid x \neq 2\}$, Range $= \{y \mid y \neq 0\}$
iii no x-intercept, y-intercept $-\frac{3}{2}$
iv as $x \to 2^-$, $y \to -\infty$ as $x \to \infty$, $y \to 0^+$
as $x \to 2^+$, $y \to \infty$ as $x \to -\infty$, $y \to 0^-$
v

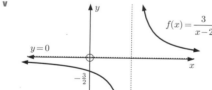

$$f(x) = \frac{3}{x-2}$$
$$y = 0$$
$$-\frac{3}{2}$$
$$x = 2$$

b i vertical asymptote $x = -1$, horizontal asymptote $y = 2$
ii Domain $= \{x \mid x \neq -1\}$, Range $= \{y \mid y \neq 2\}$
iii x-intercept $\frac{1}{2}$, y-intercept -1
iv as $x \to -1^-$, $y \to \infty$ as $x \to \infty$, $y \to 2^-$
as $x \to -1^+$, $y \to -\infty$ as $x \to -\infty$, $y \to 2^+$
v

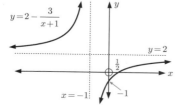

$$y = 2 - \frac{3}{x+1}$$
$$y = 2$$
$$\frac{1}{2}$$
$$x = -1$$
$$-1$$

c i vertical asymptote $x = 2$, horizontal asymptote $y = 1$
ii Domain $= \{x \mid x \neq 2\}$, Range $= \{y \mid y \neq 1\}$
iii x-intercept -3, y-intercept $-\frac{3}{2}$
iv as $x \to 2^-$, $y \to -\infty$ as $x \to \infty$, $y \to 1^+$
as $x \to 2^+$, $y \to \infty$ as $x \to -\infty$, $y \to 1^-$
v

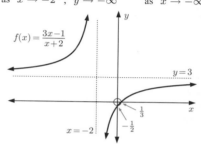

$$f(x) = \frac{x+3}{x-2}$$
$$y = 1$$
$$-3$$
$$-\frac{3}{2}$$
$$x = 2$$

d i vertical asymptote $x = -2$, horizontal asymptote $y = 3$
ii Domain $= \{x \mid x \neq -2\}$, Range $= \{y \mid y \neq 3\}$
iii x-intercept $\frac{1}{3}$, y-intercept $-\frac{1}{2}$
iv as $x \to -2^-$, $y \to \infty$ as $x \to \infty$, $y \to 3^-$
as $x \to -2^+$, $y \to -\infty$ as $x \to -\infty$, $y \to 3^+$
v

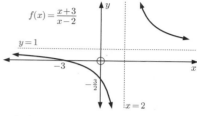

$$f(x) = \frac{3x-1}{x+2}$$
$$y = 3$$
$$\frac{1}{3}$$
$$-\frac{1}{2}$$
$$x = -2$$

2 a Domain $= \{x \mid x \neq -\frac{d}{c}\}$ **b** Vertical asymptote $= -\frac{d}{c}$
c Horizontal asymptote $= \frac{a}{c}$

EXERCISE 2G

1 a i

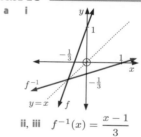

$$1$$
$$-\frac{1}{3}$$
$$-\frac{1}{3}$$
$$1$$
$$f^{-1}$$
$$y = x$$
$$f$$

ii, iii $f^{-1}(x) = \dfrac{x-1}{3}$

b i

$$\frac{1}{2}$$
$$-2$$
$$-\frac{1}{2}$$
$$-2$$
$$f$$
$$y = x \quad f^{-1}$$

ii, iii $f^{-1}(x) = 4x - 2$

2 a i $f^{-1}(x) = \dfrac{x-5}{2}$
ii

$$y = x$$
$$f$$
$$5$$
$$-\frac{5}{2}$$
$$-\frac{5}{2}$$
$$5$$
$$f^{-1}$$

b i $f^{-1}(x) = -2x + \dfrac{3}{2}$
ii

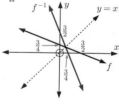

$$f^{-1}$$
$$y = x$$
$$\frac{3}{2}$$
$$\frac{3}{4}$$
$$\frac{3}{2}$$
$$\frac{3}{4}$$
$$f$$

c i $f^{-1}(x) = x - 3$
ii

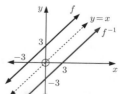

$$f$$
$$y = x$$
$$f^{-1}$$
$$3$$
$$-3$$
$$3$$
$$-3$$

3 a
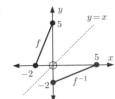

b

c
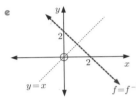

d

e
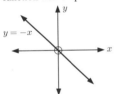

f

4 a $\{x \mid -2 \leqslant x \leqslant 0\}$ **b** $\{y \mid 0 \leqslant y \leqslant 5\}$
c $\{x \mid 0 \leqslant x \leqslant 5\}$ **d** $\{y \mid -2 \leqslant y \leqslant 0\}$

5 a f and f^{-1} are the same. They are self-inverse functions.
b For example, any linear function with slope $= -1$.
c For example, any of $y = \dfrac{a}{x}$, $a \in \mathbb{R}$, $a \neq 0, 1$.

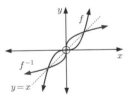

Note: There may be other answers.

Note: There may be other answers.

6 Range $= \{y \mid -2 \leqslant y < 3\}$

7 $f(x)$ is the same as $(f^{-1})^{-1}(x)$

8

9 $f^{-1}(x) = \dfrac{1}{x}$ and $f(x) = \dfrac{1}{x}$ $\therefore$ $f = f^{-1}$
$\therefore$ f is a self-inverse function

10 a $y = \dfrac{3x - 8}{x - 3}$ is symmetrical about $y = x$,
$\therefore$ f is a self-inverse function.
b $f^{-1}(x) = \dfrac{3x - 8}{x - 3}$ and $f(x) = \dfrac{3x - 8}{x - 3}$
$\therefore$ $f = f^{-1}$ $\therefore$ f is a self-inverse function

11 a $f^{-1}(x) = 2x + 2$
b i $(f \circ f^{-1})(x) = x$ **ii** $(f^{-1} \circ f)(x) = x$

12 a 10

b $f^{-1}(x) = \dfrac{x - 5}{2}$ and $f^{-1}(-3) = -4$
$g^{-1}(x) = 8 - 2x$ and $g^{-1}(6) = -4$
$\therefore$ $g^{-1}(6) - f^{-1}(-3) = 0$
c $x = 3$

13 a i 25   **ii** 16   **b** $x = 1$

14 $(f^{-1} \circ g^{-1})(x) = \dfrac{x + 3}{8}$ and $(g \circ f)^{-1}(x) = \dfrac{x + 3}{8}$

15 a Is not **b** Is **c** Is **d** Is **e** Is

16 a The inverse function must also be a function and must therefore satisfy the vertical line test, which it can only do if the original function satisfies the horizontal line test.
b i is the only one

REVIEW SET 2A

1 a i Domain $= \{x \mid x \in \mathbb{R}\}$ **ii** Range $= \{y \mid y > -4\}$
iii Yes
b i Domain $= \{x \mid x \in \mathbb{R}\}$ **ii** Range $= \{2\}$ **iii** Yes
c i Domain $= \{x \mid x \in \mathbb{R}\}$
ii Range $= \{y \mid y \leqslant -1$ or $y \geqslant 1\}$ **iii** No
d i Domain $= \{x \mid x \in \mathbb{R}\}$
ii Range $= \{y \mid -5 \leqslant y \leqslant 5\}$ **iii** Yes

2 a 0   **b** -15 **c** $-\dfrac{5}{4}$ **3** $a = -6$, $b = 13$

4 a $x^2 - x - 2$ **b** $x^4 - 7x^2 + 10$

5 a i Domain $= \{x \mid x \in \mathbb{R}\}$, Range $= \{y \mid y \geqslant -5\}$
ii x-int -1, 5, y-int $-\dfrac{25}{9}$ **iii** is a function
b i Domain $= \{x \mid x \in \mathbb{R}\}$, Range $= \{y \mid y = 1$ or $-3\}$
ii no x-intercepts, y-intercept 1   **iii** is a function

6 a
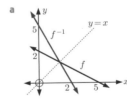

b

7 $a = 1$, $b = -1$

8 a
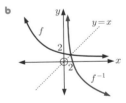

b

9 a $f^{-1}(x) = \dfrac{x - 2}{4}$ **b** $f^{-1}(x) = \dfrac{3 - 4x}{5}$

10 a $f(-3) = (-3)^2 = 9$ **b** 169   **c** $x = -4$
$g(-\tfrac{4}{3}) = 1 - 6(-\tfrac{4}{3}) = 9$

11 $(f^{-1} \circ h^{-1})(x) = (h \circ f)^{-1}(x) = x - 2$

REVIEW SET 2B

1 a Domain $= \{x \mid x \in \mathbb{R}\}$, Range $= \{y \mid y \geqslant -4\}$
b Domain $= \{x \mid x \neq 0, x \neq 2\}$,
Range $= \{y \mid y \leqslant -1$ or $y > 0\}$

2 a $2x^2 + 1$ **b** $4x^2 - 12x + 11$

3 a

b

4 a $x = 0$ **b**

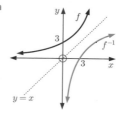

$y = \dfrac{1}{x^2}$

c Domain $= \{x \mid x \neq 0\}$, Range $= \{y \mid y > 0\}$

5 a $a = 2$, $b = -1$
   b Domain $= \{x \mid x \neq 2\}$, Range $= \{y \mid y \neq -1\}$

6 a vertical asymptote $x = 2$, horizontal asymptote $y = -4$
   b Domain $= \{x \mid x \neq 2\}$, Range $= \{y \mid y \neq -4\}$
   c as $x \to 2^-$, $y \to \infty$ as $x \to \infty$, $y \to -4^-$
      as $x \to 2^+$, $y \to -\infty$ as $x \to -\infty$, $y \to -4^+$
   d x-intercept $-\frac{1}{4}$, y-intercept $\frac{1}{2}$
   e

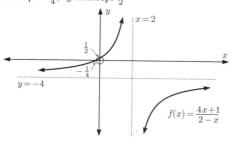

$x = 2$
$\frac{1}{2}$
$-\frac{1}{4}$
$y = -4$
$f(x) = \dfrac{4x+1}{2-x}$

7 a $(g \circ f)(x) = \dfrac{2}{3x+1}$ **b** $x = -\frac{1}{2}$
   c i vertical asymptote $x = -\frac{1}{3}$,
      horizontal asymptote $y = 0$
   ii

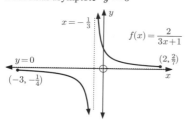

$x = -\frac{1}{3}$
$f(x) = \dfrac{2}{3x+1}$
$y = 0$
$(2, \frac{2}{7})$
$(-3, -\frac{1}{4})$

   iii Range $= \{y \mid y \leqslant -\frac{1}{4} \text{ or } y \geqslant \frac{2}{7}\}$

8 a   **b** $f^{-1}(x) = \dfrac{x+7}{2}$

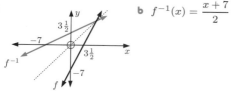

$3\frac{1}{2}$
-7
$3\frac{1}{2}$
f^{-1}
-7
f

9 a

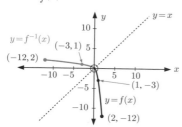

$y = x$
$y = f^{-1}(x)$ $(-3, 1)$
$(-12, 2)$
$(1, -3)$
$y = f(x)$
$(2, -12)$

   b Range $= \{y \mid 0 \leqslant y \leqslant 2\}$
   c i $x \approx -1.83$ **ii** $x = -3$

REVIEW SET 2C

1 a Domain $= \{x \mid x \geqslant -2\}$, Range $= \{y \mid 1 \leqslant y < 3\}$
   b Domain $= \{x \in \mathbb{R}\}$, Range $= \{y \mid y = -1, 1 \text{ or } 2\}$

2 a 12   **b** $x = \pm 1$ **3 a** $x = \frac{1}{2}$ **b** $x < -7$

4 a   **b**

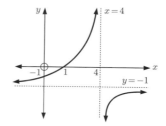

5 a $10 - 6x$ **b** $x = 2$ **6 a** $1 - 2\sqrt{x}$ **b** $\sqrt{1 - 2x}$

7 $a = 1$, $b = -6$, $c = 5$

8 a   **b**

9 a $f^{-1}(x) = \dfrac{7 - x}{4}$ **b** $f^{-1}(x) = \dfrac{5x - 3}{2}$

10 $(f^{-1} \circ h^{-1})(x) = (h \circ f)^{-1}(x) = \dfrac{4x + 6}{15}$ **11** 16

12

$x = 4$
-1 1 4
$y = -1$

EXERCISE 3A

1 a $2^1 = 2$, $2^2 = 4$, $2^3 = 8$, $2^4 = 16$, $2^5 = 32$, $2^6 = 64$
   b $3^1 = 3$, $3^2 = 9$, $3^3 = 27$, $3^4 = 81$, $3^5 = 243$,
      $3^6 = 729$
   c $4^1 = 4$, $4^2 = 16$, $4^3 = 64$, $4^4 = 256$, $4^5 = 1024$,
      $4^6 = 4096$

2 a $5^1 = 5$, $5^2 = 25$, $5^3 = 125$, $5^4 = 625$
   b $6^1 = 6$, $6^2 = 36$, $6^3 = 216$, $6^4 = 1296$
   c $7^1 = 7$, $7^2 = 49$, $7^3 = 343$, $7^4 = 2401$

3 a -1 **b** 1 **c** 1 **d** -1 **e** 1 **f** -1
   g -1 **h** -32 **i** -32 **j** -64 **k** 625 **l** -625

4 a $16\,384$ **b** 2401 **c** -3125 **d** -3125
   e $262\,144$ **f** $262\,144$ **g** $-262\,144$
   h $902.436\,039\,6$ **i** $-902.436\,039\,6$
   j $-902.436\,039\,6$

5 a $0.\overline{1}$ **b** $0.\overline{1}$ **c** $0.02\overline{7}$ **d** $0.02\overline{7}$
   e $0.012\,345\,679$ **f** $0.012\,345\,679$ **g** 1 **h** 1
   Notice that $a^{-n} = \dfrac{1}{a^n}$

6 3   **7** 7

EXERCISE 3B

1 a 5^{11} **b** d^8 **c** k^5 **d** $\frac{1}{7}$ **e** x^{10} **f** 3^{16}
   g p^{-4} **h** n^{12} **i** 5^{3t} **j** 7^{x+2} **k** 10^{3-q} **l** c^{4m}

2 a 2^2 **b** 2^{-2} **c** 2^3 **d** 2^{-3} **e** 2^5 **f** 2^{-5}
g 2^1 **h** 2^{-1} **i** 2^6 **j** 2^{-6} **k** 2^7 **l** 2^{-7}

3 a 3^2 **b** 3^{-2} **c** 3^3 **d** 3^{-3} **e** 3^1 **f** 3^{-1}
g 3^4 **h** 3^{-4} **i** 3^0 **j** 3^5 **k** 3^{-5}

4 a 2^{a+1} **b** 2^{b+2} **c** 2^{t+3} **d** 2^{2x+2} **e** 2^{n-1}
f 2^{c-2} **g** 2^{2m} **h** 2^{n+1} **i** 2^1 **j** 2^{3x-1}

5 a 3^{p+2} **b** 3^{3a} **c** 3^{2n+1} **d** 3^{d+3} **e** 3^{3t+2}
f 3^{y-1} **g** 3^{1-y} **h** 3^{2-3t} **i** 3^{3a-1} **j** 3^3

6 a $4a^2$ **b** $27b^3$ **c** a^4b^4 **d** p^3q^3 **e** $\dfrac{m^2}{n^2}$
f $\dfrac{a^3}{27}$ **g** $\dfrac{b^4}{c^4}$ **h** $1, b \neq 0$ **i** $\dfrac{m^4}{81n^4}$ **j** $\dfrac{x^3y^3}{8}$

7 a $4a^2$ **b** $36b^4$ **c** $-8a^3$ **d** $-27m^6n^6$
e $16a^4b^{16}$ **f** $\dfrac{-8a^6}{b^6}$ **g** $\dfrac{16a^6}{b^2}$ **h** $\dfrac{9p^4}{q^6}$

8 a $\dfrac{a}{b^2}$ **b** $\dfrac{1}{a^2b^2}$ **c** $\dfrac{4a^2}{b^2}$ **d** $\dfrac{9b^2}{a^4}$ **e** $\dfrac{a^2}{bc^2}$
f $\dfrac{a^2c^2}{b}$ **g** a^3 **h** $\dfrac{b^3}{a^2}$ **i** $\dfrac{2}{ad^2}$ **j** $12am^3$

9 a a^{-n} **b** b^n **c** 3^{n-2} **d** a^nb^m **e** a^{-2n-2}

10 a 1 **b** $\dfrac{4}{7}$ **c** 6 **d** 27 **e** $\dfrac{9}{16}$ **f** $\dfrac{5}{2}$
g $\dfrac{27}{125}$ **h** $\dfrac{151}{5}$

11 a 3^{-2} **b** 2^{-4} **c** 5^{-3} **d** $3^1 \times 5^{-1}$ **e** $2^2 \times 3^{-3}$
f $2^{c-3} \times 3^{-2}$ **g** $3^{2k} \times 2^{-1} \times 5^{-1}$ **h** $2^p \times 3^{p-1} \times 5^{-2}$

12 a $5^3 = 21 + 23 + 25 + 27 + 29$
b $7^3 = 43 + 45 + 47 + 49 + 51 + 53 + 55$
c $12^3 = 133 + 135 + 137 + 139 + 141 + 143 + 145 + 147$
$+ 149 + 151 + 153 + 155$

EXERCISE 3C

1 a $2^{\frac{1}{5}}$ **b** $2^{-\frac{1}{5}}$ **c** $2^{\frac{3}{2}}$ **d** $2^{\frac{5}{2}}$ **e** $2^{-\frac{1}{3}}$
f $2^{\frac{4}{3}}$ **g** $2^{\frac{3}{2}}$ **h** $2^{\frac{3}{2}}$ **i** $2^{-\frac{4}{3}}$ **j** $2^{-\frac{3}{2}}$

2 a $3^{\frac{1}{3}}$ **b** $3^{-\frac{1}{3}}$ **c** $3^{\frac{1}{4}}$ **d** $3^{\frac{3}{2}}$ **e** $3^{-\frac{5}{2}}$

3 a $7^{\frac{1}{3}}$ **b** $3^{\frac{3}{4}}$ **c** $2^{\frac{4}{5}}$ **d** $2^{\frac{5}{3}}$ **e** $7^{\frac{2}{7}}$
f $7^{-\frac{1}{3}}$ **g** $3^{-\frac{3}{4}}$ **h** $2^{-\frac{4}{5}}$ **i** $2^{-\frac{5}{3}}$ **j** $7^{-\frac{2}{7}}$

4 a 2.28 **b** 1.83 **c** 0.794 **d** 0.435 **e** 1.68
f 1.93 **g** 0.523

5 a 8 **b** 32 **c** 8 **d** 125 **e** 4
f $\dfrac{1}{2}$ **g** $\dfrac{1}{27}$ **h** $\dfrac{1}{16}$ **i** $\dfrac{1}{81}$ **j** $\dfrac{1}{25}$

EXERCISE 3D.1

1 a $x^5 + 2x^4 + x^2$ **b** $4^x + 2^x$ **c** $x + 1$
d $49^x + 2(7^x)$ **e** $2(3^x) - 1$ **f** $x^2 + 2x + 3$
g $1 + 5(2^{-x})$ **h** $5^x + 1$ **i** $x^{\frac{3}{2}} + x^{\frac{1}{2}} + 1$

2 a $4^x + 2^{x+1} - 3$ **b** $9^x + 7(3^x) + 10$
c $25^x - 6(5^x) + 8$ **d** $4^x + 6(2^x) + 9$
e $9^x - 2(3^x) + 1$ **f** $16^x + 14(4^x) + 49$
g $x - 4$ **h** $4^x - 9$ **i** $x - x^{-1}$ **j** $x^2 + 4 + \dfrac{4}{x^2}$
k $7^{2x} - 2 + 7^{-2x}$ **l** $25 - 10(2^{-x}) + 4^{-x}$

EXERCISE 3D.2

1 a $5^x(5^x + 1)$ **b** $10(3^n)$ **c** $7^n(1 + 7^{2n})$
d $5(5^n - 1)$ **e** $6(6^{n+1} - 1)$ **f** $16(4^n - 1)$

2 a $(3^x + 2)(3^x - 2)$ **b** $(2^x + 5)(2^x - 5)$ **c** $(4 + 3^x)(4 - 3^x)$
d $(5 + 2^x)(5 - 2^x)$ **e** $(3^x + 2^x)(3^x - 2^x)$ **f** $(2^x + 3)^2$
g $(3^x + 5)^2$ **h** $(2^x - 7)^2$ **i** $(5^x - 2)^2$

3 a $(2^x + 3)(2^x + 6)$ **b** $(2^x + 4)(2^x - 5)$
c $(3^x + 2)(3^x + 7)$ **d** $(3^x + 5)(3^x - 1)$
e $(5^x + 2)(5^x - 1)$ **f** $(7^x - 4)(7^x - 3)$

4 a 2^n **b** 10^a **c** 3^b **d** $\dfrac{1}{5^n}$ **e** 5^x
f $(\tfrac{3}{4})^a$ **g** 5 **h** 5^n

5 a $3^m + 1$ **b** $1 + 6^n$ **c** $4^n + 2^n$ **d** $4^x - 1$
e 6^n **f** 5^n **g** 4 **h** $2^n - 1$ **i** $\dfrac{1}{2}$

6 a $n2^{n+1}$ **b** -3^{n-1}

EXERCISE 3E

1 a $x = 3$ **b** $x = 2$ **c** $x = 4$ **d** $x = 0$
e $x = -1$ **f** $x = \frac{1}{2}$ **g** $x = -3$ **h** $x = 2$
i $x = -3$ **j** $x = -4$ **k** $x = 2$ **l** $x = 1$

2 a $x = \frac{5}{3}$ **b** $x = -\frac{3}{2}$ **c** $x = -\frac{3}{2}$ **d** $x = -\frac{1}{2}$
e $x = -\frac{2}{3}$ **f** $x = -\frac{5}{4}$ **g** $x = \frac{3}{2}$ **h** $x = \frac{5}{2}$
i $x = \frac{1}{8}$ **j** $x = \frac{9}{2}$ **k** $x = -4$ **l** $x = -4$
m $x = 0$ **n** $x = \frac{7}{2}$ **o** $x = -2$ **p** $x = -6$

3 a $x = \frac{1}{7}$ **b** has no solutions **c** $x = 2\frac{1}{2}$

4 a $x = 3$ **b** $x = 3$ **c** $x = 2$
d $x = 2$ **e** $x = -2$ **f** $x = -2$

5 a $x = 1$ or 2 **b** $x = 1$ **c** $x = 1$ or 2
d $x = 1$ **e** $x = 2$ **f** $x = 0$

EXERCISE 3F

1 a 1.4 **b** 1.7 **c** 2.8 **d** 0.4

2 a $x \approx 1.6$ **b** $x \approx -0.7$

3 $y = 2^x$ has a horizontal asymptote of $y = 0$

4 a
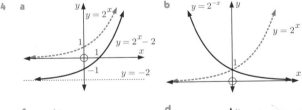

b

c
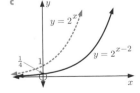

d
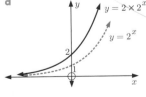

5 a
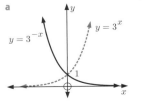

b
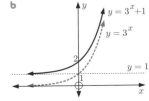

c

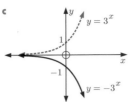

$y = 3^x$

$y = -3^x$

d

$y = 3^x$

$y = 3^{x-1}$

$\frac{1}{3}$

2 a 50

b **i** 76
ii 141
iii 400

c

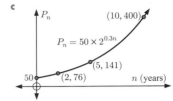

$P_n = 50 \times 2^{0.3n}$

$(10, 400)$

$(5, 141)$

$(2, 76)$

n (years)

3 a 12 bears   **b** 146 bears   **c** 248% increase

4 a **i** V_0 **ii** $2V_0$ **b** 100%
c 183% increase, it is the percentage increase at $50°C$ compared with $20°C$

6 a i

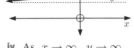

$y = 2^x + 1$

$y = 1$

ii Domain: $\{x \mid x \in \mathbb{R}\}$
Range: $\{y \mid y > 1\}$
iii $y \approx 3.67$

iv As $x \to \infty$, $y \to \infty$
As $x \to -\infty$, $y \to 1$ from above
v $y = 1$

b i

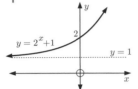

$y = 2$

$y = 2 - 2^x$

ii Domain: $\{x \mid x \in \mathbb{R}\}$
Range: $\{y \mid y < 2\}$
iii $y \approx -0.665$

iv As $x \to \infty$, $y \to -\infty$
As $x \to -\infty$, $y \to 2$ from below
v $y = 2$

c i

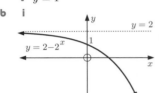

$y = 2^{-x} + 3$

$y = 3$

ii Domain: $\{x \mid x \in \mathbb{R}\}$
Range: $\{y \mid y > 3\}$
iii $y \approx 3.38$

iv As $x \to \infty$, $y \to 3$ from above
As $x \to -\infty$, $y \to \infty$
v $y = 3$

d i

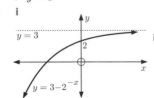

$y = 3$

$y = 3 - 2^{-x}$

ii Domain: $\{x \mid x \in \mathbb{R}\}$
Range: $\{y \mid y < 3\}$
iii $y \approx 2.63$

iv As $x \to \infty$, $y \to 3$ from below
As $x \to -\infty$, $y \to -\infty$
v $y = 3$

EXERCISE 3G.2

1 a 250 g   **b** **i** 112 g   **ii** 50.4 g   **iii** 22.6 g
c   **d** ≈ 346 years

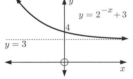

$W(t)$

$W(t) = 250 \times (0.998)^t$

$(400, 112)$

$(800, 50.4)$

$(1200, 22.6)$

t

2 a $100°C$ **c**

b **i** $81.2°C$
ii $75.8°C$
iii $33.9°C$

$T(t)$

$T(t) = 100 \times 2^{-0.02t}$

$(20, 75.8)$

$(78, 33.9)$

$(15, 81.2)$

t (min)

3 a **i** $22°C$ **b**
ii $6°C$
iii $-2°C$
iv $-6°C$

$T(t)$

$T(t) = -10 + 32 \times 2^{-0.2t}$

$(5, 6)$ $(15, -6)$

$(10, -2)$ t (min)

c Never, since $32 \times 2^{-0.2t}$ is always > 0

4 a 1000 g   **c**
b **i** 812 g
ii 125 g
iii 9.31×10^{-7} g
d 221 years
e $1000(1 - 2^{-0.03t})$ g

W_t (grams)

$(10, 812)$

$W_t = 1000 \times 2^{-0.03t}$

$(100, 125)$

t (years)

5 a W_0 **b** 12.9%   **c** 45 000 years

EXERCISE 3H

1 The graph of $y = e^x$ lies between $y = 2^x$ and $y = 3^x$.

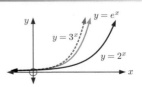

$y = e^x$

$y = 3^x$

$y = 2^x$

EXERCISE 3G.1

1 a 100 grams   **c**
b **i** 132 g
ii 200 g
iii 528 g

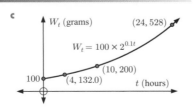

W_t (grams) $(24, 528)$

$W_t = 100 \times 2^{0.1t}$

$(10, 200)$

$(4, 132.0)$ t (hours)

2 One is the other reflected in the y-axis.

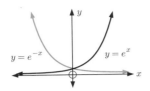

3 a

4 a $e^x > 0$ for all x
  b i 0.000 000 004 12   ii 970 000 000

5 a ≈ 7.39 b ≈ 20.1 c ≈ 2.01 d ≈ 1.65
  e ≈ 0.368

6 a $e^{\frac{1}{2}}$ b $e^{-\frac{1}{2}}$ c e^{-2} d $e^{\frac{3}{2}}$

7 a $e^{0.18t}$ b $e^{0.004t}$ c $e^{-0.005t}$ d $\approx e^{-0.167t}$

8 a 10.074 b 0.099 261 c 125.09 d 0.007 994 5
  e 41.914 f 42.429 g 3540.3 h 0.006 342 4

9

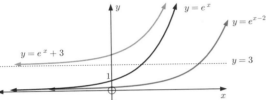

Domain of f, g, and h is $\{x \mid x \in \mathbb{R}\}$
Range of f is $\{y \mid y > 0\}$, Range of g is $\{y \mid y > 0\}$
Range of h is $\{y \mid y > 3\}$

10

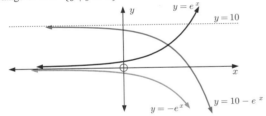

Domain of f, g, and h is $\{x \mid x \in \mathbb{R}\}$
Range of f is $\{y \mid y > 0\}$, Range of g is $\{y \mid y < 0\}$
Range of h is $\{y \mid y < 10\}$

11 a $e^{2x} + 2e^x + 1$ b $1 - e^{2x}$ c $1 - 3e^x$

12 a i 2 g
    ii 2.57 g
    iii 4.23 g
    iv 40.2 g
  b

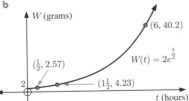

13 a $x = \frac{1}{2}$ b $x = -4$

14 a i 64.6 amps b
    ii 16.7 amps
  c 28.8 seconds

15 a $f^{-1}(x) = \log_e x$

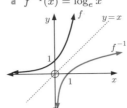

  b Domain of f^{-1} is $\{x \mid x > 0\}$,
    Range of f^{-1} is $\{y \mid y \in \mathbb{R}\}$

REVIEW SET 3A

1 a -1 b 27 c $\frac{2}{3}$ **2** a $a^6 b^7$ b $\dfrac{2}{3x}$ c $\dfrac{y^2}{5}$

3 a i 81 ii $\frac{1}{3}$ b $k = 9$

4 a $\dfrac{1}{x^5}$ b $\dfrac{2}{a^2 b^2}$ c $\dfrac{2a}{b^2}$ **5** a 3^{3-2a} b $3^{\frac{5}{2} - \frac{9}{2}x}$

6 a 4 b $\frac{1}{9}$ **7** a $\dfrac{m}{n^2}$ b $\dfrac{1}{m^3 n^3}$ c $\dfrac{m^2 p^2}{n}$ d $\dfrac{16 n^2}{m^2}$

8 a $9 - 6e^x + e^{2x}$ b $x - 4$ c $2^x + 1$

9 a $x = -2$ b $x = \frac{3}{4}$ c $x = -\frac{1}{4}$

10 a **C** b **E** c **A** d **B** e **D**

11 a y^2 b y^{-1} c $\dfrac{1}{\sqrt{y}}$ (or $y^{-\frac{1}{2}}$)

REVIEW SET 3B

1 a 2^{n+2} b $-\frac{6}{7}$ c $3\frac{3}{8}$ d $\dfrac{4}{a^2 b^4}$

2 a 2.28 b 0.517 c 3.16 **3** a 3 b 24 c $\frac{3}{4}$

4 a $\frac{1}{\sqrt{2}} + 1 \approx 1.71$ **5**
  b $a = -1$

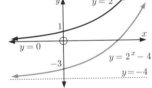

6 a 80°C c
  b i 26.8°C
    ii 9.00°C
    iii 3.02°C
  d ≈ 12.8 min

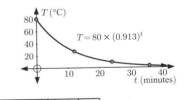

7 a

x	-2	-1	0	1	2
y	$-4\frac{8}{9}$	$-4\frac{2}{3}$	-4	-2	4

  b as $x \to \infty$, c
    $y \to \infty$;
    as $x \to -\infty$,
    $y \to -5$ (above)
  d $y = -5$

8 a

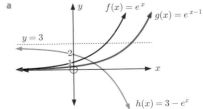

b Domain of f, g, and h is $\{x \mid x \in \mathbb{R}\}$
Range of f is $\{y \mid y > 0\}$, Range of g is $\{y \mid y > 0\}$,
Range of h is $\{y \mid y < 3\}$

9 **a**

x	-2	-1	0	1	2
y	-1	1	2	$2\frac{1}{2}$	$2\frac{3}{4}$

b as $x \to \infty$, $y \to 3$ (below); as $x \to -\infty$, $y \to -\infty$
c   **d** $y = 3$

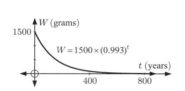

$y = 3$

$y = 3 - 2^{-x}$

10 **a** 1500 g   **c**
b **i** 90.3 g
ii 5.44 g
d 386 years

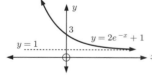

W (grams)

1500

$W = 1500 \times (0.993)^t$

t (years)

400   800

REVIEW SET 3C

1 **a** $x \approx 1.5$ **b** $x \approx -0.6$ **c** $x \approx 1.1$

2 **a** a^{21} **b** $p^4 q^6$ **c** $\dfrac{4b}{a^3}$

3 **a** 2^{-3} **b** 2^7 **c** 2^{12} **4** **a** $\dfrac{1}{b^3}$ **b** $\dfrac{1}{ab}$ **c** $\dfrac{a}{b}$

5 2^{2x} **6** **a** 5^0 **b** $5^{\frac{3}{2}}$ **c** $5^{-\frac{1}{4}}$ **d** 5^{2a+6}

7 **a** $1 + e^{2x}$ **b** $2^{2x} + 10(2^x) + 25$ **c** $x - 49$

8 **a** $x = 5$ **b** $x = -4$ **9** $k = \frac{3}{2}$

10 **a** $x = 4$ **b** $x = -\frac{2}{5}$

11 **a**

x	-2	-1	0	1	2
y	15.8	6.44	3	1.74	1.27

b as $x \to \infty$, $y \to 1$ (above); as $x \to -\infty$, $y \to \infty$
c   **d** $y = 1$

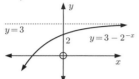

y

3

$y = 2e^{-x} + 1$

$y = 1$

x

EXERCISE 4A

1 **a** 4   **b** -3 **c** 1   **d** 0   **e** $\frac{1}{2}$ **f** $\frac{1}{3}$
g $-\frac{1}{4}$ **h** $1\frac{1}{2}$ **i** $\frac{2}{3}$ **j** $1\frac{1}{2}$ **k** $1\frac{1}{3}$ **l** $3\frac{1}{2}$

2 **a** n **b** $a + 2$ **c** $1 - m$ **d** $a - b$

3 **a** $10^{0.7782}$ **b** $10^{1.7782}$ **c** $10^{3.7782}$ **d** $10^{-0.2218}$
e $10^{-2.2218}$ **f** $10^{1.1761}$ **g** $10^{3.1761}$ **h** $10^{0.1761}$
i $10^{-0.8239}$ **j** $10^{-3.8239}$

4 **a** **i** 0.477   **ii** 2.477   **b** $\log 300 = \log(3 \times 10^2)$

5 **a** **i** 0.699   **ii** -1.301 **b** $\log 0.05 = \log(5 \times 10^{-2})$

6 **a** $x = 100$ **b** $x = 10$ **c** $x = 1$
d $x = \frac{1}{10}$ **e** $x = 10^{\frac{1}{2}}$ **f** $x = 10^{-\frac{1}{2}}$
g $x = 10\,000$ **h** $x = 0.000\,01$ **i** $x \approx 6.84$
j $x \approx 140$ **k** $x \approx 0.0419$ **l** $x \approx 0.000\,631$

EXERCISE 4B

1 **a** $10^2 = 100$ **b** $10^4 = 10\,000$ **c** $10^{-1} = 0.1$
d $10^{\frac{1}{2}} = \sqrt{10}$ **e** $2^3 = 8$ **f** $3^2 = 9$
g $2^{-2} = \frac{1}{4}$ **h** $3^{1.5} = \sqrt{27}$ **i** $5^{-\frac{1}{2}} = \frac{1}{\sqrt{5}}$

2 **a** $\log_2 4 = 2$ **b** $\log_4 64 = 3$ **c** $\log_5 25 = 2$
d $\log_7 49 = 2$ **e** $\log_2 64 = 6$ **f** $\log_2(\frac{1}{8}) = -3$
g $\log_{10} 0.01 = -2$ **h** $\log_2(\frac{1}{2}) = -1$ **i** $\log_3(\frac{1}{27}) = -3$

3 **a** 5   **b** -2 **c** $\frac{1}{2}$ **d** 3   **e** 6   **f** 7   **g** 2
h 3   **i** -3 **j** $\frac{1}{2}$ **k** 2   **l** $\frac{1}{2}$ **m** 5   **n** $\frac{1}{3}$
o n, $a > 0$ **p** $\frac{1}{3}$ **q** -1, $t > 0$ **r** $\frac{3}{2}$ **s** 0
t 1

4 **a** ≈ 2.18 **b** ≈ 1.40 **c** ≈ 1.87 **d** ≈ -0.0969

5 **a** $x = 8$ **b** $x = 2$ **c** $x = 3$ **d** $x = 14$

6 **a** 2   **b** 2   **c** -1 **d** $\frac{3}{4}$ **e** $-\frac{1}{2}$ **f** $\frac{5}{2}$
g $-\frac{3}{2}$ **h** $-\frac{3}{4}$ **i** 2, $x > 0$ **j** $\frac{1}{2}$, $x > 0$
k 3, $m > 0$ **l** $\frac{3}{2}$, $x > 0$ **m** -1, $n > 0$
n -2, $a > 0$ **o** $-\frac{1}{2}$, $a > 0$ **p** $\frac{5}{2}$, $m > 0$

EXERCISE 4C.1

1 **a** $\log 16$ **b** $\log 20$ **c** $\log 8$ **d** $\log \dfrac{p}{m}$
e 1   **f** $\log 2$ **g** $\log 24$ **h** $\log_2 6$
i $\log 0.4$ **j** 1   **k** $\log 200$
l $\log(10^t \times w)$ **m** $\log_m\left(\dfrac{40}{m^2}\right)$ **n** 0
o $\log(0.005)$ **p** $\log_5(\frac{5}{2})$ **q** 2   **r** $\log 28$

2 **a** $\log 96$ **b** $\log 72$ **c** $\log 8$ **d** $\log_3(\frac{25}{8})$
e 1   **f** $\log \frac{1}{2}$ **g** $\log 20$ **h** $\log 25$
i $\log_n\left(\dfrac{n^2}{10}\right)$

3 **a** 2   **b** $\frac{3}{2}$ **c** 3   **d** $\frac{1}{2}$ **e** -2 **f** $-\frac{3}{2}$

4 For example, for **a**, $\log 9 = \log 3^2 = 2 \log 3$

5 **a** $p + q$ **b** $2q + r$ **c** $2p + 3q$ **d** $r + \frac{1}{2}q - p$
e $r - 5p$ **f** $p - 2q$

6 **a** $x + z$ **b** $z + 2y$ **c** $x + z - y$ **d** $2x + \frac{1}{2}y$
e $3y - \frac{1}{2}z$ **f** $2z + \frac{1}{2}y - 3x$

7 **a** 0.86   **b** 2.15   **c** 1.075

EXERCISE 4C.2

1 **a** $\log y = x \log 2$ **b** $\log y \approx 1.30 + 3 \log b$
c $\log M = \log a + 4 \log d$ **d** $\log T \approx 0.699 + \frac{1}{2} \log d$
e $\log R = \log b + \frac{1}{2} \log l$ **f** $\log Q = \log a - n \log b$
g $\log y = \log a + x \log b$ **h** $\log F \approx 1.30 - \frac{1}{2} \log n$
i $\log L = \log a + \log b - \log c$ **j** $\log N = \frac{1}{2} \log a - \frac{1}{2} \log b$
k $\log S \approx 2.30 + t \log 2$ **l** $\log y = m \log a - n \log b$

2 **a** $D = 2e$ **b** $F = \dfrac{5}{t}$ **c** $P = \sqrt{x}$ **d** $M = b^2 c$
e $B = \dfrac{m^3}{n^2}$ **f** $N = \dfrac{1}{\sqrt[3]{p}}$ **g** $P = 10x^3$ **h** $Q = \dfrac{a^2}{x}$

3 a $\log_2 y = \log_2 3 + x$ **b** $x = \log_2\left(\dfrac{y}{3}\right)$

c i $x = 0$ **ii** $x = 2$ **iii** $x \approx 3.32$

4 a $x = 9$ **b** $x = 2$ or 4 **c** $x = 25\sqrt{5}$
d $x = 200$ **e** $x = 5$ **f** $x = 3$

EXERCISE 4D.1

1 a 2 **b** 3 **c** $\frac{1}{2}$ **d** 0 **e** -1 **f** $\frac{1}{3}$ **g** -2
h $-\frac{1}{2}$

2 a 3 **b** 9 **c** $\frac{1}{5}$ **d** $\frac{1}{4}$

3 x does not exist such that $e^x = -2$ or 0

4 a a **b** $a+1$ **c** $a+b$ **d** ab **e** $a-b$

5 a $e^{1.7918}$ **b** $e^{4.0943}$ **c** $e^{8.6995}$ **d** $e^{-0.5108}$
e $e^{-5.1160}$ **f** $e^{2.7081}$ **g** $e^{7.3132}$ **h** $e^{0.4055}$
i $e^{-1.8971}$ **j** $e^{-8.8049}$

6 a $x \approx 20.1$ **b** $x \approx 2.72$ **c** $x = 1$
d $x \approx 0.368$ **e** $x \approx 0.006\,74$ **f** $x \approx 2.30$
g $x \approx 8.54$ **h** $x \approx 0.037\,0$

EXERCISE 4D.2

1 a $\ln 45$ **b** $\ln 5$ **c** $\ln 4$ **d** $\ln 24$
e $\ln 1 = 0$ **f** $\ln 30$ **g** $\ln(4e)$ **h** $\ln\left(\frac{6}{e}\right)$
i $\ln 20$ **j** $\ln(4e^2)$ **k** $\ln\left(\frac{20}{e^2}\right)$ **l** $\ln 1 = 0$

2 a $\ln 972$ **b** $\ln 200$ **c** $\ln 1 = 0$ **d** $\ln 16$ **e** $\ln 6$
f $\ln\left(\frac{1}{3}\right)$ **g** $\ln\left(\frac{1}{2}\right)$ **h** $\ln 2$ **i** $\ln 16$

3 For example, for **a**, $\ln 27 = \ln 3^3 = 3\ln 3$

4 Hint: In **d**, $\ln\left(\dfrac{e^2}{8}\right) = \ln e^2 - \ln 2^3$

5 a $D = ex$ **b** $F = \dfrac{e^2}{p}$ **c** $P = \sqrt{x}$

d $M = e^3 y^2$ **e** $B = \dfrac{t^3}{e}$ **f** $N = \dfrac{1}{\sqrt[3]{g}}$

g $Q \approx 8.66 x^3$ **h** $D \approx 0.518 n^{0.4}$

EXERCISE 4E

1 a $x = \dfrac{1}{\log 2}$ **b** $x = \dfrac{\log 20}{\log 3}$ **c** $x = \dfrac{2}{\log 4}$

d $x = 4$ **e** $x = -\dfrac{1}{\log(\frac{3}{4})}$ **f** $x = -5$

2 a $x = \ln 10$ **b** $x = \ln 1000$ **c** $x = \ln 0.15$
d $x = 2\ln 5$ **e** $x = \frac{1}{2}\ln 18$ **f** $x = 0$

3 a $t = \dfrac{\log R - \log 200}{0.25\log 2}$ **b i** $t \approx 6.34$ **ii** $t \approx 11.3$

4 a $x = \dfrac{\log M - \log 20}{-0.02\log 5}$ **b i** $x = -50$ **ii** $x \approx -76.1$

5 a $x = -\dfrac{\log(0.03)}{\log 2}$ **b** $x = \dfrac{10\log\left(\frac{10}{3}\right)}{\log 5}$

c $x = \dfrac{-4\log\left(\frac{1}{8}\right)}{\log 3}$ **d** $x = \frac{1}{2}\ln 42$

e $x = -\frac{100}{3}\ln(0.001)$ **f** $x = \frac{10}{3}\ln\left(\frac{27}{41}\right)$

6 a $x = \ln 2$ **b** $x = 0$ **c** $x = \ln 2$ or $\ln 3$ **d** $x = 0$
e $x = \ln 4$ **f** $x = \ln\left(\dfrac{3+\sqrt{5}}{2}\right)$ or $\ln\left(\dfrac{3-\sqrt{5}}{2}\right)$

7 a $(\ln 3,\, 3)$ **b** $(\ln 2,\, 5)$ **c** $(0,\, 2)$ and $(\ln 5,\, -2)$

EXERCISE 4F

1 a ≈ 2.26 **b** ≈ -10.3 **c** ≈ -2.46 **d** ≈ 5.42

2 a $x \approx -4.29$ **b** $x \approx 3.87$ **c** $x \approx 0.139$

3 a $x = \dfrac{\log 3}{\log 5}$ **b** $x = \dfrac{\log\left(\frac{1}{8}\right)}{\log 3}$ **c** $x = -1$ **4** $x = 16$

EXERCISE 4G

1 a i domain is
$\{x \mid x > -1\}$,
range is
$\{y \mid y \in \mathbb{R}\}$
ii VA is $x = -1$,
x and y-intercepts 0
iv $x = -\frac{2}{3}$
v $f^{-1}(x) = 3^x - 1$

iii
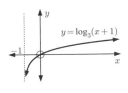

b i domain is
$\{x \mid x > -1\}$,
range is
$\{y \mid y \in \mathbb{R}\}$
ii VA is $x = -1$,
x-intercept 2,
y-intercept 1
iv $x = 8$
v $f^{-1}(x) = 3^{1-x} - 1$

iii
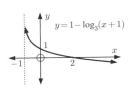

c i domain is
$\{x \mid x > 2\}$,
range is
$\{y \mid y \in \mathbb{R}\}$
ii VA is $x = 2$,
x-intercept 27,
no y-intercept
iv $x = 7$
v $f^{-1}(x) = 5^{2+x} + 2$

iii
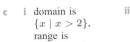

d i domain is
$\{x \mid x > 2\}$,
range is
$\{y \mid y \in \mathbb{R}\}$
ii VA is $x = 2$,
x-intercept 7,
no y-intercept
iv $x = 27$
v $f^{-1}(x) = 5^{1-x} + 2$

iii

e i domain is
$\{x \mid x > 0\}$,
range is
$\{y \mid y \in \mathbb{R}\}$
ii VA is $x = 0$,
x-intercepts $\pm\sqrt{2}$,
no y-intercept
iv $x = \pm 2$
v $f^{-1}(x) = 2^{\frac{1-x}{2}}$

iii
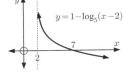

2 a i $f^{-1}(x)$
$= \ln(x - 5)$
iii domain of f is
$\{x \mid x \in \mathbb{R}\}$,
range is $\{y \mid y > 5\}$
domain of f^{-1} is
$\{x \mid x > 5\}$,
range is $\{y \mid y \in \mathbb{R}\}$

ii
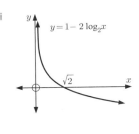

iv f has a HA $y = 5$, f has y-int 6
  f^{-1} has a VA $x = 5$, f^{-1} has x-int 6

b i $f^{-1}(x)$
      $= \ln(x+3) - 1$

   ii
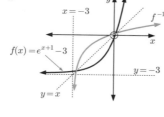

   iii domain of f is
       $\{x \mid x \in \mathbb{R}\}$,
       range is
       $\{y \mid y > -3\}$
       domain of f^{-1} is
       $\{x \mid x > -3\}$,
       range is
       $\{y \mid y \in \mathbb{R}\}$

   iv f has a HA $y = -3$, x-int $\ln 3 - 1$, y-int $e - 3$
      f^{-1} has a VA $x = -3$, x-int $e - 3$, y-int $\ln 3 - 1$

c i $f^{-1}(x)$
      $= e^{x+4}$

   ii
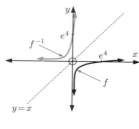

   iii domain of f is
       $\{x \mid x > 0\}$,
       range of f is
       $\{y \mid y \in \mathbb{R}\}$
       domain of f^{-1} is
       $\{x \mid x \in \mathbb{R}\}$,
       range is
       $\{y \mid y > 0\}$

   iv f has a VA $x = 0$, x-int e^4
      f^{-1} has a HA $y = 0$, y-int e^4

d i $f^{-1}(x)$
      $= 1 + e^{x-2}$

   ii
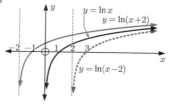

   iii domain of f is
       $\{x \mid x > 1\}$,
       range is
       $\{y \mid y \in \mathbb{R}\}$
       domain of f^{-1} is
       $\{x \mid x \in \mathbb{R}\}$,
       range is $\{y \mid y > 1\}$

   iv f has a VA $x = 1$,
      x-int $1 + e^{-2}$
      f^{-1} has a HA $y = 1$,
      y-int $1 + e^{-2}$

3 $f^{-1}(x) = \frac{1}{2}\ln x$

   a $(f^{-1} \circ g)(x) = \frac{1}{2}\ln(2x-1)$

   b $(g \circ f)^{-1}(x) = \frac{1}{2}\ln\left(\dfrac{x+1}{2}\right)$

4 a A is $y = \ln x$
      as its x-intercept
      is 1
   c $y = \ln x$ has
      VA $x = 0$
      $y = \ln(x - 2)$
      has VA $x = 2$
      $y = \ln(x + 2)$
      has VA $x = -2$

   b
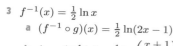

5 $y = \ln(x^2) = 2\ln x$, so she is correct.
   This is because the y-values are twice as large for $y = \ln(x^2)$
   as they are for $y = \ln x$.

6 a $f^{-1} : x \mapsto \ln(x - 2) - 3$
   b i $x < -5.30$ ii $x < -7.61$ iii $x < -9.91$
      iv $x < -12.2$ Conjecture HA is $y = 2$

c as $x \to \infty$, $f(x) \to \infty$,
   as $x \to -\infty$, $e^{x+3} \to 0$ and $f(x) \to 2$
   $\therefore$ HA is $y = 2$

d VA of f^{-1} is $x = 2$, domain of f^{-1} is $\{x \mid x > 2\}$

EXERCISE 4H

1 a 3.90 h   b 15.5 h

3 a, b see graph below   c i $n \approx 2.82$ weeks

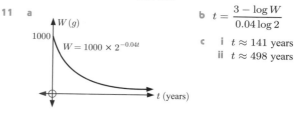

   $\therefore$ approximately 2.8 weeks

4 In 6.17 years, or 6 years 62 days

5 8.65 years, or 8 years 237 days

6 a $\dfrac{8.4\%}{12} = 0.7\% = 0.007$, $r = 1 + 0.007 = 1.007$

   b after 74 months

7 a 17.3 years   b 92.2 years   c 115 years

8 **Hint:** Set $V = 40$, solve for t.

9 a

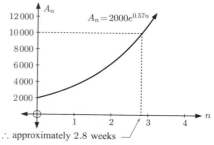

   b ≈ 4.32 weeks   c $t = \dfrac{\log P - 3}{\log 2}$

10 a 50.7 min   b 152 min

11 a

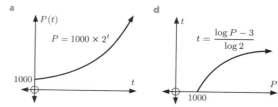

   b $t = \dfrac{3 - \log W}{0.04 \log 2}$

   c i $t \approx 141$ years
      ii $t \approx 498$ years

12 a 10 000 years   b 49 800 years

13 **Hint:** $t = \dfrac{-50 \log(0.1)}{\log 2}$ 14 12.9 seconds

REVIEW SET 4A

1 a 3   b 8   c -2 d $\frac{1}{2}$ e 0
   f $\frac{1}{4}$ g -1 h $\frac{1}{2}$, $k > 0$

2 a $\frac{1}{2}$ b $-\frac{1}{3}$ c $a + b + 1$

3 a $\ln 144$ b $\ln\left(\frac{3}{2}\right)$ c $\ln\left(\dfrac{25}{e}\right)$ d $\ln 3$

4 a $\frac{3}{2}$ b -3 c $2x$ d $1 - x$

5 **a** $\log 144$ **b** $\log_2\left(\frac{16}{9}\right)$ **c** $\log_4 80$

6 **a** $\log P = \log 3 + x\log b$ **b** $\log m = 3\log n - 2\log p$

7 **Hint:** Use change of base rule.

8 **a** $T = \dfrac{x^2}{y}$ **b** $K = n\sqrt{t}$

9 **a** $5\ln 2$ **b** $3\ln 5$ **c** $6\ln 3$

10

Function	Domain	Range
$y = \log_2 x$	$x > 0$	$y \in \mathbb{R}$
$y = \ln(x+5)$	$x > -5$	$y \in \mathbb{R}$

11 **a** $2A + 2B$ **b** $A + 3B$ **c** $3A + \frac{1}{2}B$
   d $4B - 2A$ **e** $3A - 2B$

12 **a** $x = 0$ or $\ln\left(\frac{2}{3}\right)$ **b** $x = e^2$

REVIEW SET 4B

1 **a** $\approx 10^{1.5051}$ **b** $\approx 10^{-2.8861}$ **c** $\approx 10^{-4.0475}$

2 **a** $x = \frac{1}{8}$ **b** $x \approx 82.7$ **c** $x \approx 0.0316$

3 **a** $k \approx 3.25 \times 2^x$ **b** $Q = P^3 R$ **c** $A \approx \dfrac{B^5}{400}$

4 **a** $x = \dfrac{\log 7}{\log 5}$ **b** $x = 2$

5 **a** 2500 g   **d**
   b 3290 years
   c 42.3%

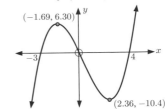
$$W_t = 2500 \times 3^{-\frac{t}{3000}}$$

6 **Hint:** $2^{4x} - 5 \times 2^{3x} = 0$

7 **a** $x = e^5$ **b** $x = e^{-\frac{2}{3}}$ **c** $x = \ln 400$
   d $x = \dfrac{\ln 11 - 1}{2}$ **e** $x = 2\ln 30$

8 **a** 3 years   **b** 152%

9 **a** $g^{-1}(x)$ **b**
   $= \ln\left(\dfrac{x+5}{2}\right)$

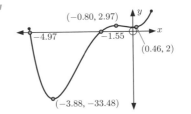

   c domain of g is $\{x \mid x \in \mathbb{R}\}$,
   range is $\{y \mid y > -5\}$
   domain of g^{-1} is
   $\{x \mid x > -5\}$,
   range is $\{y \mid y \in \mathbb{R}\}$

   d g has horizontal asymptote $y = -5$,
   x-intercept is $\ln\left(\frac{5}{2}\right) \approx 0.916$, y-intercept is -3
   g^{-1} has vertical asymptote $x = -5$,
   x-intercept is -3, y-intercept is ≈ 0.916

10 **a** 9   **b** $\ln 5$

REVIEW SET 4C

1 **a** $\frac{3}{2}$ **b** $\frac{2}{3}$ **c** $a + b$

2 **a** x^4 **b** 5   **c** $\frac{1}{2}$ **d** $3x$ **e** $-x$ **f** $\log x$

3 **a** $\approx e^{2.9957}$ **b** $\approx e^{8.0064}$ **c** $\approx e^{-2.5903}$

4 **a** $x = 1000$ **b** $x \approx 4.70$ **c** $x \approx 6.28$

5 **a** $\ln 3$ **b** $\ln 4$ **c** $\ln 125$

6 **a** $\log M = \log a + n\log b$ **b** $\log T = \log 5 - \frac{1}{2}\log l$
   c $\log G = 2\log a + \log b - \log c$

7 **a** $x \approx 5.19$ **b** $x \approx 4.29$ **c** $x \approx -0.839$

8 **a** $x = \ln 3$ **b** $x = \ln 3$ or $\ln 4$

9 **a** $P = TQ^{1.5}$ **b** $M = \dfrac{e^{1.2}}{\sqrt{N}}$

10 **a** domain is   **d**
   $\{x \mid x > -2\}$
   range is
   $\{y \mid y \in \mathbb{R}\}$
   b VA is $x = -2$,
   x-intercept is 7,
   y-intercept is ≈ -1.37
   c $g^{-1}(x) = 3^{x+2} - 2$

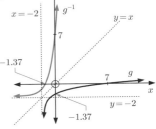

11 **a** 13.9 weeks   **b** 41.6 weeks   **c** 138 weeks

EXERCISE 5A

1 **a** **i** x-intercepts -3, 0, and 4, no y-intercept
   ii max. turning point $(-1.69, 6.30)$
       min. turning point $(2.36, -10.4)$
   iii none
   iv Domain $= \{x \mid x \in \mathbb{R}\}$, Range $= \{y \mid y \in \mathbb{R}\}$
   v

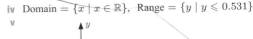

   b **i** x-intercepts -4.97 and -1.55, y-intercept 2
   ii min. turning points $(-3.88, -33.5)$, $(0, 2)$
       and max. turning points $(-0.805, 2.97)$
   iii none   **iv** Domain $= \{x \mid -5 \leqslant x \leqslant 1\}$,
                    Range $= \{y \mid -33.5 \leqslant y \leqslant 12.8\}$
   v

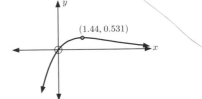

   c **i** x-intercept 0, y-intercept 0
   ii max. turning point $(1.44, 0.531)$ **iii** none
   iv Domain $= \{x \mid x \in \mathbb{R}\}$, Range $= \{y \mid y \leqslant 0.531\}$
   v

d **i** x-intercepts -1 and 1, y-intercept 0.25
   ii max. turning point $(-0.5, 0.333)$
   iii vertical asymptote of $x = -2$,
       no horizontal asymptote
   iv Domain $= \{x \mid -5 \leqslant x \leqslant 5, \ x \neq 2\}$,
       Range $= \{y \mid y \leqslant 0.333\}$
   v

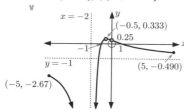

e **i** y-intercept 0.5, no x-intercepts   **ii** none
   iii horizontal asymptotes of $y = 0$, $y = 1$
   iv Domain $= \{x \mid x \in \mathbb{R}\}$, Range $= \{y \mid 0 < y < 1\}$
   v

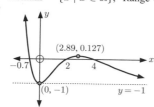

f **i** x-intercepts -0.767, 2 and 4, y-intercept -1
   ii min. turning point $(0, -1)$
       and max. turning point $(2.89, 0.127)$
   iii horizontal asymptote of $y = -1$
   iv Domain $= \{x \mid x \in \mathbb{R}\}$, Range $= \{y \mid y \geqslant -1\}$
   v

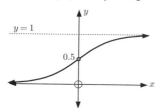

2 **a**

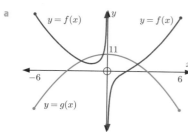

   b $x = -0.373$
       and -2.14

3 **a** max. 28.0
   b **i** max. 6.27 **ii** max. 4.03 **iii** max. 6.27
                                                  $x = -0.753$
4   or $x = 0.753$

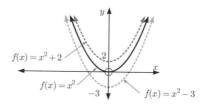

5 **a**

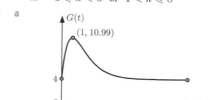

   b one solution
   c **i** $0 < k < 1$ **ii** $k = 0$ or 1
       iii $-3 \leqslant k < 0$ or $1 < k \leqslant 8$ **iv** no solutions

6 **a**

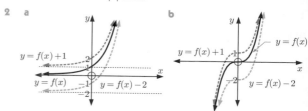

   b Highest level 11.0 mmol/L when $t = 1$ h after evening
       meal.
   c 2.46 h

EXERCISE 5B

1 **a** $2x$ **b** $x + 2$ **c** $\dfrac{x}{2}$ **d** $2x + 3$

2 **a** $9x^2$ **b** $\dfrac{x^2}{4}$ **c** $3x^2$ **d** $2x^2 - 4x + 7$

3 **a** $64x^3$ **b** $4x^3$ **c** $x^3 + 3x^2 + 3x + 1$
   d $2x^3 + 6x^2 + 6x - 1$

4 **a** 4^x **b** $2^{-x} + 1$ **c** $2^{x-2} + 3$ **d** $2^{x+1} + 3$

5 **a** $-\dfrac{1}{x}$ **b** $\dfrac{2}{x}$ **c** $\dfrac{2 + 3x}{x}$ **d** $\dfrac{2x + 1}{x - 1}$

EXERCISE 5C

1 **a, b**

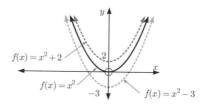

   c **i** If $b > 0$, the function is translated vertically upwards
       through b units.
       ii If $b < 0$, the function is translated vertically
       downwards $|b|$ units.

2 **a**   **b**

c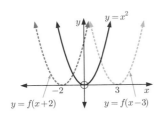

d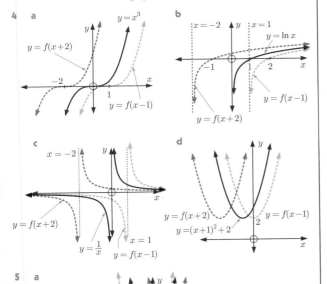

3 a

b i If $a > 0$, the graph is translated a units right.
ii If $a < 0$, the graph is translated $|a|$ units left.

4 a   **b**

c **d**

5 a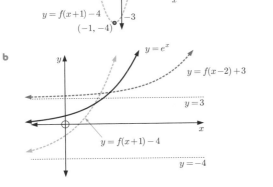

b

c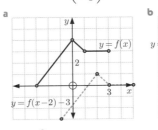

6 A translation of $\begin{pmatrix} 2 \\ -3 \end{pmatrix}$.

a 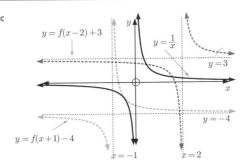 **b**

$y = f(x-2) - 3$

$y = f(x-2) - 3$

7 $g(x) = x^2 - 8x + 17$

8 a i $(3, 2)$ **ii** $(0, 11)$ **iii** $(5, 6)$

b i $(-2, 4)$ **ii** $(-5, 25)$ **iii** $(-1\frac{1}{2}, 2\frac{1}{4})$

EXERCISE 5D

1 a 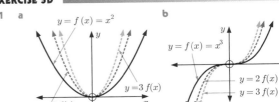 **b**

$y = f(x) = x^2$

$y = 3f(x)$

$y = 2f(x)$

$y = f(x) = x^3$

$y = 2f(x)$

$y = 3f(x)$

c 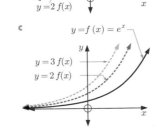 **d**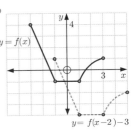

$y = f(x) = e^x$

$y = 3f(x)$

$y = 2f(x)$

$y = 3f(x)$

$y = 2f(x)$

$y = f(x) = \ln x$

e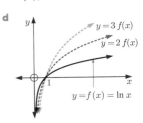

$y = 3f(x)$

$y = f(x) = \frac{1}{x}$

$y = 2f(x)$

2 a 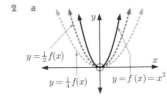 **b**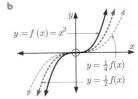

$y = \frac{1}{2}f(x)$

$y = \frac{1}{4}f(x)$

$y = f(x) = x^2$

$y = f(x) = x^3$

$y = \frac{1}{4}f(x)$

$y = \frac{1}{2}f(x)$

c

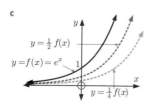

$y = \frac{1}{2} f(x)$

$y = f(x) = e^x$

$y = \frac{1}{4} f(x)$

3 a

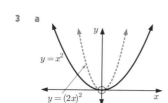

$y = x^2$

$y = (2x)^2$

b

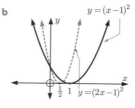

$y = (x-1)^2$

$\frac{1}{2}$ 1 $y = (2x-1)^2$

c

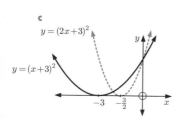

$y = (2x+3)^2$

$y = (x+3)^2$

-3 $-\frac{3}{2}$

4 a

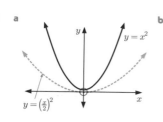

$y = x^2$

$y = \left(\frac{x}{2}\right)^2$

b

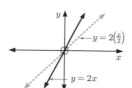

$y = 2\left(\frac{x}{2}\right)$

$y = 2x$

c

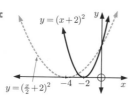

$y = (x+2)^2$

$y = \left(\frac{x}{2}+2\right)^2$

-4 -2

5 a

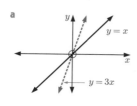

$y = x$

$y = 3x$

b

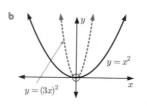

$y = x^2$

$y = (3x)^2$

c

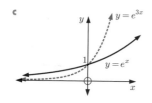

$y = e^{3x}$

$y = e^x$

1

6 a

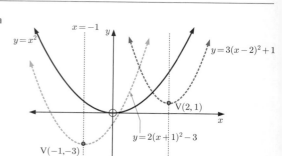

$y = x^2$

$x = -1$

$y = 3(x-2)^2 + 1$

V(2, 1)

$y = 2(x+1)^2 - 3$

V(−1, −3)

$x = 2$

b

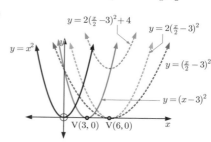

$y = 2\left(\frac{x}{2} - 3\right)^2 + 4$

$y = 2\left(\frac{x}{2} - 3\right)^2$

$y = x^2$

$y = \left(\frac{x}{2} - 3\right)^2$

$y = (x-3)^2$

V(3, 0) V(6, 0)

c

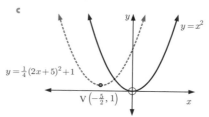

$y = \frac{1}{4}(2x+5)^2 + 1$

$V\left(-\frac{5}{2}, 1\right)$

7 a i $\left(\frac{3}{2}, -15\right)$ ii $\left(\frac{1}{2}, 6\right)$ iii $(-1, 3)$

  b i $\left(4, \frac{1}{3}\right)$ ii $\left(-6, \frac{2}{3}\right)$ iii $(-14, 1)$

EXERCISE 5E

1 a

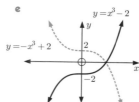

$y = -3x$ $y = 3x$

b

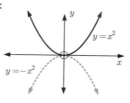

$y = e^x$

1

-1

$y = -e^x$

c

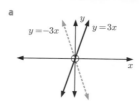

$y = x^2$

$y = -x^2$

d

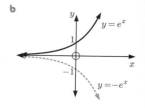

$y = \ln x$

1

$y = -\ln x$

e

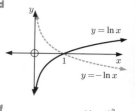

$y = x^3 - 2$

$y = -x^3 + 2$

2

-2

f

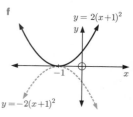

$y = 2(x+1)^2$

-1

$y = -2(x+1)^2$

2 a i $f(-x) = -2x + 1$ **ii** $f(-x) = x^2 - 2x + 1$
   iii $f(-x) = -x^3$

b i

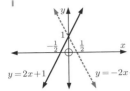

$y = 2x+1$ $y = -2x+1$

ii

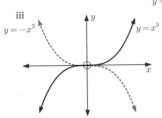

$y = x^2 + 2x + 1$ $y = x^2 - 2x + 1$

iii

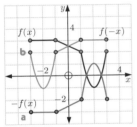

$y = -x^3$ $y = x^3$

3 $g(x) = \ln x - x^3$ **4** $g(x) = x^4 + 2x^3 - 3x^2 - 5x - 7$

5 a i $(3, 0)$ **ii** $(2, 1)$ **iii** $(-3, -2)$
   b i $(7, 1)$ **ii** $(-5, 0)$ **iii** $(-3, 2)$
6 a i $(-2, -1)$ **ii** $(0, 3)$ **iii** $(1, 2)$
   b i $(-5, -4)$ **ii** $(0, 3)$ **iii** $(-2, 3)$

7

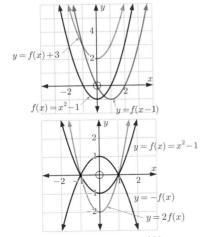

$f(x)$ $f(-x)$ $-f(x)$

8 a A rotation about the origin through $180°$.   **b** $(-3, 7)$
   c $(5, 1)$

EXERCISE 5F

1 a, b x-intercepts are ± 1, y-intercept is -1

$y = f(x) + 3$ $f(x) = x^2 - 1$ $y = f(x-1)$

$y = f(x) = x^2 - 1$ $y = -f(x)$ $y = 2f(x)$

c i a vertical translation of $\begin{pmatrix} 0 \\ 3 \end{pmatrix}$
   ii a horizontal translation of $\begin{pmatrix} 1 \\ 0 \end{pmatrix}$

iii a vertical stretch with scale factor 2
iv a reflection in the x-axis

d

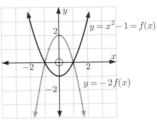

$y = x^2 - 1 = f(x)$ $y = -2f(x)$

A vertical stretch with scale factor -2.
e $(-1, 0)$ and $(1, 0)$

2 a i A vertical stretch with scale factor 3.
   ii $g(x) = 3f(x)$
   b i A vertical translation of $\begin{pmatrix} 0 \\ -2 \end{pmatrix}$.   **ii** $g(x) = f(x) - 2$
   c i A vertical stretch with scale factor $\frac{1}{2}$.
   ii $g(x) = \frac{1}{2}f(x)$

3 a

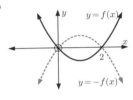

$y = f(x)$ $y = -f(x)$

b

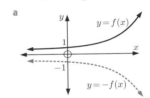

$y = f(x)$ $y = -f(x)$

c

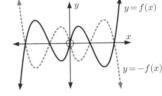

$y = f(x)$ $y = -f(x)$

4 a

$y = f(-x)$ $y = f(x)$

b

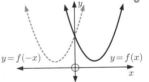

$y = f(-x)$ $y = f(x)$

c

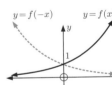

$y = f(-x)$ $y = f(x)$ $y = 1$
$x = -2$ $x = 2$

5 a A   **b** B   **c** D   **d** C

6

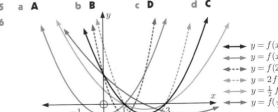

$y = f(x)$
$y = f(x+2)$
$y = f(2x)$
$y = 2f(x)$
$y = \frac{1}{2}f(x)$
$y = f(\frac{1}{2}x)$

7

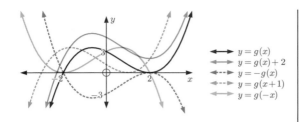

- $y = g(x)$
- $y = g(x) + 2$
- $y = -g(x)$
- $y = g(x+1)$
- $y = g(-x)$

8

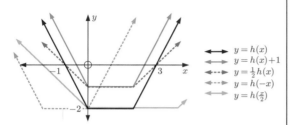

- $y = h(x)$
- $y = h(x) + 1$
- $y = \frac{1}{2}h(x)$
- $y = h(-x)$
- $y = h(\frac{x}{2})$

REVIEW SET 5A

1   **a** 3   **b** $4x^2 - 4x$ **c** $x^2 + 2x$ **d** $3x^2 - 6x - 2$

2   **a** 5   **b** $-x^2 + x + 5$ **c** $5 - \frac{1}{2}x - \frac{1}{4}x^2$ **d** $-x^2 - 3x + 5$

3 $g(x) = 3x^3 - 11x^2 + 14x - 6$

4

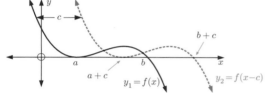

$y_1 = f(x)$ $y_2 = f(x-c)$

5

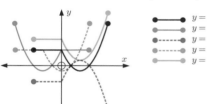

- $y = f(x)$
- $y = f(-x)$
- $y = -f(x)$
- $y = f(x+2)$
- $y = f(x) + 2$

6

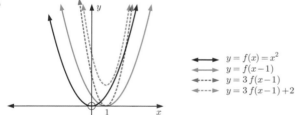

- $y = f(x) = x^2$
- $y = f(x-1)$
- $y = 3f(x-1)$
- $y = 3f(x-1) + 2$

7   **a**

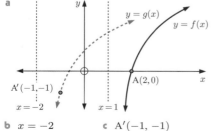

$y = g(x)$ $y = f(x)$ A(2, 0)   A′(−1, −1) $x = -2$ $x = 1$

   b $x = -2$ **c** A′(−1, −1)

REVIEW SET 5B

1

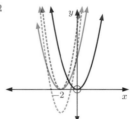

$x = -1$ −3   1   −3   V(−1, −4)

2

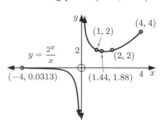

- $y = f(x) = x^2$
- $y = f(x+2)$
- $y = 2f(x+2)$
- $y = 2f(x+2) - 3$

3   **a** no

   b horizontal asymptote $y = 0$,   vertical asymptote $x = 0$

   c min. turning point (1.44, 1.88)

   d

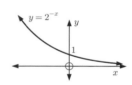

(4, 4)   (1, 2) $y = \frac{2^x}{x}$ (2, 2)   (−4, 0.0313)   (1.44, 1.88)

4   **a**

$y = 2^{-x}$

   b   **i** true   **ii** false   **iii** false   **iv** true

5   **a** $g(x) = (x-1)^2 + 8$ **b** $\{y \mid y \geqslant 4\}$ **c** $\{y \mid y \geqslant 8\}$

6   **a**   **i** $y = \dfrac{1}{x-1} - 2$

     ii

$y = \frac{1}{x}$ $y = -2$ $y = \frac{1}{x-1} - 2$ $x = 1$

For $y = \dfrac{1}{x}$,   VA is $x = 0$,   HA is $y = 0$

For $y = \dfrac{1}{x-1} - 2$,   VA is $x = 1$,   HA is $y = -2$

     iii For $y = \dfrac{1}{x}$,   domain is $\{x \mid x \neq 0\}$,

                         range is $\{y \mid y \neq 0\}$

        For $y = \dfrac{1}{x-1} - 2$,   domain is $\{x \mid x \neq 1\}$,

                             range is $\{y \mid y \neq -2\}$

b i $y = 2^{x-1} - 2$

ii

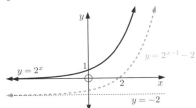

For $y = 2^x$, HA is $y = 0$, no VA
For $y = 2^{x-1} - 2$, HA is $y = -2$, no VA

iii For $y = 2^x$, domain is $\{x \mid x \in \mathbb{R}\}$,
  range is $\{y \mid y > 0\}$
For $y = 2^{x-1} - 2$, domain is $\{x \mid x \in \mathbb{R}\}$,
  range is $\{y \mid y > -2\}$

c i $y = \log_4(x - 1) - 2$

ii

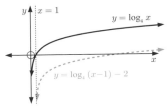

For $y = \log_4 x$, VA is $x = 0$, no HA
For $y = \log_4(x - 1) - 2$, VA is $x = 1$, no HA

iii For $y = \log_4 x$, domain is $\{x \mid x > 0\}$,
  range is $\{y \in \mathbb{R}\}$
For $y = \log_4(x - 1) - 2$, domain is $\{x \mid x > 1\}$,
  range is $\{y \in \mathbb{R}\}$

7

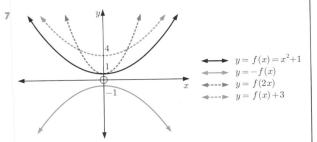

$y = f(x) = x^2 + 1$
$y = -f(x)$
$y = f(2x)$
$y = f(x) + 3$

REVIEW SET 5C

1 a i $(-2, 1.8)$ **ii** $x = 0$ **iii** $y = 2$
iv x-intercepts -3.2, -0.75

b

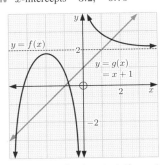

c $(-3.65, -2.65)$, $(-0.8, 0.2)$, and $(1.55, 2.55)$

2

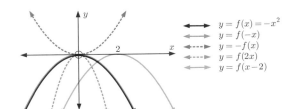

$y = f(x) = -x^2$
$y = f(-x)$
$y = -f(x)$
$y = f(2x)$
$y = f(x-2)$

3 a

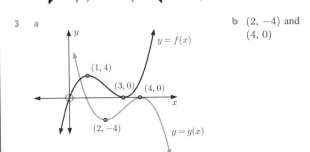

b $(2, -4)$ and $(4, 0)$

4 $g(x) = -x^2 - 6x - 7$

5

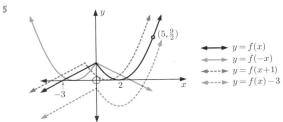

$y = f(x)$
$y = f(-x)$
$y = f(x+1)$
$y = f(x) - 3$

6 $g(x) = x^3 + 6x^2 + 8x + 10$

7 a i $y = 3x + 8$ **ii** $y = 3x + 8$
b $f(x + k) = a(x + k) + b = ax + b + ka = f(x) + ka$

EXERCISE 6A

1 a 4, 13, 22, 31   **b** 45, 39, 33, 27
c 2, 6, 18, 54   **d** 96, 48, 24, 12

2 a Starts at 8 and each term is 8 more than the previous term. Next two terms 40, 48.
b Starts at 2, each term is 3 more than the previous term; 14, 17.
c Starts at 36, each term is 5 less than the previous term; 16, 11.
d Starts at 96, each term is 7 less than the previous term; 68, 61.
e Starts at 1, each term is 4 times the previous term; 256, 1024.
f Starts at 2, each term is 3 times the previous term; 162, 486.
g Starts at 480, each term is half the previous term; 30, 15.
h Starts at 243, each term is $\frac{1}{3}$ of the previous term; 3, 1.
i Starts at 50 000, each term is $\frac{1}{5}$ of the previous term; 80, 16.

3 a Each term is the square of the term number; 25, 36, 49.
b Each term is the cube of the term number; 125, 216, 343.
c Each term is $n(n + 1)$ where n is the term number; 30, 42, 56.

4 a 79, 75   **b** 1280, 5120   **c** 625, 1296
d 13, 17   **e** 16, 22   **f** 6, 12

EXERCISE 6B

1   a 1   b 13   c 79

2   a 7, 9, 11, 13   b

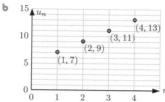

3   a 2, 4, 6, 8, 10   b 4, 6, 8, 10, 12
    c 1, 3, 5, 7, 9   d −1, 1, 3, 5, 7
    e 5, 7, 9, 11, 13   f 13, 15, 17, 19, 21
    g 4, 7, 10, 13, 16   h 1, 5, 9, 13, 17

4   a 2, 4, 8, 16, 32   b 6, 12, 24, 48, 96
    c 3, $\frac{3}{2}$, $\frac{3}{4}$, $\frac{3}{8}$, $\frac{3}{16}$ d −2, 4, −8, 16, −32

5   17, 11, 23, −1, 47

EXERCISE 6C.1

1   a 73   b 65   c $21\frac{1}{2}$

2   a 101   b −107   c $a + 14d$

3   a $u_1 = 6$, $d = 11$ b $u_n = 11n − 5$ c 545
    d yes, u_{30} e no

4   a $u_1 = 87$, $d = −4$ b $u_n = 91 − 4n$ c −69   d u_{97}

5   b $u_1 = 1$, $d = 3$ c 169   d $u_{150} = 448$

6   b $u_1 = 32$, $d = −\frac{7}{2}$ c −227   d $n \geqslant 68$

7   a $k = 17\frac{1}{2}$ b $k = 4$ c $k = 4$ d $k = 0$
    e $k = −2$ or 3   f $k = −1$ or 3

8   a $u_n = 6n − 1$ b $u_n = −\frac{3}{2}n + \frac{11}{2}$
    c $u_n = −5n + 36$ d $u_n = −\frac{3}{2}n + \frac{1}{2}$

9   a $6\frac{1}{4}, 7\frac{1}{2}, 8\frac{3}{4}$ b $3\frac{5}{7}, 8\frac{3}{7}, 13\frac{1}{7}, 17\frac{6}{7}, 22\frac{4}{7}, 27\frac{2}{7}$

10 a $u_1 = 36$, $d = −\frac{2}{3}$ b u_{100} 11 $u_{7692} = 100\,006$

EXERCISE 6C.2

1   a Month 1 = 5 cars   Month 4 = 44 cars
      Month 2 = 18 cars   Month 5 = 57 cars
      Month 3 = 31 cars   Month 6 = 70 cars
    b The constant difference $d = 13$.   c 148 cars
    d 20 months

2   a $u_1 = 34$, $d = 7$ b 111 online friends   c 18 weeks

3   a Day 1 = 97.3 tonnes,   Day 2 = 94.6 tonnes,
      Day 3 = 91.9 tonnes
    b $d = −2.7$, the cattle eat 2.7 tonnes of hay each day.
    c $u_{25} = 32.5$. After 25 days (that is, July 25th) there will be
      32.5 tonnes of hay left.
    d 16.3 tonnes

EXERCISE 6D.1

1   a $b = 18$, $c = 54$ b $b = 2\frac{1}{2}$, $c = 1\frac{1}{4}$
    c $b = 3$, $c = −1\frac{1}{2}$

2   a 96   b 6250   c 16

3   a 6561   b $\frac{19\,683}{64}$ c 16   d ar^8

4   a $u_1 = 5$, $r = 2$ b $u_n = 5 \times 2^{n−1}$, $u_{15} = 81\,920$

5   a $u_1 = 12$, $r = −\frac{1}{2}$
    b $u_n = 12 \times (−\frac{1}{2})^{n−1}$, $u_{13} = \frac{3}{1024}$

6   $u_1 = 8$, $r = −\frac{3}{4}$, $u_{10} \approx −0.600\,677\,490\,2$

7   $u_1 = 8$, $r = \frac{1}{\sqrt{2}}$ Hint: $u_n = 2^3 \times (2^{−\frac{1}{2}})^{n−1}$

8   a $k = \pm 14$ b $k = 2$ c $k = −2$ or 4

9   a $u_n = 3 \times 2^{n−1}$ b $u_n = 32 \times (−\frac{1}{2})^{n−1}$
    c $u_n = 3 \times (\pm\sqrt{2})^{n−1}$ d $u_n = 10 \times (\pm\sqrt{2})^{1−n}$

10 a $u_9 = 13\,122$ b $u_{14} = 2916\sqrt{3} \approx 5050.66$
    c $u_{18} \approx 0.000\,091\,55$

EXERCISE 6D.2

1   a i ≈ 1550 ants   ii ≈ 4820 ants   b ≈ 12.2 weeks

2   a ≈ 278   b Year 2047

3   a i ≈ 73   ii ≈ 167   b ≈ 30.5 years

4   a i ≈ 2860   ii ≈ 184\,000   b ≈ 14.5 years

EXERCISE 6D.3

1   a \$3993.00   b \$993.00   2 €11\,470.39

3   a ¥43\,923   b ¥13\,923   4 \$23\,602.32

5   ¥148\,024.43   6 £51\,249.06   7 \$14\,976.01

8   £11\,477.02   9 €19\,712.33   10 ¥19\,522.47

EXERCISE 6E

1   a i $S_n = 3 + 11 + 19 + 27 + \ldots + (8n − 5)$ ii 95
    b i $S_n = 42 + 37 + 32 + \ldots + (47 − 5n)$ ii 160
    c i $S_n = 12 + 6 + 3 + 1\frac{1}{2} + \ldots + 12(\frac{1}{2})^{n−1}$ ii $23\frac{1}{4}$
    d i $S_n = 2 + 3 + 4\frac{1}{2} + 6\frac{3}{4} + \ldots + 2(\frac{3}{2})^{n−1}$ ii $26\frac{3}{8}$
    e i $S_n = 1 + \frac{1}{2} + \frac{1}{4} + \frac{1}{8} + \ldots + \frac{1}{2^{n−1}}$ ii $1\frac{15}{16}$
    f i $S_n = 1 + 8 + 27 + 64 + \ldots + n^3$ ii 225

2   a 24   b 27   c 10   d 25   e 168   f 310

3   $\sum_{n=1}^{20} (3n − 1) = 610$

5   a $1 + 2 + 3 + \ldots + (n − 2) + (n − 1) + n$
    b
    $$
    \begin{array}{ccccccc}
    1 & + & 2 & + & 3 & + \ldots + (n−1) + & n \\
    + \; n & + & (n−1) & + & (n−2) + \ldots + & 2 & + \; 1 \\
    \hline
    n+1 & + & n+1 & + & n+1 + \ldots + & n+1 & + \; n+1
    \end{array}
    $$
    c $S_n = \dfrac{n(n+1)}{2}$ d $a = 16$, $b = 3$

EXERCISE 6F

1   a 820   b $3087\frac{1}{2}$ c −1460   d −740

2   a 1749   b 2115   c $1410\frac{1}{2}$

3   a 160   b −630   c 135   4 203   5 $−115\frac{1}{2}$

6   18   7 a 65   b 1914   c 47\,850

8   a 14\,025   b 71\,071   c 3367

9   a $u_n = 2n − 1$ c $S_1 = 1$, $S_2 = 4$, $S_3 = 9$, $S_4 = 16$

10 56, 49   11 10, 4, −2 or −2, 4, 10

12 2, 5, 8, 11, 14 or 14, 11, 8, 5, 2

EXERCISE 6G.1

1   a 23.9766 ≈ 24.0   b ≈ 189\,134   c ≈ 4.000
    d ≈ 0.5852

2   a $S_n = \dfrac{3 + \sqrt{3}}{2}\left((\sqrt{3})^n − 1\right)$ b $S_n = 24(1 − (\frac{1}{2})^n)$
    c $S_n = 1 − (0.1)^n$ d $S_n = \dfrac{40}{3}(1 − (−\frac{1}{2})^n)$

3 **a** $u_1 = 3$ **b** $r = \frac{1}{3}$ **c** $u_5 = \frac{1}{27}$

4 **a** 3069   **b** $\frac{4095}{1024} \approx 4.00$ **c** $-134\,217\,732$

5 **c** \$26\,361.59

6 **a** $\frac{1}{2}, \frac{3}{4}, \frac{7}{8}, \frac{15}{16}, \frac{31}{32}$ **b** $S_n = \dfrac{2^n - 1}{2^n}$

c $1 - (\frac{1}{2})^n = \dfrac{2^n - 1}{2^n}$ **d** as $n \to \infty$, $S_n \to 1$

e As $n \to \infty$, the sum of the fractions approaches the area of a 1×1 unit square.

EXERCISE 6G.2

1 **a** **i** $u_1 = \frac{3}{10}$ **ii** $r = 0.1$ **b** $S = \frac{1}{3}$

2 **a** $\frac{4}{9}$ **b** $\frac{16}{99}$ **c** $\frac{104}{333}$ **4** **a** 54   **b** 14.175

5 **a** 1   **b** $4\frac{2}{7}$ **6** $u_1 = 9$, $r = \frac{2}{3}$

7 $u_1 = 8$, $r = \frac{1}{5}$ and $u_1 = 2$, $r = \frac{4}{5}$

8 **b** $S_n = 19 - 20 \times 0.9^n$ **c** 19 seconds

REVIEW SET 6A

1 **a** arithmetic, $d = -8$
   b geometric, $r = 1$ or arithmetic, $d = 0$
   c geometric, $r = -\frac{1}{2}$ **d** neither   **e** arithmetic, $d = 4$

2 $k = -\frac{11}{2}$ **3** $u_n = 33 - 5n$, $S_n = \frac{n}{2}(61 - 5n)$

4 $k = \pm\frac{2\sqrt{3}}{3}$ **5** $u_n = \frac{1}{6} \times 2^{n-1}$ or $-\frac{1}{6} \times (-2)^{n-1}$

6 21, 19, 17, 15, 13, 11

7 **a** $u_n = 89 - 3n$ **b** $u_n = \dfrac{2n + 1}{n + 3}$
   c $u_n = 100(0.9)^{n-1}$

8 **a** $1 + 4 + 9 + 16 + 25 + 36 + 49 = 140$
   b $\frac{4}{3} + \frac{5}{4} + \frac{6}{5} + \frac{7}{6} + \frac{8}{7} + \frac{9}{8} + \frac{10}{9} + \frac{11}{10} \approx 9.43$

9 **a** $10\frac{4}{5}$ **b** $16 + 8\sqrt{2}$ **10** 27 metres

11 **a** $u_n = 3n + 1$

REVIEW SET 6B

1 **b** $u_1 = 6$, $r = \frac{1}{2}$ **c** 0.000\,183

2 **a** 81   **b** $-1\frac{1}{2}$ **c** 375

3 **a** 1587   **b** $47\frac{253}{256} \approx 48.0$ **4** $u_{12} = 10\,240$

5 **a** €8415.31   **b** €8488.67   **c** €8505.75

6 **a** 42   **b** $u_{n+1} - u_n = 5$ **c** $d = 5$ **d** 1672

7 $u_n = \left(\frac{3}{4}\right)2^{n-1}$ **a** 49\,152   **b** 24\,575.25

8 $u_{11} = \frac{8}{19\,683} \approx 0.000\,406$ **9** **a** 17   **b** $255\frac{511}{512} \approx 256$

10 **a** $\frac{1331}{2100} \approx 0.634$ **b** $6\frac{8}{15}$ **11** \$13\,972.28

12 **a** ≈ 3470 **b** Year 2029

REVIEW SET 6C

1 **a** $d = -5$ **b** $u_1 = 63$, $d = -5$ **c** -117
   d $u_{54} = -202$

2 **a** $u_1 = 3$, $r = 4$ **b** $u_n = 3 \times 4^{n-1}$, $u_9 = 196\,608$

3 $u_n = 73 - 6n$, $u_{34} = -131$

4 **a** $\displaystyle\sum_{k=1}^{n}(7k - 3)$ **b** $\displaystyle\sum_{k=1}^{n}\left(\frac{1}{2}\right)^{k+1}$

5 **a** 70   **b** ≈ 241 **c** $\frac{64}{1875}$

6 12   **7** **a** £18\,726.65   **b** £18\,855.74

8 **a** $u_1 = 54$, $r = \frac{2}{3}$ and $u_1 = 150$, $r = -\frac{2}{5}$

b $|r| < 1$ in both cases, so the series will converge.
   For $u_1 = 54$, $r = \frac{2}{3}$, $S = 162$
   For $u_1 = 150$, $r = -\frac{2}{5}$, $S = 107\frac{1}{7}$

9 **a** 35.5 km   **b** 1183 km   **10** **a** $0 < x < 1$ **b** $35\frac{5}{7}$

EXERCISE 7A

1 **a** $p^3 + 3p^2q + 3pq^2 + q^3$ **b** $x^3 + 3x^2 + 3x + 1$
   c $x^3 - 9x^2 + 27x - 27$ **d** $8 + 12x + 6x^2 + x^3$
   e $27x^3 - 27x^2 + 9x - 1$ **f** $8x^3 + 60x^2 + 150x + 125$
   g $8a^3 - 12a^2b + 6ab^2 - b^3$ **h** $27x^3 - 9x^2 + x - \frac{1}{27}$
   i $8x^3 + 12x + \dfrac{6}{x} + \dfrac{1}{x^3}$

2 **a** $1 + 4x + 6x^2 + 4x^3 + x^4$
   b $p^4 - 4p^3q + 6p^2q^2 - 4pq^3 + q^4$
   c $x^4 - 8x^3 + 24x^2 - 32x + 16$
   d $81 - 108x + 54x^2 - 12x^3 + x^4$
   e $1 + 8x + 24x^2 + 32x^3 + 16x^4$
   f $16x^4 - 96x^3 + 216x^2 - 216x + 81$
   g $16x^4 + 32x^3b + 24x^2b^2 + 8xb^3 + b^4$
   h $x^4 + 4x^2 + 6 + \dfrac{4}{x^2} + \dfrac{1}{x^4}$
   i $16x^4 - 32x^2 + 24 - \dfrac{8}{x^2} + \dfrac{1}{x^4}$

3 **a** $x^5 + 10x^4 + 40x^3 + 80x^2 + 80x + 32$
   b $x^5 - 10x^4y + 40x^3y^2 - 80x^2y^3 + 80xy^4 - 32y^5$
   c $1 + 10x + 40x^2 + 80x^3 + 80x^4 + 32x^5$
   d $x^5 - 5x^3 + 10x - \dfrac{10}{x} + \dfrac{5}{x^3} - \dfrac{1}{x^5}$

4 **a** 1   6   15   20   15   6   1
   b **i** $x^6 + 12x^5 + 60x^4 + 160x^3 + 240x^2 + 192x + 64$
   ii $64x^6 - 192x^5 + 240x^4 - 160x^3 + 60x^2 - 12x + 1$
   iii $x^6 + 6x^4 + 15x^2 + 20 + \dfrac{15}{x^2} + \dfrac{6}{x^4} + \dfrac{1}{x^6}$

5 **a** $a = 2$ and $b = e^x$ **b** $T_3 = 6e^{2x}$ and $T_4 = e^{3x}$

6 **a** $7 + 5\sqrt{2}$ **b** $161 + 72\sqrt{5}$ **c** $232 - 164\sqrt{2}$

7 **a** $64 + 192x + 240x^2 + 160x^3 + 60x^4 + 12x^5 + x^6$
   b 65.944\,160\,601\,201

8 $2x^5 + 11x^4 + 24x^3 + 26x^2 + 14x + 3$ **9** **a** 270   **b** 4320

EXERCISE 7B

1 $0! = 1$, $1! = 1$, $2! = 2$, $3! = 6$, $4! = 24$, $5! = 120$, $6! = 720$, $7! = 5040$, $8! = 40\,320$, $9! = 362\,880$, $10! = 3\,628\,800$

2 **a** 30   **b** 100   **c** 21   **3** **a** n **b** $(n + 2)(n + 1)$

4 **a** 3   **b** 6   **c** 35   **d** 210

5 **a** **i** 28   **ii** 28
   b The 3rd and 7th elements in row 8 of Pascal's triangle are the same due to its symmetry.

EXERCISE 7C

1 **a** $1^{11} + \binom{11}{1}(2x)^1 + \binom{11}{2}(2x)^2 + ... + \binom{11}{10}(2x)^{10} + (2x)^{11}$
   b $(3x)^{15} + \binom{15}{1}(3x)^{14}\left(\frac{2}{x}\right)^1 + \binom{15}{2}(3x)^{13}\left(\frac{2}{x}\right)^2 + ...$
   $.... + \binom{15}{14}(3x)^1\left(\frac{2}{x}\right)^{14} + \left(\frac{2}{x}\right)^{15}$
   c $(2x)^{20} + \binom{20}{1}(2x)^{19}\left(-\frac{3}{x}\right)^1 + \binom{20}{2}(2x)^{18}\left(-\frac{3}{x}\right)^2 + ...$
   $.... + \binom{20}{19}(2x)^1\left(-\frac{3}{x}\right)^{19} + \left(-\frac{3}{x}\right)^{20}$

2 **a** $T_6 = \binom{15}{5}(2x)^{10}5^5$ **b** $T_4 = \binom{9}{3}(x^2)^6y^3$
   c $T_{10} = \binom{17}{9}x^8\left(-\frac{2}{x}\right)^9$ **d** $T_9 = \binom{21}{8}(2x^2)^{13}\left(-\frac{1}{x}\right)^8$

3 **a** $T_{r+1} = \binom{7}{r} x^{7-r} a^r$ **b** $a = -2$

4 **a** $\binom{10}{5} 3^5 2^5$ **b** $\binom{6}{3} 2^3 (-3)^3$ **c** $\binom{6}{3} 2^3 (-3)^3$

   d $\binom{12}{4} 2^8 (-1)^4$

5 **a** $\binom{15}{5} 2^5$ **b** $\binom{9}{3} (-3)^3$

6 **a**
```
            1   1
          1   2   1
        1   3   3   1
      1   4   6   4   1
    1   5  10  10   5   1
  1   6  15  20  15   6   1
```
   b **i** 2
      ii 4
      iii 8
      iv 16
      v 32

   c The sum of the numbers in row n of Pascal's triangle is 2^n.
   d Let $x = 1$, in the expansion of $(1+x)^n$.

7 **a** $\binom{8}{6} = 28$ **b** $2\binom{9}{3} 3^6 x^6 - \binom{9}{4} 3^5 x^6 = 91\,854 x^6$

8 $T_3 = \binom{6}{2} (-2)^2 x^8 y^8$

9 **a** $84x^3$ **b** $n = 6$ and $k = -2$ **10** $a = 2$

REVIEW SET 7A

1 15

2 **a** $x^3 - 6x^2 y + 12xy^2 - 8y^3$
   b $81x^4 + 216x^3 + 216x^2 + 96x + 16$

3 60

4 $(a+b)^6 = a^6 + 6a^5 b + 15a^4 b^2 + 20a^3 b^3 + 15a^2 b^4 + 6ab^5 + b^6$
   a $x^6 - 18x^5 + 135x^4 - 540x^3 + 1215x^2 - 1458x + 729$
   b $1 + \dfrac{6}{x} + \dfrac{15}{x^2} + \dfrac{20}{x^3} + \dfrac{15}{x^4} + \dfrac{6}{x^5} + \dfrac{1}{x^6}$

5 $362 + 209\sqrt{3}$ **6** **a** 7   **b** $\binom{6}{4} \times 3^2 = 135$

7 **a** $a = e^x$ and $b = -e^{-x}$
   b $(a+b)^4 = e^{4x} - 4e^{2x} + 6 - 4e^{-2x} + e^{-4x}$

REVIEW SET 7B

1 2500   **2** 64.964 808   **3** $\binom{12}{6} \times 2^6 \times (-3)^6$

4 $8\binom{6}{2} x^5 - 6\binom{6}{1} x^5 = 84x^5$ **5** $k = 180$ **6** $c = 3$

7 **a** $2^n + \binom{n}{1} 2^{n-1} x^1 + \binom{n}{2} 2^{n-2} x^2 + \binom{n}{3} 2^{n-3} x^3 + \ldots.$
   $\ldots. + \binom{n}{n-1} 2^1 x^{n-1} + x^n$
   b 3^n **Hint:** Let $x = 1$ in **a**.

EXERCISE 8A

1 **a** $\frac{\pi}{2}^c$ **b** $\frac{\pi}{3}^c$ **c** $\frac{\pi}{6}^c$ **d** $\frac{\pi}{10}^c$ **e** $\frac{\pi}{20}^c$

   f $\frac{3\pi}{4}^c$ **g** $\frac{5\pi}{4}^c$ **h** $\frac{3\pi}{4}^c$ **i** $2\pi^c$ **j** $4\pi^c$

   k $\frac{7\pi}{4}^c$ **l** $3\pi^c$ **m** $\frac{\pi}{5}^c$ **n** $\frac{4\pi}{9}^c$ **o** $\frac{23\pi}{18}^c$

2 **a** 0.641^c **b** 2.39^c **c** 5.55^c **d** 3.83^c **e** 6.92^c

3 **a** $36°$ **b** $108°$ **c** $135°$ **d** $10°$ **e** $20°$
   f $140°$ **g** $18°$ **h** $27°$ **i** $210°$ **j** $22.5°$

4 **a** $114.59°$ **b** $87.66°$ **c** $49.68°$ **d** $182.14°$
   e $301.78°$

5 **a**

Degrees	0	45	90	135	180	225	270	315	360
Radians	0	$\frac{\pi}{4}$	$\frac{\pi}{2}$	$\frac{3\pi}{4}$	π	$\frac{5\pi}{4}$	$\frac{3\pi}{2}$	$\frac{7\pi}{4}$	2π

   b

Deg.	0	30	60	90	120	150	180	210	240	270	300	330	360
Rad.	0	$\frac{\pi}{6}$	$\frac{\pi}{3}$	$\frac{\pi}{2}$	$\frac{2\pi}{3}$	$\frac{5\pi}{6}$	π	$\frac{7\pi}{6}$	$\frac{4\pi}{3}$	$\frac{3\pi}{2}$	$\frac{5\pi}{3}$	$\frac{11\pi}{6}$	2π

EXERCISE 8B

1 **a** **i** 49.5 cm   **ii** 223 cm^2 **b** **i** 23.0 cm   **ii** 56.8 cm^2
2 **a** 3.14 m   **b** 9.30 m^2 **3** **a** 5.91 cm   **b** 18.9 cm
4 **a** 0.686^c **b** 0.6^c
5 **a** 0.75^c, 24 cm^2 **b** 1.68^c, 21 cm^2 **c** 2.32^c, 126.8 cm^2
6 10 cm, 25 cm^2
8 **a** 11.7 cm   **b** 11.7   **c** 37.7 cm   **d** 3.23^c
9 **a** $\alpha \approx 18.43$ **b** $\theta \approx 143.1$ **c** 387 m^2
10 25.9 cm   **11** **b** 2 h 24 min   **12** 227 m^2

EXERCISE 8C

1 **a** **i** A$(\cos 26°, \sin 26°)$, B$(\cos 146°, \sin 146°)$,
      C$(\cos 199°, \sin 199°)$
   ii A$(0.899, 0.438)$, B$(-0.829, 0.559)$,
      C$(-0.946, -0.326)$
   b **i** A$(\cos 123°, \sin 123°)$, B$(\cos 251°, \sin 251°)$,
      C$(\cos(-35°), \sin(-35°))$
   ii A$(-0.545, 0.839)$, B$(-0.326, -0.946)$,
      C$(0.819, -0.574)$

2

θ (degrees)	0°	90°	180°	270°	360°	450°
θ (radians)	0	$\frac{\pi}{2}$	π	$\frac{3\pi}{2}$	2π	$\frac{5\pi}{2}$
sine	0	1	0	-1	0	1
cosine	1	0	-1	0	1	0
tangent	0	undef	0	undef	0	undef

3 **a** **i** $\frac{1}{\sqrt{2}} \approx 0.707$ **ii** $\frac{\sqrt{3}}{2} \approx 0.866$

   b

θ (degrees)	30°	45°	60°	135°	150°	240°	315°
θ (radians)	$\frac{\pi}{6}$	$\frac{\pi}{4}$	$\frac{\pi}{3}$	$\frac{3\pi}{4}$	$\frac{5\pi}{6}$	$\frac{4\pi}{3}$	$\frac{7\pi}{4}$
sine	$\frac{1}{2}$	$\frac{1}{\sqrt{2}}$	$\frac{\sqrt{3}}{2}$	$\frac{1}{\sqrt{2}}$	$\frac{1}{2}$	$-\frac{\sqrt{3}}{2}$	$-\frac{1}{\sqrt{2}}$
cosine	$\frac{\sqrt{3}}{2}$	$\frac{1}{\sqrt{2}}$	$\frac{1}{2}$	$-\frac{1}{\sqrt{2}}$	$-\frac{\sqrt{3}}{2}$	$-\frac{1}{2}$	$\frac{1}{\sqrt{2}}$
tangent	$\frac{1}{\sqrt{3}}$	1	$\sqrt{3}$	-1	$-\frac{1}{\sqrt{3}}$	$\sqrt{3}$	-1

4 **a** **i** 0.985   **ii** 0.985   **iii** 0.866   **iv** 0.866
      v 0.5   **vi** 0.5   **vii** 0.707   **viii** 0.707
   b $\sin(180° - \theta) = \sin \theta$ as the points have the same
      y-coordinate
   d **i** 135°   **ii** 129°   **iii** $\frac{2\pi}{3}$ **iv** $\frac{5\pi}{6}$

5 **a** **i** 0.342   **ii** -0.342 **iii** 0.5   **iv** -0.5
      v 0.906   **vi** -0.906 **vii** 0.174   **viii** -0.174
   b $\cos(180° - \theta) = -\cos \theta$
   d **i** 140°   **ii** 161°   **iii** $\frac{4\pi}{5}$ **iv** $\frac{3\pi}{5}$

6 **a** ≈ 0.6820 **b** ≈ 0.8572 **c** ≈ -0.7986
   d ≈ 0.9135 **e** ≈ 0.9063 **f** ≈ -0.6691

7 **a**

Quadrant	Degree measure	Radian measure	$\cos \theta$	$\sin \theta$	$\tan \theta$
1	$0° < \theta < 90°$	$0 < \theta < \frac{\pi}{2}$	+ve	+ve	+ve
2	$90° < \theta < 180°$	$\frac{\pi}{2} < \theta < \pi$	$-$ve	+ve	$-$ve
3	$180° < \theta < 270°$	$\pi < \theta < \frac{3\pi}{2}$	$-$ve	$-$ve	+ve
4	$270° < \theta < 360°$	$\frac{3\pi}{2} < \theta < 2\pi$	+ve	$-$ve	$-$ve

b **i** 1 and 4   **ii** 2 and 3   **iii** 3   **iv** 2

8 a $A\widehat{O}Q = 180° - \theta$ or $\pi - \theta$ radians

b [OQ] is a reflection of [OP] in the y-axis and so Q has coordinates $(-\cos\theta, \sin\theta)$.

c $\cos(180° - \theta) = -\cos\theta$, $\sin(180° - \theta) = \sin\theta$

9 a

θ^c	$\sin\theta$	$\sin(-\theta)$	$\cos\theta$	$\cos(-\theta)$
0.75	0.682	−0.682	0.732	0.732
1.772	0.980	−0.980	−0.200	−0.200
3.414	−0.269	0.269	−0.963	−0.963
6.25	−0.0331	0.0331	0.999	0.999
−1.17	−0.921	0.921	0.390	0.390

b $\sin(-\theta) = -\sin\theta$, $\cos(-\theta) = \cos\theta$

c **i** Q has coordinates $(\cos(-\theta), \sin(-\theta))$ or $(\cos\theta, -\sin\theta)$ (since it is the reflection of P in the x-axis).

$\therefore$ $\cos(-\theta) = \cos\theta$ and $\sin(-\theta) = -\sin\theta$.

ii $\cos(2\pi - \theta) = \cos(-\theta) = \cos\theta$ {from **c i**}

EXERCISE 8D.1

1 a $\cos\theta = \pm\frac{\sqrt{3}}{2}$ **b** $\cos\theta = \pm\frac{2\sqrt{2}}{3}$ **c** $\cos\theta = \pm 1$

d $\cos\theta = 0$

2 a $\sin\theta = \pm\frac{3}{5}$ **b** $\sin\theta = \pm\frac{\sqrt{7}}{4}$ **c** $\sin\theta = 0$

d $\sin\theta = \pm 1$

3 a $\sin\theta = \frac{\sqrt{5}}{3}$ **b** $\cos\theta = -\frac{\sqrt{21}}{5}$ **c** $\cos\theta = \frac{4}{5}$

d $\sin\theta = -\frac{12}{13}$

4 a $-\frac{1}{2\sqrt{2}}$ **b** $-2\sqrt{6}$ **c** $\frac{1}{\sqrt{2}}$ **d** $-\frac{\sqrt{7}}{3}$

5 a $\sin x = \frac{2}{\sqrt{13}}$, $\cos x = \frac{3}{\sqrt{13}}$

b $\sin x = \frac{4}{5}$, $\cos x = -\frac{3}{5}$

c $\sin x = -\sqrt{\frac{5}{14}}$, $\cos x = -\frac{3}{\sqrt{14}}$

d $\sin x = -\frac{12}{13}$, $\cos x = \frac{5}{13}$

6 $\sin x = \frac{-k}{\sqrt{k^2+1}}$, $\cos x = \frac{-1}{\sqrt{k^2+1}}$

EXERCISE 8D.2

1 a $\theta \approx 1.33$ or 4.47 **b** $\theta \approx 0.592$ or 5.69

c $\theta \approx 0.644$ or 2.50 **d** $\theta = \frac{\pi}{2}$ or $\frac{3\pi}{2}$

e $\theta \approx 0.876$ or 4.02 **f** $\theta \approx 0.674$ or 5.61

g $\theta \approx 0.0910$ or 3.05 **h** $\theta \approx 1.52$ or 4.66

i $\theta \approx 1.35$ or 1.79

2 a $\theta \approx 1.82$ or 4.46 **b** $\theta = 0$ or π

c $\theta \approx 1.88$ or 5.02 **d** $\theta \approx 3.58$ or 5.85

e $\theta \approx 1.72$ or 4.86 **f** $\theta \approx 1.69$ or 4.59

g $\theta \approx 1.99$ or 5.13 **h** $\theta \approx 2.19$ or 4.10

i $\theta \approx 3.83$ or 5.60

EXERCISE 8E

1

	a	b	c	d	e
$\sin\theta$	$\frac{1}{\sqrt{2}}$	$\frac{1}{\sqrt{2}}$	$-\frac{1}{\sqrt{2}}$	0	$-\frac{1}{\sqrt{2}}$
$\cos\theta$	$\frac{1}{\sqrt{2}}$	$-\frac{1}{\sqrt{2}}$	$\frac{1}{\sqrt{2}}$	-1	$-\frac{1}{\sqrt{2}}$
$\tan\theta$	1	-1	-1	0	1

2

	a	b	c	d	e
$\sin\beta$	$\frac{1}{2}$	$\frac{\sqrt{3}}{2}$	$-\frac{1}{2}$	$-\frac{\sqrt{3}}{2}$	$-\frac{1}{2}$
$\cos\beta$	$\frac{\sqrt{3}}{2}$	$-\frac{1}{2}$	$-\frac{\sqrt{3}}{2}$	$\frac{1}{2}$	$\frac{\sqrt{3}}{2}$
$\tan\beta$	$\frac{1}{\sqrt{3}}$	$-\sqrt{3}$	$\frac{1}{\sqrt{3}}$	$-\sqrt{3}$	$-\frac{1}{\sqrt{3}}$

3 a $\cos 120° = -\frac{1}{2}$, $\sin 120° = \frac{\sqrt{3}}{2}$, $\tan 120° = -\sqrt{3}$

b $\cos(-45°) = \frac{1}{\sqrt{2}}$, $\sin(-45°) = -\frac{1}{\sqrt{2}}$, $\tan(-45°) = -1$

4 a $\cos 90° = 0$, $\sin 90° = 1$ **b** $\tan 90°$ is undefined

5 a $\frac{3}{4}$ **b** $\frac{1}{4}$ **c** 3 **d** $\frac{1}{4}$ **e** $-\frac{1}{4}$ **f** 1

g $\sqrt{2}$ **h** $\frac{1}{2}$ **i** $\frac{1}{2}$ **j** 2 **k** -1 **l** $-\sqrt{3}$

6 a $30°, 150°$ **b** $60°, 120°$ **c** $45°, 315°$

d $120°, 240°$ **e** $135°, 225°$ **f** $240°, 300°$

7 a $\frac{\pi}{4}, \frac{5\pi}{4}$ **b** $\frac{3\pi}{4}, \frac{7\pi}{4}$ **c** $\frac{\pi}{3}, \frac{4\pi}{3}$

d $0, \pi, 2\pi$ **e** $\frac{\pi}{6}, \frac{7\pi}{6}$ **f** $\frac{2\pi}{3}, \frac{5\pi}{3}$

8 a $\frac{\pi}{6}, \frac{11\pi}{6}, \frac{13\pi}{6}, \frac{23\pi}{6}$ **b** $\frac{7\pi}{6}, \frac{11\pi}{6}, \frac{19\pi}{6}, \frac{23\pi}{6}$ **c** $\frac{3\pi}{2}, \frac{7\pi}{2}$

9 a $\theta = \frac{\pi}{3}, \frac{5\pi}{3}$ **b** $\theta = \frac{\pi}{3}, \frac{2\pi}{3}$ **c** $\theta = \pi$

d $\theta = \frac{\pi}{2}$ **e** $\theta = \frac{3\pi}{4}, \frac{5\pi}{4}$ **f** $\theta = \frac{\pi}{2}, \frac{3\pi}{2}$

g $\theta = 0, \pi, 2\pi$ **h** $\theta = \frac{\pi}{4}, \frac{3\pi}{4}, \frac{5\pi}{4}, \frac{7\pi}{4}$

i $\theta = \frac{5\pi}{6}, \frac{11\pi}{6}$ **j** $\theta = \frac{\pi}{3}, \frac{2\pi}{3}, \frac{4\pi}{3}, \frac{5\pi}{3}$

10 a $\theta = k\pi, \ k \in \mathbb{Z}$ **b** $\theta = \frac{\pi}{2} + k\pi, \ k \in \mathbb{Z}$

EXERCISE 8F

1 a $y = \sqrt{3}x$ **b** $y = x$ **c** $y = -\frac{1}{\sqrt{3}}x$

2 a $y = \sqrt{3}x + 2$ **b** $y = -\sqrt{3}x$ **c** $y = \frac{1}{\sqrt{3}}x - 2$

REVIEW SET 8A

1 a $\frac{2\pi}{3}$ **b** $\frac{5\pi}{4}$ **c** $\frac{5\pi}{6}$ **d** 3π

2 a $\frac{\pi}{3}$ **b** $15°$ **c** $84°$

3 a 0.358 **b** -0.035 **c** 0.259 **d** -0.731

4 a $1, 0$ **b** $-1, 0$

6 a $\sin\left(\frac{2\pi}{3}\right) = \frac{\sqrt{3}}{2}$, $\cos\left(\frac{2\pi}{3}\right) = -\frac{1}{2}$, $\tan\left(\frac{2\pi}{3}\right) = -\sqrt{3}$

b $\sin\left(\frac{8\pi}{3}\right) = \frac{\sqrt{3}}{2}$, $\cos\left(\frac{8\pi}{3}\right) = -\frac{1}{2}$, $\tan\left(\frac{8\pi}{3}\right) = -\sqrt{3}$

7 $\frac{1}{\sqrt{15}}$ **8** $\pm\frac{\sqrt{7}}{4}$ **9 a** $\frac{\sqrt{3}}{2}$ **b** 0 **c** $\frac{1}{2}$

10 a $-\frac{3}{\sqrt{13}}$ **b** $\frac{2}{\sqrt{13}}$

11 perimeter $= 12$ units, area $= 8$ units^2 **12** $\frac{\sqrt{6}}{\sqrt{11}}$

REVIEW SET 8B

1 a $(0.766, -0.643)$ **b** $(-0.956, 0.292)$

2 a 1.239^c **b** 2.175^c **c** -2.478^c

3 a $171.89°$ **b** $83.65°$ **c** $24.92°$ **d** $-302.01°$

4 111 cm^2

5 M$(\cos 73°, \sin 73°) \approx (0.292, 0.956)$
N$(\cos 190°, \sin 190°) \approx (-0.985, -0.174)$
P$(\cos 307°, \sin 307°) \approx (0.602, -0.799)$

6 $\approx 103°$

7 a $150°, 210°$ **b** $45°, 135°$ **c** $120°, 300°$

8 a $\theta = \pi$ **b** $\theta = \frac{\pi}{3}, \frac{2\pi}{3}, \frac{4\pi}{3}, \frac{5\pi}{3}$

9 a $133°$ **b** $\frac{14\pi}{15}$ **c** $174°$

10 perimeter ≈ 34.1 cm, area ≈ 66.5 cm^2

11 $r \approx 8.79$ cm, area ≈ 81.0 cm^2

12 **a** $\theta \approx 0.841$ or 5.44 **b** $\theta \approx 3.39$ or 6.03
  c $\theta \approx 1.25$ or 4.39

REVIEW SET 8C

1 **a** $72°$ **b** $225°$ **c** $140°$ **d** $330°$

2

3 **a** $0, -1$
  b $0, -1$

4 **a** $\sin(\pi - p) = m$ **b** $\sin(p + 2\pi) = m$
  c $\cos p = \sqrt{1 - m^2}$ **d** $\tan p = \dfrac{m}{\sqrt{1 - m^2}}$

5 **a** **i** $60°$ **ii** $\frac{\pi}{3}$ **b** $\frac{\pi}{3}$ units   **c** $\frac{\pi}{6}$ units^2 **6** 3

8 **a** $\frac{\sqrt{7}}{4}$ **b** $-\frac{\sqrt{7}}{3}$ **c** $-\frac{\sqrt{7}}{4}$ **9** **a** $2\frac{1}{2}$ **b** $1\frac{1}{2}$ **c** $-\frac{1}{2}$

10 **a** 0 **b** $\sin\theta$ **11** **a** $y = -\frac{1}{\sqrt{3}}x$ **b** $k = -2\sqrt{3}$

EXERCISE 9A

1 **a** 28.9 cm^2 **b** 384 km^2 **c** 28.3 cm^2 **2** $x \approx 19.0$

3 18.9 cm^2 **4** 137 cm^2 **5** 374 cm^2 **6** 7.49 cm

7 11.9 m   **8** **a** $48.6°$ or $131.4°$ **b** $42.1°$ or $137.9°$

9 $\frac{1}{4}$ is not covered

10 **a** 36.2 cm^2 **b** 62.8 cm^2 **c** 40.4 mm^2 **11** 4.69 cm^2

EXERCISE 9B

1 **a** 28.8 cm   **b** 3.38 km   **c** 14.2 m

2 $\widehat{BAC} \approx 52.0°$, $\widehat{ABC} \approx 59.3°$, $\widehat{ACB} \approx 68.7°$

3 **a** $112°$ **b** 16.2 cm^2 **4** **a** $40.3°$ **b** $107°$

5 **a** $\cos\theta = 0.65$ **b** $x \approx 3.81$

6 **a** $x = 3 + \sqrt{22}$ **b** $x = \dfrac{-3 + \sqrt{73}}{2}$ **c** $x = \frac{5}{\sqrt{3}}$

7 **a** $\theta \approx 75.2$ **b** 6.30 m

8 **a** $x \approx 10.8$ **b** $x \approx 9.21$ **9** $x \approx 1.41$ or 7.78

EXERCISE 9C.1

1 **a** $x \approx 28.4$ **b** $x \approx 13.4$ **c** $x \approx 3.79$

2 **a** $a \approx 21.3$ cm   **b** $b \approx 76.9$ cm   **c** $c \approx 5.09$ cm

EXERCISE 9C.2

1 $C \approx 62.1°$ or $C \approx 117.9°$

2 **a** $\widehat{BAC} \approx 49.5°$ **b** $\widehat{ABC} \approx 72.0°$ or $108°$
  c $\widehat{ACB} \approx 44.3°$

3 No, $\dfrac{\sin 85°}{11.4} \neq \dfrac{\sin 27°}{9.8}$ **4** $\widehat{ABC} = 66°$, $BD \approx 4.55$ cm

5 $x \approx 17.7$, $y \approx 33.1$

6 **a** $\widehat{B} = 83°$ or $97°$ **b** $\widehat{B} = 83°$
  c .... *cosine rule* as it avoids the *ambiguous case*.

7 Area ≈ 25.1 cm^2 **8** $x = 8 + \frac{11}{2}\sqrt{2}$

EXERCISE 9D

1 17.7 m   **2** 207 m   **3** $23.9°$ **4** 77.5 m

5 **a** 5.63 km   **b** $115°$
  c **i** Esko   **ii** 3.68 min   **d** $295°$

6 $9.38°$ **7** 69.1 m   **8** **a** 38.0 m   **b** 94.0 m

9 $55.1°$ **10** $AC \approx 11.7$ km, $BC \approx 8.49$ km

11 **a** 74.9 km^2 **b** 7490 hectares   **12** 9.12 km

13 85.0 mm   **14** 10.1 km   **15** 29.2 m   **16** 37.6 km

REVIEW SET 9A

1 14 km^2

2 If the unknown is an angle, use the cosine rule to avoid an ambiguous case.

3 **a** $x = 3$ or 5 **b** Kady can draw
2 triangles:

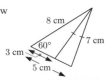

4 $\frac{12}{13}$ **5** 42 km

REVIEW SET 9B

1 **a** $x \approx 34.1$ **b** $x \approx 18.9$

2 $AC \approx 12.6$ cm, $A \approx 48.6°$, $C \approx 57.4°$ **3** 113 cm^2

4 7.32 m   **5** 204 m   **6** 560 m, bearing $079.7°$

REVIEW SET 9C

1 **a** $x \approx 41.5$ **b** $x \approx 15.4$ **2** $x \approx 47.5$ or 132.5

3 $\widehat{EDG} \approx 74.4°$ **4** **a** $10\,600$ m^2 **b** 1.06 ha

5 179 km, bearing $352°$

6 **a** The information
given could give
two triangles:
  b ≈ 2.23 m^3

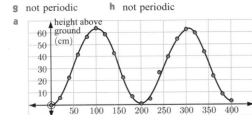

EXERCISE 10A

1 **a** periodic   **b** periodic   **c** periodic
  d not periodic   **e** periodic   **f** periodic
  g not periodic   **h** not periodic

2 **a**

  b A curve can be fitted to the data.
  c The data is periodic.
   i $y = 32$ (approx.)   **ii** ≈ 64 cm
   iii ≈ 200 cm   **iv** ≈ 32 cm

3 **a**
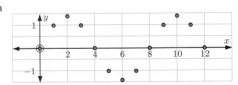

Data exhibits periodic behaviour.

  b
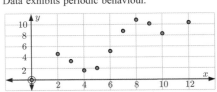

Not enough information to say data is periodic.

EXERCISE 10B.1

1 a
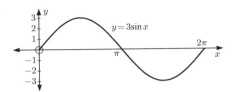

b
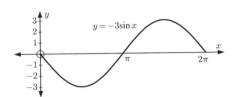

c
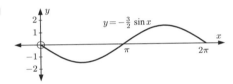

d
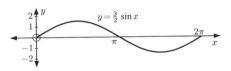

2 a
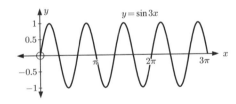

b
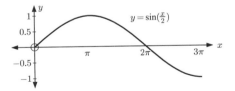

c
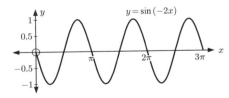

3 a $\frac{\pi}{2}$ b $\frac{\pi}{2}$ c 6π d $\frac{10\pi}{3}$

4 a $b = \frac{2}{5}$ b $b = 3$ c $b = \frac{1}{6}$ d $b = \frac{\pi}{2}$ e $b = \frac{\pi}{50}$

EXERCISE 10B.2

1 a
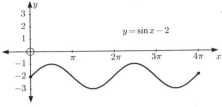

b
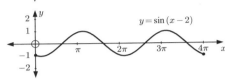

c
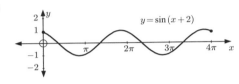

d
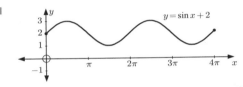

e
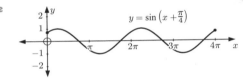

f
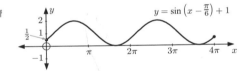

2 a $\frac{2\pi}{5}$ b 8π c π 3 a $\frac{2}{3}$ b 20 c $\frac{1}{50}$ d $\frac{\pi}{25}$

4 a vert. translation -1 b horiz. translation $\frac{\pi}{4}$ right

   c vert. stretch, factor 2 d horiz. stretch, factor $\frac{1}{4}$

   e vert. stretch, factor $\frac{1}{2}$ f horiz. stretch, factor 4

   g reflection in the x-axis   h translation $\begin{pmatrix} -2 \\ -3 \end{pmatrix}$

   i vert. stretch, factor 2, followed by a horiz. stretch, factor $\frac{1}{3}$

   j translation $\begin{pmatrix} \frac{\pi}{3} \\ 2 \end{pmatrix}$

EXERCISE 10C

1 a $T \approx 6.5 \sin \frac{\pi}{6}(t - 4.5) + 20.5$

2 a $T \approx 4.5 \sin \frac{\pi}{6}(t - 10.5) + 11.5$

3 a $T \approx 9.5 \sin \frac{\pi}{6}(t - 10.5) - 9.5$

   b A reasonable fit but not perfect.

4 a $H \approx 7 \sin 0.507(t - 3.1)$

b

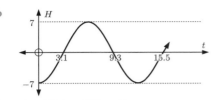

5 $H = 10\sin(\frac{\pi}{50}(t-25)) + 12$

EXERCISE 10D

1 a $y = \cos x + 2$

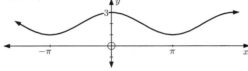

b $y = \cos x - 1$

c $y = \cos\left(x - \frac{\pi}{4}\right)$

d $y = \cos\left(x + \frac{\pi}{6}\right)$

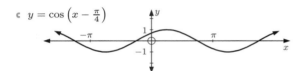

e $y = \frac{2}{3}\cos x$

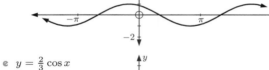

f $y = \frac{3}{2}\cos x$

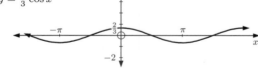

g $y = -\cos x$

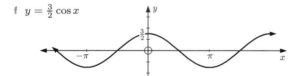

h $y = \cos\left(x - \frac{\pi}{6}\right) + 1$

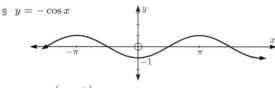

i $y = \cos\left(x + \frac{\pi}{4}\right) - 1$

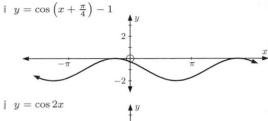

j $y = \cos 2x$

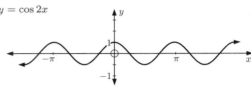

k $y = \cos\left(\frac{x}{2}\right)$

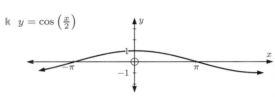

l $y = 3\cos 2x$

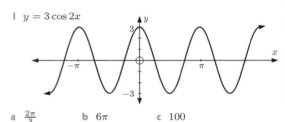

2 a $\frac{2\pi}{3}$ **b** 6π **c** 100

3 $|a| =$ amplitude, $b = \dfrac{2\pi}{\text{period}}$, $c =$ horizontal translation, $d =$ vertical translation

4 a $y = 2\cos 2x$ **b** $y = \cos\left(\frac{x}{2}\right) + 2$

c $y = -5\cos\left(\frac{\pi}{3}x\right)$

EXERCISE 10E

1 a **i** $y = \tan\left(x - \frac{\pi}{2}\right)$

ii $y = -\tan x$

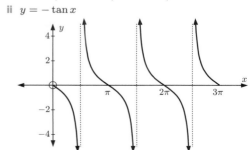

iii $y = \tan 3x$

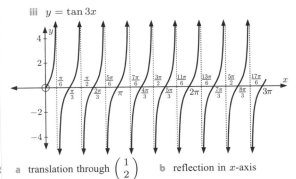

2 a translation through $\begin{pmatrix} 1 \\ 2 \end{pmatrix}$ **b** reflection in x-axis

   c horizontal stretch, factor $\frac{1}{2}$ and vertical stretch with factor 2

3 a π **b** $\frac{\pi}{3}$ **c** $\frac{\pi}{n}$

EXERCISE 10F

1 a 1   **b** undefined   **c** 1

2 a π **b** 6π **c** π

3 a $b = 1$ **b** $b = 3$ **c** $b = 2$ **d** $b = \frac{\pi}{2}$

4 a

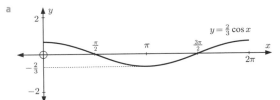

b

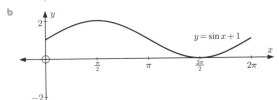

c

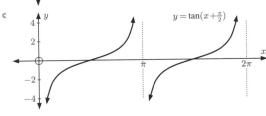

d

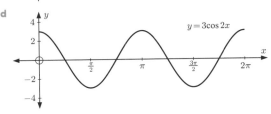

e

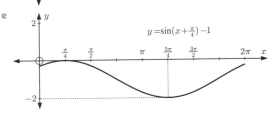

f

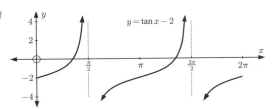

$y = \tan x - 2$

5

	a	b	c	d	e	f
maximum value	1	3	undef.	4	3	-2
minimum value	-1	-3	undef.	2	-1	-4

6 a vertical stretch, factor $\frac{1}{2}$ **b** horizontal stretch, factor 4

   c reflection in the x-axis

   d vertical translation down 2 units

   e horizontally translate $\frac{\pi}{4}$ units to the left

   f reflection in the y-axis

7 $m = 2$, $n = -3$ **8** $p = \frac{1}{2}$, $q = 1$

REVIEW SET 10A

1 a no   **b** yes

2

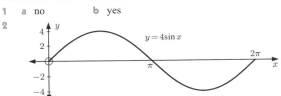

$y = 4\sin x$

3 a minimum $= 0$, maximum $= 2$

   b minimum $= -2$, maximum $= 2$

4 a 10π **b** $\frac{\pi}{2}$ **c** 4π **d** $\frac{\pi}{3}$

5

Function	Period	Amplitude
$y = -3\sin(\frac{x}{4}) + 1$	8π	3
$y = \tan 2x$	$\frac{\pi}{2}$	undefined
$y = 3\cos \pi x$	2	3

Function	Domain	Range
$y = -3\sin(\frac{x}{4}) + 1$	$x \in \mathbb{R}$	$-2 \leqslant y \leqslant 4$
$y = \tan 2x$	$x \neq \pm\frac{\pi}{4}, \pm\frac{3\pi}{4}, \dots$	$y \in \mathbb{R}$
$y = 3\cos \pi x$	$x \in \mathbb{R}$	$-3 \leqslant y \leqslant 3$

6 a $y = -4\cos 2x$ **b** $y = \cos\frac{\pi}{4}x + 2$

REVIEW SET 10B

1 a

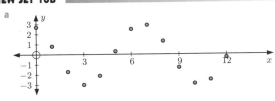

approximately periodic

b

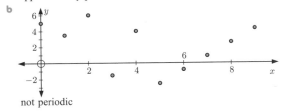

not periodic

2

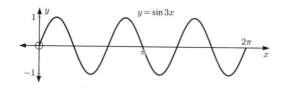

$y = \sin 3x$

3 a 6π **b** $\frac{\pi}{4}$

4

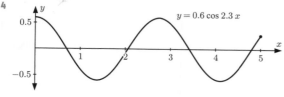

$y = 0.6 \cos 2.3\,x$

5 a maximum: $-5°C$, minimum: $-79°C$
 b $T \approx 37\sin(0.008\,98n) - 42$ **c** ≈ 700 Mars days

6 a maximum $= 2$, minimum $= -8$
 b maximum $= 1\frac{1}{3}$, minimum $= \frac{2}{3}$

REVIEW SET 10C

1 a The function repeats itself over and over in a horizontal direction, in intervals of length 8 units.
 b i 8   **ii** 5   **iii** -1

2 a $\frac{1}{3}$ **b** 24   **c** $\frac{2\pi}{9}$

3 a

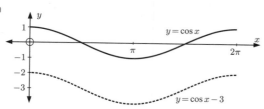

$y = \sin\left(x - \frac{\pi}{3}\right) + 2$

 b $1 \leqslant k \leqslant 3$

4 a

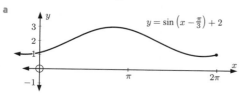

$y = \cos x$
$y = \cos x - 3$

 b

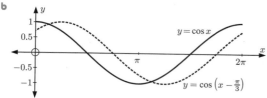

$y = \cos x$
$y = \cos\left(x - \frac{\pi}{3}\right)$

 c

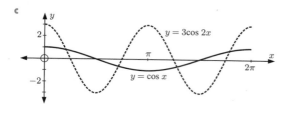

$y = 3\cos 2x$
$y = \cos x$

---

d

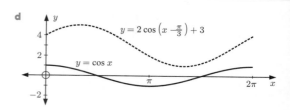

$y = 2\cos\left(x - \frac{\pi}{3}\right) + 3$
$y = \cos x$

5 a $T \approx 7.05\sin\frac{\pi}{6}(t - 10.5) + 24.75$

6 a translation through $\begin{pmatrix} \frac{\pi}{3} \\ 1 \end{pmatrix}$

 b a vertical stretch of factor 2 followed by a reflection in the x-axis

 c a horizontal stretch, factor $\frac{1}{3}$

EXERCISE 11A.1

1 a $x \approx 0.3,\ 2.8,\ 6.6,\ 9.1,\ 12.9$ **b** $x \approx 5.9,\ 9.8,\ 12.2$
2 a $x \approx 1.2,\ 5.1,\ 7.4$ **b** $x \approx 4.4,\ 8.2,\ 10.7$
3 a $x \approx 0.4,\ 1.2,\ 3.5,\ 4.3,\ 6.7,\ 7.5,\ 9.8,\ 10.6,\ 13.0,\ 13.7$
 b $x \approx 1.7,\ 3.0,\ 4.9,\ 6.1,\ 8.0,\ 9.3,\ 11.1,\ 12.4,\ 14.3,\ 15.6$
4 a i ≈ 1.6 **ii** ≈ -1.1
 b i $x \approx 1.1,\ 4.2,\ 7.4$ **ii** $x \approx 2.2,\ 5.3$

EXERCISE 11A.2

1 a $x \approx 0.446,\ 2.70,\ 6.73,\ 8.98$
 b $x \approx 2.52,\ 3.76,\ 8.80,\ 10.0$
 c $x \approx 0.588,\ 3.73,\ 6.87,\ 10.0$
2 a $x \approx -0.644,\ 0.644$ **b** $x \approx -4.56,\ -1.42,\ 1.72,\ 4.87$
 c $x \approx -2.76,\ -0.384,\ 3.53$
3 a $x \approx 1.08,\ 4.35$ **b** $x \approx 0.666,\ 2.48$
 c $x \approx 0.171,\ 4.92$ **d** $x \approx 1.31,\ 2.03,\ 2.85$
4 $x \approx -0.951,\ 0.234,\ 5.98$

EXERCISE 11A.3

1 a $x = \frac{\pi}{3},\ \frac{5\pi}{3},\ \frac{7\pi}{3},\ \frac{11\pi}{3}$ **b** $x = \frac{\pi}{4},\ \frac{3\pi}{4},\ \frac{9\pi}{4},\ \frac{11\pi}{4}$
 c $x = \frac{\pi}{4},\ \frac{5\pi}{4},\ \frac{9\pi}{4},\ \frac{13\pi}{4}$
2 a $x = -\frac{5\pi}{3},\ -\frac{4\pi}{3},\ \frac{\pi}{3},\ \frac{2\pi}{3}$ **b** $x = -\frac{5\pi}{4},\ -\frac{3\pi}{4},\ \frac{3\pi}{4},\ \frac{5\pi}{4}$
 c $x = -\frac{5\pi}{4},\ -\frac{\pi}{4},\ \frac{3\pi}{4},\ \frac{7\pi}{4}$
3 a $0 \leqslant 2x \leqslant 4\pi$ **b** $0 \leqslant \frac{x}{3} \leqslant \frac{2\pi}{3}$
 c $\frac{\pi}{2} \leqslant x + \frac{\pi}{2} \leqslant \frac{5\pi}{2}$ **d** $-\frac{\pi}{6} \leqslant x - \frac{\pi}{6} \leqslant \frac{11\pi}{6}$
 e $-\frac{\pi}{2} \leqslant 2\left(x - \frac{\pi}{4}\right) \leqslant \frac{7\pi}{2}$ **f** $-2\pi \leqslant x \leqslant 0$
4 a $-3\pi \leqslant 3x \leqslant 3\pi$ **b** $-\frac{\pi}{4} \leqslant \frac{x}{4} \leqslant \frac{\pi}{4}$
 c $-\frac{3\pi}{2} \leqslant x - \frac{\pi}{2} \leqslant \frac{\pi}{2}$ **d** $-\frac{3\pi}{2} \leqslant 2x + \frac{\pi}{2} \leqslant \frac{5\pi}{2}$
 e $-2\pi \leqslant -2x \leqslant 2\pi$ **f** $0 \leqslant \pi - x \leqslant 2\pi$
5 a $x = \frac{\pi}{3},\ \frac{5\pi}{3},\ \frac{7\pi}{3}$ **b** $x = \frac{\pi}{6},\ \frac{5\pi}{6},\ \frac{7\pi}{6},\ \frac{11\pi}{6},\ \frac{13\pi}{6},\ \frac{17\pi}{6}$
 c $x = 0,\ \frac{4\pi}{3},\ 2\pi$
6 a $x = \frac{2\pi}{3},\ \frac{4\pi}{3},\ \frac{8\pi}{3},\ \frac{10\pi}{3},\ \frac{14\pi}{3}$
 b $x = -330°,\ -210°,\ 30°,\ 150°$
 c $x = \frac{5\pi}{6},\ \frac{7\pi}{6},\ \frac{17\pi}{6}$ **d** $x = -\frac{5\pi}{3},\ -\pi,\ \frac{\pi}{3},\ \pi$
 e $x = -\frac{13\pi}{6},\ -\frac{3\pi}{2},\ -\frac{\pi}{6},\ \frac{\pi}{2},\ \frac{11\pi}{6},\ \frac{5\pi}{2}$ **f** $x = 0,\ \frac{3\pi}{2},\ 2\pi$
 g $x = \frac{\pi}{2},\ \frac{3\pi}{2},\ \frac{5\pi}{2}$
 h $x = -\frac{8\pi}{9},\ -\frac{4\pi}{9},\ -\frac{2\pi}{9},\ \frac{2\pi}{9},\ \frac{4\pi}{9},\ \frac{8\pi}{9}$
 i $x = 0,\ \frac{\pi}{4},\ \frac{\pi}{2},\ \frac{3\pi}{4},\ \pi$ **j** $x = 0,\ \frac{\pi}{6},\ \pi,\ \frac{7\pi}{6},\ 2\pi$

7 $\theta = \frac{\pi}{3}, \frac{4\pi}{3}$

 a $x = \frac{\pi}{2}, \frac{3\pi}{2}$ b $x = \frac{\pi}{12}, \frac{\pi}{3}, \frac{7\pi}{12}, \frac{5\pi}{6}, \frac{13\pi}{12}, \frac{4\pi}{3}, \frac{19\pi}{12}, \frac{11\pi}{6}$
 c $x = \frac{\pi}{3}, \frac{2\pi}{3}, \frac{4\pi}{3}, \frac{5\pi}{3}$

8 a $x = 0°, 90°, 180°$ b $x = \frac{\pi}{4}, \frac{5\pi}{4}, \frac{9\pi}{4}$

9 a
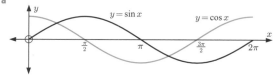

 b $x = \frac{\pi}{4}$ or $\frac{5\pi}{4}$

10 a $x = \frac{3\pi}{4}$ or $\frac{7\pi}{4}$ b $x = \frac{\pi}{12}, \frac{5\pi}{12}, \frac{3\pi}{4}, \frac{13\pi}{12}, \frac{17\pi}{12}, \frac{7\pi}{4}$
 c $x = \frac{\pi}{6}, \frac{2\pi}{3}, \frac{7\pi}{6}, \frac{5\pi}{3}$

EXERCISE 11B

1 a 22 m   b 100 s   c $t \approx 31.5$ s, 68.5 s, 132 s, 168 s
2 a i 7500 grasshoppers   ii 10 300 grasshoppers
 b 10 500 grasshoppers, when $t = 4$ weeks
 c i at $t = 1\frac{1}{3}$ wks and $6\frac{2}{3}$ wks   ii at $t = 9\frac{1}{3}$ wks
 d $2.51 \leqslant t \leqslant 5.49$
3 a 20 m   b at $t = \frac{3}{4}$ minute   c 3 minutes
 d
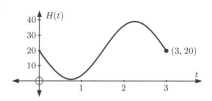

4 a 400 water buffalo
 b i 577 water buffalo   ii 400 water buffalo
 c 650, which is the maximum population.
 d 150, after 3 years   e $t \approx 0.262$ years
5 a $H(t) = 3\cos(\frac{\pi t}{2}) + 4$ b $t \approx 1.46$ s
6 a i true   ii true   b 116.8 cents L^{-1}
 c on the 5th, 11th, 19th, and 25th days
 d 98.6 cents L^{-1} on the 1st and 15th days

EXERCISE 11C.1

1 a $2\sin\theta$ b $3\cos\theta$ c $2\sin\theta$ d $\sin\theta$
 e $-2\tan\theta$ f $-3\cos^2\theta$
2 a 3   b -2 c -1 d $3\cos^2\theta$
 e $4\sin^2\theta$ f $\cos\theta$ g $-\sin^2\theta$ h $-\cos^2\theta$
 i $-2\sin^2\theta$ j 1   k $\sin\theta$ l $\sin\theta$
3 a $2\tan x$ b $\tan^2 x$ c $\sin x$ d $\cos x$
 e $5\sin x$ f $\dfrac{2}{\cos x}$
4 a $1 + 2\sin\theta + \sin^2\theta$ b $\sin^2\alpha - 4\sin\alpha + 4$
 c $\tan^2\alpha - 2\tan\alpha + 1$ d $1 + 2\sin\alpha\cos\alpha$
 e $1 - 2\sin\beta\cos\beta$ f $-4 + 4\cos\alpha - \cos^2\alpha$
5 $\sin^2 x - \tan^2 x$

EXERCISE 11C.2

1 a $(1 - \sin\theta)(1 + \sin\theta)$
 b $(\sin\alpha + \cos\alpha)(\sin\alpha - \cos\alpha)$
 c $(\tan\alpha + 1)(\tan\alpha - 1)$ d
 e $\cos\phi(2 + 3\cos\phi)$ f $3\,s$
 g $(\tan\theta + 3)(\tan\theta + 2)$ h $(2\cos$
 i $(3\cos\alpha + 1)(2\cos\alpha - 1)$
2 a $1 + \sin\alpha$ b $\tan\beta - 1$ c c
 d $\cos\phi + \sin\phi$ e $\dfrac{1}{\sin\alpha - \cos\alpha}$ f $\dfrac{\cos}{2}$

EXERCISE 11D

1 a $\frac{24}{25}$ b $-\frac{7}{25}$ c $-\frac{24}{7}$ 2 a $-\frac{7}{9}$ b $\frac{1}{9}$
3 a $\cos\alpha = \frac{-\sqrt{5}}{3}$ b $\sin 2\alpha = \frac{4\sqrt{5}}{9}$
4 a $\sin\beta = \frac{-\sqrt{21}}{5}$ b $\sin 2\beta = \frac{-4\sqrt{21}}{25}$
5 a $\frac{1}{3}$ b $\frac{2\sqrt{2}}{3}$ 6 $\frac{3}{2}$
7 a $\sin 2\alpha$ b $2\sin 2\alpha$ c $\frac{1}{2}\sin 2\alpha$ d $\cos 2\beta$
 e $-\cos 2\phi$ f $\cos 2N$ g $-\cos 2M$ h $\cos 2\alpha$
 i $-\cos 2\alpha$ j $\sin 4A$ k $\sin 6\alpha$ l $\cos 8\theta$
 m $-\cos 6\beta$ n $\cos 10\alpha$ o $-\cos 6D$ p $\cos 4A$
 q $\cos\alpha$ r $-2\cos 6P$
9 a $x = 0, \frac{2\pi}{3}, \pi, \frac{4\pi}{3}, 2\pi$ b $x = \frac{\pi}{2}, \frac{3\pi}{2}$ c $x = 0, \pi, 2\pi$

EXERCISE 11E

1 a $x = 0, \pi, \frac{7\pi}{6}, \frac{11\pi}{6}, 2\pi$ b $x = \frac{\pi}{3}, \frac{\pi}{2}, \frac{3\pi}{2}, \frac{5\pi}{3}$
 c $x = \frac{\pi}{3}, \pi, \frac{5\pi}{3}$ d $x = \frac{7\pi}{6}, \frac{3\pi}{2}, \frac{11\pi}{6}$ e no solutions
2 a $x = 0, \frac{2\pi}{3}, \frac{4\pi}{3}, 2\pi$ b $x = \frac{\pi}{3}, \frac{5\pi}{3}$ c $x = \frac{\pi}{2}, \frac{7\pi}{6}, \frac{11\pi}{6}$
 d $x = 0, \frac{\pi}{6}, \frac{\pi}{2}, \frac{5\pi}{6}, \pi, \frac{7\pi}{6}, \frac{3\pi}{2}, \frac{11\pi}{6}, 2\pi$
 e $x = \frac{\pi}{4}$ f $x = \frac{\pi}{6}, \frac{5\pi}{6}$

REVIEW SET 11A

1 a $x \approx 115°, 245°, 475°, 605°$ b $x \approx 25°, 335°, 385°$
2 a $x = \frac{7\pi}{6}, \frac{11\pi}{6}, \frac{19\pi}{6}, \frac{23\pi}{6}$ b $x = -\frac{7\pi}{4}, -\frac{5\pi}{4}, \frac{\pi}{4}, \frac{3\pi}{4}$
3 a $\frac{4\pi}{9}, \frac{5\pi}{9}, \frac{10\pi}{9}, \frac{11\pi}{9}, \frac{16\pi}{9}, \frac{17\pi}{9}$ b $\frac{3\pi}{4}, \frac{7\pi}{4}, \frac{11\pi}{4}$
4 $x = 0, \frac{3\pi}{2}, 2\pi, \frac{7\pi}{2}, 4\pi$
5 a $1 - \cos\theta$ b $\dfrac{1}{\sin\alpha + \cos\alpha}$ c $\dfrac{-\cos\alpha}{2}$
6 $\cos\alpha = -\frac{\sqrt{7}}{4}$, $\sin 2\alpha = \frac{3\sqrt{7}}{8}$

REVIEW SET 11B

1 a $x \approx 0.392, 2.75, 6.68$ b $x \approx 5.42$
2 a $x \approx 1.12, 5.17, 7.40$ b $x \approx 0.184, 4.62$
3 a $\frac{120}{169}$ b $\frac{119}{169}$ c $\frac{120}{119}$
4 a i $x \approx 1.33, 4.47, 7.61$ ii $x \approx 5.30$
  iii $x \approx 2.83, 5.97, 9.11$
 b i $x = -\frac{\pi}{2}, \frac{\pi}{2}$ ii $x = -\frac{2\pi}{3}, -\frac{\pi}{6}, \frac{\pi}{3}, \frac{5\pi}{6}$
  iii $x = -\frac{2\pi}{3}, -\frac{\pi}{3}, \frac{\pi}{3}, \frac{2\pi}{3}$
 c $x \approx 0.612, 3.754, 6.895$
5 a $x \approx 1.27, 5.02$ b $x = \frac{\pi}{12}, \frac{\pi}{4}, \frac{3\pi}{4}, \frac{11\pi}{12}, \frac{17\pi}{12}, \frac{19\pi}{12}$
 c $x \approx 1.09, 2.05$
6 a 5000   b 3000, 7000   c $0.5 < t < 2.5$ and $6.5 < t \leqslant 8$
7 $x \approx 1.37, 5.44, 7.65$

$\frac{7\pi}{6}, \frac{11\pi}{6}$

$\frac{\pi}{3}, \pi, \frac{5\pi}{3}$

d $-\cos\theta$

b i $\overrightarrow{FE}, \overrightarrow{BC}$
  ii $\overrightarrow{DE}, \overrightarrow{EF}, \overrightarrow{FE}, \overrightarrow{FA}, \overrightarrow{AF}, \overrightarrow{AB}, \overrightarrow{BA}, \overrightarrow{BC}, \overrightarrow{CB}, \overrightarrow{CD}, \overrightarrow{DC}$
c $\overrightarrow{FC}$ (or $\overrightarrow{CF}$)

EXERCISE 12B.1

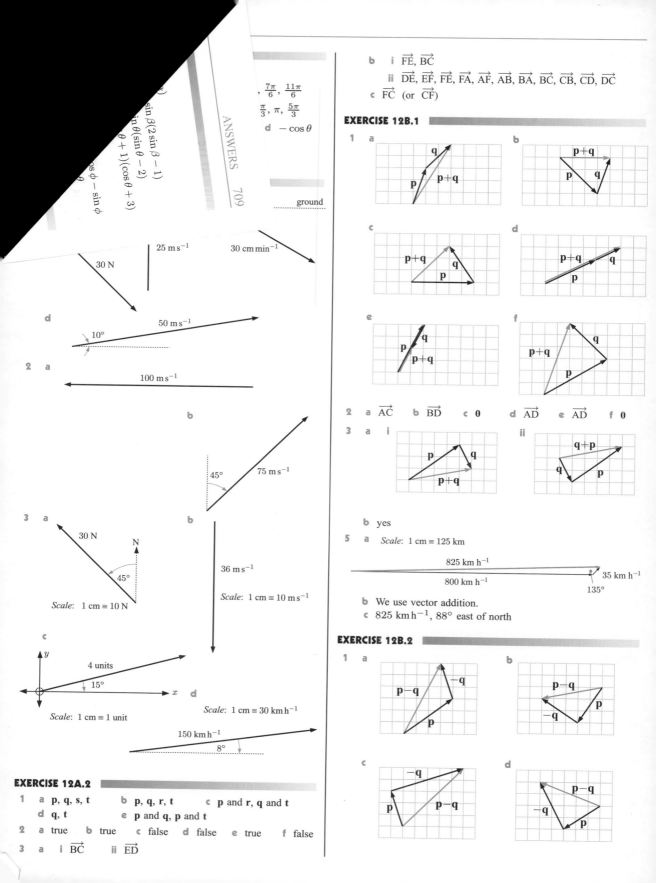

1 a, b, c, d, e, f (vector diagrams showing $\mathbf{p}+\mathbf{q}$)

2 a $\overrightarrow{AC}$ b $\overrightarrow{BD}$ c $\mathbf{0}$ d $\overrightarrow{AD}$ e $\overrightarrow{AD}$ f $\mathbf{0}$

3 a i, ii (vector diagrams)

b yes

5 a *Scale:* 1 cm ≡ 125 km

825 km h^{-1}
800 km h^{-1}
35 km h^{-1}
135°

b We use vector addition.
c 825 km h^{-1}, 88° east of north

EXERCISE 12B.2

1 a, b, c, d (vector diagrams showing $\mathbf{p}-\mathbf{q}$)

ground

25 m s^{-1} 30 cm min^{-1}

30 N

d
10°
50 m s^{-1}

2 a
100 m s^{-1}

b
45°
75 m s^{-1}

3 a
30 N
N
45°
Scale: 1 cm ≡ 10 N

b
36 m s^{-1}
Scale: 1 cm ≡ 10 m s^{-1}

c
y
4 units
15°
x
Scale: 1 cm ≡ 1 unit

d
Scale: 1 cm ≡ 30 km h^{-1}
150 km h^{-1}
8°

EXERCISE 12A.2

1 a p, q, s, t   b p, q, r, t   c p and r, q and t
  d q, t   e p and q, p and t
2 a true b true c false d false e true f false
3 a i $\overrightarrow{BC}$ ii $\overrightarrow{ED}$

2 a

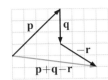

b

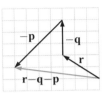

c

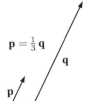

3 a $\overrightarrow{AB}$ **b** $\overrightarrow{AB}$ **c** $\mathbf{0}$ **d** $\overrightarrow{AD}$ **e** $\mathbf{0}$ **f** $\overrightarrow{AD}$

EXERCISE 12B.3

1 a $t = r + s$ **b** $r = -s - t$
c $r = -p - q - s$ **d** $r = q - p + s$
e $p = t + s + r - q$ **f** $p = -u + t + s - r - q$

2 a **i** $r + s$ **ii** $-t - s$ **iii** $r + s + t$
b **i** $p + q$ **ii** $q + r$ **iii** $p + q + r$

EXERCISE 12B.4

1 a   **b**   **c**   **d**

  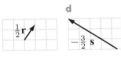

e   **f**

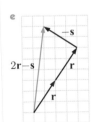 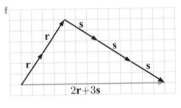

g   **h**

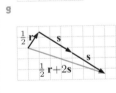 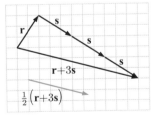

2 a   **b**   **c**

  $p = 2q$

d   **e**

$p = \frac{1}{3}q$ $p = -3q$

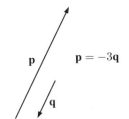

3 a

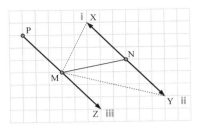

b a parallelogram

4 a $-p$ **b** $p + q$ **c** $\frac{1}{2}(p + q)$ **d** $\frac{1}{2}(q - p)$

5 a b **b** $2b$ **c** $b - a$ **d** $b - a$

EXERCISE 12C

1 a $\begin{pmatrix} 7 \\ 3 \end{pmatrix}$, $7i + 3j$ **b** $\begin{pmatrix} -6 \\ 0 \end{pmatrix}$, $-6i$

c $\begin{pmatrix} 2 \\ -5 \end{pmatrix}$, $2i - 5j$ **d** $\begin{pmatrix} 0 \\ 6 \end{pmatrix}$, $6j$

e $\begin{pmatrix} -6 \\ 3 \end{pmatrix}$, $-6i + 3j$ **f** $\begin{pmatrix} -5 \\ -5 \end{pmatrix}$, $-5i - 5j$

2 a $3i + 4j$ **b** $2i$ **c** $2i - 5j$ **d** $-i - 3j$

  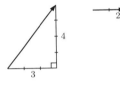 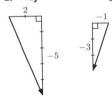

3 a $\begin{pmatrix} -4 \\ -1 \end{pmatrix}$, $-4i - j$ **b** $\begin{pmatrix} -1 \\ -5 \end{pmatrix}$, $-i - 5j$

c $\begin{pmatrix} 2 \\ 0 \end{pmatrix}$, $2i$ **d** $\begin{pmatrix} 3 \\ -4 \end{pmatrix}$, $3i - 4j$

e $\begin{pmatrix} -3 \\ 4 \end{pmatrix}$, $-3i + 4j$ **f** $\begin{pmatrix} 3 \\ 5 \end{pmatrix}$, $3i + 5j$

4 a $\begin{pmatrix} 1 \\ 2 \end{pmatrix}$ **b** $\begin{pmatrix} -1 \\ 3 \end{pmatrix}$ **c** $\begin{pmatrix} 0 \\ -5 \end{pmatrix}$ **d** $\begin{pmatrix} 4 \\ -2 \end{pmatrix}$

5 $\begin{pmatrix} 0 \\ 0 \end{pmatrix}$

EXERCISE 12D

1 a 5 units   **b** 5 units   **c** 2 units
d $\sqrt{8}$ units   **e** 3 units

2 a $\sqrt{2}$ units   **b** 13 units   **c** $\sqrt{17}$ units
d 3 units   **e** $|k|$ units

3 a unit vector   **b** unit vector   **c** not a unit vector
d unit vector   **e** not a unit vector

4 a $k = \pm 1$ **b** $k = \pm 1$ **c** $k = 0$
d $k = \pm\frac{1}{\sqrt{2}}$ **e** $k = \pm\frac{\sqrt{3}}{2}$

5 $p = \pm 3$

EXERCISE 12E

1 **a** $\begin{pmatrix} -2 \\ 6 \end{pmatrix}$ **b** $\begin{pmatrix} -2 \\ 6 \end{pmatrix}$ **c** $\begin{pmatrix} -1 \\ -1 \end{pmatrix}$ **d** $\begin{pmatrix} -1 \\ -1 \end{pmatrix}$

e $\begin{pmatrix} -5 \\ -3 \end{pmatrix}$ **f** $\begin{pmatrix} -5 \\ -3 \end{pmatrix}$ **g** $\begin{pmatrix} -6 \\ 4 \end{pmatrix}$ **h** $\begin{pmatrix} -4 \\ 1 \end{pmatrix}$

2 **a** $\begin{pmatrix} -3 \\ 7 \end{pmatrix}$ **b** $\begin{pmatrix} -4 \\ -3 \end{pmatrix}$ **c** $\begin{pmatrix} -8 \\ -1 \end{pmatrix}$ **d** $\begin{pmatrix} -6 \\ 9 \end{pmatrix}$

e $\begin{pmatrix} 0 \\ -5 \end{pmatrix}$ **f** $\begin{pmatrix} 6 \\ -9 \end{pmatrix}$

3 **a** $\mathbf{a} + \mathbf{0} = \begin{pmatrix} a_1 \\ a_2 \end{pmatrix} + \begin{pmatrix} 0 \\ 0 \end{pmatrix} = \begin{pmatrix} a_1 + 0 \\ a_2 + 0 \end{pmatrix} = \begin{pmatrix} a_1 \\ a_2 \end{pmatrix} = \mathbf{a}$

b $\mathbf{a} - \mathbf{a} = \begin{pmatrix} a_1 \\ a_2 \end{pmatrix} - \begin{pmatrix} a_1 \\ a_2 \end{pmatrix} = \begin{pmatrix} a_1 - a_1 \\ a_2 - a_2 \end{pmatrix} = \begin{pmatrix} 0 \\ 0 \end{pmatrix} = \mathbf{0}$

4 **a** $\begin{pmatrix} -3 \\ -15 \end{pmatrix}$ **b** $\begin{pmatrix} -1 \\ 2 \end{pmatrix}$ **c** $\begin{pmatrix} 0 \\ 14 \end{pmatrix}$ **d** $\begin{pmatrix} 5 \\ -3 \end{pmatrix}$

e $\begin{pmatrix} \frac{5}{2} \\ \frac{11}{2} \end{pmatrix}$ **f** $\begin{pmatrix} -7 \\ 7 \end{pmatrix}$ **g** $\begin{pmatrix} 5 \\ 11 \end{pmatrix}$ **h** $\begin{pmatrix} 3 \\ \frac{17}{3} \end{pmatrix}$

5 **a** $\begin{pmatrix} 8 \\ -1 \end{pmatrix}$ **b** $\begin{pmatrix} 8 \\ -1 \end{pmatrix}$ **c** $\begin{pmatrix} 8 \\ -1 \end{pmatrix}$

6 **a** $\sqrt{13}$ units **b** $\sqrt{17}$ units **c** $5\sqrt{2}$ units **d** $\sqrt{10}$ units
e $\sqrt{29}$ units

7 **a** $\sqrt{10}$ units **b** $2\sqrt{10}$ units **c** $2\sqrt{10}$ units **d** $3\sqrt{10}$ units
e $3\sqrt{10}$ units **f** $2\sqrt{5}$ units **g** $8\sqrt{5}$ units **h** $8\sqrt{5}$ units
i $\sqrt{5}$ units **j** $\sqrt{5}$ units

EXERCISE 12F

1 **a** $\begin{pmatrix} 2 \\ 4 \end{pmatrix}$ **b** $\begin{pmatrix} -2 \\ 5 \end{pmatrix}$ **c** $\begin{pmatrix} 3 \\ -3 \end{pmatrix}$ **d** $\begin{pmatrix} 1 \\ -5 \end{pmatrix}$

e $\begin{pmatrix} 6 \\ -5 \end{pmatrix}$ **f** $\begin{pmatrix} 1 \\ 3 \end{pmatrix}$

2 **a** $(4, 2)$ **b** $(2, 2)$ **3** **a** $\begin{pmatrix} 2 \\ 1 \end{pmatrix}$ **b** $(3, 3)$

4 **a** $\begin{pmatrix} 5 \\ 1 \end{pmatrix}$ **b** $\begin{pmatrix} -5 \\ -1 \end{pmatrix}$ **c** $D(-1, -2)$

5 **a** $\overrightarrow{AB} = \begin{pmatrix} 4 \\ k-3 \end{pmatrix}$, $|\overrightarrow{AB}| = \sqrt{16 + (k-3)^2} = 5$ units
b $k = 0$ or 6

6 **a** $\overrightarrow{AB} = \begin{pmatrix} 2 \\ 3 \end{pmatrix}$, $\overrightarrow{AC} = \begin{pmatrix} 3 \\ -3 \end{pmatrix}$
b $\overrightarrow{BC} = \overrightarrow{BA} + \overrightarrow{AC} = -\overrightarrow{AB} + \overrightarrow{AC}$ **c** $\overrightarrow{BC} = \begin{pmatrix} 1 \\ -6 \end{pmatrix}$

7 **a** $\begin{pmatrix} -5 \\ 4 \end{pmatrix}$ **b** $\begin{pmatrix} 1 \\ 2 \end{pmatrix}$ **c** $\begin{pmatrix} 6 \\ -5 \end{pmatrix}$

8 **a** $M(1, 4)$ **b** $\overrightarrow{CA} = \begin{pmatrix} 7 \\ 5 \end{pmatrix}$, $\overrightarrow{CM} = \begin{pmatrix} 5 \\ 3 \end{pmatrix}$, $\overrightarrow{CB} = \begin{pmatrix} 3 \\ 1 \end{pmatrix}$

EXERCISE 12G

1 **a**

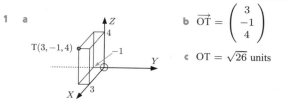

b $\overrightarrow{OT} = \begin{pmatrix} 3 \\ -1 \\ 4 \end{pmatrix}$

c $OT = \sqrt{26}$ units

2 **a**

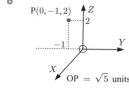

OP = 3 units

b

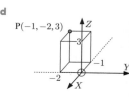

OP $= \sqrt{5}$ units

c

$P(3, 1, 4)$

d

$P(-1, -2, 3)$

3 **a** $\overrightarrow{AB} = \begin{pmatrix} 4 \\ -1 \\ -3 \end{pmatrix}$, $\overrightarrow{BA} = \begin{pmatrix} -4 \\ 1 \\ 3 \end{pmatrix}$
b $AB = \sqrt{26}$ units, $BA = \sqrt{26}$ units

4 $\overrightarrow{OA} = \begin{pmatrix} 3 \\ 1 \\ 0 \end{pmatrix}$, $\overrightarrow{OB} = \begin{pmatrix} -1 \\ 1 \\ 2 \end{pmatrix}$, $\overrightarrow{AB} = \begin{pmatrix} -4 \\ 0 \\ 2 \end{pmatrix}$

5 **a** $\overrightarrow{NM} = \begin{pmatrix} 5 \\ -4 \\ -1 \end{pmatrix}$ **b** $\overrightarrow{MN} = \begin{pmatrix} -5 \\ 4 \\ 1 \end{pmatrix}$
c $MN = \sqrt{42}$ units

6 **a** $\overrightarrow{OA} = \begin{pmatrix} -1 \\ 2 \\ 5 \end{pmatrix}$, $OA = \sqrt{30}$ units

b $\overrightarrow{AB} = \begin{pmatrix} 3 \\ -2 \\ -2 \end{pmatrix}$, $AB = \sqrt{17}$ units

c $\overrightarrow{AC} = \begin{pmatrix} -2 \\ -1 \\ -5 \end{pmatrix}$, $AC = \sqrt{30}$ units

d $\overrightarrow{CB} = \begin{pmatrix} 5 \\ -1 \\ 3 \end{pmatrix}$, $CB = \sqrt{35}$ units

e ABC is scalene, and not right angled.

7 **a** $\sqrt{13}$ units **b** $\sqrt{14}$ units **c** 3 units

9 **a** right angled **b** straight line (not a triangle)

10 **a** $|\overrightarrow{AB}| = \sqrt{158}$ units, $|\overrightarrow{BC}| = \sqrt{129}$ units,
$|\overrightarrow{AC}| = \sqrt{29}$ units, and $29 + 129 = 158$
b area ≈ 30.6 units^2

11 $(0, 3, 5)$, $r = \sqrt{3}$ units

12 **a** $(0, y, 0)$ **b** $(0, 2, 0)$ and $(0, -4, 0)$

13 **a** $a = 5$, $b = 6$, $c = -6$ **b** $a = 4$, $b = 2$, $c = 1$

14 **a** $k = \pm \frac{\sqrt{11}}{4}$ **b** $k = \pm \frac{2}{3}$

15 **a** $r = 2$, $s = 4$, $t = -7$ **b** $r = -4$, $s = 0$, $t = 3$

16 **a** $\overrightarrow{AB} = \begin{pmatrix} 2 \\ -5 \\ -1 \end{pmatrix}$, $\overrightarrow{DC} = \begin{pmatrix} 2 \\ -5 \\ -1 \end{pmatrix}$
b ABCD is a parallelogram.

17 **a** $S(-2, 8, -3)$ **b** midpoints are at $(-\frac{1}{2}, 3, 1)$

EXERCISE 12H

1 a $x = \frac{1}{2}q$ b $x = 2n$ c $x = -\frac{1}{3}p$
d $x = \frac{1}{2}(r - q)$ e $x = \frac{1}{5}(4s - t)$ f $x = 3(4m - n)$

2 a $x = \begin{pmatrix} 4 \\ -6 \\ -5 \end{pmatrix}$ b $x = \begin{pmatrix} 1 \\ -\frac{2}{3} \\ \frac{5}{3} \end{pmatrix}$ c $x = \begin{pmatrix} \frac{3}{2} \\ -1 \\ \frac{5}{2} \end{pmatrix}$

3 $\overrightarrow{AB} = \begin{pmatrix} 3 \\ 4 \\ -2 \end{pmatrix}$, $AB = \sqrt{29}$ units

4 a $\overrightarrow{AB} = 4i - 5j - k$ b $\sqrt{42}$ units

5 a $\sqrt{10}$ b $\sqrt{6}$ c $2\sqrt{10}$ d $2\sqrt{10}$
e $-3\sqrt{6}$ f $3\sqrt{6}$ g $3\sqrt{2}$ h $\sqrt{14}$

6 $\overrightarrow{AC} = -i - 2k$

8 $C(5, 1, -8)$, $D(8, -1, -13)$, $E(11, -3, -18)$

9 a parallelogram b parallelogram c not parallelogram

10 a $D(9, -1)$ b $R(3, 1, 6)$ c $X(2, -1, 0)$

11 a $\overrightarrow{BD} = \frac{1}{2}a$ b $\overrightarrow{AB} = b - a$ c $\overrightarrow{BA} = -b + a$
d $\overrightarrow{OD} = b + \frac{1}{2}a$ e $\overrightarrow{AD} = b - \frac{1}{2}a$ f $\overrightarrow{DA} = \frac{1}{2}a - b$

12 a $\begin{pmatrix} -1 \\ 5 \\ -1 \end{pmatrix}$ b $\begin{pmatrix} -3 \\ 4 \\ -2 \end{pmatrix}$ c $\begin{pmatrix} -3 \\ 6 \\ -5 \end{pmatrix}$

13 a $\begin{pmatrix} 3 \\ 1 \\ -2 \end{pmatrix}$ b $\begin{pmatrix} 1 \\ -3 \\ 4 \end{pmatrix}$ c $\begin{pmatrix} 1 \\ 4 \\ -9 \end{pmatrix}$

d $\begin{pmatrix} -1 \\ \frac{3}{2} \\ -\frac{7}{2} \end{pmatrix}$ e $\begin{pmatrix} 1 \\ -4 \\ 7 \end{pmatrix}$ f $\begin{pmatrix} 4 \\ 2 \\ -2 \end{pmatrix}$

14 a $\sqrt{11}$ units b $\sqrt{14}$ units c $\sqrt{38}$ units

d $\sqrt{3}$ units e $\begin{pmatrix} \sqrt{11} \\ -3\sqrt{11} \\ 2\sqrt{11} \end{pmatrix}$ f $\begin{pmatrix} -\frac{1}{\sqrt{11}} \\ \frac{1}{\sqrt{11}} \\ \frac{3}{\sqrt{11}} \end{pmatrix}$

15 a $a = \frac{1}{3}$, $b = 2$, $c = 1$ b $a = 1$, $b = -1$, $c = 2$
c $a = 4$, $b = -1$

EXERCISE 12I

1 $r = 3$, $s = -9$ **2** $a = -6$, $b = -4$

3 a $\overrightarrow{AB} \parallel \overrightarrow{CD}$, $AB = 3CD$
b $\overrightarrow{RS} \parallel \overrightarrow{KL}$, $RS = \frac{1}{2}KL$ opposite direction
c A, B, and C are collinear and $AB = 2BC$

4 a $\overrightarrow{PR} = \begin{pmatrix} -1 \\ -3 \\ 3 \end{pmatrix}$, $\overrightarrow{QS} = \begin{pmatrix} -2 \\ -6 \\ 6 \end{pmatrix}$, $2\overrightarrow{PR} = \overrightarrow{QS}$
b $PR = \frac{1}{2}QS$

5 a $\begin{pmatrix} 4 \\ 8 \end{pmatrix}$ b $\begin{pmatrix} -1 \\ -2 \end{pmatrix}$

6 a $\frac{1}{\sqrt{5}}(i + 2j)$ b $\frac{1}{\sqrt{13}}(2i - 3k)$ c $\frac{1}{3}(2i - 2j + k)$

7 a $\frac{3}{\sqrt{5}}\begin{pmatrix} 2 \\ -1 \end{pmatrix}$ b $\frac{2}{\sqrt{17}}\begin{pmatrix} 1 \\ 4 \end{pmatrix}$

8 a $\overrightarrow{AB} = \begin{pmatrix} 2\sqrt{2} \\ -2\sqrt{2} \end{pmatrix}$ b $\overrightarrow{OB} = \begin{pmatrix} 3 + 2\sqrt{2} \\ 2 - 2\sqrt{2} \end{pmatrix}$
c $B(3 + 2\sqrt{2}, \ 2 - 2\sqrt{2})$

9 a $\pm\frac{1}{3}\begin{pmatrix} 2 \\ -1 \\ -2 \end{pmatrix}$ b $\pm\frac{2}{3}\begin{pmatrix} -2 \\ -1 \\ 2 \end{pmatrix}$

10 a $\sqrt{2}\begin{pmatrix} -1 \\ 4 \\ 1 \end{pmatrix}$ b $\frac{5}{3}\begin{pmatrix} 1 \\ 2 \\ 2 \end{pmatrix}$

EXERCISE 12J

1 a 7 b 22 c 29 d 66 e 52 f 3 g 5 h 1

2 a 2 b 2 c 14 d 14 e 4 f 4

3 a -1 b $94.1°$ **4** a $\approx 140°$ b $\approx 114°$

5 a 1 b 1 c 0 **6** a 5 b -9

7 a i ±12 ii 6
b i $a \bullet b$ is not 0 ii 12 units
c i $c = d$ ii $c = -d$

8 a $(\cos\theta, \sin\theta)$
b $\overrightarrow{BP} = \begin{pmatrix} \cos\theta + 1 \\ \sin\theta \end{pmatrix}$, $\overrightarrow{AP} = \begin{pmatrix} \cos\theta - 1 \\ \sin\theta \end{pmatrix}$
c $\overrightarrow{AP} \bullet \overrightarrow{BP} = \cos^2\theta + \sin^2\theta - 1$
$\therefore \ \overrightarrow{AP} \bullet \overrightarrow{BP} = 0$
d The angle in a semi-circle is a right angle.

10 a $t = 6$ b $t = -8$ c $t = 0$ or 2

11 a $t = -\frac{3}{2}$ b $t = -\frac{6}{7}$ c $t = \frac{-1 \pm \sqrt{5}}{2}$

12 b **Hint:** Show $a \bullet b = b \bullet c = a \bullet c = 0$
c i $t = -\frac{3}{2}$ ii $t = -\frac{5}{6}$

13 a $\widehat{BAC}$ is a right angle b not right angled
c $\widehat{BAC}$ is a right angle d $\widehat{ACB}$ is a right angle

14 $\overrightarrow{AB} \bullet \overrightarrow{AC} = 0$, $\therefore \ \widehat{BAC}$ is a right angle

15 b $|\overrightarrow{AB}| = \sqrt{14}$ units, $|\overrightarrow{BC}| = \sqrt{14}$ units,
ABCD is a rhombus
c 0, the diagonals of a rhombus are perpendicular

16 a $k\begin{pmatrix} -2 \\ 5 \end{pmatrix}$, $k \neq 0$ b $k\begin{pmatrix} 2 \\ -1 \end{pmatrix}$, $k \neq 0$

c $k\begin{pmatrix} 1 \\ 3 \end{pmatrix}$, $k \neq 0$ d $k\begin{pmatrix} 3 \\ 4 \end{pmatrix}$, $k \neq 0$

e $k\begin{pmatrix} 0 \\ 1 \end{pmatrix}$, $k \neq 0$

17 **Hint:** Choose a vector $\begin{pmatrix} a \\ b \\ c \end{pmatrix}$, where a and b are integers.

Solve for c such that $\begin{pmatrix} a \\ b \\ c \end{pmatrix} \bullet \begin{pmatrix} 1 \\ 2 \\ -1 \end{pmatrix} = 0$.

18 $\widehat{ABC} \approx 62.5°$, the exterior angle $\approx 117.5°$

19 a $54.7°$ b $60°$ c $35.3°$

20 a $30.3°$ b $54.2°$ **21** a $M(\frac{3}{2}, \frac{5}{2}, \frac{3}{2})$ b $51.5°$

22 a $t = 0$ or -3 b $r = -2$, $s = 5$, $t = -4$

23 a $74.5°$ b $72.5°$

REVIEW SET 12A

1 a

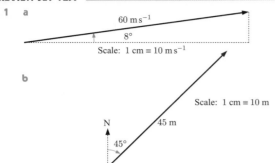

60 m s⁻¹

8°

Scale: 1 cm ≡ 10 m s⁻¹

b

Scale: 1 cm ≡ 10 m

N

45 m

45°

2 a $\overrightarrow{AC}$ b $\overrightarrow{AD}$

3 a $q = p + r$ b $l = k - j + n - m$ 4 $\begin{pmatrix} 1 \\ 4 \end{pmatrix}$

5 a $p + q$ b $\frac{3}{2}p + \frac{1}{2}q$ 6 $m = 5, \ n = -\frac{1}{2}$

7 $\begin{pmatrix} 8 \\ -8 \\ 7 \end{pmatrix}$ 8 a -13 b -36 10 $k = 6$

11 $t\begin{pmatrix} 5 \\ 4 \end{pmatrix}, \ t \neq 0$ 12 a i $p + q$ ii $\frac{1}{2}p + \frac{1}{2}q$

13 a $a \bullet b = -4$ b $b \bullet c = 10$ c $a \bullet c = -10$

14 $a = -2, \ b = 0$

15 a $q + r$ b $r + q, \ DB = AC, \ [DB] \parallel [AC]$

16 a $t = -4$ b $\overrightarrow{LM} = \begin{pmatrix} 5 \\ -3 \\ -4 \end{pmatrix}, \ \overrightarrow{KM} = \begin{pmatrix} -2 \\ -2 \\ -1 \end{pmatrix}$

$\therefore \ \widehat{M} = 90°$

REVIEW SET 12B

1 a   b

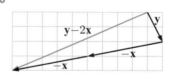

x+y   x   y

y−2x   y   −x   −x

2 $AB = AC = \sqrt{53}$ units and $BC = \sqrt{46}$ units

$\therefore \ \triangle$ is isosceles

3 a $\sqrt{13}$ units   b $\sqrt{10}$ units   c $\sqrt{109}$ units

4 $r = 4, \ s = 7$

5 a $\begin{pmatrix} -6 \\ 1 \\ 3 \end{pmatrix}$ b $\sqrt{46}$ units   c $(-1, 3\frac{1}{2}, \frac{1}{2})$ 6 $c = \frac{50}{3}$

7 $\begin{pmatrix} 1 \\ -\frac{5}{3} \\ -\frac{2}{3} \end{pmatrix}$ 8 $64.0°$ 9 $(0, 0, 1)$ and $(0, 0, 9)$

10 $t = \frac{2}{3}$ or -3 11 a 8   b $62.2°$

12 a $\overrightarrow{AC} = -p + r, \ \overrightarrow{BC} = -q + r$

13 $\pm\frac{4}{\sqrt{14}}(3i - 2j + k)$ 14 $16.1°$

15 a $k = \pm\frac{1}{2}$ b $-\frac{5}{\sqrt{14}}\begin{pmatrix} 3 \\ 2 \\ -1 \end{pmatrix}$

REVIEW SET 12C

1 a $\overrightarrow{PQ}$ b $\overrightarrow{PR}$

2 a $\begin{pmatrix} 3 \\ -3 \\ 11 \end{pmatrix}$ b $\begin{pmatrix} 7 \\ -3 \\ -26 \end{pmatrix}$ c $\sqrt{74}$ units

3 a $AB = \frac{1}{2}CD, \ [AB] \parallel [CD]$ b C is the midpoint of [AB].

4 a $\overrightarrow{PQ} = \begin{pmatrix} -3 \\ 12 \\ 3 \end{pmatrix}$ b $\sqrt{162}$ units   c $\sqrt{61}$ units

5 a $r + q$ b $-p + r + q$ c $r + \frac{1}{2}q$ d $-\frac{1}{2}p + \frac{1}{2}r$

6 a $x = \begin{pmatrix} -1 \\ \frac{1}{3} \\ \frac{2}{3} \end{pmatrix}$ b $x = \begin{pmatrix} 1 \\ -10 \\ 2 \end{pmatrix}$ 7 $v \bullet w = \pm 6$

8 $t = 2 \pm \sqrt{2}$ 9 $\widehat{K} \approx 123.7°, \ \widehat{L} \approx 11.3°, \ \widehat{M} = 45°$

10 a $k = \pm\frac{12}{13}$ b $k = \pm\frac{1}{\sqrt{3}}$ 11 $40.7°$

13 $\overrightarrow{OT} = \begin{pmatrix} 4 \\ 8 \end{pmatrix}$ or $\begin{pmatrix} 2 \\ -2 \end{pmatrix}$ 14 a 10   b $61.6°$

15 $\sin\theta = \frac{2}{\sqrt{5}}$

EXERCISE 13A

1 a

6 m s⁻¹   1 m s⁻¹ $\therefore$ 7 m s⁻¹

7 m s⁻¹

b

6 m s⁻¹ $\therefore$ 5 m s⁻¹

5 m s⁻¹   1 m s⁻¹

2 a $1.34 \ m s^{-1}$

b i 30° to the right of straight across   ii $1.04 \ m s^{-1}$

3 a $24.6 \ km h^{-1}$ b $\approx 170°$

4 a 82.5 m   b 23.3° to the left of straight across   c 48.4 s

5 a The plane's speed in still air would be $\approx 437 \ km h^{-1}$.

The wind slows the plane down to $400 \ km h^{-1}$.

b 4.65° north of due east

EXERCISE 13B

1 a i $\begin{pmatrix} x \\ y \end{pmatrix} = \begin{pmatrix} 3 \\ -4 \end{pmatrix} + t\begin{pmatrix} 1 \\ 4 \end{pmatrix}, \ t \in \mathbb{R}$

ii $x = 3 + t, \ y = -4 + 4t, \ t \in \mathbb{R}$ iii $4x - y = 16$

b i $\begin{pmatrix} x \\ y \end{pmatrix} = \begin{pmatrix} 5 \\ 2 \end{pmatrix} + t\begin{pmatrix} -2 \\ 5 \end{pmatrix}, \ t \in \mathbb{R}$

ii $x = 5 - 2t, \ y = 2 + 5t, \ t \in \mathbb{R}$ iii $5x + 2y = 21$

c i $\begin{pmatrix} x \\ y \end{pmatrix} = \begin{pmatrix} -6 \\ 0 \end{pmatrix} + t\begin{pmatrix} 3 \\ 7 \end{pmatrix}, \ t \in \mathbb{R}$

ii $x = -6 + 3t, \ y = 7t, \ t \in \mathbb{R}$ iii $7x - 3y = -42$

d i $\begin{pmatrix} x \\ y \end{pmatrix} = \begin{pmatrix} -1 \\ 11 \end{pmatrix} + t\begin{pmatrix} -2 \\ 1 \end{pmatrix}, \ t \in \mathbb{R}$

ii $x = -1 - 2t, \ y = 11 + t, \ t \in \mathbb{R}$ iii $x + 2y = 21$

2 a $x = -1 + 2t, \ y = 4 - t, \ t \in \mathbb{R}$

b Points are: $(-1, 4), (1, 3), (5, 1), (-3, 5), (-9, 8)$

3 a When $t = 1, \ x = 3, \ y = -2, \ \therefore$ yes   b $k = -5$

4 a $(0, 8)$ b It is a non-zero scalar multiple of $\begin{pmatrix} -1 \\ 3 \end{pmatrix}$

c $\begin{pmatrix} x \\ y \end{pmatrix} = \begin{pmatrix} 0 \\ 8 \end{pmatrix} + s\begin{pmatrix} 1 \\ -3 \end{pmatrix}, \ s \in \mathbb{R}$

5 a i $\begin{pmatrix} x \\ y \\ z \end{pmatrix} = \begin{pmatrix} 1 \\ 3 \\ -7 \end{pmatrix} + t \begin{pmatrix} 2 \\ 1 \\ 3 \end{pmatrix}, \; t \in \mathbb{R}$

ii $x = 1 + 2t, \; y = 3 + t, \; z = -7 + 3t, \; t \in \mathbb{R}$

b i $\begin{pmatrix} x \\ y \\ z \end{pmatrix} = \begin{pmatrix} 0 \\ 1 \\ 2 \end{pmatrix} + t \begin{pmatrix} 1 \\ 1 \\ -2 \end{pmatrix}, \; t \in \mathbb{R}$

ii $x = 6, \; y = 1 + t, \; z = 2 - 2t, \; t \in \mathbb{R}$

c i $\begin{pmatrix} x \\ y \\ z \end{pmatrix} = \begin{pmatrix} -2 \\ 2 \\ 1 \end{pmatrix} + t \begin{pmatrix} 1 \\ 0 \\ 0 \end{pmatrix}, \; t \in \mathbb{R}$

ii $x = -2 + t, \; y = 2, \; z = 1, \; t \in \mathbb{R}$

d i $\begin{pmatrix} x \\ y \\ z \end{pmatrix} = \begin{pmatrix} 0 \\ 2 \\ -1 \end{pmatrix} + t \begin{pmatrix} 2 \\ -1 \\ 3 \end{pmatrix}, \; t \in \mathbb{R}$

ii $x = 2t, \; y = 2 - t, \; z = -1 + 3t, \; t \in \mathbb{R}$

6 a $\begin{pmatrix} x \\ y \\ z \end{pmatrix} = \begin{pmatrix} 1 \\ 2 \\ 1 \end{pmatrix} + t \begin{pmatrix} -2 \\ 1 \\ 1 \end{pmatrix}, \; t \in \mathbb{R}$

b $\begin{pmatrix} x \\ y \\ z \end{pmatrix} = \begin{pmatrix} 0 \\ 1 \\ 3 \end{pmatrix} + t \begin{pmatrix} 3 \\ 0 \\ -4 \end{pmatrix}, \; t \in \mathbb{R}$

c $\begin{pmatrix} x \\ y \\ z \end{pmatrix} = \begin{pmatrix} 1 \\ 2 \\ 5 \end{pmatrix} + t \begin{pmatrix} 0 \\ -3 \\ 0 \end{pmatrix}, \; t \in \mathbb{R}$

d $\begin{pmatrix} x \\ y \\ z \end{pmatrix} = \begin{pmatrix} 0 \\ 1 \\ -1 \end{pmatrix} + t \begin{pmatrix} 5 \\ -2 \\ 4 \end{pmatrix}, \; t \in \mathbb{R}$

7 a $\left(-\frac{1}{2}, \frac{9}{2}, 0\right)$ **b** $(0, 4, 1)$ **c** $(4, 0, 9)$

8 $(0, 7, 3)$ and $\left(\frac{20}{3}, -\frac{19}{3}, -\frac{11}{3}\right)$

EXERCISE 13C

1 $33.7°$ **2** $\mathbf{b}_1 \bullet \mathbf{b}_2 = 0$ **3** $75.5°$

4 a $28.6°$ **b** $x = -\frac{48}{7}$

5 a $78.7°$ **b** $63.4°$ **c** $63.4°$ **d** $71.6°$

EXERCISE 13D

1 a $(1, 2)$ **b** [graph with points $(1,2)$, $(3,-3)$, $(5,-8)$, $(7,-13)$]

c $\begin{pmatrix} 2 \\ -5 \end{pmatrix}$

d $\sqrt{29}$ cm s^{-1}

2 a $\begin{pmatrix} x \\ y \end{pmatrix} = \begin{pmatrix} 2 \\ 3 \end{pmatrix} + t \begin{pmatrix} 4 \\ -5 \end{pmatrix}, \; t \geqslant 0$ **b** $(8, -4.5)$

c 45 minutes

3 a $\begin{pmatrix} -3 + 2t \\ -2 + 4t \end{pmatrix}$ **d** [graph]

b $\begin{pmatrix} 2 \\ 8 \end{pmatrix}$

c i $t = 1.5$ s
   ii $t = 0.5$ s

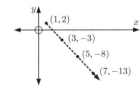

4 a i $(-4, 3)$ **ii** $\begin{pmatrix} 12 \\ 5 \end{pmatrix}$ **iii** 13 m s^{-1}

b i $(3, 0, 4)$ **ii** $\begin{pmatrix} 2 \\ -1 \\ -2 \end{pmatrix}$ **iii** 3 m s^{-1}

5 a $\begin{pmatrix} 120 \\ -90 \end{pmatrix}$ **b** $\begin{pmatrix} 20\sqrt{5} \\ 10\sqrt{5} \end{pmatrix}$ **6** $\begin{pmatrix} -12 \\ 30 \\ -84 \end{pmatrix}$

7 a A is at $(4, 5)$, B is at $(1, -8)$

b For A it is $\begin{pmatrix} 1 \\ -2 \end{pmatrix}$. For B it is $\begin{pmatrix} 2 \\ 1 \end{pmatrix}$.

c For A, speed is $\sqrt{5}$ km h^{-1}. For B, speed is $\sqrt{5}$ km h^{-1}.

d $\begin{pmatrix} 1 \\ -2 \end{pmatrix} \bullet \begin{pmatrix} 2 \\ 1 \end{pmatrix} = 0$

8 a $\begin{pmatrix} x_1 \\ y_1 \end{pmatrix} = \begin{pmatrix} -5 \\ 4 \end{pmatrix} + t \begin{pmatrix} 3 \\ -1 \end{pmatrix}$

$\therefore \; x_1(t) = -5 + 3t, \; y_1(t) = 4 - t$

b speed $= \sqrt{10}$ km min^{-1}

c a minutes later, $(t - a)$ min have elapsed.

$\therefore \; \begin{pmatrix} x_2 \\ y_2 \end{pmatrix} = \begin{pmatrix} 15 \\ 7 \end{pmatrix} + (t - a) \begin{pmatrix} -4 \\ -3 \end{pmatrix}$

$\therefore \; x_2(t) = 15 - 4(t - a), \; y_2(t) = 7 - 3(t - a)$

d Torpedo is fired at 1:35:28 pm and the explosion occurs at 1:37:42 pm.

9 a $\begin{pmatrix} -3 \\ 1 \\ -0.5 \end{pmatrix}$ **b** ≈ 19.2 km h^{-1}

c $\begin{pmatrix} x \\ y \\ z \end{pmatrix} = \begin{pmatrix} 6 \\ 9 \\ 3 \end{pmatrix} + t \begin{pmatrix} -3 \\ 1 \\ -0.5 \end{pmatrix}, \; t \in \mathbb{R}$ **d** 1 hour

EXERCISE 13E

1 a $\frac{3}{5}\sqrt{5}$ units **b** $\frac{1}{2}\sqrt{2}$ units **c** $\frac{9}{2}\sqrt{2}$ units

d 0 units

2 a $6\mathbf{i} - 6\mathbf{j}$ **b** $\begin{pmatrix} 6 - 6t \\ -6 + 8t \end{pmatrix}$

c when $t = \frac{3}{4}$ hours

d $t = 0.84$ and position is $(0.96, 0.72)$

3 a $\begin{pmatrix} -120 \\ -40 \end{pmatrix}$ **b** $\begin{pmatrix} x \\ y \end{pmatrix} = \begin{pmatrix} 200 \\ 100 \end{pmatrix} + t \begin{pmatrix} -120 \\ -40 \end{pmatrix}$

c $(80, 60)$ **d** $|\overrightarrow{OP}| = \sqrt{80^2 + 60^2} = 100$ km

e at 1:45 pm and $d_{min} \approx 31.6$ km   **f** 2:30 pm

4 a A$(18, 0)$ and B$(0, 12)$ **b** R is at $\left(x, \frac{36 - 2x}{3}\right)$

c $\overrightarrow{PR} = \begin{pmatrix} x - 4 \\ \frac{36-2x}{3} \end{pmatrix}$ and $\overrightarrow{AB} = \begin{pmatrix} -18 \\ 12 \end{pmatrix}$

d $\left(\frac{108}{13}, \frac{84}{13}\right)$ and distance ≈ 7.77 km

5 a A$(3, -4)$ and B$(4, 3)$

b for A $\begin{pmatrix} -1 \\ 2 \end{pmatrix}$, for B $\begin{pmatrix} -3 \\ -2 \end{pmatrix}$ **c** $82.9°$

d at $t = 1.5$ hours

6 a $(2, -1, 4)$ **b** $\sqrt{27}$ units

7 a $\left(2, \frac{1}{2}, \frac{5}{2}\right)$ **b** $\sqrt{\frac{3}{2}}$ units

EXERCISE 13F

1 a

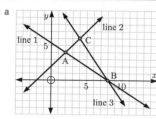

b A(2, 4),
B(8, 0),
C(4, 6)

c BC = BA
= $\sqrt{52}$ units
∴ isosceles △

2 a

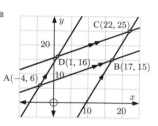

b A(−4, 6),
B(17, 15),
C(22, 25),
D(1, 16)

3 a A(2, 3), B(8, 6), C(5, 0)
b AB = BC = $\sqrt{45}$ units, AC = $\sqrt{18}$ units

4 a P(10, 4), Q(3, −1), R(20, −10)
b $\overrightarrow{PQ} = \begin{pmatrix} -7 \\ -5 \end{pmatrix}$, $\overrightarrow{PR} = \begin{pmatrix} 10 \\ -14 \end{pmatrix}$, $\overrightarrow{PQ} \bullet \overrightarrow{PR} = 0$
c $\widehat{QPR} = 90°$ **d** 74 units²

5 a A is at (2, 5), B(18, 9), C(14, 25), D(−2, 21)
b $\overrightarrow{AC} = \begin{pmatrix} 12 \\ 20 \end{pmatrix}$ and $\overrightarrow{DB} = \begin{pmatrix} 20 \\ -12 \end{pmatrix}$
  i $\sqrt{544}$ units   **ii** $\sqrt{544}$ units   **iii** 0
c Diagonals are perpendicular and equal in length, and as their midpoints are both (8, 15), ABCD is a square.

EXERCISE 13G

1 a They intersect at (1, 2, 3), angle ≈ 10.9°.
b Lines are skew, angle ≈ 62.7°.
c They are parallel, ∴ angle = 0°.
d They are skew, angle ≈ 11.4°.
e They intersect at (−4, 7, −7), angle ≈ 40.2°.
f They are parallel, ∴ angle = 0°.
g They are coincident, ∴ angle = 0°

REVIEW SET 13A

1 a $\begin{pmatrix} x \\ y \end{pmatrix} = \begin{pmatrix} -6 \\ 3 \end{pmatrix} + t \begin{pmatrix} 4 \\ -3 \end{pmatrix}$
b $x = -6 + 4t, \ y = 3 - 3t, \ t \in \mathbb{R}$ **c** $3x + 4y = -6$

2 $m = 10$

3 a (5, 2)   **b** $\begin{pmatrix} 4 \\ 10 \end{pmatrix}$ is a non-zero scalar multiple of $\begin{pmatrix} 2 \\ 5 \end{pmatrix}$
c $\begin{pmatrix} x \\ y \end{pmatrix} = \begin{pmatrix} 5 \\ 2 \end{pmatrix} + s \begin{pmatrix} 4 \\ 10 \end{pmatrix}$

4 a $x = 2 + t, \ y = 4t, \ z = 1 - 3t, \ t \in \mathbb{R}$
b Use $\cos\theta = \dfrac{|\ \overrightarrow{PQ} \ \bullet \ \overrightarrow{QR}\ |}{|\ \overrightarrow{PQ}\ ||\ \overrightarrow{QR}\ |}$

5 a A(5, 2), B(6, 5), C(8, 3)
b $|\ \overrightarrow{AB}\ | = \sqrt{10}$ units, $|\ \overrightarrow{BC}\ | = \sqrt{8}$ units, $|\ \overrightarrow{AC}\ | = \sqrt{10}$ units
c isosceles

6 a OABC is a rhombus.
So, its diagonals
bisect its angles.

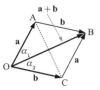

b $\begin{pmatrix} x \\ y \\ z \end{pmatrix} = \begin{pmatrix} 7 \\ 3 \\ -4 \end{pmatrix} + t \begin{pmatrix} 0 \\ \frac{1}{3} \\ \frac{1}{3} \end{pmatrix}$, $t \in \mathbb{R}$

c $(7, 3\frac{3}{4}, -3\frac{1}{4})$

7 (4, 1, −3) and (1, −5, 0)

8 a

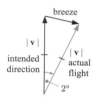

b i isosceles triangle ∴ 2 remaining angles = 89° each, breeze makes angle of 180 − 89 = 91° to intended direction of the arrow.
  ii bisect angle 2° and use $\sin 1° = \dfrac{\frac{1}{2} \text{ speed}}{|\mathbf{v}|}$
  ∴ speed = $2\,|\mathbf{v}|\sin 1°$

REVIEW SET 13B

1 $\begin{pmatrix} x \\ y \end{pmatrix} = \begin{pmatrix} 0 \\ 8 \end{pmatrix} + t \begin{pmatrix} 5 \\ 4 \end{pmatrix}$, $t \in \mathbb{R}$

2 a i $-6\mathbf{i} + 10\mathbf{j}$ **ii** $-5\mathbf{i} - 15\mathbf{j}$
  iii $(-6 - 5t)\mathbf{i} + (10 - 15t)\mathbf{j}$
b $t = 0.48$ h
c shortest distance ≈ 8.85 km, so will miss reef

3 a i $\begin{pmatrix} x \\ y \end{pmatrix} = \begin{pmatrix} 2 \\ -3 \end{pmatrix} + t \begin{pmatrix} 4 \\ -1 \end{pmatrix}$, $t \in \mathbb{R}$
  ii $x = 2 + 4t, \ y = -3 - t, \ t \in \mathbb{R}$
b i $\begin{pmatrix} x \\ y \\ z \end{pmatrix} = \begin{pmatrix} -1 \\ 6 \\ 3 \end{pmatrix} + t \begin{pmatrix} 6 \\ -8 \\ -3 \end{pmatrix}$, $t \in \mathbb{R}$
  ii $x = -1 + 6t, \ y = 6 - 8t, \ z = 3 - 3t, \ t \in \mathbb{R}$

4 a 11.5° east of due north   **b** ≈ 343 km h⁻¹   **5** 8.13°

6 a X23, $x_1 = 2 + t, \ y_1 = 4 - 3t, \ t \geqslant 0$
b Y18, $x_2 = 13 - t, \ y_2 = 3 - 2a + at, \ t \geqslant 2$
c interception occurred at 2:22:30 pm
d bearing ≈ 193°, ≈ 4.54 units per minute

7 a intersecting at (4, 3, 1), angle ≈ 44.5°
b skew, angle ≈ 71.2°

REVIEW SET 13C

1 $2\sqrt{10}(3\mathbf{i} - \mathbf{j})$

2 a (−4, 3)   **b** (28, 27)   **c** $\begin{pmatrix} 8 \\ 6 \end{pmatrix}$ **d** 10 m s⁻¹

3 a (KL) is parallel to (MN) as $\begin{pmatrix} 5 \\ -2 \end{pmatrix}$ is parallel to $\begin{pmatrix} -5 \\ 2 \end{pmatrix}$
b (KL) is perpendicular to (NK) as $\begin{pmatrix} 5 \\ -2 \end{pmatrix} \bullet \begin{pmatrix} 4 \\ 10 \end{pmatrix} = 0$
  and (NK) is perpendicular to (MN) as $\begin{pmatrix} 4 \\ 10 \end{pmatrix} \bullet \begin{pmatrix} -5 \\ 2 \end{pmatrix} = 0$

c K(7, 17), L(22, 11), M(33, −5), N(3, 7) **d** 261 units^2

4 30.5°

5 **a** $|\overrightarrow{AB}| = \sqrt{22}$ units

  b A lies on the line **r** where $\lambda = -3$ and B lies on **r** where $\lambda = 0$ ∴ the line between A and B is the same as line **r**, so it can be described by **r**.

  c 70.5°

6 **a** Road A: $\begin{pmatrix} x \\ y \end{pmatrix} = \begin{pmatrix} -9 \\ 2 \end{pmatrix} + t \begin{pmatrix} 4 \\ -3 \end{pmatrix}$, $t \in \mathbb{R}$

  Road B: $\begin{pmatrix} x \\ y \end{pmatrix} = \begin{pmatrix} 6 \\ -18 \end{pmatrix} + s \begin{pmatrix} 5 \\ 12 \end{pmatrix}$, $s \in \mathbb{R}$

  b Road B, 13 km

7 **a** $\overrightarrow{AB} \bullet \overrightarrow{AC} = \begin{pmatrix} -2 \\ -1 \\ 6 \end{pmatrix} \bullet \begin{pmatrix} 5 \\ 2 \\ 2 \end{pmatrix} = 0$

  b **i** $x = 4 - 2t$, $y = 2 - t$, $z = -1 + 6t$, $t \in \mathbb{R}$

   ii $x = 4 + 5s$, $y = 2 + 2s$, $z = -1 + 2s$, $s \in \mathbb{R}$

EXERCISE 14A

1 **a** 7 **b** 7 **c** 11 **d** 16 **e** 0 **f** 5

2 **a** 5 **b** 7 **c** c

3 **a** −2 **b** 7 **c** −1 **d** 1

4 **a** −3 **b** 5 **c** −1 **d** 6 **e** −4 **f** −8

  g 1 **h** 2 **i** 5

EXERCISE 14B

1 **a** **i** as $x \to 0^-$, $f(x) \to -\infty$

    as $x \to 0^+$, $f(x) \to \infty$

    as $x \to \infty$, $f(x) \to 0^+$

    as $x \to -\infty$, $f(x) \to 0^-$

    vertical asymptote $x = 0$, horizontal asymptote $y = 0$

   ii $\lim\limits_{x \to -\infty} f(x) = 0$, $\lim\limits_{x \to \infty} f(x) = 0$

  b **i** as $x \to -3^-$, $f(x) \to \infty$

    as $x \to -3^+$, $f(x) \to -\infty$

    as $x \to \infty$, $f(x) \to 3^-$

    as $x \to -\infty$, $f(x) \to 3^+$

    vertical asymptote $x = -3$, horizontal asymptote $y = 3$

   ii $\lim\limits_{x \to -\infty} f(x) = 3$, $\lim\limits_{x \to \infty} f(x) = 3$

  c **i** as $x \to -\frac{2}{3}^-$, $f(x) \to -\infty$

    as $x \to -\frac{2}{3}^+$, $f(x) \to \infty$

    as $x \to \infty$, $f(x) \to -\frac{2}{3}^+$

    as $x \to -\infty$, $f(x) \to -\frac{2}{3}^-$

    vertical asymptote $x = -\frac{2}{3}$,

    horizontal asymptote $y = -\frac{2}{3}$

   ii $\lim\limits_{x \to -\infty} f(x) = -\frac{2}{3}$, $\lim\limits_{x \to \infty} f(x) = -\frac{2}{3}$

  d **i** as $x \to 1^-$, $f(x) \to \infty$,

    as $x \to 1^+$, $f(x) \to -\infty$,

    as $x \to \infty$, $f(x) \to -1^-$

    as $x \to -\infty$, $f(x) \to -1^+$

    vertical asymptote $x = 1$, horizontal asymptote $y = -1$

   ii $\lim\limits_{x \to -\infty} f(x) = -1$, $\lim\limits_{x \to \infty} f(x) = -1$

  e **i** as $x \to \infty$, $y \to 1^-$ horizontal asymptote $y = 1$

    as $x \to -\infty$, $y \to 1^-$ no vertical asymptote

   ii $\lim\limits_{x \to -\infty} f(x) = 1$, $\lim\limits_{x \to \infty} f(x) = 1$

  f **i** as $x \to \infty$, $f(x) \to 0^+$

    as $x \to -\infty$, $f(x) \to 0^-$

    horizontal asymptote $y = 0$

    no vertical asymptote

   ii $\lim\limits_{x \to -\infty} f(x) = 0$, $\lim\limits_{x \to \infty} f(x) = 0$

2 **a**

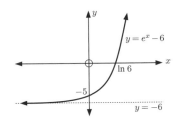

  b **i** $\lim\limits_{x \to -\infty} (e^x - 6) = -6$

   ii $\lim\limits_{x \to \infty} (e^x - 6)$ does not exist

    $y = -6$ is a horizontal asymptote of $y = e^x - 6$.

3 $\lim\limits_{x \to -\infty} (2e^{-x} - 3)$ does not exist, $\lim\limits_{x \to \infty} (2e^{-x} - 3) = -3$

EXERCISE 14C

1 **a**

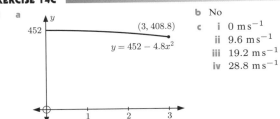

  b No

  c **i** 0 m s^{-1}

   ii 9.6 m s^{-1}

   iii 19.2 m s^{-1}

   iv 28.8 m s^{-1}

2 **a**

x	Point B	Gradient of [AB]
0	(0, 0)	2
1	(1, 1)	3
1.5	(1.5, 2.25)	3.5
1.9	(1.9, 3.61)	3.9
1.99	(1.99, 3.9601)	3.99
1.999	(1.999, 3.996 001)	3.999

x	Point B	Gradient of [AB]
5	(5, 25)	7
3	(3, 9)	5
2.5	(2.5, 6.25)	4.5
2.1	(2.1, 4.41)	4.1
2.01	(2.01, 4.0401)	4.01
2.001	(2.001, 4.004 001)	4.001

  b $\lim\limits_{x \to 2} \dfrac{x^2 - 4}{x - 2} = 4$

  The gradient of the tangent to $y = x^2$ at the point (2, 4) is 4.

EXERCISE 14D

1 **a** 3 **b** 0 **2** **a** 4 **b** −1 **3** $f(2) = 3$, $f'(2) = 1$

EXERCISE 14E

1 **a** **i** 1 **ii** 0 **iii** $3x^2$ **iv** $4x^3$ **b** $f'(x) = nx^{n-1}$

2 **a** 2 **b** $2x - 3$ **c** $-2x + 5$

3 **a** $\dfrac{dy}{dx} = -1$ **b** $\dfrac{dy}{dx} = 4x + 1$ **c** $\dfrac{dy}{dx} = 3x^2 - 4x$

4 a 12   **b** 108   **5 a** 3   **b** −12   **c** 9   **d** 10

6 a $\dfrac{dy}{dx} = 3x^2 - 3$ **b** $(-1, 2)$ and $(1, -2)$

REVIEW SET 14A

1 a −1   **b** −1   **c** 8

2 a $f'(x) = 2x + 2$ **b** $\dfrac{dy}{dx} = -6x$ **3** 3

4 a $f'(t) = -9.6t$ m s^{-1}
   b 19.2 m s^{-1} (the − sign indicates travelling downwards)

REVIEW SET 14B

1 a as $x \to -\frac{2}{3}^-$, $f(x) \to \infty$,
   as $x \to -\frac{2}{3}^+$, $f(x) \to -\infty$,
   as $x \to \infty$, $f(x) \to \frac{1}{3}^-$
   as $x \to -\infty$, $f(x) \to \frac{1}{3}^+$
   vertical asymptote $x = -\frac{2}{3}$, horizontal asymptote $y = \frac{1}{3}$

b $\lim\limits_{x \to -\infty} \dfrac{x-7}{3x+2} = \frac{1}{3}$, $\lim\limits_{x \to \infty} \dfrac{x-7}{3x+2} = \frac{1}{3}$

2 a

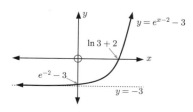

$y = e^{x-2} - 3$
$\ln 3 + 2$
$e^{-2} - 3$
$y = -3$

b $\lim\limits_{x \to -\infty} (e^{x-2} - 3) = -3$,   **c** $y = -3$
   $\lim\limits_{x \to \infty} (e^{x-2} - 3)$ does not exist

3 b i 12.2   **ii** 12.02   **iii** 12
   c The gradient of the tangent to $y = 2x^2$ at $(3, 18)$ is 12.

4 $\lim\limits_{x \to \infty} \left(\dfrac{2x+3}{4-x}\right) = \lim\limits_{x \to -\infty} \left(\dfrac{2x+3}{4-x}\right) = -2$

REVIEW SET 14C

1 a −3   **b** 3   **c** −1

2 a

$y = \dfrac{2+x}{x-4}$
$y = 1$
-2
$-\frac{1}{2}$
$x = 4$

b as $x \to 4^-$, $y \to -\infty$, as $x \to \infty$, $y \to 1^+$,
   as $x \to 4^+$, $y \to \infty$, as $x \to -\infty$, $y \to 1^-$
   vertical asymptote $x = 4$, horizontal asymptote $y = 1$

c $\lim\limits_{x \to -\infty} \dfrac{2+x}{x-4} = 1$, $\lim\limits_{x \to \infty} \dfrac{2+x}{x-4} = 1$

3 $f'(1) = 2$

4 a $\dfrac{dy}{dx} = 4x$ **b** gradient $= 16$ **c** when $x = -3$

EXERCISE 15A

1 a $3x^2$ **b** $6x^2$ **c** $14x$ **d** $\dfrac{3}{\sqrt{x}}$

e $\dfrac{1}{\sqrt[3]{x^2}}$ **f** $2x + 1$ **g** $-4x$ **h** $2x + 3$

i $2x^3 - 12x$ **j** $\dfrac{6}{x^2}$ **k** $-\dfrac{2}{x^2} + \dfrac{6}{x^3}$

l $2x - \dfrac{5}{x^2}$ **m** $2x + \dfrac{3}{x^2}$ **n** $-\dfrac{1}{2x\sqrt{x}}$

o $8x - 4$ **p** $3x^2 + 12x + 12$

2 a $7.5x^2 - 2.8x$ **b** $2\pi x$ **c** $-\dfrac{2}{5x^3}$

d 100   **e** 10   **f** $12\pi x^2$

3 a 6   **b** $\dfrac{3\sqrt{x}}{2}$ **c** $2x - 10$

d $2 - 9x^2$ **e** $2x - 1$ **f** $-\dfrac{2}{x^3} + \dfrac{3}{\sqrt{x}}$

g $4 + \dfrac{1}{4x^2}$ **h** $6x^2 - 6x - 5$

4 a 4   **b** $-\dfrac{16}{729}$ **c** −7   **d** $\dfrac{13}{4}$ **e** $\dfrac{1}{8}$ **f** −11

5 $b = 3$, $c = -4$

6 a $\dfrac{2}{\sqrt{x}} + 1$ **b** $\dfrac{1}{3\sqrt[3]{x^2}}$ **c** $\dfrac{1}{x\sqrt{x}}$

d $2 - \dfrac{1}{2\sqrt{x}}$ **e** $-\dfrac{2}{x\sqrt{x}}$ **f** $6x - \frac{3}{2}\sqrt{x}$

g $\dfrac{-25}{2x^3\sqrt{x}}$ **h** $2 + \dfrac{9}{2x^2\sqrt{x}}$

7 a $\dfrac{dy}{dx} = 4 + \dfrac{3}{x^2}$, $\dfrac{dy}{dx}$ is the gradient function of $y = 4x - \dfrac{3}{x}$ from which the gradient at any point can be found.

b $\dfrac{dS}{dt} = 4t + 4$ m s^{-1}, $\dfrac{dS}{dt}$ is the instantaneous rate of change in position at the time t, or the velocity function.

c $\dfrac{dC}{dx} = 3 + 0.004x$ $ per toaster, $\dfrac{dC}{dx}$ is the instantaneous rate of change in cost as the number of toasters changes.

EXERCISE 15B.1

1 a $g(f(x)) = (2x + 7)^2$ **b** $g(f(x)) = 2x^2 + 7$
   c $g(f(x)) = \sqrt{3 - 4x}$ **d** $g(f(x)) = 3 - 4\sqrt{x}$
   e $g(f(x)) = \dfrac{2}{x^2 + 3}$ **f** $g(f(x)) = \dfrac{4}{x^2} + 3$

2 a $g(x) = x^3$, $f(x) = 3x + 10$
   b $g(x) = \dfrac{1}{x}$, $f(x) = 2x + 4$
   c $g(x) = \sqrt{x}$, $f(x) = x^2 - 3x$
   d $g(x) = \dfrac{10}{x^3}$, $f(x) = 3x - x^2$

EXERCISE 15B.2

1 a u^{-2}, $u = 2x - 1$ **b** $u^{\frac{1}{2}}$, $u = x^2 - 3x$
   c $2u^{-\frac{1}{2}}$, $u = 2 - x^2$ **d** $u^{\frac{1}{3}}$, $u = x^3 - x^2$
   e $4u^{-3}$, $u = 3 - x$ **f** $10u^{-1}$, $u = x^2 - 3$

2 a $8(4x - 5)$ **b** $2(5 - 2x)^{-2}$ **c** $\frac{1}{2}(3x - x^2)^{-\frac{1}{2}} \times (3 - 2x)$
   d $-12(1 - 3x)^3$ **e** $-18(5 - x)^2$

f $\frac{1}{3}(2x^3 - x^2)^{-\frac{2}{3}} \times (6x^2 - 2x)$ g $-60(5x-4)^{-3}$

h $-4(3x-x^2)^{-2} \times (3-2x)$ i $6(x^2 - \frac{2}{x})^2 \times (2x + \frac{2}{x^2})$

3 a $-\frac{1}{\sqrt{3}}$ b -18 c -8 d -4 e $-\frac{3}{32}$ f 0

4 $a=3,\ b=1$ **5** $a=2,\ b=1$

6 a $\dfrac{dy}{dx} = 3x^2,\quad \dfrac{dx}{dy} = \frac{1}{3}y^{-\frac{2}{3}}$ **Hint:** Substitute $y = x^3$

  b $\dfrac{dy}{dx} \times \dfrac{dx}{dy} = \dfrac{dy}{dy} = 1$

EXERCISE 15C

1 a $2x-1$ b $4x+2$ c $2x(x+1)^{\frac{1}{2}} + \frac{1}{2}x^2(x+1)^{-\frac{1}{2}}$

2 a $2x(2x-1) + 2x^2$ b $4(2x+1)^3 + 24x(2x+1)^2$

  c $2x(3-x)^{\frac{1}{2}} - \frac{1}{2}x^2(3-x)^{-\frac{1}{2}}$

  d $\frac{1}{2}x^{-\frac{1}{2}}(x-3)^2 + 2\sqrt{x}(x-3)$

  e $10x(3x^2-1)^2 + 60x^3(3x^2-1)$

  f $\frac{1}{2}x^{-\frac{1}{2}}(x-x^2)^3 + 3\sqrt{x}(x-x^2)^2(1-2x)$

3 a -48 b $406\frac{1}{4}$ c $\frac{13}{3}$ d $\frac{11}{4}$

4 b $x=3$ or $\frac{3}{5}$ c $x \leqslant 0$ d $x=0$

  e As we approach the point $x=0$ from the right, the curve has steeper and steeper gradient and approaches vertical.

5 $x=-1$ and $x=-\frac{5}{3}$

EXERCISE 15D

1 a $\dfrac{7}{(2-x)^2}$ b $\dfrac{2x(2x+1) - 2x^2}{(2x+1)^2}$

  c $\dfrac{(x^2-3) - 2x^2}{(x^2-3)^2}$ d $\dfrac{\frac{1}{2}x^{-\frac{1}{2}}(1-2x) + 2\sqrt{x}}{(1-2x)^2}$

  e $\dfrac{2x(3x-x^2) - (x^2-3)(3-2x)}{(3x-x^2)^2}$

  f $\dfrac{(1-3x)^{\frac{1}{2}} + \frac{3}{2}x(1-3x)^{-\frac{1}{2}}}{1-3x}$

2 a 1 b 1 c $-\frac{7}{324}$ d $-\frac{28}{27}$

3 b i never $\{\dfrac{dy}{dx}$ is undefined at $x=-1\}$

    ii $x \leqslant 0$ and $x=1$

4 b i $x = -2 \pm \sqrt{11}$ ii $x = -2$

  c $\dfrac{dy}{dx}$ is zero when the tangent to the function is horizontal (gradient 0), at its turning points or points of horizontal inflection. $\dfrac{dy}{dx}$ is undefined at vertical asymptotes.

EXERCISE 15E

1 a $4e^{4x}$ b e^x c $-2e^{-2x}$ d $\frac{1}{2}e^{\frac{x}{2}}$

  e $-e^{-\frac{x}{2}}$ f $2e^{-x}$ g $2e^{\frac{x}{2}} + 3e^{-x}$

  h $\dfrac{e^x - e^{-x}}{2}$ i $-2xe^{-x^2}$ j $e^{\frac{1}{x}} \times \dfrac{-1}{x^2}$

  k $20e^{2x}$ l $40e^{-2x}$ m $2e^{2x+1}$

  n $\frac{1}{4}e^{\frac{x}{4}}$ o $-4xe^{1-2x^2}$ p $-0.02e^{-0.02x}$

2 a $e^x + xe^x$ b $3x^2e^{-x} - x^3e^{-x}$ c $\dfrac{xe^x - e^x}{x^2}$

  d $\dfrac{1-x}{e^x}$ e $2xe^{3x} + 3x^2e^{3x}$ f $\dfrac{xe^x - \frac{1}{2}e^x}{x\sqrt{x}}$

  g $\frac{1}{2}x^{-\frac{1}{2}}e^{-x} - x^{\frac{1}{2}}e^{-x}$ h $\dfrac{e^x + 2 + 2e^{-x}}{(e^{-x}+1)^2}$

3 a 108 b -1 c $\frac{9}{\sqrt{19}}$

4 $k=-9$ **5** a $\dfrac{dy}{dx} = 2^x \ln 2$ **6** $(0,0)$ or $(2, \frac{4}{e^2})$

EXERCISE 15F

1 a $\dfrac{1}{x}$ b $\dfrac{2}{2x+1}$ c $\dfrac{1-2x}{x-x^2}$

  d $-\dfrac{2}{x}$ e $2x \ln x + x$ f $\dfrac{1 - \ln x}{2x^2}$

  g $e^x \ln x + \dfrac{e^x}{x}$ h $\dfrac{2 \ln x}{x}$ i $\dfrac{1}{2x\sqrt{\ln x}}$

  j $\dfrac{e^{-x}}{x} - e^{-x} \ln x$ k $\dfrac{\ln(2x)}{2\sqrt{x}} + \dfrac{1}{\sqrt{x}}$ l $\dfrac{\ln x - 2}{\sqrt{x}(\ln x)^2}$

  m $\dfrac{4}{1-x}$ n $\ln(x^2+1) + \dfrac{2x^2}{x^2+1}$

2 a $\ln 5$ b $\dfrac{3}{x}$ c $\dfrac{4x^3+1}{x^4+x}$ d $\dfrac{1}{x-2}$

  e $\dfrac{6}{2x+1}[\ln(2x+1)]^2$ f $\dfrac{1 - \ln(4x)}{x^2}$

  g $-\dfrac{1}{x}$ h $\dfrac{1}{x\ln x}$ i $\dfrac{-1}{x(\ln x)^2}$

3 a $\dfrac{-1}{1-2x}$ b $\dfrac{-2}{2x+3}$ c $1 + \dfrac{1}{2x}$

  d $\dfrac{1}{x} - \dfrac{1}{2(2-x)}$ e $\dfrac{1}{x+3} - \dfrac{1}{x-1}$ f $\dfrac{2}{x} + \dfrac{1}{3-x}$

  g $\dfrac{9}{3x-4}$ h $\dfrac{1}{x} + \dfrac{2x}{x^2+1}$ i $\dfrac{2x+2}{x^2+2x} - \dfrac{1}{x-5}$

4 2 **5** $a=3,\ b=-e$

EXERCISE 15G

1 a $2\cos(2x)$ b $\cos x - \sin x$

  c $-3\sin(3x) - \cos x$ d $\cos(x+1)$ e $2\sin(3-2x)$

  f $\dfrac{5}{\cos^2(5x)}$ g $\frac{1}{2}\cos(\frac{x}{2}) + 3\sin x$

  h $\dfrac{3\pi}{\cos^2(\pi x)}$ i $4\cos x + 2\sin(2x)$

2 a $2x - \sin x$ b $\dfrac{1}{\cos^2 x} - 3\cos x$

  c $e^x \cos x - e^x \sin x$ d $-e^{-x}\sin x + e^{-x}\cos x$

  e $\dfrac{\cos x}{\sin x}$ f $2e^{2x}\tan x + \dfrac{e^{2x}}{\cos^2 x}$

  g $3\cos(3x)$ h $-\frac{1}{2}\sin(\frac{x}{2})$ i $\dfrac{6}{\cos^2(2x)}$

  j $\cos x - x\sin x$ k $\dfrac{x\cos x - \sin x}{x^2}$ l $\tan x + \dfrac{x}{\cos^2 x}$

3 a $2x\cos(x^2)$ b $-\dfrac{1}{2\sqrt{x}}\sin(\sqrt{x})$ c $-\dfrac{\sin x}{2\sqrt{\cos x}}$

  d $2\sin x \cos x$ e $-3\sin x \cos^2 x$

  f $-\sin x \sin(2x) + 2\cos x \cos(2x)$ g $\sin x \sin(\cos x)$

  h $-12\sin(4x)\cos^2(4x)$ i $-\dfrac{\cos x}{\sin^2 x}$

$\mathbf{j}$ $\dfrac{2\sin(2x)}{\cos^2(2x)}$ $\mathbf{k}$ $-\dfrac{8\cos(2x)}{\sin^3(2x)}$ $\mathbf{l}$ $\dfrac{-12}{\cos^2(\frac{x}{2})\tan^4(\frac{x}{2})}$

4 $\mathbf{a}$ $-\frac{9}{8}$ $\mathbf{b}$ 0

EXERCISE 15H

1 $\mathbf{a}$ 6 $\mathbf{b}$ $\dfrac{3}{2x^{\frac{5}{2}}}$ $\mathbf{c}$ $12x - 6$

$\mathbf{d}$ $\dfrac{12 - 6x}{x^4}$ $\mathbf{e}$ $24 - 48x$ $\mathbf{f}$ $\dfrac{20}{(2x - 1)^3}$

2 $\mathbf{a}$ $-6x$ $\mathbf{b}$ $2 - \dfrac{30}{x^4}$ $\mathbf{c}$ $-\frac{9}{4}x^{-\frac{5}{2}}$ $\mathbf{d}$ $\dfrac{8}{x^3}$

$\mathbf{e}$ $6(x^2 - 3x)(5x^2 - 15x + 9)$ $\mathbf{f}$ $2 + \dfrac{2}{(1 - x)^3}$

3 $\mathbf{a}$ 9 $\mathbf{b}$ 10 $\mathbf{c}$ 12 $\mathbf{d}$ 6

5 $\mathbf{a}$ $x = 1$ **6**
$\mathbf{b}$ $x = 0, \pm\sqrt{6}$

x	-1	0	1
$f(x)$	$-$	0	$+$
$f'(x)$	$+$	$-$	$+$
$f''(x)$	$-$	0	$+$

8 $\mathbf{b}$ $f''(x) = 3\sin x\cos 2x + 6\cos x\sin 2x$

9 $\mathbf{a}$ $\dfrac{1}{x^2}$ $\mathbf{b}$ $\dfrac{1}{x}$ $\mathbf{c}$ $\dfrac{2}{x^2}(1 - \ln x)$

10 $\mathbf{a}$ 0 $\mathbf{b}$ 3 $\mathbf{c}$ 0 $\mathbf{d}$ 6

11 **Hint:** Find $\dfrac{dy}{dx}$ and $\dfrac{d^2y}{dx^2}$ and substitute into the equation.

REVIEW SET 15A

1 $\mathbf{a}$ -17 $\mathbf{b}$ -17 $\mathbf{c}$ -6 **2** $\mathbf{a}$ $6x - 4x^3$ $\mathbf{b}$ $1 + \dfrac{1}{x^2}$

3 $(0, 0)$ **4** $\mathbf{a}$ $3x^2e^{x^3 + 2}$ $\mathbf{b}$ $\dfrac{1}{x + 3} - \dfrac{2}{x}$

6 $\mathbf{a}$ $5\cos(5x)\ln x + \dfrac{\sin(5x)}{x}$

$\mathbf{b}$ $\cos x\cos(2x) - 2\sin x\sin(2x)$

$\mathbf{c}$ $-2e^{-2x}\tan x + \dfrac{e^{-2x}}{\cos^2 x}$

7 $\dfrac{\sqrt{3}}{2}$

8 $\mathbf{a}$ $f'(x) = 8x(x^2 + 3)^3$

$\mathbf{b}$ $g'(x) = \dfrac{\frac{1}{2}x(x + 5)^{-\frac{1}{2}} - 2(x + 5)^{\frac{1}{2}}}{x^3}$

9 $\mathbf{a}$ $\frac{23}{4}$ $\mathbf{b}$ $-\frac{1}{8\sqrt{2}}$

REVIEW SET 15B

1 $\mathbf{a}$ $\dfrac{dy}{dx} = 5 + 3x^{-2}$ $\mathbf{b}$ $\dfrac{dy}{dx} = 4(3x^2 + x)^3(6x + 1)$

$\mathbf{c}$ $\dfrac{dy}{dx} = 2x(1 - x^2)^3 - 6x(x^2 + 1)(1 - x^2)^2$

2 $(-2, 19)$ and $(1, -2)$

3 $\mathbf{a}$ $-2(5 - 4x)^{-\frac{1}{2}}$ $\mathbf{b}$ $-4(5 - 4x)^{-\frac{3}{2}}$

4 $\mathbf{a}$

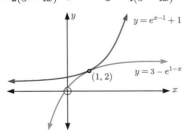

b $(1, 2)$ **c** gradient is $e^0 = 1$ for both
d The tangents to each of the curves at this point are the same line.

5 $\mathbf{a}$ $\dfrac{3x^2 - 3}{x^3 - 3x}$ $\mathbf{b}$ $\dfrac{e^x(x - 2)}{x^3}$ **6** $x = -\frac{1}{2}, \frac{3}{2}$

7 $\mathbf{a}$ $\pi + 1$ $\mathbf{b}$ 2 $\mathbf{c}$ $-\dfrac{\sqrt{2}}{2}$

8 $\dfrac{dy}{dx} = 3b\cos(bx) + 2a\sin(2x)$, $a = 2$, $b = -1$ or 1

9 $\mathbf{a}$ $10 - 10\cos(10x)$ $\mathbf{b}$ $\tan x$

$\mathbf{c}$ $5\cos(5x)\ln(2x) + \dfrac{\sin(5x)}{x}$

REVIEW SET 15C

1 $\mathbf{a}$ $\dfrac{dy}{dx} = 3x^2(1 - x^2)^{\frac{1}{2}} - x^4(1 - x^2)^{-\frac{1}{2}}$

$\mathbf{b}$ $\dfrac{dy}{dx} = \dfrac{(2x - 3)(x + 1)^{\frac{1}{2}} - \frac{1}{2}(x^2 - 3x)(x + 1)^{-\frac{1}{2}}}{x + 1}$

2 $\mathbf{a}$ $\dfrac{d^2y}{dx^2} = 36x^2 - \dfrac{4}{x^3}$ $\mathbf{b}$ $\dfrac{d^2y}{dx^2} = 6x + \frac{3}{4}x^{-\frac{5}{2}}$

3 $(1, e)$

4 $\mathbf{a}$ $f'(x) = \dfrac{e^x}{e^x + 3}$ $\mathbf{b}$ $f'(x) = \dfrac{3}{x + 2} - \dfrac{1}{x}$ **5** 0

6 $\mathbf{a}$ $f'(x) = \frac{1}{2}x^{-\frac{1}{2}}\cos(4x) - 4x^{\frac{1}{2}}\sin(4x)$,

$f''(x) = -\frac{1}{4}x^{-\frac{3}{2}}\cos(4x) - 4x^{-\frac{1}{2}}\sin(4x)$

$- 16x^{\frac{1}{2}}\cos(4x)$

$\mathbf{b}$ $f'(\frac{\pi}{16}) \approx -0.455$, $f''(\frac{\pi}{8}) \approx -6.38$

8 $\mathbf{a}$ $x \approx -11.7$ or $x \approx -0.255$
$\mathbf{b}$ $x \approx -1.73$ or $x \approx 1.73$
$\mathbf{c}$ $x = -3$ or $x = 0$ or $x = 3$

9 $\mathbf{a}$ $f(x) = -5\sin 4x$ $\mathbf{b}$ $x = \frac{\pi}{8}, \frac{3\pi}{8}, \frac{5\pi}{8}, \frac{7\pi}{8}$

EXERCISE 16A

1 $\mathbf{a}$ $y = -7x + 11$ $\mathbf{b}$ $4y = x + 8$ $\mathbf{c}$ $y = -2x - 2$
$\mathbf{d}$ $y = -2x + 6$ $\mathbf{e}$ $y = -5x - 9$ $\mathbf{f}$ $y = -5x - 1$

2 $\mathbf{a}$ $6y = -x + 57$ $\mathbf{b}$ $7y = -x + 26$ $\mathbf{c}$ $3y = x + 11$
$\mathbf{d}$ $6y = -x + 43$

3 $\mathbf{a}$ $y = 21$ and $y = -6$ $\mathbf{b}$ $(\frac{1}{2}, 2\sqrt{2})$
$\mathbf{c}$ $k = -5$ $\mathbf{d}$ $y = -3x + 1$

4 $\mathbf{a}$ $a = -4$, $b = 7$ $\mathbf{b}$ $a = 2$, $b = 4$

5 $\mathbf{a}$ $3y = x + 5$ $\mathbf{b}$ $9y = x + 4$
$\mathbf{c}$ $16y = x - 3$ $\mathbf{d}$ $y = -4$

6 $\mathbf{a}$ $y = 2x - \frac{7}{4}$ $\mathbf{b}$ $y = -27x - \frac{242}{3}$
$\mathbf{c}$ $57y = -4x + 1042$ $\mathbf{d}$ $2y = x + 1$

7 $a = 4$, $b = 3$

8 $\mathbf{a}$ $x + ey = 2$ $\mathbf{b}$ $x + 3y = 3\ln 3 - 1$
$\mathbf{c}$ $2x + e^2y = \frac{2}{e^2} - e^2$

10 $\mathbf{a}$ $y = x$ $\mathbf{b}$ $y = x$ $\mathbf{c}$ $2x - y = \frac{\pi}{3} - \frac{\sqrt{3}}{2}$ $\mathbf{d}$ $x = \frac{\pi}{4}$

11 $\mathbf{a}$ $(-4, -64)$ $\mathbf{b}$ $(4, -31)$
$\mathbf{c}$ does not meet the curve again

12 $\mathbf{a}$ $f'(x) = 2x - \dfrac{8}{x^3}$ $\mathbf{b}$ $x = \pm\sqrt{2}$ $\mathbf{c}$ tangent is $y = 4$

13 A is $(\frac{2}{3}, 0)$, B is $(0, -2e)$

14 **a** $y = (2a-1)x - a^2 + 9$; $y = 5x$, contact at $(3, 15)$
$y = -7x$, contact at $(-3, 21)$

b $y = 0$, $y = 27x + 54$ **c** $y = -\sqrt{14}x + 4\sqrt{14}$

15 $y = e^a x + e^a(1-a)$ so $y = ex$ is the tangent to $y = e^x$ from the origin

16 **a**
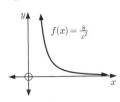
$f(x) = \frac{8}{x^2}$

b $16x + a^3 y = 24a$

c A is $(\frac{3}{2}a, 0)$,

B is $(0, \dfrac{24}{a^2})$

d Area $= \dfrac{18}{a}$ units^2,

area $\to 0$ as $a \to \infty$

17 $\approx 63.43°$

18 **a** **Hint:** They must have the same y-coordinate at $x = b$ and the same gradient.

c $a = \frac{1}{2e}$ **d** $y = e^{-\frac{1}{2}}x - \frac{1}{2}$

EXERCISE 16B

1 **a** **i** $x \geqslant 0$ **ii** never
  b **i** never   **ii** $-2 < x \leqslant 3$
  c **i** $x \leqslant 2$ **ii** $x \geqslant 2$
  d **i** all real x **ii** never
  e **i** $1 \leqslant x \leqslant 5$ **ii** $x \leqslant 1$, $x \geqslant 5$
  f **i** $2 \leqslant x < 4$, $x > 4$ **ii** $x < 0$, $0 < x \leqslant 2$

2 **a** increasing for $x \geqslant 0$, decreasing for $x \leqslant 0$
  b decreasing for all x
  c increasing for $x \geqslant -\frac{3}{4}$, decreasing for $x \leqslant -\frac{3}{4}$
  d increasing for $x \geqslant 0$, never decreasing
  e decreasing for $x > 0$, never increasing
  f incr. for $x \leqslant 0$ and $x \geqslant 4$, decr. for $0 \leqslant x \leqslant 4$
  g increasing for all x
  h increasing for $x > 0$, never decreasing
  i increasing for $-\sqrt{\frac{2}{3}} \leqslant x \leqslant \sqrt{\frac{2}{3}}$,
    decreasing for $x \leqslant -\sqrt{\frac{2}{3}}$, $x \geqslant \sqrt{\frac{2}{3}}$
  j decr. for $x \leqslant -\frac{1}{2}$, $x \geqslant 3$, incr. for $-\frac{1}{2} \leqslant x \leqslant 3$
  k decreasing for all x
  l decreasing for $x \leqslant -1$, increasing for $x \geqslant -1$
  m increasing for $x \geqslant 0$, decreasing for $x \leqslant 0$
  n increasing for $x \geqslant -\frac{3}{2} + \frac{\sqrt{5}}{2}$ and $x \leqslant -\frac{3}{2} - \frac{\sqrt{5}}{2}$
    decreasing for $-\frac{3}{2} - \frac{\sqrt{5}}{2} \leqslant x \leqslant -\frac{3}{2} + \frac{\sqrt{5}}{2}$
  o increasing for $x \leqslant 2 - \sqrt{3}$, $x \geqslant 2 + \sqrt{3}$
    decreasing for $2 - \sqrt{3} \leqslant x \leqslant 2 + \sqrt{3}$
  p increasing for $x \geqslant 1$, decreasing for $0 \leqslant x \leqslant 1$

3 **a**

b increasing for $-1 \leqslant x \leqslant 1$
  decreasing for $x \leqslant -1$, $x \geqslant 1$

4 **a**

b increasing for $-1 \leqslant x < 1$
  decreasing for $x \leqslant -1$, $x > 1$

5 **a**

b increasing for $-1 \leqslant x < 1$, $1 < x \leqslant 3$
  decreasing for $x \leqslant -1$, $x \geqslant 3$

6 **a** increasing for $x \geqslant \sqrt{3}$ and $x \leqslant -\sqrt{3}$
    decreasing for $-\sqrt{3} \leqslant x < -1$, $-1 < x < 1$,
    $1 < x \leqslant \sqrt{3}$
  b increasing for $x \geqslant 0$, decreasing for $x \leqslant 0$
  c increasing for $x \geqslant 2$, decreasing for $x < 1$, $1 < x \leqslant 2$
  d increasing for $x \leqslant -1$,
    decreasing for $-1 \leqslant x < 0$, $x > 0$

EXERCISE 16C

1 **a** A - local max, B - stationary inflection, C - local min.
  b
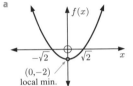

  c **i** $x \leqslant -2$, $x \geqslant 3$ **ii** $-2 \leqslant x \leqslant 3$
  d
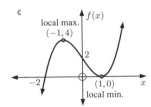

2 **a**
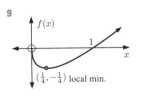

b
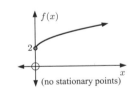

c

d
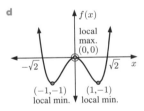

e

f
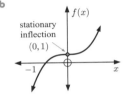

g

h
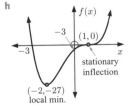

i

j
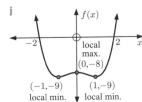
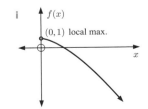

3 $x = -\dfrac{b}{2a}$, local min if $a > 0$, local max if $a < 0$

4 **a** local maximum at $(1, e^{-1})$
   b local max. at $(-2, 4e^{-2})$, local min. at $(0, 0)$
   c local minimum at $(1, e)$ **d** local maximum at $(-1, e)$

5 $a = 9$

6 **a** $a = -12$, $b = -13$
   b $(-2, 3)$ local max. $(2, -29)$ local min

7 **a** $x > 0$

8 **a**
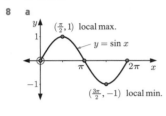
$(\frac{\pi}{2}, 1)$ local max.
$y = \sin x$
$(\frac{3\pi}{2}, -1)$ local min.

   b
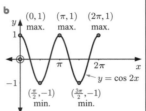
$(0, 1)$ $(\pi, 1)$ $(2\pi, 1)$
max. max. max.
$y = \cos 2x$
$(\frac{\pi}{2}, -1)$ $(\frac{3\pi}{2}, -1)$
min. min.

   c
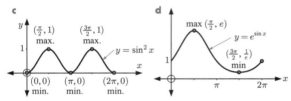
$(\frac{\pi}{2}, 1)$ $(\frac{3\pi}{2}, 1)$
max. max.
$y = \sin^2 x$
$(0, 0)$ $(\pi, 0)$ $(2\pi, 0)$
min. min. min.

   d
max $(\frac{\pi}{2}, e)$
$y = e^{\sin x}$
$(\frac{3\pi}{2}, \frac{1}{e})$
min

   e
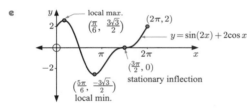
local max.
$(\frac{\pi}{6}, \frac{3\sqrt{3}}{2})$
$(2\pi, 2)$
$y = \sin(2x) + 2\cos x$
$(\frac{3\pi}{2}, 0)$
stationary inflection
$(\frac{5\pi}{6}, \frac{-3\sqrt{3}}{2})$
local min.

9 $P(x) = -9x^3 - 9x^2 + 9x + 2$

10 **a** greatest value is 63 when $x = 5$,
      least value is -18 when $x = 2$
   b greatest value is 4 when $x = 3$ and $x = 0$,
      least value is -16 when $x = -2$.

12 Hint: Show that as $x \to 0$, $f(x) \to -\infty$,
      and as $x \to \infty$, $f(x) \to 0$.

13 Hint: Show that $f(x) \geqslant 1$ for all $x > 0$.

EXERCISE 16D.1

1 a

Point	$f(x)$	$f'(x)$	$f''(x)$
A	$+$	$-$	$+$
B	$-$	0	$+$
C	$+$	$+$	0
D	$+$	0	$-$
E	0	$-$	$-$

   b B is a local minimum, D is a local maximum
   c C is a non-stationary point of inflection

2 **a** no inflection   **b** stationary inflection at $(0, 2)$
   c non-stationary inflection at $(2, 3)$
   d stationary inflection at $(-2, -3)$
   e stationary inflection at $(0, 2)$
     non-stationary inflection at $(-\frac{4}{3}, \frac{310}{27})$
   f no inflection

3 **a** **i** local minimum at $(0, 0)$ **v**
     ii no points of inflection
     iii decreasing for $x \leqslant 0$,
      increasing for $x \geqslant 0$
     iv function is concave up
      for all x

$(0, 0)$ local min.

   b **i** stationary inflection at $(0, 0)$ **v**
     ii stationary inflection at $(0, 0)$
     iii increasing for all
      real x
     iv concave down for $x \leqslant 0$,
      concave up for $x \geqslant 0$
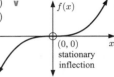
$(0, 0)$ stationary inflection

   c **i** $f'(x) \neq 0$, no stationary points   **v**
     ii no points of inflection
     iii increasing for $x \geqslant 0$,
      never decreasing
     iv concave down for $x \geqslant 0$,
      never concave up

   d **i** local max. at $(-2, 29)$ **v**
     local min. at $(4, -79)$
     ii non-stationary
     inflection at $(1, -25)$
     iii increasing for
     $x \leqslant -2$, $x \geqslant 4$
     decreasing for
     $-2 \leqslant x \leqslant 4$
     iv concave down for
     $x \leqslant 1$,
     concave up for $x \geqslant 1$
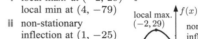
local max. $(-2, 29)$ non-stationary inflection $(1, -25)$ $(4, -79)$ local min

   e **i** stat. inflect. at $(0, -2)$ **v**
     local min. at $(-1, -3)$
     ii stat. inflect. at $(0, -2)$
     non-stationary inflection
     at $(-\frac{2}{3}, -\frac{70}{27})$
     iii increasing for $x \geqslant -1$,
     decreasing for $x \leqslant -1$
     iv concave down for
     $-\frac{2}{3} \leqslant x \leqslant 0$
     concave up for
     $x \leqslant -\frac{2}{3}$, $x \geqslant 0$
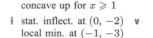
non-stationary inflection $(-\frac{2}{3}, -\frac{70}{27})$ local min. $(-1, -3)$ $(0, -2)$ stationary inflection

   f **i** local min. at   **v**
     $(1, 0)$
     ii no points of
     inflection
     iii increasing for
     $x \geqslant 1$,
     decreasing for
     $x \leqslant 1$
     iv concave up for
     all x

$y = (x-1)^4$ local min $(1, 0)$

   g **i** local minimum at $(-\sqrt{2}, -1)$ and $(\sqrt{2}, -1)$,
     local maximum at $(0, 3)$
     ii non-stationary inflection at $(\sqrt{\frac{2}{3}}, \frac{7}{9})$
     non-stationary inflection at $(-\sqrt{\frac{2}{3}}, \frac{7}{9})$
     iii increasing for $-\sqrt{2} \leqslant x \leqslant 0$, $x \geqslant \sqrt{2}$
     decreasing for $x \leqslant -\sqrt{2}$, $0 \leqslant x \leqslant \sqrt{2}$
     iv concave down for $-\sqrt{\frac{2}{3}} \leqslant x \leqslant \sqrt{\frac{2}{3}}$
     concave up for $x \leqslant -\sqrt{\frac{2}{3}}$, $x \geqslant \sqrt{\frac{2}{3}}$

v
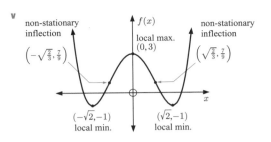

non-stationary inflection
$\left(-\sqrt{\frac{2}{3}}, \frac{7}{9}\right)$

$f(x)$

local max. $(0, 3)$

non-stationary inflection
$\left(\sqrt{\frac{2}{3}}, \frac{7}{9}\right)$

$(-\sqrt{2}, -1)$ local min.

$(\sqrt{2}, -1)$ local min.

h **i** no stationary points
ii no inflections
iii increasing for $x > 0$, never decreasing
iv concave down for $x > 0$, never concave up

v
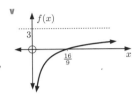

$f(x)$

3

$\frac{16}{9}$

4 **a** $A\left(\frac{\ln 3}{2}, 0\right)$, $B(0, -2)$ **b** $f'(x) = 2e^{2x} > 0$ for all x
  c $f''(x) = 4e^{2x} > 0$ for all x
  d
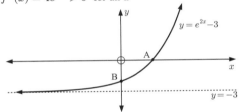

y

$y = e^{2x} - 3$

A

B

x

$y = -3$

  e as $x \to -\infty$, $e^{2x} \to 0$ $\therefore$ $e^{2x} - 3 \to -3^+$

5 **a** $f(x)$: x-int. at $x = \ln 3$, y-int. at $y = -2$
    $g(x)$: x-int. at $x = \ln\left(\frac{5}{3}\right)$, y-int. at $y = -2$
  b $f(x)$: as $x \to \infty$, $f(x) \to \infty$
       as $x \to -\infty$, $f(x) \to -3$ (above)
     $g(x)$: as $x \to \infty$, $g(x) \to 3$ (below)
       as $x \to -\infty$, $g(x) \to -\infty$
  c intersect at $(0, -2)$ and $(\ln 5, 2)$
  d
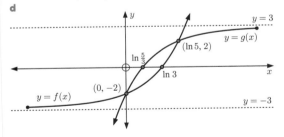

y

$y = 3$

$y = g(x)$

$(\ln 5, 2)$

$\ln \frac{5}{3}$

$\ln 3$ x

$(0, -2)$

$y = f(x)$

$y = -3$

6 **a** $P(\frac{1}{2} \ln 3, 0)$,
    $Q(0, -2)$

  b $\dfrac{dy}{dx} = e^x + 3e^{-x}$
    > 0 for all x

  c y is concave down below the x-axis and concave up above the x-axis

  d

y

-2

$\left(\frac{1}{2} \ln 3, 0\right)$
non-stationary inflection

x

7 **a** $x = \dfrac{e^3 + 1}{2} \approx 10.5$ **b** no, $\therefore$ there is no y-int.
  c gradient $= 2$ **d** Domain $= \{x \mid x > \frac{1}{2}\}$

e $f''(x) = \dfrac{-4}{(2x - 1)^2} < 0$ for all $x > \frac{1}{2}$, so $f(x)$ is concave down
f
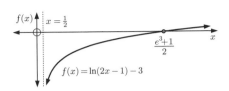

$f(x)$ $x = \frac{1}{2}$

$\frac{e^3 + 1}{2}$ x

$f(x) = \ln(2x - 1) - 3$

8 **a** $x > 0$
  b $f'(x) > 0$ for all $x > 0$, so $f(x)$ is always increasing. Its gradient is always positive. $f''(x) < 0$ for all $x > 0$, so $f(x)$ is concave down for all $x > 0$.
  c
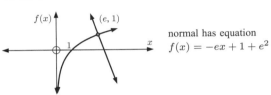

$f(x)$

$(e, 1)$

1 x

normal has equation $f(x) = -ex + 1 + e^2$

9 **a** $f(x)$ does not have any x or y-intercepts
  b as $x \to \infty$, $f(x) \to \infty$
     as $x \to -\infty$, $f(x) \to 0^-$
  c local minimum at $(1, e)$ **d** **i** $x > 0$ **ii** $x < 0$
  e
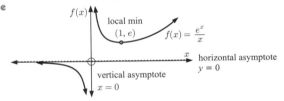

$f(x)$

local min $(1, e)$

$f(x) = \dfrac{e^x}{x}$

horizontal asymptote $y = 0$

x

vertical asymptote $x = 0$

  f $ey = -2x - 3$

10 **a** There is a local maximum at $\left(0, \frac{1}{\sqrt{2\pi}}\right)$.
    $f(x)$ is incr. for all $x \leqslant 0$ and decr. for all $x \geqslant 0$.
  b non-stationary inflections at $\left(-1, \frac{1}{\sqrt{2e\pi}}\right)$ and $\left(1, \frac{1}{\sqrt{2e\pi}}\right)$
  c as $x \to \infty$, $f(x) \to 0^+$
     as $x \to -\infty$, $f(x) \to 0^+$
  d
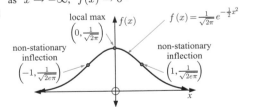

local max $\left(0, \frac{1}{\sqrt{2\pi}}\right)$

$f(x)$

$f(x) = \frac{1}{\sqrt{2\pi}} e^{-\frac{1}{2}x^2}$

non-stationary inflection $\left(-1, \frac{1}{\sqrt{2e\pi}}\right)$

non-stationary inflection $\left(1, \frac{1}{\sqrt{2e\pi}}\right)$

x

EXERCISE 16D.2

1 **a**
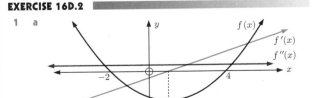

y

$f(x)$

$f'(x)$

$f''(x)$

-2

4 x

min

b

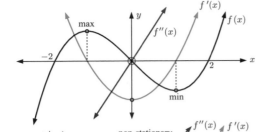

c

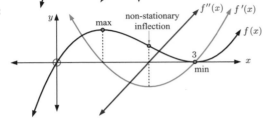

2 a

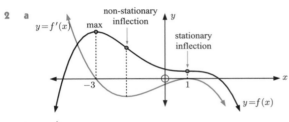

b

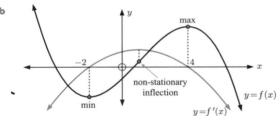

REVIEW SET 16A

1 $y = 4x + 2$ **2** $x = 1$

3 a $x = -3$ **b** x-int. $\frac{2}{3}$, y-int. $-\frac{2}{3}$

  c $f'(x) = \dfrac{11}{(x+3)^2}$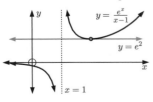

  d no stationary points

4 $y = \dfrac{e}{2}x + \dfrac{1}{e} - \dfrac{e}{2}$ **6** $a = \frac{5}{2}$, $b = -\frac{3}{2}$

8 a y-intercept at $y = -1$, no x-intercept
  b $f(x)$ is defined for all $x \neq 1$
  c $f'(x) \leqslant 0$ for $x < 1$ and $1 < x \leqslant 2$
    and $f'(x) > 0$ for $x \geqslant 2$
    $f''(x) > 0$ for $x > 1$, $f''(x) < 0$ for $x < 1$
    The function is decreasing for all defined values of $x \leqslant 2$,
    and increasing for all $x \geqslant 2$. The curve is concave down
    for $x < 1$ and concave up for $x > 1$.
  d   **e** tangent is $y = e^2$

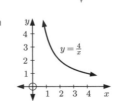

9 $a = -14$, $b = 21$ **10** $a = 64$ **11** P(0, 7.5), Q(3, 0)

12

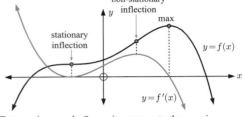

13 Tangent is $y = \ln 3$, so it never cuts the x-axis.

REVIEW SET 16B

1 $y = 7$, $y = -25$ **2** $\frac{3267}{152}$ units^2

3 a $a = -6$
  b local max. $(-\sqrt{2}, 4\sqrt{2})$,   local min. $(\sqrt{2}, -4\sqrt{2})$
  c

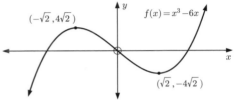

4 $p = 1$, $q = -8$ **5** $(-2, -25)$ **6** $a = \frac{1}{2}$

7 a local minimum at (0, 1)   **b** as $x \to \infty$, $f(x) \to \infty$
  c $f''(x) = e^x$,   thus $f(x)$ is concave up for all x.
  d

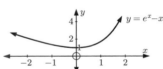

8 $y = \frac{1}{5}x - \frac{11}{5}$ (or $x - 5y = 11$)

10 $g(x) = -2x^2 + 6x + 3$

11 a for $0 \leqslant x \leqslant \frac{\pi}{2}$ and $\frac{3\pi}{2} \leqslant x \leqslant 2\pi$
  b increasing for $\frac{3\pi}{2} \leqslant x \leqslant 2\pi$, decreasing for $0 \leqslant x \leqslant \frac{\pi}{2}$
  c

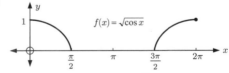

12

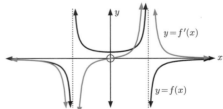

13 a

  b $y = -\dfrac{4}{k^2}x + \dfrac{8}{k}$

  c A$(2k, 0)$,   B$\left(0, \dfrac{8}{k}\right)$

  d Area = 8 units^2

  e $k = 2$

REVIEW SET 16C

1 $y = 16x - \frac{127}{2}$

2 a $f(3) = 2$, $f'(3) = -1$ **b** $f(x) = x^2 - 7x + 14$

3 $a = -1$, $b = 2$

4 a $a = 2$ and the tangent is $y = 3x - 1$ **b** $(-4, -13)$

5 $(0, \ln 4 - 1)$

6 a local maximum at $(-2, 51)$, local minimum at $(3, -74)$
non-stationary inflection at $(\frac{1}{2}, -11\frac{1}{2})$

b increasing for
$x \leqslant -2$, $x \geqslant 3$
decreasing for
$-2 \leqslant x \leqslant 3$

c concave down
for $x \leqslant \frac{1}{2}$,
concave up
for $x \geqslant \frac{1}{2}$

d

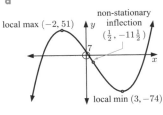

local max $(-2, 51)$
non-stationary inflection $(\frac{1}{2}, -11\frac{1}{2})$
local min $(3, -74)$

7 $BC = \frac{8\sqrt{10}}{3}$ **Hint:** The normal is $y = -3x + 8$.

8 a y-intercept at $y = 0$, x-intercept at $x = 0$ and $x = 2$

b local maximum at $\left(\frac{2}{3}, \frac{32}{27}\right)$, local minimum at $(2, 0)$,
non-stationary inflection at $\left(\frac{4}{3}, \frac{16}{27}\right)$

c

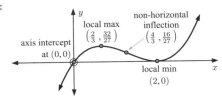

axis intercept at $(0,0)$
local max $\left(\frac{2}{3}, \frac{32}{27}\right)$
non-horizontal inflection $\left(\frac{4}{3}, \frac{16}{27}\right)$
local min $(2,0)$

9 a $2x + 3y = \frac{2\pi}{3} + 2\sqrt{3}$ **b** $\sqrt{2}y - 4x = 1 - 2\pi$

10 $a = 9$, $b = 2$, $f''(-2) = -18$ **11** $4y = 3x + 5$

12 a $x > 0$ **b** Sign diag of $f'(x)$

Sign diag of $f''(x)$

$f(x)$ is increasing for all $x > 0$ and is concave downwards for all $x > 0$.

c

$(1, 1)$

d normal is
$x + 2y = 3$

13

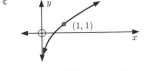

max
NSPI
min
$y = f'(x)$
$y = f(x)$

EXERCISE 17A.1

1 a 7 m s^{-1} **b** $(h + 5)$ m s^{-1}

c 5 m s$^{-1} = s'(1)$ is the instantaneous velocity at $t = 1$ s

d average velocity $= (2t + h + 3)$ m s^{-1},
$\lim\limits_{h \to 0} (2t + h + 3) = 2t + 3$ m s^{-1} is the instantaneous velocity at time t seconds

2 a -14 cm s^{-1} **b** $(-8 - 2h)$ cm s^{-1}

c -8 cm s$^{-1} = s'(2)$
$\therefore$ instantaneous velocity $= -8$ cm s^{-1} at $t = 2$

d $-4t = s'(t) = v(t)$ is the instantaneous velocity at time t seconds

3 a $\frac{2}{3}$ cm s^{-2} **b** $\frac{2\sqrt{1+h} - 2}{h}$ cm s^{-2}

c 1 cm s$^{-2} = v'(1)$ is the instantaneous accn. at $t = 1$ s

d $\frac{1}{\sqrt{t}}$ cm s$^{-2} = v'(t)$, the instantaneous accn. at time t

4 a velocity at $t = 4$ **b** acceleration at $t = 4$

EXERCISE 17A.2

1 a $v(t) = 2t - 4$ cm s^{-1}, $a(t) = 2$ cm s^{-2}

$s(t)$ $+$ $-$ $+$ 1 3
$v(t)$ $-$ $+$ 2
$a(t)$ $+$

b $s(0) = 3$ cm, $v(0) = -4$ cm s^{-1}, $a(0) = 2$ cm s^{-2}
The object is initially 3 cm to the right of the origin and is moving to the left at 4 cm s^{-1}. It is accelerating at 2 cm s^{-2} to the right.

c $s(2) = -1$ cm, $v(2) = 0$ cm s^{-1}, $a(2) = 2$ cm s^{-2}
The object is instantaneously stationary, 1 cm to the left of the origin and is accelerating to the right at 2 cm s^{-2}.

d At $t = 2$, $s(2) = 1$ cm to the left of the origin.

e **f** $0 \leqslant t \leqslant 2$

-1 0 3 s

2 a $v(t) = 98 - 9.8t$ m s^{-1}, $a(t) = -9.8$ m s^{-2}

$s(t)$ $+$ 0
$v(t)$ $+$ $-$ 10
$a(t)$ $-$

b $s(0) = 0$ m above the ground, $v(0) = 98$ m s^{-1} skyward

c $t = 5$ s Stone is 367.5 m above the ground and moving skyward at 49 m s^{-1}. Its speed is decreasing.
$t = 12$ s Stone is 470.4 m above the ground and moving groundward at 19.6 m s^{-1}. Its speed is increasing.

d 490 m **e** 20 seconds

3 a 1.2 m

b $s'(t) = 28.1 - 9.8t$ represents the instantaneous velocity of the ball.

c $t = 2.87$ s. The ball has reached its maximum height and is instantaneously at rest.

d 41.5 m

e i 28.1 m s^{-1} **ii** 8.5 m s^{-1} **iii** 20.9 m s^{-1}
$s'(t) \geqslant 0$ when the ball is travelling upwards.
$s'(t) \leqslant 0$ when the ball is travelling downwards.

f 5.78 s

g $s''(t)$ is the rate of change of $s'(t)$, or the instantaneous acceleration.

4 b 69.6 m s^{-1}

5 a $v(t) = 12 - 6t^2$ cm s^{-1}, $a(t) = -12t$ cm s^{-2}

b $s(0) = -1$ cm, $v(0) = 12$ cm s^{-1}, $a(0) = 0$ cm s^{-2}
Particle started 1 cm to the left of the origin and was travelling to the right at a constant speed of 12 cm s^{-1}.

c $t = \sqrt{2}$ s, $s(\sqrt{2}) = 8\sqrt{2} - 1$ cm

d i $t \geqslant \sqrt{2}$ s **ii** never

6 a $v(t) = 3t^2 - 18t + 24$ m s^{-1} $a(t) = 6t - 18$ m s^{-2}

$+$ $-$ $+$ 2 4 t
$-$ $+$ 3 t

b $x(2) = 20$, $x(4) = 16$

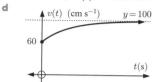

c **i** $0 \leqslant t \leqslant 2$ and $3 \leqslant t \leqslant 4$ **ii** $0 \leqslant t \leqslant 3$
d 28 m

7 **a** $v(t) = 100 - 40e^{-\frac{t}{5}}$ cm s^{-1}, $a(t) = 8e^{-\frac{t}{5}}$ cm s^{-2}
b $s(0) = 200$ cm on positive side of origin
$v(0) = 60$ cm s^{-1}, $a(0) = 8$ cm s^{-2}
c as $t \to \infty$, $v(t) \to 100$ cm s^{-1} (below)
d

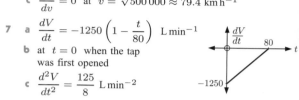

e after 3.47 s

8 **a** $x(0) = -1$ cm, $v(0) = 0$ cm s^{-1}, $a(0) = 2$ cm s^{-2}
b At $t = \frac{\pi}{4}$ seconds, the particle is $(\sqrt{2} - 1)$ cm left of the origin, moving right at $\sqrt{2}$ cm s^{-1}, with increasing speed.
c changes direction when $t = \pi$, $x(\pi) = 3$ cm
d increasing for $0 \leqslant t \leqslant \frac{\pi}{2}$ and $\pi \leqslant t \leqslant \frac{3\pi}{2}$

9 **Hint:** $s'(t) = v(t)$ and $s''(t) = a(t) = g$
Show that $a = \frac{1}{2}g$, $b = v(0)$, $c = 0$.

EXERCISE 17B

1 **a** $118\,000   **b** $\dfrac{dP}{dt} = 4t - 12$, $1000s per year
c $\dfrac{dP}{dt}$ is the rate of change in profit with time
d **i** $0 \leqslant t \leqslant 3$ years   **ii** $t > 3$ years
e minimum profit is $100\,000 when $t = 3$
f $\left.\dfrac{dP}{dt}\right|_{t=4} = 4$ Profit is increasing at $4000 per year after 4 years.
$\left.\dfrac{dP}{dt}\right|_{t=10} = 28$ Profit is increasing at $28\,000 per year after 10 years.
$\left.\dfrac{dP}{dt}\right|_{t=25} = 88$ Profit is increasing at $88\,000 per year after 25 years.

2 **a** 19 000 m^3 per minute   **b** 18 000 m^3 per minute

3 **a** **i** $Q(0) = 100$ **ii** $Q(25) = 50$ **iii** $Q(100) = 0$
b **i** decr. 1 unit per year   **ii** decr. $\frac{1}{\sqrt{2}}$ units per year
c $Q'(t) = -\dfrac{5}{\sqrt{t}} < 0$

4 **a** 0.5 m
b $t = 4$: 9.17 m, $t = 8$: 12.5 m, $t = 12$: 14.3 m
c $t = 0$: 3.9 m year^{-1}, $t = 5$: 0.975 m year^{-1},
$t = 10$: 0.433 m year^{-1}
d as $\dfrac{dH}{dt} = \dfrac{97.5}{(t+5)^2} > 0$, for all $t \geqslant 0$, the tree is always growing, and $\dfrac{dH}{dt} \to 0$ as t increases

5 **a** $C'(x) = 0.0009x^2 + 0.04x + 4$ dollars per pair
b $C'(220) = $56.36 per pair. This estimates the additional cost of making one more pair of jeans if 220 pairs are currently being made.
c $56.58   This is the actual increase in cost to make an extra pair of jeans (221 rather than 220).

d $C''(x) = 0.0018x + 0.04$.
$C''(x) = 0$ when $x = -22.2$. This is where the rate of change is a minimum, however it is out of the bounds of the model (you cannot make < 0 jeans!).

6 **a** **i** €4500   **ii** €4000
b **i** decrease of €210.22 per km h^{-1}
ii increase of €11.31 per km h^{-1}
c $\dfrac{dC}{dv} = 0$ at $v = \sqrt[3]{500\,000} \approx 79.4$ km h^{-1}

7 **a** $\dfrac{dV}{dt} = -1250\left(1 - \dfrac{t}{80}\right)$ L min^{-1}
b at $t = 0$ when the tap was first opened
c $\dfrac{d^2V}{dt^2} = \dfrac{125}{8}$ L min^{-2}

This shows that the rate of change of V is constantly increasing, so the outflow is decreasing at a constant rate.

8 **a** The near part of the lake is 2 km from the sea, the furthest part is 3 km.
b $\dfrac{dy}{dx} = \dfrac{3}{10}x^2 - x + \dfrac{3}{5}$.
$\left.\dfrac{dy}{dx}\right|_{x=\frac{1}{2}} = 0.175$, height of hill is increasing as gradient is positive.
$\left.\dfrac{dy}{dx}\right|_{x=1\frac{1}{2}} = -0.225$, height of hill is decreasing as gradient is negative.
$\therefore$ top of the hill is between $x = \frac{1}{2}$ and $x = 1\frac{1}{2}$.
c 2.55 km from the sea, 63.1 m deep

9 **a** $k = \frac{1}{50}\ln 2 \approx 0.0139$
b **i** 20 grams   **ii** 14.3 grams   **iii** 1.95 grams
c 9 days and 6 minutes (216 hours)
d **i** -0.0693 g h^{-1} **ii** -2.64×10^{-7} g h^{-1}
e **Hint:** You should find $\dfrac{dW}{dt} = -\frac{1}{50}\ln 2 \times 20e^{-\frac{1}{50}\ln 2t}$

10 **a** $k = \frac{1}{15}\ln\left(\frac{19}{3}\right) \approx 0.123$ **b** 100°C
c $c = -k \approx -0.123$
d **i** decreasing at 11.7°C min^{-1}
ii decreasing at 3.42°C min^{-1}
iii decreasing at 0.998°C min^{-1}

11 **a** 43.9 cm   **b** 10.4 years
c **i** growing at 5.45 cm per year
ii growing at 1.88 cm per year

12 **a** $A(0) = 0$
b **i** $k = \dfrac{\ln 2}{3}$ (≈ 0.231)
ii 0.728 litres of alcohol produced per hour

13 $\frac{21}{\sqrt{2}}$ cm^2 per degree

14 **a** rising at 2.73 m per hour   **b** rising

15 **a** $-34\,000\pi$ units per second   **b** $V'(t) = 0$

16 **b** **i** 0   **ii** 1   **iii** ≈ 1.11

EXERCISE 17C

1 250 items

2 b

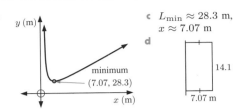

c $L_{min} \approx 28.3$ m, $x \approx 7.07$ m

d

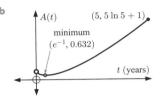

14.1 m

7.07 m

3 50 fittings   **4** 10 blankets   **5** 14.8 km h^{-1}

6 a at 4.41 months old   **b**

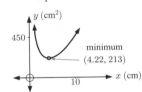

$A(t)$ $(5, 5\ln 5 + 1)$

minimum $(e^{-1}, 0.632)$

t (years)

7 Maximum hourly cost is $680.95 when 150 hinges are made per hour. Minimum hourly cost is $529.80 when 104 hinges are made per hour.

8 a $2x$ cm   **b** $V = 200 = 2x \times x \times h$

c Hint: Show $h = \dfrac{100}{x^2}$ and substitute into the surface area equation.

d

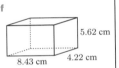

y (cm^2)

450

minimum $(4.22, 213)$

10   x (cm)

e $SA_{min} \approx 213$ cm^2, $x \approx 4.22$ cm

f

5.62 cm

8.43 cm   4.22 cm

9 20 kettles   **10** $C\left(\dfrac{1}{\sqrt{2}}, e^{\left(-\frac{1}{2}\right)}\right)$

11 a recall that $V_{cylinder} = \pi r^2 h$ and that 1 L $= 1000$ cm^3

b recall that $SA_{cylinder} = 2\pi r^2 + 2\pi r h$

c

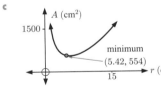

A (cm^2)

1500

minimum $(5.42, 554)$

15   r (cm)

d $A \approx 554$ cm^2, $r \approx 5.42$ cm

e

5.42 cm

10.84 cm

12 b $\theta \approx 1.91$, $A \approx 237$ cm^2 **13 b** 6 cm $\times$ 6 cm

14 a $0 \leqslant x \leqslant 63.7$

b $l = 100$ m, $x = \frac{100}{\pi} \approx 31.83$ m, $A = \frac{20\,000}{\pi} \approx 6366$ m^2

15 after 13.8 weeks   **16** after 40 minutes

17 a $D(x) = \sqrt{x^2 + (24-x)^2}$

0   12   24 x

b $\dfrac{d[D(x)]^2}{dx} = 4x - 48$

c Smallest $D(x) \approx 17.0$ m

17 m

12 m

18 c $\theta = 30°$, $A \approx 130$ cm^2

19 a Hint: Show that $AC = \frac{\theta}{360} \times 2\pi \times 10$

b Hint: Show that $2\pi r = AC$

c Hint: Use the result from **b** and Pythagoras' theorem.

d $V = \frac{1}{3}\pi \left(\frac{\theta}{36}\right)^2 \sqrt{100 - \left(\frac{\theta}{36}\right)^2}$

e

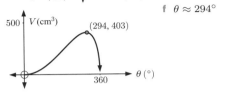

500   V (cm^3) $(294, 403)$

360   θ (°)

f $\theta \approx 294°$

20 a Hint: Use the cosine rule.

b 3553 km^2

$-$ $+$
4.605 t
0

c 5:36 pm

21 1 hour 34 min 53 s when $\theta \approx 36.9°$ **22** 9.87 m

REVIEW SET 17A

1 a $v(t) = (6t^2 - 18t + 12)$ cm s^{-1}, $a(t) = (12t - 18)$ cm s^{-2}

$v(t)$: $+$ $-$ $+$ t
       0   1   2

$a(t)$: $-$ $+$ t
       0    $1\frac{1}{2}$

b $s(0) = 5$ cm to left of origin
$v(0) = 12$ cm s^{-1} towards origin
$a(0) = -18$ cm s^{-2} (reducing speed)

c At $t = 2$, particle is 1 cm to the left of the origin, is stationary and is accelerating towards the origin.

d $t = 1$, $s = 0$ and $t = 2$, $s = -1$

e

$t = 0$ $t = 2$
              $t = 1$ s
-5 -1 0

f Speed is increasing for $1 \leqslant t \leqslant 1\frac{1}{2}$ and $t \geqslant 2$.

2 b $k = 9$

3 a $x(0) = 3$ cm, $x'(0) = 2$ cm s^{-1}, $x''(0) = 0$ cm s^{-2}

b $t = \frac{\pi}{4}$ s and $\frac{3\pi}{4}$ s   **c** 4 cm

4 6 cm from each end

5 a $v(t) = 2 + \dfrac{4}{(t+1)^2}$ cm s^{-1}

$+$ t
0

$a(t) = -\dfrac{8}{(t+1)^3}$ cm s^{-2}

$-$ t
0

b The particle is at O, moving right at 3 cm s^{-1}, and slowing down at 1 cm s^{-2}.

c The particle never changes direction

d

$t = 0$ $t = 1$

-4 0 s

e i never   **ii** never

6 $x = \dfrac{k}{2}\left(1 - \dfrac{1}{\sqrt{3}}\right)$

7 a $v(0) = 0$ cm s^{-1}, $v(\frac{1}{2}) = -\pi$ cm s^{-1}, $v(1) = 0$ cm s^{-1}, $v(\frac{3}{2}) = \pi$ cm s^{-1}, $v(2) = 0$ cm s^{-1}

b $0 \leqslant t \leqslant 1$, $2 \leqslant t \leqslant 3$, $4 \leqslant t \leqslant 5$, etc.
So, for $2n \leqslant t \leqslant 2n + 1$, $n \in \{0, 1, 2, 3, ...\}$

REVIEW SET 17B

1 a 60 cm   **b i** 4.24 years   **ii** 201 years

c i 16 cm per year   **ii** 1.95 cm per year

2 **a** $v(t) = -8e^{-\frac{t}{10}} - 40$ m s^{-1}

$a(t) = \frac{4}{5}e^{-\frac{t}{10}}$ m s^{-2} $\{t \geqslant 0\}$

b $s(0) = 80$ m,

$v(0) = -48$ m s^{-1},

$a(0) = 0.8$ m s^{-2}

c as $t \to \infty$,

$v(t) \to -40$ m s^{-1} (below)

e $t = 10\ln 2$ seconds

d

3 **a** **i** \$535 **ii** \$1385.79

b **i** $-$\$0.267 per km h^{-1} **ii** \$2.33 per km h^{-1}

c 51.3 km h^{-1}

4 **a** $v(t) = 3 - \dfrac{1}{2\sqrt{t+1}}$ $a(t) = \dfrac{1}{4(t+1)^{\frac{3}{2}}}$

b $x(0) = -1$, $v(0) = 2.5$, $a(0) = 0.25$

Particle is 1 cm to the left of the origin, is travelling to the right at 2.5 cm s^{-1}, and accelerating at 0.25 cm s^{-2}.

c Particle is 21 cm to the right of the origin, is travelling to the right at 2.83 cm s^{-1}, and accelerating at 0.009 26 cm s^{-2}.

d never changes direction

e never decreasing

5 **a** \$20 000   **b** \$146.53 per year

6 100 or 101 shirts, \$938.63 profit

7 **b** $A = 200x - 2x^2 - \frac{1}{2}\pi x^2$ **c**

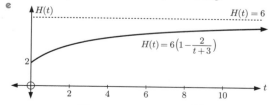

28.0 m

56.0 m

REVIEW SET 17C

1 **a** $y = \dfrac{1}{x^2}$, $x > 0$ **c** base is 1.26 m square, height 0.630 m

2 **a** $v(t) = 15 + \dfrac{120}{(t+1)^3}$ cm s^{-1}, $a(t) = \dfrac{-360}{(t+1)^4}$ cm s^{-2}

b At $t = 3$, particle is 41.25 cm to the right of the origin, moving to the right at 16.88 cm s^{-1} and decelerating at 1.41 cm s^{-2}.

c speed is never increasing

3 $A\left(\dfrac{1}{2}, \dfrac{1}{e}\right)$

4 **a** 2 m   **b** $H(3) = 4$ m, $H(6) = 4\frac{2}{3}$ m, $H(9) = 5$ m

c $H'(0) = \frac{4}{3}$ m year^{-1}, $H'(3) = \frac{1}{3}$ m year^{-1}

$H'(6) = \frac{4}{27}$ m year^{-1}, $H'(9) = \frac{1}{12}$ m year^{-1}

d $H'(t) = \dfrac{12}{(t+3)^2} > 0$ for all $t \geqslant 0$

$\therefore$ the height of the tree is always increasing.

e

$H(t) = 6\left(1 - \dfrac{2}{t+3}\right)$ $H(t) = 6$

5 **a** $v(t) = 25 - \dfrac{10}{t}$ cm min^{-1}, $a(t) = \dfrac{10}{t^2}$ cm min^{-2}

b $s(e) = 25e - 10$ cm, $v(e) = 25 - \dfrac{10}{e}$ cm min^{-1},

$a(e) = \dfrac{10}{e^2}$ cm min^{-2}

c As $t \to \infty$, $v(t) \to 25$ cm min^{-1} from below

d 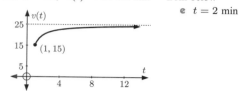   **e** $t = 2$ min

6 **b** $\dfrac{d[A(x)]^2}{dx} = 5000x - 4x^3$

Area is a maximum when $x \approx 35.4$, $A = 1250$ m^2.

7 **b** $\dfrac{1}{\sqrt{2}}$ m above the floor

EXERCISE 18A.1

1 **a** **i** 0.6 units^2 **ii** 0.4 units^2 **b** 0.5 units^2

2 **a** 0.737 units^2 **b** 0.653 units^2

3

n	A_L	A_U
10	2.185 0	2.485 0
25	2.273 6	2.393 6
50	2.303 4	2.363 4
100	2.318 4	2.348 4
500	2.330 3	2.336 3

converges to $\frac{7}{3}$

4 **a** **i**

n	A_L	A_U
5	0.160 00	0.360 00
10	0.202 50	0.302 50
50	0.240 10	0.260 10
100	0.245 03	0.255 03
500	0.249 00	0.251 00
1000	0.249 50	0.250 50
10 000	0.249 95	0.250 05

ii

n	A_L	A_U
5	0.400 00	0.600 00
10	0.450 00	0.550 00
50	0.490 00	0.510 00
100	0.495 00	0.505 00
500	0.499 00	0.501 00
1000	0.499 50	0.500 50
10 000	0.499 95	0.500 05

iii

n	A_L	A_U
5	0.549 74	0.749 74
10	0.610 51	0.710 51
50	0.656 10	0.676 10
100	0.661 46	0.671 46
500	0.665 65	0.667 65
1000	0.666 16	0.667 16
10 000	0.666 62	0.666 72

iv

n	A_L	A_U
5	0.618 67	0.818 67
10	0.687 40	0.787 40
50	0.738 51	0.758 51
100	0.744 41	0.754 41
500	0.748 93	0.750 93
1000	0.749 47	0.750 47
10 000	0.749 95	0.750 05

b **i** $\frac{1}{4}$ **ii** $\frac{1}{2}$ **iii** $\frac{2}{3}$ **iv** $\frac{3}{4}$ **c** area $= \dfrac{1}{a+1}$

5 a

n	Rational bounds for π
10	$2.9045 < \pi < 3.3045$
50	$3.0983 < \pi < 3.1783$
100	$3.1204 < \pi < 3.1604$
200	$3.1312 < \pi < 3.1512$
1000	$3.1396 < \pi < 3.1436$
10 000	$3.1414 < \pi < 3.1418$

b $n = 10\,000$

EXERCISE 18A.2

1 a

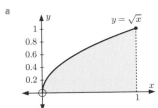

b

n	A_L	A_U
5	0.5497	0.7497
10	0.6105	0.7105
50	0.6561	0.6761
100	0.6615	0.6715
500	0.6656	0.6676

c $\int_0^1 \sqrt{x}\,dx \approx 0.67$

2 a

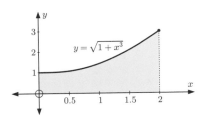

b $A_L = \dfrac{2}{n} \displaystyle\sum_{i=0}^{n-1} \sqrt{1+x_i^3}$, $A_U = \dfrac{2}{n} \displaystyle\sum_{i=1}^{n} \sqrt{1+x_i^3}$

c

n	A_L	A_U
50	3.2016	3.2816
100	3.2214	3.2614
500	3.2373	3.2453

d $\int_0^2 \sqrt{1+x^3}\,dx \approx 3.24$

3 a 18   **b** 4.5   **c** 2π

EXERCISE 18B

1 a **i** $\dfrac{x^2}{2}$ **ii** $\dfrac{x^3}{3}$ **iii** $\dfrac{x^6}{6}$ **iv** $-\dfrac{1}{x}$

  v $-\dfrac{1}{3x^3}$ **vi** $\dfrac{3}{4}x^{\frac{4}{3}}$ **vii** $2\sqrt{x}$

b The antiderivative of x^n is $\dfrac{x^{n+1}}{n+1}$ $(n \neq -1)$.

2 a **i** $\frac{1}{2}e^{2x}$ **ii** $\frac{1}{5}e^{5x}$ **iii** $2e^{\frac{1}{2}x}$ **iv** $100e^{0.01x}$

  v $\frac{1}{\pi}e^{\pi x}$ **vi** $3e^{\frac{x}{3}}$

b The antiderivative of e^{kx} is $\dfrac{1}{k}e^{kx}$.

3 a $\dfrac{d}{dx}(x^3 + x^2) = 3x^2 + 2x$

  $\therefore$ the antiderivative of $6x^2 + 4x = 2x^3 + 2x^2$

b $\dfrac{d}{dx}(e^{3x+1}) = 3e^{3x+1}$

  $\therefore$ the antiderivative of $e^{3x+1} = \frac{1}{3}e^{3x+1}$

c $\dfrac{d}{dx}(x\sqrt{x}) = \frac{3}{2}\sqrt{x}$

  $\therefore$ the antiderivative of $\sqrt{x} = \frac{2}{3}x\sqrt{x}$

d $\dfrac{d}{dx}(2x+1)^4 = 8(2x+1)^3$

  $\therefore$ the antiderivative of $(2x+1)^3 = \frac{1}{8}(2x+1)^4$

EXERCISE 18C

1 a $\frac{1}{4}$ units^2 **b** $2\frac{1}{3}$ units^2 **c** $\frac{2}{3}$ units^2

3 a $3\frac{3}{4}$ units^2 **b** $24\frac{2}{3}$ units^2 **c** $\frac{-2+4\sqrt{2}}{3}$ units^2

  d ≈ 3.48 units^2 **e** 2 units^2 **f** ≈ 3.96 units^2

4 $\frac{9\pi}{4}$ units^2

5 c **i** $\int_0^1 (-x^2)\,dx = -\frac{1}{3}$, the area between $y = -x^2$
  and the x-axis from $x = 0$ to $x = 1$ is $\frac{1}{3}$ units^2.

  ii $\int_0^1 (x^2 - x)\,dx = -\frac{1}{6}$, the area between $y = x^2 - x$
  and the x-axis from $x = 0$ to $x = 1$ is $\frac{1}{6}$ units^2.

  iii $\int_{-2}^0 3x\,dx = -6$, the area between $y = 3x$
  and the x-axis from $x = -2$ to $x = 0$ is 6 units^2

  d $-\pi$

EXERCISE 18D

1 $\dfrac{dy}{dx} = 7x^6$; $\int x^6\,dx = \frac{1}{7}x^7 + c$

2 $\dfrac{dy}{dx} = 3x^2 + 2x$; $\int (3x^2 + 2x)\,dx = x^3 + x^2 + c$

3 $\dfrac{dy}{dx} = 2e^{2x+1}$; $\int e^{2x+1}\,dx = \frac{1}{2}e^{2x+1} + c$

4 $\dfrac{dy}{dx} = 8(2x+1)^3$; $\int (2x+1)^3\,dx = \frac{1}{8}(2x+1)^4 + c$

5 $\dfrac{dy}{dx} = \frac{3}{2}\sqrt{x}$; $\int \sqrt{x}\,dx = \frac{2}{3}x\sqrt{x} + c$

6 $\dfrac{dy}{dx} = -\dfrac{1}{2x\sqrt{x}}$; $\int \dfrac{1}{x\sqrt{x}}\,dx = -\dfrac{2}{\sqrt{x}} + c$

7 $\dfrac{dy}{dx} = -2\sin 2x$; $\int \sin 2x\,dx = -\frac{1}{2}\cos 2x + c$

8 $\dfrac{dy}{dx} = -5\cos(1-5x)$; $\int \cos(1-5x)\,dx = -\frac{1}{5}\sin(1-5x) + c$

9 $\int (2x-1)(x^2 - x)^2\,dx = \frac{1}{3}(x^2 - x)^3 + c$

11 $\dfrac{dy}{dx} = \dfrac{-2}{\sqrt{1-4x}}$; $\int \dfrac{1}{\sqrt{1-4x}}\,dx = -\frac{1}{2}\sqrt{1-4x} + c$

12 $2\ln(5 - 3x + x^2) + c$ {since $5 - 3x + x^2$ is > 0}

EXERCISE 18E.1

1 a $\dfrac{x^5}{5} - \dfrac{x^3}{3} - \dfrac{x^2}{2} + 2x + c$ **b** $\frac{2}{3}x^{\frac{3}{2}} + e^x + c$

  c $3e^x - \ln x + c$, $x > 0$ **d** $\frac{2}{5}x^{\frac{5}{2}} - 2\ln x + c$, $x > 0$

  e $-2x^{-\frac{1}{2}} + 4\ln x + c$, $x > 0$

  f $\frac{1}{8}x^4 - \frac{1}{5}x^5 + \frac{3}{4}x^{\frac{4}{3}} + c$ **g** $\frac{1}{3}x^3 + 3\ln x + c$, $x > 0$

  h $\frac{1}{2}\ln x + \frac{1}{3}x^3 - e^x + c$, $x > 0$

  i $5e^x + \frac{1}{12}x^4 - 4\ln x + c$, $x > 0$

2 **a** $-3\cos x - 2x + c$ **b** $2x^2 - 2\sin x + c$
 c $-\cos x - 2\sin x + e^x + c$ **d** $\frac{2}{7}x^3\sqrt{x} + 10\cos x + c$
 e $\frac{1}{9}x^3 - \frac{1}{6}x^2 + \sin x + c$ **f** $\cos x + \frac{4}{3}x\sqrt{x} + c$

3 **a** $\frac{1}{3}x^3 + \frac{3}{2}x^2 - 2x + c$ **b** $\frac{2}{5}x^{\frac{5}{2}} - 2x^{\frac{1}{2}} + c$
 c $2e^x + \frac{1}{x} + c$ **d** $-2x^{-\frac{1}{2}} - 8x^{\frac{1}{2}} + c$
 e $\frac{4}{3}x^3 + 2x^2 + x + c$ **f** $\frac{1}{2}x^2 + x - 3\ln x + c,\ x > 0$
 g $\frac{4}{3}x^{\frac{3}{2}} - 2x^{\frac{1}{2}} + c$ **h** $2x^{\frac{1}{2}} + 8x^{-\frac{1}{2}} - \frac{20}{3}x^{-\frac{3}{2}} + c$
 i $\frac{1}{4}x^4 + x^3 + \frac{3}{2}x^2 + x + c$

4 **a** $\frac{2}{3}x^{\frac{3}{2}} + \frac{1}{2}\sin x + c$ **b** $2e^t + 4\cos t + c$
 c $3\sin t - \ln|t| + c$

5 **a** $y = 6x + c$ **b** $y = \frac{4}{3}x^3 + c$
 c $y = \frac{10}{3}x\sqrt{x} - \frac{1}{3}x^3 + c$ **d** $y = -\frac{1}{x} + c$
 e $y = 2e^x - 5x + c$ **f** $y = x^4 + x^3 + c$

6 **a** $y = x - 2x^2 + \frac{4}{3}x^3 + c$ **b** $y = \frac{2}{3}x^{\frac{3}{2}} - 4\sqrt{x} + c$
 c $y = x + 2\ln|x| + \frac{5}{x} + c$

7 **a** $f(x) = \frac{1}{4}x^4 - \frac{10}{3}x\sqrt{x} + 3x + c$
 b $f(x) = \frac{4}{3}x^{\frac{3}{2}} - \frac{12}{5}x^{\frac{5}{2}} + c$ **c** $f(x) = 3e^x - 4\ln|x| + c$

EXERCISE 18E.2

1 **a** $f(x) = x^2 - x + 3$ **b** $f(x) = x^3 + x^2 - 7$
 c $f(x) = e^x + 2\sqrt{x} - 1 - e$ **d** $f(x) = \frac{1}{2}x^2 - 4\sqrt{x} + \frac{11}{2}$

2 **a** $f(x) = \frac{x^3}{3} - 4\sin x + 3$
 b $f(x) = 2\sin x + 3\cos x - 2\sqrt{2}$

3 **a** $f(x) = \frac{1}{3}x^3 + \frac{1}{2}x^2 + x + \frac{1}{3}$
 b $f(x) = 4x^{\frac{5}{2}} + 4x^{\frac{3}{2}} - 4x + 5$
 c $f(x) = -\cos x - x + 4$ **d** $f(x) = \frac{1}{3}x^3 - \frac{16}{3}x + 5$

EXERCISE 18F

1 **a** $\frac{1}{8}(2x+5)^4 + c$ **b** $\frac{1}{2(3-2x)} + c$ **c** $\frac{-2}{3(2x-1)^3} + c$
 d $\frac{1}{32}(4x-3)^8 + c$ **e** $\frac{2}{9}(3x-4)^{\frac{3}{2}} + c$ **f** $-4\sqrt{1-5x} + c$
 g $-\frac{3}{5}(1-x)^5 + c$ **h** $-2\sqrt{3-4x} + c$

2 **a** $-\frac{1}{3}\cos(3x) + c$ **b** $-\frac{1}{2}\sin(-4x) + x + c$
 c $6\sin\left(\frac{x}{2}\right) + c$ **d** $-\frac{3}{2}\cos(2x) + e^{-x} + c$
 e $-\cos\left(2x + \frac{\pi}{6}\right) + c$ **f** $3\sin\left(\frac{\pi}{4} - x\right) + c$
 g $\frac{1}{2}\sin(2x) - \frac{1}{2}\cos(2x) + c$
 h $-\frac{2}{3}\cos(3x) + \frac{5}{4}\sin(4x) + c$
 i $\frac{1}{16}\sin(8x) + 3\cos x + c$

3 **a** $y = \frac{1}{3}(2x-7)^{\frac{3}{2}} + 2$ **b** $(-8, -19)$

4 **a** $\frac{1}{2}x + \frac{1}{4}\sin(2x) + c$ **b** $\frac{1}{2}x - \frac{1}{4}\sin(2x) + c$
 c $\frac{3}{2}x + \frac{1}{8}\sin(4x) + c$ **d** $\frac{5}{2}x + \frac{1}{12}\sin(6x) + c$
 e $\frac{1}{4}x + \frac{1}{32}\sin(8x) + c$ **f** $\frac{3}{2}x + 2\sin x + \frac{1}{4}\sin(2x) + c$

5 **a** $\frac{1}{2}(2x-1)^3 + c$ **b** $\frac{1}{5}x^5 - \frac{1}{2}x^4 + \frac{1}{3}x^3 + c$
 c $-\frac{1}{12}(1-3x)^4 + c$ **d** $x - \frac{2}{3}x^3 + \frac{1}{5}x^5 + c$
 e $-\frac{8}{3}(5-x)^{\frac{3}{2}} + c$ **f** $\frac{1}{7}x^7 + \frac{3}{5}x^5 + x^3 + x + c$

6 **a** $2e^x + \frac{5}{2}e^{2x} + c$ **b** $\frac{3}{5}e^{5x-2} + c$
 c $-\frac{1}{3}e^{7-3x} + c$ **d** $\frac{1}{2}\ln|2x-1| + c$
 e $-\frac{5}{3}\ln|1-3x| + c$ **f** $-e^{-x} - 2\ln|2x+1| + c$
 g $\frac{1}{2}e^{2x} + 2x - \frac{1}{2}e^{-2x} + c$ **h** $-\frac{1}{2}e^{-2x} - 4e^{-x} + 4x + c$
 i $\frac{1}{2}x^2 + 5\ln|1-x| + c$

7 **a** $y = x - 2e^x + \frac{1}{2}e^{2x} + c$
 b $y = x - x^2 + 3\ln|x+2| + c$
 c $y = -\frac{1}{2}e^{-2x} + 2\ln|2x-1| + c$

8 Both are correct. Recall that:
$$\frac{d}{dx}(\ln(Ax)) = \frac{d}{dx}(\ln A + \ln x) = \frac{1}{x}, \quad A, x > 0$$

9 $p = -\frac{1}{4}, \ f(x) = \frac{1}{2}\cos(\frac{1}{2}x) + \frac{1}{2}$

11 **a** $f(x) = -e^{-2x} + 4$
 b $f(x) = x^2 + 2\ln|1-x| + 2 - 2\ln 2$
 c $f(x) = \frac{2}{3}x^{\frac{3}{2}} - \frac{1}{8}e^{-4x} + \frac{1}{8}e^{-4} - \frac{2}{3}$

12 $x - \frac{1}{2}\cos(2x) + c$ **13** $\frac{1}{4}\sin 2x + 2\sin x + \frac{3}{2}x + c$

EXERCISE 18G

1 **a** $\frac{1}{5}(x^3+1)^5 + c$ **b** $\frac{1}{3}e^{x^3+1} + c$ **c** $\frac{1}{5}\sin^5 x + c$
2 **a** $\frac{1}{4}(2+x^4)^4 + c$ **b** $2\sqrt{x^2+3} + c$
 c $\frac{2}{3}(x^3+x)^{\frac{3}{2}} + c$ **d** $\frac{1}{8(1-x^2)^4} + c$
3 **a** $e^{1-2x} + c$ **b** $e^{x^2} + c$ **c** $2e^{\sqrt{x}} + c$ **d** $-e^{x-x^2} + c$
4 **a** $\ln|x^2+1| + c$ **b** $-\frac{1}{2}\ln|2-x^2| + c$
 c $\ln|x^2-3x| + c$ **d** $2\ln|x^3-x| + c$
5 **a** $-2(\cos x)^{\frac{1}{2}} + c$ **b** $-\ln|\cos x| + c$
 c $\frac{2}{3}(\sin x)^{\frac{3}{2}} + c$ **d** $-\frac{1}{2}\cos(x^2) + c$

EXERCISE 18H

1 **a** $\int_1^4 \sqrt{x}\,dx \approx 4.67$, $\int_1^4(-\sqrt{x})\,dx \approx -4.67$
 b $\int_0^1 x^7\,dx = \frac{1}{8}$, $\int_0^1(-x^7)\,dx = -\frac{1}{8}$
2 **a** $\frac{1}{3}$ **b** $\frac{7}{3}$ **c** $\frac{8}{3}$ **d** 1
3 **a** -4 **b** 6.25   **c** 2.25   **4** **a** $\frac{1}{3}$ **b** $\frac{2}{3}$ **c** 1
5 **a** $\frac{1}{4}$ **b** $\frac{2}{3}$ **c** $e-1$ (≈ 1.72)   **d** $\frac{1}{2}$
 e $1\frac{1}{2}$ **f** $6\frac{2}{3}$ **g** $\ln 3$ (≈ 1.10)   **h** $\frac{1}{2}$
 i ≈ 1.52 **j** 2   **k** $e-1$ (≈ 1.72)   **l** $\frac{1}{3}$
6 $\frac{\pi}{8} + \frac{1}{4}$ **7** $\frac{\pi}{4}$
8 **a** ≈ 1.30 **b** ≈ 1.49 **c** ≈ -0.189
10 **a** $m = -5$ **b** $m = -1$ or $\frac{4}{3}$
11 **a** 6.5   **b** -9 **c** 0   **d** -2.5
12 **a** 2π **b** -4 **c** $\frac{\pi}{2}$ **d** $\frac{5\pi}{2} - 4$
13 **a** $\int_2^7 f(x)\,dx$ **b** $\int_1^9 g(x)\,dx$ **14** **a** -5 **b** 4
15 **a** 4   **b** 0   **c** -8 **d** $k = -\frac{7}{4}$ **16** 0

REVIEW SET 18A

1 **a** 2π units^2 **b** 4 units^2

2 **a** $8\sqrt{x} + c$ **b** $-\frac{3}{2}\ln|1-2x| + c$

c $-\frac{1}{4}\cos(4x-5) + c$ **d** $-\frac{1}{3}e^{4-3x} + c$

3 **a** $12\frac{4}{9}$ **b** $\sqrt{2}$ **4** $\dfrac{dy}{dx} = \dfrac{x}{\sqrt{x^2-4}};$ $\int$ is $\sqrt{x^2-4} + c$

5 $b = \frac{\pi}{4}, \frac{3\pi}{4}$ **6** $\dfrac{9x}{2} - 4\sin x + \frac{1}{4}\sin(2x) + c$

7 $\dfrac{d}{dx}(3x^2 + x)^3 = 3(3x^2 + x)^2(6x+1)$

$\int(3x^2+x)^2(6x+1)\,dx = \frac{1}{3}(3x^2+x)^3 + c$

8 **a** 6 **b** 3 **9** $e^{\sin x} + c$ **10** $f\left(\frac{\pi}{2}\right) = 3 - \frac{\pi}{2}$

11 $\frac{\pi}{12} - \frac{1}{4}$ **12** **a** $\frac{1}{4}(x^2+1)^4 + c$ **b** **i** $\frac{15}{4}$ **ii** $-\frac{609}{8}$

REVIEW SET 18B

1 **a**

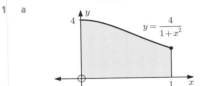

b

n	A_L	A_U
5	2.9349	3.3349
50	3.1215	3.1615
100	3.1316	3.1516
500	3.1396	3.1436

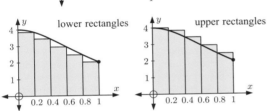

lower rectangles   upper rectangles

c $\displaystyle\int_0^1 \dfrac{4}{1+x^2}\,dx \approx 3.1416$

2 **a** $y = \frac{1}{5}x^5 - \frac{2}{3}x^3 + x + c$ **b** $y = 400x + 40e^{-\frac{x}{2}} + c$

3 **a** 3.528 **b** 2.963 **4** $\dfrac{2(\ln x)}{x}, \ \frac{1}{2}(\ln x)^2 + c$

5 $f(x) = 3x^3 + 5x^2 + 6x - 1$ **6** $a = \ln\sqrt{2}$

7 **a** 1.236 17 **b** 1.952 49

8 **a** $f(x) = \frac{1}{4}x^4 + \frac{1}{3}x^3 - \frac{10}{3}x + 3$ **b** $3x + 26y = 84$

9 **a** $e^{3x} + 6e^{2x} + 12e^x + 8$ **b** $\frac{1}{3}e^3 + 3e^2 + 12e - 7\frac{1}{3}$

10 $\frac{19}{384}$

REVIEW SET 18C

1 **a** $-2e^{-x} - \ln|x| + 3x + c$ **b** $\frac{1}{2}x^2 - 2x + \ln|x| + c$

c $9x + 3e^{2x-1} + \frac{1}{4}e^{4x-2} + c$

2 $f(x) = \frac{1}{3}x^3 - \frac{3}{2}x^2 + 2x + 2\frac{1}{6}$ **3** $\frac{2}{3}(\sqrt{5} - \sqrt{2})$

4 $\frac{\pi}{6} + \frac{\sqrt{3}}{4}$ **5** $e^{-\pi}$

6 if $n \neq -1$, $\quad\dfrac{1}{2(n+1)}(2x+3)^{n+1} + c$

if $n = -1$, $\quad\frac{1}{2}\ln|2x+3| + c$

7 $a = \frac{1}{3}$, $f'(x) = 2\sqrt{x} + \frac{1}{3\sqrt{x}}$ is never 0 as $\sqrt{x} \geqslant 0$ for all x

$\therefore$ $f'(x) > 0$ for all x

8 $a = 0$ or ± 3

9 **a** $A = \frac{17}{4}$, $B = \frac{25}{4}$ **b** $\int_0^2 (4 - x^2)\,dx \approx \frac{21}{4}$

10 **a** $2\sqrt{x^2-5} + c$ **b** $\frac{14\sqrt{7}}{3}$

EXERCISE 19A

1 **a** 30 units^2 **b** $\frac{9}{2}$ units^2 **c** $\frac{27}{2}$ units^2 **d** 2 units^2

2 **a** $\frac{1}{3}$ units^2 **b** 2 units^2 **c** $63\frac{3}{4}$ units^2

d $(e-1)$ units^2 **e** $20\frac{5}{6}$ units^2 **f** 18 units^2

g $\ln 4$ units^2 **h** $\ln 3$ units^2 **i** $4\frac{1}{2}$ units^2

j $\left(2e - \frac{2}{e}\right)$ units^2

3 $\frac{2}{3}$ units^2 **4** **a** $\int_1^4 \ln x\,dx \approx 2.55$ units^2

b $\int_1^{\frac{\pi}{2}} x\sin x\,dx \approx 0.699$ units^2

c $\int_0^{2.8} x^2 e^{-x}\,dx \approx 1.06$ units^2

EXERCISE 19B

1 **a** $4\frac{1}{2}$ units^2 **b** $(1 + e^{-2})$ units^2 **c** $1\frac{5}{27}$ units^2

d 2 units^2 **e** $2\frac{1}{4}$ units^2 **f** $\left(\frac{\pi}{2} - 1\right)$ units^2 **g** $\frac{\pi}{2}$ units^2

2 $10\frac{2}{3}$ units^2

3 **a, b**

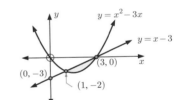

c $1\frac{1}{3}$ units^2

4 $\frac{1}{3}$ units^2

5 **a, b**

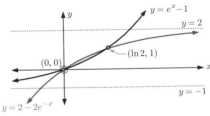

c enclosed area $= 3\ln 2 - 2$ (≈ 0.0794) units^2

6 $\frac{1}{2}$ units^2

7

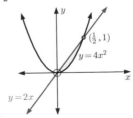

enclosed area $= \frac{1}{12}$ units^2

8 **a**

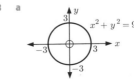

b $\frac{9\pi}{4}$ units^2 $(\approx 7.07$ units$^2)$

9   **a** $40\frac{1}{2}$ units^2 **b** 8 units^2 **c** 8 units^2

10   **a** C_1 is $y = \sin 2x$, C_2 is $y = \sin x$ **b** $A(\frac{\pi}{3}, \frac{\sqrt{3}}{2})$
   c $2\frac{1}{2}$ units^2

11   **a** $\int_3^5 f(x)\,dx = -$ (area between $x = 3$ and $x = 5$)
   b $\int_1^3 f(x)\,dx - \int_3^5 f(x)\,dx + \int_5^7 f(x)\,dx$

12   **a** C_1 is $y = \cos^2 x$, C_2 is $y = \cos(2x)$
   b $A(0, 1)$, $B(\frac{\pi}{4}, 0)$, $C(\frac{\pi}{2}, 0)$, $D(\frac{3\pi}{4}, 0)$, $E(\pi, 1)$
   c Area $= \int_0^\pi (\cos^2 x - \cos 2x)\,dx$

13   **a** 2.88 units^2 **b** 4.97 units^2 **14** $k \approx 1.737\,7$

15 $b \approx 1.310\,4$ **16** $a = \sqrt{3}$

EXERCISE 19C.1

1   110 m

2   **a** **i** travelling forwards
          ii travelling backwards (opposite direction)
   b 16 km   **c** 8 km from starting point (on positive side)

3   **a**   **b** 9.75 km

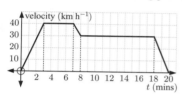

EXERCISE 19C.2

1   **a** $s(t) = t - t^2 + 2$ cm   **b** $\frac{1}{2}$ cm   **c** 0 cm

2   **a** $s(t) = \frac{1}{3}t^3 - \frac{1}{2}t^2 - 2t$ cm   **b** $5\frac{1}{6}$ cm
   c $1\frac{1}{2}$ cm left of its starting point

3   **a** $s(t) = 32t + 2t^2 + 16$ m
   b no change of direction
      so displacement $= s(t_1) - s(0) = \int_0^{t_1} (32 + 4t)\,dt$
   c acceleration $= 4$ m s^{-2}

4 $\frac{\sqrt{3}+2}{4}$ m   **5** **a** 41 units   **b** 34 units   **6** **b** 2 m

7   **a** 40 m s^{-1} **f**
   b 47.8 m s^{-1}
   c 1.39 seconds
   d as $t \to \infty$, $v(t) \to 50^-$
   e $a(t) = 5e^{-0.5t}$ and as
      $e^x > 0$ for all x,
      $a(t) > 0$ for all t.
   g 134.5 m

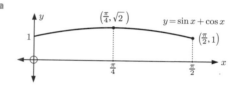

8   **a** $v(t) = \dfrac{1}{t+1} - 1$ m s^{-2} **b** $s(t) = \ln|t+1| - t$ metres
   c $s(2) = \ln|3 - 2| \approx -0.901$ m, $v(2) = -\frac{2}{3}$ m s^{-1},
      $a(2) = -\frac{1}{9}$ m s^{-2}
      The object is approximately 0.901 m to the left of the origin,
      travelling left at $\frac{2}{3}$ m s^{-1}, with acceleration $-\frac{1}{9}$ m s^{-2}.

9   **a** $v(t) = \dfrac{t^2}{20} - 3t + 45$ m s^{-1}
   b $\int_0^{60} v(t)\,dt = 900$. The train travels a total of 900 m in
      the first 60 seconds.

10   **a** Show that $v(t) = 100 - 80e^{-\frac{1}{20}t}$ m s^{-1} and as $t \to \infty$,
      $v(t) \to 100$ m s^{-1}.
   b 370.4 m

EXERCISE 19D.1

1   **a** 36π units^3 **b** 8π units^3 **c** $\frac{127\pi}{7}$ units^3
   d $\frac{255\pi}{4}$ units^3 **e** $\frac{992\pi}{5}$ units^3 **f** $\frac{250\pi}{3}$ units^3
   g $\frac{\pi}{2}$ units^3 **h** $\frac{40\pi}{3}$ units^3

2   **a** 18.6 units^3 **b** 30.2 units^3

3   **a** 186π units^3 **b** $\frac{146\pi}{5}$ units^3 **c** $\frac{\pi}{2}(e^8 - 1)$ units^3

4   **a** a circle
   b Volume of revolution $= \pi \int_a^b y^2\,dx$
                               $= \int_0^4 \pi(4\sqrt{x})^2\,dx$
   c 128π units^3

5   **a** 63π units^3 **b** ≈ 198 cm^3

6   **a** a cone of base radius r and height h
   b $y = -\left(\frac{r}{h}\right)x + r$ **c** $V = \frac{1}{3}\pi r^2 h$

7   **a** a sphere of radius r

8   **a** π units^3 **b** $\frac{\pi^2}{8} + \frac{\pi}{4}$ units^3

9   **a**

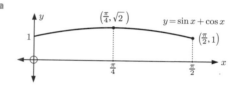

   b $\pi\left(\frac{\pi}{4} + \frac{1}{2}\right)$ units^3

EXERCISE 19D.2

1   **a** $A(-1, 3)$, $B(1, 3)$ **b** $\frac{136\pi}{15}$ units^3

2   **a** $A(2, e)$ **b** $\pi(e^2 + 1)$ units^3

3   **a** $A(1, 1)$ **b** $\frac{11\pi}{6}$ units^3 **4**   **a** $A(5, 1)$ **b** $\frac{9\pi}{2}$ units^3

REVIEW SET 19A

1 $A = \int_a^b [f(x) - g(x)]\,dx + \int_b^c [g(x) - f(x)]\,dx$
                               $+ \int_c^d [f(x) - g(x)]\,dx$

2   **a** $2 + \pi$ units^2 **b** -2 units^2 **c** π units^2

3   no, total area shaded $= \int_{-1}^1 f(x)\,dx - \int_1^3 f(x)\,dx$

4 $k = \sqrt[3]{16}$

5   **Hint:** Show that the areas represented by the integrals can be
      arranged to form a $1 \times e$ unit rectangle.

6   4.5 units^2

7   **a** $v(t)$:

   b The particle moves in the positive direction initially, then at
      $t = 2$, $6\frac{2}{3}$ m from its starting point, it changes direction. It
      changes direction again at $t = 4$, $5\frac{1}{3}$ m from its starting
      point, and at $t = 5$, it is $6\frac{2}{3}$ m from its starting point again.
   c $6\frac{2}{3}$ m   **d** $9\frac{1}{3}$ m

8 $(3 - \ln 4)$ units^2

REVIEW SET 19B

1   **a** $a(t) = 2 - 6t$ m s^{-2} **b** $s(t) = t^2 - t^3 + c$ m
   c -4 m (4 m to the left)

2   **a** local maximum at $(1, \frac{1}{2})$, local minimum at $(-1, -\frac{1}{2})$

b as $x \to \infty$, $f(x) \to 0^+$,   as $x \to -\infty$, $f(x) \to 0^-$

c

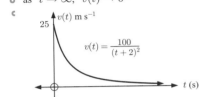

$f(x) = \dfrac{x}{1+x^2}$ $(1, \frac{1}{2})$ local max.

$(-1, -\frac{1}{2})$ local min.

d 0.805 units^2

3 2.35 m

4 **a** $v(0) = 25$ m s^{-1}, $v(3) = 4$ m s^{-1}

b as $t \to \infty$, $v(t) \to 0^+$

c

$v(t)$ m s^{-1}

25

$v(t) = \dfrac{100}{(t+2)^2}$

t (s)

d 3 seconds **e** $a(t) = \dfrac{-200}{(t+2)^3}$ m s^{-2}, $t \geqslant 0$ **f** $k = \frac{1}{5}$

5 **a** 0 and -0.7292 **b** 0.2009 units^2 **6** $m = \frac{\pi}{3}$

7 **a** $a \approx 0.8767$ **b** ≈ 0.1357 units^2

8 **a** $\pi \left(\frac{3\pi}{32} - \frac{1}{8\sqrt{2}} \right)$ units^3 **b** ≈ 124 units^3

REVIEW SET 19C

1 **a** $v(t) = 3t^2 - 30t + 27$ cm s^{-1}

b $\int_0^6 (3t^2 - 30t + 27) \, dt = s(6) - s(0) = -162$ cm

(162 cm to the left of the origin)

2 **a**

$y = \sin x$

$y = \sin^2 x$

π

b $(1 - \frac{\pi}{4})$ units^2

3 $a = \ln 3$, $b = \ln 5$ **4** $(\frac{\pi^2}{2} - 2)$ units^2

5 $(2 - \frac{\pi}{2})$ units^2 **6** $k = 1\frac{1}{3}$

7 **a** 312π units^3 **b** 402π units^3 **c** 2π units^3

d $\pi \left(\frac{3\pi - 8}{4} \right)$ units^3

8 **a** $\frac{128\pi}{3}$ units^3 **9** $\frac{\pi}{2}$ units^3

EXERCISE 20A

1 **a** Heights can take any value from 170 cm to 205 cm, e.g., 181.37 cm.

b

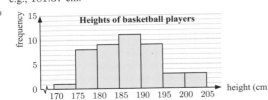

Heights of basketball players

frequency

height (cm)

170 175 180 185 190 195 200 205

c The modal class is $185 \leqslant H < 190$ cm, as this occurred the most frequently.

d slightly positively skewed

2 **a** Continuous numerical, but has been rounded to become discrete numerical data.

b

Time (min)	Tally	Frequency
0 - 9	卌 I	6
10 - 19	卌 卌 卌 卌 卌 I	26
20 - 29	卌 卌 III	13
30 - 39	卌 IIII	9
40 - 49	卌 I	6

c positively skewed

d The modal travelling time class is 10 - 19 minutes.

3 **a** column graph   **b** frequency histogram

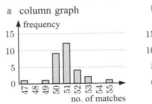

frequency

no. of matches

frequency

length (cm)

4 **a** 20   **b** 58.3%   **c** **i** 1218   **ii** 512

EXERCISE 20B.1

1 **a** **i** 5.61   **ii** 6   **iii** 6

b **i** 16.3   **ii** 17   **iii** 18

c **i** 24.8   **ii** 24.9   **iii** 23.5

2 **a** A: 6.46, B: 6.85   **b** A: 7, B: 7

c The data sets are the same except for the last value, and the last value of A is less than the last value of B, so the mean of A is less than the mean of B.

d The middle value of the data sets is the same, so the median is the same.

3 **a** mean: \$29 300, median: \$23 500, mode: \$23 000

b The mode is the lowest value, so does not take the higher values into account.

c No, since the data is positively skewed, the median is not in the centre.

4 **a** mean: 3.19, median: 0, mode: 0

b The data is very positively skewed so the median is not in the centre.

c The mode is the lowest value so does not take the higher values into account.

d yes, 21 and 42   **e** no

5 **a** 44   **b** 44   **c** **i** 40.2   **ii** increase mean to 40.3

6 \$185 604   **7** 3144 km   **8** 116   **9** 17.25 goals per game

10 **a** mean = \$163 770, median = \$147 200 (differ by \$16 570)

b **i** mean selling price   **ii** median selling price

11 $x = 15$ **12** $a = 5$ **13** 37   **14** 14.8

15 6 and 12   **16** 7 and 9

EXERCISE 20B.2

1 **a** 1 head   **b** 1 head   **c** 1.43 heads

2 **a** **i** 2.96 phone calls   **ii** 2 phone calls   **iii** 2 phone calls

c positively skewed

d The mean takes into account the larger numbers of phone calls.

e the mean

b

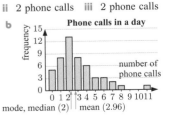

Phone calls in a day

frequency

number of phone calls

0 1 2 3 4 5 6 7 8 9 10 11

mode, median (2) mean (2.96)

3 a **i** 49 matches   **ii** 49 matches   **iii** 49.0 matches
  b no
  c The sample of only 30 is not large enough. The company could have won its case by arguing that a larger sample would have found an average of 50 matches per box.

4 a **i** 2.61 children   **ii** 2 children   **iii** 2 children
  b This school has more children per family than the average Australian family.
  c positive
  d The mean is larger than the median and the mode.

5 a

Donation	Frequency
1	7
2	9
3	2
4	4
5	8

  b 30
  c **i** $2.90
    ii $2
    iii $2
  d the mode

6 a $x = 5$ **b** 75%
7 a **i** 5.63 **ii** 6 **iii** 6   **b** **i** 6.81 **ii** 7 **iii** 7
  c the mean   **d** yes
8 a ≈ 70.9 g   **b** ≈ 210 g   **c** 139 g   **9** 10.1 cm
10 a mean for A ≈ 50.7, mean for B ≈ 49.9
  b No, as to the nearest match, A is 51 and B is 50.
11 a **i** €31 500 **ii** €28 000 **iii** €33 300   **b** The mode.

EXERCISE 20B.3

1 31.7
2 a 70   **b** $\approx 411\,000$ litres, ≈ 411 kL   **c** ≈ 5870 L
3 a 125 people   **b** ≈ 119 marks   **c** $\frac{3}{25}$ **d** 28%

EXERCISE 20C

1 a **i** 6 **ii** $Q_1 = 4$, $Q_3 = 7$ **iii** 7 **iv** 3
  b **i** 17.5 **ii** $Q_1 = 15$, $Q_3 = 19$ **iii** 14 **iv** 4
  c **i** 24.9 **ii** $Q_1 = 23.5$, $Q_3 = 26.1$ **iii** 7.7 **iv** 2.6
2 a median = 2.45, $Q_1 = 1.45$, $Q_3 = 3.8$
  b range = 5.2, IQR = 2.35
  c **i** ...... greater than 2.45 min
    ii ...... less than or equal to 3.8 min
    iii The minimum waiting time was 0 minutes and the maximum waiting time was 5.2 minutes. The waiting times were spread over 5.2 minutes.
3 a **i** 124 cm   **ii** $Q_1 = 116$ cm, $Q_3 = 130$ cm
  b **i** ...... 124 cm tall   **ii** ...... 130 cm tall
  c **i** 29 cm **ii** 14 cm   **d** ...... over 14 cm
4

measure	median	mode	range	interquartile range
a value	11	9	13	6
b	18	14	26	12

5 a **i** 7 **ii** 6 **iii** 5 **iv** 7 **v** 2
  b **i** 10 **ii** 7 **iii** 6 **iv** 8 **v** 2

EXERCISE 20D

1 a **i** 35 **ii** 78 **iii** 13 **iv** 53 **v** 26
  b **i** 65 **ii** 27
2 a **i** ...... was 98, ... was 25
    ii ...... greater than or equal to 70
    iii ...... at least 85 marks **iv** ..... between 55 and 85 .....
  b 73   **c** 30

3 a **i** min = 3, $Q_1 = 5$, median = 6, $Q_3 = 8$, max = 10
  ii
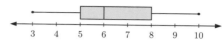
  iii range = 7 **iv** IQR = 3
  b **i** min = 0, $Q_1 = 4$, median = 7, $Q_3 = 8$, max = 9
  ii
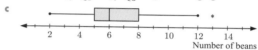
  iii range = 9 **iv** IQR = 4

4 a

Statistic	Year 9	Year 12
min value	1	6
Q_1	5	10
median	7.5	14
Q_3	10	16
max value	12	17.5

  b **i** Year 9: 11, Year 12: 11.5
    ii Year 9: 5, Year 12: 6
  c **i** true
    ii not enough information to tell

5 a median = 6, $Q_1 = 5$, $Q_3 = 8$ **b** 3
  c
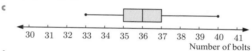
Number of beans

6 a 12   **b** lower: 13.5, upper: 61.5   **c** 13.2 and 65
7 a Min = 33, $Q_1 = 35$, $Q_2 = 36$, $Q_3 = 37$, Max = 40
  b **i** 7 **ii** 2
  c
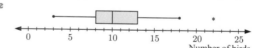
Number of bolts
  d no
8 a median = 10, $Q_1 = 8$, $Q_3 = 13$ **b** 5
  c lower = 0.5, upper = 20.5   **d** Yes, 22.
  e

Number of birds

9 A I   **B** IV   **C** III   **D** II
10 a discrete   **c**

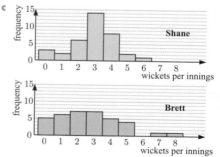

wickets per innings

  d There are no outliers for Shane.
    Brett has outliers of 7 and 8.
  e Shane's distribution is reasonably symmetrical.   Brett's distribution is positively skewed.
  f Shane has a higher mean (≈ 2.89 wickets) compared with Brett (≈ 2.67 wickets).   Shane has a higher median (3 wickets) compared with Brett (2.5 wickets).   Shane's modal number of wickets is 3 (14 times) compared with Brett, who has two modal values of 2 and 3 (7 times each).

g Shane's range is 6 wickets, compared with Brett's range of 8 wickets. Shane's IQR is 2 wickets, compared with Brett's IQR of 3 wickets. Brett's wicket taking shows greater spread or variability.

h

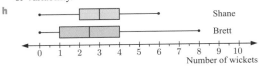

i Generally, Shane takes more wickets than Brett and is a more consistent bowler.

11 a continuous

c For the 'new type' of globes, 191 hours could be considered an outlier. However, it could be a genuine piece of data, so we will include it in the analysis.

d The mean and median are $\approx 25\%$ and $\approx 19\%$ higher for the 'new type' of globe compared with the 'old type'.

	Old type	New type
Mean	107	134
Median	110.5	132
Mode	87, 111, 113	131, 133
Range	56	84
IQR	19	18.5

The range is higher for the 'new type' of globe (but has been affected by the 191 hours).
The IQR for each type of globe is almost the same.

e

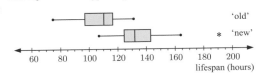

f For the 'old type' of globe, the data is bunched to the right of the median, hence the distribution is negatively skewed.
For the 'new type' of globe, the data is bunched to the left of the median, hence the distribution is slightly positively skewed.

g The manufacturer's claim, that the 'new type' of globe has a 20% longer life than the 'old type' seems to be backed up by the 25% higher mean life and 19.5% higher median life.

EXERCISE 20E

1

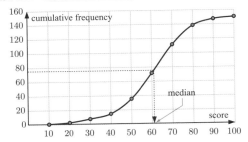

a ≈ 61 **b** ≈ 91 students   **c** ≈ 76 students

d 23 (or 24) students   **e** 75 marks

2 a

Length (x cm)	Frequency	Cumulative frequency
$24 \leqslant x < 27$	1	1
$27 \leqslant x < 30$	2	3
$30 \leqslant x < 33$	5	8
$33 \leqslant x < 36$	10	18
$36 \leqslant x < 39$	9	27
$39 \leqslant x < 42$	2	29
$42 \leqslant x < 45$	1	30

b

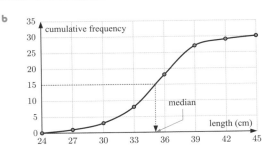

c median ≈ 35 cm

d actual median = 34.5, $\therefore$ a good approximation

3 a 9   **b** $\approx 28.3\%$ **c** 7 cm   **d** IQR ≈ 2.4 cm

e 10 cm, which means that 90% of the seedlings have a height of 10 cm or less.

4 a 26 years   **b** 36%   **c** **i** 0.527   **ii** 0.0267

5 a 27 min   **b** 29 min   **c** 31.3 min

d IQR ≈ 4.3 min   **e** 28 min 10 s

f

Time t (mins)	$21 \leqslant t < 24$	$24 \leqslant t < 27$	$27 \leqslant t < 30$
Number of competitors	5	15	30

Time t (mins)	$30 \leqslant t < 33$	$33 \leqslant t < 36$
Number of competitors	20	10

6 a 2270 h   **b** $\approx 71\%$ **c** 65 or 66

EXERCISE 20F.1

1 a Sample A

b

	A	B
$\overline{x}$	8	8

c

	A	B
s	2	1.06

Sample A has a larger standard deviation, which agrees with part **a**. That is, Sample A has a wider spread.

d The standard deviation is calculated using all data values, not just two.

2 a

	$\overline{x}$	s
Andrew	25	4.97
Brad	30.5	12.6

b Andrew

3 a Rockets: range $= 11$, $\overline{x} = 5.7$;
Bullets: range $= 11$, $\overline{x} = 5.7$

b We suspect the Rockets, they have two zeros.

c Rockets: $s = 3.9$ $\leftarrow$ greater variability
Bullets: $s \approx 3.29$

d standard deviation

4 a We suspect variability in standard deviation since the factors may change every day.

b **i** sample mean   **ii** sample standard deviation

c less variability

5 a $\overline{x} = 69$, $s \approx 6.05$ **b** $\overline{x} = 79$, $s \approx 6.05$

c The distribution has simply shifted by 10 kg. The mean increases by 10 kg and the standard deviation remains the same.

6 a $\overline{x} = 1.01$ kg; $s = 0.17$ **b** $\overline{x} = 2.02$ kg; $s = 0.34$

c Doubling the values doubles the mean and the standard deviation.

7 a 0.809   **b** 0.150

c the extreme value greatly increases the standard deviation

EXERCISE 20F.2

1 a $s_n \approx 6.77$ kg $\therefore$ $\sigma \approx 6.77$ kg   b $\mu \approx 93.8$ kg

2 a $\overline{x} \approx 77.5$ g, $s_n \approx 7.44$ g   b $\mu \approx 77.5$ g, $\sigma \approx 7.44$ g

EXERCISE 20F.3

1 a $\overline{x} \approx 1.72$ children, $s_n \approx 1.67$ children
  b $\mu \approx 1.72$ children, $\sigma \approx 1.67$ children

2 a $\overline{x} \approx 14.5$ years, $s_n \approx 1.75$ years
  b $\mu \approx 14.5$ years, $\sigma \approx 1.75$ years

3 a $\overline{x} \approx 37.3$ toothpicks, $s_n \approx 1.45$ toothpicks
  b $\mu \approx 37.3$ toothpicks, $\sigma \approx 1.45$ toothpicks

4 a $\overline{x} \approx 48.3$ cm, $s_n \approx 2.66$ cm
  b $\mu \approx 48.3$ cm, $\sigma \approx 2.66$ cm

5 a $\overline{x} \approx \$390.30$, $s_n \approx \$15.87$
  b $\mu \approx \$390.30$, $\sigma \approx \$15.87$

REVIEW SET 20A

1 a   i 3.15 cm   ii 4.5 cm
  b

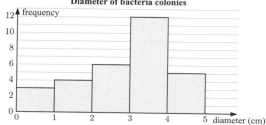

Diameter of bacteria colonies

  c The distribution is slightly negatively skewed.

2 $a = 8$, $b = 6$

3 a

Distribution	Girls	Boys
shape	pos. skewed	approx. symm.
median	36 s	34.5 s
mean	36 s	34.45 s
modal class	34.5 - 35.5 s	34.5 - 35.5 s

  b The girls' distribution is positively skewed and the boys' distribution is approximately symmetrical. The median and mean swim times for boys are both about 1.5 seconds lower than for girls. Despite this, the distributions have the same modal class because of the skewness in the girls' distribution. The analysis supports the conjecture that boys generally swim faster than girls with less spread of times.

4

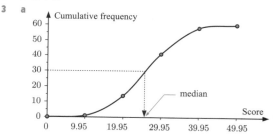

5 a 58.5 s
  b 6 s
  c 53 s

6 a $p = 12$, $m = 6$
  c $\frac{254}{30} = \frac{127}{15}$

  b

Measure	Value
mode	9
median	9
range	4

7 a 88 students   b $m \approx 24$

  c

Time t (min)	$5 \leqslant t < 10$	$10 \leqslant t < 15$	$15 \leqslant t < 20$
Frequency	20	40	48

Time t (min)	$20 \leqslant t < 25$	$25 \leqslant t < 30$	$30 \leqslant t < 35$
Frequency	42	28	17

Time t (min)	$35 \leqslant t < 40$
Frequency	5

REVIEW SET 20B

1 a highest = 97.5 m, lowest = 64.6 m
  b use groups $60 \leqslant d < 65$, $65 \leqslant d < 70$, ...
  c

Distances thrown by Thabiso

Distance (m)	Tally	Frequency
$60 \leqslant d < 65$	|	1
$65 \leqslant d < 70$	|||	3
$70 \leqslant d < 75$	ⵊⵊ	5
$75 \leqslant d < 80$	||	2
$80 \leqslant d < 85$	ⵊⵊ |||	8
$85 \leqslant d < 90$	ⵊⵊ |	6
$90 \leqslant d < 95$	|||	3
$95 \leqslant d < 100$	||	2
	Total	30

  d

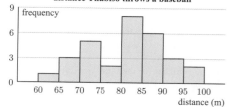

Frequency histogram displaying the distance Thabiso throws a baseball

  e   i ≈ 81.1 m   ii ≈ 83.1 m

2 b $k + 3$

3 a

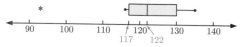

  b ≈ 25.9 c ≈ 12.0 d $\overline{x} \approx 26.0$, $s \approx 8.31$

4 a $\overline{x} \approx 33.6$ L, $s \approx 7.63$ L   b $\mu \approx 33.6$ L, $\sigma \approx 7.63$ L

5 a   i 101.5   ii 98   iii 105.5   b 7.5
  c $\overline{x} = 100.2$, $s \approx 7.59$

6 a $\overline{x} \approx 49.6$, $s \approx 1.60$
  b Does not justify claim. Need a larger sample.

7 a $\sigma \approx 11.65$ b $Q_1 = 117$, $Q_3 = 130$ c yes, 93
  d

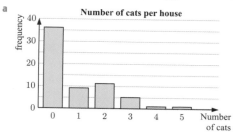

8 a

Number of cats per house

  b positively skewed   c   i 0   ii 0.87   iii 0

d The mean, as it suggests that some people have cats. (The mode and median are both 0.)

REVIEW SET 20C

1 a discrete

b

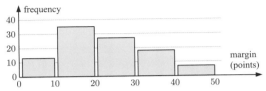

c No, as we do not know each individual data value, only the intervals they fall in.

2 a $x = 7$ **b** $s^2 \approx 10.2$ **3** ≈ 414 customers

4 a

	A	B
Min	11	11.2
Q_1	11.6	12
Median	12	12.6
Q_3	12.6	13.2
Max	13	13.8

b

		A	B
i	Range	2	2.6
ii	IQR	1	1.2

c **i** We know the members of squad A generally ran faster because their median time is lower.
ii We know the times in squad B are more varied because their range and IQR are higher.

5 a $\bar{x} = €103.51$, $s \approx €19.40$ **b** $\mu = €103.51$, $\sigma \approx €19.40$

6 a No, extreme values have less effect on the standard deviation of a larger population.
b **i** mean   **ii** standard deviation
c A low standard deviation means that the weight of biscuits in each packet is, on average, close to 250 g.

7 a 120 students   **b** 65 marks   **c** 54 and 75
d 21 marks   **e** 73% of them   **f** 82 marks

EXERCISE 21A

1 a A scatter diagram consists of points plotted on a set of axes where the independent variable is placed on the horizontal axis and the dependent variable on the vertical axis.
b Correlation refers to the relationship or association between two variables.
c Positive correlation describes the relationship when increasing the independent variable generally results in the dependent variable increasing.
d Negative correlation describes the relationship when increasing the independent variable generally results in the dependent variable decreasing.
e An outlier is a data point that does not fit the general trend of the data and is isolated from the main body of data.

2 a **i** no correlation   **ii** zero
iii non-linear   **iv** no outliers
b **i** positive correlation   **ii** weak
iii roughly linear   **iv** no outliers
c **i** negative correlation   **ii** moderate
iii non-linear   **iv** one outlier
d **i** positive correlation   **ii** moderate
iii linear   **iv** no outliers
e **i** negative correlation   **ii** strong
iii linear   **iv** one outlier

f **i** positive correlation   **ii** moderate
iii non-linear   **iv** no outliers

3 a

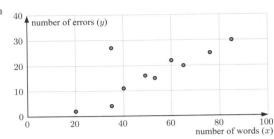

b **i** C   **ii** G   **iii** I
c positive, strong correlation   **d** It is approximately linear.

4 a

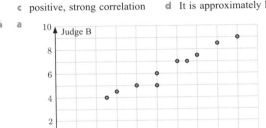

b There appears to be a **strong, positive** correlation between Judge A's scores and Judge B's scores. This means that as Judge A's scores increase, Judge B's scores **increase**.
c No

EXERCISE 21B

1 a **B**   **b** **A**   **c** **D**   **d** **C**   **e** **E**
2 a $r = 1$ **b** $r = -1$ **c** $r = 0$
3 a

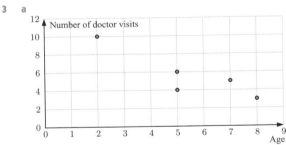

b $r \approx -0.892$ **c** strong, negative correlation

4 a

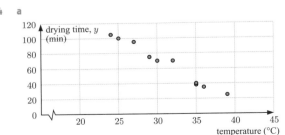

b $r \approx -0.987$ **c** very strong, negative correlation

5 a

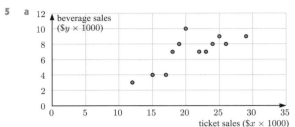

b $r \approx 0.776$ **c** moderate, positive correlation

6 a

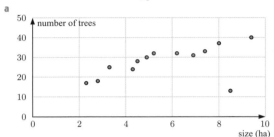

b Positive, since more trees can be planted in a larger space.

c $r \approx 0.520$ **d** Yes, the point $(8.5, 13)$.   **e** $r \approx 0.943$

EXERCISE 21C

1 a i

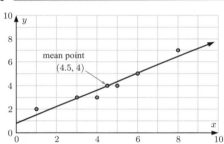

ii $y \approx 0.7x + 0.8$

b i

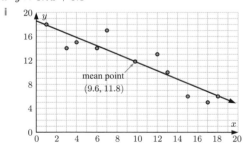

ii $y \approx -0.7x + 18.6$

c i

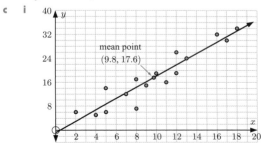

ii $y \approx 1.9x - 0.8$

2 a, c

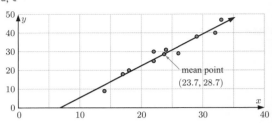

b very strong, positive correlation   **d** $y \approx 1.7x - 12$

e About 31 break-ins.

3 a, d

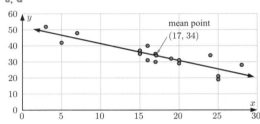

b $r \approx -0.878$

c There is a strong, negative correlation between *number of speed cameras* and *number of car accidents*.

e At $y \approx 52$. This means that we would expect a city with no speed cameras to have approximately 52 car accidents.

EXERCISE 21D

1 a $y \approx 0.712x + 0.797$ **b** $y \approx -0.707x + 18.6$

c $y \approx 1.88x - 0.797$

2 $y \approx 1.72x - 12.2$

3 a

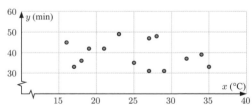

b $r \approx -0.219$

c There is weak, negative correlation between *temperature* and *time*.

d No, as there is only a weak correlation between the variables.

4 a $r \approx -0.924$

b There is a strong, negative correlation between the *petrol price* and the *number of customers*.

c $y \approx -4.27x + 489$

EXERCISE 21E

1 a $y \approx -5.75x + 245$ **b** 84 minutes

c Quite reliable as we are interpolating.

2 a $y \approx 0.350x - 0.293$

b i $\approx \$12\,000$

ii Not very reliable; we are extrapolating and the variables are only moderately correlated.

3 a

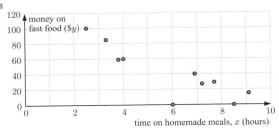

b $y \approx -12.7x + 116$ **c** $r \approx -0.868$

d slope ≈ -12.7. For each extra hour spent on homemade meals, a family spends about $12.70 less each week on fast food.
  y-intercept ≈ 116 If no time is spent on homemade meals, a family will spend $116 each week on fast food.

e $x = 5$, $y \approx 52.89$
  The family spends about $52.89 on fast food each week. It is reasonably reliable as it is an interpolation and the variables are strongly correlated.

4 a

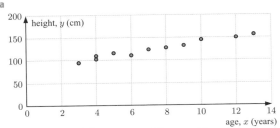

b $y \approx 5.98x + 80.0$ **c** 10 years old

d slope ≈ 5.98
  Every year a child grows about 5.98 cm taller.

e 200 cm - This prediction is not very reliable, as it is an extrapolation well beyond the upper pole. Most girls have finished growing taller before 20 years.

5 a

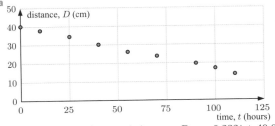

b very strong, negative correlation   **c** $D \approx -0.232t + 40.0$

d **i** $D \approx 21.4$ cm   **ii** $t \approx 172$ hours

e part **d i**, as it is an interpolation and **d ii** was extrapolated

6 a

t	1	2	3	4	5
M	3.6	5.7	9.1	14.6	23.3
$\ln M$	1.28	1.74	2.21	2.68	3.15

b

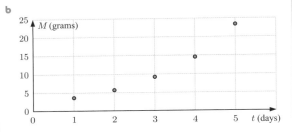

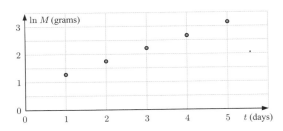

The scatter diagram of $\ln M$ against t is linear.

c $\ln M \approx 0.468t + 0.809$

d **Hint:** $e^{\ln M} \approx e^{0.468t+0.809}$ **e** 2.25 g

7 a As t increases, Q decreases.   **b** No

c

$\sqrt{t}$	1.41	3.16	4.47	5.48	7.07	8.06	8.94
Q	119	98	82	70	50	40	30

d The graph of Q against $\sqrt{t}$ is approximately linear.

e $m \approx -11.9$, $c \approx 135$ **f** **i** ≈ 135 mg   **ii** 76.0 mg

g The answer in **f ii** is more likely to be reliable, as it is an interpolation and **f i** was extrapolated.

8 a

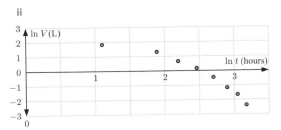

b **i**

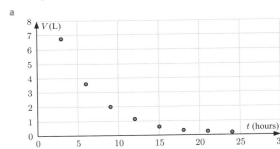

ii

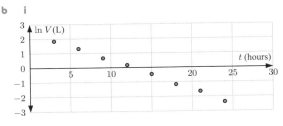

c $V \approx 12.1 \times (0.818)^t$ **d** ≈ 4.43 litres   **e** ≈ 10.5 litres

REVIEW SET 21A

1 a **i** moderate, negative correlation   **ii** non-linear

  b **i** strong, positive correlation   **ii** linear

2 a, c

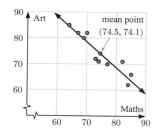

b There is a strong, negative, linear correlation between Mathematics and Art marks.

3 a

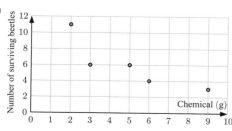

b moderate, negative correlation

4 a, b

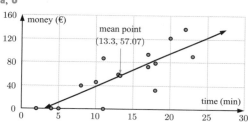

c There is a moderate positive linear correlation between *time in the store* and *money spent*.

5 a, b

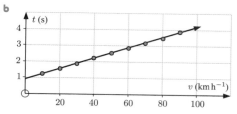

c i 2.55 seconds   ii 4.2 seconds
d The estimate in c i, as it is an interpolation.

REVIEW SET 21B

1 a

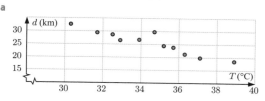

b $r \approx -0.928$, a strong negative linear relationship exists between the variables.
c $d = -1.64T + 82.3$ d $50.0°C$

2 a

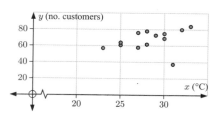

b $r \approx 0.314$ c Yes, the point $(31, 35)$.   d $r \approx 0.801$
e There is a moderate, positive linear correlation between the *number of customers* and the *noon temperature*.

3 a, d

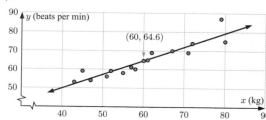

b There is a strong, positive correlation between *weight* and *pulse rate*.
c $(60, 64.6)$ e $y \approx 0.738x + 20.3$
f 68 beats per minute. This is an interpolation, so the estimate is reliable.

4 a number of waterings, n b $f \approx 34.0n + 19.3$
c

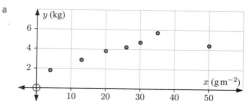

d i 104 $(n = 2.5)$,   359 $(n = 10)$
  ii $n = 10$ is unreliable as it is outside the poles and over watering could be a problem. $n = 2.5$ is reliable.

5 a

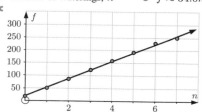

$(50, 4.4)$ is the outlier.
b i $r \approx 0.798$ ii $r \approx 0.993$
c i $y \approx 0.0672x + 2.22$ ii $y \approx 0.119x + 1.32$
d The one which excludes the outlier.
e Too much fertiliser often kills the plants, or makes them sick.

REVIEW SET 21C

1 a There is a moderate positive correlation between *hours of study* and *marks obtained*.
b The number of marks is greater than 50, so the outlier appears to be an error. It should be discarded.

2 a

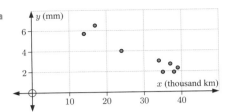

b $r \approx -0.951$

c There is a very strong, negative correlation between *tread depth* and *number of km travelled*.

3 a, e

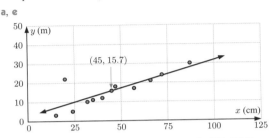

b (20, 22)   **c** tall and thin   **d** (45, 15.7)

f $y \approx 0.289x + 2.72$

g ≈ 37 m. This is an extrapolation, so the prediction may not be reliable.

4 a

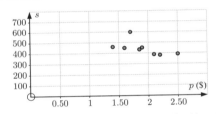

b Yes, the point (1.7, 597) is an outlier. It should not be deleted as there is no evidence that it is a mistake.

c $s \approx -116p + 665$

d No, the prediction would not be accurate, as that much extrapolation is unreliable.

5 a

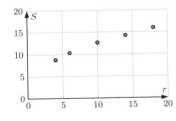

b

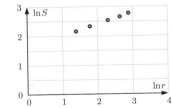

c $s \approx 5.04 \times r^{0.396}$ **d** $\approx 11.5 \ km\,h^{-1}$

EXERCISE 22A

1 a ≈ 0.779 **b** ≈ 0.221

2 a ≈ 0.487 **b** ≈ 0.051 **c** ≈ 0.731

3 a 43 days   **b i** ≈ 0.0465 **ii** ≈ 0.186 **iii** ≈ 0.465

4 a ≈ 0.0895 **b** ≈ 0.126

EXERCISE 22B

1 a {A, B, C, D}   **b** {BB, BG, GB, GG}

c {ABCD, ABDC, ACBD, ACDB, ADBC, ADCB, BACD, BADC, BCAD, BCDA, BDAC, BDCA, CABD, CADB, CBAD, CBDA, CDAB, CDBA, DABC, DACB, DBAC, DBCA, DCAB, DCBA}

d {GGG, GGB, GBG, BGG, GBB, BGB, BBG, BBB}

2 a

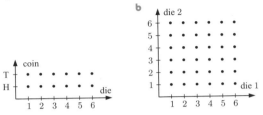

b

c

d

3 a

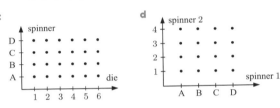

b

c

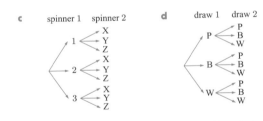

d

EXERCISE 22C.1

1 a $\frac{1}{5}$ **b** $\frac{1}{3}$ **c** $\frac{7}{15}$ **d** $\frac{4}{5}$ **e** $\frac{1}{5}$ **f** $\frac{8}{15}$

2 a 4   **b i** $\frac{2}{3}$ **ii** $\frac{1}{3}$

3 a $\frac{1}{4}$ **b** $\frac{1}{9}$ **c** $\frac{4}{9}$ **d** $\frac{1}{36}$ **e** $\frac{1}{18}$ **f** $\frac{1}{6}$

g $\frac{1}{12}$ **h** $\frac{1}{3}$

4 a $\frac{1}{7}$ **b** $\frac{2}{7}$ **c** $\frac{124}{1461}$ **d** $\frac{237}{1461}$ {remember leap years}

5 a {AKN, ANK, KAN, KNA, NAK, NKA}

b i $\frac{1}{3}$ **ii** $\frac{1}{3}$ **iii** $\frac{2}{3}$ **iv** $\frac{2}{3}$

6 a {GGG, GGB, GBG, BGG, GBB, BGB, BBG, BBB}

b i $\frac{1}{8}$ **ii** $\frac{1}{8}$ **iii** $\frac{1}{8}$ **iv** $\frac{3}{8}$ **v** $\frac{1}{2}$ **vi** $\frac{7}{8}$

7 a {ABCD, ABDC, ACBD, ACDB, ADBC, ADCB, BACD, BADC, BCAD, BCDA, BDAC, BDCA, CABD, CADB, CBAD, CBDA, CDAB, CDBA, DABC, DACB, DBAC, DBCA, DCAB, DCBA}

b i $\frac{1}{2}$ **ii** $\frac{1}{2}$ **iii** $\frac{1}{2}$ **iv** $\frac{1}{2}$

EXERCISE 22C.2

1

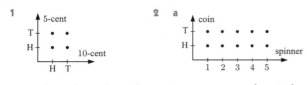

a $\frac{1}{4}$ **b** $\frac{1}{4}$ **c** $\frac{1}{2}$ **d** $\frac{3}{4}$

2 a

b 10 **c** **i** $\frac{1}{10}$ **ii** $\frac{1}{5}$
 iii $\frac{3}{5}$ **iv** $\frac{3}{5}$

3 a $\frac{1}{36}$ **b** $\frac{1}{18}$ **c** $\frac{5}{9}$ **d** $\frac{11}{36}$ **e** $\frac{5}{18}$
 f $\frac{25}{36}$ **g** $\frac{1}{6}$ **h** $\frac{5}{18}$ **i** $\frac{2}{9}$ **j** $\frac{13}{18}$

EXERCISE 22D

1 a $\frac{259}{537} \approx 0.482$ **b** $\frac{197}{537} \approx 0.367$ **c** $\frac{115}{537} \approx 0.214$
 d $\frac{225}{259} \approx 0.869$ **e** $\frac{34}{115} \approx 0.296$

2 a 7510 **b** **i** ≈ 0.325 **ii** ≈ 0.653 **iii** ≈ 0.243

3 a ≈ 0.428 **b** ≈ 0.240 **c** ≈ 0.758
 d ≈ 0.257 **e** ≈ 0.480

EXERCISE 22E.1

1 a $\frac{6}{7}$ **b** $\frac{36}{49}$ **c** $\frac{216}{343}$ **2 a** $\frac{1}{8}$ **b** $\frac{1}{8}$

3 a 0.0096 **b** 0.8096 **4 a** $\frac{1}{16}$ **b** $\frac{15}{16}$

5 a 0.56 **b** 0.06 **c** 0.14 **d** 0.24

6 a $\frac{8}{125}$ **b** $\frac{12}{125}$ **c** $\frac{27}{125}$

EXERCISE 22E.2

1 a $\frac{14}{55}$ **b** $\frac{1}{55}$ **2 a** $\frac{7}{15}$ **b** $\frac{7}{30}$ **c** $\frac{7}{15}$

3 a $\frac{3}{100}$ **b** $\frac{3}{100} \times \frac{2}{99} \approx 0.000\,606$
 c $\frac{3}{100} \times \frac{2}{99} \times \frac{1}{98} \approx 0.000\,006\,18$ **d** $\frac{97}{100} \times \frac{96}{99} \times \frac{95}{98} \approx 0.912$

4 a $\frac{4}{7}$ **b** $\frac{2}{7}$ **5 a** $\frac{10}{21}$ **b** $\frac{1}{21}$

EXERCISE 22F

1 a

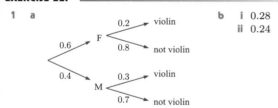

b **i** 0.28
 ii 0.24

2 a

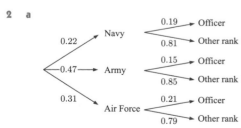

b **i** ≈ 0.177 **ii** ≈ 0.958 **iii** ≈ 0.864

3 a

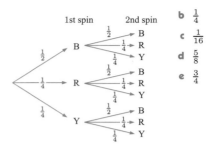

b $\frac{1}{4}$
c $\frac{1}{16}$
d $\frac{5}{8}$
e $\frac{3}{4}$

4

$P(\text{win}) = \frac{7}{50}$

5 0.032 **6** $\frac{17}{40}$ **7** $\frac{9}{38}$ **8 a** $\frac{11}{30}$ **b** $\frac{19}{30}$

EXERCISE 22G

1 a $\frac{20}{49}$ **b** $\frac{10}{21}$

2 a

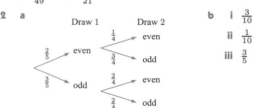

b **i** $\frac{3}{10}$
 ii $\frac{1}{10}$
 iii $\frac{3}{5}$

3 a $\frac{2}{9}$ **b** $\frac{5}{9}$

4 a **i** $\frac{1}{3}$ **ii** $\frac{2}{15}$ **iii** $\frac{4}{15}$ **iv** $\frac{4}{15}$
 b These are all the possible outcomes, so their probabilities must sum to 1.

5 a

Spin 1   Spin 2

$\frac{1}{4}$ → B

$\frac{3}{4}$ → R $\frac{1}{4}$ → B
  $\frac{3}{4}$ → R

b $\frac{7}{16}$

6 a $\frac{1}{5}$ **b** $\frac{3}{5}$ **c** $\frac{4}{5}$ **7** $\frac{19}{45}$

8 a $\frac{2}{100} \times \frac{1}{99} \approx 0.000\,202$ **b** $\frac{98}{100} \times \frac{97}{99} \approx 0.960$
 c $1 - \frac{98}{100} \times \frac{97}{99} \approx 0.0398$

9 $\frac{7}{33}$ **10** 7 to start with

EXERCISE 22H.1

1 a $A = \{1, 2, 3, 6\}$,
 $B = \{2, 4, 6, 8, 10\}$

b

c **i** $n(A) = 4$
 ii $A \cup B = \{1, 2, 3, 4, 6, 8, 10\}$
 iii $A \cap B = \{2, 6\}$

2 a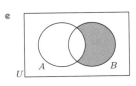

b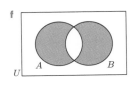

c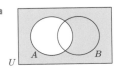

d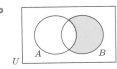

e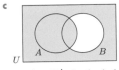

f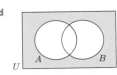

3 a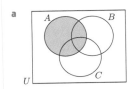

A' is shaded.

b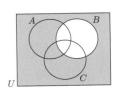

$A' \cap B$ is shaded.

c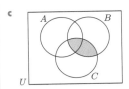

$A \cup B'$ is shaded.

d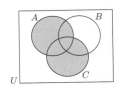

$A' \cap B'$ is shaded.

4 a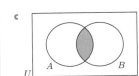

b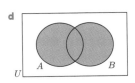

c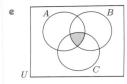

d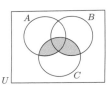

e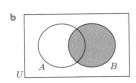

f

5 a 29   **b** 17   **c** 26   **d** 5

6 a 65   **b** 9   **c** 4   **d** 52

7 a

Venn diagram: A and B with regions 6, 5, 1, and 2 outside. U.

b i $\frac{12}{14} = \frac{6}{7}$

ii $\frac{3}{14}$

8 a $\frac{19}{40}$ **b** $\frac{1}{2}$ **c** $\frac{4}{5}$ **d** $\frac{5}{8}$ **e** $\frac{13}{40}$

9 a $\frac{19}{25}$ **b** $\frac{13}{25}$ **c** $\frac{6}{25}$ **10 a** $\frac{7}{15}$ **b** $\frac{1}{15}$ **c** $\frac{2}{15}$

11 a $a = 3$, $b = 3$

b i $\frac{12}{40} = \frac{3}{10}$ **ii** $\frac{4}{40} = \frac{1}{10}$ **iii** $\frac{7}{40}$

   iv $\frac{15}{40} = \frac{3}{8}$ **v** $\frac{25}{40} = \frac{5}{8}$

EXERCISE 22H.2

1 For each of these, draw **two** diagrams. Shade the first with the LHS set and the second with the RHS set.

2 a i $n(A) = 14$ **ii** $n(B) = 19$ **iii** 2   **iv** 31

3 a i $\dfrac{b+c}{a+b+c+d}$ **ii** $\dfrac{b}{a+b+c+d}$

   iii $\dfrac{a+b+c}{a+b+c+d}$ **iv** $\dfrac{a+b+c}{a+b+c+d}$

b $P(A \cup B) = P(A) + P(B) - P(A \cap B)$

EXERCISE 22I

1 0.6   **2** 0.2   **3** 0.35

4 a

Venn diagram: M and P with regions 18, 22, 10, and 0 outside. U.

22 study both

b i $\frac{9}{25}$ **ii** $\frac{11}{20}$

5 a $\frac{3}{8}$ **b** $\frac{7}{20}$ **c** $\frac{1}{5}$ **d** $\frac{15}{23}$

6 a $\frac{14}{25}$ **b** $\frac{4}{5}$ **c** $\frac{1}{5}$ **d** $\frac{5}{23}$ **e** $\frac{9}{14}$ **7** $\frac{5}{6}$

8 a $\frac{13}{20}$ **b** $\frac{7}{20}$ **c** $\frac{11}{50}$ **d** $\frac{7}{25}$ **e** $\frac{4}{7}$ **f** $\frac{1}{4}$

9 a $\frac{3}{5}$ **b** $\frac{2}{3}$ **10 a** 0.46   **b** $\frac{14}{23}$ **11** $\frac{70}{163}$

12 a 0.45   **b** 0.75   **c** 0.65

13 a 0.0484   **b** 0.393   **14** $\frac{2}{3}$

EXERCISE 22J

1 $P(R \cap S) = 0.4 + 0.5 - 0.7 = 0.2$ and $P(R) \times P(S) = 0.2$
∴ are independent events

2 a $\frac{7}{30}$ **b** $\frac{7}{12}$ **c** $\frac{7}{10}$ No, as $P(A \mid B) \neq P(A)$

3 a 0.35   **b** 0.85   **c** 0.15   **d** 0.15   **e** 0.5

4 $\frac{14}{15}$ **5 a** $\frac{91}{216}$ **b** 26

6 Hint: Show $P(A' \cap B') = P(A') P(B')$
using a Venn diagram and $P(A \cap B)$

7 0.9

8 a i $\frac{13}{20}$ **ii** $\frac{7}{10}$ **b** No, as $P(C \mid D) \neq P(C)$

REVIEW SET 22A

1 ABCD, ABDC, ACBD, ACDB, ADBC, ADCB, BACD, BADC, BCAD, BCDA, BDAC, BDCA, CABD, CADB, CBAD, CBDA, CDAB, CDBA, DABC, DACB, DBAC, DBCA, DCAB, DCBA

   a $\frac{1}{2}$ **b** $\frac{1}{3}$

2 **a** $P(A') = 1 - m$ **b** $0 \leqslant m \leqslant 1$

   c **i** $2m(1 - m)$ **ii** $2m - m^2$

3 **a** $\frac{3}{8}$ **b** $\frac{1}{8}$ **c** $\frac{5}{8}$ **4** **a** $\frac{2}{5}$ **b** $\frac{13}{15}$ **c** $\frac{4}{15}$

5 **a** 0   **b** 0.45   **c** 0.8

6 **a** Two events are independent if the occurrence of either event does not affect the probability that the other occurs. For A and B independent, $P(A) \times P(B) = P(A \text{ and } B)$.

   b Two events A and B are mutually exclusive if they have no common outcomes. $P(A \text{ or } B) = P(A) + P(B)$

7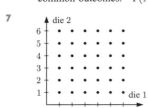

   a $\frac{2}{9}$

   b $\frac{5}{12}$

8 **a** $\frac{1}{4}$ **b** $\frac{37}{40}$ **c** $\frac{2}{5}$ **9** $\frac{5}{9}$

REVIEW SET 22B

1 P(N wins)

$= \frac{44}{125}$

$= 0.352$

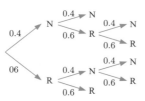

2 **a** $\frac{4}{500} \times \frac{3}{499} \times \frac{2}{498} \approx 0.000\,000\,193$

   b $1 - \frac{496}{500} \times \frac{495}{499} \times \frac{494}{498} \approx 0.0239$

3 **a** ≈ 0.259 **b** ≈ 0.703

4 **a**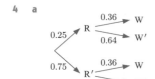

   b **i** 0.09   **ii** 0.52

   c That the two events (rain and wind) are independent.

5 $1 - 0.9 \times 0.8 \times 0.7 = 0.496$

6 **a** **i** 0.89   **ii** 20   **b** **i** 0.077   **ii** 0.11   **c** 0.81

7 **a**

	Female	Male	Total
Smoker	20	40	60
Non-smoker	70	70	140
Total	90	110	200

   b **i** $\frac{7}{20}$ **ii** $\frac{1}{2}$ **c** **i** ≈ 0.121 **ii** ≈ 0.422

8 **a**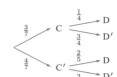

   b **i** $\frac{3}{28}$

      ii $\frac{23}{35}$

REVIEW SET 22C

1 BBBB, BBBG, BBGB, BGBB, GBBB, BBGG, BGBG, BGGB, GGBB, GBBG, GBGB, BGGG, GBGG, GGBG, GGGB, GGGG.

   P(2 children of each sex) $= \frac{3}{8}$

2 **a** $\frac{5}{33}$ **b** $\frac{19}{66}$ **c** $\frac{5}{11}$ **d** $\frac{16}{33}$

3 **a** **i** $\frac{3}{25}$ **ii** $\frac{24}{25}$ **iii** $\frac{11}{12}$ **b** **i** $\frac{11}{115}$ **ii** $\frac{104}{115}$

4 **a** $\frac{5}{8}$ **b** $\frac{1}{4}$

5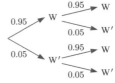

  0.9975

6 **a** $\frac{31}{70}$ **b** $\frac{21}{31}$

7 **a**

	Men	Women	Total
Tea	15	24	39
Coffee	35	26	61
Total	50	50	100

   b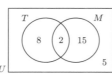

   c **i** 0.39

      ii $\frac{35}{61} \approx 0.574$

8 **a**

   b **i** $\frac{1}{15}$

      ii $\frac{2}{17}$

9 **b** ≈ 0.9876 **c** **i** ≈ 0.547 **ii** ≈ 0.266

   d A 20 year old of either gender is expected to live for longer than 30 years, so it is unlikely the insurance company will have to pay out the policy.

EXERCISE 23A

1 **a** continuous   **b** discrete   **c** continuous   **d** continuous

   e discrete   **f** discrete   **g** continuous   **h** continuous

2 **a** **i** $X =$ the height of water in the rain gauge

      ii $0 \leqslant X \leqslant 400$ mm   **iii** continuous

   b **i** $X =$ stopping distance   **ii** $0 \leqslant X \leqslant 50$ m

      iii continuous

   c **i** number of switches until failure

      ii any integer $\geqslant 1$ **iii** discrete

3 a $X = 1, 2, 3,$ or 4

b
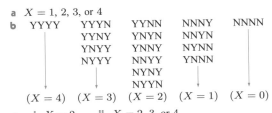

YYYY	YYYN	YYNN	NNNY	NNNN
	YYNY	YNYN	NNYN	
	YNYY	YNYN	NYNN	
	NYYY	NNYY	YNNN	
		NYNY		
		NYYN		

$(X = 4)$ $(X = 3)$ $(X = 2)$ $(X = 1)$ $(X = 0)$

c i $X = 2$ **ii** $X = 2, 3,$ or 4

4 a $X = 0, 1, 2,$ or 3

b
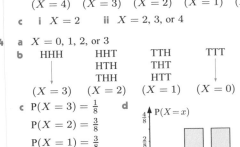

HHH	HHT	TTH	TTT
	HTH	THT	
	THH	HTT	

$(X = 3)$ $(X = 2)$ $(X = 1)$ $(X = 0)$

c $P(X = 3) = \frac{1}{8}$
$P(X = 2) = \frac{3}{8}$
$P(X = 1) = \frac{3}{8}$
$P(X = 0) = \frac{1}{8}$

d

EXERCISE 23B

1 a $k = 0.2$ **b** $k = \frac{1}{7}$

2 a $P(2) = 0.1088$
b $a = 0.5488$ is the probability that Jason does not hit a home run in a game.
c $P(1) + P(2) + P(3) + P(4) + P(5) = 0.4512$ and is the probability that Jason will hit one or more home runs in a game.
d
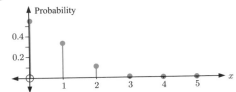

3 a $\sum P(x_i) > 1$ **b** $P(5) < 0$ which is not possible

4 a X is the number of hits that Sally has in each match.
$X = 0, 1, 2, 3, 4,$ or 5
b $k = 0.23$
c i $P(X \geqslant 2) = 0.79$ **ii** $P(1 \leqslant X \leqslant 3) = 0.83$

5 a
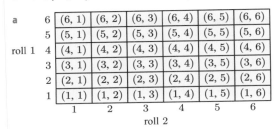

	6	(6, 1)	(6, 2)	(6, 3)	(6, 4)	(6, 5)	(6, 6)
	5	(5, 1)	(5, 2)	(5, 3)	(5, 4)	(5, 5)	(5, 6)
roll 1	4	(4, 1)	(4, 2)	(4, 3)	(4, 4)	(4, 5)	(4, 6)
	3	(3, 1)	(3, 2)	(3, 3)	(3, 4)	(3, 5)	(3, 6)
	2	(2, 1)	(2, 2)	(2, 3)	(2, 4)	(2, 5)	(2, 6)
	1	(1, 1)	(1, 2)	(1, 3)	(1, 4)	(1, 5)	(1, 6)
		1	2	3	4	5	6

roll 2

b $P(0) = 0,\ P(1) = 0,\ P(2) = \frac{1}{36},\ P(3) = \frac{2}{36},$
$P(4) = \frac{3}{36},\ P(5) = \frac{4}{36},\ P(6) = \frac{5}{36},\ P(7) = \frac{6}{36},$
$P(8) = \frac{5}{36},\ P(9) = \frac{4}{36},\ P(10) = \frac{3}{36},\ P(11) = \frac{2}{36},$
$P(12) = \frac{1}{36}$

c
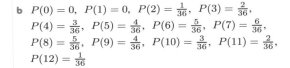

6 a $k = \frac{1}{12}$ **b** $k = \frac{12}{25}$

7 a $P(0) = 0.1975k;\ P(1) = 0.0988k;\ P(2) = 0.0494k;$
$P(3) = 0.0247k;\ P(4) = 0.0123k$
b $k = \frac{81}{31}\ (\approx 2.61),\ P(X \geqslant 2) = \frac{7}{31} \approx 0.226$

8 a $P(0) = 0.665$ **b** $P(X \geqslant 1) = 0.335$

9 a

x	0	1	2
$P(X = x)$	$\frac{3}{28}$	$\frac{15}{28}$	$\frac{10}{28}$

b

x	0	1	2	3
$P(X = x)$	$\frac{1}{56}$	$\frac{15}{56}$	$\frac{30}{56}$	$\frac{10}{56}$

10 a   **b** $\frac{1}{6}$
d $\frac{15}{26}$

			Die 2			
	1	2	3	4	5	6
1	2	3	4	5	6	7
2	3	4	5	6	7	8
3	4	5	6	7	8	9
Die 1 4	5	6	7	8	9	10
5	6	7	8	9	10	11
6	7	8	9	10	11	12

c

d	2	3	4	5	6	7	8	9	10	11	12
$P(D = d)$	$\frac{1}{36}$	$\frac{2}{36}$	$\frac{3}{36}$	$\frac{4}{36}$	$\frac{5}{36}$	$\frac{6}{36}$	$\frac{5}{36}$	$\frac{4}{36}$	$\frac{3}{36}$	$\frac{2}{36}$	$\frac{1}{36}$

11 a   **c** $\frac{1}{6}$
d $\frac{2}{5}$

			Die 2			
	1	2	3	4	5	6
1	0	1	2	3	4	5
2	1	0	1	2	3	4
3	2	1	0	1	2	3
Die 1 4	3	2	1	0	1	2
5	4	3	2	1	0	1
6	5	4	3	2	1	0

b

N	0	1	2	3	4	5
$P(N = n)$	$\frac{6}{36}$	$\frac{10}{36}$	$\frac{8}{36}$	$\frac{6}{36}$	$\frac{4}{36}$	$\frac{2}{36}$

EXERCISE 23C

1 102 days   **2 a** $\frac{1}{8}$ **b** 25   **3** 30 times

4 $1.50   **5** 15 days   **6** 27

7 a i 0.55   **ii** 0.29   **iii** 0.16
b i 4125   **ii** 2175   **iii** 1200

8 a i $\frac{1}{6}$ **ii** $\frac{1}{3}$ **iii** $\frac{1}{2}$
b i $1.33   **ii** $0.50   **iii** $3.50
c lose 50 cents   **d** lose $50

9 a €3.50   **b** $-$€0.50, no   **c i** $k = 3.5$ **ii** $k > 3.5$

10 a £2.75   **b** £3.75   **11 a** $k = 0.03$ **b** $\mu = 0.74$

12 $\mu = 2.5$

13 a

m	1	2	3	4	5	6
$P(M = m)$	$\frac{1}{36}$	$\frac{3}{36}$	$\frac{5}{36}$	$\frac{7}{36}$	$\frac{9}{36}$	$\frac{11}{36}$

b $\mu \approx 4.47$

14 a $P(X \leqslant 3) = \frac{1}{12}$, $P(4 \leqslant X \leqslant 6) = \frac{1}{3}$,

$P(7 \leqslant X \leqslant 9) = \frac{5}{12}$, $P(X \geqslant 10) = \frac{1}{6}$

c $a = 5$ **d** organisers would lose $1.17 per game

e $2807

EXERCISE 23D.1

1 a $(p+q)^4 = p^4 + 4p^3q + 6p^2q^2 + 4pq^3 + q^4$

b $4(\frac{1}{2})^3(\frac{1}{2}) = \frac{1}{4}$

2 a $(p+q)^5 = p^5 + 5p^4q + 10p^3q^2 + 10p^2q^3 + 5pq^4 + q^5$

b i $5\left(\frac{1}{2}\right)^4\left(\frac{1}{2}\right) = \frac{5}{32}$ **ii** $10\left(\frac{1}{2}\right)^2\left(\frac{1}{2}\right)^3 = \frac{5}{16}$

iii $\left(\frac{1}{2}\right)^4\left(\frac{1}{2}\right) = \frac{1}{32}$

3 a $\left(\frac{2}{3}+\frac{1}{3}\right)^4 = \left(\frac{2}{3}\right)^4 + 4\left(\frac{2}{3}\right)^3\left(\frac{1}{3}\right) + 6\left(\frac{2}{3}\right)^2\left(\frac{1}{3}\right)^2$

$+ 4\left(\frac{2}{3}\right)\left(\frac{1}{3}\right)^3 + \left(\frac{1}{3}\right)^4$

b i $\left(\frac{2}{3}\right)^4 = \frac{16}{81}$ **ii** $6\left(\frac{2}{3}\right)^2\left(\frac{1}{3}\right)^2 = \frac{8}{27}$ **iii** $\frac{8}{9}$

4 a $\left(\frac{3}{4}+\frac{1}{4}\right)^5 = \left(\frac{3}{4}\right)^5 + 5\left(\frac{3}{4}\right)^4\left(\frac{1}{4}\right)^1 + 10\left(\frac{3}{4}\right)^3\left(\frac{1}{4}\right)^2$

$+ 10\left(\frac{3}{4}\right)^2\left(\frac{1}{4}\right)^3 + 5\left(\frac{3}{4}\right)\left(\frac{1}{4}\right)^4 + \left(\frac{1}{4}\right)^5$

b i $10\left(\frac{3}{4}\right)^3\left(\frac{1}{4}\right)^2 = \frac{135}{512}$ **ii** $\frac{53}{512}$ **iii** $\frac{47}{128}$

5 a ≈ 0.154 **b** ≈ 0.973

EXERCISE 23D.2

1 a The binomial distribution applies, as tossing a coin has two possible outcomes (H or T) and each toss is independent of every other toss.

b The binomial distribution applies, as this is equivalent to tossing one coin 100 times.

c The binomial distribution applies as we can draw out a red or a blue marble with the same chances each time.

d The binomial distribution does not apply as the result of each draw is dependent upon the results of previous draws.

e The binomial distribution does not apply, assuming that ten bolts are drawn without replacement. We do not have a repetition of independent trials.

2 a ≈ 0.0305 **b** ≈ 0.265 **3** $\approx 0.000\,864$

4 a ≈ 0.268 **b** ≈ 0.800 **c** ≈ 0.200

5 a ≈ 0.476 **b** ≈ 0.840 **c** ≈ 0.160 **d** ≈ 0.996

6 a ≈ 0.231 **b** ≈ 0.723 **c** 1.25 apples

7 a ≈ 0.0280 **b** $\approx 0.002\,46$ **c** ≈ 0.131 **d** ≈ 0.710

8 a i ≈ 0.998 **ii** ≈ 0.807 **b** 105 students

9 a i ≈ 0.290 **ii** ≈ 0.885 **b** 18.8

10 ≈ 0.0341 **11** at least 4 dice

12 a ≈ 0.863 **b** ≈ 0.475 **13** ≈ 0.837

EXERCISE 23D.3

1 a i $\mu = 3$, $\sigma = 1.22$

ii

x_i	0	1	2	3
$P(x_i)$	0.0156	0.0938	0.2344	0.3125

x_i	4	5	6
$P(x_i)$	0.2344	0.0938	0.0156

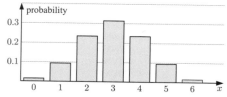

iii The distribution is bell-shaped.

b i $\mu = 1.2$, $\sigma = 0.980$

ii

x_i	0	1	2	3
$P(x_i)$	0.2621	0.3932	0.2458	0.0819

x_i	4	5	6
$P(x_i)$	0.0154	0.0015	0.0001

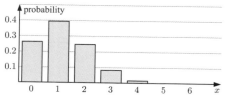

iii The distribution is positively skewed.

c i $\mu = 4.8$, $\sigma = 0.980$

ii

x_i	0	1	2	3
$P(x_i)$	0.0001	0.0015	0.0154	0.0819

x_i	4	5	6
$P(x_i)$	0.2458	0.3932	0.2621

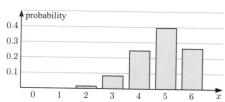

iii The distribution is negatively skewed and is the exact reflection of **b**.

2 $\mu = 5$, $\sigma = 1.58$

3 a $\mu = 1.2$, $\sigma = 1.07$ **b** $\mu = 28.8$, $\sigma = 1.07$

4 $\mu = 3.9$, $\sigma \approx 1.84$

REVIEW SET 23A

1 a $a = \frac{5}{9}$ **b** $\frac{4}{9}$ **2** 4.8 defectives

3 a $k = 0.05$ **b** 0.15   **c** 1.7

4 a $\left(\frac{3}{5}+\frac{2}{5}\right)^4 = \left(\frac{3}{5}\right)^4 + 4\left(\frac{3}{5}\right)^3\left(\frac{2}{5}\right) + 6\left(\frac{3}{5}\right)^2\left(\frac{2}{5}\right)^2$

$+ 4\left(\frac{3}{5}\right)\left(\frac{2}{5}\right)^3 + \left(\frac{2}{5}\right)^4$

b i $\frac{216}{625}$ **ii** $\frac{328}{625}$

5 a i $\frac{1}{10}$ **ii** $\frac{3}{5}$ **iii** $\frac{3}{10}$ **b** $1\frac{1}{5}$

6 a £7   **b** No, she would lose £1 per game in the long run.

7 a $k = \binom{7}{x}$ **b** $\mu = \frac{7}{3} \approx 2.33$, $\sigma^2 = \frac{14}{9} \approx 1.56$

8 a

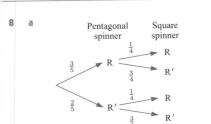

Pentagonal spinner → Square spinner

b $\frac{11}{20}$

c i $P(X=1) = \binom{10}{1}\left(\frac{11}{20}\right)^1 \left(\frac{9}{20}\right)^9$,

$P(X=9) = \binom{10}{9}\left(\frac{11}{20}\right)^9 \left(\frac{9}{20}\right)^1$

ii It is more likely that exactly one red will occur 9 times.

REVIEW SET 23B

1 a $k = \frac{8}{5}$ **b** 0.984 **c** 2.55 **d** 0.75

2 a 0.302 **b** 0.298 **c** 0.561 **3** 6.43 surgeries

4 a 0.849 **b** 2.56×10^{-6} **c** 0.991 **d** 0.000 246

5 a 42 donations **b** 0.334

6 a i 0.100 **ii** 0.114 **b** 3.41 games

7 a $n = 120$, $p = \frac{1}{4}$

b i ≈ 0.0501 **ii** ≈ 0.878 **iii** ≈ 0.172

REVIEW SET 23C

1 a $k = \frac{12}{11}$ **b** $k = \frac{1}{2}$

2 a

x	0	1	2	3	4
$P(X=x)$	0.0625	0.25	0.375	0.25	0.0625

b $\mu = 2$ **c** 1

3 a $\left(\frac{4}{5} + \frac{1}{5}\right)^5 = \left(\frac{4}{5}\right)^5 + 5\left(\frac{4}{5}\right)^4\left(\frac{1}{5}\right) + 10\left(\frac{4}{5}\right)^3\left(\frac{1}{5}\right)^2$
$+ 10\left(\frac{4}{5}\right)^2\left(\frac{1}{5}\right)^3 + 5\left(\frac{4}{5}\right)\left(\frac{1}{5}\right)^4 + \left(\frac{1}{5}\right)^5$

b i ≈ 0.0205 **ii** ≈ 0.205

4 $\mu = 480$, $\sigma \approx 17.0$ **5 a** 0.259 **b** 0.337 **c** 0.922

6 a i $\frac{2}{5}$ **ii** $\frac{1}{10}$ **iii** $\frac{1}{10}$ **b** $2.70

7 a ≈ 0.0660 **b** ≈ 0.563

EXERCISE 24A

1

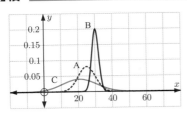

2 a, b The mean volume (or diameter) is likely to occur most often with variations around the mean occurring symmetrically as a result of random variations in the production process.

3 a 0.683 **b** 0.477

4 a 15.9% **b** 84.1% **c** 97.6% **d** 0.13%

5 3 times **6 a** 5 **b** 32 **c** 137 competitors

7 a 459 babies **b** 446 babies **8 a** 0.954 **b** 2.9

9 a $\mu = 176$ g, $\sigma = 24$ g **b** 81.9%

10 a i 34.1% **ii** 47.7%

b i 0.136 **ii** 0.159 **iii** 0.0228 **iv** 0.841
c $k = 178$

11 a $\mu = 155$ cm, $\sigma = 12$ cm **b** 0.84

12 a 84.1% **b** 2.28% **c i** 2.15% **ii** 95.4%
d i 97.7% **ii** 2.28%

13 a ≈ 41 days **b** ≈ 254 days **c** ≈ 213 days

EXERCISE 24B

1 a 0.341 **b** 0.383 **c** 0.106

2 a 0.341 **b** 0.264 **c** 0.212 **d** 0.945
e 0.579 **f** 0.383

3 0.378 **4 a** 90.4% **b** 4.78%

5 a 0.003 33 **b** 61.5% **c** 23 eels

6 a 0.303 **b** 0.968 **c** 0.309

7 a 10.3% **b** 0.544 **8 a** 84.1% **b** 0.880

EXERCISE 24C

1 a z-scores: Geography ≈ 1.61
English ≈ 1.82 Biology $= 0.9$
Mandarin ≈ 2.33 Maths ≈ 2.27

b Mandarin, Maths, English, Geography, Biology

2 a Physics -0.463, Chemistry 0.431, Maths 0.198, German 0.521, Biology -0.769

b German, Chemistry, Maths, Physics, Biology

3 a

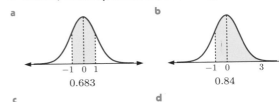

0.683

b

0.84

c

0.341

d

0.977

e

0.841

f

0.159

4 a $a = -1$, $b = 2$ **b** $a = -0.5$, $b = 0$
c $a = 0$, $b = 3$

5 a

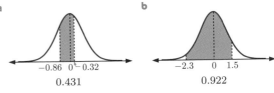

0.431

b

0.922

c

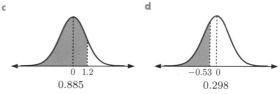

0.885

d

0.298

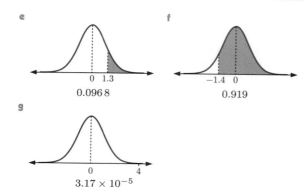

e   f

0 1.3   −1.4 0
0.096 8   0.919

g

0   4
3.17×10^{-5}

6 a i $z_1 \approx -0.859$, $z_2 \approx 1.18$ ii 0.687

EXERCISE 24D.1

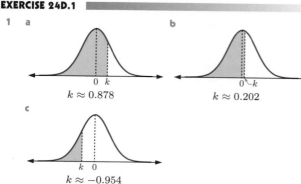

1 a   b

0 k   0 k
$k \approx 0.878$ $k \approx 0.202$

c

k 0
$k \approx -0.954$

2 a   b

k   20   20   k
$k \approx 18.8$ $k \approx 23.5$

c

20
k
$k = 20$

3 a   b

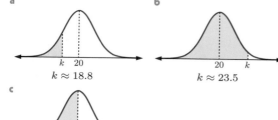

38.7 k   k   38.7
$k \approx 49.2$ $k \approx 31.8$

4 a $a \approx 21.4$ b $a \approx 21.8$ c $a \approx 2.82$
5 82.9   6 24.7 cm   7 75.2 mm   8 65.6%
9 between 502 mL and 504 mL

EXERCISE 24D.2

1 112.4   2 0.193 m   3 $96.50   4 4:01:24 pm
5 a $\mu \approx 52.4$, $\sigma \approx 21.6$ b $\mu \approx 52.4$, $\sigma \approx 21.6$, 54.4%
6 a $\mu \approx 4.00$ cm, $\sigma \approx 0.003\,53$ cm   b 0.604
7 a $\mu = 2.00$ cm, $\sigma = 0.0305$ cm   b 0.736

REVIEW SET 24A

1 a 2.28%   b 95.4%   c 68.3%
2 a i 2.28%   ii 84%   b 0.341
3 a $a = 6.3$ grams   b $b \approx 32.3$ grams
4 a Harri's score is 2 standard deviations below the mean.
   b 97.7%   c 17
5 $k \approx 2$ 6 29.5 m   7 a 0.136   b 0.341
8 a 2.28%   b 84.1%   c 81.9%

REVIEW SET 24B

1 a 68.3%   b 95.4%   c 81.9%   d 13.6%
2 a i 81.9%   ii 84.1%   b 0.477   c $x \approx 61.9$
3 $\mu \approx 31.2$ mm
4 a $\mu = 29.0$, $\sigma \approx 10.7$ b i 0.713   ii 0.250
5 a 6.68%   b 0.854
6 a 1438 candidates   b 71.1 marks
7 a 0.260   b 29.3 weeks
8 a $\mu = 61.2$, $\sigma \approx 22.6$ b ≈ 0.244
9 a The relative difficulty of each test is not known.
   b z-score for English = 1, z-score for Chemistry = 1
   $\therefore$ Kerry's performance relative to the rest of the class is the
      same in both tests.

REVIEW SET 24C

1 a mean is 18.8, standard deviation is 2.6   b 13.6 to 24.0
2 a 0.364   b 0.356   c $k \approx 18.2$
3 0.207   4 $\mu \approx 80.0$ cm   5 0.0708
6 a 68.3%   b 0.0884   7 $\sigma \approx 0.501$ mL   8 0.403

EXERCISE 25A

1 a $r = 3$ b 2×3^{19} 2 Hint: $u_1 = \ln 2 = d$
3 a $b^2 x$ b $2\ln b + x$ c $x = \dfrac{2\ln b}{b^2 - 1}$
4 a $(b, 2)$ b y-intercept is $2 - 2b^2$, x-intercepts are $b \pm 1$
   c i $b = -2$ ii $b < -2$ iii $b = \dfrac{1 \pm \sqrt{17}}{4}$
5 a $x^3 - 6x^2 + 12x - 8$ b 29
6 a 1   b 3   c $\{x \mid x \leqslant \frac{1}{2},\ x \in \mathbb{R}\}$
   d $\{y \mid y \geqslant 0,\ y \in \mathbb{R}\}$
7 a a b $-b$ c a d $\dfrac{a}{\sqrt{1 - a^2}}$
8 a $x = 0, \pi, 2\pi$ b $x = \frac{\pi}{3}, \frac{5\pi}{3}$
9 a

Constant	a	b	c	d	e	h
Sign	> 0	< 0	> 0	< 0	> 0	$= 0$

Constant	Δ of $f(x)$	Δ of $g(x)$
Sign	< 0	> 0

10 a $\frac{\pi}{3}$ b 6 cm
11 a no
    b 3 is not in the range of f. In fact, the range is $\{y \mid y \geqslant 6\}$.
12 a $p = 1$ b $\sqrt{6p^2 + 60}$
13 a $\overrightarrow{BA} = \begin{pmatrix} 3 \\ 1 \\ 1 \end{pmatrix}$, $\overrightarrow{BC} = \begin{pmatrix} 1 \\ 1 \\ -3 \end{pmatrix}$ b both are $\sqrt{11}$ units
    c a rhombus   d i $\frac{1}{11}$ ii $\frac{\sqrt{120}}{11}$ iii $2\sqrt{30}$ units^2

14 a g **b i** $m - a$ **ii** $\left(\dfrac{j+k}{2}\right) - \left(\dfrac{c+d}{2}\right)$

15 a 35, 6.4   **b** 19.5, 3.2   **c** 57.5, 9.6

17 a

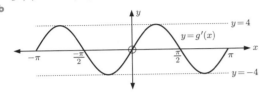

$f'(x)$ $f''(x)$ $y = 2a$

18 a $g'(x) = 4\sin(2x)$

b

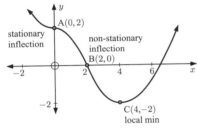

$y = 4$ $y = g'(x)$ $y = -4$

c $x = -\pi, -\frac{\pi}{2}, 0, \frac{\pi}{2}, \pi$ $\therefore$ 5 solutions

d M is at $(-\pi, 0)$, $(0, 0)$, or $(\pi, 0)$

19 a $P(A \cup B) = x + 0.57$ **b** $x = 0.16$

20

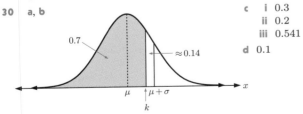

stationary inflection   A(0, 2)

non-stationary inflection   B(2, 0)

C(4, −2) local min

21 b $\left(\frac{1}{2}, \frac{1}{2}\right)$ **c i** $x > 0$ **ii** $x < \frac{1}{2}$

22 a $v(t) = k - 8e^{2t}$ m s^{-1} **b** $k = 72$

23 a $x = 3$ **b** $x = \dfrac{5 - \ln 8}{2}$ **c** $x = 3$

24 a 1 m s^{-1}, the initial velocity

b 0, uniform (constant) velocity

c 4, 4 m displacement on $1 \leqslant t \leqslant 3$

25 a -8 **b** $k = \frac{1}{2}$ **26 b** $\frac{\pi}{4} - \frac{1}{2}$ **27** $a = 0.3, b = 0.2$

28 a $r = \dfrac{1}{e^2}$ **b** e^{-199} **c** $\dfrac{e^3}{e^2 - 1}$

29 a 15   **b** 15

c $x^6 - 12x^5 + 60x^4 - 160x^3 + 240x^2 - 192x + 64$

30 a, b

0.7 ≈ 0.14 μ $\mu + \sigma$ k

c i 0.3
ii 0.2
iii 0.541
d 0.1

31 a 70%

b i $m \approx 27$ **ii** $n \approx 35$ **iii** $p \approx 42$ **iv** $q = 100$

32 a $p = 10\sqrt{3}$ **b** $x + \sqrt{3}y = 40$

33 a $v(t) = t - \frac{3}{2}\sin(2t + \frac{\pi}{2}) + 6\frac{1}{2}$ cm s^{-1}

b $\dfrac{\pi + 26}{4}$ cm s^{-1}

34 b $\frac{1}{3}\ln\left(\frac{7}{2}\right)$ **35 a** $-\dfrac{\sqrt{21}}{5}$ **b** $-\dfrac{2}{\sqrt{21}}$ **c** $-\dfrac{4\sqrt{21}}{25}$

36 a $\frac{5}{2}\sqrt{2}$ **b i** $310 + 155\sqrt{2}$ **ii** $320 + 160\sqrt{2}$

37 a $\begin{pmatrix} -2 \\ 2 \\ 6 \end{pmatrix}$ **b** $\sqrt{11}$ units s^{-1}

c $x = 3 - 2t$, $y = 1 + 2t$, $z = -2 + 6t$, $t \geqslant 0$

38 a

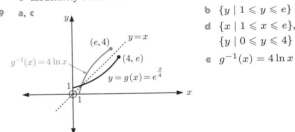

Camera B vs Camera A

b yes   (Camera A = 7, Camera B = 9)

c moderately consistent

39 a, c

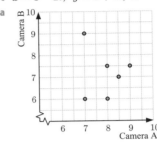

$(e, 4)$ $y = x$ $g^{-1}(x) = 4\ln x$ $(4, e)$ $y = g(x) = e^{\frac{x}{4}}$

b $\{y \mid 1 \leqslant y \leqslant e\}$
d $\{x \mid 1 \leqslant x \leqslant e\}$, $\{y \mid 0 \leqslant y \leqslant 4\}$
e $g^{-1}(x) = 4\ln x$

40 b ii RS $= 5\sqrt{3}$ cm

iii perimeter $= 15 + 5\sqrt{3}$ cm,   area $= \frac{25}{2}\sqrt{3}$ cm^2

41 a $f'(x) = -\frac{1}{2}x + 3$ **b i** $x + 2y = 20$ **ii** $(12, 4)$

c i $\int_2^6 (-\frac{1}{4}x^2 + 3x + 4)\, dx$ **ii** $46\frac{2}{3}$ units^2

iii $\pi \int_2^6 (-\frac{1}{4}x^2 + 3x + 4)^2\, dx$

42 a i $r = -3$ **ii** -4×3^{13}

b i $x = 4$ or -1

ii $S = 8$ when $x = 4$; when $x = -1$, S does not exist

c i -55 **ii** -2300

43 a $\begin{pmatrix} -1 \\ -3 \\ -7 \end{pmatrix}$ **b** $\dfrac{1}{\sqrt{59}}\begin{pmatrix} 1 \\ 3 \\ 7 \end{pmatrix}$ **c** no

d $a = \frac{1}{5}$ **e** $\overrightarrow{OM} = \frac{1}{2}(5\mathbf{i} + \mathbf{j} - 9\mathbf{k})$

f $\mathbf{r}_1 = \frac{1}{2}\begin{pmatrix} 5 \\ 1 \\ -9 \end{pmatrix} + t\begin{pmatrix} 3 \\ 2 \\ -1 \end{pmatrix}$, $t \in \mathbb{R}$

g i $\begin{pmatrix} 3 \\ 2 \\ -1 \end{pmatrix} \neq k\begin{pmatrix} 2 \\ -3 \\ 1 \end{pmatrix}$ for some $k \in \mathbb{R}$

ii $m = -45\frac{1}{2}$ **iii** $P(-30\frac{1}{2}, -21\frac{1}{2}, 6\frac{1}{2})$

44 a $\tan^{-1}\left(\frac{1}{2}\right)$ **b** $\tan^{-1}\left(\dfrac{\sqrt{3}}{2}\right)$

45 a i $a = -1$ **ii** $x = 6$ **iii** 16

b **i** $y = 12 - x$ **ii** $y^2 = x^2 + 64 - 16x\cos\theta$
   vi $8\sqrt{5}$ units^2 when $x = y = 6$ **vii** isosceles

46 **a** $f^{-1}(x) = \dfrac{x+3}{4}$, $g^{-1}(x) = x - 2$

   b $(f \circ g^{-1})(x) = 4x - 11$ **c** $x = \dfrac{47}{15}$

   d **i, iv**

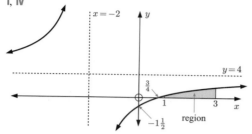

   ii $A = 4$, $B = -11$ **iii** $12 - 11\ln 4$

47 **a** The probabilities do not add to 1.
   b $a + b = 0.3$, $0 \leqslant a \leqslant 0.3$, $0 \leqslant b \leqslant 0.3$
   c **i** 0.16   **ii** 0.84

48 **a**

   b $\dfrac{2}{5}$
   c $\dfrac{7}{15}$
   d $\dfrac{1}{2}$
   e \$7.40

49 **a**

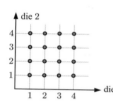

   b $X = 2, 3, 4, 5, 6, 7, 8$
   c **i** $\dfrac{3}{16}$
       ii $\dfrac{5}{8}$
   d $d = 8\dfrac{1}{3}$

50 **a** 0 cm s^{-2}, $\left(\dfrac{3\pi}{2} - 1\right)$ cm s^{-2}

   b $v(t) = \dfrac{3}{2}t^2 + \cos t + 2$ cm s^{-1}

   c $\left(\dfrac{\pi^3}{16} + \pi + 1\right)$ cm, which is positive as $\pi > 3$.

   d The integral is the displacement in the first $\dfrac{\pi}{2}$ seconds.

51 **a** $a = 7$, $b = \dfrac{\pi}{8}$, $c = 1$, $d = 10$

   b **i** $A'(7, 28)$ **ii** $y = 14\sin\dfrac{\pi}{8}(x - 3) + 14$
     iii a vertical stretch of factor $\dfrac{1}{2}$, followed by a translation
        of $\begin{pmatrix} -2 \\ 3 \end{pmatrix}$.

52 **a** $(2^x + 4)(2^x - 5)$ **b** $x = \log_2 5$

   c **i** $x = \dfrac{1}{p}$ **ii** $x = \dfrac{1}{3p + 1}$

53 **b** $2a - b$ when $x = \dfrac{3\pi}{4}, \dfrac{7\pi}{4}$
   c Max TPs: $(0, a)$, (π, a), $(2\pi, a)$
     Min TPs: $(\dfrac{\pi}{2}, b - a)$, $(\dfrac{3\pi}{2}, b - a)$

54 **c** $S(x)$ **d** $\dfrac{1}{[C(x)]^2}$

55 **a** $P(0) = 20\,000$ **b** $P'(t) = \dfrac{30\,000\,e^{-\frac{t}{4}}}{(1 + 2e^{-\frac{t}{4}})^2}$

c Use the fact that $e^{-\frac{t}{4}}$ is never negative.
   $P(t)$ is increasing for all $t \geqslant 0$

d $P''(t) = \dfrac{7500e^{-\frac{t}{4}}(2e^{-\frac{t}{4}} - 1)}{(1 + 2e^{-\frac{t}{4}})^3}$

e 3750 per year when $t = 4\ln 2$ years   **f** $P(t) \to 60\,000^-$

g

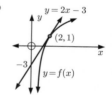

56 **a** $-\dfrac{1}{3}e^{1 - x^3} + c$

57 **a** $\{y \mid -1 \leqslant y \leqslant 1\}$ **b** 2 solutions
   c $-3\sin x\cos^2 x$ **d** π units^3

58 **a** $25\sin\alpha$ cm^2 **b** $\left(\dfrac{25\pi}{2} - 25\sin\alpha\right)$ cm^2
   c $A_{\max} = \dfrac{25\pi}{2}$ cm^2 when $\alpha = 0$ or π
     $A_{\min} = 25(\dfrac{\pi}{2} - 1)$ cm^2 when $\alpha = \dfrac{\pi}{2}$

59 **a** **i** $h = 4$ **ii** $k = 18$ **iii** $a = -2$ **b** $18\dfrac{2}{3}$ units^2

60 **a** **i** $x = 1$ **ii** $x = \sqrt[5]{7}$ **b** $x = 0$ or 1

61 **a** **ii** $\theta = \dfrac{\pi}{3}$ **b** $\cos x = \dfrac{1 - \sqrt{3}}{2}$

62 $u_1 = 2$, $u_n = 3n^2 - 3n + 3$, $n > 1$

63 $x = -\dfrac{3\pi}{2}$ or $\dfrac{\pi}{2}$ **64** **a** $-e^2$ **b** $e^2 - 3$

65 $(0, -1, -1)$

66 **a** $y = 2x - 3$ **b**
   c $f'(x) > 0$ for all $x \in \mathbb{R}$
     $\therefore$ $f(x)$ is monotone
     increasing
   d $\dfrac{3}{2} < x < 2$

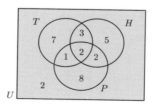

67 **a**

   b **i** $\dfrac{5}{30} = \dfrac{1}{6}$
      ii $\dfrac{13}{30}$
      iii $\dfrac{8}{30} = \dfrac{4}{15}$
      iv $\dfrac{23}{30}$
      v $\dfrac{1}{30}$

69 $a = \dfrac{1}{2}$ **70** $P(A \cup B) = 1$ or $P(A \cap B) = 0$

71 $\theta = -\dfrac{11\pi}{12}, -\dfrac{7\pi}{12}, \dfrac{\pi}{12}, \dfrac{5\pi}{12}$

72 **a** $\{x \mid x < 0$ or $x > 2\}$ **b** $\dfrac{1}{x} + \dfrac{1}{x - 2}$
   c $4x - 3y = 12 - 3\ln 3$

73 **a** $\dfrac{24}{49}$ **b** $\dfrac{16}{25}$ **74** **a** ≈ 0.341 **b** $\sigma \approx 5$

75 $a = \dfrac{3}{5}$ **76** $\dfrac{8}{x}$

77 **a, d**

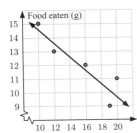

b strong, negative, linear correlation

c $(\overline{x}, \overline{y}) = (15.4, 12)$ **e** $F \approx -0.47t + 19.2$

f 16.9 grams   **g** may be unreliable as it is an extrapolation

78 **a** $(0, 4)$, a translation of $\begin{pmatrix} 2 \\ 1 \end{pmatrix}$

b $(0, 6)$, a translation of $\begin{pmatrix} 2 \\ 0 \end{pmatrix}$ followed by a vertical stretch of factor 2

c $(-1, 0)$, a translation of $\begin{pmatrix} 0 \\ -3 \end{pmatrix}$ followed by a horizontal stretch of factor $\frac{1}{2}$

d $(3, -2)$, a reflection in $y = x$

79 $y = 4\sin\left(\frac{\pi}{2}x\right) - 1$ **80** **a** $x = 0$ **b** $x = 0.2$ or 0.3

81 **a** 121   **b** 2

82 **a** **i** 4 kg
        ii 2.1 kg

        c ≈ 4.25 kg

b

Weight (w grams)	Frequency
$0 \leqslant w < 1$	1
$1 \leqslant w < 2$	2
$2 \leqslant w < 3$	5
$3 \leqslant w < 4$	12
$4 \leqslant w < 5$	8
$5 \leqslant w < 6$	6
$6 \leqslant w < 7$	3
$7 \leqslant w < 8$	2
$8 \leqslant w < 9$	1

83 **a** $\dfrac{3x}{x - 2}$ **b** $\dfrac{2x + 1}{x - 1}$ **84** **a** $\dfrac{13}{21}$ **b** $\dfrac{11}{21}$

85 $x = \dfrac{2}{a^2 - 1}$

86 **a** $a^5 - 5a^4b + 10a^3b^2 - 10a^2b^3 + 5ab^4 - b^5$ **b** 1

        c $32x^5 + 80x^3 + 80x + \dfrac{40}{x} + \dfrac{10}{x^3} + \dfrac{1}{x^5}$

87 **a** $a^2 - 2$ **b** $a^3 - 3a$

88 **a** **i** $A(4, 0)$, $B(-4, 0)$ **ii** $C(0, 2)$, $D(0, -2)$

        b $y = \sqrt{4 - \dfrac{x^2}{4}}$ **c** area $= 4\displaystyle\int_0^4 \sqrt{4 - \dfrac{x^2}{4}}\, dx$

        d volume $= \dfrac{64\pi}{3}$ units^3

89 **a**

x	0	$\frac{\pi}{4}$	$\frac{\pi}{2}$	$\frac{3\pi}{4}$	π	$\frac{5\pi}{4}$	$\frac{3\pi}{2}$	$\frac{7\pi}{4}$	2π
$f(0)$	0	$\frac{1}{2}$	1	$\frac{1}{2}$	0	$\frac{1}{2}$	1	$\frac{1}{2}$	0

b

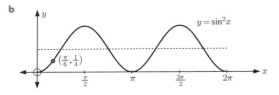

c when $x = \frac{\pi}{6}$, $y = \frac{1}{4}$ ✓   **d** $\{y \mid 0 \leqslant y \leqslant 1\}$

e $\frac{\pi}{2}$ units^2 **f** $x - y = \frac{\pi}{4} - \frac{1}{2}$

90 **a** $f'(x) = 1 - x^{-2}$, $x = 1$ **b** $A(1, 2)$ **c** .... is at least 2

        d **i** no solutions   **ii** one solution   **iii** two solutions

91 **a** $\mathbf{r} = \begin{pmatrix} 2 \\ 0 \\ -3 \end{pmatrix} + t\begin{pmatrix} 1 \\ -1 \\ 2 \end{pmatrix}$, $t \in \mathbb{R}$

        b $x = 2 + t$, $y = -t$, $z = -3 + 2t$, $t \in \mathbb{R}$

        c it represents any point on the line   **d** $\begin{pmatrix} t + 3 \\ -t - 3 \\ 2t - 8 \end{pmatrix}$

        e $6t - 10$ **f** $t = \frac{5}{3}$ **g** $\left(\frac{11}{3}, -\frac{5}{3}, \frac{1}{3}\right)$

92 **a** **i** a is the minimum value of X **ii** b is Q$_1$
        iii c is the median   **iv** d is Q$_3$
        v e is the maximum value of X
        b **i** the range   **ii** the IQR   **c** **i** 0.5   **ii** 0.75
        d

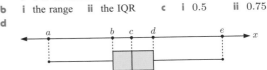

EXERCISE 25B

1 $n = 30$

2 **a, c**

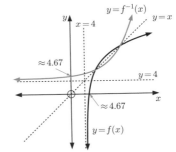

        b $x \approx 4.82$ **d** $x + 5y = 15$

3 $-\dfrac{84}{125}$

4 **a** $\$7500$ **b** **i** $\$10\,245$ **ii** $\$19\,118$
        c 36.6% increase   **d** ≈ 11.1 years

5 **a** 1950   **b** 10 500

6 **a** $x = \pm 1$ **b** $x = \pm\dfrac{3}{2\sqrt{5}}$ **c** $x = -\frac{1}{5}$
        d $x = -\frac{1}{2}$ or $\frac{2}{5}$

7 **a** $r \approx 35.4$ cm   **b** ≈ 1530 cm^2 **c** 59.4 cm

8 **a**

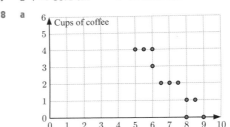

        b $r \approx -0.937$ **c** strong, negative correlation

9 a

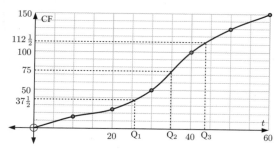

b i $y = 1$ **ii** 2 **iii** 60 **iv** 1
c $y = \sin\left(\frac{\pi}{30}x\right) + 1$

10 a $m = 4$, $n = \frac{\pi}{4}$, $p = 1$, $r = 8$ **b** ≈ 5.17
c $x = 2\frac{1}{3}$

11 a $\approx 30.9°$ **c** No, as equations have inconsistent solutions
d $(-8, 2\frac{1}{2}, -\frac{1}{2})$ **e** $a = -5\frac{1}{2}$

12 a x-intercepts are -1 and β, y-intercept is $-\beta$
b, c

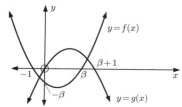

13 a

Time (min)	f	Cumulative frequency
$0 < t \leqslant 10$	15	15
$10 < t \leqslant 20$	10	25
$20 < t \leqslant 30$	25	50
$30 < t \leqslant 40$	50	100
$40 < t \leqslant 50$	30	130
$50 < t \leqslant 60$	20	150

b i ≈ 35 min **ii** ≈ 17.5 min **iii** ≈ 0.5

14 $\frac{37}{675} \approx 0.0548$

15 a $(0.86)^5 \approx 0.470$
b No, it is $\binom{5}{3}(0.86)^3(0.14)^2$ where $\binom{5}{3} = 10$.

16 $\frac{1}{2}$

17 a z-score for 100 m ≈ -1.86 **b** the 100 m
z-score for 200 m ≈ -1.70

18 a $0, \approx 1.46$

b

c $y \approx 1.64x - 0.820$ **d** P(0.955, 0.544)

19 a i $\frac{1208}{1797} \approx 0.672$ **ii** $\frac{415}{589} \approx 0.705$
b Method is OK. Although not strictly binomial, the binomial distribution is very close in this case.

20 a $-12e^{1-4x}$ **b** $-\frac{3}{4}e^{1-4x} + c$ **c** ≈ 2.04

21 a A$(1, 0)$, B$(\pi, 0)$ **b** C(2.128, 0.641)
c (1.101, 0.086) **d** a non-stationary inflection

22 a 185 months **b** ≈ 370 months

23 a $+ 80x^4 + 80x^2 + 32$
b $\frac{1}{11}x^{11} + \frac{10}{9}x^9 + \frac{40}{7}x^7 + 16x^5 + \frac{80}{3}x^3 + 32x + c$

24 a $f(x) = -4(x-1)^2 + 4$ **b** $x \approx 0.106$ and $x \approx 1.89$
c i $A \approx \int_{0.106}^{1.89} [f(x) - g(x)]\,dx$ **ii** ≈ 4.77 units^2

25 b $P(B) = 0.6$, $P(A) = 0.2$

26 a $\overline{x} = 70.5$ kg **b** 76 kg
c i $\sigma \approx 15.1$ kg
ii ≈ 1.92 standard deviations above the mean

27 a ≈ 0.0355 **b** ≈ 0.974

28 a i ≈ 0.544 **ii** ≈ 0.456 **b i** $(0.97)^n$ **ii** $n = 12$

29 a i

1st	2nd

$\frac{10}{15}$ W, $\frac{9}{14}$ W, $\frac{5}{14}$ G, $\frac{5}{15}$ G, $\frac{10}{14}$ W, $\frac{4}{14}$ G

ii $\frac{11}{21}$ **b** $n = 6$

30 $\mu \approx 679$ kg, $\sigma \approx 173$ kg **31 a** 4 horses **b** 11.4 days

32 a $z = 0.1$ **b** $y = 0.1$ **c** $x = 0.7$

33 a $m = -1$, $n = 2$
b i $g(x) = -\dfrac{1}{x+2}$ **iv**
ii VA is $x = -2$,
HA is $y = 0$
iii $-\frac{1}{2}$

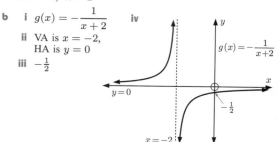

34 a i $(-1, 3)$ **ii** $(39, 23)$ **b** ≈ 44.7 m **d** no

35 $k \approx -0.969$

36 a A$(0, 1)$, B$\left(2, \dfrac{1}{e^4}\right)$ **b** ≈ 0.882 units^2

37 a 0.8 **b i** ≈ 0.0881 **ii** ≈ 0.967

38 a $\mu \approx 40.4$ **b** ≈ 0.0117 **c** $a \approx 55.8$

39 a

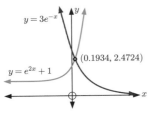

$y = 3e^{-x}$

$y = e^{2x} + 1$

(0.1934, 2.4724)

b $x \approx 0.1934$

40 a

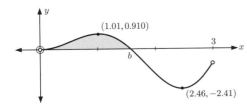

(1.01, 0.910)

(2.46, −2.41)

b Range is $\{y \mid -2.41 \leqslant y \leqslant 0.910\}$ **c** $b = \frac{\pi}{2}$
d $A \approx 0.785$

41 b $3x + e^{\frac{3\pi}{2}} y = 1 + \frac{3\pi}{2}$ **c** ≈ 0.0847 units^2

42 b $x = 0$, $x = \frac{\pi}{2}$ are VAs   **c** 2 when $x = \frac{\pi}{4}$
d ≈ 2.046

43 a   **i** ≈ 0.0362 **ii** ≈ 0.610 **iii** ≈ 0.566
b $k \approx 74.4$ **c** $a \approx 81.0$, $b \approx 102$ **d** ≈ 0.506

44 a $\begin{pmatrix} 2 \\ 3 \\ -5 \end{pmatrix}$, $\sqrt{38}$ units   **b** D(4, 3, 2)

c F(7, −4, −2)   **d** 33, $\frac{11}{3\sqrt{38}}$ **e** $3\sqrt{221}$ units^2

45 a $t = \frac{1}{4}$ **b** 2.675   **c** It is the mean of the Y distribution.

46 a $e - 2 \approx 0.718$
b

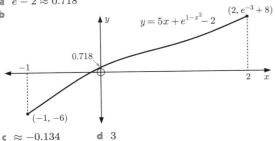

$y = 5x + e^{1-x^2} - 2$

(2, e^{-3} + 8)

0.718

(−1, −6)

c ≈ -0.134 **d** 3

47 a $a \approx 17.2$, $b \approx 30.0$
b   **i** ≈ 0.649 **ii** ≈ 0.334 **iii** 0.5

48 a

$x = 3$

$y = -2$

$y = \dfrac{6 - 2x}{x + 3}$

b as $x \to -3^-$, $y \to -\infty$
as $x \to -3^+$, $y \to \infty$
as $x \to \infty$, $y \to 2^+$
as $x \to -\infty$, $y \to 2^-$
VA is $x = -3$, HA is $y = -2$

c $\displaystyle\lim_{x \to -\infty} \frac{6 - 2x}{x + 3} = -2$, $\displaystyle\lim_{x \to \infty} \frac{6 - 2x}{x + 3} = -2$

49 a A(−3, 4, −2)   **b** Yes, at (4, −3, 5)   **c** $\approx 75.0°$

50 a A(1, 0), B(2, 0), C(0, 2)   **b** $y = 0$ is a HA
d local max. at $x \approx -0.618$,   local min. at $x \approx 1.62$
f $x \approx 2.05$ **g** area ≈ 0.959 units^2

51 a 0   **b** $\left(1, \dfrac{1}{e}\right)$ **c** $\left(2, \dfrac{2}{e^2}\right)$ **d** ≈ 0.330 units^2

52 a

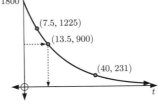

die 2

die 1

b $\dfrac{11}{36}$

c   **i** ≈ 0.227
ii ≈ 0.635

53 b $a = -3\frac{1}{2}$, $b = 5$ **c** D(10, −11, 11)

54 a DB ≈ 4.09 m,   BC ≈ 9.86 m
b $\widehat{ABE} \approx 68.2°$, $\widehat{DBC} \approx 57.5°$ **c** ≈ 17.0 m^2
d ≈ 10.9 m

55 a $a = -1$, $b = 2$ **b** y-intercept is $-2\frac{1}{2}$

c $\dfrac{-1-\sqrt{21}}{2}$ and $\dfrac{-1+\sqrt{21}}{2}$ **d** D$\left(-\frac{1}{2}, -2\frac{1}{3}\right)$

e   **i** $A = -\displaystyle\int_{\frac{\sqrt{21}-1}{2}}^{k} \left(-1 + \frac{3}{x^2 + x - 2}\right) dx$

ii ≈ 0.558 units^2

56 a   **i** The probability of a randomly selected customer buying both a goldfish and a tortoise is 0.12.

ii

G T

a b c
0.18   0.12   0.28

U 0.42

iii G and T are independent since P(G) × P(T) = P($G \cap T$)

b   **iii** $b \approx 0.104$, $a \approx 0.124$ **iv** ≈ 0.228

57 a 1800 g   **b**   **i** ≈ 1225 g   **ii** ≈ 231 g
c

W_t

1800

(7.5, 1225)

(13.5, 900)

(40, 231)

t

d ≈ 13.5 years   **e** ≈ 56.3 years

58 b   **i** $\approx 0.927^c$ **ii** $\approx 0.644^c$
c   **i** ≈ 2.16 cm^2 **ii** ≈ 29.3 cm^2

59 a $x = 3$ **b** $x = \dfrac{\ln 2}{\ln 3}$ (or $\log_3 2$)

60 a

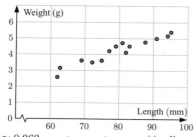

b $r \approx 0.962$ **c** very strong, positive linear correlation

d $y \approx 0.072\,9x - 1.57$ **e i** ≈ 6.45 g   **ii** 3.53 g

f The prediction in **e ii** is more likely to be reliable, as it is an interpolation.

61 a $2p^2 - p^4$ **b** $p \approx 0.541$

62 a $\frac{3}{5}$ **b** 2.2 cm   **c** Two - 5 cm or 2.2 cm

63 ≈ 6.40 cm   **64** ≈ 0.114 **65** ≈ 0.842

66 a $a = 13$, $b = 12$, $c = \frac{\pi}{30}$, $d = 15$ **b** ≈ 24.9 m

67 a $a = 2$, $b = -\sqrt{3}$ **b** $x \approx -1.05$, 0.524, 2.09

68 a $x = \frac{\pi}{2}$ **b** $f''(x) = e^{\sin^2 x}(\sin^2 2x + 2\cos 2x)$

   c $\approx (0.999, 2.03)$, $\approx (2.14, 2.03)$

69 $31\frac{1}{7}$ or $47\frac{6}{7}$

70 a $f'(x) = e^{1-2x^2}(1 - 4x^2)$, $f''(x) = e^{1-2x^2}(16x^3 - 12x)$

   b local min at $\left(-\frac{1}{2}, \frac{-\sqrt{e}}{2}\right)$, local max at $\left(\frac{1}{2}, \frac{\sqrt{e}}{2}\right)$

   c $x = 0$ or $\pm\frac{\sqrt{3}}{2}$

   d as $x \to \infty$, $f(x) \to 0^+$

   as $x \to -\infty$, $f(x) \to 0^-$

   e

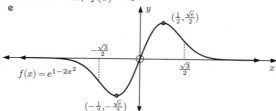

71 a $\bar{x} \approx 16.0$ **b** $\sigma \approx 2.48$

72 b Hint: $-1 \leqslant \cos\theta \leqslant 1$ for all θ.

   c $\theta \approx 1.02$, 2.59, 4.16, 5.73

73 a no solutions exist   **b** $x \approx 3.82$

74 a $k = 2$ **b** $\mu = 3.2$ **c** $\frac{47}{50}$

75 a $f'(x) = 6\cos^3 x - 5\cos x$

   c local max. at $(0.421, 0.272)$, $(2.72, 0.272)$,
   local min. at $\left(\frac{\pi}{2}, -1\right)$

   d

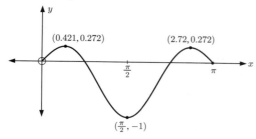

76 a i

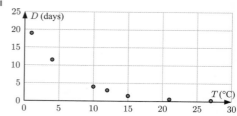

   ii

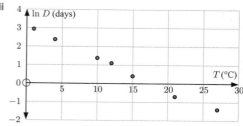

   iii

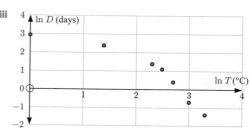

b The graph of $\ln D$ against T illustrates a linear relationship. The equation is $\ln D \approx -0.172T + 3.10$.

c $D \approx 22.2 \times (0.842)^T$ **d** ≈ 6.66 days